THE
WRITER'S
HANDBOOK
1997

THE WRITER'S COMPANION

*The essential guide
to being published*

Barry Turner

The Writer's Companion is a route map through the media
jungle, an indispensable guide for established writers
and newcomers alike who seek to make the best
commercial use of their talents.

Drawing on the cumulative experiences of its sister volume,
The Writer's Handbook, which is now in its tenth year, *The
Writer's Companion* is packed with a wealth of
practical advice taking in:

- book publishing
- freelance journalism
- film and television
- radio drama
- theatre and poetry

Everyday concerns, financial and legal, from how to avoid
contractual pitfalls to minimising the risk of libel are given
full coverage and there is up-to-date advice on raising
funds for creative projects on stage and screen.

Published by Macmillan

THE
WRITER'S
HANDBOOK
1997

EDITOR

BARRY TURNER

MACMILLAN

First published 1988
This edition published 1996 by
MACMILLAN
an imprint of Macmillan General Books,
25 Eccleston Place, London SW1W 9NF
and Basingstoke
Associated companies throughout the world

10 9 8 7 6 5 4 3 2 1

A CIP catalogue record for this book is available from the British Library

ISBN 0–333–642058

Typeset by Heronwood Press
Printed and bound in Great Britain
by Mackays of Chatham PLC, Kent

If you would like an entry in *The Writer's Handbook 1998*,
please write or send a fax to:
The Writer's Handbook,
45 Islington Park Street,
London N1 1QB.
Fax 0171 359 6026

Contents

Preface

A tenth birthday is a good excuse for a party. It is not simply the longevity (in publishing terms) of *The Writer's Handbook* that we celebrate but ten glorious editions of healthy growth. When we started, *The Writer's Handbook* had 500 pages including a 20-page index. Now it is 700 pages with twice as many words to the page. The index alone takes up over 80 pages.

The expansion reflects partly a development of editorial confidence. We have learned from experience just how much information needs to be garnered to provide an authoritative reference book. But the accumulation of words and pages also shows how the writing business has developed over the years. Notwithstanding the doom merchants who are for ever predicting the imminent demise of all forms of literary endeavour, opportunities for writers have multiplied in the last decade. More books, magazines and newspapers are published, more television and radio is transmitted, more theatre is produced and more films are made. If the dooms have a point at all, it is that the nature of the business has changed so that what was once a closed shop for a select band of writers has now opened up to competition.

Nowhere is this more obvious than in book publishing where technology has simplified production to a point where virtually anyone can publish their life's work, however bizarre. It may not succeed in the marketplace but then again, it may catch the public imagination and become a best seller. Some of the richest authors devote their talents to specialist interests – gardening, pets, hiking, country sports, travel – that rarely qualify for a mention in the literary pages of the national press.

The new age of multimedia will create yet more opportunities for budding writers. The diehards will bemoan the threat to conventional publishing but there is no reason why the book should not thrive alongside the CD-ROM in the same way that film has accommodated itself to television. 'More means worse', Kingsley Amis once famously remarked but in reality more means more, neither better nor worse. It all depends on what we make of life's chances. Ten years with *The Writer's Handbook* reveal clear evidence of exciting prospects for all writers. The next ten years will show if the challenge has been met.

In the midst of change, some elements of continuity can be noted. In the first edition of *The Writer's Handbook* I gave thanks to Jill Fenner who 'assisted' with the research. Now Jill is the mainstay of the editorial team, a creator of order out of chaos. Jill, in turn, leans on Jayne Jenkinson who sets us up for the printer. Other long-serving allies are Peter Finch who contributes the poetry section and Pat Kernon who gives advice on coping with the Inland Revenue and Customs and Excise. Our editor at Macmillan, Dominic Taylor, is relatively new to the game which has its advantages since he casts a fresh eye on the work. Dominic is our insurance against becoming stale.

A tenth anniversary tribute must also be paid to Julian Ashby, who started it all with an idea that no one, least of all me, took altogether seriously and to my agent Michael Motley who has put up with a curmudeongly client for more years than either of us can remember.

Feel free to spot the errors in this latest edition. You know who to blame.

Barry Turner

Pile 'em High and Sell 'em Cheap

The Book Clubs are having a hard time. Can they meet the challenge of a free market?

How time flies! It is barely a year since *The Bookseller*, the trade's voice of conservatism, asked melodramatically, 'What will save the Net Book Agreement?' A few days later, back came the answer, a loud raspberry blown in unison by all the leading booksellers and publishers. The century old price fixing system duly collapsed and died, a relic of the days when customers were supposed to be grateful for whatever producers decided to throw at them. And since then? Well, the repercussions have been less dramatic than either the doom merchants or the apostles of unfettered free enterprise predicted. After a bout of discounting to put some life into the Christmas trade, high street businesses settled back to normal, that is remained pretty well static. This has been interpreted by diehards to mean that the NBA lives in spirit. They are wrong.

For a more accurate judgement of what is happening to the book trade, look at the broad picture. It helps, for a start, to put the demise of the NBA into long term perspective. Its end was not as sudden as the panic headlines suggested. For years, publishers have been sidestepping the NBA with deals that precluded the high street bookshops. The trend appears most obviously in the direct sale of non-net school books to local education authorities and of children's books via mail order and the shelves of leading supermarkets. That direct sales by publishers at a discount (or, as they like to say, a pre-publication price) have leapt in recent years helps to explain the otherwise curious discrepancy between modest retail growth and the buoyant profits of the conglomerates. Then there are the book clubs.

Book clubs have been with us for a long time, having made their first appearance in the 1930s. But until recently they were tightly constrained by a publishers agreement not to make books available for cheap editions until at least nine months after their publication as trade hardbacks. This obvi-

'One cannot remind oneself too often that neglect of true talent is the sad but inevitable corollary of the overpraise of junk.' **Giles Auty**, *The Spectator*

'More books are being published and remaindered and pulped very rapidly. There is an immense amount being produced, but very little of it seems to be of commanding stature. Talent, scarce in itself, is going into the competing media of television, film and their allied arts.'
Professor George Steiner

ous advantage to booksellers was enhanced by the knowledge that if a title proved popular its subsequent paperback version would be in the shops well in time to compete with a book club offer. Authors were kept happy in the belief that anything sold by the clubs was a bonus on normal sales – a welcome boost to income, however modest.

Restraints on their activities were accepted by book clubs uncomplainingly. Indeed, they went out of their way to reinforce the regulations by imposing their own stuffy rules. Potential members had to sign up for a minimum period and guarantee to buy a certain number of books in order to qualify for concessions. Book club editions were characterised by tatty design and dull uniformity.

But with the progressive undermining of the NBA the book clubs have had to sharpen their act. No longer are they the only, or even the major source of 'cheap' books. To maintain their competitive edge, they have poured money into presentation and promotion. In a business that is notoriously penny-pinching in displaying its wares, the clubs spend around £22 million on direct marketing.

Of even greater concern to conventional bookshops, club editions have been moving closer to first publication dates. In many cases the gap has narrowed from the conventional nine months to three or less and there are already examples of the two editions appearing virtually simultaneously. Conditions of club membership, meanwhile, have been reduced to a formality.

Ironically, the formal ending of the NBA is seen as the first major setback in the growth of the book clubs whose share of the UK hardback market is around 20 per cent. Having prospered on tactics that circumvented the NBA they now find themselves up against the challenge of discounted books and cheap editions appearing on every prime retail site across the country. That this has not happened so far is merely an indication that in publishing, as in all industries, policy changes take time to work through the system. Be sure that in every publisher's boardroom, the earnest young men and women of marketing are being given Brownie points for coming up with schemes to sell the most books at the best possible prices. This could be via book clubs but it could just as easily be achieved, say, by negotiating exclusive deals with the supermarkets.

'What separates the talented from the successful is hard work.'
Stephen King

The book clubs have the armoury to fight back. The first among equals, Book Club Associates, with two million members and an annual turnover of around £140 million, is the UK's biggest direct marketer. Its customer database, containing several million names, is an asset of incalculable value. Interviews with chief executive Manfred Herriger hint at fundamental changes in BCA terms. Exclusivity may soon be the name of the game. And why not? For certain types of book, publishers might serve their own and their authors' best interests by allowing the book clubs to take the lead. Some titles would then appear first in club promotions before making their debut in the book shops. Such a reversal in the natural order of things would, of course, set up a wail of protest from the big retailers. But they too could make their bids for exclusivity - by dropping the outmoded practice of sale or return (how many other shopkeepers can rely on this fail safe?) in favour of buying firm from publishers.

The death of the NBA could be the rebirth of book marketing. Prepare for exciting times.

'Even now we are drowning in information. There are more words produced each year than in the whole period of history up to 1914.' **Martin Brooks**, *FT Information*

Book Clubs listing

Artists' Choice
PO Box 3, Huntingdon, Cambridgeshire
PE18 0QX
☎01832 710201   Fax 01832 710488
Specialises in books for the amateur artist at all levels of ability.

BCA (Book Club Associates)
87 Newman Street, London W1P 4EN
☎0171 637 0341   Fax 0171 291 3525
Has 19 book clubs, most of them catering for specific interests: Ancient & Medieval History Book Club, The Arts Guild, The Book Club of Ireland, Book of the Month Club, Children's Book of the Month Club, Classical Music Direct, The English Book Club, Executive World, Fantasy and Science Fiction, History Guild, Home Computer Club, The Literary Guild, Military and Aviation Book Society, Music Direct, Mystery and Thriller Guild, The New Home & Garden Guild, Quality Paperbacks Direct, Railway Book Club, World Books.

Bookmarks Club
265 Seven Sisters Road, Finsbury Park, London N4 2DE
☎0181 802 6145   Fax 0181 802 3835
New and recent books of interest to Socialists

at discount prices. Write, phone or fax for latest list.

Books for Children (Time-Life UK)
4 Furzeground Way, Stockley Park, Uxbridge, Middlesex UB11 1DP
☎0181 606 3090   Fax 0181 606 3099
Hardcover and paperback books for children from newly-born to aged 12. Also occasional adult non-fiction - cookery, family interest, parenting guides.

The Bookworm Club
Heffers Booksellers, 20 Trinity Street, Cambridge CB2 3ND
☎01223 568650   Fax 01223 568591
Sells paperback books for children through schools.

Cygnus Book Club
PO Box 15, Llandeilo, Carmarthenshire SA19 9DB
☎01550 777693   Fax 01550 777569
'Books which make people think.' Information books on spirituality, complementary healthcare, environmental issues, plus some management and education titles.

The Folio Society
44 Eagle Street, London WC1R 4FS
☎0171 400 4200   Fax 0171 400 4242

Fine editions of classic titles and reference; also some children's classics.

Letterbox Library
Children's Book Cooperative,
Unit 2D/2nd Floor, Leroy House,
436 Essex Road, London N1 3QP
☎0171 226 1633   Fax 0171 226 1768

Hard and softcover, non-sexist and multi-cultural books for children from one to teenage.

Poetry Book Society
Book House, 45 East Hill, London
SW18 2QZ
☎0181 870 8403   Fax 0181 877 1615

Readers Union Ltd
PO Box 6, Brunel House, Newton Abbot,
Devon TQ12 2DW
☎01626 336424   Fax 01626 664463

Has eight book clubs, all dealing with specific interests: Country Sports Book Society, Craftsman Book Society, Creative Living Book Club, Equestrian Book Society, Gardeners Book Society, Needlecraft Book Society, Photo-graphic Book Society, Ramblers and Climbers Book Society.

Scholastic School Book Club
Villiers House, Clarendon Avenue,
Leamington Spa, Warwickshire CV 32 5PR
☎01926 887799   Fax 01926 883331

Runs five book clubs: See-Saw (3-6 year-olds), Lucky (6-9), Chip (9-11), Scene (11-15), and Teacher's Bookshelf (professional resources for teachers).

The Softback Preview
(Time-Life UK)
4 Furzeground Way, Stockley Park, Uxbridge,
Middlesex UB11 1DP
☎0181 606 3073   Fax 0181 606 3099

Mainly non-fiction.

The Women's Book Club
The Women's Press, 34 Great Sutton Street,
London EC1V 0DX
☎0171 251 3007   Fax 0171 608 1938

'Best women writers from more than 70 publishers.' Fiction, biography and autobiography; popular mind, body and spirit; health and self-help; also a collection of women's studies, social issues and current affairs.

UK Publishers

AA Publishing

The Automobile Association, Fanum House, Basingstoke, Hampshire RG21 2EA
☎01256 201234   Fax 01256 492335

Managing Director *John Howard*
Editorial Director *Michael Buttler*
Approx. Annual Turnover £26 million

Publishes maps, atlases and guidebooks, motoring and leisure. About 100 titles a year.

Authors' Rating Benefiting from a clearly defined market, the AA has advanced strongly in the publication of maps and tour guides. Travel writers who really know how to churn out the facts are among the beneficiaries.

Abacus

See **Little, Brown & Co (UK)**

ABC – All Books For Children (a division of The All Children's Co. Ltd)

33 Museum Street, London WC1A 1LD
☎0171 436 6300   Fax 0171 240 6923

Managing Director *Sue Tarsky*

Publishes children's titles only, including the successful *Angelina Ballerina* and *Ned* books and toys. About 40 titles a year. *Specialises* in co-editions worldwide. **SoftbABCks** paperback imprint launched 1991 and **FactbABCks** non-fiction imprint launched 1995. Unsolicited material welcome but no novels. All material should be addressed to *Carol MacKenzie*, the Editorial Department; s.a.e. essential for return.
Royalties paid twice-yearly.

ABC–Clio Ltd

Old Clarendon Iron Works, 35a Great Clarendon Street, Oxford OX2 6AT
☎01865 311350   Fax 01865 311358

Managing Director *Tony Sloggett*
Editorial Director *Dr Robert G. Neville*

Formerly Clio Press Ltd. *Publishes* academic and general reference work, social sciences and humanities. Markets, outside North America, the CD-ROM publications of the American parent company. Art Bibliographies *S. Pape*. Series *World Bibliographical; International Organisations; World Photographers; Clio Montessori*.
Royalties paid twice-yearly.

Abington Publishing

See **Woodhead Publishing Ltd**

Absolute Press

Scarborough House, 29 James Street West, Bath, Avon BA1 2BT
☎01225 316013   Fax 01225 445836

Managing/Editorial Director *Jon Croft*

Founded 1980. *Publishes* food and wine-related subjects as well as travel guides and the *Streetwise Maps* series of city maps. About 10 titles a year. Also publishes English translations of plays considered to be world masterpieces under the **Absolute Classics** imprint. *Outlines*, launched in autumn 1996, is a new series of monographs on gay and lesbian creative artists. No unsolicited mss. Synopses and ideas for books welcome.
Royalties paid twice-yearly.

Abson Books London

5 Sidney Square, London E1 2EY
☎0171 790 4737   Fax 0171 790 7346

Chairman *M. J. Ellison*

Founded 1971 in Bristol. *Publishes* language glossaries, literary quizzes and puzzles. No unsolicited mss; synopses and ideas for books welcome.
Royalties paid twice-yearly.

Academic Press

See **Harcourt Brace and Company Ltd**

Academy Books

35 Pretoria Avenue, London E17 7DR
☎0181 521 7647   Fax 0181 503 6655

Chairman/Managing Director *Tony Freeman*
Approx. Annual Turnover £150,000

Founded 1990 as a self-publishing venture for specialist transport titles. *Publishes* non-fiction, mostly historical and technological, with a strong bias towards transport. Titles *Daimler: An Illustrated History; The Godfather of Rolls Royce; Edsel, The Motor Industry's Titanic; Bentley, The Overdrive Cars; The Nyasaland Survey Papers; The Culwick Papers; Panther, The Inside Story of the Panther Car Company; Selling the Dream, Advertising the American Car 1930-1980*. Unsolicited mss, synopses and ideas welcome. Synopses should be accompanied by sample chapter or example of previously published work. Mss must be supplied on computer disk prior to acceptance. Packaging undertaken on specialist academic and specialist transport titles for some clients. Several magazines handled on a contract basis.

Royalties paid monthly.

Academy Group Ltd
42 Leinster Gardens, London W2 3AN
☎0171 402 2141   Fax 0171 723 9540
Chairman *H. D. Köhler*
Managing Director *John Stoddart*
Approx. Annual Turnover £3 million

FOUNDED 1969. Part of VCH Verlagsgesellschaft mbh, Germany. *Publishes* architecture, art and design. Welcomes unsolicited mss, synopsis and ideas. CONTACTS *Maggie Toy* **Architecture/Architectural Design**; *Nicola Kearton* **Art & Design**.

Royalties paid annually.

Acair Ltd
Unit 7, 7 James Street, Stornoway, Isle of Lewis, Scotland HS1 2QN
☎01851 703020   Fax 01851 703294
Manager *Joan Morrison*

Specialising in matters pertaining to the Gaidhealtachd, Acair publishes books on Scottish history, culture and the Gaelic language. 75% of their children's books are targeted at primary school usage and are published exclusively in Gaelic.

Royalties paid twice-yearly.

Ace Books
1268 London Road, London SW16 4ER
☎0181 679 8000   Fax 0181 679 6069
Approx. Annual Turnover £500,000

Publishing arm of Age Concern England. *Publishes* related non-fiction only. No fiction. About 18 titles a year. Unsolicited mss, synopses and ideas welcome.

Acropolis Books
See **Anness Publishing Ltd**

Actinic Press
See **Cressrelles Publishing Co. Ltd**

Addison Wesley Longman Ltd
Edinburgh Gate, Harlow, Essex CM20 2JE
☎01279 623623   Fax 01279 431059
Contracts & Copyrights Department
   Brenda Gvozdanovic

FOUNDED 1724 by Thomas Longman. Restruc-tured in 1994 to focus solely on educational publishing. A subsidiary of Pearson plc. *Publishes* a range of curriculum subjects, inclu-ding English language teaching for students at primary and secondary school level, college and university. All unsolicited mss should be addressed to the Manager, Contracts and Copyrights Department.

Royalties twice-yearly. *Overseas associates* worldwide.

Authors' Rating Now the world's third biggest educational publisher with the US as a prime market. Keen to develop titles on CD-ROM.

Adelphi
See **David Campbell Publishers Ltd**

Adlard Coles Ltd
See **A & C Black (Publishers) Ltd**

Adlib
See **Scholastic Ltd**

African Books Collective
The Jam Factory, 27 Park End Street, Oxford OX1 1HU
☎01865 726686   Fax 01865 793298

FOUNDED 1990. Collectively owned by its 17 founder member publishers. Exclusive distrib-ution in N. America, UK, Europe and Commonwealth countries outside Africa for 48 African member publishers. Aims to promote and disseminate African-published material outside Africa. No unsolicited mss.

Airlife Publishing Ltd
101 Longden Road, Shrewsbury, Shropshire SY3 9EB
☎01743 235651   Fax 01743 232944
Chairman/Managing Director
   A. D. R. Simpson
Editorial Head *Peter Coles*
Approx. Annual Turnover £3 million

IMPRINTS

Airlife *Publishes* specialist aviation titles, both technical and general, for pilots, historians and enthusiasts. About 35 titles a year. TITLES *Air Pilot's Manuals; The Source Book of the RAF; Diary of an Aviator; Jets: Airliners of the Golden Age.*

   Swan Hill Press covers country sport, nat-ural history, travel and adventure, wildlife art. About 25 titles a year. TITLES *The Whitehead Encyclopedia of Deer; Minton – The First 200 Years; Salmon Flyfishing – The Dynamics Approach; Voice From the Wilderness.*

About 12 sailing and yachting titles a year are published under the **Waterline Books** imprint. TITLES *Hand Reef & Steer; High Performance Sailing; Dinghy Systems; Voyaging on a Small Income.*

Unsolicited mss, synopses and ideas for books welcome.

Royalties paid annually, twice-yearly by arrangement.

Ian Allan Ltd

Coombelands House, Coombelands Lane, Addlesdown, Surrey KT15 1HY
☎01932 855909   Fax 01932 854750

Chairman *David Allan*
Managing Director *Martin Kenny*

Publishes atlases and maps, aviation, hobbies, guidebooks, defence and militaria, nautical, reference, transport, travel and topography. About 100 titles a year. Send sample chapter and synopsis (with s.a.e.). Manages distribution and sales for third party publishers.

IMPRINT **Dial House** sport, leisure, cookery, gardening.

J. A. Allen & Co. Ltd

1 Lower Grosvenor Place, Buckingham Palace Road, London SW1W 0EL
☎0171 834 0090   Fax 0171 976 5836

Chairman/Managing Director *Joseph A. Allen*
Publishing Director *Caroline Burt*
Editor *Jane Lake*
Approx. Annual Turnover £700,000

FOUNDED 1926 as part of J. A. Allen & Co. (The Horseman's Bookshop) Ltd, and became a separate independent company in 1960. *Publishes* equine and equestrian non-fiction and fiction. About 20 titles a year. Mostly commissioned, but willing to consider unsolicited mss of technical/instructional material related to all aspects of horses and horsemanship.

Royalties paid twice-yearly.

Allen Lane
See **Penguin Books Ltd**

Allison & Busby

179 King's Cross Road, London WC1X 9BZ
☎0171 833 1042   Fax 0171 833 1044

Managing Director/Editor *Peter Day*
Rights *Sarah Fulford*

FOUNDED 1967. *Publishes* literary fiction and non-fiction, including 20th-century classics, writers' guides and crime. About 36 titles a year. Send synopsis with two sample chapters. No replies without s.a.e..

Amber Lane Press Ltd

Cheorl House, Church Street, Charlbury, Oxfordshire OX7 3PR
☎01608 810024   Fax 01608 810024

Chairman *Brian Clark*
Managing Director/Editorial Head *Judith Scott*

FOUNDED 1979 to publish modern play texts. *Publishes* plays and books on the theatre. About 4 titles a year. TITLES *Steaming; Pack of Lies; The Dresser* (play texts); *Playwrights' Progress - Patterns of Postwar British Drama* Colin Chambers & Mike Prior; *The Sound of One Hand Clapping: A Guide to Writing for the Theatre* Sheila Yeger. 'Expressly *not* interested in poetry.' No unsolicited mss. Synopses and ideas welcome.

Royalties paid twice-yearly.

Amsco
See **Omnibus Press**

Andersen Press Ltd

20 Vauxhall Bridge Road, London SW1V 2SA
☎0171 973 9720   Fax 0171 233 6263

Managing Director/Publisher *Klaus Flugge*
Editorial Director *Denise Johnstone-Burt*
Editor, Fiction *Audrey Adams*

FOUNDED 1976 by Klaus Flugge and named after Hans Christian Andersen. *Publishes* children's high-quality picture books and hardback fiction. Seventy per cent of their books are sold as co-productions abroad. TITLES *Not Now Bernard* David McKee; *A Dark, Dark Tale* Ruth Brown; *I Want My Potty* Tony Ross; *Badger's Parting Gift* Susan Varley; *Teddy, Where Are You?* Ralph Steadman; *Jack's Fantastic Voyage* Michael Foreman; *Cry of the Wolf* Melvin Burgess. Unsolicited mss welcome for picture books; synopsis in the first instance for books for young readers up to age 12.

Royalties paid twice-yearly.

Anness Publishing Ltd

Boundary Studios, 1-7 Boundary Row, London SE1 8HP
☎0171 401 2077   Fax 0171 633 9499

Chairman/Managing Director *Paul Anness*
Publisher/Partner *Joanna Lorenz*

FOUNDED 1989. Successful, small entrepreneurial company: international packager and publisher of highly illustrated co-edition titles. *Publishes* illustrated general non-fiction: cookery, crafts, interior design, gardening, photography, decorating, lifestyle and children's. About 120 titles a year. Unsolicited summaries and proposals welcome, no manucripts.

IMPRINTS **Lorenz Books; Acropolis Books; Anness Publishing**.

Antique Collectors' Club

5 Church Street, Woodbridge,
Suffolk IP12 1DS
☎01394 385501   Fax 01394 384434
Managing Director *Diana Steel*
Sales Director *Brian Cotton*

FOUNDED 1966. Has a five-figure membership spread over the United Kingdom and the world. The Club's magazine *Antique Collecting* is sold on a subscription basis (currently £19.50 p.a.) and is published 10 times a year. It is sent free to members who may also buy the Club's books at special pre-publication prices. *Publishes* specialist books on antiques and collecting. The price guide series was introduced in 1968 with the first edition of *The Price Guide to Antique Furniture*. Subject areas include furniture, silver/jewellery, metalwork, glass, textiles, art reference, ceramics, horology. Also books on architecture and gardening. RECENT TITLES *Garden Antiques* Alistair Morris; *Wedgwood* Robin Reilly; *Turkoman Rugs* Uwe Jourdan; *The Rose and the Clematis* John Howells. Unsolicited synopses and ideas for books welcome. No mss.

Royalties paid quarterly as a rule, but can vary.

Anvil Press Poetry Ltd

69 King George Street, London SE10 8PX
☎0181 858 2946   Fax 0181 858 2946
Editorial Director *Peter Jay*

FOUNDED 1968 to promote English and foreign poetry, both classic and contemporary, in translation. English list includes Peter Levi and Carol Ann Duffy. Anvil has now developed to the point at which most of its new titles are new volumes by their regulars. Preliminary enquiry required for translations. Unsolicited book-length collections of poems are welcome from writers whose work has appeared in poetry magazines.

Authors' Rating Distancing himself from the aggressive marketing tactics paraded by some other houses, Peter Jay is said to be the least likely of all publishers to sign a fashionable poet for merely commercial reasons but he has had great success with younger poets.

Apollos

See **Inter-Varsity Press**

Apple

See **Quarto Publishing** under **UK Packagers**

Appletree Press Ltd

19–21 Alfred Street, Belfast BT2 8DL
☎01232 243074   Fax 01232 246756
Managing Director *John Murphy*
Senior Editor *Douglas Marshall*
Gift Books Editor *Nicola Lavery*

FOUNDED 1974. *Publishes* cookery and other small-format gift books, plus general non-fiction of Irish and Scottish interest. TITLES *Little Cookbook* series (about 40 titles); *Ireland: The Complete Guide; Northern Ireland: The Background to the Conflict*. No unsolicited mss; send initial letter or synopsis. Appletree's London office is at Aquarius House, 80–82 Chiswick High Road, London W4 1SY (Tel: 0181 987 9439), but all editorial approaches should be sent to Belfast.

Royalties paid twice-yearly in the first year, annually thereafter. For the *Little Cookbook* Series, a standard fee is paid.

Arc Publications

Nanholme Mill, Shaw Wood Road,
Todmorden, Lancashire OL14 6DA
☎01706 812338   Fax 01706 818948
Publishers *Rosemary Jones, Angela Jarman, Tony Ward*
General Editor *Tony Ward*
Associate Editors *Michael Hulse* (International), *David Morley* (UK)

FOUNDED in 1969 to specialise in the publication of contemporary poetry from new and established writers both in the UK and abroad. Runs the annual **Northern Short Story Competition** and *publishes* an anthology of winning entries. AUTHORS include Dinah Hawken (New Zealand), W. N. Herbert, Jonathan Davidson, Rose Ausländer (Austria), Robert Gray (Australia), John Hartley Williams, Jackie Wills, Don Coles (Canada), Ian Pope, Michael O'Louglin (Ireland). 8 titles a year. Authors submitting material should ensure that it is compatible with the current list and should enclose s.a.e. if they wish mss to be returned.

Arena

See **Ashgate Publishing Co. Ltd**

Argus Books

See **Nexus Special Interests**

Aris & Phillips Ltd

Teddington House, Warminster, Wiltshire
BA12 8PQ
☎01985 213409   Fax 01985 212910
Managing/Editorial Director *Adrian Phillips*
Editor, Hispanic Classics *Lucinda Phillips*

FOUNDED 1972 to publish books on Egyptology. A family firm which has remained independent. *Publishes* academic, classical, oriental and hispanic. About 20 titles a year. With such a highly specialised list, unsolicited mss and synopses are not particularly welcome, but synopses will be considered.

Royalties paid twice-yearly.

Arkana
See **Penguin Books Ltd**

Arms & Armour Press
See **Cassell**

Arnefold
See **George Mann Books**

Edward Arnold
See **Hodder Headline plc**

Arrow
See **Random House UK Ltd**

Artech House
Portland House, Stag Place, London
SW1E 5XA
☎0171 973 8077   Fax 0171 630 0166
Managing Director (USA) *William M. Bazzy*
Commissioning Editor *Dr Julie Lancashire*

FOUNDED 1969. European office of Artech House Inc., Boston. *Publishes* electronic engineering, especially telecommunications, computer communications, computer science, optoelectronics and solid-state materials and devices (books, software and videos). 50-60 titles a year. Unsolicited mss and synopses considered.

Royalties paid twice-yearly.

Ashgate Publishing Co. Ltd
Gower House, Croft Road, Aldershot, Hampshire GU11 3HR
☎01252 331551   Fax 01252 344405
Chairman/Managing Director *Nigel Farrow*

FOUNDED 1967. *Publishes* professional and academic books in social sciences, arts and humanities. Associated companies include Edward Elgar Publishing Ltd.

IMPRINTS

Arena *Jo Gooderham* Social work and policy; *John Hindley* Aviation, construction and technical. **Avebury** *Sarah Markham* Research monographs on social science. **Dartmouth** *John Irwin* Political science, international relations and legal studies. **Gower** *Christopher Simpson*

Business and management titles. **Scolar Press** *Pamela Edwards* Art history; *Ravel Lynch* Music and literary studies; *Alec McAulay* History. **Variorum** *John Smedley* Collected studies on history. Unsolicited mss welcome. Synopses and ideas for books considered.

Royalties paid as per contract.

Ashmolean Museum Publications
Ashmolean Museum, Beaumont Street,
Oxford OX1 2PH
☎01865 278009   Fax 01865 278018
Publisher/Editorial Head *Ian Charlton*
Approx. Annual Turnover £200,000

The Ashmolean Museum, which is wholly owned by Oxford University, was founded in 1683. The first publication appeared in 1890 but publishing did not really start in earnest until the 1960s. *Publishes* European and Oriental fine and applied arts, European archaeology and ancient history, Egyptology and numismatics, for both adult and children's markets. About 8 titles a year. No fiction, American/African art, ethnography, modern art or post-medieval history.

IMPRINTS

Ashmolean Museum Publications and **Griffith Institute** (Egyptology imprint). TITLES *Coinage of the Crusades and the Latin East; Treasures of the Ashmolean Museum; Principles of Egyptian Art; Bridging East and West: Japanese Ceramics from the Kozan Studio*. No unsolicited mss; synopses and ideas welcome.

Royalties paid annually.

Associated University Presses (AUP)
See **Golden Cockerel Press Ltd**

The Athlone Press
1 Park Drive, London NW11 7SG
☎0181 458 0888   Fax 0181 201 8115
Managing Director *Doris Southam*
Editorial Head *Brian Southam*

FOUNDED 1949 as the publishing house of the University of London. Now wholly independent, but preserves links with the University via an academic advisory board. *Publishes* archaeology, architecture, art, economics, film studies, history, medical, music, Japan, oriental, philosophy, politics, religion, science, sociology, zoology, women's/feminist issues. Anticipated developments in the near future: more emphasis on cultural studies, history of ideas, women's/feminist studies and environmental issues, including medicine. About 35 titles a year. Unsolicited mss, synopses and ideas for academic books welcome.

Royalties paid annually. *Overseas associates* The Athlone Press, 165 First Avenue, Atlantic Highlands, NJ 07716, USA.

Atlantic Europe Publishing Co. Ltd
Greys Court Farm, Greys Court,
Nr Henley on Thames, Oxon RG9 4PG
☎01491 628188   Fax 01491 628189
Directors *Dr B. J. Knapp, D. L. R. McCrae*

Closely associated, since 1990, with Earthscape Editions packaging operation. *Publishes* full-colour, highly illustrated children's non-fiction in hardback for international co-editions. Not interested in any other material. Main focus is on National Curriculum titles, especially in the fields of mathematics, science, technology, social history and geography. About 15 titles a year. Unsolicited synopses and ideas for books welcome but s.a.e. essential for return of submissions.

Royalties or fees paid depending on circumstance.

Attic Books
The Folly, Rhosgoch, Painscastle, Builth
Wells, Powys LD2 3JY
☎01497 851205
Managing Director/Editorial Head *Jack Bowyer*

FOUNDED 1984 by its architect owners. *Publishes* books on building crafts, architecture and engineering. Mostly technical books for the industry, dealing mainly with restoration and conservation.

Royalties paid annually.

AUP (Associated University Presses)
See **Golden Cockerel Press Ltd**

Aurum Press Ltd
25 Bedford Avenue, London WC1B 3AT
☎0171 637 3225   Fax 0171 580 2469
Chairman *André Deutsch*
Managing Director *Bill McCreadie*
Editorial Director *Piers Burnett*

FOUNDED 1977. Formerly owned by Andrew Lloyd Webber's Really Useful Group, now owned jointly by Piers Burnett, Bill McCreadie and Sheila Murphy (Marketing & Rights Director), all of whom worked together in the 70s for André Deutsch. Committed to producing high-quality, illustrated/non-illustrated adult non-fiction in the areas of general

human interest, art and craft, lifestyle and travel. About 40 titles a year.

Royalties paid twice-yearly.

Autumn Publishing Ltd
First Floor, North Barn, Appledram Barns,
Birdham Road, Near Chichester, West Sussex
PO20 7EQ
☎01243 531660   Fax 01243 774433
Managing Director *Campbell Goldsmid*
Editorial Director *Ingrid Goldsmid*

FOUNDED 1976. Publisher of highly illustrated non-fiction: mainly children's, including activity books. About 20 titles a year. Unsolicited synopses and ideas for books welcome if they come within relevant subject areas.

Payment varies according to contract; generally a flat fee.

Avebury
See **Ashgate Publishing Co. Ltd**

B & W Publishing
233 Cowgate, Edinburgh EH1 1NQ
☎0131 220 5551   Fax 0131 220 5552
Joint Managing Directors *Campbell Brown, Steven Wiggins*

FOUNDED 1990. *Publishes* fiction, memoirs, sport and guidebooks. 15 titles in 1995 with around 60 titles in print. Unsolicited mss, synopses and ideas for books welcome. No children's books.

Royalties paid twice-yearly.

Baillière Tindall
See **Harcourt Brace and Company Ltd**

Bantam/Bantam Press
See **Transworld Publishers Ltd**

Barefoot Books Ltd
PO Box 95, Kingswood, Bristol,
Avon BS15 5BH
☎0117 9328885   Fax 0117 9328887
Rights & Management:
18 Highbury Terrace, London N5 1UP
☎0171 704 6453 Fax 0171 359 5798
Managing Director *Nancy Traversy*
Publisher *Tessa Strickland (at Bristol office)*
Approx. Annual Turnover £400,000

FOUNDED in 1993. *Publishes* high-quality children's picture books, particularly new and traditional stories from a wide range of cultures. 25 titles in 1996. No unsolicited mss.

Royalties paid twice-yearly.

N. Barnard

See **Haynes Publishing**

Barny Books

The Cottage, Hough on the Hill,
Nr Grantham, Lincolnshire NG32 2BB
☎01400 250246

Managing Director/Editorial Head *Molly Burkett*
Business Manager *Ian Smith*
Approx. Annual Turnover £10,000

FOUNDED with the aim of encouraging new writers and illustrators. *Publishes* mainly children's books. TITLES *Once Upon a Wartime* series, Molly Burkett; *No Spots for the Leopard* B. Seshadri; *The Fox Run* Joan Baker; *Tom Goes to the Seaside* Divya Malde; *Orston - History of a Nottinghamshire Village* Paul Barnes. Too small a concern to have the staff/resources to deal with unsolicited mss. Writers with strong ideas should approach Molly Burkett by letter in the first instance. Also runs a readership and advisory service for new writers (£10 fee for short stories or illustrations; £20 fee for full-length stories).
Royalties division of profits 50/50.

Authors' Rating Friendliest and gentlest of small publishers with a genuine feel for what attracts children to the bookshelves.

Baron Birch

See **The Barracuda Collection/Quotes Ltd**

The Barracuda Collection/ Quotes Ltd

The Book Barn, Church Way, Whittlebury, Northamptonshire NN12 8XS
☎01327 858301   Fax 01327 858302

Publisher *Clive Birch*

Barracuda was formed in 1974, Quotes in 1985. *Publishes* local and natural history, country and sporting life, military, transport, church, family and institutional histories. About 30 titles a year.

IMPRINTS
The Barracuda Collection TITLES *The Book of Raddiffe; The Book of Kingston.* **Quotes in Camera** TITLES *Kent Buses; Hull & E. Yorkshire.* **Saga** TITLES *Murder in Old Buckinghamshire.* **Sporting & Leisure Press** TITLES *Crystal Palace F.C. 1905-1994.* **Baron Birch** TITLES *On the Move; Care in Crisis.* Synopses and ideas for books welcome with sample mss page, extent of words and pictures.
Royalties paid annually.

Barrie & Jenkins

See **Random House UK Ltd**

Bartholomew

See **HarperCollins Publishers Ltd**

B. T. Batsford Ltd

4 Fitzhardinge Street, London W1H 0AH
☎0171 486 8484   Fax 0171 487 4296

Chief Executive *Jules Perel*
Chairman *Gerard Mizrahi*
Approx. Annual Turnover £5 million

FOUNDED in 1843 as a bookseller, and began publishing in 1874. An independent publisher until 1996 when it was bought by **Labyrinth Publishing UK Ltd**. A world leader in books on chess, arts and craft. *Publishes* non-fiction: archaeology, school reference, cinema, crafts and hobbies, numismatics, equestrian, fashion and costume, graphic design, horticulture, botany and gardening. Acquired Faber chess list in 1994. About 130 titles a year.

DIVISIONS **Arts & Crafts; Archaeology & Ancient History; Chess; Horticulture; Country Sports; Graphic Design**.
Royalties paid twice in first year, annually thereafter.

Authors' Rating Gone at last! After more than 150 years in the business Batsford has finally succumbed to a tempting offer - and from a three-year-old upstart. But **Labyrinth** is one of the fastest growing media groups while Batsford is virtually static. This could soon change not least with opportunities for Batsford to push into the US market.

Bay View Books Ltd

The Red House, 25-26 Bridgeland Street, Bideford, Devon EX39 2PZ
☎01237 479225/421285   Fax 01237 421286

Managing Directors *Charles Herridge, Bridgid Herridge*

FOUNDED 1986. *Publishes* transport books only, including series: all-colour classic car restoration guides; A-Zs of cars, motorcycles and racing cars. About 10 titles a year.
Payment varies according to contract.

BBC Books

80 Wood Lane, London W12 0TT
☎0181 576 2623   Fax 0181 576 2858

Director Books/Audio Publishing *Christopher Weller*
Editorial Director *Sheila Ableman*
Approx. Annual Turnover £25 million

BBC Books is a division of BBC Worldwide Publishing. *Publishes* TV tie-in titles, including books which, though linked with BBC television or radio, may not simply be the 'book of the series'. Books with no television or radio link are of little interest. About 80 titles a year. TITLES *Delia Smith's Winter Collection; Jancis Robinson's Wine Course; People's Century.* Unsolicited mss (which come in at the rate of about 15 weekly) are rarely read. However, strong ideas well expressed will always be considered, and promising letters stand a chance of further scrutiny.

IMPRINTS
Network Books A new range of non-fiction tie-ins to TV programmes broadcast on channels other than BBC1 or BBC2. Includes cookery, gardening, crafts, plus some children's fiction. 4 titles in 1995.
BBC Penguin A co-publishing deal which gives BBC Books a mass-market paperback outlet. 20 tie-in titles in 1995.
Royalties paid twice-yearly.

Authors' Rating Entitled to first refusal on all books based on BBC programmes, this publisher has a promotion budget to die for. Think of all that free advertising that comes with the screen and radio credits. There are critics who suggest that BBC Books – though undoubtedly a success story – could do more to exploit the big names of broadcasting but as Heather Holden–Brown, senior commissioning editor, points out 'Everyone thinks that because millions are listening or watching they'll want to buy the book, but that isn't so'. There is no magic formula for bestsellers.

BBC Penguin
See **BBC Books Ltd**

Bedford Square Press
See **NCVO Publications**

Belair
See **Folens Ltd**

Bellew Publishing Co. Ltd
Nightingale Centre, 8 Balham Hill, London SW12 9EA
☎0181 673 5611   Fax 0181 675 3542
Chairman *Ian McCorquodale*
Managing Director *Ib Bellew*
Approx. Annual Turnover £600,000
FOUNDED 1983. Publisher and packager. *Publishes* craft, art and design, fiction, illustrated non-fiction, general interest, religion and politics. About 15 titles a year. TITLES *We Believe* Alfred Gilbey; *The Awakening of Willie Ryland* Tom Hart; *Chronicle* Alan Wall; *On Depiction:*

Critical Essays on Art Avigdor Arikha. No unsolicited mss. Synopses with specimen chapters welcome.
Royalties paid annually.

Benn Technical Books
See **Tolley Publishing Co. Ltd**

Berg Publishers Ltd
150 Cowley Road, Oxford OX4 1JJ
☎01865 245104   Fax 01865 791165
Managing Director *Peter Cowell*
Editorial Director *Kathryn Earle*
Approx. Annual Turnover £600,000
Also **Oswald Wolff Books** imprint. *Publishes* scholarly books in the fields of history, social sciences and humanities. About 45 titles a year. No unsolicited mss. Synopses and ideas for books welcome.
Royalties paid annually.

Berkswell Publishing Co. Ltd
PO Box 420, Warminster, Wiltshire BA12 9XB
☎01985 840189   Fax 01985 840189
Managing Director *John Stidolph*
Approx. Annual Turnover £250,000
FOUNDED 1974. *Publishes* illustrated books, royalty, heritage, country sports, biography and books about Wessex. No fiction. About 4 titles a year. Unsolicited mss, synopses and ideas for books welcome.
Royalties paid according to contract.

Berlitz Publishing Co. Ltd
Berlitz House, Peterley Road, Oxford OX4 2TX
☎01865 747033   Fax 01865 779700
Chairman *H. Yokoi*
Managing Director *R. Kirkpatrick*
Approx. Annual Turnover £6 million
FOUNDED 1970. Part of Berlitz International, which also comprises language instruction and translation divisions. *Publishes* travel and language-learning products only: travel guides, phrasebooks and language courses. 150 titles in 1995. DIVISION **Berlitz Publishing** *Julian Parish* TITLES *Pocket Guides; Discover Guides; Berlitz Complete Guide to Cruising and Cruise Ships; Business Phrase Books; Berlitz Live.* No unsolicited mss.

BFI Publishing
British Film Institute, 21 Stephen Street, London W1P 2LN
☎0171 255 1444   Fax 0171 436 7950
Head of Publishing *Edward Buscombe*

Approx. Annual Turnover £500,000
FOUNDED 1982. Part of the **British Film Institute**. *Publishes* academic and general film/television-related books. About 30 titles a year. TITLES *Film Classics* (series); *Claiming the Real* Brian Winston; *The Scorsese Connection* Lesley Stern; *David Lynch* Michel Chion. Unsolicited synopses and ideas preferred to complete mss.
Royalties paid annually.

Bible Society
Stonehill Green, Westlea, Swindon, Wiltshire SN5 7DG
☎01793 418100   Fax 01793 418118
Executive Director *Neil Crosbie*
Approx. Annual Turnover £4 million
The Bible Society was founded in 1804 and was granted a royal charter in 1948. It is now part of a worldwide fellowship of Bible Societies, working in over 180 countries. A mission agency with the specific task of enabling the Church to use the Bible in her mission. *Publishes* Bibles, Bible-related resources, group study, religious education and video materials. TITLES *The Good News Bible; Just Looking; Learn New Testament Greek; Finding Faith Today*. 12 titles in 1995. Unsolicited synopses and ideas welcome. No Christian biography, fiction, poetry, general religious or commentaries.
Royalties paid twice-yearly.

Clive Bingley Books
See **Library Association Publishing Ltd**

A. & C. Black (Publishers) Ltd
35 Bedford Row, London WC1R 4JH
☎0171 242 0946   Fax 0171 831 8478
Chairman *Charles Black*
Deputy Chairman *David Gadsby*
Managing Directors *Charles Black, Jill Coleman*
Approx. Annual Turnover £6.5 million
Publishes children's and educational books, including music, for 3–15-year-olds, arts and crafts, ceramics, fishing, ornithology, nautical, reference, sport, theatre and travel. About 125 titles a year. Acquisitions brought the Herbert Press' art, design and general books, Adlard Coles sailing list and Christopher Helm's natural history and ornithology lists into A. & C. Black's stable.
IMPRINTS **Adlard Coles; Christopher Helm; Herbert Press** (see entry). TITLES *New Mermaid* drama series; *Who's Who; Writers' & Artists' Yearbook; Know the Game* sports series; *Blue Guides* travel series. Initial enquiry appreciated before submission of mss.
Royalties payment varies according to contract.

Black Ace Books
Ellemford Farmhouse, Duns, Berwickshire TD11 3SG
☎01361 890370   Fax 01361 890287
Managing Director *Hunter Steele*
FOUNDED 1991. *Publishes* new fiction, Scottish and general; some non-fiction including history and philosophy. 16 titles in print. IMPRINTS **Black Ace Books, Black Ace Paperbacks** TITLES *The Hawthorn Hedge* Mercedes Clarasó; *On My Way Weeping* Steve McGiffen; *The Sound of My Voice* Ron Butlin; *House of Lies* Colin Mackay. No unsolicited mss. Preliminary letter essential with large s.a.e. for details of current requirements. Will respond to ideas (with s.a.e.) but does not commission books on the basis of synopses. No poetry, children's, cookery, DIY, religion.
Royalties paid twice-yearly.

Black Dagger Crime
See **Chivers Press Ltd**

Black Lace
See **Virgin Publishing**

Black Spring Press Ltd
63 Harlescott Road, Nunhead, London SE15 3DA
☎0171 639 2492   Fax 0171 639 2508
Managing Director/Editor *Simon Pettifar*
FOUNDED 1986. *Publishes* fiction, literary criticism, biography, theatre and cinema studies. About 5 titles a year. TITLES *And the Ass Saw the Angel* Nick Cave; *Death of a Lady's Man* Leonard Cohen; *My Original Sin* Marie-Victoire Rouillier; *The Terrible News* collection of Russian short stories by Zamyatin, Babel, Karms, *et al*; *The Mortdecai Trilogy* Kyril Bonfiglioli. No unsolicited mss.
Royalties paid twice-yearly.

Black Swan
See **Transworld Publishers Ltd**

Blackie
See **Penguin Books Ltd**

Blackstaff Press Ltd
3 Galway Park, Dundonald, Belfast BT16 0AN
☎01232 487161   Fax 01232 489552
Director/Editorial Head *Anne Tannahill*
FOUNDED 1971. *Publishes* mainly, but not exclusively, Irish interest books, fiction, poetry, history, politics, illustrated and fine editions, natural history and folklore. About 25 titles a year.

Unsolicited mss considered, but preliminary submission of synopsis plus short sample of writing preferred. Return postage *must* be enclosed.
Royalties paid twice-yearly.

Authors' Rating Past winner of the *Sunday Times* Small Publisher of the Year Award, this Belfast publisher is noted for a strong backlist, 'wonderfully well-presented catalogues and promotional material'.

Blackwell Publishers Ltd
108 Cowley Road, Oxford OX4 1JF
☎01865 791100   Fax 01865 791347
Chairman *Nigel Blackwell*
Managing Director *René Olivieri*

FOUNDED 1922. Rapid growth since the 1970s included the establishment of a wholly owned distribution company, Marston Book Services, a joint venture with **Polity Press** (see book entry). The focus is on international research journals and undergraduate textbooks in social sciences, business and humanities; computer-aided instruction on p.c. applications; corporate training. About 300 titles a year and over 100 journals.

DIVISIONS/IMPRINTS
Books *Philip Carpenter, John Davey* **Journals** *Sue Corbett, Claire Andrews* **Shakespeare Head Press** *John Davey* **New Business** *Stephan Chambers*. Unsolicited synopses with specimen chapter and table of contents welcome.
Royalties paid annually. *Overseas associates* Blackwell Publishers Inc., Cambridge, Massachusetts; InfoSource Inc., Orlando, Florida.

Authors' Rating The latest venture for this fast-growing company is computer-based training and assessment for the further and higher education markets. The move away from print could be accelerated by the American connection which is proving to be a highly fruitful investment.

Blackwell Science Ltd
Osney Mead, Oxford OX2 0EL
☎01865 206206   Fax 01865 721205
Chairman *Nigel Blackwell*
Managing Director *Robert Campbell*
Editorial Director *Peter Saugman*
Approx. Annual Turnover (Group)
   £85 million

FOUNDED 1939. Part of the Blackwell Group, Oxford, which has seen rapid growth since the 1970s, culminating in expansion into Europe in the late 1980s with the acquisition of Medizinische Zeitschriften Verlagsgesellschaft (MZV), Vienna; Ueberreuter Wissenschaft

Verlag (now Blackwell Wissenschafts-Verlag), Berlin; Arnette, Paris; more recently, Grosse Verlag, Germany; and the academic publishing of Paul Parey. Also 75% owner of Danish general publisher Munksgaard. *Publishes* medical, professional and science. About 230 titles a year, plus 220 journals. TITLES *Diseases of the Liver and Biliary System* Sherlock; *Essential Immunology* Roitt; *Textbook of Dermatology* Rook. Unsolicited mss and synopses welcome.
Royalties paid annually. *Overseas subsidiaries* in USA, Australia, Paris, Berlin and Vienna; editorial offices in London and Edinburgh.

Authors' Rating Journals are more important to Blackwell Science than books and it will not be long before books are pushed into third place by CD-ROMs. Sales in Europe are impressive in part thanks to acquisition or link-up with continental publishers.

Blake Publishing
3 Bramber Court, 2 Bramber Road, London W14 9PB
☎0171 381 0666   Fax 0171 381 6868
Chairman *David Blake*
Managing Director *John Blake*
Approx. Annual Turnover £1 million

FOUNDED 1991 and rapidly expanding. *Publishes* mass-market non-fiction. No cookery, children's, specialist or non-commercial. 25 titles in 1995. No unsolicited mss; synopses and ideas welcome. Please enclose s.a.e..
Royalties paid twice-yearly.

Authors' Rating Tabloid version of book publishing with an 'unashamedly mass-market' list. Strong on sale of serial rights.

Blandford Press
See **Cassell**

Bloodaxe Books Ltd
PO Box 1SN, Newcastle upon Tyne NE99 1SN
☎0191 232 5988   Fax 0191 222 0020
Chairman *Simon Thirsk*
Managing/Editorial Director *Neil Astley*

Publishes poetry, literature and criticism, and related titles by British, Irish, European, Commonwealth and American writers. 95 per cent of their list is poetry. About 50 titles a year. TITLES include two major anthologies, *The New Poetry* Hulse, Kennedy and Morley (eds); *Sixty Women Poets* Linda France (ed); *The Gaze of the Gorgon* Tony Harrison - winner of the **Whitbread Award** for poetry in 1992; *No Truth With the Furies* R. S. Thomas (Nobel

Prize nominee); *Selected Poems* Jenny Joseph. Unsolicited poetry mss welcome. Authors of other material should write first with details of their work.

Royalties paid annually.

Authors' Rating 'The liveliest and most innovative poetry house', according to the editor of *Poetry Review*. Strong on women's poetry and on translations.

Bloomsbury Publishing Plc
2 Soho Square, London W1V 6HB
☎0171 494 2111   Fax 0171 434 0151
Chairman/Managing Director *Nigel Newton*
Publishing Directors *Liz Calder, David Reynolds, Kathy Rooney*

FOUNDED 1986 by Nigel Newton, David Reynolds, Alan Wherry and Liz Calder. Over the following years Bloomsbury titles were to appear regularly on *The Sunday Times* bestseller list and many of its authors have gone on to win prestigious literary prizes. In 1991 Nadine Gordimer won the **Nobel Prize for Literature**, Michael Ondaatje's *The English Patient* won the 1992 **Booker Prize** and Tobias Wolff's *In Pharaoh's Army* won the 1994 **Esquire/Volvo/Waterstone's Non-Fiction Award**. Publishes literary fiction and non-fiction, including general reference and children's books. TITLES *The Best of Friends* Joanna Trollope; *Debatable Land* Candia McWilliam; *The Piano* Jane Campion; *Crossing the River* Caryl Phillips; *The Robber Bride* Margaret Atwood; *Thomas Hardy; The Definitive Biography* Martin Seymour-Smith; *The Unlikely Spy* Paul Henderson; *Bloomsbury Thesaurus; Guide to Human Thought; Guide to Women's Literature; Bloomsbury Classics.* Unsolicited mss and synopses welcome; no poetry.

Royalties paid twice-yearly.

Authors' Rating There have been times in its ten-year history when the hatchets have been out for Bloomsbury, a quality general publisher which has prospered against the odds. Ambitious investments made when general confidence was low are now beginning to pay off.

Boatswain Press
See **Kenneth Mason Publications Ltd**

Bobcat
See **Omnibus Press**

Bodley Head
See **Random House UK Ltd**

The Book Guild Ltd
Temple House, 25-26 High Street, Lewes, East Sussex BN7 2LU
☎01273 472534   Fax 01273 476472
Chairman *George M. Nissen CBE*
Managing Director *Carol Biss*

FOUNDED 1982. *Publishes* fiction, academic, general, naval and military, autobiography, art. Expanding children's list. Approx. 75 titles a year.

DIVISIONS/TITLES
Children's *Underneath the Underground* Anthea Turner and Wendy Turner; *Spuddy* Pat Hill. **Fiction** *Making a Killing* William M. Johnson; *Isabel's Choice* Joan Bovell-Eberhardt. **Academic** *The Alternative Shakespeare* A. M. Challinor; *The Rainbow Shell* Frederick Jarvis. **Military** *Corporal Haggis* Frank and Julian Akers Douglas; *To Be a Chindit* Phil Sharpe. **Autobiography** *Baby in the Bathwater* Gordon Schaffer; *Century Story* Claudia Parsons. **General** *The Weimar Insanity* Christopher Thurndall; *The Making of Brazil* N. P. Macdonald. **Art** *Blake, Palmer, Linnell & Co.* David Linnell; *The Life and Work of James Ward* Oliver Beckett.

IMPRINTS **Temple House Books** Fiction: *Drug Squad* Brian Windmill. Non-fiction: *Colditz, Last Stop* Jack Pringle; *The Fitzroy* Sally Fiber. Unsolicited mss. Ideas and synopses welcome.

Royalties paid twice-yearly.

Authors' Rating Trawls for authors in the small ads columns of the literary pages who may be asked to cover their own production costs.

Bookmarks Publications
265 Seven Sisters Road, Finsbury Park, London N4 2DE
☎0181 802 6145   Fax 0181 802 3835
Managing Director *Lee Humber*
Approx. Annual Turnover £75,000

FOUNDED 1979 to promote the international socialist movement. Has close links with the Socialist Workers Party and its internationally related organisations. *Publishes* politics, economics, labour history, trade unionism, international affairs. About 7 titles a year. TITLES *Socialists in the Trade Unions; Economics of the Madhouse; History of Communism in Britain.* Unsolicited synopses and ideas welcome as long as they are compatible with existing policy. No unsolicited mss.

Royalties paid annually. *Overseas associates* Chicago, USA; Melbourne, Australia.

Boulevard Books & The Babel Guides

8 Aldbourne Road, London W12 0LN
☎0181 743 5278   Fax 0181 743 5278
Managing Director *Ray Keenoy*
Sales & Promotion *Siân Williams*

Specialises in contemporary world fiction by young writers in English translation. Existing or forthcoming series of fiction from Brazil, Italy, Latin America, Portugal and Greece. The Babel Guides series of popular guides to fiction in translation started in 1995.

DIVISONS

Latin American *Ray Keenoy* TITLES *Dragons* Caio Abreu; *Tattoo* Ednodio Quintero. **Italian** *Fiorenza Conte* TITLES *The Toy Catalogue* Sandra Petrignani; *Run!* Valeria Viganò; *Old Heaven, New Earth* Ginevra Bompiani. **Brazil** *Dr David Treece* TITLES *From the Heart of Brazil* (anthology). **Portugal** *Dr Hilary Owen* TITLES *Women of the Sea* (anthology); **Greece** *Marina Coriolano-Likourezos*; **Babel Guides to Fiction in Translation** *Ray Keenoy* series editor TITLES *Babel Guide to Italian Fiction in Translation, Babel Guide to the Fiction of Portugal, Brazil & Africa in Translation* (Keenoy & Treece).

Suggestions and proposals for translations of contemporary fiction welcome. Also seeking contributors to forthcoming Babel Guides (all literatures).

Royalties paid twice-yearly.

Bowker-Saur Ltd

Maypole House, Maypole Road,
East Grinstead, West Sussex RH19 1HU
☎01342 330100   Fax 01342 330191
Managing Director *Charles Halpin*
Publishers *Geraldine Turpie, Yolanda Dolling*

Owned by Reed Elsevier, Bowker-Saur is the UK division of Reed Reference Publishing. *Publishes* library reference, library science, bibliography, biography, African studies, politics and world affairs, business and professional directories. Unsolicited mss will not be read. Approach with ideas only.

Royalties paid annually.

Boxtree

2nd Floor, Broadwall House, 21 Broadwall,
London SE1 9PL
☎0171 928 9696   Fax 0171 928 5632
Chairman *Peter Roche*
Managing Director *David Inman*
Publishing Directors *Adrian Sington, Michael Alcock*

Editorial Directors *Humphrey Price, Susanna Wadeson*
Approx. Annual Turnover £9 million

FOUNDED 1987. *Publishes* books linked to and about television; also video and music. About 250 titles a year. Children's imprint **Sapling** and New Age imprint **Newleaf** launched in 1995. TITLES *Oliver Otter* Kate Veale; *Second Act* Joan Collins; *Garden Doctors* (Channel 4); *Diary of an England Manager* Terry Venables; *Queen* CD-ROM, also Robert Carrier and Anton Mossiman. See **Stop Press**

Royalties paid twice-yearly.

Authors' Rating Described by *The Bookseller* as 'one of the publishing successes of the 1990s', Boxtree has developed a strong list of television and film tie-in books. The latest development is a new children's imprint called Sapling.

Marion Boyars Publishers Ltd

24 Lacy Road, London SW15 1NL
☎0181 788 9522   Fax 0181 789 8122
Managing Director/Editorial Director *Marion Boyars*
Editor, Non-fiction *Ken Hollings*

FOUNDED 1975, formerly Calder and Boyars. *Publishes* biography and autobiography, economics, fiction, literature and criticism, medical, music, philosophy, poetry, politics and world affairs, psychology, religion and theology, sociology and anthropology, theatre and drama, film and cinema, women's studies. About 30 titles a year. AUTHORS include Georges Bataille, Ingmar Bergman, Heinrich Böll, Jean Cocteau, Clive Collins, Julian Green, Ivan Illich, Pauline Kael, Ken Kesey, Kenzaburo Oe, Michael Ondaatje, Hubert Selby, Igor Stravinsky, Frederic Tuten, Eudora Welty, Judith Williamson. Unsolicited mss not welcome for fiction; submissions from agents preferred. Unsolicited synopses and ideas welcome for non-fiction.

Royalties paid annually. *Overseas associates* Marion Boyars Publishers Inc., 237 East 39th Street, New York, NY 10016, USA.

Authors' Rating Where have all the intellectuals gone? Maybe not every one to Marion Boyars but her list is cerebral, to put it mildly. So beset is she by unsolicited mss that she has a mind to charge an administration fee 'by arrangement'. Who can blame her?

Boydell & Brewer Ltd

PO Box 9, Woodbridge, Suffolk IP12 3DF
☎01394 411320

Publishes non-fiction only. All books commissioned. No unsolicited material.

BPS Books

St Andrews House, 48 Princess Road East,
Leicester LE1 7DR
☎0116 2549568   Fax 0116 2470787

Publications Manager *Joyce Collins*
Editor *Susan Pacitti*

Book publishing division of the British
Psychological Society. *Publishes* a wide range of
academic and applied psychology, including
specialist monographs, textbooks for teachers,
managers, doctors, nurses, social workers, and
schools material; plus general psychology. 10–
15 titles a year. Proposals considered.

Bracken Books
See **Random House UK Ltd**

Brampton Publications
See **SB Publications**

Brassey's (UK) Ltd

33 John Street, London WC1N 2AT
☎0171 753 7777   Fax 0171 753 7794

Chairman *Lord Holme of Cheltenham*
Managing Director *Jenny Shaw MA*
Approx. Annual Turnover £2.65 million

Began life as *Brassey's Naval Annual* in 1886 to
become the most important publisher of serious
defence-related material in the world. Owned
by Robert Stephen Holdings. *Publishes* books
and journals on defence, international relations,
military history, maritime and aeronautical subjects and defence terminology. Launced its new
imprint **Brassey's Sports** in 1996 with the
International Olympic Committee's Official
Handbook *The IOC Olympic Companion 1996*

IMPRINTS **Brassey's (UK)**; **Brassey's Inc**;
Brassey's Sports; **Conway Maritime Press**
naval history and ship modelling; **Putnam
Aeronautical Books** technical and reference.
Royalties paid annually.

Nicholas Brealey Publishing Ltd

21 Bloomsbury Way, London WC1A 2TH
☎0171 430 0224   Fax 0171 404 8311

Managing Director *Nicholas Brealey*

FOUNDED 1992 with a backlist of major titles
from The Industrial Society. Independent non-
fiction publisher focusing on high-profile, practical books for business that inspire, enable, inform
and entertain. *Publishes* 'readable reference' on
management, employment, law, training and
human resources. TITLES *Coaching for Performance;
Head to Head; Reengineering the Corporation; NLP
at Work; Megatrends Asia; The Fifth Discipline
Fieldbook; China Wakes; Transforming the Bottom*

Line; Snapshots from Hell. No fiction, poetry or
leisure titles. No unsolicited mss; synopses and
ideas welcome.
Royalties paid twice-yearly.

Authors' Rating A recent entry into the
booming management book market, Nicholas
Brealey looks to be succeeding in breaking
away from the usual computer-speak business
manuals to publish information and literate
texts. Lead titles have a distinct trans-Atlantic
feel.

The Breedon Books Publishing Co. Ltd

44 Friar Gate, Derby DE1 1DA
☎01332 384235   Fax 01332 292755

Chairman/Managing Director *A. C. Rippon*
Approx. Annual Turnover £1 million

FOUNDED 1983. *Publishes* autobiography, biography, heritage and sport. 32 titles in 1995.
Unsolicited mss, synopses and ideas welcome if
accompanied by s.a.e.. No poetry or fiction.
Royalties paid annually.

Breese Books Ltd

164 Kensington Park Road, London
W11 2ER
☎0171 727 9426   Fax 0171 229 3395

Chairman/Managing Director *Martin Breese*

FOUNDED 1975 to produce specialist conjuring
books and then went on to establish a more
general list, linking up with German, Italian,
French and US publishers. *Publishes* fiction,
crime, biography, self-hypnosis, bibliography,
meditation, ESP and related fields, music and
conjuring titles. About 20 titles a year.

IMPRINTS
Breese Books TITLES *Even if They Fail* David
Holbrook; *Exit Mr Punch* Mignon Warner;
Foxtrot, Oscar, X-Ray James Neat. **Breese
Books Paperbacks** TITLES *Self-hypnosis and
Other Mind Expanding Techniques* Charles
Tebbetts; *The Gourmet Detective* Peter King;
The Dreamer's Guide series. Unsolicited mss not
welcome but synopses plus 10 sample mss
pages will be considered.
Royalties paid twice-yearly. *Distributed* by
Clipper Distribution.

Brimax Books
See **Reed Books**

Bristol Classical Press
See **Gerald Duckworth & Co. Ltd**

British Academic Press
See **I. B. Tauris & Co. Ltd**

The British Academy
20-21 Cornwall Terrace, London NW1 4QP
☎0171 487 5966   Fax 0171 224 3807
Publications Officer *J. M. H. Rivington*
Publications Assistant *J. English*

FOUNDED 1901. The primary body for promoting scholarship in the humanities, the Academy publishes many series stemming from its own long-standing research projects, or series of lectures and conference proceedings. Main subjects include history, philosophy and archaeology. About 10-15 titles a year. SERIES *Auctores Britannici Medii Aevi; Early English Church Music; Fontes Historiae Africanae; Records of Social and Economic History.* Proposals for these series are welcome and are forwarded to the relevant project committees. The British Academy is a registered charity and does not publish for profit.

Royalties paid only when titles have covered their costs.

The British Library
Marketing & Publishing Office, 41 Russell Square, London WC1B 3DG
☎0171 412 7704   Fax 0171 412 7768
Managing Director *Jane Carr*
Publishing Manager *David Way*
Approx. Annual Turnover £750,000

FOUNDED 1979 as the publishing arm of The British Library's London Collections to publish works based on the historic collections and related subjects. *Publishes* bibliographical reference, manuscript studies, illustrated books based on the Library's collections, and book arts. TITLES *The Image of the World: 20 Centuries of World Maps; Women Bookbinders 1880 - 1920; Five Hundred Years of Printing; The Lindisfarne Gospels; The Gutenberg Bible.* About 30 titles a year. Unsolicited mss, synopses and ideas welcome if related to the history of the book, book arts or bibliography. No fiction or general non-fiction.

Royalties paid annually.

British Museum Press
46 Bloomsbury Street, London WC1B 3QQ
☎0171 323 1234   Fax 0171 436 7315
Managing Director *Patrick Wright*
Head of Publishing *Emma Way*

The book publishing division of The British Museum Company Ltd. FOUNDED 1973 as British Museum Publications Ltd; relaunched 1991 as British Museum Press. *Publishes* ancient history, archaeology, ethnography, art history, exhibition catalogues, guides, children's books, and all official publications of the British Museum. Around 50 titles a year. TITLES *Dictionary of Ancient Egypt; The Medieval Garden, Landmarks in Print Collecting; The Classical Cookbook; The Kingdom of Kush.* Synopses and ideas for books welcome.

Royalties paid twice-yearly.

The Brockhampton Press
See **Hodder Headline plc**

John Brown Publishing Ltd
The Boathouse, Crabtree Lane, Fulham, London SW6 6LU
☎0171 470 2400   Fax 0171 381 3930
Chairman/Managing Director *John Brown*

FOUNDED 1986. *Publishes* adult comic annuals; *Viz* magazine; strange phenomena. 10 titles in 1995. DIVISION **Fortean Times Books** *Mike Dash* TITLES *Book of Weird Sex; Book of Strange Dreams; Fortean Studies Vol II.* IMPRINT **Old Rope Books** *Chris Donald.* Does not welcome unsolicited mss.

Royalties paid twice-yearly.

WCB Brown
See **Times Mirror International Publishers Ltd**

Brown, Son & Ferguson, Ltd
4-10 Darnley Street, Glasgow G41 2SD
☎0141 429 1234   Fax 0141 420 1694
Chairman/Joint Managing Director
  T. Nigel Brown

FOUNDED 1850. *Specialises* in nautical textbooks, both technical and non-technical. Also Boy Scout/Girl Guide books, and Scottish one-act/three-act plays. Unsolicited mss, synopses and ideas for books welcome.

Royalties paid annually.

Brown Watson Ltd
The Old Mill, 76 Fleckney Road, Kibworth Beauchamp, Leicestershire LE8 0HG
☎0116 2796333   Fax 0116 2796303
Managing Director *Michael B. McDonald*

FOUNDED 1980. *Publishes* children's books only. About 150 titles a year. Most books are commissioned. Unsolicited mss and synopses are not welcome.

Authors' Rating Children's books for the cheaper end of the market. Authors must work fast to make money.

Bucknell University Press
See **Golden Cockerel Press Ltd**

Burns & Oates
See **Search Press**

Business Books
See **Random House UK Ltd**

Business Education Publishers Ltd
Leighton House, 10 Grange Crescent,
Sunderland, Tyne & Wear SR2 7BN
☎0191 567 4963   Fax 0191 514 3277
Managing Director *P. M. Callaghan*
Approx. Annual Turnover £350,000

FOUNDED 1981. *Publishes* business education,
economics and law for BTEC and GNVQ reading. Currently expanding into further and higher
education, computing, community health services, travel and tourism, occasional papers for
institutions and local government administration.
Unsolicited mss and synopses welcome.
Royalties paid annually.

Butterworth Heinemann UK
See **Reed Educational and Professional
Publishing**

Cadogan Books plc
London House, Park Gate Road, London
SW11 4NQ
☎0171 738 1961   Fax 0171 924 5491
Chairman *Bill Colegrave*
Publisher *Rachel Fielding*
Approx. Annual Turnover £1.2 million

Now merged with **David Campbell
Publishers Ltd**. *Publishes* the *Cadogan Travel
Guide* series, and chess and bridge titles. About
55 titles a year. No unsolicited mss; send introductory letter with synopsis only. Synopses and
ideas welcome.
Royalties paid twice-yearly.

Authors' Rating Having achieved a strong
base in travel publishing, Cadogan is branching
out. Last year brought the launch of a chess
service on the Microsoft Network to supplement an acquired chess and bridge list; now
there is a merger with **David Campbell
Publishers** whose prize possession is the
Everyman Library. Further expansion is
planned.

Calder Publications Ltd
179 Kings Cross Road, London
WC1X 9BZ
☎0171 833 1300
**Chairman/Managing Director/Editorial
Head** *John Calder*

Formerly John Calder (Publishers) Ltd. A publishing company which has grown around the
tastes and contacts of John Calder, the iconoclast
of the literary establishment. The list has a reputation for controversial and opinion-forming
publications; Samuel Beckett is perhaps the most
prestigious name. The list includes all of
Beckett's prose and poetry. *Publishes* autobiography, biography, drama, literary fiction, literary
criticism, music, opera, poetry, politics, sociology. AUTHORS Roy Calne, Marguerite Duras,
Erich Fried, Trevor Hoyle, P. J. Kavanagh,
Robert Pinget, Alain Robbe-Grillet, Nathalie
Sarraute, Julian Semyonov, Claude Simon,
Howard Barker (plays), ENO opera guides. All
approaches must be accompanied by s.a.e. if a
reply is required. *No unsolicited material.*
Royalties paid annually.

Authors' Rating Operating in Paris and
London and points between, John Calder is
said to be 'overflowing with geniuses and
eccentric talents'. But according to the publisher, times are hard and there is never enough
money to pay all the bills. He is much revered
in France as a free and far-ranging intellectual.

California University Press
See **University Presses of California,
Columbia & Princeton Ltd**

Cambridge University Press
The Edinburgh Building, Shaftesbury Road,
Cambridge CB2 2RU
☎01223 312393   Fax 01223 315052
Chief Executive *A. K. Wilson*
Managing Director, Publishing *R. J. Mynott*

The oldest press in the world. Over the last few
years CUP has been diversifying into reference,
electronic, legal and medical publishing and has
expanded its activities in Europe, the Far East,
Latin America, Australia and the USA. Recent
developments include editorial offices at
Stanford University, California, Cape Town,
South Africa and Barcelona; new offices in
Bologna and Mexico; the acquisition of
Grotius Publications (International Law);
major National Curriculum and ELT course
publications; Cambridge Encyclopedia programme;   the   Cambridge   International

Dictionary of English; low-price editions for the developing world; new Cambridge Guides and Illustrated Histories; the paperback imprint **Canto**. *Publishes* academic/educational books for international English-language markets, at all levels from primary school to postgraduate. Also bibles and over 100 academic journals. Over 20,000 authors in 100 different countries, and about 1500 new titles a year.

PUBLISHING GROUPS
Bibles *L. M. Hieatt* **ELT** *C. J. F. Hayes* **Education** *S. A. Seddon* **Humanities** *A. M. C. Brown* **Social Sciences** *M. Y. Holdsworth* **Journals** *C. Guettler* **Reference** *A. du Plessis* **Science, Technology, Medicine and Electronic Publishing** *S. Mitton*. Synopses and ideas for educational, ELT and academic books are welcomed (preferable to the submission of unsolicited mss). No fiction or poetry. *Royalties* paid twice-yearly.

Authors' Rating With its strong overseas presence, CUP has taken the bold step of setting up a Spanish language publishing programme. With sluggish home sales, this could be an example that other publishers will be keen to follow.

Camden Large Print
See **Chivers Press Ltd**

David Campbell Publishers Ltd
79 Berwick Street, London W1V 3PF
☎0171 287 0035   Fax 0171 287 0038
Chairman *Alewyn Birch*
Managing Director *David Campbell*
Approx. Annual Turnover £3.5 million
FOUNDED 1990 with the acquisition of **Everyman's Library** (established 1906) bought from **J. M. Dent**. Now merged with **Cadogan Books plc**. *Publishes* classics of world literature and travel guides. AUTHORS include Bulgakov, Bellow, Borges, Forster, Grass, Mann, Nabokov, Orwell, Rushdie, Updike and Waugh. No unsolicited mss; ideas or synopsis welcome. IMPRINT **Adelphi** Illustrated books.
Royalties paid annually.

Campbell Books
See **Macmillan Publishers Ltd**

Canongate Books Ltd
14 High Street, Edinburgh EH1 1TE
☎0131 557 5111   Fax 0131 557 5211
Joint Managing Directors *Jamie Byng, Hugh Andrew*
Approx. Annual Turnover £800,000
FOUNDED 1973. Independent again, following

a management buyout in September 1994. *Publishes* general fiction and non-fiction, children's fiction (age 8+), and Scottish interest. Also has an audio list (see under **Audio Books**).
IMPRINTS **Canongate Classics** adult paperback series; **Kelpie** children's paperback fiction series; **Payback Press** Afro-American, Black orientated fiction and non-fiction; music, history, politics, biography and poetry. About 60 titles a year. Synopses preferred to complete mss.
Royalties paid twice-yearly.

Authors' Rating An independent Scottish publisher with a flair for original ideas.

Canterbury Press Norwich
See **Hymns Ancient & Modern Ltd**

Canto
See **Cambridge University Press**

Jonathan Cape Ltd
See **Random House UK Ltd**

Carcanet Press Ltd
402 Corn Exchange Buildings, Manchester M4 3BQ
☎0161 834 8730   Fax 0161 832 0084
Chairman *Kate Gavron*
Managing Director/Editorial Director *Michael Schmidt*
Since 1969 Carcanet has grown from an undergraduate hobby into a substantial venture. Robert Gavron bought the company in 1983 and it has established strong Anglo-European and Anglo-Commonwealth links. *Publishes* poetry, academic, literary biography, fiction in translation and translations. About 40 titles a year, including the *P. N. Review* (six issues yearly). AUTHORS John Ashbery, Edwin Morgan, Elizabeth Jennings, Iain Crichton Smith, Natalia Ginzburg, Eavan Boland, Stuart Hood, Leonardo Sciascia, Christine Brooke-Rose, Pier Paolo Pasolini, C. H. Sisson, Donald Davie.
Royalties paid annually.

Authors' Rating One of the leaders of the poetry revival in the eighties, Carcanet shows how quality can be profitable. William Boyd says of Carcanet that it is 'everything an independent publisher should be'.

Cardiff Academic Press
St Fagans Road, Fairwater, Cardiff CF5 3AE
☎01222 560333   Fax 01222 554909
Marketing Manager *Mary de Lange*
Academic publisher.

Carlton Books Ltd

20 St Anne's Court, Wardour Street, London
W1V 3AW
☎0171 734 7338   Fax 0171 434 1196

Managing Director *Jonathan Goodman*
Approx. Annual Turnover £6.7 million

FOUNDED 1992. Owned by Carlton Communications, Carlton books are aimed at the mass market for subjects such as computer games, popular science and rock'n'roll. *Publishes* illustrated leisure and entertainment. Prime UK customers include the Book Club and W H Smith. A second arm of the company, established late 1992, was set up to create a promotional books business. No unsolicited mss; synopses and ideas welcome.

Royalties paid twice-yearly.

Authors' Rating Linked to the largest programme producer in the ITV network, Carlton Books has built a reputation on co-editions for the international market. Now it is moving into television tie-ins. Noted for speed of taking a book from first idea to publication.

Frank Cass & Co Ltd

Newbury House, 890-900 Eastern Avenue, Newbury Park, Ilford, Essex IG2 7HH
☎0181 599 8866   Fax 0181 599 0984

Managing Director *Frank Cass*
Managing Editor *Robert Easton*

Publishes Africa, development, strategic and military studies, education, history, literature, Middle East, politics and world affairs plus over 40 academic journals. TITLES *Anwar Sadat: Visionary Who Dared* Joseph Finklestone; *Violence in Southern Africa* ed. J. E. Spence; *Ethnicity, Gender and the Subversion of Nationalism* eds. Fiona Wilson and Bodil Folke Frederikson.

DIVISIONS
Woburn Press Educational list. TITLES *The First Teenagers: The Lifestyle of Young Wage-Earners in Interwar Britain* David Fowler; *Teaching Science* eds. Jenny Frost *et al.* **Vallentine Mitchell/Jewish Chronicle Publications** Books of Jewish interest. TITLES *Will We Have Jewish Grandchildren? Jewish Continuity and How to Achieve It* Chief Rabbi Dr Jonathan Sacks; *New Women's Writing From Israel* Risa Domb; *Library of Holocaust Testimonies* series: *An End to Childhood* Miriam Akavia; *Jewish Year Book; Jewish Travel Guide.* Unsolicited mss considered but synopsis with covering letter preferred.

Royalties paid annually.

Cassell

Wellington House, 125 Strand, London
WC2R 0BB
☎0171 420 5555   Fax 0171 240 7261

Chairman/Managing Director *Philip Sturrock*
Approx. Annual Turnover £20 million

FOUNDED 1848 by John Cassell. Bought by Collier Macmillan in 1974, then by CBS Publishing Europe in 1982. Finally returned to independence in 1986 as Cassell plc and a string of acquisitions followed: Tycooly's book publishing division; Link House Books (now Blandford Publishing Ltd); Mansell; then Mowbray and Ward Lock, publisher of Mrs Beeton, (in print continuously since 1861); Victor Gollancz in 1992 and Pinter Publishers Ltd in February 1995. *Publishes* business, education and academic, general non-fiction, primary and secondary school books, poetry, religion. About 800 titles a year.

IMPRINTS
Cassell *Alison Goff* (general books) TITLES *Cassell Concise English Dictionary; French Country Crafts* Marie-Pierre Moine; *Brewer's Politics – A Dictionary of Phrase and Fable* Nicholas Comfort; *Wisley Handbooks.* PAPERBACK IMPRINTS **Indigo** Mike Petty; **Vista** *Richard Evans.*

    Cassell (academic books) and **Mansell** TITLES *Reflective Teaching in Primary Schools* Pollard; *Practical Counselling Skills* Nelson-Jones; *Index of English Literary Manuscripts* Peter Beal.

    Arms & Armour Press *Roderick Dymott* TITLES *The Royal Air Force: An Illustrated History* Michael Armitage; *Waterloo: New Perspectives* David Hamilton-William.

    Blandford Press *Alison Goff* TITLES *Insects in Flight* John Brackenbury; *A Dictionary of Dream Symbols* Eric Ackroyd; *Play the Game Series.*

    Studio Vista *Alison Goff* TITLES *The Beginner's Guide to Painting in Watercolour* Jenny Rodwell.

    Ward Lock *Alison Goff* TITLES *How to be a Supergardener* Alan Titchmarsh; *Mrs Beeton's Book of Cookery and Household Management* Bridget Jones (ed.).

    Victor Gollancz *Liz Knights* TITLES *Fever Pitch* Nick Hornby; *Maskerade* Terry Pratchett; *Official and Confidential* A. Summers.

    Geoffrey Chapman *Ruth McCurry* TITLES *Cardinal Hume and the Changing Face of English Catholicism* Peter Stanford; *New Jerome Biblical Commentary* Brown, Fitzmyer, Murphy (eds.).

    Mowbray *Ruth McCurry* TITLES *Robert Runcie* Adrian Hastings; *Celebrating Common Prayer.*

New Orchard Editions *Alan Smith* TITLES *Natural History of Britain's Coasts* Eric Foothill; *One Hour Garden* Laurence Fleming.

Leicester University Press *Janet Joyce* (history archaeology, museum and cultural studies) TITLES *The Origins of Anglo Saxon Kingdoms; The Archaeology of Society in the Holy Land.*

Pinter Publishers Ltd *Janet Joyce* (social sciences and humanities) TITLES *Globalisation and Interdependence in the International Political Economy; An Introduction to Systemic Functional Linguistics.*

Royalties payment depends on sales potential and varies between imprints; generally twice-yearly, but annually for Arms & Armour Press.

Authors' Rating Dedicated to growth by acquisition, Cassell has a formidable reputation for reviving companies once thought to be on their last legs. Ward Lock, Gollancz and Blandford are among the famous names now recovering under Cassell management. New paperback lists – Vista and Indigo – are off to a promising start.

Kyle Cathie Ltd

20 Vauxhall Bridge Road, London SW1V 2SA
☎0171 973 9710   Fax 0171 821 9258

Publisher/Managing Director *Kyle Cathie*
Senior Commissioning Editor *Catherine Bradley*

FOUNDED 1990 to publish and promote 'books we have personal enthusiasm for'. *Publishes* non-fiction: history, natural history, health, biography, food and drink, craft, gardening and reference. TITLES *Irish Traditional Cooking* Darina Allen; *Bob Flowerdew's Complete Fruit Book*; *The Complete Verse of Rudyard Kipling.* About 40 titles a year. No unsolicited mss. 'Synopses and ideas are considered in the fields in which we publish.'
Royalties paid twice-yearly.

Authors' Rating A refugee from big-time publishing who has made good as a small independent producing books which might not otherwise find a home.

Catholic Truth Society

192 Vauxhall Bridge Road, London SW1V 1PD
☎0171 834 4392   Fax 0171 630 1124

Chairman *Rt. Rev. Mgr. Peter Smith*
General Secretary *Fergal Martin*
Approx. Annual Turnover £500,000

FOUNDED originally in 1869 and re-founded in 1884. *Publishes* religious books – Roman Catholic and ecumenical. TITLES *My Lourdes Diary* Ellen Ryder; *The Human Face of Jesus*

Bernard O'Connor; *Saints' Names for Boys and Girls* J. J. Dwyer; *Prayer in a Busy Life* Bishop John Crowley; *The Second World War* Pope John Paul II. Unsolicited mss, synopses and ideas welcome if appropriate to their list.
Royalties paid annually.

Causeway Press Ltd

PO Box 13, 129 New Court Way, Ormskirk, Lancashire L39 5HP
☎01695 576048   Fax 01695 570714

Chairman/Managing Director
  M. Haralambos
Approx. Annual Turnover £1.7 million

FOUNDED in 1982. *Publishes* educational textbooks only. 18 titles in 1995. TITLES *Causeway Maths Series; Discovering History Series; Economics/Business Studies; Sociology: A New Approach; Causeway GNVQ: Intermediate Business.* Unsolicited mss, synopses and ideas welcome.
Royalties paid annually.

CBA Publishing

Bowes Morrell House, 111 Walmgate, York YO1 2UA
☎01904 671417   Fax 01904 671384

Managing Editor *Christine Pietrowski*
Approx. Annual Turnover £25,000

Publishing arm of the **Council for British Archaeology**. *Publishes* academic archaeology reports, practical handbooks, yearbook, *British Archaeology* (monthly magazine), monographs, archaeology and education. TITLES *Architecture in Roman Britain; Life and Death in Spitalfields 1700 to 1850; Moorland Monuments: Studies in the Archaeology of N. E. Yorkshire; Biological Evidence from 16-22 Coppergate, York; Recording a Church: an Illustrated Glossary.*
Royalties not paid.

CBD Research Ltd

Chancery House, 15 Wickham Road, Beckenham, Kent BR3 5JS
☎0181 650 7745   Fax 0181 650 0768

Chairman *G. P. Henderson*
Managing Director *S. P. A. Henderson*
Approx. Annual Turnover £300,000

FOUNDED 1961. *Publishes* directories and other reference guides to sources of information. Increased output over the last few years. About 8 titles a year planned. No fiction.

IMPRINT **Chancery House Press** non-fiction of an esoteric/specialist nature for 'serious researchers and the dedicated hobbyist'. Unsolicited mss, synopses and ideas welcome.
Royalties paid quarterly.

Centaur Press

Fontwell, Arundel, West Sussex BN18 0TA
☎01243 543302

Managing Director *Jon Wynne-Tyson*

FOUNDED 1954. A one-man outfit publishing some 20 titles a year at its peak. Then became increasingly preoccupied with humane education and reduced output to around 5 titles a year. After a semi-dormant period in the 1980s, Centaur went on to launch *The Kinship Library*, a series on the philosophy, politics and application of humane education, with special focus on the subject of animal rights and its relevance to the human condition.

IMPRINT **Linden Press** TITLES *Victims of Science; The Universal Kinship; Publishing Your Own Book.*

Authors' Rating With Centaur 40-plus and himself 70-plus, and with turnover too modest to tempt conglomerate predators, Jon Wynne-Tyson wants to sell out to a compatible firm or entrepreneur wanting a starter list. Submissions not encouraged until new owner found.

Century

See **Random House UK Ltd**

Chadwyck-Healey Ltd

The Quorum, Barnwell Road, Cambridge CB5 8SW
☎01223 215512   Fax 01223 215513

Chairman *Sir Charles Chadwyck-Healey*
Managing Director *Steven Hall*
Editorial Head *Alison Moss*

FOUNDED 1973. *Publishes* on microform and CD-ROM, with a few reference works/guides to their own microform collections. No monographs. About 50 titles a year. TITLES *The English Satirical Print; Theatre in Focus; Index of Manuscripts in The British Library*. No unsolicited mss. Synopses/ideas welcome for reference works only.

Royalties paid annually.

Chambers Harrap Ltd

See **Larousse plc**

Chancery House Press

See **CBD Research Ltd**

Chansitor Publications Ltd

See **Hymns Ancient & Modern Ltd**

Chapman

4 Broughton Place, Edinburgh EH1 3RX
☎0131 557 2207   Fax 0131 556 9565

Managing Editor *Joy Hendry*

A venture devoted to publishing works by the best of the Scottish writers, both up-and-coming and established, published in *Chapman* magazine, Scotland's leading literary quarterly. Has expanded publishing activities considerably over the last two years and is now publishing a wider range of works though the broad policy stands. *Publishes* poetry, drama, short stories, books of contemporary importance in 20th-century Scotland. About 4 titles a year. TITLES *Carlucco and the Queen of Hearts; The Blasphemer* George Rosie; *Gold of Kildonan; Songs of the Grey Coast* George Gunn; *The Collected Shorter Poems* Tom Scott. No unsolicited mss; synopses and ideas for books welcome.

Royalties paid annually.

Geoffrey Chapman

See **Cassell**

Paul Chapman Publishing Ltd

144 Liverpool Road, London N1 1LA
☎0171 609 5315   Fax 0171 700 1057

Managing Director *Paul R. Chapman*
Editorial Director *Marianne Lagrange*

Publishes business, management, accountancy and finance, education, geography, environment, planning and economics, for the academic and professional markets.

Royalties paid twice-yearly.

Chapmans Publishers

See **The Orion Publishing Group Ltd**

Chatto & Windus Ltd

See **Random House UK Ltd**

Cherrytree Press Children's Books

See **Chivers Press Ltd**

Child's Play (International) Ltd

Ashworth Road, Bridgemead, Swindon, Wiltshire SN5 7YD
☎01793 616286   Fax 01793 512795

Chairman *Michael Twinn*

FOUNDED 1972. This Swindon-based publisher has pioneered learning-through-play since the early days of its inception. *Publishes* children's books: picture books, fiction, science, art, activity books and dictionaries. TITLES *Dear Santa; Big Hungry Bear; Percy's Face Paint Party; Ten in a Bed; Wally Whale; One Odd Old Owl*. Unsolicited mss welcome. Send s.a.e. for return or response. Expect to wait 1-2 months for a reply.

Royalties payment varies according to contract.

Chivers Press Ltd

Windsor Bridge Road, Bath, Avon BA2 3AX
☎01225 335336   Fax 01225 310771
Managing Director *Simon D. Gibbs*

Part of the Gieves Group. *Publishes* reprints for libraries mainly, in large-print editions, including biography and autobiography, children's, crime, fiction and spoken word cassettes. No unsolicited material.

IMPRINTS **Chivers Large Print; Gunsmoke Westerns; Galaxy Children's Large Print; Camden Large Print; Paragon Softcover Large Print; Cherrytree Press Children's Books; Windsor Large Print; Black Dagger Crime. Chivers Audio Books** (see under **Audio Books**.
Royalties paid twice-yearly.

Christian Focus Publications

Geanies House, Fearn, Tain, Ross-shire
IV20 1TW
☎01862 87541   Fax 01862 87699
Chairman *R. W. M. Mackenzie*
Managing Director *William Mackenzie*
Editorial Head *Malcolm Maclean*
Approx. Annual Turnover £500,000

FOUNDED 1979 to produce children's books for the co-edition market. Now a major producer of Christian books. *Publishes* Christianity, adult and children's, including some children's fiction. About 45 titles a year. Unsolicited mss, synopses and ideas welcome from Christian writers. Publishes for all English-speaking markets, as well as the UK. Books produced for Australia, USA, Canada, South Africa.
Royalties paid twice-yearly.

Churchill Livingstone

Robert Stevenson House, 1-3 Baxter's Place, Leith Walk, Edinburgh EH1 3AF
☎0131 556 2424   Fax 0131 558 1278
Managing Director *Andrew Stevenson*
Publishing Director *Jennifer Mitchell*
Director, Nursing and Allied Health, Medical Education *Peter Shepherd*

Originally an amalgamation of E. & S. Livingstone and J. & A. Churchill in the early 1970s. Now part of Pearson Professional. *Publishes* books, journals and loose-leaf material in medicine, nursing and allied health matters, plus complementary therapies. About 150 titles a year. No unsolicited mss. Synopses and ideas welcome.
Royalties paid annually. *Overseas associates* worldwide.

Authors' Rating Churchill Livingstone is the leading medical publisher.

Cicerone Press

2 Police Square, Milnthorpe, Cumbria
LA7 7PY
☎015395 62069   Fax 015395 63417
Managing Director *Dorothy Unsworth*
Editorial Director *Walt Unsworth*

FOUNDED 1969. Guidebook publisher for outdoor enthusiasts. About 30 titles a year. No fiction or poetry. TITLES *Tour of Monte Rosa* (2 vols.); *A Trekker's Handbook; Everest – A Trekker's Guide.* No unsolicited mss; synopses and ideas considered.
Royalties paid twice-yearly.

Clarendon Press

See **Oxford University Press**

Claridge Press

33 Canonbury Park South, London N1 2JW
☎0171 226 7791   Fax 0171 354 0383
Chairman/Managing Director/Editorial Head *Roger Scruton*
Managing Editor *Merrie Cave*

FOUNDED 1987. Developed from the quarterly *Salisbury Review* (see under **Magazines**). *Publishes* current affairs – political, philosophical and sociological – from a right-wing viewpoint. SERIES *Thinkers of our Time.* TITLES *Falsification of the Good; Understanding Youth; Some Turn to Mecca to Pray: Islamic Values in the Modern World; KGB Lawsuits.* Unsolicited mss welcome within given subject areas.
Royalties paid according to contract.

Authors' Rating As the only house devoted to publishing the works of conservative thinkers, Claridge proclaims itself to be 'Britain's most backward-looking publisher'.

Clarion

See **Elliot Right Way Books**

T. & T. Clark

59 George Street, Edinburgh EH2 2LQ
☎0131 225 4703   Fax 0131 220 4260
Managing Director/Editorial Head *Geoffrey Green*

FOUNDED 1821. *Publishes* religion, theology, law and philosophy, for academic and professional markets. About 35 titles a year, including journals. TITLES include *Church Dogmatics* Karl Barth; *A Textbook of Christian Ethics* ed. Robin Gill; *Scottish Law Directory; The Law of Contracts and Related Obligations in Scotland* David M. Walker. Unsolicited mss, synopses and ideas for books welcome.
Royalties paid annually.

James Clarke & Co.
PO Box 60, Cambridge CB1 2NT
☎01223 350865   Fax 01223 366951
Managing Director *Adrian Brink*

Parent company of **Lutterworth Press**. *Publishes* scholarly and academic works, mainly theological, directory and reference titles. TITLES *The Encyclopedia of the Early Church; The Libraries' Directory*. Approach in writing with ideas in the first instance.

Clio Press Ltd
See **ABC–Clio International**

Richard Cohen Books Ltd
The Basement Offices, 7 Manchester Square, London W1M 5RE
☎0171 935 2099   Fax 0171 935 2199
Chairman/Managing Director *Richard Cohen*
Approx. Annual Turnover £1 million

FOUNDED in 1994. *Publishes* fiction, biography, current affairs, travel, history, politics, the arts, and sport. First titles published in 1995 with plans to expand from 20 books a year to 30. No erotica, DIY, children's, reference, science fiction, fantasy, or historical romance.

DIVISIONS **RCB General Books** *Richard Cohen* TITLES *Memoirs* Al Alvarez; *Mrs Rochester* Emma Tennant; *Running Free* Robin Knox-Johnston; *Alastair Cooke* Nick Clarke. No unsolicited mss; synopses and ideas welcome.
Royalties paid twice-yearly.

Authors' Rating With less than a year in the market place it is still too early to judge the prospects for Richard Cohen. Authors wish him well. He has flair and is responsive to ideas. But a general lift in the market would not come amiss.

Frank Coleman Publishing Ltd
Enterprise Way, Maulden Road, Flitwick, Bedfordshire MK45 5BW
☎01525 712261   Fax 01525 718205
Managing Director *Neil Goldman*
Approx. Annual Turnover £100,000

Publishes children's books. Unsolicited mss, synopses and ideas welcome.
Royalties paid annually.

Peter Collin Publishing Ltd
1 Cambridge Road, Teddington, Middlesex TW11 8DT
☎0181 943 3386   Fax 0181 943 1673
Chairman *P. H. Collin*

FOUNDED 1985. *Publishes* dictionaries only, including specialised dictionaries in English for students and specialised bilingual dictionaries for translators (French, German, Swedish, Spanish, Greek). About 5 titles a year. Synopses and ideas welcome. No unsolicited mss; copy must be supplied on disk.
Royalties paid twice-yearly.

Collins
See **HarperCollins Publishers Ltd**

Collins & Brown
London House, Great Eastern Wharf, Parkgate Road, London SW11 4NQ
☎0171 924 2575   Fax 0171 924 7725
Chairman *Cameron Brown*
Managing Director *Mark Collins*
Approx. Annual Turnover £4.75 million

FOUNDED 1989. Independent publisher. *Publishes* illustrated non-fiction: practical photography, crafts, gardening, illustrated letters and history. No fiction, children's, poetry or local interest. About 50 titles a year.

No unsolicited mss; outlines with s.a.e. only.
Royalties paid twice-yearly.

Colonsay Books
See **House of Lochar**

Columbia University Press
See **University Presses of California, Columbia & Princeton Ltd**

Condé Nast Books
See **Random House UK Ltd**

Condor
See **Souvenir Press Ltd**

Conran Octopus
See **Reed Books**

Constable & Co. Ltd
3 The Lanchesters, 162 Fulham Palace Road, London W6 9ER
☎0181 741 3663   Fax 0181 748 7562
Chairman/Managing Director *Benjamin Glazebrook*
Editorial Director *Carol O'Brien*
Approx. Annual Turnover £2.6 million

FOUNDED in 1890 by Archibald Constable, a grandson of Walter Scott's publisher. Controlling interest was bought by Benjamin Glazebrook in 1967 and the remaining 48% was purchased by Hutchinson, now owned by

Random House, in 1968. A small but select publisher whose list includes Muriel Spark and Francis King. *Publishes* archaeology, architecture and design, biography and autobiography, cookery, fiction, guidebooks, history and antiquarian, natural history, psychology, sociology and anthropology, travel and topography, wines and spirits. About 75 titles a year. TITLES *Reality and Dreams* Muriel Spark; *Life in an Irish Country House* Mark Bence-Jones; *Yesterday Came Suddenly* Francis King. Unsolicited mss, synopses and ideas for books welcome.

Royalties paid twice-yearly.

Authors' Rating Said by **The Society of Authors** to be the only publisher ready to take on the entire cost of having an index professionally prepared. Usually the cost is shared with an author. Also distinguished by paying authors at least two-thirds of income from the sale of paperback rights.

Consultants Bureau
See **Plenum Publishing Ltd**

Consumers' Association
See **Which? Books/Consumers' Association**

Conway Maritime Press
See **Brassey's (UK) Ltd**

Thomas Cook Publishing
PO Box 227, Peterborough PE3 8BQ
☎01733 268943   Fax 01733 267052
Head of Publishing *Jennifer Rigby*
Approx. Annual Turnover £1.7 million

Part of the Thomas Cook Group Ltd, publishing commenced in 1873 with the first issue of Cook's Continental Timetable. *Publishes* guidebooks, maps and timetables. 12 titles in 1995. No unsolicited mss; synopses and ideas welcome as long as they are travel-related.

Royalties paid annually.

Leo Cooper/Pen & Sword Books Ltd
190 Shaftesbury Avenue, London WC2H 8JL
☎0171 836 3141   Fax 0171 240 9247
Chairman *Sir Nicholas Hewitt*
Managing Director *Leo Cooper*

FOUNDED 1990 following the acquisition of the Leo Cooper imprint from Octopus Publishing. *Publishes* military history, naval and aviation history, autobiography and biography. About 40 titles a year. Unsolicited synopses and ideas welcome; no unsolicited mss.

Royalties paid twice-yearly. *Associated company* **Wharncliffe Publishing Ltd**.

Corgi
See **Transworld Publishers Ltd**

Cornwall Books
See **Golden Cockerel Press Ltd**

Coronet Books
See **Hodder Headline plc**

Countryside Books
2 Highfield Avenue, Newbury, Berkshire
RG14 5DS
☎01635 43816   Fax 01635 551004
Publisher *Nicholas Battle*

FOUNDED 1976. *Publishes* mainly paperbacks on regional subjects, generally by county. Local history, genealogy, walking and photographic, some transport. Over 250 titles available in 1994. Unsolicited mss and synopses welcome but, regretfully, no fiction, poetry or personal memories.

Royalties paid twice-yearly.

Crabtree Publishing
73 Lime Walk, Headington, Oxford OX3 7AD
☎01865 67575   Fax 01865 750079
President *Peter Crabtree*
Editorial Director *Bobbie Kalman*

FOUNDED 1980. *Publishes* ecological and educational books in series. About 12 titles a year. SERIES *Animals and Their Ecosystems; Lands, Peoples and Culture; The Arctic World; Endangered Animals; Historic Communities; Crabtree Environment; Primary Ecology.* New series: *The Crabapples; Great African Americans* and *The Wonders of the World.*

Royalties paid twice-yearly.

CRC Press
See **Times Mirror International Publishers Ltd**

Cressrelles Publishing Co. Ltd
10 Station Road Industrial Estate, Colwall, Malvern, Worcestershire WR13 6RN
☎01684 540154
Managing Director *Leslie Smith*

Publishes a range of general books, drama and chiropody titles.

IMPRINTS **Actinic Press** specialises in chiropody; **J. Garnet Miller Ltd** plays and theatre texts; **Kenyon-Deane** plays and drama textbooks.

Croom Helm
See **Routledge**

Crossway
See **Inter-Varsity Press**

The Crowood Press Ltd
The Stable Block, Crowood Lane, Ramsbury, Marlborough, Wiltshire SN8 2HR
☎01672 520320   Fax 01672 520280
Chairman *John Dennis*
Managing Director *Ken Hathaway*

Publishes sport and leisure titles, including animal and land husbandry, climbing and walking, maritime, country sports, equestrian, fishing and shooting; also chess and bridge, crafts, dogs, gardening, natural history and motoring. About 70 titles a year. Preliminary letter preferred in all cases.
Royalties paid annually.

James Currey Publishers
54B Thornhill Square, London N1 1BE
☎0171 609 9026   Fax 0171 609 9605
Chairman/Managing Director *James Currey*

FOUNDED 1985. A small specialist publisher. *Publishes* academic books on Africa, the Caribbean and Third World: history, anthropology, economics, sociology, politics and literary criticism. Approach in writing with synopsis if material is 'relevant to our needs'.
Royalties paid annually.

Curzon Press Ltd
St John's Studios, Church Road, Richmond, Surrey TW9 2QA
☎0181 948 5322   Fax 0181 332 6735
Managing Director *Malcolm G. Campbell*

Specialised scholarly publishing house. *Publishes* academic/scholarly books on history and archaeology, languages and linguistics, philosophy, religion and theology, sociology and anthropology, cultural studies and reference, all in the context of Africa and Asia. IMPRINT **Japan Library**.

Cygnus Arts
See **Golden Cockerel Press Ltd**

Dalesman Publishing Co. Ltd
Stable Courtyard, Broughton Hall, Skipton, West Yorkshire BD23 3AE
☎01756 701381   Fax 01756 701326
Editor (books) *Robert Flanagan*
Editor (magazines) *Terry Fletcher*

Publishers of *Dalesman*, *Cumbria* and *Pennine* magazines and regional books covering Yorkshire and the Lake District. Subjects include crafts and hobbies, geography and geology, guidebooks, history and antiquarian, humour, travel and topography. Unsolicited mss considered on all subjects. About 20 titles a year.
Royalties paid annually.

Terence Dalton Ltd
Water Street, Lavenham, Sudbury, Suffolk CO10 9RN
☎01787 247572   Fax 01787 248247
Director/Editorial Head *Elisabeth Whitehair*

FOUNDED 1967. Part of Lavenham Holdings plc, a family company. *Publishes* non-fiction: aviation and maritime history, river series and East Anglian interest. 1 title in 1995. TITLES *Imperial Airways and the First British Airline* Capt. Archie Jackson. No unsolicited mss; send synopsis with two or three sample chapters. Ideas welcome.
Royalties paid annually.

The C. W. Daniel Co. Ltd
1 Church Path, Saffron Walden, Essex CB10 1JP
☎01799 521909   Fax 01799 513462
Managing Director *Ian Miller*
Approx. Annual Turnover £1 million

FOUNDED in 1902 by a man who knew Tolstoy, the company was taken over by its present directors in 1973. Output has increased following the acquisition in 1980 of health and healing titles from the Health Science Press, and the purchase of Neville Spearman Publishers' metaphysical list in 1985. *Publishes* New Age: alternative healing and metaphysical. About 15 titles a year. No fiction, diet or cookery. Unsolicited synopses and ideas welcome; no unsolicited mss.
Royalties paid annually.

Darf Publishers Ltd
277 West End Lane, London NW6 1QS
☎0171 431 7009   Fax 0171 431 7655
Chairman/Managing Director
   M. B. Fergiani
Editorial Head *A. Bentaleb*
Approx. Annual Turnover £500,000

FOUNDED 1982 to publish books and reprints on the Middle East, history, theology and travel. *Publishes* geography, history, language, literature, oriental, politics, theology and travel. About 10 titles a year. TITLES *Moslems in Spain*; *Travels of Ibn Battuta*; *The Barbary Corsairs*; *Elementary*

Arabic; Travels in Syria and the Holy Land Burckhardt.

Royalties paid annually. *Overseas associates* Dar Al-Fergiani, Cairo and Tripoli.

Dartmouth

See **Ashgate Publishing Co. Ltd**

Darton, Longman & Todd Ltd

1 Spencer Court, 140-142 Wandsworth High Street, London SW18 4JJ

☎0181 875 0155   Fax 0181 875 0133

Editorial Director *Morag Reeve*

Approx. Annual Turnover £1 million

FOUNDED by Michael Longman, who broke away from Longman Green in 1959 when they decided to cut their religious list. In July 1990 DLT became a common ownership company, owned and run by staff members. The company is a leading ecumenical, predominantly Christian, publisher, with a strong emphasis on spirituality and the ministry and mission of the Church. About 50 titles a year. TITLES include *Jerusalem Bible; New Jerusalem Bible; God of Surprises; Audacity to Believe.* Sample material for books on theological or spiritual subjects considered.

Royalties paid twice-yearly.

David & Charles Publishers

Brunel House, Forde Road, Newton Abbot, Devon TQ12 4PU

☎01626 61121   Fax 01626 334998

Publishing Director *Piers Spence*

FOUNDED 1960 as a specialist company. Family-controlled until 1990 when it was acquired by the **Reader's Digest Association Ltd**. *Publishes* crafts and hobbies, art techniques, gardening, equestrian and countryside, natural history and field guides. No fiction, poetry, memoirs or children's. About 50 titles a year. TITLES *Jo Verso's Cross Stitch for Beginners; Hillier Gardener's Guide to Trees and Shrubs; The Encyclopedia of Fungi; The Artist's Guide to Mixing Colours; The Countryman's Year.* Unsolicited mss will be considered if return postage is included, synopses and ideas welcome.

Royalties paid twice-yearly.

Authors' Rating Hopes for the reinvigoration of David & Charles have received a setback with the Reader's Digest decision to hive off a division that apparently does not fit their growth strategy. Bids are invited for a company that was bought by Reader's Digest in 1990 for over £10 million and is now thought to be worth £5 million or less.

Christopher Davies Publishers Ltd

PO Box 403, Swansea, West Glamorgan SA1 4YF

☎01792 648825   Fax 01792 648825

Managing Director/Editorial Head
  Christopher T. Davies

Approx. Annual Turnover £100,000

FOUNDED 1949 to promote and expand Welsh-language publications. By the 1970s the company was publishing over 50 titles a year but a subsequent drop in Welsh sales led to the establishment of a small English list which has continued. *Publishes* biography, cookery, history and literature of Welsh interest. About 4 titles a year. TITLES *English/Welsh Dictionaries; Chronicle of Welsh Events; Famous Cricketers of Glamorgan.* No unsolicited mss. Synopses and ideas for books welcome.

Royalties paid twice-yearly.

Authors' Rating A favourite for Celtic readers and writers.

Giles de la Mare Publishers Ltd

3 Queen Square, London WC1N 3AU

☎0171 465 0045   Fax 0171 465 0034

Chairman/Managing Director *Giles de la Mare*

Approx. Annual Turnover £60,000

FOUNDED 1995 and commenced publishing in April 1996. *Publishes* mainly non-fiction, especially art and architecture, biography, history, music. Unsolicited mss, synopses and ideas welcome after initial telephone call.

Royalties paid twice-yearly.

Debrett's Peerage Ltd

73-77 Britannia Road, PO Box 357, London SW6 2JY

☎0171 736 6524   Fax 0171 731 7768

Chairman *Ian McCorquodale*

Managing Director *R. M. Summers*

General Manager *Jonathan Parker*

FOUNDED 1769. The company's main activity (in conjunction with **Macmillan**) is the quinquennial *Debrett's Peerage and Baronetage* (published in 1995) and annual *Debrett's People of Today* (also available on CD-ROM). Debrett's general books are published under licence through **Headline**.

Royalties paid twice-yearly.

Dedalus Ltd

Langford Lodge, St Judith's Lane, Sawtry, Cambridgeshire PE17 5XE

☎01487 832382   Fax 01487 832382

Chairman *Juri Gabriel*

Managing Director *George Barrington*
Approx. Annual Turnover £175,000

FOUNDED 1983. *Publishes* contemporary European fiction and classics, literary fantasy anthologies and original literary action in the fields of magic realism, surrealism, the grotesque and bizarre. 16 titles in 1995.

TITLES *The Decadent Cookbook; The Arabian Nightmare* Robert Irwin; *Pfitz* Andrew Crumey; *Memoirs of a Gnostic Dwarf* David Madsen; *Music in a Foreign Language* Andrew Crumey (winner of the **Saltire Best First Book Award** in 1994). Welcomes submissions for original fiction and books suitable for its list but 'most people sending work in have no idea of what kind of books Dedalus publishes and merely waste their efforts'. Particularly interested in intellectually clever and unusual fiction. A letter about the author should always accompany any submission. No replies without s.a.e..

DIVISIONS/IMPRINTS **Original Fiction in Paperback; Contemporary European Fiction 1992–1997; Dedalus European Classics; Surrealism; Empire of the Senses; Literary Concept Books.**

Royalties paid annually. *Overseas associates* Hippocrene Books, Inc., New York; Ariadne Press, California.

Authors' Rating A small publisher triumphing against powerful competition by the simple expedient of putting quality first.

University of Delaware
See **Golden Cockerel Press Ltd**

J. M. Dent
See **The Orion Publishing Group Ltd**

André Deutsch Children's Books
See **Scholastic Ltd**

André Deutsch Ltd
106 Great Russell Street, London WC1B 3LJ
☎0171 580 2746   Fax 0171 631 3253
Chairman *T. G. Rosenthal*
Managing Director *Tim Forrester*
Submissions *David Wilson*
Approx. Annual Turnover £2.5 million

FOUNDED in 1950 by André Deutsch, who sold the company between 1984 and 1987 and ended his long association with it in 1991. By then a major fiction list had been established, with writers like V. S. Naipaul, Philip Roth and Norman Mailer among the *literati*. *Publishes* fiction, poetry and non-fiction, particularly biography, current affairs, history, cricket, politics and photographic.

About 60 titles a year now following the sale of Deutsch's children's list to **Scholastic Publications Ltd** in 1991. In 1995 the company was acquired by audio and video publisher and distributor VCI Plc, of which it is now a wholly owned but separately managed subsidiary whose editorial policy remains unchanged apart from the addition of some high profile books by sporting heroes such as George Graham. AUTHORS Malcolm Bradbury, Joan Brady, Paul Erdman, Carlos Fuentes, William Gaddis, Gail Godwin, George V. Higgins, Bohumil Hrabal, Dan Jacobson, Molly Keane, Tom Sharpe, David Thomson, Gore Vidal. Unsolicited mss, synopses and ideas for books considered.

Royalties paid twice-yearly.

Authors' Rating In a mind-boggling turnaround, Deutsch is now the publishing arm of a video company. The deal with Video Collection International ends Deutsch's independence but keeps the name alive. Since VCI is associated with Hat Trick Productions, television tie-in books can be expected.

Dial House
See **Ian Allan Ltd**

Disney
See **Ladybird Books Ltd**

Dolphin Book Co. Ltd
Tredwr, Llangrannog, Llandysul, Dyfed SA44 6BA
☎01239 654404   Fax 01239 654002
Managing Director *Martin L. Gili*
Approx. Annual Turnover £5000

FOUNDED 1957. A small publishing house specialising in Catalan, Spanish and South American books for the academic market. TITLES *Elegies de Bierville/Bierville Elegies* Carles Riba, Catalan text with English translation by J. L. Gili; *The Discerning Eye Studies* presented to Robert Pring-Mill; *The Late Poetry of Pablo Neruda* Christopher Perriam; *Hispanic Linguistic Studies in Honour of F. W. Hodcroft; Salvatge cor/Savage Heart* Carles Riba; Catalan text with English translations by J. L. Gili. Unsolicited mss not welcome. Approach by letter.

Royalties paid annually.

John Donald Publishers Ltd
138 St Stephen Street, Edinburgh EH3 5AA
☎0131 225 1146   Fax 0131 220 0567
Publishing & Production *Donald Morrison*
Commissioning Editor *Russell Walker*

Publishes academic and scholarly, agriculture,

archaeology, architecture, economics, textbooks, guidebooks, local, military and social history, religious, sociology and anthropology. About 30 titles a year.

Royalties paid annually.

Donhead Publishing Ltd

Lower Coombe, Donhead St Mary,
Shaftesbury, Dorset SP7 9LYU
☎01747 828422

Contact *Jill Pearce*

FOUNDED 1990 to specialise in publishing how-to books for building practitioners; particularly interested in building conservation material. *Publishes* building and architecture only. 6 titles a year. TITLES *Encyclopaedia of Architectural Terms; A Good Housekeeping Guide to Churches and their Contents; Cleaning Historic Buildings; Brickwork; Practical Stone Masonry; Conservation of Timber Buildings; Journal of Architectural Conservation* (3 issues yearly). Unsolicited mss, synopses and ideas welcome.

Dorling Kindersley Ltd

9 Henrietta Street, London WC2E 8PS
☎0171 836 5411   Fax 0171 836 7570

Chairman *Peter Kindersley*
Deputy Chairman *Christopher Davis*

FOUNDED 1974. Packager and publisher of illustrated non-fiction: cookery, crafts, gardening, health, natural history and children's information books. Launched a US imprint in 1991. About 175-200 titles a year.

DIVISIONS **Adult; Children's; Direct; Education; Multimedia; Vision** (video). TITLES *Eyewitness Guides; BMA Complete Family Health Encyclopedia; RHS Gardener's Encyclopedia of Plants and Flowers; Children's Illustrated Encyclopedia*. Unsolicited synopses and ideas for books welcome.

Authors' Rating Among the first to take on the challenge of CD-ROM, DK multimedia products are now nine per cent of turnover – and rising. Part of the secret for DK's multimedia success is the experience the company has built up on team projects for conventional publishing. Highly illustrated information books involve a huge amount of in-house design and editorial. A DK writer need never feel alone.

Doubleday

See **Transworld Publishers Ltd**

DP Publications Ltd

Aldine Place, 142-144 Uxbridge Road,
London W12 8AW
☎0181 746 0044   Fax 0181 743 8692

Managing Director *R. J. Chapman*
Publishing Director *Catherine Tilley*

FOUNDED 1972. Part of BPP Holdings plc. *Publishes* accounting, business, computing and mathematics textbooks for higher and further education. Unsolicited synopses and ideas for books welcome. Authors sought for active-learning material in business, accounting and computing in further and higher education.

Royalties paid twice-yearly.

Dragon's World

7-9 St Georges Square, London
SW1V 2HX
☎0171 630 9955   Fax 0171 630 9921

Managing Director *Hubert Schaafsma*

FOUNDED 1975. *Publishes* fantasy art, natural history, children's non-fiction (ages 7-11), contemporary album cover art, fine art, design, craft, photography, DIY, folklore, illustrated children's classics and fables. About 50 titles a year.

IMPRINTS **Dragon's World** General illustrated non-fiction, notably natural history, with a major pocket guide series. **Paper Tiger Books** Fantasy art. Unsolicited mss, synopses and ideas for books welcome.

Drake Educational Associates

St Fagans Road, Fairwater, Cardiff CF5 3AE
☎01222 560333   Fax 01222 554909

Contact *R. G. Drake*

Educational publishers.

Dryden Press

See **Harcourt Brace and Company Limited**

Gerald Duckworth & Co. Ltd

The Old Piano Factory, 48 Hoxton Square,
London N1 6PB
☎0171 729 5986   Fax 0171 729 0015

Managing Director *Robin Baird-Smith*
Editorial Director *Deborah Blake*

FOUNDED 1898. A joint ownership company. Some of the company's early credits include authors like Hilaire Belloc, August Strindberg, Henry James and John Galsworthy. *Publishes* academic material in the main, with some trade books, including fiction. About 80 titles a year.

IMPRINTS **Bristol Classical Press** Classical texts and modern languages; **Paperduck** Paperback imprint. No unsolicited mss; synopses and sample chapters only. Enclose s.a.e. or return postage for response/return.

Royalties paid twice-yearly at first, annually thereafter.

Martin Dunitz Ltd

The Livery House, 7-9 Pratt Street, London
NW1 0AE
☎0171 482 2202   Fax 0171 267 0159

Chairman/Managing Director *Martin
Dunitz*

FOUNDED 1978. Dunitz sold the successful
Positive Health Guides series to former Macdonald
in the 80s and now concentrates solely on specialist medical and dental titles aimed at an international market, with co-editions for the USA
and Europe. The company won the Queen's
Award for Export Achievement (1991). 20-30
titles a year. Unsolicited synopses and ideas welcome but no mss. Co-publisher of *Journal of
Cytokines and Molecular Therapy*.
Royalties paid twice-yearly.

Dunrod Press

8 Brown's Road, Newtownabbey,
Co. Antrim BT36 8RN
☎01232 832362   Fax 01232 848780

Managing Director/Editorial Head *Ken
Lindsay*

FOUNDED 1979. *Publishes* politics and world
affairs. About 3 titles a year. Preliminary letter
essential. Synopses and ideas for books welcome.
Royalties paid annually.

Dutton

See **Penguin Books Ltd**

Eagle

See **Inter Publishing Ltd**

Earthscan Publications Ltd

See **Kogan Page Ltd**

East-West Publications

8 Caledonia Street, London N1 9DZ
☎0171 837 5061   Fax 0171 278 4429

Chairman *L. W. Carp*
Managing Director *B. G. Thompson*
Approx. Annual Turnover £250,000

FOUNDED in the early 1970s. *Publishes* Eastern
religions/philosophy and children's books. No
unsolicited material. Enquiries in writing only.
DIVISIONS **East-West Publications** *L. W.
Carp* TITLES *The Sacred Mountain; Nirvana Tao;
Nada Brahma*; **Gallery Children's Books** *B.
G. Thompson* TITLES *A Child's Garden of Verses;
Our Old Nursery Rhymes; Baby's Album*.
Royalties paid twice-yearly.

Ebury Press

See **Random House UK Ltd**

Economist Books

See **Penguin Books Ltd**

Edinburgh University Press Ltd

22 George Square, Edinburgh EH8 9LF
☎0131 650 4218/Polygon: 650 4689 Fax 0131
662 0053

Managing Director *Vivian Bone*
Editorial Director *Jackie Jones*

Publishes academic and scholarly books and
journals: archaeology, botany, history, Islamic
studies, law and jurisprudence, linguistics, literary criticism, philosophy, politics, social sciences, Scottish studies, theology. About 100
titles a year.
IMPRINT **Polygon** *Marion Sinclair* Creative
writing and Scottish studies. *Publishes* international fiction and poetry. SERIES *Sigma* (apho-
risms, anarchisms and surreal); *Determinations*
(Scottish cultural polemics); *Living Memory* (oral
history). No unsolicited mss for EUP titles; mss
welcome for Polygon but must be accompanied
by s.a.e. for reply/return; letter/synopsis preferred in the first instance, particularly for EUP.
Royalties paid annually.

Element Books

The Old School House, The Courtyard, Bell
Street, Shaftesbury, Dorset SP7 8BP
☎01747 851448   Fax 01747 855721

Chairman/Publisher *Michael Mann*
Managing Director *David Alexander*
Editorial Director *Julia McCutchen*
Approx. Annual Turnover £7 million

FOUNDED 1978. An independent general pub-
lishing house whose policy is 'to make available
knowledge and information to aid humanity in a
time of major transition'. *Publishes* general non-
fiction in hardback and paperback, including
full-colour, illustrated and gift books. TITLES
*Trance Dane; The Illustrated Encyclopedia of
Essential Oils; I Ching; Nostradamus; The Mayan
Prophecies* SERIES Elements Of; Little Books; The
Natural Way; Self Help; Health Essentials;
Element Guides; Chinese Horoscopes for
Lovers; Colour Health Reference Series; Earth
Quest. Unsolicited mss, synopses and ideas
welcome. No fiction or poetry. 'We are always
interested to hear from authors who have an
original contribution to make based on quality
and integrity.'
Royalties paid twice-yearly.

Authors' Rating Very popular with way-out
authors. Books about 'black magic or witchcraft or psychic phenomena' are turned away
but Michael Mann does want to hear from

authors who are 'concerned about ... the heart of religion, the mystical side of the great traditions. There have been some problems with royalties – but more a case of late payment than no payment at all.

Elliot Right Way Books

Kingswood Buildings, Lower Kingswood, Tadworth, Surrey KT20 6TD
☎01737 832202   Fax 01737 830311

Managing Directors *Clive Elliot, Malcolm G. Elliot*

FOUNDED 1946 by Andrew G. Elliot. *Publishes* how-to titles and instruction books on a multifarious list of subjects including cookery, DIY, family financial and legal matters, family health and fitness, fishing, looking after pets and horses, motoring, popular education, puzzles, jokes and quizzes. All the early books were entitled *The Right Way to ...* but this format became too restrictive. No fiction.
IMPRINTS **Right Way** Instructional paperbacks in B format; **Clarion** Promotional/bargain series of 'how-to' books. Unsolicited mss, synopses and ideas for books welcome.
Royalties paid annually.

Ellipsis London Ltd

55 Charlotte Road, London EC2A 3QT
☎0171 739 3157   Fax 0171 739 3175

Contact *Tom Neville*

FOUNDED 1992. A subsidiary of Zurich-based Artemis Verlags AG following a management buyout in 1994. *Publishes* architecture. About 8–10 titles a year. No unsolicited mss, synopses or ideas.
Royalties paid annually.

Aidan Ellis Publishing

Cobb House, Nuffield, Henley on Thames, Oxfordshire RG9 5RT
☎01491 641496   Fax 01491 641678

Partners/Editorial Heads *Aidan Ellis, Lucinda Ellis*

Approx. Annual Turnover £220,000

FOUNDED in 1971. *Publishes* fiction and general trade books. About 12 titles a year.
DIVISIONS **Non-Fiction** TITLES *The Royal Gardens at Windsor Great Park* Charles Lyte; *Gardening Down a Rabbit-hole* Josephine Saxton; *Waves: The Real Sea* Maurice Grant. **Fiction** AUTHORS include José Miguel Roig, David MacSweeney, Alan Bloom and Dana Fuller Ross. Unsolicited synopses and ideas for books (with s.a.e.) welcome.
Royalties paid twice-yearly. *Overseas associates* worldwide.

Elm Publications

Seaton House, Kings Ripton, Huntingdon, Cambridgeshire PE17 2NJ
☎01487 773254   Fax 01487 773359

Managing Director *Sheila Ritchie*

FOUNDED 1977. *Publishes* textbooks, teaching aids, educational resources, educational software and languages, in the fields of business and management for adult learners. Books and teaching/training resources are generally commissioned to meet specific business, management and other syllabuses. About 30 titles a year. Ideas are welcome for new textbooks – first approach in writing with outline or by a brief telephone call.
Royalties paid annually.

Elsevier Science Ltd

The Boulevard, Langford Lane, Kidlington, Oxford OX5 1GB
☎01865 843000   Fax 01865 843010

Managing Director *Michael Boswood*

Parent company **Elsevier**, Amsterdam. Now incorporates **Pergamon Press**. *Publishes* academic and professional reference books, scientific, technical and medical books, journals, CD-ROMs and magazines.
DIVISIONS **Elsevier Advanced Technology** *Nick Baker*; **Elsevier Trends Journals** *David Bousfield*; **Elsevier and Pergamon** *Barbara Barrett, Michael Mabe, Chris Lloyd, Peter Shepherd, Jim Gilgunn-Jones, Gerry Dorey*. Unsolicited mss, synopses and ideas for books welcome.
Royalties paid annually.

Authors' Rating An offshoot of the largest Dutch publisher. Refreshingly open with authors in the tradition of northern European publishers – early news on print runs and royalties paid promptly.

Elvendon Press

See **William Reed Directories**

Emissary Publishing

PO Box 33, Bicester, Oxfordshire OX6 7PP
☎01869 323447   Fax 01869 324096

Editorial Director *Val Miller*

FOUNDED 1992. *Publishes* humorous paperback books. About 12 titles a year. Runs an annual 'Peter Pook Humorous Novel Competition' and publishes the winning novel (s.a.e. for details). No unsolicited mss or synopses. Contact by letter in the first instance (with s.a.e. for reply).
Royalties paid twice-yearly.

Enitharmon Press
36 St George's Avenue, London N7 0HD
☎0171 607 7194 Fax 0171 607 8694
Director *Stephen Stuart-Smith*
FOUNDED 1969 by Alan Clodd. An independent company with an enterprising editorial policy, Enitharmon has established itself as one of Britain's leading poetry presses. Patron of 'the new and the neglected', Enitharmon prides itself on the success of its collaborations between writers and artists. *Publishes* poetry, literary criticism, fiction, art and photography. About 20 titles a year. TITLES include *The Language of Yes* Kevin Crossley-Holland; *Collected Poems* Ruth Pitter; *Green Resistance* Anna Adams; *Selected Poems* Frances Cornford; *Gift of Work* Martyn Crucefix; *Selected Essays* David Gascoyne and Edward Upward's memoir of Christopher Isherwood. Limited editions include: *Burning Waters* Victor Pasmore; *The Unknown Masterpiece* Callum Innes, and a collaboration between Blake Morrison and Paula Rego. No unsolicited mss.
Royalties paid according to contract. *Distribution* in Europe by Password (Books) Ltd, Manchester; in the USA by Dufour Editions Inc., Chester Springs, PA 19425.

Epworth Press
c/o Methodist Publishing House, 20 Ivatt Way, Peterborough, Cambridgeshire PE3 7PG
☎01733 332202 Fax 01733 331201
Chairman *Graham Slater*
Editor *Dr C. S. Rodd*
Formerly based in Manchester, Epworth now operates from Peterborough. *Publishes* Christian books only: philosophy, theology, biblical studies, pastoralia and social concern. No fiction, poetry or children's. A series based on the text of the *Revised English Bible*, entitled *Epworth Commentaries*, has proved very successful and two new series *Exploring Methodism* and *Thinking Things Through* have just been launched. About 10 titles a year. TITLES *Worshipping God Together* (*Companion to the Lectionary* vol 6) ed. M. J. Townsend; *The Making of a Quaker* (life of Roger Wilson) Fred Brown; *Ezekiel* C. Biggs; *The Pastoral Epistles* Margaret Davies. Unsolicited mss considered but write to enquire in the first instance. Authors wishing to have their mss returned must send sufficient postage.
Royalties paid annually.

Eros Plus
See **Titan Books**

Euromonitor
60-61 Britton Street, London EC1M 5NA
☎0171 251 8024 Fax 0171 608 3149
Chairman *R. N. Senior*
Managing Director *T. J. Fenwick*
Approx. Annual Turnover £5 million
FOUNDED 1972. International business information publisher specialising in library and professional reference books, market reports, electronic databases, journals and CD-ROMs. *Publishes* business reference, market analysis and information directories only. About 80-85 titles a year.
DIVISIONS **Market Direction** *S. Holmes*; **Reference Books & Reports** *S. Leckey*; **Directories** *M. McGrath*. TITLES *Credit & Charge Cards: The International Market*; *Europe in the Year 2000*; *European Marketing Handbook*; *European Directory of Trade and Business Associations*; *World Retail Directory and Sourcebook*.
Royalties payment is generally by flat fee.

Europa Publications Ltd
18 Bedford Square, London WC1B 3JN
☎0171 580 8236 Fax 0171 636 1664
Chairman *C. H. Martin*
Managing Director *P. A. McGinley*
Approx. Annual Turnover £5 million
Owned by Staples Printers Ltd. FOUNDED 1926 with the publication of the first edition of *The Europa Year Book*. *Publishes* annual reference books on political, economic and commercial matters. About 3 titles a year. No fiction, biography or poetry. Enquiries in writing only.
Royalties paid annually.

Evangelical Press of Wales
Bryntirion House, Bridgend, Mid-Glamorgan CF31 4DX
☎01656 655886 Fax 01656 656095
Chairman *Reverend S. Jones*
Chief Executive *G. Wyn Davies*
Approx. Annual Turnover £85,000
Owned by the Evangelical Movement of Wales. *Publishes* Christian books. 4 titles in 1995. TITLES *Christian Handbook; Voices from the Welsh Revival; Why Does God Allow War?; I Will Never Become a Christian.* No unsolicited mss; synopses and ideas welcome.
Royalties paid twice-yearly.

Evans Brothers Ltd
2A Portman Mansions, Chiltern Street, London W1M 1LE
☎0171 935 7160 Fax 0171 487 5034
Managing Director *Stephen Pawley*

International Publishing Director
  Brian Jones
Managing Editor Su Swallow
Approx. Annual Turnover £3 million
FOUNDED 1908 by Robert and Edward Evans. Originally published educational journals, books for primary schools and teacher education. After rapid expansion into popular fiction and drama, both were sacrificed to a major programme of educational books for schools in East and West Africa. A new UK programme was launched in 1986 followed by the acquisition of **Hamish Hamilton**'s non-fiction list for children in 1990. *Publishes* UK children's and educational books, and educational books for Africa, the Caribbean and Far East. About 70 titles a year. Unsolicited mss, synopses and ideas for books welcome.
  Royalties paid annually. *Overseas associates* in Kenya, Cameroon, Sierra Leone; Evans Bros (Nigeria Publishers) Ltd.

Everyman
See **The Orion Publishing Group Ltd**

Everyman's Library
See **David Campbell Publishers Ltd**

University of Exeter Press
Reed Hall, Streatham Drive, Exeter, Devon EX4 4QR
☎01392 263066   Fax 01392 263064
Publisher Simon Baker
FOUNDED 1956. *Publishes* academic books: archaeology, classical studies, mining, history, maritime studies, English literature (especially medieval), linguistics, European studies, modern languages and literature, American studies, cultural studies, Arabic studies and books on Exeter and the South West. About 40 titles a year. Unsolicited mss welcomed in the subject areas mentioned above.
  Royalties paid annually.

Exley Publications Ltd
16 Chalk Hill, Watford, Hertfordshire WD1 4BN
☎01923 248328   Fax 01923 818733
Managing/Editorial Director Helen Exley
FOUNDED 1976. Independent family company. *Publishes* gift books, quotation anthologies, social stationery and humour. All in series only – no individual titles. Has a substantial children's non-fiction list. About 65 titles a year.
DIVISIONS
Gift Series TITLES *To a Very Special Friend, Daughter, Mother, ...; The Fanatics Guide to Golf,*

Cats, Dads, etc; The Crazy World of Aerobics, Golf, Learning to Drive; Golf, Book Lovers, Dog, Friendship Quotations; So-Much-More-Than-A-Card Collection. No unsolicited mss. 'Joke and gag writers are very badly needed. Also writers who can create personal "messages", rather like not-too-sugary greetings cards.'

Faber & Faber Ltd
3 Queen Square, London WC1N 3AU
☎0171 465 0045   Fax 0171 465 0034
Chairman/Managing Director Matthew Evans
Approx. Annual Turnover £8.8 million
Geoffrey Faber and Richard de la Mare founded the company in the 1920s, with T. S. Eliot as an early recruit to the board. The original list was based on contemporary poetry and plays (the distinguished backlist includes Eliot, Auden and MacNeice). *Publishes* poetry and drama, art, children's, fiction, film, music, politics, biography, specialist cookery and wine. Unsolicited mss will be considered; synopses and ideas for books welcome. Return postage required.

DIVISIONS
Children's Janice Thomson AUTHORS Gene Kemp, Russell Stannard, Susan Price; **Cookery and Wine** Belinda Matthews TITLES *Simple French Cuisine; Pastability; Burgundy;* **Fiction** Julian Loose AUTHORS P. D. James, Peter Carey, William Golding, Milan Kundera, Mario Vargas Llosa, Garrison Keillor, Paul Auster; **Plays** Peggy Butcher; **Film** Walter Donohue. AUTHORS Samuel Beckett, Alan Bennett, David Hare, Tom Stoppard, John Boorman, Woody Allen, Martin Scorsese, Quentin Tarantino; **Poetry** Christopher Reid AUTHORS Seamus Heaney, Ted Hughes, Douglas Dunn, Tom Paulin, Simon Armitage; **Non-fiction** Julian Loose TITLES *Faber Book of Science; On Flirtation.*
  Royalties paid twice-yearly. *Overseas office* Boston.

Authors' Rating With one of the strongest backlists of any publisher (providing up to 40 per cent of income), Faber still has a knack for spotting long distance runners – P. D. James and Alan Bennett among them.

FactbABCks
See **ABC – All Books For Children**

Fairleigh Dickinson University Press
See **Golden Cockerel Press**

Falmer Press

27 Palmeira Mansions, Church Road, Hove, East Sussex BN3 2FA
☎01273 775154   Fax 01273 205612

Managing/Editorial Director *Malcolm Clarkson*

Part of **Taylor & Francis**. *Publishes* educational books/materials for all levels. Largely commissioned. Unsolicited mss considered.
Royalties paid annually.

Farming Press Books & Videos

Wharfedale Road, Ipswich, Suffolk IP1 4LG
☎01473 241122   Fax 01473 240501

Manager *Roger Smith*

Owned by United News & Media plc. *Publishes* specialist books/videos on farming, plus a range of humorous and countryside titles. About 35 books and videos a year. No unsolicited mss; synopses and ideas welcome provided material is suitable for their list.
Royalties paid twice-yearly.

Fernhurst Books

Duke's Path, High Street, Arundel, West Sussex BN18 9AJ
☎01903 882277   Fax 01903 882715

Chairman/Managing Director *Tim Davison*

FOUNDED 1979. For people who love watersports. *Publishes* practical, highly illustrated handbooks on sailing and watersports. No unsolicited mss; synopses and ideas welcome.
Royalties paid twice-yearly.

Finborough Seminars

See **Tolley Publishing Co. Ltd**

Findhorn Press

The Park, Findhorn, Moray IV36 0TZ
☎01309 690582   Fax 01309 690036

Partners *Karin Bogliolo, Thierry Bogliolo*
Approx. Annual Turnover £200,000

FOUNDED 1971. *Publishes* mind, body, spirit, new age and healing. 14 titles in 1995. Unsolicited mss, synopses and ideas welcome if they come within their subject areas.
Royalties paid twice-yearly.

First & Best in Education Ltd

32 Nene Valley Business Park, Oundle, Peterborough PE8 4HJ
☎01832 275716   Fax 01832 278281

Publisher *Tony Attwood*
Senior Editors *Kirsty Meadows, Vivienne Hill*

Publishes educational books of all types for all ages as well as business books. All books are published

as being suitable for photocopying and as electronic books. Currently launching 20 new titles a month and 'keenly looking for new authors all the time'. TITLES *Getting Ready to Start School; Primary School Curriculum Policy; Science for Me; Attention Deficit Disorder.* IMPRINT **Multi-Sensory Learning** (see entry). Also publishers of *Schools Internet.* In the first instance send s.a.e. for details of requirements and current projects.
Royalties normally 12% paid twice-yearly.

Fitzjames Press

See **Motor Racing Publications**

Flamingo

See **HarperCollins Publishers Ltd**

Flicks Books

29 Bradford Road, Trowbridge, Wiltshire BA14 9AN
☎01225 767728   Fax 01225 760418

Publishing Director *Matthew Stevens*

FOUNDED 1986. Devoted solely to publishing books on the cinema and related media. 5 titles in 1995. TITLES *Queen of the 'B's: Ida Lupino Behind the Camera* ed Annette Kuhn; *By Angels Driven: The Films of Derek Jarman* ed Chris Lippard. Unsolicited mss, synopses and ideas within the subject area are welcome.
Royalties paid twice yearly.

Flint River Press Ltd

See **Philip Wilson Publishers Ltd**

Floris Books

15 Harrison Gardens, Edinburgh EH11 1SH
☎0131 337 2372   Fax 0131 346 7516

Managing Director *Christian Maclean*
Editor *Christopher Moore*
Approx. Annual Turnover £350,000

FOUNDED 1977. *Publishes* books related to the Steiner movement, including arts & crafts, children's, the Christian Community, history, religious, science, social questions and Celtic studies. No unsolicited mss. Synopses and ideas for books welcome.
Royalties paid annually.

Fodor's

See **Random House UK Ltd**

Folens Limited

Albert House, Apex Business Centre, Boscombe Road, Dunstable, Bedfordshire LU5 4RL
☎01582 472788   Fax 01582 472575

Chairman *Dirk Folens*

Managing Director *Malcolm Watson*

FOUNDED 1987. Leading educational publisher. 150 titles in 1995. IMPRINTS **Folens**; **Belair** *Patricia Harrison*. Unsolicited mss, synopses and ideas for educational books welcome.

Royalties paid annually.

Fontana
See **HarperCollins Publishers Ltd**

Fortean Times Books
See **John Brown Publishing Ltd**

G. T. Foulis & Co Ltd
See **Haynes Publishing**

W. Foulsham & Co.
The Publishing House, Bennetts Close, Cippenham, Berkshire SL1 5AP
☎01753 526769   Fax 01753 535003
Chairman *R. S. Belasco*
Managing Director *B. A. R. Belasco*
Approx. Annual Turnover £2.2 million

FOUNDED 1816 and now one of the few remaining independent family companies to survive takeover. *Publishes* non-fiction on most subjects including astrology, gardening, cookery, DIY, business, hobbies, sport, health and marriage. No fiction. IMPRINT **Quantum** Mind, Body and Spirit titles. Unsolicited mss, synopses and ideas welcome. Around 60 titles a year.

Royalties paid twice-yearly.

Fount
See **HarperCollins Publishers Ltd**

Fountain Press Ltd
2 Gladstone Road, Kingston-upon-Thames, Surrey KT1 3HD
☎0181 541 4050   Fax 0181 547 3022
Managing Director *H. M. Ricketts*
Approx. Annual Turnover £600,000

FOUNDED 1923 when it was part of the Rowntree Trust Group. Owned by the British Electric Traction Group until 1982 when it was bought out by the present managing director. *Publishes* mainly photography, health, music, natural history and travel. About 25 titles a year. TITLES *Photography Yearbook*; *Wildlife Photographer of the Year*; *Antique and Collectable Cameras*; *Camera Manual* (series). Unsolicited mss and synopses are welcome.

Royalties paid twice-yearly.

Authors' Rating Highly regarded for production values, Fountain has the reputation for

involving authors in every stage of the publishing process.

Fourmat Publishing
See **Tolley Publishing Co. Ltd**

Fourth Estate Ltd
6 Salem Road, London W2 4BU
☎0171 727 8993   Fax 0171 792 3176
Chairman/Managing Director *Victoria Barnsley*
Publishing Director *Christopher Potter*
Approx. Annual Turnover £2.5 million

FOUNDED 1984. Independent publisher with strong reputation for literary fiction and up-to-the-minute non-fiction. *Publishes* fiction, popular science, current affairs, biography, humour, self-help, travel, design and architecture, reference. About 75 titles a year.

DIVISIONS
Literary Fiction/Non-fiction *Christopher Potter* TITLES *Hanging Up* Delia Ephron; *Wonder Boys* Michael Chabon; *The Stone Diaries* Carol Shields; *The Shipping News* E. Annie Proulx; *Revolution in the Head* Ian MacDonald; *Bestseller* Celia Brayfield; *Out of Control* Kevin Kelly; **General Fiction/Non-Fiction** TITLES *Real Good Food* Nigel Slater; *Mrs Merton's Friendship Book; Che Guevara's Motorcycle Diaries*. No unsolicited mss; synopses welcome.

IMPRINTS **Guardian Books** in association with *The Guardian*.

Royalties paid twice-yearly.

Authors' Rating Quality publisher with a distinctive voice. Takes on subjects other publishers choose to avoid. Editorial expansion includes the development of a new commercial fiction list. The latest move is into film and TV tie-in publishing.

Free Association Books Ltd
57 Warren Street, London W1P 5PA
☎0171 388 3182   Fax 0171 388 3187
Chairman/Finance Director *T. E. Brown*
Managing Director *Gill Davies*

Publishes psychoanalysis and psychotherapy, cultural studies, sexuality and gender, women's studies, applied social sciences. TITLES *Mad to be Normal; A Doctor's Dilemma; Winnicott's Words; Unhappy Children*. Always write a letter in the first instance accompanied by a book outline.

Royalties paid twice-yearly. *Overseas associates* New York University Press, USA; Astam, Australia.

W. H. Freeman

Macmillan Press, Houndsmill, Basingstoke, Hampshire RG21 6XS
☎01256 29242 Fax 01256 330688
President *Robert Beiwen* (New York)
Sales Director *Elizabeth Warner*

Part of W. H. Freeman & Co., USA. *Publishes* academic, agriculture, animal care and breeding, archaeology, artificial intelligence, biochemistry, biology and zoology, chemistry, computer science, economics, educational and textbooks, engineering, geography and geology, mathematics and statistics, medical, natural history, neuroscience, palaeontology, physics, politics and world affairs, psychology, sociology and anthropology, and veterinary. Freeman's editorial office is in New York (Basingstoke is a sales and marketing office only) but unsolicited mss can go through Basingstoke. Those which are obviously unsuitable will be sifted out; the rest will be forwarded to New York.
Royalties paid annually.

Samuel French Ltd

52 Fitzroy Street, London W1P 6JR
☎0171 387 9373 Fax 0171 387 2161
Chairman *Charles R. Van Nostrand*
Managing Director *John Bedding*

FOUNDED 1830 with the object of acquiring acting rights and publishing plays. Part of **Samuel French Inc.**, New York. *Publishes* plays only. About 50 titles a year. Unsolicited mss considered only after initial submission of synopsis and specimen scene. Such material should be addressed to the Performing Rights Department.
Royalties paid twice-yearly.

Authors' Rating The darling of amdram (a booming specialist market), Samuel French has cornered the publication of play texts and the permissions (around £50 a night for amateurs) for their performance. Editorial advisers give serious attention to new material but a high proportion of the list is staged before it goes into print. Non-established writers are advised to try one-act plays, much in demand by the amateur dramatic societies but rarely turned out by well-known playwrights.

David Fulton (Publishers) Ltd

2 Barbon Close, Great Ormond Street, London WC1N 3JX
☎0171 405 5606 Fax 0171 831 4840
Chairman/Managing Director *David Fulton*
Editorial Director *John Owens*

Approx. Annual Turnover £600,000
FOUNDED 1987. *Publishes* non-fiction: books for teachers and teacher training at B.Ed and PGCE levels for primary, secondary and special education; geography for undergraduate and professional. In 1995 David Fulton set up a Fulton Fellowship (see under **Bursaries, Fellowships and Grants**). About 50 titles a year. No unsolicited mss; synopses and ideas for books welcome.
Royalties paid twice-yearly.

Funfax/Junior Funfax

See **Henderson Publishing Ltd**

Gaia Books Ltd

66 Charlotte Street, London W1P 1LR
☎0171 323 4010 Fax 0171 323 0435
Also at: 20 High Street, Stroud, Gloucestershire GL5 1AS
☎01453 752985 Fax 01453 752987
Managing Director *Joss Pearson*

FOUNDED 1983. *Publishes* ecology, health, natural living and mind, body & spirit, mainly in practical self-help illustrated reference form. About 12 titles a year. TITLES *Gaia: The Practical Science of Planetary Medicine; Step-by-Step Tai Chi; The Gaia Atlas of Planet Management.* Outlines and mss with s.a.e. considered. Most projects conceived in-house.

Gairm Publications

29 Waterloo Street, Glasgow G2 6BZ
☎0141 221 1971 Fax 0141 221 1971
Chairman *Prof. Derick S. Thomson*

FOUNDED 1952 to publish the quarterly Gaelic periodical *Gairm* and soon moved into publishing other Gaelic material. Acquired an old Glasgow Gaelic publishing firm, Alexander MacLaren & Son, in 1970. *Publishes* a wide range of Gaelic and Gaelic-related books: dictionaries, grammars, handbooks, children's, fiction, poetry, biography, music and song.

Galaxy Children's Large Print

See **Chivers Press Ltd**

Gallery Children's Books

See **East-West Publications**

J. Garnet Miller Ltd

See **Cressrelles Publishing Co. Ltd**

Garnet Publishing Ltd

8 Southern Court, South Street, Reading, Berkshire RG1 4QS
☎01734 597847 Fax 01734 597356

Managing Director *Ken Banerji*

FOUNDED 1992 and purchased Ithaca Press in the same year. *Publishes* art, architecture, photography, archive photography, cookery, travel classics, travel, comparative religion, Islamic culture and history, Arabic fiction in translation. Core subjects are Middle Eastern but list is rapidly expanding to be more general. Published 48 titles 1995.

IMPRINTS

Ithaca Press *Adel Kamal* Specialises in postgraduate academic works on the Middle East, political science and international relations. TITLES *Distant Neighbours*; *Emergent Regional Powers and International Relations in the Gulf*; *Feminism and Islam*; *Jerusalem Today*; *The Middle East into the 21st Century*. **Garnet Publishing** *Anna Watson* TITLES *The Heritage of Oman*; *Arab Women Writers* series (winner of the 1995 WiP New Venture Award); *Traditional Spanish Cooking*; *Mezze*; *Christian Art in Byzantine Syria*; *South Africa, Korea, Tibet - Caught in Time* series; *Patchwork Handbook, Patchwork Quilts for Beds*. Unsolicited mss not welcome – write with outline and ideas first. Not interested in sport or general fiction.

Royalties paid twice-yearly. *Sister companies*: All Prints, Beirut; Garnet France, Paris.

The Gay Men's Press (GMP Publishers Ltd)

PO Box 247, Swaffham, Norfolk PE37 8PA
☎01366 328101   Fax 01366 328102

Directors *David Fernbach, Aubrey Walter*

Publishes primarily books by gay authors about gay-related issues: art, photography, biography and autobiography, literary fiction and popular (historical romance to crime and science fiction), health and leisure. No poetry. Works should generally be submitted by the author on disk.

DIVISIONS

Art & Photography *Aubrey Walter*; **General Books (including Fiction)** *David Fernbach*. TITLES *Mother Clap's Molly House* Rictor Norton; *Halfway Home* Paul Monette; *Gaveston* Chris Hunt; *Trouble with the Law?* Caroline Gooding; *Rodeo Pantheon* Delmas Hale; *Younger Days* Ian David Baker. Send synopsis with sample chapters rather than complete mss.

Royalties negotiable.

Stanley Gibbons Publications

5 Parkside, Christchurch Road, Ringwood, Hampshire BH24 3SH
☎01425 472363   Fax 01425 470247

Chairman *P. I. Fraser*

Managing Director *A. J. Pandit*
Editorial Head *D. Aggersberg*
Approx. Annual Turnover £3 million

Long-established force in the philatelic world with over a hundred years in the business. *Publishes* philatelic reference catalogues and handbooks. Approx. 15 titles a year. Reference works relating to other areas of collecting may be considered. TITLES *Stanley Gibbons British Commonwealth Stamp Catalogue*; *Collect British Stamps*; *How to Arrange and Write Up a Stamp Collection*; *Stamps of the World*; *Collect Aircraft on Stamps*. Monthly publication *Gibbons Stamp Monthly* (see under **Magazines**). Unsolicited mss, synopses and ideas welcome.

Royalties by negotiation.

Robert Gibson & Sons Glasgow Limited

17 Fitzroy Place, Glasgow G3 7SF
☎0141 248 5674   Fax 0141 221 8219

Chairman/Managing Director *R. G. C. Gibson*

FOUNDED 1850 and went public in 1886. *Publishes* educational books only, and has been agent for the Scottish Certificate of Education Examination Board since 1902. About 40 titles a year. Unsolicited mss preferred to synopses/ideas.

Royalties paid annually.

Ginn & Co

See **Reed Educational and Professional Publishing**

Mary Glasgow Publications

See **Stanley Thornes (Publishers) Ltd**

Godsfield Press Ltd

Laurel House, Station Approach, Alresford, Hampshire SO24 9JH
☎01962 735633   Fax 01962 735320

Approx. Annual Turnover £0.5 million

Publishes mind/body/spirit titles in colour for adults and children.

Golden Cockerel Press Ltd

16 Barter Street, London WC1A 2AH
☎0171 405 7979   Fax 0171 404 3598

Directors *Tamar Lindesay, Andrew Lindesay*

FOUNDED 1980 to distribute titles for US-based Associated University Presses Inc., New Jersey. *Publishes* academic titles mostly: art, film, history, literary criticism, music, philosophy, sociology and special interest. About 120 titles a year.

IMPRINTS
AUP: Bucknell University Press; University of Delaware; Fairleigh Dickinson University Press; Lehigh University Press; Susquehanna University Press; **Cygnus Arts** Non-academic books on the arts; **Cornwall Books** Trade hardbacks. Unsolicited mss, synopses and ideas for academic books welcome.

Authors' Rating Very much attuned to American interests with trans-Atlantic spelling and punctuation predominating. Purists may find the process wearisome but those who persevere win through to a wider market.

Victor Gollancz
See **Cassell**

Gomer Press
Wind Street, Llandysul, Dyfed SA44 4BQ
☎01559 362371   Fax 01559 363758
Chairman/Managing Director J. H. Lewis
FOUNDED 1892. Publishes adult fiction and non-fiction, children's fiction and educational material in English and Welsh. About 100 titles a year (80 Welsh; 20 English).
   IMPRINTS **Gomer Press** Dr D. Elis-Gruffydd; **Pont Books** Mairwen Prys Jones. No unsolicited mss, synopses or ideas.
   Royalties paid twice-yearly.

Gower
See **Ashgate Publishing Co. Ltd**

GPC Books
See **University of Wales Press**

Grafton
See **HarperCollins Publishers Ltd**

Graham & Trotman
See **Kluwer Law International**

Graham & Whiteside Ltd
Tuition House, 5-6 Francis Grove, London SW19 4DT
☎0181 947 1011   Fax 0181 947 1163
Managing Director Alastair M. W. Graham
FOUNDED 1995. Publishes annual directories for the business and professional market with titles dating back to 1975 originally published by Graham & Trotman. TITLES 15 annual directories, including: Major Companies of Europe; Major Companies of the Arab World; Major Companies of the Far East and Australasia. Proposals for new projects welcome.
   Royalties paid annually.

Graham-Cameron Publishing
The Studio, 23 Holt Road, Sheringham, Norfolk NR26 8NB
☎01263 821333   Fax 01263 821334
Editorial Director Mike Graham-Cameron
Art Director Helen Graham-Cameron
FOUNDED 1984 as a packaging operation. Publishes illustrated books for children, institutions and business; also biography, education and social history. TITLES Up From the Country; In All Directions; The Holywell Story; Let's Look at Dairying. Please do not send unsolicited mss.
   Royalties paid annually. Subsidiary company: Graham-Cameron Illustration (agency).

Granta Books
2-3 Hanover Yard, Noel Road, London N1 8BE
☎0171 704 9776   Fax 0171 704 0474
Publisher Frances Coady
FOUNDED 1979. Publishes literary fiction, reportage and travel, and general non-fiction. About 35 titles a year. No unsolicited mss; synopses and sample chapters welcome.
   Royalties paid twice-yearly.

Authors' Rating Generous investment by Granta's American owner has led the way to a relaunch promised for 1997. The emphasis will be on 'good writing and challenging ideas' with a mix of new and established writers. Frances Coady hopes to find books 'quite unlike anything you've read before'. The cross fertilization with Granta magazine will continue to mutual benefit.

Granville Publishing
102 Islington High Street, London N1 8EG
☎0171 226 2904
Managing Director John Murray-Browne
Approx. Annual Turnover 'very small'
FOUNDED 1983. Publishes literature reprints only. No unsolicited mss.

W. Green (Scotland)
See **Sweet & Maxwell Ltd**

Green Books
Foxhole, Dartington, Totnes, Devon TQ9 6EB
☎01803 863843   Fax 01803 863843
Chairman Satish Kumar
Managing Editor John Elford
Approx. Annual Turnover £120,000
FOUNDED in 1987 with the support of a number of Green organisations. Closely associated with

Resurgence magazine. *Publishes* high-quality books on a wide range of Green issues, particularly ideas, philosophy and the practical application of Green values. No fiction or books for children. TITLES *Forest Gardening* Robert A. de J. Hart; *Eco-Renovation* Edward Harland; *The Growth Illusion* Richard Douthwaite; *The Living Tree* John Lane; *Tongues in Trees* Kim Taplin. No unsolicited mss. Synopses and ideas welcome. *Royalties* paid twice-yearly.

Green Print
See **Merlin Press Ltd**

Greenhill Books/ Lionel Leventhal Ltd
Park House, 1 Russell Gardens, London NW11 9NN
☎0181 458 6314   Fax 0181 905 5245
Managing Director *Lionel Leventhal*

FOUNDED 1984 by Lionel Leventhal (ex-**Arms & Armour Press**). *Publishes* aviation, military and naval books, and its Napoleonic Library series. Synopses and ideas for books welcome. No unsolicited mss.
Royalties paid twice-yearly.

Gresham Books
See **Woodhead Publishing Ltd**

Gresham Books Ltd
PO Box 61, Henley on Thames, Oxfordshire RG9 3LQ
☎01734 403789   Fax 01734 403789
Managing Director *Mary V. Green*
Approx. Annual Turnover £175,000

Bought by Mary Green from Martins Publishing Group in 1980. A small specialist publishing house. *Publishes* hymn and service books for schools and churches, also craft-bound choir and orchestral folders and Records of Achievement. TITLES include music and melody editions of *Hymns for Church and School*; *The School Hymnal*; *Praise and Thanksgiving*. No unsolicited material but ideas welcome.

Grey Seal Books
28 Burgoyne Road, London N4 1AD
☎0181 340 6061   Fax 0181 342 8102
Chairman *John E. Duncan*

FOUNDED 1990. *Publishes* comparative religion, Islam and futures studies. About 6 titles a year. No unsolicited mss; synopses and ideas welcome.
Royalties paid annually.

Griffith Institute
See **Ashmolean Museum Publications Ltd**

Grisewood & Dempsey
See **Larousse plc**

Grove's Dictionary of Music
See **Macmillan Publishers Ltd**

Grub Street
The Basement, 10 Chivalry Road, London SW11 1HT
☎0171 924 3966   Fax 0171 738 1009
Managing Directors *John Davies,*
    Anne Dolamore

FOUNDED 1982. *Publishes* cookery, health and aviation history books. About 20 titles a year. TITLES *Complete Middle Cookbook; Everyday Diabetic Cookbook; Above the Trenches; Aces High*. Unsolicited mss and synopses welcome in the above categories.
Royalties paid twice-yearly.

Grune & Stratton
See **Harcourt Brace and Company Limited**

Guardian Books
See **Fourth Estate Ltd**

Guild of Master Craftsman Publications Ltd
166 High Street, Lewes, East Sussex BN7 1XU
☎01273 477374   Fax 01273 478606
Chairman *A.E. Phillips*
Approx. Annual Turnover £2 million

FOUNDED 1979. Part of G.M.C. Services Ltd. *Publishes* woodworking and craft books and magazines. 20 titles in 1995. Unsolicited mss, synopses and ideas for books welcome. No fiction.
Royalties paid twice-yearly.

Guinness Publishing Ltd
33 London Road, Enfield, Middlesex EN2 6DJ
☎0181 367 4567   Fax 0181 367 5912
Chairman *Ian Chapman, CBE*
Managing Director *Christopher Irwin*
Joint Publishing Directors *Ian Castello-Cortes, Michael Feldman*

FOUNDED 1954 to publish *The Guinness Book of Records*, now the highest-selling copyright book in the world, published in 35 languages. In the late 1960s the company set about expanding its list with a wider range of print and electronic titles. About 50 titles a year. Ideas and synopses for books welcome if they come within their fields of sport, human achievement (with the emphasis on facts and feats), popular music and family reference.

Authors' Rating Said by *The Bookseller* to be 'a strong contender for the title of most profitable adult trade publisher', all activity is centred on the founding title. The emphasis now is on using the Guinness name to broaden the publishing base.

Gunsmoke Westerns
See **Chivers Press Ltd**

Gwasg Prifysgol Cymru
See **University of Wales Press**

Peter Haddock Ltd
Pinfold Lane Industrial Estate, Bridlington, East Yorkshire YO16 5BT
☎01262 678121   Fax 01262 400043
Managing Director *Peter Haddock*
Contact *Pat Hornby*

FOUNDED 1952. *Publishes* children's picture story and activity books. About 200 series a year. Ideas for picture books welcome.
Royalties payments vary according to each contract.

Authors' Rating Cheap end of the market. Writers need to work fast to make a living.

Peter Halban Publishers
42 South Molton Street, London W1Y 1HB
☎0171 491 1582   Fax 0171 629 5381
Directors *Peter Halban, Martine Halban*

FOUNDED 1986. Independent publisher. *Publishes* biography, autobiography and memoirs, history, philosophy, theology, politics, literature and criticism, Judaica and world affairs. 4–5 titles a year. No unsolicited material. Approach by letter in first instance.
Royalties paid twice-yearly for first two years, thereafter annually in December.

Robert Hale Ltd
Clerkenwell House, 45–47 Clerkenwell Green, London EC1R 0HT
☎0171 251 2661   Fax 0171 490 4958
Chairman/Managing Director *John Hale*

FOUNDED 1936. Family-owned company. *Publishes* adult fiction (but not interested in category crime, romance or science fiction) and nonfiction. No specialist material (education, law, medical or scientific). Acquired **NAG Press Ltd** in 1993 with its list of horological, gemmologi-

cal, jewellery and metalwork titles. Over 200 titles a year. TITLES *The History of Hell* Alice Turner; *The English Pub* Peter Haydon; *21st Century Synonym & Antonym Finder* Barbara Ann Kipfer; *Breadmaking at Home* Harold Bagust; *Queen Victoria in Switzerland* Peter Arengo-Jones; *Gem Identification Made Easy* Matlins & Bonnano; *Simeon's Bride* Alison G. Taylor. Unsolicited mss, synopses and ideas for books welcome.
Royalties paid twice-yearly.

Authors' Rating Takes good care of authors but can be tough on advances. Favours the popular end of the fiction market.

The Hambledon Press
102 Gloucester Avenue, London NW1 8HX
☎0171 586 0817   Fax 0171 586 9970
Chairman/Managing Director/Editorial Head *Martin Sheppard*

FOUNDED 1980. *Publishes* English and European history from post-classical to modern. Currently expanding its list to include history titles with a wider appeal. 25–30 titles a year. TITLES *Jane Austen and Food* Maggie Lane; *Dilke, The Lost Prime Minister* David Nicholls; *Riddles in Stone* Richard Hayman. No unsolicited mss; send preliminary letter. Synopses and ideas welcome.
Royalties paid annually. *Overseas associates* **The Hambledon Press (USA)**, Ohio.

Hamish Hamilton Ltd/ Hamish Hamilton Children's
See **Penguin Books Ltd**

Hamlyn/Hamlyn Children's Books
See **Reed Books**

Harcourt Brace and Company Limited
24–28 Oval Road, London NW1 7DX
☎0171 267 4466
Fax 0171 482 2293/485 4752
Managing Director *Bill Barnett*

Owned by US parent company. *Publishes* scientific, technical and medical books, college textbooks, educational & occupational test. No unsolicited mss.

IMPRINTS **Academic Press; Baillière Tindall; Dryden Press; Grune & Stratton; Holt Rinehart and Winston; T. & A. D. Poyser; W. B. Saunders & Co. Ltd.; Saunders Scientific Publications.**

Harlequin Mills & Boon Ltd

Eton House, 18-24 Paradise Road,
Richmond, Surrey TW9 1SR
☎0181 948 0444   Fax 0181 288 2899
Chairman *John T. Boon*
Managing Director *A. Flynn*
Editorial Director *Karin Stoecker*

FOUNDED 1908. Owned by the Canadian-based Torstar Group. *Publishes* romantic fiction and historical romance. Over 600 titles a year.

IMPRINTS

Mills & Boon Romances (50-55,000 words) contemporary romances with international settings, focusing intensely on hero and heroine, with happy endings assured. **Mills & Boon Temptation** *Lesley Stonehouse* (60-65,000 words) Modern, sensual love stories where characters face dilemmas and choices in fast-paced plots. **Love On Call** *Elizabeth Johnson* (50-55,000 words) Modern medical practice provides a unique background to love stories. **Legacy of Love** *Elizabeth Johnson* (75-80,000 words) Historical romances. **Mira** *Linda Fildew* (minimum 100,000 words) Individual women's fiction.

Silhouette Desire, **Special Edition**, **Sensation** and **Intrigue** imprints are handled by US-based **Silhouette Books** (see **US Publishers**). Unsolicited mss welcome for imprints other than Silhouette.

Tip sheets and guidelines for the Harlequin Mills & Boon series available from Harlequin Mills & Boon Editorial Dept. (please send s.a.e.). Also available (at £9.99 inc. VAT, p&p): *And Then He Kissed Her*, a 40-minute audio cassette with advice on characterisation, plot, dialogue, etc plus *Behind The Hearts and Flowers*, a 28-page booklet containing practical advice on preparing a manuscript.

Royalties paid twice-yearly.

Authors' Rating If there is a single message to emerge from HMB it is that love conquers all. But rivals for consumer affections are claiming that the romance market is getting tougher and racier. HMB is updating its product and sales are still impressive but there is still a risk of falling behind the times.

Harley Books

Martins, Great Horkesley, Colchester, Essex
CO6 4AH
☎01206 271216   Fax 01206 271182
Managing Director *Basil Harley*

FOUNDED 1983. Natural history publishers specialising in entomological and botanical books. Definitive, high-quality illustrated reference works. TITLES *The Moths and Butterflies of Great Britain and Ireland; Spiders of Great Britain and Ireland; Dragonflies of Europe; The Flora of Hampshire.*

Royalties paid twice-yearly in the first year, annually thereafter.

HarperCollins Publishers Ltd

77-85 Fulham Palace Road, London
W6 8JB
☎0181 741 7070   Fax 0181 307 4440
Also at: Freepost PO Box, Glasgow G4 0NB
☎☎0141 772 3200   Fax 0141 306 3119
Executive Chairman/Publisher *Eddie Bell*
Managing Director *Adrian Bourne*
Approx. Annual Turnover £200 million

Publisher of high-profile authors like Jeffrey Archer, James Herbert, Fay Weldon and Len Deighton. Owned by News Corporation. Since 1991 there has been a period of consolidated focus on key management issues within the HarperCollins empire. This has led to various imprints being phased out in favour of others, among them Grafton and Fontana, which have been merged under the HarperCollins paperback imprint. Title output has been reduced by about 20%.

DIVISIONS

Trade *David Young*, Divisional Managing Director, *Stuart Profitt*, Publisher; **Fiction** *Malcolm Edwards*, *Nick Sayers*; **Non-Fiction** *Michael Fishwick*. IMPRINTS **Collins Crime**; **Flamingo** (literary fiction, both hardback and paperback); **HarperCollins Paperbacks**; **Tolkein**; **HarperCollins Science Fiction and Fantasy**; **Fontana Press**; **HarperCollins**. Over 650 titles a year, hardback and paperback. No longer accepts unsolicited submissions.

Thorsons *Eileen Campbell*, Divisional Managing Director IMPRINTS **Pandora Press**; **Thorsons** Health, nutrition, business, parenting, popular psychology, positive thinking, self-help, divination, therapy, recovery, feminism, women's issues, mythology, religion, yoga, tarot, personal development, sexual politics, biography, history, popular culture. About 250 titles a year.

Children's *Ian Craig* IMPRINTS **Picture Lions**; **HarperCollins Audio** (see under **Audio Books**); **Jets**; **Collins Tracks**; **Collins Non-Fiction** Quality picture books and book and tape sets for under 7s; all categories of fiction for the 6-14 age group; dictionaries and general reference for pre-school and primary.

About 250 titles a year. No longer accepts unsolicited mss.

Reference *Robin Wood*, Divisional Managing Director IMPRINTS **HarperCollins; Collins New Naturalist Library; Collins Gems; Collins Willow** (sport); **Janes** (military) Encyclopedias, guides and handbooks, phrase books and manuals on popular reference, art instruction, cookery and wine, crafts, DIY, gardening, military, natural history, pet care, Scottish, sports and pastimes. About 120 titles a year.

Educational *Kate Harris*, Divisional Managing Director Textbook publishing for schools and FE colleges (5–18-year-olds): all subjects for primary education; strong in English, history, geography, science and technology for secondary education; and sociology, business studies and economics in FE. (Former Holmes McDougall, Unwin Hyman, Mary Glasgow Primary Publications, and part of Harcourt, Brace & Co. educational imprints have been incorporated under Collins Educational.) About 90 titles a year.

Dictionaries *Robin Wood* IMPRINTS **Collins; Collins Cobuild; Collins Gem** Includes the *Collins English Dictionary* range with dictionaries and thesauruses, *Collins Bilingual Dictionary* range (French, German, Spanish, Italian, etc.), and the *Cobuild* series of English dictionary, grammars and EFL books. About 50 titles a year.

HarperCollege   *Kate   Harris*   IMPRINT **HarperCollins College** Selected US academic titles, mostly imported from College Division, Basic Books, Harper Business and Harper Perennial. Most of the titles stocked are university-level texts, previously published under the Harper & Row and Scott Foresman imprints. A programme to publish UK editions of some of these commenced in 1994. Strength areas are economics, psychology, allied health and business. About 550 titles stocked in the UK.

HarperCollins World *Robin Wood*. IMPRINTS **HarperCollins US; Australia; New Zealand; Canada; India** General trade titles imported into the UK market.

Religious *Eileen Campbell*, Divisional Managing Director A broad-based religious publisher across all denominations. IMPRINTS **HarperCollins; Fount; Marshall Pickering** Extensive range covering both popular and academic spirituality, music and reference.

Marshall Pickering, bibles, missals, prayer books, and hymn books. About 150 titles a year.

HarperCollins Cartographic *Jeremy Westwood* The cartographic division, with Bartholomew and Times Books now conjoined as one division. IMPRINTS **Bartholomew; Collins; HarperCollins Audiobooks** (see under **Audio Books**); **Invincible Press; Longman Nicholson; Nicholson/Ordnance Survey; Sun Crosswords; Times Atlases; Times Books; Times Crosswords;** Maps, atlases and guides (Bartholomew; Collins; Collins Longman; Times Atlases); leisure maps; educational titles (Collins Longman); London titles (Nicholson); waterway guides (Nicholson/ Ordnance Survey); sports titles for *The Sun* and *News of the World* (Invincible Press); reference and non-fiction (Times Books). About 30 titles a year.

HarperCollins Interactive *Steve Paul* Supports the company's electronic publishing activities on CD-ROM, floppy disk and on-line. *Specialises* in special interest, children's, reference and interactive fiction.

Broadcasting Consultancy *Cresta Norris* Newly formed to exploit TV and film rights across the country.

Authors' Rating A sharp dip in profits led to a signal of displeasure from Rupert Murdoch and, soon afterwards, the departure of chief executive George Craig. His successor, Anthea Disney, lately of News Corps Internet projects, is thought to have ideas for bringing HarperCollins closer to other media interests in the group. Serialisation of Jeffrey Archer's opus in *The Sunday Times* could be the first indication of mutual back-scratching. His $30 million three-book deal is described by the author's biographer 'the worst deal in the history of publishing'.

Harrap Publishing Group Ltd
See **Larousse plc**

Harvard University Press
Fitzroy House, 11 Chenies Street, London WC1E 7ET
☎0171 306 0603   Fax 0171 306 0604

Director *William Sisler*
General Manager *Ann Sexsmith*

Part of **Harvard University Press**, USA. *Publishes* academic and scholarly works in history, politics, philosophy, economics, literary criticism, psychology, sociology, anthropology, women's studies, biological sciences, astronomy, history of science, art, music, film, reference. All mss go to the American office: 79 Garden Street, Cambridge, MA 02138.

The Harvill Press Ltd

84 Thornhill Road, London N1 1RD
☎0171 609 1119   Fax 0171 609 2019
Chairman *Christopher MacLehose*
Managing Director *John Mitchinson*
Editorial Director *Guido Waldman*
Managing Editor *Sarah Westcott*

FOUNDED in 1947, the list was bought by Collins in 1959, of which it remained an imprint until returning to its original independent status in early 1995. *Publishes* literature in translation (especially Russian, Italian and French), literature, quality thrillers, illustrated books and Africana, plus an occasional poetry anthology. 50-60 titles in 1995. AUTHORS Mikhail Bulgakov, Raymond Carver, Richard Ford, Alan Garner, Peter Høeg, Robert Hughes, Giuseppe T. di Lampedusa, Peter Matthiessen, Cees Nooteboom, Boris Pasternak, Georges Perec, Aleksandr Solzhenitsyn, Marguerite Yourcenar. Mss usually submitted by foreign publishers and agents. Synopses and ideas welcome. No educational or technical books.
Royalties paid twice-yearly.

Authors' Rating Still working in as an independent after a buyout from HarperCollins, Harvill is one of the rare UK publishers to take European literature seriously. Over half the output goes to make what Christopher MacLehose calls 'a bridge between culture, so that the best writers can cross in and out of Britain'. The two-way traffic means that Harvill's English language writers tend to do well in Europe. Relations with authors are said to be close and friendly.

Haynes Publishing

Sparkford, Near Yeovil, Somerset BA22 7JJ
☎01963 440635   Fax 01963 440825
Chairman *John H. Haynes*
Approx. Annual Turnover £20 million

FOUNDED in 1960 by John H. Haynes. A family-run business. The mainstay of its programme has been the *Owners' Workshop Manual*, first published in the mid 1960s and still running off the presses today. Indeed the company maintains a strong bias towards motoring and transport titles. *Publishes* DIY workshop manuals for cars and motorbikes, railway, aviation, military, maritime, model-making, and general leisure under imprints.

IMPRINTS
G. T. Foulis & Co. Cars and motoring-related books; **J. H. Haynes & Co. Ltd** *Scott Mauck* Workshop manuals; **Oxford Illustrated Press** Photography, sports and games, gardening, travel and guidebooks; **N. Barnard** Home and leisure titles; **Oxford Publishing Co.** Railway titles; **Patrick Stephens Ltd** *Darryl Reach* Motoring, rail, aviation, military, maritime, model-making. Unsolicited mss welcome if they come within the subject areas covered.
Royalties paid annually. *Overseas associates* Haynes Publications Inc., California, USA.

Authors' Rating Sluggish sales for workshop manuals - Haynes' core business - has led to expansion into the home and leisure market starting with the launch of a *Decorate Your Home* series. Dedicated to providing information that is easily understood but never superficial, Haynes prides itself on meticulous research.

Hazar Publishing Ltd

147 Chiswick High Road, London W4 2DT
☎0181 742 8578   Fax 0181 994 1407
**Managing Director/Editorial Head
   (Children's)** *Gregory Hill*
Editorial Head (Adult) *Marie Clayton*
Approx. Annual Turnover £700,000

FOUNDED 1993, Hazar is a new independent publisher of high-quality illustrated books. *Publishes* children's fiction and adult non-fiction: design and architecture. Planning to expand the children's list. About 15 titles a year. Welcome unsolicited mss, synopses and ideas.
Royalties paid twice-yearly.

Hazleton Publishing

3 Richmond Hill, Richmond, Surrey
TW10 6RE
☎0181 948 5151   Fax 0181 948 4111
Chairman/Managing Director *R. F. Poulter*

Publisher of the leading Grand Prix annual *Autocourse*, now in its 46th edition. *Publishes* high-quality motor sport titles including annuals. TITLE *British Motorsport Year 1995–1996*. About 13 titles a year. No unsolicited mss; synopses and ideas welcome. Interested in all motor sport titles.
Royalties payment varies.

Headline

See **Hodder Headline plc**

Headstart

See **Hodder Headline plc**

Headway
See **Hodder Headline plc**

Health Education Authority
Publishing Department, Hamilton House,
Mabledon Place, London WC1H 9TX
☎0171 413 1846   Fax 0171 413 0339
Managing Director Simon Boyd
Approx. Annual Turnover £600,000

Publishes mass media information leaflets, training manuals, professional guides, open learning for the Health Education Authority. 70 titles in 1995. TITLES *Stopping Smoking Made Easier; Enjoy Healthy Eating; Getting Active, Feeling Fit; Parents, Schools and Sex Education; Promoting Physical Activity in Primary Health Care.* No unsolicited mss; synopses and ideas welcome.
Royalties paid twice-yearly.

Heinemann (William)/ Heinemann Young Books
See **Reed Books**

Heinemann Educational/ Heinemann English Language Teaching
See **Reed Educational and Professional Publishing**

Helicon Publishing
42 Hythe Bridge Street, Oxford OX1 2EP
☎01865 204204   Fax 01865 204205
Managing Director David Attwooll
Publishing Director Michael Upshall
Editorial Director Anne-Lucie Norton

FOUNDED 1992 from the management buy-out of former Random Century's reference division. Led by David Attwooll, the buy-out (for an undisclosed sum) included the Hutchinson Encyclopedia titles and databases, along with other reference titles. Random maintain a close relationship, representing Helicon to the trade. Helicon is increasing the range of reference titles, particularly in history, science and current affairs and is maintaining its lead in electronic publishing. TITLES *History of the World* J. M. Roberts; *Enquire Within* Moira Bremner.

Christopher Helm Publishers Ltd
See **A. & C. Black (Publishers) Ltd**

Henderson Publishing Limited
The Salt House, Tide Mill Way, Woodbridge, Suffolk IP12 1BY
☎01394 380622   Fax 01394 380618
Managing Director Barrie Henderson

Commissioning Editor Lucy Bater
Approx. Annual Turnover £5 million

FOUNDED 1990. *Publishes* non-fiction novelty and information books for children. Most ideas are generated in-house to specific formats across the range of imprints. Unsolicited mss, synopses and ideas for books welcome. Maximum length 7500 words; 3500 for Junior Funfax titles. No poetry, long fiction or teenage subject matter.
IMPRINTS **Funfax; Junior Funfax; Mad Jack Activity Packs; Henderson Study System**.

Ian Henry Publications Ltd
20 Park Drive, Romford, Essex
RM1 4LH
☎01708 749119   Fax 01621 850862
Managing Director Ian Wilkes

FOUNDED 1976. *Publishes* local history, transport history and Sherlockian pastiches. 8–10 titles a year. TITLES *Tales of the East Coast; Grandfather's Romford; The Hampstead Poisonings; Wivenhoe & Brightlingsea Railway.* No unsolicited mss. Synopses and ideas for books welcome.
Royalties paid twice-yearly.

The Herbert Press Ltd
35 Bedford Row, London WC1R 4JH
☎0171 404 5621   Fax 0171 404 7706
Managing Director/Editorial Director David Herbert

Publishes archaeology, architecture and design, botanical art, crafts and hobbies, exhibition catalogues, fashion and costume, fine art and art history, photography. About 8 titles a year. Unsolicited mss welcome.
Royalties paid twice-yearly.

Nick Hern Books
14 Larden Road, London W3 7ST
☎0181 740 9539   Fax 0181 746 2006
Chairman/Managing Director Nick Hern
Approx. Annual Turnover £250,000

FOUNDED 1988. Fully independent since 1992. *Publishes* books on theatre: from how-to and biography to plays. About 30 titles a year. No unsolicited playscripts. Scripts, ideas and proposals for other theatre material welcome. Not interested in material unrelated to the theatre.

High Risk Books
See **Serpent's Tail**

Highland Books
See **Inter Publishing Ltd**

Hippo
See **Scholastic Ltd**

HMSO Books
St Crispins, Duke Street, Norwich, Norfolk
NR3 1PD
☎01603 622211   Fax 01603 695582
Controller & Chief Executive *Mike Lynn*
Approx. Annual Turnover £340 million

FOUNDED 1786. Government publisher of material sponsored by Parliament, government departments and other official bodies. No unsolicited material. The Controller is responsible for the administration of Crown and parliamentary copyright. The contact point for any copyright queries is 01603 695506.

Authors' Rating Britain's largest publisher by title output could enter the private sector within a year if government plans for a sell-off are realised. Top title is the *Highway Code* which outsells every other book except the Bible.

Hobsons Publishing
Bateman Street, Cambridge CB2 1LZ
☎01223 354551   Fax 01223 323154
Chairman/Managing Director *Martin Morgan*
Approx. Annual Turnover £17.7 million

FOUNDED 1973. A division of Harmsworth Publishing Ltd, part of the Daily Mail & General Trust. *Publishes* course and career guides, under exclusive licence and royalty agreements for CRAC (Careers Research and Advisory Bureau); computer software; directories and specialist titles for employers, government departments and professional associations. TITLES *Graduate Employment and Training; The Student HelpBook Series; Degree Course Guides; The Which Degree Series; Which University* (CD-ROM); *The POSTGRAD Series: The Directory of Graduate Studies; The Directory of Higher Education; The Directory of Further Education; CRAC GNVQ Assignment Series; CRAC Core Skills Series.* Also publisher of *Johansens Hotel Guides*.

Authors' Rating Formula publishing based on a close and shrewd analysis of the education and business markets.

Hodder & Stoughton
See **Hodder Headline plc**

Hodder Headline plc
338 Euston Road, London NW1 3BH
☎0171 873 6000   Fax 0171 873 6024
Group Chief Executive *Tim Hely Hutchinson*

Deputy Chief Executive *Mark Opzoomer*
Approx. Annual Turnover £80 million

Formed in June 1993 through the merger of **Headline Book Publishing** and **Hodder & Stoughton**. Headline was formed in 1986 and had grown dramatically, whereas Hodder & Stoughton was 125 years old with a diverse range of publishing.

DIVISIONS
Headline Book Publishing Managing Director *Sian Thomas* **Non-fiction** *Alan Brooke*; **Fiction** *Jane Morpeth. Publishes* commercial fiction (hardback and paperback) and popular non-fiction including biography, cinema, design and film, food and wine, countryside, TV tie-ins and sports yearbooks. IMPRINTS **Headline**; **Headline Feature**; **Headline Review**; **Headline Delta Liaison** (erotic fiction). AUTHORS Raymond Blanc, Harry Bowling, Martina Cole, Josephine Cox, John Francome, Dean Koontz, Richard Laymon, Lyn Macdonald, Ellis Peters and Peter Scudamore.

Hodder & Stoughton General Managing Director *Martin Nield*, Deputy Managing Director *Sue Fletcher*. **Non-fiction** *Roland Philipps*; **Horror** *Nick Austin*; **Sceptre** *Carole Welch*; **Fiction** *Carolyn Mays, Carolyn Caughey*; **Audio** (See under **Audio Books**). *Publishes* commercial and literary fiction; biography, autobiography, history, self-help, humour, travel and other general interest non-fiction; audio. IMPRINTS **Hodder & Stoughton; Coronet; New English Library; Sceptre.** AUTHORS Elizabeth Adler, Melvyn Bragg, John le Carré, James Clavell, Edwina Currie, Stephen King, Stephen Leather, Gavin Lyall, Ed McBain, Hilary Norman and Mary Stewart, Terry Waite.

Hodder & Stoughton Educational Managing Director *Brian Steven.* **Humanities, Science & Mathematics** *David Lea;* **Language, Business and Psychology** *Tim Gregson-Williams.* Textbooks for the primary, secondary, tertiary and further education sectors and for self-improvement. IMPRINTS **Hodder & Stoughton Educational; Teach Yourself; Headway**.

Hodder Children's Books Managing Director *Mary Tapissier,* Publishing Director *Fiona Kenshole.* IMPRINTS **Hodder & Stoughton; Knight; Picture Knight; Hodder Dargaud; Headstart; Test Your Child**. AUTHORS Goscinny & Uderzo (*Asterix*), Rolf Harris, Mick Inkpen, Christopher Pike.

Hodder & Stoughton Religious Managing Director *Charles Nettleton.* **Bibles & Liturgical** *Emma Sealey;* **Christian paperbacks** *James Catford.* Bibles, commentaries, liturgical works (both printed and software), and a wide range of Christian paperbacks. IMPRINTS **New International Version of the Bible**; **Hodder Christian paperbacks**.

Edward Arnold Managing Director *Richard Stileman*. **Humanities** *Chris Wheeler*, **Medical, Science and Engineering** *Nicki Dennis*. Academic and professional books and journals.

The Brockhampton Press Managing Director *John Maxwell*. Promotional books.

Royalties paid twice-yearly.

Authors' Rating It is a measure of Hodder Headline's growth rate that one of its problems is in finding a US partner capable of exploiting the range of output. With an annual list of well over 2000 titles, Hodder Headline has shown impressive growth in education and audio books. Authors praise regular and frequent updates on sales figures. Their worry is that Hodder Headline may carry its enthusiasm for aggressive selling, i.e. discounting, to the point where royalties are adversely affected. The Hodder & Stoughton general list has nearly 20 per cent first-time authors.

Holmes McDougall
See **HarperCollins Publishers Ltd**

Holt Rinehart & Winston
See **Harcourt Brace and Company Limited**

Honeyglen Publishing Ltd
56 Durrels House, Warwick Gardens, London W14 8QB
☎0171 602 2876   Fax 0171 602 2876
Directors *N. S. Poderegin, J. Poderegin*

FOUNDED 1983. *Publishes* history, philosophy of history, biography and selective fiction. No children's or science fiction. TITLES *The Soul of India; A Child of the Century* Amaury de Riencourt; *With Duncan Grant in South Turkey* Paul Roche; *Vladimir, The Russian Viking* Vladimir Volkoff; *The Dawning* Milka Bajic-Poderegin; *Quicksand* Louise Hide. Unsolicited mss welcome. No synopses or ideas.

Authors' Rating Highly commended in *The Sunday Times* survey of small independent publishers.

House of Lochar
Isle of Colonsay, Argyll PA61 7YR
☎01951 200232   Fax 01951 200232
Chairman *Kevin Byrne*
Managing Director *Georgina Hobhouse*
Approx. Annual Turnover £80,000

FOUNDED 1995 on the basis of some 24 titles formerly published by Thomas and Lochar of Nairn. *Publishes* Scottish non-fiction – history, topography, transport. IMPRINTS **House of Lochar** *Kevin Byrne* TITLES *Country Houses of Scotland; Dog-Collar Diary; The Drove Roads of Scotland; Fearchair a'Ghunna*. **Colonsay Books** *Georgina Hobhouse* TITLES *Summer in the Hebrides; Place Names of Colonsay and Oronsay; Antiquities of Colonsay*. No poetry, fiction or books unrelated to Scotland or Celtic theme. Unsolicited mss, synopses and ideas welcome if relevant to subjects covered.

Royalties paid annually.

How To Books Ltd
Plymbridge House, Estover Road, Plymouth, Devon PL6 7PZ
☎01752 202369   Fax 01752 202369
Publisher/Managing Director *Roger Ferneyhough*

The first titles were published in 1987 by **Northcote House Publishers**. By 1991 the list had grown so much and was expanding at such a rate that Roger Ferneyhough set up a separate company, with 25 titles in print and a programme of some 20 new titles a year. There are now 150 titles in the series, many in revised and updated new editions. TITLES take the form of 'how to achieve a specific goal or benefit' in the areas of employment, business, education, family reference, international opportunities and self-development: *How to Become an Au Pair; How to Survive Divorce; How to Master Languages*. Well-structured proposals from qualified and experienced professionals welcome.

Royalties paid annually.

The University of Hull Press/ The Lampada Press
Cottingham Road, Hull, North Humberside HU6 7RX
☎01482 465322   Fax 01482 465936
Secretary *Miss J. M. Smith*

The University of Hull Press *publishes* books of academic merit and those that command a wide general market. TITLES *Superior Force: The Conspiracy Behind the Escape of Goeben and Breslau* Geoffrey Miller; *The Desperate Faction? The Jacobites of North-East England 1688-1745* Leo Gooch; *Aspects of Political Censorship 1914-1918* Tania Rose. The Lampada Press *publishes* well-researched popular works, mainly of local interest. Welcomes unsolicited mss, synopses and ideas for books.

Royalties paid annually. *Overseas representatives*:

Paul & Company Publishers Consortium Inc., USA; St Clair Press, Australia.

Human Horizons
See **Souvenir Press Ltd**

Human Science Press
See **Plenum Publishing Ltd**

Hunt & Thorpe
Laurel House, Station Approach, Alresford, Hampshire SO24 9JH
☎01962 735633 Fax 01962 735320
Approx. Annual Turnover £1.5 million

Publishes children's and religious titles only. About 25 titles a year. Unsolicited material welcome.

C. Hurst & Co.
38 King Street, London WC2E 8JZ
☎0171 240 2666 Fax 0171 240 2667
Chairman/Managing Director *Christopher Hurst*
Editorial Heads *Christopher Hurst, Michael Dwyer*

FOUNDED 1967. An independent company, cultivating a concern for literacy, detail and the visual aspects of the product. *Publishes* contemporary history, politics and social science. About 20 titles a year. TITLES *The Origins of Japanese Trade Supremacy; The Rwanda Crisis – History of a Genocide; Churchill to Major – the Prime Ministership since 1945; Yugoslavia's Bloody Collapse.* No unsolicited mss. Synopses and ideas welcome.
Royalties paid twice in first year, annually thereafter.

Hutchinson Books Ltd
See **Random House UK Ltd**

Hymns Ancient & Modern Ltd
St Mary's Works, St Mary's Plain, Norwich, Norfolk NR3 3BH
☎01603 616563 Fax 01603 624483
Chairman *Very Rev. Dr Henry Chadwick KBE*
Publisher *G. A. Knights*

Publishes hymn books for churches, schools and other institutions. All types of religious books, both general and educational.
IMPRINTS **The Canterbury Press Norwich** General religious books TITLES *Pilgrim's Guide to the Holy Land; Diary of a Country Parson; Management and Ministry; Lower Than the Angels.* **Chansitor Publications Ltd** TITLES *The Sign; Home Words* – two monthly, nationwide parish

magazine inserts. **Religious and Moral Education Press** Religious books for schools, primary, middle secondary, assembly material, etc. **G. J. Palmer & Sons Ltd** TITLES *Church Times* (see under **Magazines**). Ideas welcome; no mss.
Royalties paid annually.

IBC Publishing
37–41 Mortimer Street, London W1N 7JX
☎0171 637 4383 Fax 0171 636 6414
Managing Director *Tony Powell*

Owned by International Business Communications (Holdings) plc. *Publishes* the *Banking Technology* magazine and a range of legal, tax, financial, management and business to business books, newsletters and directories aimed at senior management and professional practices. About 50 titles a year. Unsolicited synopses and ideas welcome, but initial approach in writing preferred.
Royalties paid twice-yearly.

Icon Books
52 High Street, Trumpington, Cambridge CB2 2LS
☎01223 847474 Fax 01223 844884
Managing Director *Peter Pugh*
Editorial Head *Richard Appignanesi*

FOUNDED 1992. *Publishes* 'Beginners' – cartoon introductions to the key figures and issues in the history of science, psychology, philosophy, religion and the arts. 9 titles in 1995. TITLES *Freud for Beginners; Einstein for Beginners; Buddha for Beginners; Postmodernism for Beginners.* No unsolicited mss; synopses and ideas for informative non-fiction welcome.
Royalties paid twice-yearly. *Overseas Associates* Totem Books, USA.

Impact Books Ltd
Axe and Bottle Court, 70 Newcomen Street, London SE1 1YT
☎0171 403 3541 Fax 0171 407 6437
Managing Director *Jean-Luc Barbanneau*
Approx. Annual Turnover £150,000

FOUNDED 1985 by Jean-Luc Barbanneau, also Managing Director of Websters International Publishers. *Publishes* travel, practical guides, reference, illustrated books. About 20 titles a year. TITLES *By Bicycle in Ireland* (new edition) M. Ryle; *Chasing the Lizard's Tail* J. Finke; *French Glossary of Banking Terms.* Unsolicited mss not welcome – send detailed synopses and sample chapters first.
Royalties paid twice-yearly.

Institute of Personnel and Development

IPD House, Camp Road, London SW19 4UX
☎0181 263 3387

Part of IPD Enterprises Limited. *Publishes* management and training. 36 titles in 1995. Unsolicited mss, synopses and ideas welcome.
Royalties paid annually.

Inter Publishing Ltd

St Nicholas House, The Mount, Guildford, Surrey GU2 4NH
☎01483 306309   Fax 01483 579196

Managing Director *David Wavre*
Approx. Annual Turnover £400,000

FOUNDED 1990. *Publishes* religious plus some gift and music books. About 24 titles a year. IMPRINTS **Eagle, Highland Books**. Unsolicited mss, synopses and ideas for books welcome.
Royalties paid quarterly.

Inter-Varsity Press

38 De Montfort Street, Leicester LE1 7GP
☎0116 2551754   Fax 0116 2542044

Chairman *Ralph Evershed*
Chief Executive *Frank Entwistle*

FOUNDED mid-30s as the publishing arm of Universities and Colleges Christian Fellowship, it has expanded to wider Christian markets worldwide. *Publishes* Christian belief and lifestyle, reference and bible commentaries. About 50 titles a year. No secular material or anything which fails to empathise with orthodox Protestant Christianity.
    IMPRINTS **IVP, Apollos, Crossway** TITLES *The Bible Speaks Today; Sociology through the Eyes of Faith* Campolo & Fraser. No unsolicited mss; synopses and ideas welcome.
Royalties paid twice-yearly.

Intrigue

See **Harlequin Mills & Boon Ltd**

Invincible Press

See **HarperCollins Publishers Ltd**

Richard D. Irwin/Irwin Professional Publishers

See **Times Mirror International Publishers Ltd**

Isis Publishing Limited

7 Centremead, Osney Mead, Oxford OX2 0ES
☎01865 250333   Fax 01865 790358

Managing Director *John Durrant*

Publishes large-print books - fiction and non-fiction; audio books (see under **Audio Books**). TITLES *The Colour of Magic* Terry Pratchett; *The Book of Guys* Garrison Keillor; *The Rise and Fall of the House of Windsor*. No unsolicited mss as Isis undertake no original publishing.
Royalties paid twice-yearly.

Ithaca Press

See **Garnet Publishing Ltd**

IVP

See **Inter-Varsity Press**

JAI Press Ltd

The Courtyard, 28 High Street, Hampton Hill, Middlesex TW12 1PD
☎0181 943 9296   Fax 0181 943 9317

Chairman *Herbert M. Johnson*
Managing Director *Piers R. Allen*

FOUNDED 1976. Owned by JAI Press, Inc., USA. *Publishes* research-level scholarly publications in business, economics, social sciences, computer sciences, chemistry and life sciences, spanning the complete range of social and economic sciences, natural, pure and applied physical sciences. *Specialises* in the publication of research serials and monograph series, as well as journals. About 150 titles a year. TITLES *Advances in Biosensors; Research in Organizational Behavior; Research in Accounting in Emerging Economies; Studies in Qualitative Methodology.* No undergraduate texts. Unsolicited mss discouraged. Synopses and ideas welcome.
    Royalties paid annually. *Overseas associates* JAI Press, Inc., Greenwich, Connecticut, USA.

Arthur James Ltd

4 Broadway Road, Evesham, Worcestershire WR11 6BH
☎01386 446566   Fax 01386 446717

Editorial Office: Deershot Lodge, Park Lane, Ropley, Nr Alresford, Hampshire SO24 0BE

Managing Director *Ian Carlile*
Editorial Director *Mr J. Hunt*
Approx. Annual Turnover £165,000

FOUNDED 1944 by a Fleet Street journalist, A. J. Russell. *Publishes* day books, devotional classics, psychological, healing, religious, social work and *New Testament* translations. AUTHORS William Barclay, Jacques Duquesne, Monica Furlong, Rosemary Harthill, Sara Maitland, John Skinner, Chuck Spezzano, Angela Tilby, Robert Van de Weyer, Marina Warner. No unsolicited mss.
    Royalties paid annually. *Overseas associates* Buchanan, Australia; Omega, New Zealand.

Jane's Information Group

163 Brighton Road, Coulsdon, Surrey
CR5 2NH
☎0181 700 3700   Fax 0181 763 1006
Managing Director *Alfred Rolington*
Approx. Annual Turnover £18 million

FOUNDED 1898 by Fred T. Jane with the publication of *All The World's Fighting Ships*. Now part of The Thomson Corporation. In recent years, management has been focusing on growth opportunities in its core business and on enhancing the performance of initiatives like Jane's yearbooks on CD-ROM. *Publishes* reviews and yearbooks on defence, aerospace and transport topics, with details of equipment and systems; plus directories and strategic studies. Also *Jane's Defence Weekly* (see under **Magazines**).

DIVISIONS
Publishing *Robert Hutchinson* TITLES *Jane's Defence Weekly; Jane's International Defense Review; Jane's Intelligence Review; Jane's Defence Systems Modernisation; Jane's Navy International; Defence, Aerospace Yearbooks.* **Electronic and Commercial Publishing** *Sarah Thomas* TITLES *Jane's Airport Review; Foreign Report; Jane's Sentinel* (regional security assessment); *Transportation Yearbooks;* CD-ROM and electronic development and publication. Unsolicited mss, synopses and ideas for books welcome.

Royalties paid twice-yearly. *Overseas associates* Jane's Information Group Inc., USA.

Janus Publishing Company Ltd

Edinburgh House, 19 Nassau Street, London
W1N 7RE
☎0171 580 7664   Fax 0171 636 5756
Managing Director *Ronald Ross Stanton*

Publishes fiction, human interest, memoirs/biography, mind, body and spirit, religion and theology, social questions, popular science, history, spiritualism and the paranormal, poetry, children and young adults. About 50 titles. TITLES *Are They Really so Awful* Christopher Challis; *Between Life and Death* Ben A. Soifer; *The Great Defender* Sarah F. Morrison; *The Wicker Cage* Kathleen Kinder; *Stalin's Little Guest* Janka Goldberger. Unsolicited mss welcome.

Royalties paid twice-yearly. Agents in the USA, Australia, South Africa and Asia.

Authors' Rating Authors may be asked to cover their own productions costs.

Japan Library
See **Curzon Press Ltd**

Jarrold Publishing

Whitefriars, Norwich, Norfolk NR3 1TR
☎01603 763300   Fax 01603 662748
Managing Director *Antony Jarrold*

Part of Jarrold & Sons Ltd, long-established printing/publishing company. *Publishes* UK travel, leisure and calendars. Material tends to be of a high pictorial content. About 30 titles a year. Unsolicited mss, synopses and ideas welcome but approach in writing before submitting anything to Donald Greig, Senior Editor.

Royalties paid twice-yearly.

Jets
See **HarperCollins Publishers Ltd**

Jewish Chronicle Publications
See **Frank Cass & Co Ltd**

Michael Joseph Ltd
See **Penguin Books Ltd**

Kahn & Averill

9 Harrington Road, London SW7 3ES
☎0181 743 3278   Fax 0181 743 3278
Managing Director *Mr M. Kahn*

FOUNDED 1967 to publish children's titles but now specialises in music titles. A small independent publishing house. *Publishes* music and general non-fiction. No unsolicited mss; synopses and ideas for books considered.

Royalties paid twice-yearly.

Karnak House

300 Westbourne Park Road, London
W11 1EH
☎0171 221 6490   Fax 0171 221 6490
Chairman *Dimela Yekwai*
Managing Director *Amon Saba Saakana*

FOUNDED 1979. *Publishes* anthropology, education, Egyptology, history, language and linguistics, literary criticism, music, parapsychology, prehistory. No poetry, humour or sport. About 12 titles a year. No unsolicited mss; send introduction or synopsis with one sample chapter. Synopses and ideas welcome.

Royalties paid twice-yearly. *Overseas subsidiaries*: The Antef Institute, and Karnak House, Illinois, USA.

Richard Kay Publications

80 Sleaford Road, Boston, Lincolnshire
PE21 8EU
☎01205 353231
Managing Editor *Richard Allday*

FOUNDED 1970. Non-profit motivated publisher of local interest (Lincs.) material: dialect, history, autobiography and biography, philosophy, medico-political and contemporary dissent on current affairs. About 6 titles a year. TITLES *Winceby and the Battle; Alcoholism: A Terminal Disease; William Brewster: The Father of New England; Woods and Doggeybaw – A Lincolnshire Dialect Dictionary.* No unsolicited mss; synopses and ideas welcome.

Royalties paid if appropriate.

Kelpie
See **Canongate Books Ltd**

Kenilworth Press Ltd
Addington, Buckingham, Buckinghamshire MK18 2JR
☎01296 715101   Fax 01296 715148
Chairman/Managing Director *David Blunt*
Approx. Annual Turnover £500,000

FOUNDED 1989 with the acquisition of Threshhold Books. The UK's principal instructional equestrian publisher, producing the official books of the British Horse Society, the famous *Threshold Picture Guides*, and a range of authoritative titles sold around the world. About 10 titles a year.

IMPRINTS **Kenilworth Press** TITLES *British Horse Society Manuals*; *The International Warmblood Horse*; *Course Design & Construction for Horse Trials*; *Eventing Insights*; *Lungeing and Long-Reining.* **Threshold Books** TITLES *Threshold Picture Guides 1–38.* Unsolicited mss, synopses and ideas welcome but only for titles concerned with the care or riding of horses or ponies.

Royalties paid twice-yearly.

Kenyon-Deane
See **Cressrelles Publishing Co. Ltd**

Laurence King
71 Great Russell Street, London WC1B 3BN
☎0171 831 6351   Fax 0171 831 8356
Chairman *Robin Hyman*
Managing Director *Laurence King*

FOUNDED 1991. Publishing imprint of UK packager **Calmann & King Ltd** (see under **UK Packagers**). *Publishes* full-colour illustrated books on art history, the decorative arts, carpets, photography and design. Unsolicited material welcome.

Royalties paid twice-yearly.

Kingfisher
See **Larousse plc**

Jessica Kingsley Publishers Ltd
116 Pentonville Road, London N1 9JB
☎0171 833 2307   Fax 0171 837 2917
Managing Director *Jessica Kingsley*
Production Manager *Anna French*
Editors *Tricia Dever, Rosie Barker*

FOUNDED 1987. Independent publisher of social and behavioural sciences, including arts therapies, child psychology, psychotherapy (especially forensic psychotherapy), social work, regional studies and higher education policy. Approx. 65 titles in 1996, including *Autism: An Inside-Out Approach* Donna Williams. 'We welcome suggestions for books and proposals from prospective authors, especially in the areas of social issues and working with children. Proposals should consist of an outline of the book, a contents list, assessment of the market, and author's c.v.. Complete manuscript should not be sent.'

Kingsway Publications
Lottbridge Drove, Eastbourne, East Sussex BN23 6NT
☎01323 410930   Fax 01323 411970
Chairman *Peter Fenwick*
Joint Managing Directors *John Paculabo, Brian Davies*
Editorial Contact *Mrs J. Oldroyd*
Approx. Annual Turnover £1.5 million

Part of Kingsway Communications Ltd, a charitable trust with Christian objectives. *Publishes* Christian books: Bibles, Christian testimonies, renewal issues, devotional. No poetry please. About 40 titles a year.

IMPRINT **Kingsway** TITLES *The Life Application Bible*; *The Father Heart of God* Floyd McClung; *Growing in the Prophetic* Mike Bickle; *Questions of Life* Nicky Gumble. Unsolicited mss welcome, but partial submissions/synopses preferred. Return postage appreciated; all submissions should be addressed to the Editorial Department.

Royalties paid annually.

Kluwer Academic Publishers
PO Box 55, Lancaster LA1 1PE
☎01524 34996   Fax 01524 32144
Managing Director *Mr J. Smith*
Head of Medical Division *Helen Liepmann*
Approx. Annual Turnover £1.5 million

A member of the Dutch Kluwer Group, publisher of approximately 200 scholarly journals and 500 titles a year across an extensive range of scientific disciplines. Kluwer Academic

(UK) specialises in medical, scientific and technical publishing at the postgraduate level. *Publishes* research monographs, postgraduate textbooks, colour atlases and texts for family physicians. Particular areas of medical specialisation include cardiology, nephrology, radiology, oncology, pathology, neurosciences and immunology.

Kluwer Law International
Sterling House, 66 Wilton Road, London SW1V 1DE
☎0171 821 1123   Fax 0171 630 5229
Director of Operations *Marcel Nieuwenhuis*

FOUNDED 1995. Parent company: Wolters Kluwer Group. Kluwer Law International consists of three components: the law list of Graham & Trotman, Kluwer Law and Taxation and Martinus Nyhoff. *Publishes* international law. Plans to publish 200 titles a year. Unsolicited synopses and ideas for books on law at an international level welcome.

Royalties paid annually. North American sales and marketing: Kluwer Law International, 675 Massachusetts Avenue, Cambridge, MA 02139.

Knight
See **Hodder Headline plc**

Charles Knight Publishing
See **Tolley Publishing Co Ltd**

Kogan Page Ltd
120 Pentonville Road, London N1 9JN
☎0171 278 0433   Fax 0171 837 3768/6348
Managing Director *Philip Kogan*
Approx. Annual Turnover £8 million

FOUNDED 1967 by Philip Kogan to publish *The Industrial Training Yearbook*. Member of the Euro Business Publishing Network. In 1992 acquired Earthscan Publications and launched a new management research series. *Publishes* business and management reference books and monographs, education and careers, marketing, personal finance, personnel, small business, training and industrial relations, transport, plus journals. Further expansion is planned, particularly in the professional and human resource areas, yearbooks and directories, and international business reference. About 240 titles a year.

DIVISIONS
Kogan Page *Pauline Goodwin, Philip Mudd, Peter Chadwick*. TITLES *Training and Enterprise Directory*; *British Vocational Qualifications*. SERIES *Working for Yourself*; *Careers*; *Better Management Skills*.

Earthscan Publications *Jonathan Sinclair Wilson* Has close associations with the International Institute for Environment and Development and with the Worldwide Fund for Nature. *Publishes* Third World issues and their global implications, and general environmental titles, both popular and academic. About 30 titles a year. TITLES *European Environmental Technology Directory*. Unsolicited mss, synopses and ideas for books welcome.

Royalties paid twice-yearly.

Authors' Rating Now the largest independent publisher of business books, Kogan Page rewards good ideas with strong marketing, particularly in airports and other gathering points for young executives.

Labyrinth Publishing (UK) Ltd
See under **UK Packagers**

Ladybird Books Ltd
Beeches Road, Loughborough, Leicestershire LE11 2NQ
☎01509 268021   Fax 01509 234672
Chair *Peter Mayer*
Managing Director *A. D. Forbes Watson*
Publishing Director *M. H. Gabb*
International Director *D. King*
Approx. Annual Turnover £19 million

FOUNDED in the 1860s. Introduced just before the First World War, the Ladybird name and format was fully established as a result of the development of a children's list during the Second World War. In the early 1960s the commercial print side of the operation was abandoned in favour of publishing Ladybird titles only and in 1971 the company was bought by the Pearson Longman Group. From 1st January 1995, Ladybird has been integrated into the Penguin Group. *Publishes* children's consumer books for the mass market internationally. About 200 titles a year.

IMPRINTS
Ladybird; Key Words Reading Scheme; Picture Ladybird; Ladybird Discovery Storybooks; Disney. TITLES *Favourite Tales; Read it Yourself; Say The Sounds Reading Scheme; Read With Me Reading Scheme; Disney; Beatrix Potter; Mumfie; Spot; Activity Books; Practice at Home National Curriculum Series; Learning at Home; First Focus* range; plus the Ladybird audio cassette/book series (see entry under **Audio Books**). Unsolicited mss relating to published areas are welcome.

The Lampada Press
See **The University of Hull Press**

Langley Publishing Ltd
32 Sheen Park, Richmond, Surrey
TW9 1UW
☎0181 948 0937
Chairman *Tim Little*
FOUNDED 1995. *Publishes* management training
and personal development. 4 titles in 1995.
Straightforward Guides series *Bill Peters* TITLES
*Answering the Tough Interview Question; Power CVs
and Interview Letters – That Really Work; Making
Effective Presentations.* Unsolicited mss welcome,
'but our style is important – ask for the Authors'
Information Pack first'. Synopses and ideas wel-
come.
   Royalties paid quarterly.

Larousse plc
Elsley House, 24–30 Great Titchfield Street,
London W1P 7AD
☎0171 631 0878   Fax 0171 323 4694
Managing Director *John Clement*
FOUNDED 1994 when owners, Groupe de la
Cité (publisher of the Larousse dictionaries in
France), merged its UK operations of
Grisewood & Dempsey and **Chambers
Harrap Ltd.** Larousse publishes under the
Kingfisher, Chambers, and **Larousse**
imprints.

IMPRINTS
Chambers *Robert Allen, Min Lee* Editorial
offices: 43–45 Annandale Street, Edinburgh
EH7 4AZ. ☎0131 557 4571 Fax: 0131 557
2936. *Publishes* dictionaries, reference, and
local interest. The imprint was founded in the
early 1800s to publish self-education books,
but soon diversified into dictionaries and other
reference works. Acquired by Groupe de la
Cité in 1989. The acquisition of **Harrap
Publishing Group**'s core business strength-
ened its position in the dictionary market,
adding bilingual titles, covering almost all the
major European languages, to its English-language dictionaries. Send synopsis with accompanying letter rather than completed mss.
   Kingfisher *Chester Fisher* (Based at London
address above.) Founded in 1973 by **Grisewood
& Dempsey Ltd.** *Publishes* children's fiction and
non-fiction in hardback and paperback: story
books, rhymes and picture books, fiction and
poetry anthologies, young non-fiction, activity
books, general series and reference.
   Larousse *Jim Miles* (illustrated reference)
Robert Allen (dictionaries and reference).

Editorial offices in both London and Edinburgh.
Publishes adult reference and dictionaries.
   Royalties paid bi-annually where applicable.

Lawrence & Wishart Ltd
99A Wallis Road, London E9 5LN
☎0181 533 2506   Fax 0181 533 7369
Managing Director *Sally Davison*
Editors *Sally Davison, Ruth Borthwick*
FOUNDED 1936. An independent publisher
with a substantial backlist. *Publishes* current
affairs, cultural politics, economics, history,
politics and education. 15–20 titles a year.
TITLES *Reclaiming Truth: A Contribution to a
Critique of Cultural Relativism; The Acceptable
Face of Feminism, A History of the Women's
Institute; The Body Language: The Meaning of
Modern Sport; Leadership and Democracy: The
History of NUPE, Vol. 2, 1928-93.* Synopses
preferred to complete mss. Ideas welcome.
   Royalties paid annually, unless by arrange-
ment.
Authors' Rating One of the few genuine
left-wing publishers. Authors should expect to
surrender profit to principles.

Legacy of Love
See **Harlequin Mills & Boon Ltd**

Legend
See **Random House UK Ltd**

Lehigh University Press
See **Golden Cockerel Press Ltd**

Leicester University Press
See **Cassell**

Lennard Publishing
See **Lennard Associates Ltd** under **UK
Packagers**

Charles Letts
See **New Holland (Publishers) Ltd**

Liaison
See **Hodder Headline plc**

John Libbey & Co. Ltd
13 Smiths Yard, Summerley Street, London
SW18 4HR
☎0181 947 2777   Fax 0181 947 2664
Chairman/Managing Director *John Libbey*
FOUNDED 1979. *Publishes* medical books only.
TITLES *Progress in Obesity Research; Current
Problems in Epilepsy.* About 20 titles a year.

Synopses and ideas welcome for both specialist areas. *Overseas subsidiaries* John Libbey Eurotext Ltd, France; John Libbey-Cic, Italy.

Librapharm Ltd

Gemini House, 162 Craven Road, Newbury, Berkshire RG14 5NR
☎01635 522651   Fax 01635 522651
Chairman *Dr R. B. Smith*
Managing Director *Dr P. L. Clarke*
Approx. Annual Turnover £500,000

FOUNDED 1995 as a partial buyout from Kluwer Academic Publishers (UK) academic list. *Publishes* medical and scientific books and periodicals. 8 titles a year. IMPRINT **Petroc Press**. TITLES *Fry's Common Diseases; Neighbour: The Inner Consultation; Current Medical Research and Opinion* (journal). Unsolicited mss, synopses and ideas for medical books welcome.
Royalties paid twice-yearly.

Library Association Publishing

7 Ridgmount Street, London WC1E 7AE
☎0171 636 7543   Fax 0171 636 3627
Chairman *E. M. Broome*
Managing Director *Janet Liebster*

Publishing arm of **The Library Association**. *Publishes* library and information science, monographs, reference, textbooks and bibliography. About 30 titles a year.

IMPRINTS
Library Association Publishing; **Clive Bingley Books**   Over 200 titles in print, including *Walford's Guide to Reference Material* and *AACR2*. Unsolicited mss, synopses and ideas welcome provided material falls firmly within the company's specialist subject areas.
Royalties paid annually.

Frances Lincoln Ltd

4 Torriano Mews, Torriano Avenue, London, NW5 2RZ
☎0171 284 4009   Fax 0171 267 5249
Managing Director *Frances Lincoln*

FOUNDED 1977. *Publishes* highly illustrated non-fiction: gardening, interiors, health, crafts, cookery; children's picture and information books, art and religion books; and stationery. About 45 titles a year.

DIVISIONS
Adult Non-fiction *Erica Hunningher* TITLES *Monet's Garden* Vivian Russell; *Rosemary Verey's Making of a Garden*; **Children's General Fiction and Non-fiction** *Janetta Otter-Barry* TITLES *The Wanderings of Odysseus* Rosemary

Sutcliffe, illus. Alan Lee; *Amazing Grace, Grace & Family* Mary Hoffman, illus. Caroline Binch; **Children's Art and Religion** *Kate Cave* TITLES *My Sticker Art Gallery* Carole Armstrong; *Jesus of Nazareth* illus. with paintings from the National Gallery of Art, Washington. Synopses and ideas for books considered.
Royalties paid twice-yearly.

Linden Press
See **Centaur Press**

Lion Publishing

Peter's Way, Sandy Lane West, Oxford OX4 5HG
☎01865 747550   Fax 01865 747568
Approx. Annual Turnover £7 million

FOUNDED 1971. A Christian book publisher, strong on illustrated books for a popular international readership, with rights sold in 88 languages worldwide. *Publishes* a diverse list with Christian viewpoint the common denominator. All ages, from board books for children to multi-contributor adult reference, educational, paperbacks and colour co-editions and gift books. Also developing a strong multimedia list.

DIVISIONS
Adult *Lois Rock*; **Children's** *Su Box*; **Giftlines** *Meryl Doney*; **Lynx Communications** *Robin Keeley* Training resources for churches and theology textbooks. Unsolicited mss welcome provided they have a positive Christian viewpoint intended for a wide general and international readership. Synopses, proposals and ideas also welcome.
Royalties paid twice-yearly.

Little, Brown & Co. (UK)

Brettenham House, Lancaster Place, London WC2E 7EN
☎0171 911 8000   Fax 0171 911 8100
Managing Director *Philippa Harrison*
Approx. Annual Turnover £28 million

FOUNDED 1988. Part of Time-Warner Inc. Began by importing its US parent company's titles and in 1990 launched its own illustrated non-fiction list. Two years later the company took over former Macdonald & Co. *Publishes* hardback and paperback fiction, literary fiction, crime, science fiction and fantasy; and general non-fiction, including illustrated: architecture and design, fine art, photography, biography and autobiography, cinema, gardening, history, humour, travel, crafts and hobbies, reference, cookery, wines and spirits, DIY, guidebooks, natural history and nautical.

IMPRINTS
Abacus *Richard Beswick* Literary fiction and non-fiction paperbacks; **Orbit** *Colin Murray* Science fiction and fantasy; **Little Brown/Warner** *Alan Samson, Barbara Boote, Hilary Hale* Mass-market fiction and non-fiction; **X Libris** *Helen Pisano* Women's erotica; **Illustrated** *Vivien Bowler* Hardbacks; **Virago** (see entry). Approach in writing in the first instance. No unsolicited mss.
Royalties paid twice-yearly.

Authors' Rating Thriving on a mix of popular fiction and non-fiction, attention is focused on the new X Libris list of women's erotica where sales are high but uninhibited writers are hard to find.

Liverpool University Press
Senate House, Abercromby Square, Liverpool
L69 3BX
☎0151 794 2232   Fax 0151 708 6502
Managing Director/Editorial Head *Robin Bloxsidge*

The principal activity of LUP, since its foundation in 1899, has been in the humanities and social sciences. *Publishes* academic and scholarly hardback and paperback books in the fields of archaeology, education, geography, ancient and modern history, science fiction criticism, modern French literature, English literature, Hispanic languages and literature, town planning and veterinary medicine. 15-20 titles a year. TITLES *Liverpool Public Sculpture*; *Barbara Hepworth Reconsidered*; *Watching One's Tongue: Issues in Language Planning*; *A Sound Education? Local Radio and the Education of Adults*. Unsolicited mss, synopses and ideas for books welcome.
Royalties paid annually.

Livewire Books for Teenagers
See **The Women's Press**

Longman
See **Addison Wesley Longman Ltd**

Lorenz Books
See **Anness Publishing Ltd**

Love on Call
See **Harlequin Mills & Boon Ltd**

Peter Lowe (Eurobook Ltd)
PO Box 52, Wallingford, Oxfordshire
OX10 0XU
☎01865 749033   Fax 01865 749044
Managing Director *Peter Lowe*

FOUNDED 1968. *Publishes* children's natural history, popular science and illustrated adult non-fiction. No unsolicited mss; synopses and ideas (with s.a.e.) welcome. No adult fiction.

Lund Humphries Publishers Ltd
Park House, 1 Russell Gardens, London
NW11 9NN
☎0181 458 6314   Fax 0181 905 5245
Chairman *Lionel Leventhal*
Editor *Lucy Myers*

Publisher of fine art books. First title appeared in 1895. *Publishes* art, architecture, design and graphics. Publishers of exhibition catalogues in association with museums and galleries, and of the annual *Calendar of Art Exhibitions*. About 20 titles a year. There are plans to expand the graphic arts and design list in the years to come. Unsolicited mss welcome but initial introductory letter preferred. Synopses and ideas for books considered.
Royalties paid twice-yearly.

The Lutterworth Press
PO Box 60, Cambridge CB1 2NT
☎01223 350865   Fax 01223 366951
Managing Director *Adrian Brink*
Editorial Director *Colin Lester*

The Lutterworth Press dates back to the 18th century when it was founded by the Religious Tract Society. In the 19th century it was best known for its children's books, both religious and secular, including *The Boys' Own Paper*. Since 1984 it has been part of **James Clarke & Co**. *Publishes* general non-fiction: antiques and collecting, architecture and design, biography, children's books, educational and textbooks, fine art and art history, environmental, natural history, religion and theology. Sponsored and non-sponsored books. About 25 titles a year.
DIVISIONS **Children's**, **Adult**, **Religious**. TITLES *Christopher, the Holy Giant*; *Loving Letters*; *The 50th Royal Tank Regiment*; *Maskwork*; *Before the Greeks*; *Cruickshank (III)*. Initial letter with s.a.e. advised before submitting mss.
Royalties paid annually.

Authors' Rating The list is expanding but it still has its anchor in evangelical publishing. Imaginative children's list.

Lynx
See **Society for Promoting Christian Knowledge**

Lynx Communications
See **Lion Publishing**

Macdonald & Co.
See **Little, Brown & Co. (UK)**

Macmillan Publishers Ltd

25 Eccleston Place, London
SW1W 9NF
☎0171 881 8000   Fax 0171 881 8001
Chairman *Nicholas Byam Shaw*
**Managing Director, UK Book Publishing
   Group** *Adrian Soar*
Managing Director, Pan Macmillan *Sarah
   Mahaffy*
Approx. Annual Turnover £90 million
   (Book Publishing Group)

FOUNDED 1843. Macmillan is one of the largest publishing house in Britain, publishing approximately 1400 titles a year. In May 1994 the two UK book publishing companies, Pan Macmillan and Macmillan Press, were reorganised into a unified structure which, with Grove's Dictionaries of Music and The Dictionary of Art, comprises seven divisions. In 1995, Verlagsgruppe Georg von Holtzbrinck, a major German publisher, acquired a majority stake in the Macmillan Group. Unsolicited proposals, synopses and mss are welcome in all divisions of the company (with the exception of Macmillan Children's Books). Authors who wish to send material to Macmillan General Books should note that there is a central submissions procedure in operation. For these divisions, send a synopsis and the first 3-4 chapters with a covering letter and return postage to the Submissions Editor, 25 Eccleston Place, London SW1W 9NF. **See Stop Press**.

DIVISIONS
Macmillan Press Ltd Brunel Road, Houndmills, Basingstoke, Hampshire RG21 6XS ☎01256 29242 Fax 01256 479476 Managing Director *Dominic Knight*. **Journals** *H. Holt*; **Academic** *T. M. Farmiloe*; **Higher Education** *S. Kennedy*; **Further Education** *J. Winckler*; **Business and Economics** *S. Rutt*; **Reference** *S. O'Neill* (Eccleston Place address) *Publishes* textbooks, monographs and works of reference in academic, professional and vocational subjects; medical and scientific journals; directories. Publications in both hard copy and electronic format.

Macmillan Education Basingstoke (address as for Macmillan Press). Managing Director *Chris Harrison*, Publishing Director *Alison Hubert*. *Publishes* regional ELT titles and a wide list for the international education market.

Macmillan General Books (Eccleston Place address). Managing Director *Ian S. Chapman*, Editor-in-Chief *Peter Straus*. Publishes under

Macmillan, Pan, Papermac, Sidgwick & Jackson

Macmillan (FOUNDED 1865) Publisher *Maria Rejt*, Executive Editorial Director (fiction) *Suzanne Baboneau*. *Publishes* novels, detective fiction, sci-fi, fantasy and horror. Editorial Directors (non-fiction) *Georgina Morley, Catherine Hurley, Judith Hannam*. *Publishes* autobiography, biography, business and industry, crafts and hobbies, economics, gift books, health and beauty, history, humour, natural history, travel, philosophy, politics and world affairs, psychology, theatre and drama, gardening and cookery, encyclopedias.

Pan (FOUNDED 1947) Publisher *Peter Lavery*. *Publishes* fiction: novels, detective fiction, sci-fi, fantasy and horror. Non-fiction: sports and games, theatre and drama, travel, gardening and cookery, encyclopedias.

Papermac (FOUNDED 1965) Publisher *Jon Riley*, Editor *Tanya Stobbs*. Series non-fiction: history, biography, science, political economy, cultural criticism and art history.

Picador (FOUNDED 1972) Publisher *Jon Riley*, Editorial Director *Ursula Doyle*. *Publishes* literary international fiction and non-fiction.

Sidgwick & Jackson (FOUNDED 1908) Editorial Director *Georgina Morley*. *Publishes* military and war, music, pop and rock.

Macmillan Children's Books (Eccleston Place address). *Kate Wilson*; **Fiction** *Marion Lloyd*; **Non-fiction** *Susie Gibbs*; **Picture Books** *Alison Green*. IMPRINTS **Macmillan, Pan, Campbell Books**. *Publishes* novels, board books, picture books, non-fiction (illustrated and non-illustrated), poetry and novelty books in paperback and hardback.

Grove's Dictionaries of Music (Eccleston Place address). Publishing Director *Margot Levy*. *Publishes The New Grove Dictionary of Music and Musicians* ed. Stanley Sadie; and associated works.

The Dictionary of Art (Eccleston Place address). Director *Ian Jacobs*. *Publishes The Dictionary of Art* (1996) ed. Jane Shoaf Turner.

Royalties paid annually or twice-yearly depending on contract.

Authors' Rating Now part of the Holtzbrinck Group, Macmillan has raised sales and profits all round - with a little help from a cost-cutting exercise. Fewer titles are likely to be published with more emphasis on big sellers, though none quite so big as *The Macmillan Dictionary of Art* - a £30 million project - and the company's most ambitious single investment ever. Under Holtzbrinck influence, a big expansion into electronic publishing is under way.

Julia MacRae
See **Random House UK Ltd**

Magi Publications
22 Manchester Street, London W1M 5PG
☎0171 486 0925   Fax 0171 486 0926
Postal address only: 55 Crowland Avenue, Hayes, Middlesex UB3 4JP
Publisher *Monty Bhatia*
Editor *Linda Jennings*
Approx. Annual Turnover £1 million
FOUNDED 1987. *Publishes* children's picture books only. About 24 titles a year. Unsolicited mss, synopses and ideas welcome, but please telephone first.
Royalties paid annually.

Mainstream Publishing Co. (Edinburgh) Ltd
7 Albany Street, Edinburgh EH1 3UG
☎0131 557 2959   Fax 0131 556 8720
Directors *Bill Campbell, Peter MacKenzie*
Approx. Annual Turnover £2.2 million
Publishes art, autobiography/biography, current affairs, fiction, health, history, illustrated and fine editions, photography and sport, politics and world affairs, popular paperbacks. Over 60 titles a year. Ideas for books considered, but they should be preceded by a letter, synopsis and s.a.e. or return postage.
Royalties paid twice-yearly.

Authors' Rating A Scottish company aiming for a British profile. Keen on finding authors who 'can develop with us'. But Mainstream is not doing well with fiction; indeed, Bill Campbell anticipates closing the fiction list.

Mammoth Paperbacks
See **Reed Books**

Management Books 2000 Ltd
125A The Broadway, Didcot, Oxfordshire OX11 8AW
☎01235 815544   Fax 01235 817188
Managing Director *Nicholas Dale-Harris*
Approx. Annual Turnover £500,000
FOUNDED 1993 to develop a range of books for executives and managers working in the modern world of business, supplemented with information through other media like seminars, audio and video. *Publishes* business and management and sponsored titles. About 30 titles a year. Unsolicited mss, synopses and ideas for books welcome.

Manchester University Press
Oxford Road, Manchester M13 9NR
☎0161 273 5539   Fax 0161 274 3346
Publisher/Chief Executive *Francis Brooke*
Approx. Annual Turnover £1.7 million
FOUNDED at the turn of the century and now Britain's third largest university press, with a list marketed and sold internationally. Originally based on history, MUP's list has expanded to cover the humanities, social sciences and academic books from A-level texts to research monographs. *Publishes* academic and educational books in literature, cultural and media studies, history, art and architecture, politics, international law, economics and modern languages. Also more general books, notably on genealogy, history and the North-west of England. About 100 titles a year, plus journals.
DIVISIONS **Humanities** *Matthew Frost*; **History** *Vanessa Graham*; **Politics** Nicola Viinikka; **Economics** *Francis Brooke*. Unsolicited mss welcome.
Royalties paid annually.

Mandarin
See **Reed Books**

George Mann Books
PO Box 22, Maidstone, Kent ME14 1AH
☎01622 759591   Fax 01622 759591
Chairman *George Mann*
Managing Director *John Arne*
FOUNDED 1972, originally as library reprint publishers, but has moved on to other things with the collapse of the library market. *Publishes* non-fiction and selected reprints. Until further notice, not considering new fiction for publication. Launched a new imprint called Recollections in 1992 for subsidised publication of books of an autobiographical/ biographical nature, for which unlimited editorial advice and assistance can be made available. In the same year a new pamphlet series, Polemical Pamphlets, was begun.

IMPRINTS
Arnefold; **Recollections**; **George Mann**; **Polemical Pamphlets**. The latter is a paperback platform for controversial views on matters of public interest, local or national. 'Within the law, and supported by the best legal and editorial advice, we will enable anyone to disseminate to the widest possible readership, a

well-written and well-presented opinion.' Length 20-30,000 words. Production costs are generally shared. No unsolicited mss; send preliminary letter with synopsis. Material not accompanied by return postage will be neither read nor returned.

Royalties paid twice-yearly.

Mansell
See **Cassell**

Manson Publishing Ltd
73 Corringham Road, London NW11 7DL
☎0181 905 5150   Fax 0181 201 9233
Chairman/Managing Director *Michael Manson*
Approx. Annual Turnover £400,000

FOUNDED 1992. *Publishes* scientific, technical, medical and veterinary. 8 titles in 1995. No unsolicited mss; synopses and ideas will be considered.

Royalties paid twice-yearly.

Marc
See **Monarch Publications**

Marshall Pickering
See **HarperCollins Publishers Ltd**

Marston House
Marston House, Marston Magna, Yeovil, Somerset BA22 8DH
☎01935 851331   Fax 01935 851331
Managing Director/Editorial Head
Anthony Birks-Hay
Approx. Annual Turnover £200,000

FOUNDED 1989. Publishing imprint of book packager **Alphabet & Image Ltd**. *Publishes* fine art, architecture, ceramics. 4 titles a year.

Royalties paid twice-yearly, or flat fee in lieu of royalties.

Mask Noir
See **Serpent's Tail**

Kenneth Mason Publications Ltd
Dudley House, 12 North Street, Emsworth, Hampshire PO10 7DQ
☎01243 377977   Fax 01243 379136
Chairman *Kenneth Mason*
Managing Director *Piers Mason*
Approx. Annual Turnover £500,000

FOUNDED 1958. *Publishes* diet, health, fitness, nutrition and nautical. No fiction. 15 titles in 1995. Initial approach by letter with synopsis preferred. IMPRINT **Boatswain Press**.

Royalties paid twice-yearly (Jun/Dec) in first year, annually (Dec) thereafter.

Kevin Mayhew Ltd
Rattlesden, Bury St Edmunds, Suffolk IP30 0SZ
☎01449 737978   Fax 01449 737834
Chairman *Kevin Mayhew*
Managing Director *Gordon Carter*
Approx. Annual Turnover £2.5 million

FOUNDED in 1976. One of the leading sacred music and Christian book publishers in the UK. *Publishes* religious titles – liturgy, sacramental, also children's books and school resources. 120 titles in 1995. TITLES *Hymns Old and New (New Century Edition) – New Catholic Hymn Book; The Complete Organ Works of Johann Sebastian Bach*. Unsolicited synopses and ideas are welcome, but mss should be sent only after consultation.

IMPRINT **Palm Tree Press** *Kevin Mayhew* bibles and bible stories.

Royalties paid annually.

McGraw-Hill Book Co. Europe
McGraw-Hill House, Shoppenhangers Road, Maidenhead, Berkshire SL6 2QL
☎01628 23432   Fax 01628 770958
Group Vice President, Europe *Fred J. Perkins*
Editorial Director *Andrew Phillips*

FOUNDED 1899. Owned by US parent company. Began publishing in Maidenhead in 1965. *Publishes* business and economics, engineering, computer science, business computing and training for the academic, student, trade and professional markets. Around 100 titles a year. Unsolicited mss, synopses and ideas welcome.

Royalties paid twice-yearly.

Authors' Rating Having, by his own account, spent the last ten years 're-tooling' McGraw-Hill for the electronic age, chairman Joseph Dionne is ambitious to extend electronic publishing to academic journals, a move which will cut to a fraction the time it takes to disseminate research findings. First effects will be felt in the States but the UK branch of McGraw-Hill cannot be far behind.

The Medici Society Ltd
34-42 Pentonville Road, London N1 9HG
☎0171 837 7099   Fax 0171 837 9152
Art Director *Charles Howell*

FOUNDED 1908. *Publishes* illustrated children's fiction, art and nature. About 6 titles a year. No unsolicited mss; send synopses with specimen illustrations only.

Royalties paid annually.

Melrose Press Ltd

3 Regal Lane, Soham, Ely, Cambridgeshire
CB7 5BA
☎01353 721091   Fax 01353 721839
Chairman *Richard A. Kay*
Managing Director *Nicholas S. Law*
Approx. Annual Turnover £1.5 million

FOUNDED 1960. Took on its present name in
1969. *Publishes* biographical who's who reference only (not including *Who's Who*, which is
published by **A. & C. Black**).

DIVISIONS **International Biographical
Centre** *Jocelyn Timothy.* TITLES *International
Authors and Writers Who's Who; International
Who's Who in Music; Who's Who in Australasia
and the Pacific Nations; International Who's Who
in Poetry.*

Mercat Press

c/o James Thin Booksellers, 53 South Bridge,
Edinburgh EH1 1YS
☎0131 556 6743   Fax 0131 557 8149
Chairman/Managing Director *D. Ainslie
Thin*
Editorial Heads *Tom Johnstone, Seán Costello*

FOUNDED 1971 as an adjunct to the large
Scottish bookselling chain of James Thin. Began
by publishing reprints of classic Scottish literature but has since expanded into publishing new
work. In 1992 the company acquired the bulk
of the stock of Aberdeen University Press, a vic-
tim of the collapse of the Maxwell empire. The
backlist has expanded five-fold as a result to just
under 300 titles and new titles are added regularly. *Publishes* Scottish classics reprints and non-
fiction of Scottish interest, mainly historical and
literary. TITLES *Scotland's Place-names* David
Dorward; *Voices from War* ed. Ian MacDougall;
The Scots Kitchen F. Marion McNeill;
Scotichronicon Walter Bower, ed. D. E. R. Watt.
Unsolicited synopses and ideas for non-fiction
books, preferably with sample chapters, are
welcome. No new fiction. No complete mss.
Royalties paid annually.

Merehurst Ltd

Ferry House, 51-57 Lacy Road, London
SW15 1PR
☎0181 780 1177   Fax 0181 780 1714
Chief Executive Officer *Graham Fill*
Publishing Director *Shirley Patton*
Approx. Annual Turnover £3.5 million

Owned by Australian media group J. B. Fairfax
International Ltd. *Publishes* full-colour non-
fiction: cake decorating, cookery, craft, gardening, homes and interiors, children's crafts and

hobbies. About 60 titles a year. Synopses and
ideas for books welcome; no unsolicited mss.
Royalties paid twice-yearly.

Merlin Press Ltd

10 Malden Road, London NW5 3HR
☎0171 267 3399   Fax 0171 284 3092
Directors *Martin Eve, P. M. Eve, Julie Millard*

FOUNDED 1956. *Publishes* ecology, economics,
history, philosophy, left-wing politics. AUTHORS
Georg Lukács, Ernest Mandel, Istvan Meszaros,
Ralph Miliband, E. P. Thompson. About 20
titles a year. No fiction.

IMPRINTS **Green Print; Seafarer Books**
Sailing titles, with an emphasis on the traditional. No unsolicited mss; preliminary letter
essential before making any type of submission.
Royalties paid twice-yearly.

Methuen & Co.

See **Routledge**

Methuen/ Methuen Children's Books

See **Reed Books**

Metro Books

Metro Publishing Ltd, 19 Gerrard Street,
London W1V 7LA
☎0171 734 1411   Fax 0171 734 1811
Managing Director *Susanne McDadd*

FOUNDED 1995. *Publishes* general non-fiction -
family reference, (practical) health, giftbooks,
cookery, business and sport. 10 titles planned
for 1996. TITLES *The SHE Guide to Shopping
From Home; The Awfully Good Cat Joke Book;
Guide to Safe Sport.* No unsolicited mss. Send
outline, sample chapter and c.v. plus s.a.e. in
the first instance.
Royalties paid twice-yearly.

Authors' Rating New on the street, Metro is
aiming to publish up to 10 titles by the end of
the year. Big advances are out and ideas are
likely to be developed in-house. But authors
should be encouraged by the promise to fill out
royalty statements with information on where
titles are selling and at what discount. Draft
marketing plans will be included with contracts
and authors will be encouraged to attend marketing meetings.

Michelin Tyre plc

The Edward Hyde Building, 38 Clarendon
Road, Watford, Hertfordshire WD1 1SX
☎01923 415000   Fax 01923 415052

FOUNDED 1900 as travel publisher. *Publishes*

travel guides, maps and atlases, children's I-Spy books. Travel-related synopses and ideas welcome; no mss.

Midland Publishing Ltd
24 The Hollow, Earl Shilton, Leicester LE9 7NA
☎01455 847256   Fax 01455 841805
Director *N. P. Lewis*

Publishes aviation, military and railways. No wartime memoirs. No unsolicited mss; synopses and ideas welcome.
Royalties paid quarterly.

Milestone Publications
See **Scope International Ltd**

Millenium
See **The Orion Publishing Group Ltd**

Harvey Miller Publishers
Knightsbridge House, 8th Floor, 197 Knightsbridge, London SW7 1RB
☎0171 584 7676   Fax 0171 823 7969
Editorial Director *Mrs Elly Miller*

FOUNDED 1974. *Publishes* serious studies in the history of art only. Approx. 6 titles a year. No unsolicited mss; synopses and ideas welcome.
Royalties paid annually.

Mills & Boon Ltd
See **Harlequin Mills & Boon Ltd**

Minerva
See **Reed Books**

Mira
See **Harlequin Mills & Boon Ltd**

The MIT Press Ltd
Fitzroy House, 11 Chenies Street, London WC1E 7ET
☎0171 306 0603   Fax 0171 306 0604
Director *F. Urbanowski*
General Manager *A. Sexsmith*

Part of **The MIT Press**, USA. *Publishes* academic, architecture and design, art history and theory, bibliography, biography, business and industry, cinema and media studies, computer science, cultural studies and critical theory, economics, educational and textbooks, engineering, environment, linguistics, medical, music, natural history, philosophy, photography, physics, politics and world affairs, psychology, reference, scientific and technical, neurobiology and neuroscience. All mss go to the American office: 55 Hayward Street, Cambridge, Mass. 02142.

Mitchell Beazley
See **Reed Books**

Mitre
See **Monarch Publications**

Monarch Publications
Broadway House, The Broadway, Crowborough, East Sussex TN6 1HQ
☎01892 652364   Fax 01892 663329
Directors *Tony & Jane Collins*

Publish an independent list of Christian books across a wide range of concerns. About 30 titles a year. In 1994 took on *Renewal* and *Healing and Wholeness* magazines.
IMPRINTS **Monarch** Upmarket, social concern issues list covering a wide range of areas from psychology to future studies, politics, etc., all with a strong Christian dimension; **Marc** Leadership, mission and church growth titles; **Mitre** Creative writing imprint: humour and drama with a Christian dimension. Unsolicited mss, synopses and ideas welcome. 'Regretfully no poetry or fiction.'

Mondo
See **Titan Books**

Moorland Publishing Co. Ltd
Moorfarm Road, Airfield Estate, Ashbourne, Derbyshire DE6 1HD
☎01335 344486   Fax 01335 346397
Managing Director *Mr C. L. M. Porter*
Editorial Head *Mrs Tonya Monk*
Approx. Annual Turnover £1 million

FOUNDED 1971. *Publishes* travel guides and gardening titles only. SERIES *Visitor's Guide*; *Off The Beaten Track*; *Independent Travellers*; *Insiders Guides*; *Spectrum Guides*; *Caribbean Sunseekers*; *Mediterranean Sunseekers*. Agents for Little Hills Press travel titles. Unsolicited mss will be considered, but synopses accompanied by letters of introduction preferred.
Royalties paid annually.

Mosby/Mosby Wolf Publishing
See **Times Mirror International Publishers Ltd**

Motor Racing Publications
Unit 6, The Pilton Estate, 46 Pitlake, Croydon, Surrey CRO 3RY
☎0181 681 3363   Fax 0181 760 5117
Chairman/Editorial Head *John Blunsden*
Approx. Annual Turnover £500,000

FOUNDED soon after the end of World War II to concentrate on motor-racing titles. Fairly dormant in the mid 60s but was reactivated in 1968 by a new shareholding structure. John Blunsden later acquired a majority share and major expansion followed in the 70s. About 10–12 titles a year. *Publishes* motor-sporting history, classic car collection and restoration, road transport, motorcycles, off-road driving and related subjects.

IMPRINTS **Fitzjames Press; Motor Racing Publications** TITLES *Echoes of Imola* David Tremayne; *Cars in the UK Since 1945* (2 vols.) Graham Robson; *Modifying and Tuning Fiat/Lancia Twin-Cam Engines* Guy Croft; *Jaguar XJS Collector's Guide* Paul Skilleter; *Caterham Sevens* Chris Rees. Unsolicited mss, synopses and ideas in specified subject areas welcome.

Royalties paid twice-yearly.

Mowbray
See **Cassell**

Multi-Sensory Learning Ltd
34 Nene Valley Business Park, Oundle, Peterborough PE8 4HL
☎01832 274714   Fax 01832 275281
Senior Editor *Philippa Attwood*
Course Co-ordinator *Karen Robinson*

Part of **First and Best in Education Ltd**. *Publishes* materials and books related to dyslexia; the multi-sensory learning course for teachers of dyslexic children, plus numerous other items on assessment, reading, maths, music, etc. for dyslexics. Keen to locate authors able to write materials for dyslexic people and for teachers of dyslexics.

Multimedia Books Ltd
Unit L, 32–34 Gordon House Road, London NW5 1LP
☎0171 482 4248   Fax 0171 482 4203
Managing Director *Barry Winkleman*

Formerly a packaging operation but began publishing under the Prion imprint in 1987. *Publishes* illustrated non-fiction: Americana, cinema and photography, cars, guidebooks, food and drink, sex, psychology and health. About 40 titles a year. Unsolicited mss, synopses and ideas welcome.

Royalties paid twice-yearly.

John Murray (Publishers) Ltd
50 Albemarle Street, London W1X 4BD
☎0171 493 4361   Fax 0171 499 1792
Chairman *John R. Murray*
Managing Director *Nicholas Perren*

FOUNDED 1768. Independent publisher. *Publishes* general trade books, educational (secondary school and college textbooks) and Success Studybooks.

DIVISIONS **General Books** *Grant McIntyre*; **Educational Books** *Nicholas Perren*. Unsolicited material discouraged.

Royalties paid annually.

NAG Press Ltd
See **Robert Hale Ltd**

National Museums of Scotland (NMS Publishing)
Chambers Street, Edinburgh EH1 1JF
☎0131 247 4161   Fax 0131 247 4012
Managing Director *Mark Jones*
Approx. Annual Turnover £100–125,000

FOUNDED 1987 to *publish* non-fiction related to the National Museums of Scotland collections: academic and general; children's – archaeology, history, decorative arts worldwide, history of science, technology, natural history and geology. 9 titles in 1995. **NMS Publishing** *Jenni Calder* TITLES *Scotland's Past in Action* series; *The Viking-Age Gold and Silver of Scotland; Domestic Culture of the Middle East; Agates; Life in Ancient Egypt; Photography 1900; Fish Facts* (cartoon book). No unsolicited mss; only interested in synopses and ideas for books which are genuinely related to NMS collections.

Royalties paid twice-yearly.

Navigator Books
Moorhouse, Kingston, Ringwood, Hampshire BH24 3BJ
☎01425 476708   Fax 01425 480075
Managing Director *Philip Bristow*

FOUNDED 1964. *Publishes* nautical, war, achievements of older folk, nostalgia plus some fiction and children's. 22 titles in 1995. TITLES *The Race to the Cape; Ormonde to Oriana; Never Forget Nor Forgive; Fifty Years at Sea; No Safe Haven; Under Eight Flags; From Engineroom to Admiralty; Safety at Sea; Master in Sail; Aquatic Mammals; By a Slender Thread; On the Edge of Asia; Beating About the Nigerian Bush.* Prefers to hear from authors of completed works – send synopsis and sample chapter. No religious, gardening, domestic, art or technical.

Royalties paid twice-yearly.

NCVO Publications
Regent's Wharf, 8 All Saints Street, London N1 9RL
☎0171 713 6161   Fax 0171 713 6300
Head of Marketing and Publications *Angela Galvin*

Approx. Annual Turnover £140,000

FOUNDED 1992. Publishing imprint of the National Council for Voluntary Organisations, embracing former Bedford Square Press titles and NCVO's many other publications. The list reflects NCVO's role as the representative body for the voluntary sector. *Publishes* directories, management and trustee development, legal, finance and fundraising titles of primary interest to the voluntary sector. TITLES *The Voluntary Agencies Directory; Grants from Europe; Planning for the Future: An Introduction to Business; Planning for Voluntary Organisations.* Unsolicited mss, synopses and ideas for books welcome.

Royalties paid twice-yearly.

Thomas Nelson & Sons Ltd

Nelson House, Mayfield Road, Walton on Thames, Surrey KT12 5PL
☎01932 252211   Fax 01932 246109
President *Rod Gauvin*
Vice President, Finance *Nick White*
Approx. Annual Turnover £30 million

FOUNDED 1798. Part of the Thomson Corporation. Major school-book publisher covering all levels for students aged 5–19 in full and part-time education – National Curriculum, GNVQ, NVQ – for the home market, and a range for the Caribbean market. Also publishes Multimedia product (CD-ROM) for school and home learning. TITLES *Gaia: Geography, An Integrated Approach; Nelson English; Route Nationale; Maths Chest; Tricolore; Zickzack; Deutsch Heute; Route Nationale; Balanced Science.* Unsolicited mss and synopses welcome.

Royalties paid twice-yearly.

Authors' Rating Reacting to weaknesses in the school book market, Nelson is moving ahead strongly in multimedia. Developments include a joint venture with Yorkshire Television.

Network Books
See **BBC Books Ltd**

New English Library
See **Hodder Headline plc**

New Guild UK Limited

5 Cogdean Walk, Corfe Mullen, Wimborne, Dorset BH21 3XB
☎01202 601469   Fax 01202 601469
Chairman/Managing Director *Norman Stobart*
Approx. Annual Turnover £150,000

FOUNDED 1994 with the intention of providing publishing support for new writers. *Publishes* fiction and non-fiction for the adult market in paperback only. 10 titles in 1995. DIVISIONS **New Guild Publishing** *Norman Stobart* TITLES *Charlatan* Gary Orchard; *The Fourth Service* John Slader; *The Shield of Mashona* Bill Russell. **New Writer Support Services** *Juliet Wilson.* Unsolicited mss, synopses with 2-3 sample chapters welcome. No poetry. 'Our main objective is to support talented new writers.'

Royalties paid twice-yearly. *Overseas associates* New Guild SA (Pty) Ltd, Capetown, South Africa; New Guild NZ Ltd, Auckland, New Zealand. Negotiating to establish New Guild in Canada, USA and Australia.

New Holland (Publishers) Ltd

24 Nutford Place, London W1H 6DQ
☎0171 724 7773   Fax 0171 724 6184
Chairman *Gerry Struik*
Managing Director *John Beaufoy*
Editorial Heads *Charlotte Parry-Crooke, Yvonne McFarlane*
Approx. Annual Turnover £4 million

FOUNDED 1956. Relaunched 1987 with new name and editorial identity. New directions and rapid expansion transformed the small specialist imprint into a publisher of illustrated books for the international market. In 1993, they diversified further with the acquisition of the **Charles Letts Publishing Division** list. *Publishes* non-fiction, specialising in natural history, travel, cookery, cake decorating, crafts, gardening and DIY. TITLES *Dive Sites of the Philippines; Wild Thailand; Complete Garden Bird Book; Globetrotter Travel Guide Series; Design and Make Bedroom Furnishings; The Illustrated Book of Herbs.* No unsolicited mss; synopses and ideas welcome.

Royalties paid twice-yearly.

Authors' Rating New Holland's illustrated books are outstanding – the pride of the coffee-table.

New Left Books Ltd
See **Verso**

New Orchard Editions
See **Cassell**

Newleaf
See **Boxtree**

Nexus
See **Virgin Publishing**

Nexus Special Interests

Nexus House, Boundary Way,
Hemel Hempstead, Hertfordshire HP2 7ST
☎01442 66551   Fax 01442 66998
General Manager *Beverly Laughlin*

Argus Consumer Magazines and Argus Books were bought out by Nexus Media Communications in 1995 and the Nexus Special Interests imprint was established in the spring of that year. *Publishes* aviation, leisure and hobbies, modelling, electronics, health, wine and beer making, woodwork. Send synopses rather than completed mss.

Royalties paid twice-yearly.

NFER-NELSON Publishing Co. Ltd

Darville House, 2 Oxford Road
East, Windsor, Berkshire SL4 1DF
☎01753 858961   Fax 01753 856830
Managing Director *Michael Jackson*
Editorial Coordinator *Carolyn Richardson*

FOUNDED 1981. Jointly owned by the Thomson Corporation and the National Foundation for Educational Research. *Publishes* educational and psychological tests and training materials. Main interest is in educational, clinical and occupational assessment and training material. Unsolicited material welcome.

Royalties vary according to each contract.

Nicholson

See **HarperCollins Publishers Ltd**

James Nisbet & Co. Ltd

78 Tilehouse Street, Hitchin, Hertfordshire
SG5 2DY
☎01462 438331   Fax 01462 431528
Chairman *E. M. Mackenzie-Wood*

FOUNDED 1810 as a religious publisher and expanded into more general areas from around 1850 onwards. The first educational list appeared in 1926 and the company now specialises in educational material and business studies. About 5 titles a year. No fiction, leisure or religion. No unsolicited mss; synopses and ideas welcome.

Royalties paid twice-yearly.

No Exit Press

See **Oldcastle Books Ltd**

Nonesuch Press

See **Reinhardt Books Ltd**

Northcote House Publishers Ltd

Plymbridge House, Estover Road, Plymouth,
Devon PL6 7PZ
☎01752 735251   Fax 01752 695699
Managing Director *Brian Hulme*

FOUNDED 1985. Recently launched a new series of literary critical studies, in association with the British Council, called *Writers and their Work*. *Publishes* careers, education management, literary criticism, educational dance and drama. 40 titles in 1996. 'Well-thought-out proposals, including contents and sample chapter(s), with strong marketing arguments welcome.'

Royalties paid annually.

W. W. Norton & Co. Ltd

10 Coptic Street, London WC1A 1PU
☎0171 323 1579   Fax 0171 436 4553
Managing Director *R. A. Cameron*

Owned by US parent company. *Publishes* non-fiction, academic and nautical. No unsolicited material. Enquiries only in writing.

Notting Hill Electronic Publishers

31 Brunswick Gardens, London W8 4AW
☎0171 229 0591   Fax 0171 727 6641
Chairman *Andreas Whittam Smith*
Editorial Head *Ben Whittam Smith*

FOUNDED 1994. A new electronic publisher created by Andreas Whittam Smith, founder of the *Independent*. *Publishes* (on CD-ROM) arts, sport, popular science, food and wine. 5 titles in 1996. TITLES *International Athletics; Wine, Spirits & Beer; The Art of Singing; The Evolution of Life*. Welcomes synopses and ideas for CD-ROMs; no pornography or fiction.

Nottingham University Press

Manor Farm, Thrumpton, Nottingham
NG11 0AX
☎0115 9831011   Fax 0115 9831003
Managing Editor *Dr D. J. A. Cole*
Approx. Annual Turnover £150,000

A newly formed company which intends to publish across a broad range of subjects. Initially concentrated on agricultural and food sciences and now planning to branch into new areas including engineering, lifesciences, medicine and sport. 10 titles in 1995 with 20 planned for 1996. TITLES *Recent Development in Pig Nutrition; Recent Advances in Animal Nutrition; Gene Regulation by Sense and Antisense; Nutrition and Feeding of Poultry; The Distillers Directory*. Unsolicited mss, synopses and ideas welcome.

Royalties paid twice-yearly.

Michael O'Mara Books Ltd

9 Lion Yard, Tremadoc Road, London
SW4 7NQ
☎0171 720 8643   Fax 0171 627 8953

Chairman *Michael O'Mara*
Managing Director *Lesley O'Mara*
Editorial Director *David Roberts*
Approx. Annual Turnover £5 million

FOUNDED 1985. Independent publisher. *Publishes* general non-fiction, royalty, history, humour, anthologies and reference. TITLES *Diana: Her True Story* Andrew Morton; *The Seven Wonders of the World* John Romer; *I Don't Believe It!* Richard Wilson. Unsolicited mss, synopses and ideas for books welcome.
Royalties paid twice-yearly.

Oak

See **Omnibus Press**

Oberon Books

521 Caledonian Road, London
N7 9RH
☎0171 607 3637   Fax 0171 607 3629

Publishing Director *James Hogan*
Managing Director *Charles D. Glanville*

Publishes play texts (usually in conjunction with a production) and theatre books. *Specialises* in contemporary plays and translations of European classics. AUTHORS/TRANSLATORS Rodney Akland, Michel Azarna, Simon Bent, Ken Campbell, Barry Day, Marguerite Duras, Dic Edwards, Dario Fo, Jonathan Gems, Peter Gill, Graham Greene, Giles Havergal, Robert David MacDonald, Dino Mahoney, Louis Mellis, Adrian Mitchell, Gregory Motton, Stephen Mulrine, Jimmy Murphy, Meredith Oakes, Stewart Parker, David Pownall, Roland Rees, David Scinto, Colin Winslow, Charles Wood.

Octagon Press Ltd

PO Box 227, London N6 4EW
☎0181 348 9392   Fax 0181 341 5971

Managing Director *George R. Schrager*
Approx. Annual Turnover £100,000

FOUNDED 1972. *Publishes* philosophy, psychology, travel, Eastern religion, translations of Eastern classics and research monographs in series. 4–5 titles a year. Unsolicited material not welcome. Enquiries in writing only.
Royalties paid annually.

Old Rope Books

See **John Brown Publishing Ltd**

Oldcastle Books Ltd

18 Coleswood Road, Harpenden,
Hertfordshire AL5 1EQ
☎01582 761264   Fax 01582 712244

Managing Director *Ion S. Mills*

FOUNDED 1985. *Publishes* crime fiction and gambling non-fiction. 20 titles in 1995. No unsolicited mss; synopses and ideas for books within the two areas of interest welcome.
IMPRINTS **No Exit Press** TITLES *Burglar Who Thought He Was Bogart* Lawrence Block; *No Beast So Fierce* Eddie Bunker; **Oldcastle Books** TITLES *Biggest Game in Town* Al Alvarez.
Royalties paid twice-yearly.

OM Publishing

See **STL Ltd**

Omnibus Press

Book Sales/Music Sales Ltd, 8–9 Frith Street,
London W1V 5TZ
☎0171 434 0066   Fax 0171 734 2246

Editorial Head *Chris Charlesworth*

FOUNDED 1971. Independent publisher of music books, rock and pop biographies, song sheets, educational tutors, cassettes, videos and software. IMPRINTS **Amsco**; **Bobcat**; **Oak**; **Omnibus**; **Proteus**; **Wise**; **Zomba**. Unsolicited mss, synopses and ideas for books welcome.
Royalties paid twice-yearly.

Oneworld Publications

185 Banbury Road, Oxford OX2 7AR
☎01865 310597   Fax 01865 310598

Editorial Director *Juliet Mabey*

FOUNDED 1986. Distributed worldwide by **Penguin Books**. *Publishes* adult non-fiction across a range of subjects from world religions and social issues to psychology and health. 20 titles in 1995. TITLE New series on world religions launched in 1994 with *A Short History of Buddhism* and *A Short History of Islam*. AUTHORS include Geoffrey Parrinder, Keith Ward, William Montgomery Watt, Alfred Adler, Kahil Gibran. No unsolicited mss; synopses and ideas welcome, but should be accompanied by s.a.e. for return of material and/or notification of receipt. No autobiographies, fiction or poetry.
Royalties paid annually.

Onlywomen Press Ltd

40 St Lawrence Terrace, London W10 5ST
☎0181 960 7122   Fax 0181 960 7122

Editorial Director *Lilian Mohin*

FOUNDED 1974. *Publishes* radical feminist lesbian books only: fiction, poetry and non-fiction, including anthologies. About 6 titles a year. In 1995, published the first three titles in a new crime novel list, original paperbacks set in contemporary England with lesbian protagonists. TITLES *Burning Issues* Maggie Kelly; *Dirty Work* Vivien Kelly; *A Fearful Symmetry* Tash Fairbanks. Unsolicited mss, synopses and ideas welcome. Submissions should be accompanied by s.a.e. for return of material and/or notification of receipt.

Open Books Publishing Ltd
Beaumont House, Wells, Somerset BA5 2LD
☎01749 677276   Fax 01749 670760
Managing Director *Patrick Taylor*

FOUNDED 1974. *Publishes* general and gardening books. No unsolicited material. All books are commissioned.
Royalties paid twice-yearly.

Open University Press
Celtic Court, 22 Ballmoor, Buckingham, Buckinghamshire MK18 1XW
☎01280 823388   Fax 01280 823233
Managing Director *John Skelton*
Approx. Annual Turnover £3 million

FOUNDED 1977 as an imprint independent of the Open University's course materials. *Publishes* academic and professional books in the fields of education, management, sociology, health studies, politics, psychology, women's studies. No economics or anthropology. Not interested in anything outside the social sciences. About 100 titles a year. No unsolicited mss; enquiries/proposals only.
Royalties paid annually.

Orbit
See **Little, Brown & Co. (UK)**

Orchard Books
See **The Watts Publishing Group**

The Orion Publishing Group Ltd
Orion House, 5 Upper St Martin's Lane, London WC2H 9EA
☎0171 240 3444   Fax 0171 240 4822
Chairman *Lord Cuckney*
Chief Executive *Anthony Cheetham*
Managing Director *Peter Roche*
Approx. Annual Turnover £27 million

FOUNDED 1992 by Anthony and Rosemary Cheetham and Peter Roche. Incorporates Weidenfeld & Nicolson, J. M. Dent and Chapmans Publishers.

DIVISIONS
Orion *Rosemary Cheetham, Jane Wood* Hardcover fiction and non-fiction. IMPRINTS **Millenium** *Caroline Oakley* Science fiction and fantasy; **Orion Media** *Trevor Dolby* Film, theatre, television, music, multimedia; **Orion Business** *Martin Liu*.
    Weidenfeld & Nicolson *Ion Trewin, Ravi Mirchandani* General non-fiction, biography and autobiography, history and travel. IMPRINTS **J. M. Dent** *Hilary Laurie*; **Phoenix House** *Maggie McKernan* Literary fiction.
    Illustrated *Michael Dover* Illustrated non-fiction with a strong emphasis on the visual, and upmarket design, cookery, wine, gardening, art and architecture, natural history and personality-based books.
    Orion Children's Books *Judith Elliott* Children's fiction and non-fiction.
    Mass Market *Susan Lamb* IMPRINTS **Orion**; **Phoenix**; **Everyman** *Hilary Laurie*.

Authors' Rating Buoyant sales have led to a restructuring with the Weidenfeld & Nicolson imprint set to expand. The aim is to double turnover in three years.

Osprey
See **Reed Books**

Peter Owen Ltd
73 Kenway Road, London SW5 0RE
☎0171 373 5628/370 6093   Fax 0171 373 6760
Chairman *Peter Owen*
Senior Editor *Jill Foulston*

FOUNDED 1951. *Publishes* biography, general non-fiction, English literary fiction and translations, sociology. 'No middlebrow romance, thrillers or children's.' AUTHORS Jane Bowles, Paul Bowles, Shusaku Endo, Anna Kavan, Fiona Pitt-Kethley, Anaïs Nin, Jeremy Reed, Peter Vansittart. 35-40 titles a year. Unsolicited synopses welcome for non-fiction material; mss should be preceded by a descriptive letter or synopsis with s.a.e..
Royalties paid twice-yearly. *Overseas associates* worldwide.

Authors' Rating According to *The Guardian*, 'a publisher of the old and idiosyncratic school', Peter Owen works out of an Earls Court basement and claims not to draw a salary - 'We couldn't keep going if I did'. Certainly, his books are not great money spinners but they are the stuff of learned treatises and academic seminars. He has seven Nobel prizewinners on his list.

Oxford Illustrated Press/ Oxford Publishing Co.
See **Haynes Publishing**

Oxford University Press
Walton Street, Oxford OX2 6DP
☎01865 56767   Fax 01865 56646
Chief Executive *James Arnold-Baker*
Approx. Annual Turnover £200 million
A department of the university, OUP grew from the university's printing works and developed into a major publishing business in the 19th century. *Publishes* academic books in all categories: student texts, scholarly journals, schoolbooks, ELT material, dictionaries, reference, music, bibles, electronic publishing, as well as paperbacks, poetry, general non-fiction and children's books. Around 3000 titles a year.

DIVISIONS
Arts and Reference *I. S. Asquith* TITLES *Concise Oxford Dictionary*; **Educational** *F. E. Clarke* Courses for the National Curriculum; **ELT** *W. R. Andrewes* ELT courses and dictionaries; **Science, Medical & Journals** *J. R. Manger* TITLES *Birds of the Western Paleartic.*

IMPRINTS
Clarendon Press Monographs in humanities, science and social science; **Oxford Paperbacks** Trade paperbacks; **Oxford Science Publications**, **Oxford Medical Publications**, **Oxford Electronic Publications**. OUP welcomes first-class academic material in the form of proposals or accepted theses.
Royalties paid twice-yearly. *Overseas subsidiaries* Sister company in USA; also branches in Australia, Canada, East Africa, Hong Kong, India, Japan, New Zealand, Pakistan, Singapore, South Africa. Offices in Argentina, Brazil, France, Germany, Greece, Italy, Mexico, Spain, Taiwan, Thailand, Turkey, Uruguay. Joint companies in Malaysia, Nigeria and Germany.

Authors' Rating Weaknesses in high street sales and in the school market are offset by expansion in ELT of which Oxford is the market leader. Academic and reference (the third edition of the *Oxford English Dictionary* and a new *Dictionary of National Biography* are on the way) are the core business. The *Shorter English Dictionary* and the *Oxford Companion to Wine*

are global best sellers. One of the first publishers to get into multimedia, OUP has ambitious plans for joint ventures with companies like IBM and Philips. Authors usually have an affinity with the University.

Palm Tree Press
See **Kevin Mayhew Ltd**

G. J. Palmer & Sons Ltd
See **Hymns Ancient & Modern Ltd**

Pan Books Ltd
See **Macmillan Publishers Ltd**

Pandora Press
See **HarperCollins Publishers Ltd**

Paper Tiger Books
See **Dragon's World**

Paperduck
See **Gerald Duckworth & Co Ltd**

Papermac
See **Macmillan Publishers Ltd**

Paragon Softcover Large Print
See **Chivers Press Ltd**

Partridge Press
See **Transworld Publishers Ltd**

The Paternoster Press
See **STL Ltd**

Pavilion Books Ltd
26 Upper Ground, London SE1 9PD
☎0171 620 1666   Fax 0171 620 1314
Chairman *Richard Humphries*
Managing Director *Colin Webb*
Publishes biography, children's, cookery, gardening, humour, art, sport and travel. About 70 titles a year. Unsolicited mss not welcome. Synopses and ideas for non-fiction titles and children's fiction considered.
Royalties paid twice-yearly.

Authors' Rating Pavilion is moving into a new phase with ambitious investment in children's and trade books and co-editions.

Payback Press
See **Canongate Books Ltd**

Pelham Books/Pelham Studio
See **Penguin Books Ltd**

Pen & Sword Books Ltd
See **Leo Cooper**

Penguin Books Ltd
27 Wrights Lane, London W8 5TZ
☎0171 416 3000　　　Fax 0171 416 3099
Chief Executive *Peter Mayer*
Managing Director *Anthony Forbes Watson*
Editor-in-Chief, Adult Publishing *Peter Carson*
Publisher, Children's *Philippa Milnes-Smith*

Owned by Pearson plc. For more than 60 years the publisher of one of the largest paperback lists in the English language, the Penguin list embraces fiction, non-fiction, poetry, drama, classics, reference and special interest areas. Reprints and new work. In 1995, Penguin restructured its adult book publishing, creating three divisions issuing both hardback and paperback editions.

DIVISIONS
General Adult fiction and non-fiction. Publisher *Tony Lacey*, Associate Publisher *Clare Alexander* IMPRINTS **Hamish Hamilton Ltd**; **Penguin**; **Viking**. Non-fiction synopses and ideas welcome; no unsolicited fiction; no poetry.

Penguin Press Serious adult non-fiction, reference and classics. Director *Alastair Rolfe* IMPRINTS **Allen Lane**; **Arkana** Mind, body and spirit; **Buildings of England**; **Classics**; **Economist Books**; **Penguin Books**. Approach in writing only.

Michael Joseph Ltd Publishing Director *Susan Watt* IMPRINTS **Michael Joseph** Popular fiction; **Pelham**; **Pelham Studio** Illustrated books; **ROC** Science fiction and fantasy; **Signet** Mass-market fiction and non-fiction. Unsolicited mss discouraged; synopses and ideas welcome.

Frederick Warne *Sally Floyer* Classic children's publishing and merchandising including *Beatrix Potter*™; *Flower Fairies*; *Orlando*; **Ventura** *Sally Floyer* Producer and packager of *Spot* titles by Eric Hill.

Children's Hardback IMPRINTS **Blackie** *Rosemary Stones* Mainly *Topsy & Tim* titles; **Dutton** *Rosemary Stones* Novelty, picture books and fiction; **Hamish Hamilton Children's** *Jane Nissen* Fiction and picture books. Unsolicited mss, synopses and ideas welcome; **Viking Children's** *Rosemary Stones*. Fiction, non-fiction, picture books and poetry. Unsolicited mss discouraged; synopses and ideas welcome.

Children's Paperbacks IMPRINTS **Puffin** *Philippa Milnes-Smith* Leading children's paperback list publishing in virtually all fields including fiction, non-fiction, poetry and picture books, media-related titles.
Royalties paid twice-yearly. *Overseas associates* worldwide.

Authors' Rating Penguin seems to be returning to its roots. Founded on what was once thought to be the shaky assumption that the public was hungry for cheap paperbacks, Penguin over the years has moved up the price scale to join the rest of the fat cats. Now it is back to doing what it does best – churning out low-price classics and the phenomenal mini books which have sold 20 million worldwide. Staff morale suffered badly from two rounds of redundancies in 10 months but confidence is reviving – slowly.

Pentland Press Ltd
1 Hutton Close, South Church, Bishop Auckland, Co. Durham DL14 6XB
☎01388 776555　　　Fax 01388 776766
Chairman *Mr N. Law*
Managing Director *Mr A. Phillips*

FOUNDED in Edinburgh in 1982 and established offices in Cambridge and Durham, now the centre of operations. *Publishes* fiction and non-fiction - memoirs, autobiography, biography, war, social history, Scottish interest, history, maritime, religion, politics and poetry. 100 titles in 1995. Unsolicited mss, synopses and ideas welcome.
Royalties paid quarterly. *Overseas associates* Pentland Press Inc, Raleigh, North Carolina, USA.

Petroc Press
See **Librapharm Ltd**

Phaidon Press Limited
Regent's Wharf, All Saints Street, London N1 9PA
☎0171 843 1000　　　Fax 0171 843 1010
Chairman *Richard Schlagman*
Managing Director *Paula Kahn*
Editorial Heads *D. Jenkins, R. Sears, I. Blazwick*

Publishes quality books on the visual arts, including fine art, art history, architecture, design, practical art, photography, decorative arts, music and performing arts. Recently started producing videos. About 100 titles a year. Unsolicited mss welcome but 'only a small amount of unsolicited material gets published'.
Royalties paid twice-yearly.

Authors' Rating Has expanded activities to include music and video publishing. New leadership holds out the promise of happier relations with authors.

George Philip
See **Reed Books**

Phillimore & Co. Ltd
Shopwyke Manor Barn, Chichester, West
Sussex PO20 6BG
☎01243 787636   Fax 01243 787639
Chairman *Philip Harris*
Managing Director *Noel Osborne*
Approx. Annual Turnover £1 million
FOUNDED 1870 by W. P. W. Phillimore,
Victorian campaigner for local archive conservation in Chancery Lane, London. Became the
country's leading publisher of historical source
material and local histories. Somewhat dormant
in the 1960s, it was revived by Philip Harris in
1968. *Publishes* British local and family history,
including histories of institutions, buildings,
villages, towns and counties, plus guides to
research and writing in these fields. About 70
titles a year. No unsolicited mss; synopses/ideas
welcome for local or family histories.
   IMPRINTS **Phillimore** *Noel Osborne* TITLES
*Domesday Book; A History of Essex; Carlisle; The
Haberdashers' Company; Channel Island Churches;
Bolton Past; Warwickshire Country Houses.*
   Royalties paid annually.

Phoenix/Phoenix House
See **The Orion Publishing Group Ltd**

Piatkus Books
5 Windmill Street, London W1P 1HF
☎0171 631 0710   Fax 0171 436 7137
Managing Director *Judy Piatkus*
Approx. Annual Turnover £4.75 million
FOUNDED 1979 by Judy Piatkus. The company
is committed to continuing independence.
Specialises in publishing books and authors
'who we feel enthusiastic and committed to as
we like to build for long-term success as well as
short-term!' *Publishes* self-help, biography, personal growth, business and management,
careers, cookery, health and beauty, healing,
mind, body and spirit, popular psychology and
fiction. In 1996 launched a list of mass-market
non-fiction and fiction titles. About 150 titles a
year (50 of which are fiction).

DIVISIONS
Non-fiction *Gill Cormode* TITLES *Quentin
Tarantino* Wensley Clarkson; *Curry Club Cookery*
range Pat Chapman; *The Perfect CV* Tom
Jackson; *NLP* Harry Alder; *The Reflexology
Handbook* Laura Norman; *Living Magically* Gill
Edwards.

Fiction *Judy Piatkus* TITLES *Kernow and
Daughter* Malcolm Ross; *Happy are Those Who
Mourn* Andrew Greeley; *The Lost Daughters*
Jeanne Whitmee; *Kitty and Her Boys* June
Francis; *Family Reunions* Connie Monk. Piatkus
are expanding their range of books and welcome
synopses and ideas.
   Royalties paid twice-yearly.

Authors' Rating Anticipating tough times
ahead ('Every book will need to be clearly
focused to have any hope of achieving a
return.'), Judy Piatkus remains optimistic. 'We
see a wide range of opportunities for creative
marketing.'

Picador
See **Macmillan Publishers Ltd**

Pictorial
See **Souvenir Press Ltd**

Picture Knight
See **Hodder Headline plc**

Picture Lions
See **HarperCollins Publishers Ltd**

Pimlico
See **Random House UK Ltd**

Pinter Publishers Ltd
See **Cassell**

Pitkin Pictorials
See **Reed Books**

Pitman Publishing
128 Long Acre, London WC2E 9AN
☎0171 379 7383   Fax 0171 240 5771
Managing Director *Rod Bristow*
Publishing Director *Mark Allin*

Part of Pearson Professional. Publisher and supplier of business education and management
development materials. Portfolio of products
and services includes books, journals, directories, looseleafs, CD-ROMS aimed at business
education and management development in
both private and public sectors. About 250
titles a year.
   IMPRINTS **Pitman Publishing; Financial
Times; Institute of Management; NatWest
Business Handbooks; Allied Dunbar;
M&E Handbooks**. Unsolicited mss, synopses
and ideas for books and other materials welcome.
   Royalties paid annually.

Plenum Publishing Ltd

88-90 Middlesex Street, London E1 7EZ
☎0171 377 0686   Fax 0171 247 0555
Chairman *Martin E. Tash* (USA)
Managing Director *Dr Ken Derham*
Editor *Joanna Lawrence*

FOUNDED 1966. A division of **Plenum Publishing**, New York. The London office is the editorial and marketing base for the company's UK and European operations. *Publishes* postgraduate, professional and research-level scientific, technical and medical monographs, conference proceedings and reference books. About 300 titles (worldwide) a year.

IMPRINTS
Consultants Bureau; IFI Plenum Data Company; Plenum Insight; Plenum Medical Company; Plenum Press; Human Science Press. Proposals for new publications will be considered, and should be sent to the editor.
Royalties paid annually.

Pluto Press Ltd

345 Archway Road, London N6 5AA
☎0181 348 2724   Fax 0181 348 9133
Managing Director *Roger Van Zwanenberg*
Editorial Director *Anne Beech*

FOUNDED 1970. Has developed a reputation for innovatory publishing in the field of non-fiction. *Publishes* academic and scholarly books across a range of subjects including cultural studies, politics and world affairs, social sciences and socialist, feminist and Marxist books; plus self-help guides on all aspects of the media. About 50-60 titles a year. Synopses and ideas welcome.

Point

See **Scholastic Ltd**

Polemical Pamphlets

See **George Mann Books**

The Policy Press

University of Bristol, Rodney Lodge, Grange Road, Bristol, Avon BS8 4EA
☎0117 9748797   Fax 0117 9737308
Managing Director *Alison Shaw*
Approx. Annual Turnover £150,000

Incorporating the former SAUS Publications, The Policy Press *specialises* in the production of books, concise reports, practice guides, pamphlets and a journal. Material published is taken from research findings in policy studies, pro-viding critical discussion of policy initiatives and their impact; also recommendations for policy change. 25-35 titles per year. No unsolicited mss; brief synopses and ideas welcome.

Polity Press

65 Bridge Street, Cambridge CB2 1UR
☎01223 324315   Fax 01223 461385

FOUNDED 1984. All books are published in association with **Blackwell Publishers**. *Publishes* archaeology and anthropology, criminology, economics, feminism, general interest, history, human geography, literature, media and cultural studies, medicine and society, philosophy, politics, psychology, religion and theology, social and political theory, sociology. Unsolicited mss, synopses and ideas for books welcome.
Royalties paid annually.

Polygon

See **Edinburgh University Press Ltd**

Pont Books

See **Gomer Press**

Pop Universal

See **Souvenir Press Ltd**

Portland Press Ltd

59 Portland Place, London W1N 3AJ
☎0171 580 5530   Fax 0171 323 1136
Chairman *Professor A.J. Turner*
Managing Director *G.D. Jones*
Editorial Director *Rhonda Oliver*
Approx. Annual Turnover £2.5 million

FOUNDED 1990 to expand the publishing activities of the Biochemical Society (1911). *Publishes* biochemisty and medicine for graduate, postgraduate and research students. Expanding the list to include schools and general readership. 13 titles in 1995. TITLES *Techniques in Apoptosis; Postgraduate Study in the Physical Sciences; Glossary of Biochemistry and Molecular Biology; Making Sense of Science* series includes *Planet Ocean* and *The Space Place.* Unsolicited mss, synopses and ideas welcome. No fiction.
Royalties paid twice-yearly. *Overseas subsidiary* Portland Press Inc.

T. & A. D. Poyser

See **Harcourt Brace and Company Limited**

Presentations

See **Souvenir Press Ltd**

Princeton University Press
See **University Presses of California, Columbia & Princeton Ltd**

Prion
See **Multimedia Books Ltd**

Prism Press Book Publishers Ltd
The Thatched Cottage, Partway Lane, Hazelbury Bryan, Sturminster Newton, Dorset DT10 2DP
☎01258 817164   Fax 01258 817635
Managing Director *Julian King*
FOUNDED 1974. *Publishes* alternative medicine, conservation, environment, psychology, health, mysticism, philosophy, politics and cookery. About 6 titles a year at present. TITLES *Boundaries of the Soul* June Singer; *Beyond the Warming* Antony Milne; *Beyond Therapy* Guy Claxton. Synopses and ideas welcome.
   Royalties paid twice-yearly. *Overseas associates* Prism Press, USA.

Proteus
See **Omnibus Press**

Puffin
See **Penguin Books Ltd**

Putnam Aeronautical Books
See **Brassey's (UK) Ltd**

Quadrille Publishing Ltd
9 Irving Street, London WC2H 7AT
☎0171 839 7117   Fax 0171 839 7118
Chairman *Sue Thomson*
Managing Director *Alison Cathie*
Publishing Director *Anne Furniss*
FOUNDED in 1994 by four ex-directors of Conran Octopus, with a view to producing a small list of top-quality illustrated books. *Publishes* non-fiction, including cookery, gardening, interior design and decoration, craft, health and travel. 9 titles in 1995. TITLES *Country Living Needlework Collection* series; *Michelin France; Food of the Sun* Alastair Little and Richard Whittington. No unsolicited mss; synopses and ideas for books welcome. No fiction or children's books.
   Royalties paid twice-yearly.

Quantum
See **W. Foulsham & Co.**

Quartet Books
27 Goodge Street, London W1P 2LD
☎0171 636 3992   Fax 0171 637 1866
Chairman *Naim Attallah*

Managing Director *Jeremy Beales*
Publishing Director *Stella Kane*
Approx. Annual Turnover £1 million
FOUNDED 1972. Independent publisher. *Publishes* contemporary literary fiction including translations, popular culture, biography, music, history, politics and some photographic books. Unsolicited mss with return postage welcome; no poetry, romance or science fiction.
   Royalties paid twice-yearly.

Quiller Press
46 Lillie Road, London SW6 1TN
☎0171 499 6529   Fax 0171 381 8941
Managing/Editorial Director *Jeremy Greenwood*
Specialises in sponsored books and publications sold through non-book trade channels as well as bookshops. *Publishes* architecture, biography, business and industry, children's, cookery, DIY, gardening, guidebooks, humour, reference, sports, travel, wine and spirits. About 15 titles a year. TITLES *Novelty Teapots* Edward Bramah; *Crash the Ash* Auberon Waugh; *Monkey Business* Gen. Sir Cecil Blacker; *Water: The Book* Hugh Barty-King. Most ideas originate in-house – unsolicited mss not welcome unless the author sees some potential for sponsorship or guaranteed sales.
   Royalties paid twice-yearly.

Quotes Ltd/Quotes in Camera
See **The Barracuda Collection**

RAC Publishing
RAC House, Bartlett Street, South Croydon, Surrey CR2 6XW
☎0181 686 0088   Fax 0181 688 2882
Publisher *Alan Wakeford*
Publishes accommodation guides, plus high-quality road maps and atlases in association with HarperCollins.

Radcliffe Medical Press Ltd
18 Marcham Road, Abingdon, Oxon OX14 1AA
☎01235 528820   Fax 01235 528830
Managing Director *Andrew Bax*
Editorial Director *Gillian Nineham*
Approx. Annual Turnover £1.5 million
FOUNDED 1987. Medical publishers which began by specialising in books for general practice. *Publishes* clinical, management, health policy books and CD-ROM. 40 titles in 1995. Unsolicited mss, synopses and ideas welcome.

No non-medical or medical books aimed at lay audience.

Royalties paid twice-yearly. *Overseas subsidiary* Radcliffe Medical Press Inc., New York.

The Ramsay Head Press
15 Gloucester Place, Edinburgh EH3 6EE
☎0131 225 5646   Fax 0131 225 5646
Managing Directors *Conrad Wilson, Mrs Christine Wilson*

FOUNDED 1968 by Norman Wilson OBE. A small independent family publisher. *Publishes* biography, cookery, Scottish fiction and non-fiction, plus the quarterly literary magazine *Books in Scotland*. About 3-4 titles a year. TITLES *Medusa Dozen* Tessa Ransford; *The Happy Land* Howard Denton & Jim C. Wilson. Synopses and ideas for books of Scottish interest welcome.

Royalties paid twice-yearly.

Random House UK Ltd
Random House, 20 Vauxhall Bridge Road, London SW1V 2SA
☎0171 973 9000   Fax 0171 233 6058
Chief Executive *Gail Rebuck*
Executive Chairman *Simon Master*

Random's increasing focus on trade publishing, both here and in the US, has been well rewarded, with sales continuing to grow over the last year. Random House UK Ltd is the parent company of three separate publishing divisions following the Group's reorganisation under Gail Rebuck. These are: General Books division, the Group's largest publishing division; Children's Books & Enterprises; and Ebury Press Special Books division.

DIVISIONS
General Books Divided into two operating groups, allowing hardcover editors to see their books through to publication in paperback. The literary imprints Jonathan Cape and Chatto & Windus work side by side with paperback imprints Vintage and Pimlico to form one group; trade imprints Century and Hutchinson go hand-in-hand with Arrow and Legend to form the other group.

IMPRINTS
Jonathan Cape Ltd ☎0171 973 9730 Fax: 0171 233 6117 Publishing Director *Dan Franklin* Archaeology, biography and memoirs, current affairs, economics, fiction, history, philosophy, photography, poetry, politics, sociology and travel.
Chatto & Windus Ltd ☎0171 973 9740 Fax:

0171 233 6123 Publishing Director *Jonathan Burnham* Archaeology, art, belles-lettres, biography and memoirs, cookery, crime, current affairs, essays, fiction, history, illustrated and fine editions, poetry, politics, psychoanalysis, translations and travel.

Century (including **Business Books**) ☎0171 973 9670 Fax: 0171 233 6127 Publishing Director *Kate Parkin* General fiction and non-fiction, plus business management, advertising, communication, marketing, selling, investment and financial titles.

Hutchinson Books Ltd ☎0171 973 9680 Fax: 0171 233 6129 Publishing Director *Sue Freestone* General fiction and non-fiction including notably belles-lettres, current affairs, politics, travel and history.

Arrow ☎0171 973 9700 Fax: 0171 233 6127 Publishing Director *Andy McKillop* Mass-market paperback fiction and non-fiction.

Legend ☎0171 973 9700 Fax: 0171 233 6127 Editorial Director *John Jarrold* Science fiction and fantasy (hardback and paperback).

Pimlico ☎0171 973 9680 Fax: 0171 233 6129 Publishing Director *Will Sulkin* Large-format quality paperbacks in the fields of history, biography, autobiography and literature.

Vintage ☎0171 973 9700 Fax: 0171 233 6127 Publisher *Caroline Michel* Quality paperback fiction and non-fiction. Vintage was founded in 1989 by Frances Coady and has been described as one of the 'greatest literary success stories in recent British publishing'.

Children's Books ☎0171 973 9000 Fax: 0171 233 6058 Chairman *Piet Snyman*. Publishers & Publishing Directors *Caroline Roberts, Tom Maschler, Anne McNeil, Margaret Conroy*; Director New Media: *Anthony Askew*. IMPRINTS **Bodley Head; Jonathan Cape; Hutchinson; Julia MacRae; Random House; Tellastory** and the paperback imprint **Red Fox**. Picture books, fiction, non-fiction, novelties and audio cassette (see **Audio Books**). CD-ROM multimedia titles under the **Random House New Media** imprint.

Ebury Press Special Books ☎0171 973 9690 Fax: 0171 233 6057 Managing Director: *Amelia Thorpe*. Publishing Directors: *Fiona MacIntyre, Julian Shuckburgh* IMPRINTS **Ebury Press; Barrie & Jenkins; Condé Nast Books; Studio Editions; Fodor's; Ebury Press Stationery** and the paperback imprints **Vermilion; Rider** and **Bracken Books**. Art, architecture, antiques, cookery, gardening, health and beauty, homes and interiors, photography, travel and guides, puzzles and games, sport, natural history, DIY, diaries, gift stationery, reference, TV tie-ins. About 150 titles a year. Unsolicited mss, synopses and ideas for books welcome.

Royalties paid twice-yearly for the most part.

Authors' Rating Of a mixed bag of famous imprints, Jonathan Cape is 'committed to publishing new writers, not least because it is one of the most pleasurable and exciting things one can do as a publisher' (Dan Franklin). But overall, title output is down and rationalisation is more in evidence than growth. Following the lead of its American parent, Random House has set up a multimedia unit to produce titles for the UK market.

Raven
See **Robinson Publishing Ltd**

RCB General Books
See **Richard Cohen Books Ltd**

Reader's Digest Association Ltd
Berkeley Square House, Berkeley Square, London W1X 6AB
☎0171 629 8144   Fax 0171 236 5956
Managing Director *Neil McRae*
Editorial Head *Robin Hosie*
Approx. Annual Turnover £220 million

Publishes gardening, natural history, cookery, history, DIY, travel and word books. About 10 titles a year. TITLES *Illustrated Dictionary of Essential Knowledge; Good Health Fact Book; Treasures in Your Home; Good Ideas For Your Garden; Foods That Harm Foods That Heal.* Unsolicited mss, synopses and ideas for books welcome.

Reaktion Ltd
11 Rathbone Place, London W1P 1DE
☎0171 580 9928   Fax 0171 580 9935
Managing Director *Michael R. Leaman*
Approx. Annual Turnover £300,000

FOUNDED in Edinburgh in 1985 and moved to its London location in 1988. *Publishes* art history, design, architecture, history, cultural studies, travel and photography. 11 titles in 1995. TITLES *Parisian Fields* ed. Michael Sheringham; *Dismembering the Male: Men's Bodies, Britain and the Great War* Joanna Bourke; *Fruitful Sights: Garden Culture in Ming Dynasty China* Craig Clunas. No unsolicited mss; synopses and ideas welcome.

Royalties paid twice-yearly.

Reardon Publishing
56 Upper Norwood Street, Leckhampton, Cheltenham, Gloucestershire GL53 0DU
☎01242 231800
Managing Editor *Nicholas Reardon*

FOUNDED in the mid 1970s. Family-run publishing house specialising in local interest and tourism in the Cotswold area. Member of the **Outdoor Writers Guild**. *Publishes* walking and driving guides, and family history for societies. 10 titles a year. TITLES *Cotswold Walkabout; Cotswold Driveabout; The Donnington Way; The Haunted Cotswolds; The Cotswold Way.* Unsolicited mss, synopses and ideas welcome with return postage only.

Royalties paid twice-yearly.

Recollections
See **George Mann Books**

Red Fox
See **Random House UK Ltd**

William Reed Directories
Merchant House, 4A Reading Road, Pangbourne, Berkshire RG8 7LL
☎01734 844111   Fax 01734 841579
Editorial Manager *Mrs H. Turner*

FOUNDED 1978. Formerly Elvendon Press. *Specialises* in information books, magazines and booklets for government departments, national organisations, media/PR agencies and blue-chip companies. Database facility for publication of directories, yearbooks and exhibition programmes. No unsolicited mss. Preliminary letter essential.

Reed Books
Michelin House, 81 Fulham Road, London SW3 6RB
☎0171 581 9393   Fax 0171 225 9424
Chief Executive *Sandy Grant*
Approx. Annual Turnover £200 million

Reed Books (formerly the consumer books division of Reed International Books) has several offices; addresses and telephone numbers have been given if different from that above.

FICTION AND GENERAL NON-FICTION:
William Heinemann (hardback) Fax: 0171 225 9095 Publisher *Tom Weldon*, Editorial Director *Louise Moore* TITLES *The Gun Seller* Hugh Laurie; *The Sett* Ranulph Fiennes.

Mandarin (paperback) TITLES *Free to Trade* Michael Ridpath; *A Simple Life* Rosie Thomas; *The Gobbler* Adrian Edmonson.

Secker & Warburg (hardback) Fax: 0171 225 9095 Publisher *Max Eilenberg*, Editorial Director *Geoff Mulligan* TITLES *The Midden* Tom Sharpe; *The Devil's Carousel* Jeff Torrington; *Cruising Paradise* Sam Shepard. **Minerva** (paperbacks) TITLES *The Island of the Day Before* Umberto Eco; *Blake* Peter Ackroyd. No unsolicited mss.

Methuen Fax: 0171 589 9095 Publisher *Michael Earley* Plays, drama, humour, fiction, music, arts TITLES *Letters* John Betjeman; *Running Away* Leslie Thomas; *Joan's Book* Joan Littlewood. Plays by Brecht, Bond, Churchill, Mamet, Miller, Orton, Soyinka. Please write with synopsis before submitting mss.

Sinclair-Stevenson   Fax: 0171 225 9095 Senior Editorial Director *Penelope Hoare* Quality fiction and general non-fiction TITLES *Blake* Peter Ackroyd; *The Pope's Rhinoceros* Lawrence Norfolk; *Flora Britannica* Richard Mabey.

ILLUSTRATED NON-FICTION:
Hamlyn Fax: 0171 225 9528 Publisher *Laura Bamford* Popular non-fiction, particularly cookery, gardening, craft, sport, film tie-ins, rock 'n' roll, road atlases TITLES *Larousse Gastronomique; Variety Movie Guide; Sunday Times Chronicle of Sport; Hamlyn New Cookbook; Hamlyn Book of Gardening; Hamlyn Book of DIY & Decorating.*

Mitchell Beazley Fax: 0171 225 9024 Publisher *Jane Aspden* Quality illustrated reference books, particularly wine, antiques, gardening, craft and interiors. TITLES *Hugh Johnson's Pocket Wine Book; The New Joy of Sex; Miller's Antiques Price Guide.*

Osprey Second Floor, Unit 6, Spring Gardens, Citadel Place, Tinworth Street, London SE11 5EH. ☎0171 581 9393 Fax: 0171 225 9869 Managing Director *Jonathan Parker* Militaria, aviation, automotive SERIES *Men-at-Arms; Elite; Campaign; New Vanguard; Warrior; Aircraft of the Aces.* TITLES *Ayrton Senna – A Personal Tribute; Spitfire – Flying Legend; Waterloo: The Hundred Days.*

Conran Octopus 37 Shelton Street, London WC2H 9HN. ☎0171 240 6961 Fax: 0171 836 9951 Publisher *John Wallace* Quality illustrated books, particularly lifestyle, cookery, gardening TITLES Terence Conran's *Essential House Book*; Alastair Little *Keep It Simple*; David Austin *English Roses; Mothercare New Guide to Pregnancy and Childcare.*

George Philip Second Floor, Unit 6, Spring Gardens, Citadel Place, Tinworth Street, London SE11 5EH. ☎0171 581 9393 Fax: 0171 225 9841 Publisher *John Gaisford* World atlases, globes, astronomy, road atlases, encyclopaedias,

general reference TITLES *Philip's Atlas of the World; Philip's Guide to the Stars and Planets; Philip's Navigator Road Atlas Britain; Ordnance Survey Motoring Atlas Britain; Michelin Motoring Atlas France; Philip's Concise World Encyclopaedia; Philip's Atlas of World History.*

Pitkin Pictorials Healey House, Dene Road, Andover, Hampshire SP10 2AA. ☎01264 334303 Fax: 01264 334110 Publisher *Ian Corsie* Illustrated souvenir guides.

CHILDRENS
Reed Children's books Fax: 0171 225 9731 Managing Director *Jane Winterbotham*, Publishing Director *Gill Evans.*

Heinemann Young Books Quality picture books, novels and anthologies TITLES *Thomas The Tank Engine; The Jolly Postman; The Wreck of the Zanzibar*; **Methuen Children's Books** Quality picture books and fiction for babies to early teens TITLES *Winnie the Pooh; Babar; Tintin; The Wind in the Willows*; **Hamlyn** Illustrated non-fiction and reference books for children TITLES *History of Britain* series; *Dragon Islands; In the Next 3 Seconds*; **Mammoth Paperbacks** Paperback imprint of the above hardback imprints; licensed characters and tie-ins TITLES *Barbie; Muppet Treasure Island* No unsolicited mss.

Brimax Books Units 4/5, Studlands Park Industrial Estate, Exning Road, Newmarket, Suffolk CB8 7AU. ☎01638 664611 Fax: 01638 665220 Managing Director *Patricia Gillette* Mass-market board and picture books for children age groups 1–10.

Royalties paid twice-yearly/annually, according to contract in all divisions.

Authors' Rating What promised to be the sale of the century turned out to be no sale at all, at least for the time being. Early in the year Reed said it wanted to dispose of its consumer books to concentrate on electronic publishing. But when the bids failed to come up to expectations, the policy changed to commissioning fewer and better titles. The plan is to raise profits before putting the divisions back on to the auction block.

Reed Educational and Professional Publishing
Halley Court, Jordan Hill, Oxford OX2 8EJ
☎01865 311366   Fax 01865 314641
Chief Executive *William Shepherd*

Incorporating Butterworth-Heinmann, Heinemann Educational, Heinemann English

Language Teaching and Ginn in the UK; Greenwood Publishing Group, Heinemann and Rigby Inc. in the USA; Butterworth-Heinemann, Rigby Heinemann and DW Thorpe in Australia.

This division has several different offices: addresses and telephone numbers have been given if different from that above.

Heinemann Educational Fax: 01865 314140 Managing Director *Bob Osborne*, Primary: *Paul Shuter*, Secondary: *Kay Symons*. Textbooks/literature/other educational resources for primary and secondary school and further education. Mss, synopses and ideas welcome.

Heinemann English Language Teaching Fax: 01865 414193 Managing Director *Mike Esplen*, Publishing Directors *Christ Hartley* (Adult), *Sue Bale* (Schools). English language teaching books and materials.

Ginn & Co Prebendal House, Parson's Fee, Aylesbury, Bucks HP20 2QZ ☎01296 394442 Fax: 01296 393433 Managing Director *Nigel Hall*. Textbook/other educational resources for primary and secondary schools.

Butterworth Heinemann UK Linacre House, Jordan Hill, Oxford OX2 8EJ ☎01865 310366 Fax: 01865 310898 Managing Director *Philip Shaw*, Engineering & Technology: *Peter Dixon*, Business: *Kathryn Grant*, Medical: *Geoff Smalden*. Books and electronic products across business, technical, medical and open-learning fields for students and professionals.

Royalties paid twice-yearly/annually, according to contract in all divisions.

Reed Reference Publishing
See **Bowker-Saur Ltd**

Reinhardt Books Ltd
Flat 2, 43 Onslow Square, London SW7 3LR
☎0171 589 3751

Chairman/Managing Director *Max Reinhardt*
Directors *Joan Reinhardt*

FOUNDED 1887 as H. F. L. (Publishers) and was acquired by Max Reinhardt in 1947. Changed its name to the present one in 1987. First publication under the new name was Graham Greene's *The Captain and the Enemy*. Also publishes under the **Nonesuch Press** imprint. AUTHORS include Mitsumasa Anno, Alistair Cooke and Maurice Sendak. New books are no longer considered.

Royalties paid according to contract.

Religious & Moral Educational Press
See **Hymns Ancient & Modern Ltd**

Richmond House Publishing Company
Douglas House, 3 Richmond Buildings, London W1V 5AE
☎0171 437 9556   Fax 0171 287 3463

Managing Director *Gloria Gordon*
Editorial Head *Samantha Blair*
Manager *Spencer Block*

Publishes directories for the theatre and entertainment industries. Synopses and ideas welcome.

Rider
See **Random House UK Ltd**

Right Way
See **Elliot Right Way Books**

Robinson Publishing Ltd
7 Kensington Church Court, London W8 4SP
☎0171 938 3830   Fax 0171 938 4214

Managing Director *Nicholas Robinson*

Publishes fiction – horror, fantasy, science fiction; reference, puzzles, games, health and children's. 40 titles in 1995. IMPRINTS **Raven** *Mark Crean* TITLE *Celestial Dogs*; **Scarlet** *Sue Curran* TITLE *Fire and Ice*; **Robinson Children's Books** *Tom Keegan* TITLE *True Survival Stories*. No unsolicited mss; synopses and ideas welcome.

Royalties paid twice-yearly.

Robson Books Ltd
Bolsover House, 5–6 Clipstone Street, London W1P 8LE
☎0171 323 1223   Fax 0171 636 0798

Managing Director *Jeremy Robson*
Editorial Head *Louise Dixon*

FOUNDED 1973. *Publishes* mainly general non-fiction, including biography, cinema, cookery, gardening, guidebooks, health and beauty, humour, sports and games, theatre and drama and travel. About 60 titles a year. Unsolicited mss, synopses and ideas for books welcome (s.a.e. essential).

Royalties paid twice-yearly.

Authors' Rating The hard-pressed gift buyers' favourite publisher. A Robson book is always good for a laugh.

ROC
See **Penguin Books Ltd**

Rosendale Press Ltd

Premier House, 10 Greycoat Place, London
SW1P 1SB
☎0171 222 8866   Fax 0171 799 1416
Chairman *Timothy S. Green*
Editorial Director *Maureen P. Green*

FOUNDED 1985. Independent publisher of
non-fiction and illustrated books, namely food
and drink, travel, business entertainment and
family health. About 10 titles a year. TITLES
*The Top 100 Pasta Sauces; Favourite Indian Food;
The Vegetable Market Cookbook; The World of
Gold; Eating Out in Barcelona and Catalunya;
Understanding Your Baby.* Synopses and ideas for
books considered within their specialist fields
only.

Payment varies according to contract.

Roundhall

See **Sweet & Maxwell Ltd**

Roundhouse Publishing Group

PO Box 140, Oxford OX2 7FF
☎01865 512682   Fax 01865 59594
Editorial Head *Alan Goodworth*

ESTABLISHED 1991. Publisher of cinema, the-
atre and other media-related titles, and general-
interest non-fiction. TITLES *Cinema of Oliver
Stone; Cinema of Stanley Kubrick; Hitchcock: The
First Forty Four Films; Shoot the Piano Player;
Animating Culture; Toms, Coons, Mulattoes,
Mammies and Bucks.*

Represents a broad range of non-fiction
publishing houses in the UK, US, Canada and
Italy. No unsolicited mss.

Royalties paid twice-yearly.

Routledge

11 New Fetter Lane, London EC4P 4EE
☎0171 583 9855   Fax 0171 842 2298
Managing Director *Janice Price*
Publishing Director *Peter Sowden*
Publishers *Gordon Smith, Claire L'Enfant*
Approx. Annual Turnover (Group)
£20 million

The new Routledge company was formed in
1987 through an amalgamation of Routledge &
Kegan Paul, Methuen & Co., Tavistock
Publications, and Croom Helm. The **Harper-
Collins** academic list acquired in 1991 added a
substantial new list, bringing in textbooks and
monographs in social sciences. *Publishes* access,
addiction, anthropology, archaeology, Asian
studies, classical heritage and studies, counselling, criminology, development and environment, dictionaries, economics, education,
geography, health, history, Japanese studies, linguistics, literary criticism, media and culture,
Middle East, philosophy, politics, political
economy, psychiatry, psychology, reference,
social administration, social studies and sociology, women's studies. No poetry, fiction, travel
or astrology. About 750 titles a year.

Send synopses with sample chapter and c.v.
rather than complete mss.

Royalties paid annually.

Ryland Peters and Small Limited

Cavendish House, 51-55 Mortimer Street,
London W1N 7TD
☎0171 436 9090   Fax 0171 436 9790
Managing Director *David Peters*

FOUNDED 1996 – first titles published in the
autumn. *Publishes* highly illustrated lifestyle
books – gardening, cookery, craft, interior
design. No fiction. No unsolicited mss; synopses
and ideas welcome.

Royalties paid twice-yearly.

Saga

See **Barracuda Books Ltd/Quotes Ltd**

Saint Andrew Press

Board of Communication, Church of
Scotland, 121 George Street, Edinburgh
EH2 4YN
☎0131 225 5722   Fax 0131 220 3113
Publishing Manager *Lesley Ann Taylor*
Approx. Annual Turnover £225,000

FOUNDED in 1954 to publish and promote the
17-volume series *The Daily Study Bible New
Testament* by Professor William Barclay.
Owned by the Church of Scotland Board of
Communication. *Publishes* religious, Scottish
local interest and some children's books. No
fiction. 15 titles in 1995. No unsolicited mss;
synopses and ideas preferred.

Royalties paid annually.

St Paul's Bibliographies

1 Step Terrace, Winchester, Hampshire
SO22 5BW
☎01962 860524   Fax 01962 842409
Chairman/Managing Director *Robert Cross*
Approx. Annual Turnover £30,000

FOUNDED 1982. *Publishes* bibliographical reference books and works on the history of the
book. 2-3 titles a year. TITLES *A Genius for
Letters* ed. Robin Myers and Michael Harris; *A
New Introduction to Bibliography* Elspeth Huxley.

Unsolicited mss, synopses and ideas welcome if relevant to subjects covered.

Royalties paid twice-yearly.

St Pauls
St Paul's House, Middlegreen, Slough, Berkshire SL3 6BT
☎01753 520621   Fax 01753 574240
Managing Director *Karamvelil Sebastian*
Publishing division of the Society of St Paul. Began publishing in 1914 but activities were fairly limited until around 1948. *Publishes* religious material only: theology, scripture, catechetics, prayer books, children's material and biography. Unsolicited mss, synopses and ideas welcome. About 50 titles a year.

Salamander Books Ltd
129-137 York Way, London N7 9LG
☎0171 267 4447   Fax 0171 267 5112
Managing Director *Ray Bonds*
FOUNDED 1973. Independent publishing house. *Publishes* collecting, cookery and wine, music, crafts, military and aviation, pet care, sport, transport, technical and children's non-fiction. About 55 titles a year. Unsolicited synopses and ideas for books welcome.

Royalties outright fee paid instead of royalties.

Sangam Books Ltd
57 London Fruit Exchange, Brushfield Street, London E1 6EP
☎0171 377 6399   Fax 0171 375 1230
Executive Director *Anthony de Souza*
Traditionally an educational publisher of school and college level textbooks. Also *publishes* art, India, medicine, science, technology, social sciences, religion, plus some fiction in paperback.

Sapling
See **Boxtree**

W. B. Saunders & Co. Ltd/ Saunders Scientific Publications
See **Harcourt Brace and Company Ltd**

SAUS Publications
See **The Policy Press**

SB Publications
c/o 19 Grove Road, Seaford, East Sussex BN25 1TP
☎01323 893498
Managing Director *Steve Benz*

Approx. Annual Turnover £200,000
FOUNDED 1987. *Specialises* in local history, including themes illustrated by old picture postcards and photographs; also travel, guides (town, walking), maritime history and railways. 20 titles a year.

IMPRINTS **Brampton Publications** *Steve Benz* TITLES *Potteries Picture Postcards*; *Curiosities of East Sussex*; *A Dorset Quiz Book*. Also provides marketing and distribution services for local authors.

Royalties paid annually.

Scala Books
See **Philip Wilson Publishers Ltd**

Scarlet
See **Robinson Publishing Ltd**

Scarlet Press
5 Montague Road, London E8 2HN
☎0171 241 3702   Fax 0171 275 0031
Directors *Christine Considine, Avis Lewallen*
FOUNDED 1989. Independent publishing house. *Publishes* feminist non-fiction covering politics, autobiography, social policy, arts, leisure, history, lesbian and gay studies. No fiction or any 'non-woman-centred' material. About 8 titles a year. TITLES *Patient No More: The Politics of Breast Cancer* Sharon Batt; *Idols to Incubators: Reproduction Theory Through the Ages* Julia Stonehouse; *Stolen Lives: Trading Women into Sex and Slavery* Sietske Attink. Unsolicited mss, synopses and ideas welcome.

Royalties paid twice-yearly.

Sceptre
See **Hodder Headline plc**

Scholastic Ltd
Villiers House, Clarendon Avenue, Leamington Spa, Warwickshire CV32 5PR
☎01926 887799   Fax 01926 883331
Chairman *M. R. Robinson*
Managing Director *David Kewley*
Approx. Annual Turnover £25 million
FOUNDED 1964. Owned by US parent company. *Publishes* education for primary school teachers, children's fiction and non-fiction.

DIVISIONS
Scholastic Children's Books *David Fickling* Commonwealth House, 1–19 New Oxford Street, London WC1A 1NU. ☎0171 421 9000 Fax: 0171 421 9001. IMPRINTS **André Deutsch Children's Books** (hardbacks); **Adlib** (12+ fiction); **Hippo** (paperbacks);

Point (paperbacks). TITLES *Postman Pat; Rosie & Jim; Tots TV; Goosebumps; Point Horror.*

Educational Publishing *Anne Peel, Regina Nuttall* Professional books and classroom materials for primary teachers, plus magazines such as *Child Education, Junior Education, Art & Craft, Junior Focus, Infant Projects.*

Direct Marketing to Schools The largest school-based book-club operator in the UK, selling to children via their schools through four book clubs: *See-Saw, Lucky, Chip* and *Scene,* covering ages 5–13, and to teachers through *Criterion.* Also operates *Scholastic Book Fairs,* a complementary school marketing operation which sells books to children in schools.
Royalties paid twice-yearly.

SCM Press Ltd
9–17 St Albans Place, London N1 0NX
☎0171 359 8033   Fax 0171 359 0049
Managing Director *Rev. Dr John Bowden*
Approx. Annual Turnover £1 million

Publishes religion and theology, with some ethics and philosophy. About 40 titles a year. Unsolicited mss and synopses considered if sent with s.a.e.
Royalties paid annually.

Authors' Rating Leading publisher of religious ideas with well-deserved reputation for fresh thinking. At SCM, 'questioning theology is the norm'.

Scolar Press
See **Ashgate Publishing Co. Ltd**

Scope International Ltd/ Milestone Publications
Forestside House, Forestside, Rowlands Castle, Hampshire PO9 6EE
☎01705 631468   Fax 01705 631777
Managing Director/Editorial Director
    Nicholas J. Pine

Publishes business, economics, finance, privacy, tax haven and tax planning, antique porcelain.

IMPRINTS
Milestone Publications, Scope. No unsolicited mss. Approach in writing with ideas/proposals. Additional material for existing reports welcome.
Royalties paid twice-yearly.

Scottish Academic Press
56 Hanover Street, Edinburgh EH2 2DX
☎0131 225 7483   Fax 0131 225 7662
Managing Editor *Dr Douglas Grant*

FOUNDED 1969. *Publishes* academic: architecture, education, geology, history, literature, poetry, social sciences, theology.
Royalties paid annually.

Seafarer Books
See **Merlin Press Ltd**

Search Press Ltd/Burns & Oates
Wellwood, North Farm Road, Tunbridge Wells, Kent TN2 3DR
☎01892 510850   Fax 01892 515903
Managing Director *Countess de la Bédoyère*

FOUNDED 1847. Publishers to the Holy See. *Publishes* (Search Press) full-colour art, craft, needlecrafts and organic gardening; (Burns & Oates) philosophy, theology, history, spirituality, reference.

DIVISIONS
Academic *Paul Burns* TITLES include *Butler's Lives of the Saints,* new full edition, 12 volumes.
Craft *John Dalton, Clare Turner* Books on papermaking and papercrafts, painting on silk, calligraphy and embroidery, and the *Organic Handbooks* series. Synopses and ideas for books welcome.
Royalties paid annually.

Secker & Warburg
See **Reed Books**

Sensation
See **Harlequin Mills & Boon Ltd**

Serpent's Tail
4 Blackstock Mews, London N4 2BT
☎0171 354 1949   Fax 0171 704 6467
Contact *Laurence O'Toole*
Approx. Annual Turnover £650,000

FOUNDED 1986. Won the *Sunday Times* Small Publisher of the Year Award (1989) and the Ralph Lewis Award for new fiction (1992). Serpent's Tail has introduced to British audiences a number of major internationally known writers. Noted for its strong emphasis on design – including flaps on paperback covers in the continental style – and an eye for the unusual. *Publishes* contemporary fiction, including works in translation, crime, popular culture and biography. No poetry, science fiction, horror, romance or fantasy. About 40 titles a year.

IMPRINTS
Serpent's Tail TITLES *Mr Clive and Mr Page* Neil Bartlett; *Hallucinating Foucault* Patricia

Duncker; *Ocean of Sound* David Toop; **Mask Noir** TITLES *A Red Death*; *Black Betty* by Walter Mosley; *Calendar Gin* Stella Duffy; *Acid Casuals* Nicholas Blincoe; *Bayswater Bodycount* Graeme Gordon; **High Risk Books** *Rent Boy* Gary Indiana; *Spinsters* Pagan Kennedy; *Bombay Talkie* Armeena Meer. Send preliminary letter outlining proposal (include s.a.e. for reply). No unsolicited mss. Prospective authors who are not familiar with Serpent's Tail are advised to study the list before submitting anything.
Royalties normally paid yearly.

Authors' Rating A small publisher with a reputation for way-out and original subject matter.

Settle Press
10 Boyne Terrace Mews, London W11 3LR
☎0171 243 0695
Chairman/Managing Director *D. Settle*
FOUNDED 1981. *Publishes* travel, guidebooks, general non-fiction. About 12 titles a year. **Travel/Tourist Guides/General** *D. Settle* TITLES *City Break Series* (Paris, Rome, Vienna, etc.); *Where to Go Series* (Romania, Turkey, Greece, etc.); *Key To Series* (Far East, Africa, Caribbean, etc). Unsolicited synopses accepted but no mss.
Royalties paid by arrangement.

Severn House Publishers Ltd
9-15 High Street, Sutton, Surrey SM1 1DF
☎0181 770 3930   Fax 0181 770 3850
Chairman *Edwin Buckhalter*
Editorial *Deborah Smith*
FOUNDED 1974. A leader in library fiction publishing. *Publishes* hardback fiction: romance, science fiction, horror, fantasy, crime. About 120 titles a year. No unsolicited material. Synopses/proposals preferred through *bona fide* literary agents only.
Royalties paid twice-yearly. *Overseas associates* Severn House Publishers Inc., New York.

Shakespeare Head Press
See **Blackwell Publishers Ltd**

Sheffield Academic Press
Mansion House, 19 Kingfield Road, Sheffield S11 9AS
☎0114 2554433   Fax 0114 2554626
Managing Director *Mrs Jean R.K. Allen*
Approx. Annual Turnover £1.1 million
FOUNDED in 1976. Originally known as JSOT Press. Now the leading academic publisher of biblical titles. Recently expanded its list to include archaeology, literary studies, history and culture, languages. 80 titles in 1995. Unsolicited mss, synopses and ideas welcome. No fiction.
IMPRINTS **Sheffield Academic Press** *John Jarick*; **Subis** *Duncan Chambers*.
Royalties paid annually

Sheldon Press
See **Society for Promoting Christian Knowledge**

Shepheard-Walwyn (Publishers) Ltd
Suite 34, 26 Charing Cross Road, London WC2H 0DH
☎0171 240 5992   Fax 0171 379 5770
Managing Director *Anthony Werner*
Approx. Annual Turnover £150,000
FOUNDED 1972. 'We regard books as food for the mind and want to offer a wholesome diet of original ideas and fresh approaches to old subjects.' *Publishes* general non-fiction in three main areas: Scottish interest; gift books in calligraphy and/or illustrated; history, political economy, philosophy and religion. About 5 titles a year. Synopses and ideas for books welcome.
Royalties paid twice-yearly.

The Shetland Times
Prince Alfred Street, Lerwick, Shetland ZE1 0EP
☎01595 693622   Fax 01595 694637
Managing Director *Robert Wishart*
Editorial Head *Beatrice Nisbet*
FOUNDED 1872 as publishers of the local newspaper. Book publishing followed thereafter plus publication of monthly magazine, *Shetland Life*. *Publishes* anything with Shetland connections – local and natural history, maritime. 5 titles in 1995. Only interested in considering material with a Shetland theme/connection.
Royalties paid annually.

Shire Publications Ltd
Cromwell House, Church Street, Princes Risborough, Buckinghamshire HP27 9AA
☎01844 344301   Fax 01844 347080
Managing Director *John Rotheroe*
Commissioning Editor *Jackie Fearn*
FOUNDED 1967. *Publishes* original non-fiction paperbacks. About 25 titles a year. No unsolicited material; send introductory letter with detailed outline of idea.
Royalties paid annually.

Authors' Rating You don't have to live in the country to write books for Shire but it helps. With titles like *Church Fonts, Haunted Inns* and *Discovering Preserved Railways* there is a distinct rural feel to the list. Another way of putting it, to quote a *Financial Times* interview with MD John Rotheroe, Shire specialises in 'small books on all manner of obscure subjects'.

Sidgwick & Jackson
See **Macmillan Publishers Ltd**

Sigma Press
1 South Oak Lane, Wilmslow, Cheshire SK9 6AR
☎01625 531035   Fax 01625 536800
Chairman/Managing Director *Graham Beech*
FOUNDED in 1980 as a publisher of technical books. Sigma Press grew rapidly with popular computer books which are still a major part of the list. *Publishes* outdoor, leisure, local heritage, myths and legends, sports, computing. Recently launched a popular science series. Approx. 55 titles in 1995. No unsolicited mss; synopses and ideas welcome.
  DIVISIONS **Sigma Leisure** TITLES *50 Classic Walks in the Pennines; Cycling in Scotland; Lakeland Rocky Rambles*; **Sigma Press** TITLES *Communications & Networks; PC Engineer's Reference Book; Alice in Quantumland*.
  Royalties paid twice-yearly.

Signet
See **Penguin Books Ltd**

Silhouette Desire
See **Harlequin Mills & Boon Ltd**

Simon & Schuster
West Garden Place, Kendal Street, London W2 2AQ
☎0171 316 1900   Fax 0171 402 0639
Managing Director *Nick Webb*
Editorial Directors *Joanna Frank, Martin Fletcher, Helen Gummer*
FOUNDED 1986. Offshoot of the leading US publisher. *Publishes* general fiction and non-fiction in hardback and paperback. Expansion into school publishing, which started with the purchase of Blackwell's education list, has continued with the takeover of Cassell's ELT list. The academic division is based in Hemel Hempstead. No academic or technical material.
  Royalties paid twice-yearly.

Authors' Rating Best known in the States for its technology list, Simon & Schuster has made its British reputation with new fiction and children's books. But the company's single biggest advantage is being able to take in books from the American side of Simon & Schuster, an economic bonus that nonetheless makes it harder for British authors to gain a foothold.

Sinclair-Stevenson
See **Reed Books**

Skoob Books Ltd
11A-17 Sicilian Avenue, Southampton Row, London WC1A 2QH
☎0171 404 3063   Fax 0171 404 4398
Editorial office: 76A Oldfield Road, London N16 0RS. ☎/Fax 0171 275 9811.
Managing Director *I. K. Ong*
Editorial *M. Lovell*

Publishes Literary guides, cultural studies, esoterica/occult, new writing from the Orient. Unsolicited summaries with samples and s.a.e. welcome; no mss. TITLES *The Polemics of Imagination* Peter Abbs; *Skoob Booklovers Guide to London; Hitler Black Magician* Gerald Suster; *Skoob Esoterica Anthology; Haunting the Tiger* K. A. Maniam.

Smith Gryphon Ltd
Swallow House, 11-21 Northdown Street, London N1 9BN
☎0171 278 2444   Fax 0171 833 5680
Chairman/Managing Director *Robert Smith*
FOUNDED 1990. Family-owned company. *Publishes* biography, autobiography, music (mostly rock), cinema, true crime, topical issues, finance and business, wine, food and cookery, and illustrated. 20 titles in 1996. TITLES *Diana in Private* Lady Colin Campbell; *The Diary of Jack the Ripper* Shirley Harrison; *Harry's Bar Cookbook* Arrigo Cipriani; *Parkhurst Tales* Norman Parker; *Mercury* Laura Jackson. No unsolicited mss; ideas and synopses welcome.
  Royalties paid twice-yearly.

Authors' Rating Living up to its early promise, Smith Gryphon favours concentration on a select group of strong sellers.

Colin Smythe Ltd
PO Box 6, Gerrards Cross, Buckinghamshire SL9 8XA
☎01753 886000   Fax 01753 886469
Managing Director *Colin Smythe*
Approx. Annual Turnover £950,000
FOUNDED 1966. *Publishes* Anglo-Irish literature, drama, and criticism, history. About 15 titles a year. No unsolicited mss; send synopses and ideas for books in first instance.
  Royalties paid annually/twice-yearly.

Society for Promoting Christian Knowledge (SPCK)

Holy Trinity Church, Marylebone Road, London NW1 4DU
☎0171 387 5282   Fax 0171 388 2352
Publishing Director *Simon Kingston*

FOUNDED 1698, SPCK is the third oldest publisher in the country.

IMPRINTS
Sheldon Press Publisher *Joanna Moriarty* Popular medicine, health, self-help, psychology, business. **SPCK** Senior Editor *Alex Wright* Theology and academic; Editor *Lucy Gasson* Biblical studies, educational resources, mission; Editor *Naomi Starkey* Gospel and culture, worldwide; Publisher *Joanna Moriarty* Pastoral care. **Triangle** Editor *Naomi Starkey* Popular Christian paperbacks, **Lynx** Editor *Robin Keeley* Parish resources, training and youthwork textbooks.
Royalties paid annually.

Authors' Rating Religion with a strong social edge.

SoftbABCks

See **ABC – All Books for Children**

Solo Books Ltd

49–53 Kensington High Street, London W8 5ED
☎0171 376 2166   Fax 0171 938 3165
Chairman/Managing Director *Don Short*
Approx. Annual Turnover (Group)
£1.3 million

Publishing arm of **Solo Literary Agency** (see under **UK Agents**). *Publishes* biography and autobiography and celebrity books, some non-fiction and business titles. About 15 titles a year. No fiction. Unsolicited mss not welcome; approach in writing with synopses or ideas.
Royalties paid quarterly.

Solway

See **STL Ltd**

Sotheby's Publications

See **Philip Wilson Publishers Ltd**

Souvenir Press Ltd

43 Great Russell Street, London WC1B 3PA
☎0171 580 9307/8 & 637 5711/2/3 Fax 0171 580 5064
Chairman/Managing Director *Ernest Hecht*
Senior Editor *Tessa Harrow*

Independent publishing house. FOUNDED 1951. *Publishes* academic and scholarly, animal care and breeding, antiques and collecting, archaeology, autobiography and biography, business and industry, children's, cookery, crafts and hobbies, crime, educational, fiction, gardening, health and beauty, history and antiquarian, humour, illustrated and fine editions, magic and the occult, medical, military, music, natural history, philosophy, poetry, psychology, religious, sociology, sports, theatre and women's studies. About 55 titles a year. Souvenir's Human Horizons series for the disabled and their carers is one of the most preeminent in its field and recently celebrated 17 years of publishing for the disabled.

IMPRINTS
Condor; **Pictorial**; **Presentations**; **Pop Universal**; **Human Horizons**. TITLES *The Descent of the Child, Human Evolution From a New Perspective* Elaine Morgan; *The Artists' Way, A Spiritual Path to Higher Creativity* Julia Cameron; *Great Irish Tales of the Unimaginable* ed. Peter Haining; *Politically Correct Bedtime Stories* James Finn Garner; *The Specialist* Charles Sale; *How to Live with a Neurotic Cat Owner* Stephen Baker; *The Food Medicine Bible* Earl Mindell; *Singing From the Soul* José Carreras. Unsolicited mss considered but initial letter of enquiry preferred.
Royalties paid twice-yearly.

Authors' Rating After 45 years in the business, Ernest Hecht still manages to have fun with publishing. He was the only one *not* to be surprised when *Politically Correct Bedtime Stories* went into the best, bestseller list with sales of 200,000 plus. There is no recognisable pattern to Souvenir's publishing programme which ranges from the novels of Nobel Prize winner Knut Hamson to *Rear View*, 'being a brief and elegant history of bottoms'. Ernest Hecht is the living proof that an independent publisher can give cheer to authors and bank managers alike.

SPCK

See **Society for Promoting Christian Knowledge**

Neville Spearman

See **The C. W. Daniel Co. Ltd**

Special Edition

See **Harlequin Mills & Boon Ltd**

Spellmount Ltd

The Old Rectory, Staplehurst, Kent TN12 0AZ
☎01580 893730   Fax 01580 893731
Managing Director *Jamie Wilson*
Approx. Annual Turnover £200,000

FOUNDED 1983. *Publishes* non-fiction in hardcover; primarily history and military history, biography. About 20 titles a year. Synopses/ideas for books in these specialist fields welcome.

Royalties six-monthly for two years, then annually.

Spindlewood

70 Lynhurst Avenue, Barnstaple, Devon
EX31 2HY
☎01271 71612   Fax 01271 25906
Managing Director *Michael Holloway*

FOUNDED 1980. *Publishes* children's books. 6 titles in 1995. No unsolicited mss; send synopsis with sample chapter or two.

Royalties paid according to contract.

E & F N Spon

2–6 Boundary Row, London SE1 8HN
☎0171 865 0066   Fax 0171 522 9623
Managing Director *Geoffrey Burn*
Publishing Director *Phillip Read*

FOUNDED 1834 by the son and grandson of Baron de Spon, a refugee from the French Revolution, the company has always specialised in science and technology. In the 1950s, it became an imprint of Chapman & Hall and since 1987 has concentrated solely on construction-related titles. About 70 titles a year. *Publishes* architecture, building, civil and environmental engineering, landscape, planning & property (all built-environment), sports science, leisure & recreation management. TITLES *The Channel Tunnel Story; The Buildings Around Us; European Cities: Planning Systems and Property Markets; Coaching Children in Sport, Science and Golf.* Unsolicited mss, synopses and ideas welcome.

Royalties paid annually.

Sporting & Leisure Press
See **The Barracuda Collection**

Stainer & Bell Ltd

PO Box 110, 23 Gruneisen Road, London
N3 1DZ
☎0181 343 3303   Fax 0181 343 3024
Chairman *Bernard A. Braley*
Managing Directors *Carol Y. Wakefield, Keith M. Wakefield*
Publishing Manager *Nicholas Williams*
Approx. Annual Turnover £550,000

FOUNDED 1907 to publish sheet music. *Publishes* music and religious subjects related to hymnody. Unsolicited synopses/ideas for books welcome. Send letter enclosing brief précis.

Royalties paid annually.

Stam Press
See **Stanley Thornes (Publishers) Ltd**

Harold Starke Publishers Ltd

Pixey Green, Stradbroke, Near Eye, Suffolk
IP21 5NG
☎01379 388334   Fax 01379 388335
Directors *Harold K. Starke, Naomi Galinski*

Publishes adult non-fiction, medical and reference. No unsolicited mss.

Royalties paid annually.

Patrick Stephens Ltd
See **Haynes Publishing**

Stevens
See **Sweet & Maxwell Ltd**

STL Ltd

PO Box 300, Kingstown Broadway, Carlisle, Cumbria CA3 0QS
☎01228 512512   Fax 01228 514949
Publishing Director *Pieter Kwant*
Publishing Manager *Jeremy H. L. Mudditt*
Approx. Annual Turnover £1,200,000

Owns Paternoster Publishing with the following IMPRINTS **The Paternoster Press** FOUNDED 1935. *Publishes* religion and learned/church/life-related journals. About 50 titles a year. TITLES *The New International Dictionary of New Testament Theology* (4 vols) ed. Colin Brown; *Acts in its 1st Century Setting* ed. Bruce Winter. **OM Publishing** FOUNDED 1978. *Publishes* Christian books on evangelism, discipleship and mission. About 30 titles a year. TITLES *Operation World* Patrick Johnstone; *You Can Change the World* Jill Johnstone.

Solway new general religious books imprint launched in 1996.

Unsolicited mss, synopses and ideas for books welcome.

Royalties paid twice-yearly.

Studio Editions
See **Random House UK Ltd**

Studio Vista
See **Cassell**

Subis
See **Sheffield Academic Press**

Summersdale Publishers

46 West Street, Chichester, West Sussex
PO19 1RP
☎01243 771107   Fax 01243 786300
Manager *Alastair Williams*

Editor *Stewart Ferris*

FOUNDED 1990. *Publishes* non-fiction: cookery, biography, gardening, sport (including martial arts/self defence), humour, self-improvement, travel, local interest, arts/entertainment. TITLES *The Student Grub Guide; How to Chat-up Men; 101 Ways to Spend Your Lottery Millions; Real Self Defence; Successful Relationships.* 30 titles in 1996. No unsolicited mss; initial approach by letter only. Keen to work with new authors with strong, marketable ideas.
Royalties paid.

Susquehanna University Press
See **Golden Cockerel Press**

Sutton Publishing Ltd
Phoenix Mill, Far Thrupp, Stroud, Gloucestershire GL5 2BU
☎01453 731114   Fax 01453 731117
Managing Director *David Hogg*
Publishing Director *Peter Clifford*
Approx. Annual Turnover £3 million

FOUNDED 1978. Owned by Guernsey Press. *Publishes* academic, archaeology, biography, countryside, history, regional interest, local history, pocket classics (lesser known novels by classic authors), topography, transport, travel. About 240 titles a year. Send synopses rather than complete mss.
Royalties paid twice-yearly.

Swan Hill Press
See **Airlife Publishing Ltd**

Sweet & Maxwell Ltd
100 Avenue Road, London NW3 3PF
☎0171 393 7000   Fax 0171 393 7010
Managing Director *Chris Blake*
Publishing Director *Carol Tullo*

FOUNDED 1799. Part of The Thomson Corporation. *Publishes* legal and professional materials in all media, looseleaf works, journals, law reports and on CD-ROM. About 150 book titles a year, with live backlist of over 700 titles, 75 looseleaf services and more than 80 legal periodicals. Not interested in material which is non-legal. The legal and professional list is varied and contains many academic titles, as well as treatises and reference works in the legal and related professional fields.

IMPRINTS
Sweet & Maxwell; **Sweet & Maxwell Asia**; **Stevens** *Carol Tullo;* **W. Green (Scotland)**; **Round Hall/Sweet & Maxwell (Ireland)**

Anthony Kinahan (Managing Director). Ideas welcome. Writers with legal/professional projects in mind are advised to contact the company at the earliest possible stage in order to lay the groundwork for best design, production and marketing of a project.
Royalties and fees vary according to contract.

Take That Ltd
PO Box 200, Harrogate, North Yorkshire HG1 4XB
☎01423 507545   Fax 01423 507545
Chairman/Managing Director *C. Brown*

FOUNDED 1986. Independent publisher of computing, business, humour and gambling titles (books and magazines). TITLES *The Hangover Handbook; Playing Lotteries For the Big Money; Tax Loopholes; Complete Beginner's Guide to the Internet.* About 10 titles a year. Unsolicited mss for books welcome - any humour titles should be heavily illustrated.
Royalties paid twice-yearly.

Tango Books
See **Sadie Fields Productions Ltd** under **UK Packagers**

I. B. Tauris & Co. Ltd
Victoria House, Bloomsbury Square, London WC1B 4DZ
☎0171 916 1069   Fax 0171 916 1068
Chairman/Publisher *Iradj Bagherzade*
Editorial Director *Anna Enayat*

FOUNDED 1984. Independent publisher. *Publishes* general non-fiction and academic in the fields of international relations, current affairs, history, cultural studies, Middle East, East-West relations, Russia and East European studies. Joint projects with Cambridge University Centre for Middle Eastern Studies, Institute for Latin American Studies and Institute of Ismali Studies. *Distributes* The New Press (New York) outside North America. IMPRINTS **Tauris Parke Books** Illustrated books on architecture, travel, design and culture. **British Academic Press** Academic monographs. TITLES *Beginning with My Street* Czeslaw Milosz; *Who's Who in Russia and the New States* ed. Alex Pravda. Unsolicited mss, synopses and ideas for books welcome.
Royalties paid twice-yearly.

Tavistock Publications
See **Routledge**

Taxation Publishing
See **Tolley Publishing Co. Ltd**

Taylor & Francis Group

1 Gunpowder Square, London EC4A 3DE
☎0171 583 0490   Fax 0171 583 9581
Chairman *Mrs Elnora Ferguson*
Managing Director *Anthony Selvey*
Approx. Annual Turnover £23 million

FOUNDED 1798 with the launch of *Philosophical Magazine* which has been in publication ever since (now a solid state physics journal). The company is privately owned with strong academic connections among the major shareholders. **Falmer Press** (see entry) joined the group in 1979 and it doubled its size in the late '80s with the acquisition of Crane Russak in 1986 and Hemisphere Publishing Co in 1988. In 1995, acquired Erlbaum Associates Ltd, adding to the growing list of psychology publications. *Publishes* scientific, technical, education titles at university, research and professional levels. About 250 titles a year.Unsolicited mss, synopses and ideas welcome.

Royalties paid yearly. *Overseas office* Taylor & Francis Inc., Washington DC.

Authors' Rating A Queen's Award for Export Achievement is acknowledgement of the remarkable fact that 85% of Taylor & Francis's turnover comes from overseas.

Teach Yourself

See **Hodder Headline plc**

Telegraph Books

1 Canada Square, Canary Wharf, London E14 5DT
☎0171 538 6824   Fax 0171 538 6064
Owner *The Telegraph plc*
Manager *Vicky Unwin*
Approx. Annual Turnover £700,000

Concentrates on Telegraph branded books in association/collaboration with other publishers. *Publishes* general non-fiction: journalism, business and law, cookery, education, gardening, wine, guides, sport, puzzles and games, maps. 38 titles in 1995. Only interested in books if a Telegraph link exists. No unsolicited material.
Royalties paid twice-yearly.

Tellastory

See **Random House UK Ltd**

Temple House Books

See **The Book Guild Ltd**

Test Your Child

See **Hodder Headline plc**

Thames and Hudson Ltd

30-34 Bloomsbury Street, London WC1B 3QP
☎0171 636 5488   Fax 0171 636 4799
Managing Director *Thomas Neurath*
Editorial Head *Jamie Camplin*

Publishes art, archaeology, architecture and design, biography, crafts, fashion, garden and landscape design, graphics, history, illustrated and fine editions, mythology, music, photography, popular culture, travel and topography. Over 150 titles a year. SERIES *World of Art; New Horizons; Chic Simple; Celtic Design; Sacred Symbols; World Design.* TITLES *Claude Monet 1840-1926; Colour and Culture; David Hockney: A Drawing Retrospective; Derek Jarman's Garden; The Shock of the New; Chronicle of the Roman Emperors; Streetstyle; The Book of Kells; The Most Beautiful Villages of Tuscany; Victor Papanek: The Green Imperative; The Graphic Language of Neville Brody 1 & 2; The Body; The Story of Writing.* Send preliminary letter and outline before mss.
Royalties paid twice-yearly.

Authors' Rating Thames & Hudson thrives with its wonderfully accessible *World of Art* series accumulating sales of over 23 million copies.

Thames Publishing

14 Barlby Road, London W10 6AR
☎0181 969 3579   Fax 0181 969 1465
Publishing Manager *John Bishop*

FOUNDED 1970. *Publishes* music, and books about English music and musicians (not pop). About 4 titles a year. No unsolicited mss; send synopses and ideas in first instance.

Thomas and Lochar

See **House of Lochar**

Stanley Thornes (Publishers) Ltd

Ellenborough House, Wellington Street, Cheltenham, Gloucestershire GL50 1YD
☎01242 228888   Fax 01242 221914
Managing Director *David Smith*
Approx. Annual Turnover £17 million

FOUNDED 1972. Part of the Wolters-Kluwer Group. Merged with Mary Glasgow Publications in 1992. *Publishes* secondary school and college curriculum textbooks and primary school resources. About 200 titles a year. Unsolicited mss, synopses and ideas for books welcome if appropriate to specialised list.

IMPRINTS **Stam Press** technical books; **Mary Glasgow Publications** foreign-language teaching materials and teacher support.
Royalties paid annually.

Thorsons
See **HarperCollins Publishers Ltd**

Threshold Books
See **Kenilworth Press Ltd**

Times Books
See **HarperCollins Publishers Ltd**

Times Mirror International Publishers Ltd
Lynton House, 7-12 Tavistock Square,
London WC1H 9LB
☎0171 388 7676   Fax 0171 391 6555
President *Timothy Hailstone*
Vice-President of Publishing *Fiona Foley*
Approx. Annual Turnover £22 million

Part of Times Mirror Co., Los Angeles.
Acquired Wolfe Publishing at the beginning of
the 90s, broadening its horizon from the core
list of books and journals for nurses to a list
which now includes colour atlases and texts in
medicine, dentistry and veterinary science.
IMPRINTS **Richard D. Irwin**; **Irwin
Professional Publishing**; **Mosby**; **Mosby
Wolfe Publishing**; **CRC Press**; **WCB
Brown** TITLES *Handbook of Chemistry &
Physics; A Colour Atlas of Human Anatomy;
1995 Nursing Drug Reference; Guy's Hospital.*
Synopses and ideas for books welcome.
Royalties paid twice-yearly.

Sitan Books
42-44 Dolben Street, London SE1 0UP
☎0171 620 0200   Fax 0171 620 0032
Managing Director *Nick Landau*
Editorial Director *Katy Wild*

FOUNDED 1981. Now a leader in the publication of graphic novels and in film and television tie-ins. *Publishes* comic books/graphic
novels, cartoon strips, film and television titles,
science fiction and fantasy, true crime. About
70-80 titles a year.
IMPRINTS **Titan Books**; **Mondo** True
crime and the bizarre extremes of human
behaviour; **Eros Plus** Erotic fiction. TITLES
*Batman; Superman; Star Trek; Dr Who; Beginners
Guide to Japanese Animation; Star Wars; Guide to
Monster Make-up.* No unsolicited fiction or
children's books please. Ideas for film and TV
titles considered; send synopsis/outline with
sample chapter. Author guidelines available.
Royalties paid twice-yearly.

Tolkein
See **HarperCollins Publishers Ltd**

Tolley Publishing Co. Ltd
Tolley House, 2 Addiscombe Road, Croydon,
Surrey CR9 5AF
☎0181 686 9141   Fax 0181 686 3155
Chairman *G. J. S. Wilson*
Managing Director *Harry L. King*

Owned by United News & Media plc, pub-
lishers of the *Daily Express, Sunday Express* and
Daily Star. Publishes taxation, accounting, legal,
business, technical and professional books.
DIVISIONS **Tolley Publishing; Charles
Knight Publishing; Benn Technical
Books; Taxation Publishing; Fourmat
Publishing; Finborough Seminars; Payroll
Alliance.** Unsolicited mss, synopses and ideas
welcome.

Transworld Publishers Ltd
61-63 Uxbridge Road, London W5 5SA
☎0181 579 2652   Fax 0181 579 5479
Managing Director *Mark Barty-King*

FOUNDED 1950. A subsidiary of **Bantam,
Doubleday, Dell Publishing Group Inc.,**
New York, which is a wholly-owned subsidiary of Bertelsmann AG, Germany. *Publishes*
general fiction and non-fiction, children's
books, sports and leisure.

DIVISIONS
Adult Trade *Patrick Janson-Smith* **Adult
Hardback** *Ursula Mackenzie* **Adult Paperback**
Tony Mott IMPRINTS **Bantam** *Francesca Liversidge*;
Bantam Press *Sally Gaminara*; **Black Swan** *Bill
Scott-Kerr*; **Doubleday** *Marianne Velmans*;
Partridge Press *Debbie Beckerman.* AUTHORS
Catherine Cookson, Jilly Cooper, Nicholas
Evans, Frederick Forsyth, Elizabeth George,
Robert Goddard, Stephen Hawking, Terry
Pratchett, Danielle Steel, Joanna Trollope, Mary
Wesley.
   Children's & Young Adult Books *Philippa
Dickinson* IMPRINTS **Doubleday** (hardcover);
**Picture Corgi; Corgi Pups; Young Corgi;
Corgi Yearling; Corgi; Corgi Freeway**
(paperback imprints); **Bantam** (paperback).
AUTHORS Malorie Blackman, Peter Dickinson,
Francine Pascal, K. M. Peyton, Terry Prachett,
Robert Swindells, Jacqueline Wilson. Unsoli-
cited mss welcome only if preceded by prelimi-
nary letter.
   Royalties paid twice-yearly. *Overseas associates*
Transworld Australia/New Zealand, Trans-
South Africa Book Distributors.

Authors' Rating The latest to join the great
and the good who subscribe to the Minimum
Terms Agreement for authors, Transworld con-

tinues its run of success with Bantam doing particularly well as a front-line fiction publisher. It helps to have Stephen Hawking on the list. For the second year running Transworld topped the *Guardian* fastseller list - the best guide to mass paperback performance. So far, Transworld has relied on organic growth but there are hints that acquisitions may be in the offing and that there are ambitions to balance the popular books with a literary list.

Trentham Books Ltd

Westview House, 734 London Road, Stoke on Trent, Staffordshire ST4 5NP
☎01782 745567   Fax 01782 745553
Chairman/Managing Director *Dr John Eggleston*
Editorial Head *Gillian Klein*
Approx. Annual Turnover £500,000

Publishes education (nursery, school and higher), social sciences, intercultural studies, design and technology education for professional readers *not* for children and parents. No fiction. About 25 titles a year. Unsolicited mss, synopses and ideas welcome if relevant to their interests.
Royalties paid annually.

Triangle

See **Society for Promoting Christian Knowledge**

Trotman & Co. Ltd

12 Hill Rise, Richmond, Surrey TW10 6UA
☎0181 940 5668   Fax 0181 948 9267
Managing Director *Andrew Fiennes Trotman*
Publishing Director *Morfydd Jones*
Approx. Annual Turnover £2.5 million

Publishes general careers books, higher education guides, teaching support material, employment training. About 70 titles a year. TITLES *Complete Degree Course Offers* (book and CD-ROM); *How to Complete Your UCAS Form; Students' Money Matters*. Unsolicited material welcome. Also active in the educational resources market, producing recruitment brochures.
Royalties paid twice-yearly.

Two-Can Publishing Ltd

346 Old Street, London EC1V 9NQ
☎0171 613 3376   Fax 0171 613 3371
Chairman *Andrew Jarvis*
Marketing Director *Ian Grant*
Creative Director *Sara Lynn*

Approx. Annual Turnover £4 million

FOUNDED 1987 to publish innovative, high-quality material for children. *Publishes* books and magazines, including *Young Telegraph* (weekend supplement for 9–12-year-olds).
DIVISIONS **Books** *Ian Grant*; **Magazines** *Andrew Jarvis*. No unsolicited mss; send synopses and ideas in the first instance.
Royalties paid twice-yearly.

UCL Press Ltd

University College London, Gower Street, London WC1E 6BT
☎0171 380 7707   Fax 0171 413 8392
Chairman *Alexander Smith*
Publisher/Chief Executive *R. F. J. Jones*

FOUNDED 1991. *Publishes* academic books only. About 80 titles a year. No unsolicited mss; synopses and ideas welcome.
Royalties paid annually.

University Presses of California, Columbia & Princeton Ltd

1 Oldlands Way, Bognor Regis, West Sussex PO22 9SA
☎01243 842165   Fax 01243 842167

Publishes academic titles only. US-based editorial offices. Over 200 titles a year. Enquiries only.

Unwin Hyman

See **HarperCollins Publishers Ltd**

Usborne Publishing Ltd

83–85 Saffron Hill, London EC1N 8RT
☎0171 430 2800   Fax 0171 430 1562
Managing Director *Peter Usborne*
Editorial Director *Jenny Tyler*
Approx. Annual Turnover £14 million

FOUNDED 1973. *Publishes* non-fiction, fiction, puzzle books and music for children and young adults. Some titles for parents. Up to 100 titles a year. Also, **Usborne Books at Home** imprint, based at Oasis Park, Eynsham, Oxford OX8 1TU. Books are written in-house to a specific format, therefore unsolicited mss not normally welcome. Ideas which may be developed in-house considered. Keen to hear from new illustrators and designers.
Royalties paid twice-yearly.

Authors' Rating 21 years in the business of 'making books that children want to read' has given the Usborne imprint a distinctive, busy look recognisable in the bookshops at several yards. Most of the writing is done by in-house editors but there may be more opportunities for outsiders now that Usborne has launched a fiction list to run alongside the information books. Strong on direct selling.

Vallentine Mitchell
See **Frank Cass & Co Ltd**

Variorum
See **Ashgate Publishing Co. Ltd**

Ventura
See **Penguin Books Ltd**

Vermilion
See **Random House UK Ltd**

Verso
6 Meard Street, London W1V 3HR
☎0171 434 1704/437 3546
Fax 0171 734 0059
Chairman *Lucy Heller*
Managing Director *Colin Robinson*
Approx. Annual Turnover £1.7 million
Formerly New Left Books which grew out of the *New Left Review*. Publishes politics, history, sociology, economics, philosophy, cultural studies, feminism. No memoirs. TITLES *Theatres of Memory* Raphael Samuel; *The Enemy Within* Seumas Milne; *For the Sake of Argument* Christopher Hitchens; *City of Quartz* Mike Davis; *Senseless Acts of Beauty* George McKay; *Anyone but England* Mike Marqusee; *Dialectic* Roy Bhaskar; *Year 501* Noam Chomsky; *Ideology* Terry Eagleton. No unsolicited mss; synopses and ideas for books welcome.
Royalties paid annually. *Overseas office* in New York.
Authors' Rating Dubbed by *The Bookseller* as 'one of the most successful small independent publishers'.

Viking/Viking Children's
See **Penguin Books Ltd**

Vintage
See **Random House UK Ltd**

Virago Press
Little, Brown & Co. (UK), Brettenham House, Lancaster Place, London WC2E 7EN
☎0171 911 8000   Fax 0171 911 8100
Publisher *Lennie Goodings*
Approx. Annual Turnover £2.75 million
FOUNDED 1973 by Carmen Callil, with the aim of publishing a wide range of books which illuminate and celebrate all aspects of women's lives. Bought by **Little, Brown & Co. (UK)** in 1996. Most titles are published in paperback; a distin-

guished reprint list makes up one third of these, with two thirds original titles commissioned across a wide range of interest: autobiography, biography, crime, fiction, history, social issues, politics, psychology, women's studies. About 50 titles a year. TITLES *Oyster 2000* Janette Turner; *Hospital, Two or The Book of Twins and Doubles* Penelope Farmer. Telephone before sending unsolicited material.
Royalties paid twice-yearly.

Authors' Rating Beset by boardroom quarrels and the departure of key staff, Virago went through a savage cost-cutting exercise before submitting to a purchase by Little, Brown. Where this pioneer feminist publisher goes from here is still unsure.

Virgin Publishing
332 Ladbroke Grove, London W10 5AH
☎0181 968 7554   Fax 0181 968 0929
Chairman *Robert Devereux*
Managing Director *Robert Shreeve*
Approx. Annual Turnover £10 million
The Virgin Group's book publishing company. *Publishes* non-fiction, fiction and large-format illustrated books on entertainment and popular culture, particularly TV tie-ins and books about film, showbiz, sport, music, biography, autobiography, popular reference and humour. No poetry, short stories, individual novels, cartoons.
IMPRINTS Non-fiction: **Virgin** *Mal Peachey* Sport, music biography; *Rod Green* Humour, film, TV tie-ins; *Philip Dodd* Illustrated books on all above subjects. Fiction: **Virgin**; **Doctor Who**; **Black Lace**; **Nexus** Branded series of genre novels. Publisher *Peter Darvill-Evans*. Series editors: *Kerri Sharp* (erotica, crime), *Rebecca Levene* (science fiction).
Royalties paid twice-yearly.

Authors' Rating A much revitalised operation is making a bid for the popular market with series such as Black Lace erotic fiction aimed at women readers.

Volcano Press Ltd
PO Box 139, Leicester LE2 2YH
☎0116 2706714   Fax 0116 2706714
Chairman *F. Hussain*
Managing Director *A. Hussain*
FOUNDED 1992. *Publishes* academic non-fiction in the following areas: Islam, women's studies, human rights, Middle East, strategic studies and cultural studies. About 15 titles a year. TITLES *The Sociology of Islamic Fundamentalism; Islam in Britain; Islamic Fundamentalism in Britain; Women in the Islamic Struggle.* No unsolicited

mss; synopses and ideas welcome. No fiction, poetry or plays.

Royalties paid twice-yearly.

University of Wales Press
6 Gwennyth Street, Cathays, Cardiff CF2 4YD
☎01222 231919   Fax 01222 230908

Director *E. M. Thomas*
Approx. Annual Turnover £350,000

FOUNDED 1922. *Publishes* academic and scholarly books in English and Welsh, particularly humanities, modern languages and social sciences, and scholarly Celtic works. 60 titles in 1995.

IMPRINTS **GPC Books**; **Gwasg Prifysgol Cymru**; **University of Wales Press**. TITLES *The Literature of Wales - A Pocket Guide* Dafydd Johnston; *A History of Money: From Ancient Times to the Present Day* Glyn Davies; *The Anglo-Irish Agreement* Arwel Ellis Owen. Unsolicited mss considered.

Royalties paid annually; more frequently by negotiation.

Walker Books Ltd
87 Vauxhall Walk, London SE11 5HJ
☎0171 793 0909   Fax 0171 587 1123

Editors *Caroline Royds, Sally Christie, Jacqui Bailey, Lucy Ingrams, Sally Foord-Kelcey, Lesley-Anne Daniels, Sara Carroll, Lisa Riley*
Approx. Annual Turnover £23 million

FOUNDED 1979. *Publishes* illustrated children's books and children's fiction. About 300 titles a year. TITLES *Where's Wally?* Martin Handford; *Five Minutes' Peace* Jill Murphy; *Can't You Sleep, Little Bear?* Martin Waddell & Barbara Firth; *Guess How Much I Love You* Sam McBratney & Anita Jeram; *MapHead* Lesley Howarth. Unsolicited mss welcome.

Royalties paid twice-yearly.

Authors' Rating The strength is in picture books for the very young but the fiction list is developing strongly. Authors praise the friendly and efficient editors and designers. Walker has a profit-share scheme which benefits staff, illustrators and writers.

Ward Lock
See **Cassell**

Ward Lock Educational Co. Ltd
1 Christopher Road, East Grinstead, West Sussex RH19 3BT
☎01342 318980   Fax 01342 410980

Owner *Ling Kee (UK Ltd)*

Director *Vincent Winter*
Editor (Maths, Science, Geography) *Rose Hill*
Editor (English) *Diane Biston*

FOUNDED 1952. *Publishes* educational books (primary, middle, secondary, teaching manuals) for all subjects, specialising in maths, science, geography, reading and English.

Royalties paid annually.

Frederick Warne
See **Penguin Books Ltd**

Warner
See **Little, Brown & Co. (UK)**

Warner Chappell Plays Ltd
See under **UK Agents**

Waterline Books
See **Airlife Publishing Ltd**

The Watts Publishing Group
96 Leonard Street, London EC2A 4RH
☎0171 739 2929   Fax 0171 739 2318

Managing Director *Marlene Johnson*

Part of Hachette SA. *Publishes* general non-fiction, reference, information and children's (fiction, picture and novelty). About 300 titles a year.

IMPRINTS **Watts Books** *Philippa Stewart* Non-fiction and information; **Orchard Books** *Francesca Dow* Children's fiction, picture and novelty books. Unsolicited mss, synopses and ideas for books welcome.

Royalties paid twice-yearly. *Overseas associates* in Australia and New Zealand, US and Canada.

Authors' Rating Investment in marketing, including a new schools sales force, has led to an increased market share despite unfavourable conditions.

Wayland Publishers Ltd
61 Western Road, Hove, East Sussex BN3 1JD
☎01273 722561   Fax 01273 329314

Managing Director *David Smith*
Editorial Director *Stephen White-Thomson*
Approx. Annual Turnover £6 million

Part of the Wolters Kluwer Group. FOUNDED 1969. *Publishes* a broad range of subjects particularly colour-illustrated non-fiction for children of 5 years and upwards. About 300 titles a year. No unsolicited mss or synopses as all books are commissioned.

Royalties paid annually. *Overseas associates* Thomson Learning Inc., USA.

Weidenfeld & Nicolson Ltd
See **The Orion Publishing Group Ltd**

Wharncliffe Publishing Ltd
47 Church Street, Barnsley, South Yorkshire
S70 2AS
☎01226 734222   Fax 01226 734438
Chairman *Sir Nicholas Hewitt*
Managing Director *T. G. Hewitt*

Part of Barnsley Chronicle Holdings Ltd.
Wharncliffe is the book and magazine publishing
arm of an old-established, independently owned
newspaper publishing and printing house.
Publishes local and regional interest and activities,
field sports and related material. Unsolicited mss,
synopses and ideas welcome but return postage
must be included with all submissions.
  Royalties paid twice-yearly. *Associated company* **Leo Cooper/Pen & Sword Books Ltd.**

Which? Books/
Consumers' Association
2 Marylebone Road, London NW1 4DF
☎0171 830 6000   Fax 0171 830 7660
Director *Sheila McKechnie*
Head of Publishing *Gill Rowley*

FOUNDED 1957. Publishing arm of the consumer organisation, a registered charity. *Publishes*
non-fiction: information, reference and how-to
books on travel, gardening, health, personal
finance, consumer law, food, education, crafts,
DIY. Titles must offer direct value or utility to
the UK consumer. 25-30 titles a year.
  IMPRINT **Which? Books** *Gill Rowley* TITLES
*Good Food Guide; Good Skiing Guide; Good Walks
Guide; Which? Travel Guides; Which? Consumer
Guides.* No unsolicited mss; send synopses and
ideas only.
  Royalties paid twice-yearly; but owing to in-
house editorial development of many titles,
royalties are not always applicable.

Whittet Books Ltd
18 Anley Road, London W14 0BY
☎0171 603 1139   Fax 0171 603 8154
Managing Director *Annabel Whittet*

Publishes natural history, pets, horses, rural
interest and transport. Unsolicited mss, synopses and ideas for books welcome.
  Royalties paid twice-yearly.

Whurr Publishers Ltd
19B Compton Terrace, London N1 2UN
☎0171 359 5979   Fax 0171 226 5290
Chairman/Managing Director *Colin Whurr*

Approx. Annual Turnover £1 million

FOUNDED in 1987. Originally specialised in
publishing books and journals on disorders of
communication but now publishing in a number of academic and professional fields. *Publishes*
medical, nursing, psychology, psychotherapy,
business and management, dyslexia. No fiction
and general trade books. 11 titles in 1995.
Unsolicited mss, synopses and ideas welcome
within their specialist fields only.
  Royalties paid twice-yearly.

John Wiley & Sons Ltd
Baffins Lane, Chichester, West Sussex
PO19 1UD
☎01243 779777   Fax 01243 775878
Chairman *The Duke of Richmond*
Managing Director *Dr John Jarvis*
Publishing Director, STM Division
  Dr Michael Dixon
Publishing Director, Professional
  Division *Steven Mair*
Approx. Annual Turnover £42 million

FOUNDED 1807. US parent company. *Publishes*
professional, reference trade and text books,
scientific, technical and biomedical.

DIVISIONS
Behavioural & Professional Sciences
Richard Baggaley; **Physical Sciences** *Dr Ernest
Kirkwood*; **Biomedical & Natural Sciences**
Mike Davis; **Technology** *Rosemary Altoft, Ian
McIntosh*; **Wiley Chancery Law** *David Wilson*.
Unsolicited mss welcome, as are synopses and
ideas for books.
  Royalties paid annually.

Authors' Rating The latest recruit to the
ranks of the politically correct (a book about
intelligence was rejected because it made
'assertions that we find repellent') Wiley
has expanded into law, finance and management with the serious student very much in
mind.

Neil Wilson Publishing Ltd
Suite 303a, The Pentagon Centre,
36 Washington Street, Glasgow G3 8AZ
☎0141 221 1117   Fax 0141 221 5363
Chairman *Gordon Campbell*
Managing Director/Editorial Director
  Neil Wilson
Approx. Annual Turnover £225,000

FOUNDED 1992. *Publishes* Scottish interest and
history, biography, humour and hillwalking,
whisky and beer; also cookery and Irish interest.

About 10 titles a year. Unsolicited mss, synopses and ideas welcome. No fiction, politics, academic or technical.

Royalties paid twice-yearly.

Philip Wilson Publishers Ltd
143-149 Great Portland Street, London W1N 5FB
☎0171 436 4490   Fax 0171 436 4403
Chairman *Philip Wilson*
Managing Director *Antony White*

FOUNDED 1976. *Publishes* art, art history, antiques and collectables. 20 titles in 1995. DIVISIONS **Philip Wilson Publishers Ltd; Scala Books** *Anne Jackson*; **Flint River Press Ltd** *Bato Tomasevic*; **Sotheby's Publications** *Anne Jackson*.

Windrow & Greene Ltd
5 Gerrard Street, London W1V 7LJ
☎0171 287 4570   Fax 0171 494 0583
Managing Director *Alan Greene*
Editorial Director *Martin Windrow*

FOUNDED 1990 by ex-conglomerate refugees wanting to publish quality books in close consultation with authors. *Publishes* military history and hobbies, cars and motorcycling, aviation and transport, directories and specialist journals. About 28 titles a year. Unsolicited mss considered but synopses and ideas preferred in the first instance.

Royalties paid twice-yearly.

The Windrush Press
Little Window, High Street, Moreton in Marsh, Gloucestershire GL56 0LL
☎01608 652012/652025   Fax 01608 652125
Managing Director *Geoffrey Smith*
Editorial Head *Victoria Huxley*

FOUNDED 1987. Independent company. *Publishes* travel, biography, history, general, local interest. About 10 titles a year. TITLES *The Letters of Private Wheeler; Lanzarote: A Windrush Island Guide; A Traveller's History of China.* Send synopsis and letter with s.a.e..

Royalties paid twice-yearly.

Windsor Large Print
See **Chivers Press Ltd**

Wise
See **Omnibus Press**

Woburn Press
See **Frank Cass & Co Ltd**

Wolfe Publishing
See **Times Mirror International Publishers Ltd**

Oswald Wolff Books
See **Berg Publishers Ltd**

The Women's Press
34 Great Sutton Street, London EC1V 0DX
☎0171 251 3007   Fax 0171 608 1938
Publishing Director *Kathy Gale*
Approx. Annual Turnover £1 million

Part of the Namara Group. First title 1978. *Publishes* women only: quality fiction and non-fiction. Fiction usually has a female protagonist and a woman-centred theme. International writers and subject matter encouraged. Non-fiction: subjects of general interest, both practical and theoretical, to women generally; art books, feminist theory, health and psychology, literary criticism. About 50 titles a year. IMPRINTS **Women's Press Crime; Women's Press Handbooks Series; Livewire Books for Teenagers** *Laurie Critchley* Fiction and non-fiction series for young adults. Synopses and ideas for books welcome. No mss without previous letter, synopsis and sample material.

Royalties paid twice-yearly.

Woodhead Publishing Ltd
Abington Hall, Abington, Cambridge CB1 6AH
☎01223 891358   Fax 01223 893694
Chairman *Alan Jessup*
Managing Director *Martin Woodhead*
Approx. Annual Turnover £950,000

FOUNDED 1989. *Publishes* engineering, materials technology, finance and investment, food technology. TITLES *The TWI Journal* (welding research); *The International Grain/Nickel/Zinc/Tin/Silver Trade* series; *Foreign Exchange Options.* About 30 titles a year.

DIVISIONS **Woodhead Publishing** *Martin Woodhead*; **Abington Publishing** (in association with the Welding Institute) *Patricia Morrison*; **Gresham Books** (in association with the Chartered Institute of Bankers). Unsolicited material welcome.

Royalties paid annually.

Woodstock Books
The School House, South Newington, Banbury, Oxon OX15 4JJ
☎01295 720598   Fax 01295 720717
Chairman/Managing Director *James Price*
Approx. Annual Turnover £150,000

FOUNDED 1989. *Publishes* literary reprints only.

Main series: *Revolution and Romanticism, 1789–1834; Decadents, Symbolists, Anti-Decadents: Poetry of the 1890s; Literature and Nation in Victorian Ireland.* No unsolicited mss.

Wordsworth Editions Ltd
Cumberland House, Crib Street, Ware, Hertfordshire SG12 9ET
☎01920 465167   Fax 01920 462267
Editorial Office: 6 London Street, London W2 1HR.
☎0171 706 8822 Fax: 0171 706 8833
Directors *M. C. W. Trayler, E. G. Trayler*
Director/Editorial Head *C. M. Clapham*
Approx. Annual Turnover £7 million

FOUNDED 1987. *Publishes* reprints of English literature, paperback reference books, poetry, children's classics, women writers, classic erotica and American classics. About 150 titles a year. No unsolicited mss.

Authors' Rating A non-starter for living writers, Wordsworth is dedicated to high-run, low-cost editions of books everyone has heard of. The formula has proved a winner, particularly with young people, who don't mind paying a pound for required reading but resent the fiver charged by up-market publishers for essentially the same product.

World International Limited
Deanway Technology Centre, Wilmslow Road, Handforth, Cheshire SK9 3FB
☎01625 650011   Fax 01625 650040
Managing Director *Ian Findlay*
Creative Director *Michael Herridge*
Publishing Manager *Nina Filipek*

Part of the Egmont Group, Denmark. *Specialises* in children's books for home and international markets: activity, sticker, baby, early learning, novelty/character books and annuals. SERIES *Mr Men; Fun to Learn; I Can Learn; Learning Rewards.* 'Unsolicited material rarely used. World International does not accept responsibility for the return of unsolicited submissions.'

X Libris
See **Little Brown & Co. (UK)**

Y Lolfa Cyf
Talybont, Ceredigion SY24 5HE
☎01970 832304   Fax 01970 832782
Managing Directors *Robat and Enid Gruffudd*
Editor *Eiry Jones*
Approx. Annual Turnover £450,000

FOUNDED 1967. Small company which publishes mainly in Welsh. It handles all its own type-setting and printing. *Publishes* Welsh language publications; Celtic language tutors; English language books about Wales for the visitor; nationalism and sociology (English language). 30 titles in 1995. Expanding slowly. TITLES *Artists in Snowdonia* James Bogle; *The Welsh Learner's Dictionary* Heini Gruffudd; *Burning Down the Dosbarth* David Greenslade. Not interested in any English language books except political and Celtic. Write first with synopses or ideas.
Royalties paid twice-yearly.

Yale University Press (London)
23 Pond Street, London NW3 2PN
☎0171 431 4422   Fax 0171 431 3755
Managing Director/Editorial Director
John Nicoll

FOUNDED 1961. Owned by US parent company. *Publishes* academic and humanities. About 160 titles (worldwide) a year. Unsolicited mss and synopses welcome if within specialised subject areas.
Royalties paid annually.

Roy Yates Books
Smallfields Cottage, Cox Green, Rudgwick, Horsham, West Sussex RH12 3DE
☎01403 822299   Fax 01403 823012
Chairman/Managing Director *Roy Yates*
Approx. Annual Turnover £120,000

FOUNDED 1990. *Publishes* children's books only. No unsolicited material as books are adaptations of existing popular classics suitable for translation into dual-language format.
Royalties paid quarterly.

Zed Books Ltd
7 Cynthia Street, London N1 9JF
☎0171 837 4014   Fax 0171 833 3960
Approx. Annual Turnover £1 million

FOUNDED 1976. *Publishes* international and Third World affairs, development studies, women's studies, environmental studies, cultural studies and specific area studies. No fiction, children's or poetry. About 40 titles a year. DIVISIONS **Development & Environment** *Robert Molteno*; **Women's Studies, Cultural Studies** *Louise Murray.* TITLES *The Development Dictionary* ed. Wolfgang Sachs; *Staying Alive* Vandana Shiva; *The Hidden Face of Eve* Nawal el Saadawi. No unsolicited mss; synopses and ideas welcome though.
Royalties paid annually.

Zomba
See **Omnibus Press**

Biography as *Le Vice Anglais*

The enduring appeal of biography is one of the mysteries of publishing. Every bookshop has shelves stuffed with it. As a category in Whitaker's list it ranks with general fiction with over 3000 titles published last year.

The passion for biography is a trans-Atlantic phenomenon but one that is stronger in Britain than in America. It is only here, for example, that a publisher will put up good money to chronicle the life of a revered literary figure whose own work is little read. Last year, in a not untypical month, three books on Robert Graves were followed by a life of John Buchan, now best known for the Hitchcock film of his *39 Steps* and most remarkable of all, a study of F. R. Leavis, the curmudgeonly don who managed to persuade a generation of Cambridge undergraduates that literature stopped with D. H. Lawrence. All five books were generously reviewed and energetically marketed. Whether or not they sold in sufficient quantities to satisfy the publishers is unsure. But it is interesting that someone of editorial power must have thought they would sell.

There is more to biography than dead scribblers but it is right to focus on the literary sector since it was here that the current boom in life stories originated. Fifteen years ago, Christopher Sinclair-Stevenson advanced Richard Ellmann £35,000 to write a biography of Oscar Wilde. No one doubted that Ellmann was the man to do the job – his life of James Joyce had put him in the front rank of his profession – but this was to assume that the job needed to be done. Few believed that it was. Wilde had been worked over too often and too recently to justify a reprise.

In the event, Sinclair-Stevenson and Ellmann confounded the cynics. When *Oscar Wilde* finally appeared in 1987 it sold over 90,000 copies in hardback at £15 a copy. How come? That the book is cleverly constructed and gracefully written is undeniable but at 632 pages, say 250,000 words, it tells the general reader more than he could possibly want to know about Wilde and his circle. Maybe that was the conclusion of those who bought the book. In any event, the assumption of a correlation between the weight of a manuscript and its sales turned out to be grievously mistaken as Sinclair-Stevenson himself eventually discovered when Michael Holroyd's multi-volumed biography of George Bernard Shaw and Peter Ackroyd's doorstop volume on Charles Dickens stayed rooted in the bookshops.

But this is not to hedge on the popularity of lives compressed into more manageable tomes. Biographers have done well over the last decade winning enviable reputations and matching best-selling novelists on the scale of their advances.

Asked to explain their success, the lifers are disarmingly self-effacing. They could simply credit their amazing writing skills – and leave it at that. However, as one of the few who is prepared to delve deeper, Victoria Glendinning (Edith Sitwell, Vita Sackville-West, Rebecca West and Anthony Trollope) believes that the absence of any great body of British folk literature may help to account for the popularity of biography. 'Perhaps telling stories about people from the past, alias biography, has been, or has become, our folk literature, our folklore. We tend to personalise everything. There is a fascination with the character, personality and behaviour of prominent people which runs through our culture from high to popular.'

The spectrum stretches from biographies that 'illuminate not only distinguished persons but the work that they did and the society in which they lived' to scissors and paste jobs on film stars and sportsmen, 'biography as gossip' as Victoria Glendinning calls it. She sees no harm in this and much virtue. Biography, for Glendinning, is as much about our relation to the present as it is to the past:

'The instinct behind it is to hold the past in memory, not only for its own sake but in order to inspire, warn, structure or otherwise illuminate or manipulate the present – a reflective, reflexive aspect of biography, as of all history writing'.

Her view is endorsed and carried forward by Richard Holmes, biographer of Shelley, Johnson and Coleridge, who sees biography as one of the grand shaping forces of contemporary consciousness.

'By reconstructing a life through narrative, biography emphasises cause and consequence, the linked pattern of growth and change, the vivid story-line of individual responsibility and meaningful action. Biography is empirical and secular: not gospel, not hagiography, not hero-worship, not public relations. In studying the lives of others, we slowly learn the truth about ourselves. As Plutarch said, biography is a mirror to the age. We should be able to look into it freely, and without fear.'

Well, yes, up to a point. The high flying aspirations of the scholar biographer are less convincing when set in the context of publishing as an ordinary business enterprise out to make the most of its assets. Why, for example, are some subjects thought to be more biographically suited than others? A large number of those chosen are already deified by fame, recognisable to every bookshop browser.

It is no insult to Victoria Glendinning or Richard Holmes, both fine writers, to suggest that their popular appeal is enhanced by association with a name that everyone has heard of. A commonplace of publishing is that the sales of a biography are liable to benefit when it can ride in on the backs of several other books on exactly the same subject. This is why some characters (Dr Johnson and Lord Byron are each credited with over 200 biographies) are done to death.

This is also why, to reverse the Glendinning/Holmes argument, biography can distort rather than illuminate our knowledge of the world and of ourselves. Even accepting Thomas Carlyle's debatable proposition that history is 'nothing but the biographies of great men', it is manifestly not true that history comprises the *published* biographies of great men and women. Unless, of course, we are ready to accept a highly selective account of our heritage based entirely on current sales conditions in the book trade.

Biographies are published because they are easy – or easier – to sell. 'We can get behind a good biography with total commitment,' says Tim Waterstone, 'and really knock the hell out of it.' Biographies are more straightforward to produce too. Unlike a novel or a general work of non-fiction, the biography is an identifiable product before it is written. The potential market is clearly defined and can be primed well before publication.

The strength of market forces is such that a well-promoted life story of a famous figure can actually detract attention from the achievements that made him famous. Clearly, the risk is greatest with literary celebrities whose own books may slide into obscurity while their biographies live on. The Bloomsbury Group, George Orwell and Sylvia Plath, to choose at random, are almost certainly more read about than read.

Biography as an exercise in diverting the eye from the ball applies equally to figures in public life. An authoritative biography, weighed down with detailed scholarship, can be a powerful deterrent to the reappraisal of a leading politician. Lloyd George and Churchill have benefited thus. It is only recently that revisionist historians have felt bold enough to challenge the John Grigg or Martin Gilbert interpretation of events. The multi-volumes that purport to account for every waking moment in a great man's life are too easily assumed to be unchallengeable.

Biographers who pull punches have a persuasive excuse. To embark on a life with all the necessary enthusiasm and commitment is to fall in love a little with the subject. What irony it is that while biographers frequently complain of restraints on their freedom (the draconian libel laws, for example, or the thirty year rule restricting the publication of government papers) they are invariably their own strongest censors. This can work in subtle ways. Stopping short of telling the whole truth by the selective use of material or by actual suppression is a common feature of biography but more insidious is the way in which reputations are enhanced by lifting them out of context to protect them from rival claims to glory. Actors and writers are the chief beneficiaries. A biography of a film star or famous author can imply that all other contemporary actors or writers were so far off the sidelines as to be barely worth a mention.

As an agent of muddled thinking, the biographer as hero worshipper is only marginally more culpable than the biographer who offers up a revelation or two – invariably salacious – to whet the public appetite. A publisher signing up a writer to produce a life in print has two words of advice – 'Sex sells'. In a roundup of the last 15 years, Euan Ferguson recalls that 'we have learnt of Tchaikovsky's gay suicide, Larkin's onanism, Du Maurier's (and Jane Austen's) lesbianism; that Enid Blyton was emotionally dysfunctional, Graham Greene enjoyed sex on altars, and that Mahatma Gandhi's nights spent lying with two beautiful naked women – purportedly to prove the strength of his celibacy – were generally spent in much the same way as the rest of us would spend nights lying with two beautiful naked women'. Sex is a marketing ploy with a long tradition. Writing in 1934, theatre critic James Agate, who produced nine volumes of memoirs, noted that every current autobiography 'tells me at what age its author first practised masturbation, what at school he learned from his mates, and what in later life he taught his mistresses'.

Agate went on to assert that he had 'enough of Victorian fastidiousness to believe that [a man's] sex experiences should be kept to himself'. As a free range homosexual at a time when gay male sex was a crime, Agate did not, in truth, have any choice. But the question remains as to whether his observations on art and life – informed, witty and enlightening – would have gained from knowing more about his personal life. Probably not. Agate was more interesting for what he said about others than what he said about himself.

On the other hand, sex is a component of the truth. Without it, our knowledge of a life is necessarily incomplete. Getting the balance right is a tricky business. In her RSA lecture Victoria Glendinning said that she was only interested in writing about 'extraordinary people'. Where, one wonders, does this place Vita Sackville-West whose literary reputation was given a lift by Victoria Glendinning's biography which highlighted her unconventional sex life?

Maybe it is unfair to blame the biographer. A prurient readership is quick to detect the smut. It is hardly the fault of Fiona MacCarthy, who gave us a marvellous biography of Eric Gill, that the artist is now best remembered for having sex with his daughters and his dog.

For sheer readability, a good biography is hard to beat. It is an area of publishing in which British writers are pre-eminent, earning deserved credit abroad for extending the form beyond leaden academic studies. But the risk of biography getting above itself is increased by the decline of the literary novel as a force for imagination and the failure of publishers to realise that there is a market for books that put ideas before personalities.

Unless we correct the balance, the prospect is of a backward-looking culture in which, as A. S. Byatt has warned 'we substitute biography for thought'.

Irish Publishers

An Gúm

44 Sráid Uí Chonaill, Uacht, Dublin 1,
Republic of Ireland
☎00 353 1 8734700   Fax 00 353 1 8731140

Senior Editor *Caoimhín ó Marcaigh*

FOUNDED 1926. Publications branch of the
Department of Arts, Culture and the Gaellacht.
Established to provide general reading, textbooks and dictionaries in the Irish language.
Publishes educational, children's, music, lexi-
cography and general. Little fiction or poetry.
About 50 titles a year. Unsolicited mss, synopses and ideas for books welcome. Also welcomes reading copies of first and second level
school textbooks with a view to translating
them into the Irish language.
    Royalties paid annually.

Anvil Books

45 Palmerston Road, Dublin 6,
Republic of Ireland
☎00 353 1 4973628

Managing Director *Rena Dardis*

FOUNDED 1964 with the emphasis on Irish history and biography. Expansion of the list followed to include more general interest Irish
material and in 1982 The Children's Press was
established, making Anvil the first Irish publisher of mass-market children's books of Irish
interest. *Publishes* illustrated books, history,
biography (particularly 1916–22), folklore,
children's fiction (for ages 7–14) and quiz
books. No adult fiction or illustrated books for
children under 7. About 7 titles a year.
Unsolicited mss, synopses and ideas for books
welcome.

DIVISIONS
General TITLES *Guerilla Days in Ireland* Tom
Barry; *My Fight For Irish Freedom* Dan Breen;
The Workhouses of Ireland John O'Connor; *The
Norman Invasion of Ireland* Richard Roche; *On
Another Man's Wound* Ernie O'Malley. **The
Children's Press** TITLES *Young Champions*
Peter Regan; *The Secret of the Ruby Ring*
Yvonne MacGrory; *In Search of the Liberty Tree*
Tom McCaughren; *Best Friends* Pauline
Devine; *Dead Monks and Shady Deals* Mary
Arrigan.
    Royalties paid annually.

Attic Press Ltd

29 Upper Mount Street, Dublin 2,
Republic of Ireland
☎00 353 1 6616128   Fax 00 353 1 6616176

Publisher *Róisín Conroy*

FOUNDED 1988. Began life in 1984 as a forum
for information on the Irish feminist movement. *Publishes* adult and teenage fiction, and
non-fiction (history, women's studies, politics,
biography). About 22 titles a year. A second
imprint, **Basement Press**, was launched in
1994 to publish popular fiction and non-fiction
(politics, entertainment and information) by
men and women. Unsolicited mss, synopses
and ideas for books welcome. Not interested in
poetry or short stories.
    Royalties paid twice yearly.

Basement Press
See **Attic Press**

Beacon
See **Poolbeg Press Ltd**

Blackwater Press

c/o Folens Publishers, Broomhill Business
Park, Broomhill Road, Tallaght, Dublin 24,
Republic of Ireland
☎00 353 1 4515311   Fax 00 353 1 4515308

Chairman *Dirk Folens*
Managing Director *John O'Connor*

Part of Folens Publishers. *Publishes* political,
sports, fiction (*Anna O'Donovan*) and children's
(*Deidre Whelan*). 22 titles in 1995.

Boole Press

26 Temple Lane, Temple Bar, Dublin 2,
Republic of Ireland
☎00 353 1 6797655   Fax00 353 1 6792469

A division of AIC Ltd, Dublin. *Publishes* scientific and technical, medical, and conference
proceedings. About 2 titles a year.
    Royalties paid every two years.

Brandon Book Publishers Ltd

Dingle, Co. Kerry, Republic of Ireland
☎00 353 66 51463   Fax 00 353 66 51234

Managing Director *Bernie Goggin*

Approx. Annual Turnover £450,000

FOUNDED 1982 and in the 14 years since its inception Brandon has earned itself something of a reputation for new fiction authors and for challenging, often controversial, non-fiction. *Publishes* politics, biography, local history, children's, commercial and literary fiction. About 15 titles a year. Not interested in educational, scientific and technical or instruction material. Submit outlines with sample mss in the first instance. Ideas welcome.

Royalties paid annually.

Edmund Burke Publisher

Cloonagashel, 27 Priory Drive, Blackrock, Co. Dublin, Republic of Ireland
☎00 353 1 2882159   Fax 00 353 1 2834080
Chairman *Eamonn De Búrca*
Approx. Annual Turnover £100,000

Small family-run business publishing historical and topographical and fine limited-edition books relating to Ireland. TITLES *Irish Stuart Silver, Irish Names of Places* Joyce; *History of the Kingdom of Kerry* Cusack; *Scot's Mercenary Forces in Ireland* G. A. Hayes-McCoy; *The Dean's Friend* Alan Harrison; *Manners and Customs of the Ancient Irish* Eugene O'Curry. Unsolicited mss welcome. No synopses or ideas.

Royalties paid twice yearly.

Butterworth Ireland Limited

26 Upper Ormond Quay, Dublin 7, Republic of Ireland
☎00 353 1 8731555   Fax 00 353 1 8731876
Chairman *P. J. Robinson (UK)*
General Manager *Gerard Coakley*

Subsidiary of Butterworth & Co. Publishers, London, (Reed Elsevier is the holding company). *Publishes* solely law and tax books. Tax Editor *Susan Keegan*, Legal Editor *Louise Leavy*. 16 titles in 1995. Leading publisher of Irish law and tax titles. Unsolicited mss, synopses and ideas welcome for titles within the broadest parameters of tax and law.

Royalties paid twice yearly.

The Children's Press

See **Anvil Books**

Cló Iar-Chonnachta

Indreabhán, Connemara, Galway, Republic of Ireland
☎00 353 91 593307   Fax 00 353 91 593362
Chairman/Director *Micheál Ó Conghaile*

Editor *Nóirín Ní Ghrádaigh*
Approx. Annual Turnover £250,000

FOUNDED 1985. *Publishes* fiction, poetry, plays and children's, mostly in Irish but not exclusively. Also publishes cassettes of writers reading from their own works. 25 titles in 1995. Unsolicited mss, synopses and ideas for books welcome.

Royalties paid annually.

The Collins Press

Carey's Lane, The Huguenot Quarter, Cork, Republic of Ireland
☎00 353 21 271346   Fax 00 353 21 275489
Managing Director *Con Collins*

FOUNDED 1989. *Publishes* archaeology, fiction, history, photographic and travel guides. 3 titles in 1995. Unsolicited mss, synopses and ideas for books welcome. No poetry.

Royalties paid annually.

The Columba Press

Unit 55A Spruce Avenue, Stillorgan Industrial Park, Blackrock, Co. Dublin, Republic of Ireland
☎00 353 1 2942556   Fax 00 353 1 2942564
Chairman *Neil Kluepfel*
Managing Director *Seán O'Boyle*
Approx. Annual Turnover £750,000

FOUNDED 1985. Small company committed to growth. *Publishes* only religious titles. 30 titles in 1995. (Backlist of 225 titles.) TITLES *Nine Faces of God* Pat Collins; *Through the Year with George Otto Simms* Lesley Whiteside. Unsolicited ideas and synopses rather than full mss preferred.

Royalties paid twice yearly.

Cork University Press

University College, Cork, Co. Cork, Republic of Ireland
☎00 353 21 902980   Fax 00 353 21 273553
Managing Director *Sara Wilbourne*
Production Editor *Eileen O'Carroll*

FOUNDED 1925. Relaunched in 1992 the Press *publishes* academic and some trade titles. Plans to publish 20 titles in 1996. Two new bi-annual journals, *Graph*, an interdisciplinary cultural review, and *The Irish Journal of Feminist Studies*, are now part of the list. Unsolicited synopses and ideas welcome for textbooks, academic monographs, *belles lettres*, illustrated histories and journals.

Royalties paid annually.

Flyleaf Press

4 Spencer Villas, Glenageary, Co. Dublin,
Republic of Ireland
☎00 353 1 2806228   Fax 00 353 1 2830670

Managing Director *Dr James Ryan*

FOUNDED 1981 to publish natural history titles.
Now concentrating on family history and Irish
history as a background to family history. No fic-
tion. TITLES *Irish Records; Longford and its People;
Tracing Kerry Ancestors; Tracing Dublin's Ancestors.*
Unsolicited mss, synopses and ideas for books
welcome.
Royalties paid twice yearly.

Four Courts Press Ltd

Kill Lane, Blackrock, Co. Dublin,
Republic of Ireland
☎00 353 1 2892922   Fax 00 353 1 2893072

Chairman/Managing Director *Michael
Adams*
Approx. Annual Turnover £250,000

FOUNDED 1972. Has recently undergone major
changes with the expansion of its list. Art, film
studies (journals), and 17th- and 18th-century
history have been added to its existing list of
theology, philosophy, Welsh medieval history,
Celtic and medieval studies. Planning to expand into Scottish history. 15 titles in 1995.
Unsolicited mss, synopses and ideas for books
welcome.
Royalties paid annually.

Gill & Macmillan

Goldenbridge, Inchicore, Dublin 8,
Republic of Ireland
☎00 353 1 4531005   Fax 00 353 1 4541688

Managing Director *M. H. Gill*
Approx. Annual Turnover £4.5 million

FOUNDED 1968 when M. H. Gill & Son Ltd
and Macmillan Ltd formed a jointly owned
publishing company. *Publishes* biography/auto-
biography, history, current affairs, literary criticism (all mainly of Irish interest), guidebooks,
cookery, religion, theology, counselling/psy-
chology. Also professional books in law and
accountancy, and educational textbooks for
secondary and tertiary levels. About 100 titles a
year. Contacts: *Hubert Mahony* (educational);
Fergal Tobin (general); *Finola O'Sullivan* (professional); *Ailbhe O'Reilly* (tertiary textbooks).
Unsolicited synopses and ideas welcome. Not
interested in fiction or poetry.
Royalties paid subject to contract.

Institute of Public Administration

57-61 Lansdowne Road, Dublin 4,
Republic of Ireland
☎00 353 1 2697011   Fax 00 353 1 2698644

Chairman *Denis Lucey*
Director General *John Gallagher*
Publisher *Jim O'Donnell*
Approx. Annual Turnover £450,000

FOUNDED 1957 by a group of public servants,
the Institute of Public Administration is the
Irish public sector management development
agency. The publishing arm of the organisation
is one of its major activities. *Publishes* academic
and professional books and periodicals: history,
law, politics, economics and Irish public
administration for students and practitioners. 8
titles in 1995. TITLES *Administration Yearbook &
Diary; Personnel & Industrial Relations Directory;
Your Rights at Work; Decentralisation.* No unsolicited mss; synopses and ideas welcome. No
fiction or children's publishing.
Royalties paid annually.

Irish Academic Press Ltd

Kill Lane, Blackrock, Co. Dublin,
Republic of Ireland
☎00 353 1 2892922   Fax 00 353 1 2893072

Chairman *Frank Cass (London)*
Managing Editor *Michael Adams*
Approx. Annual Turnover £250,000

FOUNDED 1974. *Publishes* academic mono-
graphs and humanities. 14 titles in 1995.
Unsolicited mss, synopses and ideas welcome.
Royalties paid annually.

Irish Management Institute

Sandyford Road, Dublin 16,
Republic of Ireland
☎00 353 1 2956911   Fax 00 353 1 2955150

Chief Executive *Barry Kenny*
Approx. Annual Turnover £8 million

FOUNDED 1952. The Institute is owned by its
members (individual and corporate) and its major
activities involve management education, training and development. The book publishing arm
of the organisation was established in 1970.
Publishes management practice, interpersonal
skills and aspects of national macroeconomics.
TITLES *The Economy of Ireland; Practical Finance;
Pricing For Results; Personnel Management.* Unsolicited mss welcome provided that any case
material is relevant to Irish management practice.
Synopses and ideas also welcome.
Royalties paid annually.

The Lilliput Press

4 Rosemount Terrace, Arbour Hill, Dublin 7,
Republic of Ireland
☎00 353 1 6711647   Fax 00 353 1 6711647
Chairman *Terence Brown*
Managing Director *Antony Farrell*
Approx. Annual Turnover £180,000

FOUNDED 1984. *Publishes* non-fiction: literary,
history, autobiography and biography, ecology,
essays; fiction and poetry. About 20 titles a year.
TITLES *Beckett in Dublin* (essays); *Seventy Years
Young* (memoir); *The Growth Illusion* (ecology);
The Great Famine (history); *Trees of Ireland; North
of Naples, South of Rome; Stones of Aran*. Unsolicited mss, synopses and ideas welcome. No
children's or sport titles.
Royalties paid annually.

Marino Books

See **Mercier Press Ltd**

Mercier Press Ltd

PO Box No 5, 5 French Church Street, Cork,
Republic of Ireland
☎00 353 021 275040 Fax 00 353 021 274969
Chairman *George Eaton*
Managing Director *John F. Spillane*

FOUNDED 1944. One of Ireland's largest publishers with a list of approx 250 Irish interest titles
and a smaller range of religious titles. *Publishes*
alternative lifestyle, folklore, women's interest,
popular psychology, dual language, children's,
cookery, history, politics, poetry and fiction. No
academic books. IMPRINTS **Mercier Press** *Mary
Feehan* **Marino Books** *Jo O'Donoghue*. 25 titles
in 1995. TITLES *The Course of Irish History; The
Field; Irish High Crosses; Irish Myths & Legends;
Alternative Loves; The Great Irish Famine; A Short
History of Ireland*. Unsolicited mss, synopses/ideas
welcome.
Royalties paid annually.

The O'Brien Press Ltd

20 Victoria Road, Rathgar, Dublin 6,
Republic of Ireland
☎00 353 1 4923333   Fax 00 353 1 4922777
Chairman/Managing Director *Michael
O'Brien*
Editorial Director *Íde Ní Laoghaire*

FOUNDED 1974 to publish biography and books
on the environment. In recent years the company has become a substantial force in children's
publishing, concentrating mainly on juvenile
novels and non-fiction in the craft and history
areas. Also *publishes* business, adult fiction, popu-

lar biography, music and travel. No poetry or
academic. About 30 titles a year. Unsolicited mss
(with return postage enclosed), synopses and
ideas for books welcome.
Royalties paid annually.

Oak Tree Press

Merrion Building, Lower Merrion Street,
Dublin 2, Republic of Ireland
☎00 351 1 6761600   Fax 00 351 1 6761644
Managing Director *Brian O'Kane*

FOUNDED 1992. Part of Cork Publishing.
Specialist publisher of business and professional
books: accounting, finance, management and
law, aimed at students and practitioners in
Ireland and the UK. About 25 titles a year.
TITLES *Accounting Standards; Winning Business
Proposals; The European Handbook of Management
Consultancy; Personal Finance; Understanding
Services Management*. Unsolicited mss and syn-
opses welcome.
Royalties paid twice in the first year and
annually thereafter.

On Stream Publications Ltd

Cloghroe, Blarney, Co. Cork,
Republic of Ireland
☎00 353 21 385798   Fax 00 353 21 385798
Chairman/Managing Director *Roz Crowley*
Approx. Annual Turnover £50,000

FOUNDED 1992. Formerly Forum Publications.
Publishes cookery, wine, general health and fit-
ness, local history, railways, photography and
practical guides. About 3 titles a year. TITLES
Tom Doorley Uncorked!; The Examiner Cookbook.
Unsolicited mss, synopses and ideas welcome.
No children's books.
Royalties paid twice yearly.

Poolbeg Press Ltd

123 Baldoyle Industrial Estate, Baldoyle,
Dublin 13, Republic of Ireland
☎00 353 1 832 1477   Fax 00 353 1 832 1430
Managing Director *Philip MacDermott*
Approx. Annual Turnover £1,000,000

FOUNDED 1976 to publish the Irish short story
and has since diversified to include all areas of
fiction (literary and popular), children's fiction
and non-fiction, and adult non-fiction: history,
biography and topics of public interest. About
100 titles a year. Unsolicited mss, synopses and
ideas welcome (mss preferred). No drama.
IMPRINTS **Poolbeg** (paperback and hardback); **Children's Poolbeg**; **Beacon**.
Royalties paid bi-annually.

Real Ireland Design Ltd

27 Beechwood Close, Boghall Road, Bray,
Co. Wicklow, Republic of Ireland
☎00 353 1 2860799   Fax 00 353 1 2829962

Managing Director *Desmond Leonard*

Producers of calendars, diaries, posters, greeting cards and books, servicing the Irish tourist industry. *Publishes* photography, cookery and tourism. About 2 titles a year. No fiction. Unsolicited mss, synopses and ideas welcome.

Royalties paid twice yearly.

Relay Publications

Tyone, Nenagh, Co. Tipperary,
Republic of Ireland
☎00 353 67 31734

Managing Director *Donal A. Murphy*

FOUNDED 1980; in abeyance 1985-92. *Publishes* regional history. 3 titles in 1995. Welcomes unsolicited mss, ideas and synopses. Not interested in adult fiction.

Royalties paid twice yearly.

Roberts Rinehart Publishers

Trinity House, Charleston Road, Dublin 6,
Republic of Ireland
☎00 353 1 4976860   Fax 00 353 1 4976861

Chairman *Rick Rinehart*
Managing Director *Jack Van Zandt*
Approx. Annual Turnover £2 million

European branch of a US company first established in 1983. Particularly active in the Irish-American market. *Publishes* general non-fiction, particularly arts, environment, nature, Irish interest, photography, history and biography; and colour illustrated children's books, fiction and non-fiction. About 40 titles a year. TITLES *I am of Ireland; Ireland: The Living Landscape; Festive Food of Ireland; The IRA; Under the Black Flag; The People Who Hugged Trees.* No adult fiction.

Royal Dublin Society

Science Section, Ballsbridge, Dublin 4,
Republic of Ireland
☎00 353 1 6680866   Fax 00 353 1 6604014

President *Liam Connellan*
Approx. Annual Turnover £3000

FOUNDED 1731 to promote agriculture, science and the arts. Since then it has published books and journals to this end, hiring publishers on a contract basis. *Publishes* conference proceedings, biology and the history of Irish science. TITLES *Agricultural Development for the 21st Century; Kerry and Dexter Cattle and Other Ancient Irish Breeds – A History; The Right Trees in the Right Places.*

Royalties not generally paid.

Royal Irish Academy

19 Dawson Street, Dublin 2,
Republic of Ireland
☎00 353 1 6762570   Fax 00 353 1 6762346

Executive Secretary *Patrick Buckley*
Approx. Annual Turnover £50,000

FOUNDED in 1785, the Academy, has been publishing since 1787. Core publications are journals but more books published in last 10 years. *Publishes* academic, Irish interest and Irish language. About 7 titles a year. Welcomes mss, synopses and ideas of an academic standard.

Royalties paid once yearly, where applicable.

Tír Eolas

Newtownlynch, Doorus, Kinvara, Co. Galway,
Republic of Ireland
☎00 353 91 37452

Publisher/Managing Director *Anne Korff*
Approx. Annual Turnover £50,000

FOUNDED 1987. *Publishes* books and guides on ecology, archaeology, folklore and culture. TITLES *The Book of the Burren; The Shannon Floodlands; Not a Word of a Lie; The Book of Aran.* Unsolicited mss, synopses and ideas for books welcome. No specialist scientific and technical, fiction, plays, school textbooks or philosophy.

Royalties paid annually.

Town House and Country House

Trinity House, Charleston Road, Ranelagh,
Dublin 6, Republic of Ireland
☎00 353 1 4972399   Fax 00 353 1 4970927

Managing Director *Treasa Coady*

FOUNDED 1980. *Publishes* commercial fiction, art and archaeology, biography and environment. About 20 titles a year. TITLES *A Place of Stones; Irish Painting; The Illustrated Archaeology of Ireland; Lifelines.* Good production and design standards. Unsolicited mss, synopses and ideas welcome. No children's books.

Royalties paid twice yearly.

Veritas Publications

7-8 Lower Abbey Street, Dublin 1,
Republic of Ireland
☎00 353 1 8788177   Fax 00 353 1 8786507

Chairman *Diarmuid Murray*
Managing Director *Fr Sean Melody*

FOUNDED 1969 to supply religious textbooks to schools and later introduced a more general religious list. Part of the Catholic Communications Institute. *Publishes* religious books only. About 20 titles a year. Unsolicited mss, synopses and ideas for books welcome.

Royalties paid annually.

Wolfhound Press

68 Mountjoy Square, Dublin 1,
Republic of Ireland
☎00 353 1 8740354   Fax 00 353 1 8720207
Managing Director *Seamus Cashman*

FOUNDED 1974. Member of **Clé** – the Irish Book Publishers Association. *Publishes* art, biography, children's, drama, fiction, general non-fiction, history, law, literature, literary studies, poetry and gift books. About 30 titles a year. TITLES *Famine; Run With the Wind; Transitions.* Unsolicited mss (with synopses and s.a.e.) and ideas welcome.

Royalties paid annually.

When in Rom

A rough guide to making money with new-age technology

Multimedia multiplies. There are today two million CD-ROM drives at large in Britain providing a market for the 6000 CD-ROM titles to be released this year. Dorling Kindersley is well into the business but where DK has led the way, others have been quick to follow notably Random House and Macmillan both of which are investing heavily in reference, education and 'infotainment'.

The growth in multimedia publishing has in turn created a lively demand for writers who can work with a production team. Flexibility is the key for the aspiring multimedia writer; a readiness to accept that technology rules the words. However, there is always the risk of getting lost in the general mayhem that usually passes for team effort.

Contracts for books, newspapers, film and television give scant reference to electronic rights while deals struck directly with electronic publishers invariably undervalue writers' creative input. How writers can avoid becoming the fall guys of multimedia is spelt out in a new publication (*Guidelines for Writers in Electronic Publishing and Multimedia*) from The Authors' Licensing and Collecting Society. What follows is a summary of the advice, offered by the ALCS in cooperation with all the leading writers' organisations.

Because writing often spreads across text, illustration, film and music, publishers push hard for complete buyouts of creative rights. Royalties are difficult to administer and are liable to be more expensive. By the same token, writers are likely to gain more if they stick to a royalty-based payment rather than an outright fee.

The question of royalties versus fee depends chiefly on the nature of the product and the extent of the writer's contribution. As this may be difficult to predict before the product is ready for sale, calculations have to be based on an assessment of the amount of the writer's work likely to be included in the product.

There are a few basic questions that the writer needs to ask about the project. What is the budget? Knowing the budget for the product can help the writer to calculate what he might be paid. What are the sales' projections and when is it anticipated that the original investment will be recouped? Investment in the development of electronic products tends to be heavy, but production and distribution are relatively cheap so it is logical to link remuneration with sales. What will be the format, platform and channel of distribution? Will this product appear on CD-ROM or equivalent, or will it be distributed online. If the former, a per copy royalty is acceptable but for online distribution payment should be related to the period for which the product is available online together with the number of users.

All writers, whatever their area of activity, should try to retain copyright and reserve electronic rights or grant options unless the publisher can demonstrate an ability to exploit them to the writer's benefit.

Electronic aspects of book publishing

Writers who approach multimedia indirectly, by first producing a conventional book for example, should withhold electronic rights or grant options for limited periods or, if persuaded to grant a licence, provide for it to lapse if the rights are not exploited within a given (short) period. The best publishing contracts allow the author to retain electronic rights. This has to be the preferred option unless the publisher has electronic exploitation planned, in which case appropriate terms can be negotiated at the outset.

An alternative is for the author to grant the publishers first refusal on particular and specified electronic rights with each use being subject to the author's consent and on terms to be agreed.

If the book publisher exercises control of electronic rights by negotiating terms with an electronic publisher, the contract should specify that the electronic sub-licence will be subject to the author's approval. Although some academic publishers suggest a 50:50 division of the income from such sub-licences, the Society of Authors recommends that the income should be divided 80:20 in the author's favour, particularly when dealing with trade publishers. If it is not possible to negotiate a fixed 80:20 division, the split should improve as income from the sub-licence increases.

Licensing the electronic publication of text in fixed format

Start with the basic terms applicable to all book contracts.

- all rights not specifically granted should be retained by the author;
- the electronic publisher should not be able to assign the rights granted without written consent;
- the electronic publisher should undertake to release the product by a specific date or within a given time from delivery of the material;
- generally no option should be granted on future work;
- responsibility for clearing, and paying for, permission to use quotations/illustrations from other sources in the electronic product should be clear. Authors would expect the electronic publisher to meet any fees incurred;
- the number of free copies of the work the author should be sent should be agreed;

- the accounting clause should set out how often royalty statements will be provided, the information they will contain and when payments will be made;
- any 'competing works' restrictions should be clear and not fetter the author unduly;
- appropriate authors' rights should be administered by the ALCS;
- if the author is supplying the software, or illustration materials, such material should be covered by a separate agreement and separate payment.

The rights granted

Define the rights licensed as narrowly as possible and grant separate licences for different uses. For example, one electronic publisher could have the exclusive licence to publish an unabridged version of a novel, with another having the right to publish an abridged version.

In agreements originating from publishing houses, reference is sometimes made to licensing use in electronic form by any means 'now known or developed in the future'. Such phrases should be resisted as being insufficiently specific and possibly giving rise to litigation (cf. grant of film rights before the invention of video).

Platform
The scope of electronic publishing is expanding all the time. Limit the licence as far as possible to a particular product.

Format
Differentiate between straight reproduction of the work in the new medium (e.g. a full verbatim or abridged version for CD-ROM) and use in a 'composite work' (e.g. a collection of a dozen similar works on one CD) or in a 'multimedia work' (e.g. in conjunction with sound, film, etc.).

Duration
Many book and broadcasting contracts are for the duration of copyright. However, with electronic publishing in its infancy and changing rapidly, it is wise to limit the licence to a specified number of years (e.g. 2 to 5 years for straight text reproduction, 3 to 6 years where, for instance, the work involves customised software or multimedia development and the electronic publisher is making a larger capital investment in the product).

Remuneration

Advances and royalties
In most cases remuneration should be on a traditional advance and royalties basis, as opposed to a flat fee. But with developments in collective licensing, the system may change.

If there is doubt about payments, the electronic publisher should be asked to explain the costings, the budgets, and the rationale behind the royalties. The royalties should ideally be based on the retail price (excluding VAT), but it may be necessary to settle for a royalty on the dealer price (the price at which the product is sold to the shops) or a percentage of the electronic publisher's receipts.

Although some electronic publishers are suggesting a 'standard' royalty of 10% of their receipts (divided between creative contributors, where appropriate), one should not assume that 10% of receipts is appropriate. In many cases, production, warehousing and distribution costs are very low and therefore the royalty could be substantially higher than 10%. On the other hand, initial research, development and software costs can be high. Thus, it may be appropriate for the royalty to start 10%, or less in some circumstances, but rise to as much as 25% in stages, based on the publisher's receipts, unlike book royalties which are usually based on the published price.

Review and arbitration

Given the present uncertainties it is reasonable to ask for the royalties to be open to review, say, every three years from first production and then altered to the extent that may be 'just and equitable'. Include an arbitration clause, in case author and electronic publisher cannot agree on what is just and equitable.

Multi-author works

In the case of composite works, there is a tendency to suggest that royalties be divided pro rata between all those whose work is included. This may be logical where a royalty is being divided between a number of similar contributors (e.g. five novelists). However, it is frequently impracticable, because it is not easy to define a pro rata contribution when dealing with different forms of material. Text, for example, takes up much less disk space than pictures or music, and other types of contributor (e.g. artists, composers or the software programmer) may well be receiving a royalty too. It may be wise to delay agreement on royalties until more is known about the creative input.

Where there are large numbers of contributors, or the written amount is small, the author will probably have to settle for a fee. Ensure that the fee is paid on delivery rather than on publication, and that it is based on the material requested and delivered rather than on the amount which is used in the finished product. It may be possible to agree that further fees should be payable in specified circumstances (e.g. each time a certain number of copies has been sold, or each year that the product remains on sale).

Rental

If the electronic publisher receives income from the rental of the work, the author should be entitled to an agreed share of that income, directly or via a collecting society.

The integrity of the author's work

Book writers are accustomed to having final control over their texts, except to the extent that they may be libellous or may infringe someone else's copyright.

Where the electronic product consists entirely or largely of the writer's text (e.g. a medical book on CD-ROM), the author should not waive the *right of integrity* and ideally the contract should state that no alterations will be made without the author's consent. Where there are other major creative elements (e.g. film, sound, illustrations, etc.), the author may find it more difficult to retain ultimate control. Nevertheless, there should be provisions which ensure that the author is given the opportunity to make any revisions (or, at worst, the right to be informed well before production of changes made) and has the right to prevent the work being credited if it is unacceptable.

Credits

An author's other main moral right — the right of paternity or right to be identified as the author — has to be 'asserted' in writing, preferably in the contract.

Revised editions

It is common for authors to be under an obligation to prepare revised editions, where appropriate. Some forms of electronic publication can be updated easily and regularly. Questions to consider are whether the author should be on a retainer to update the work periodically, and whether the timing of publication of revised editions should be linked to the new book versions of the work.

Involvement in production

It is common for authors to be consulted about the jacket, illustrations and design of a book. Similarly in the case of an electronic product the author may secure the right to be consulted on the design of the electronic product as it evolves as well as its packaging. Specialists, such as medical writers, may want the opportunity to check the product from the viewpoint of the user.

Termination

The author of a book normally has the right to terminate the contract if the work goes out of print, if the publisher is in default, or if the publisher goes into liquidation, receivership or administration. There should be similar clauses in electronic publishing contracts, and the author should also have the right to terminate the contract in additional circumstances, such as:

- if sales fall below specified numbers in a given period (e.g. 100 units in each of two successive royalty periods);
- if the work is not available for more than three months or if it ceases to be listed in the electronic publisher's catalogue.

Contracts with online and database producers

As with all forms of publishing, the terms it is possible to achieve will vary with the status of the author and the relevance of the author's material to the online product/database as a whole.

The rights granted

As a general rule, authors should grant a non-exclusive licence only. It will also be necessary to be clear who is responsible for getting permission from the owners of copyright in any quotations or illustrations that may have been included in the work.

Platform

The electronic publisher should specify the ways in which access will be provided e.g. online data transmission via email only, or via the World Wide Web, etc. The contract should make clear that the author 'excludes the right to make the work available on disk or card or by any form of data carrier or by any method of data transmission other than as specified'.

Format

There are three ways work can be exploited online:

plain text: where the publisher/distributor simply makes the text, unaltered, available online and is effectively acting as agent only;

hypertext: where the text is, for instance, embedded with links whereby the reader can move to other points in the text, or in other texts. Here the publisher may add to the value of the author's text;

multimedia: the same as hypertext but including links with e.g. audio, video and other digital elements. Here, again, the publisher may add significantly to the value of the author's text.

Duration

The licence period should be a fixed, limited period e.g. 2 years for plain text; longer, e.g. 5 to 8 years, for hypertext/multimedia use, where the origination costs will be much higher.

Remuneration

Payments should be calculated on an advance and royalties or on a sum per month during which the product is available online.

Royalties should cover all forms of revenue deriving from the work, split between author and publisher, for example, as follows:

where the electronic publisher is only distributing the work 90:10;

where the electronic publisher is copy editing and formatting the material, or is involved in developmental editing: 80:20;

where the electronic publisher is adding hypertext and multimedia links: 50:50 to 75:25.

Royalties should be higher where the electronic products are being distributed on a networked basis e.g. CD-ROM-on-demand kiosks.

Guarantees of availability

The electronic publisher should undertake to release the work within a given time of delivery of the material, and guarantee to make it available online for a minimum period e.g. 18 months. Much more important than in book contracts, the electronic publisher should specify its marketing proposals (e.g. how the work will be advertised online and in print, and the promotional budget). Aim to secure an absolute undertaking that the electronic publisher will prevent unauthorised downloading or copying, or pirating. Check with the electronic publisher whether there is a practical way of withdrawing availability if and when it is appropriate.

The integrity of the author's work

It should be clear that no alterations will be made to the material, other than for the purpose of adapting it into electronic form, without the author's consent.

It is reasonable, in hypertext and multimedia contracts, that the producer is entitled to include search and other apparatus and reference materials to increase the usefulness of the produce (e.g. the database), but it should remain faithful to the overall tone and character of the underlying materials.

In hypertext and multimedia contracts, any other material used with the author's work should be subject to the author's approval, and the author should be given the chance to approve the final version of the product.

Dramatic writing for electronic products

Multimedia demands collaborative efforts that are even more complex than making films and television programmes. Writers are likely to be involved with a team from the start, rather than writing their contributions separately. This does not alter the fact that the writer creates copyright material which must be licensed or assigned in the usual way.

The rights granted

The producer may argue that an assignment of copyright is necessary to enable full exploitation of the electronic product. Assignment will automatically give the format rights to the producer, so writers who own the format should be careful not to assign copyright. Assignment leaves the writer with no rights in the material, only the contractual right to payment, and is best avoided even where the format originates elsewhere.

Licence/assignment

The technical means of exploitation permitted should be specified. Television and film contracts generally specify 'all audiovisual media whether now known or hereafter invented'. It is best to limit the media to a specified list to reserve the ability to renegotiate terms when exploitation in new media is proposed.

Territory

On current evidence electronic products only make substantial amounts of money if they are distributed in the US, so licences are likely to include this territory. Writers must consider whether a limitation on territory is in their interest or not. This will depend on whether the producer or the writer is best able to exploit in other territories, and on whether worldwide exploitation is planned. A worldwide licence may in fact be appropriate, or at least unavoidable.

Duration

Producers will initially ask for a licence for the duration of copyright. However, the current shelf-life of a CD-ROM is around two years. If the product is not being exploited, then the producer has no use for the rights. In general, therefore, limited licences are preferable to those that tie up rights for the duration of copyright.

Reservation of ancillary rights

If copyright has been assigned, writers must consider the position of the characters or format which they have created. They may be used for spin-offs of characters and situations for television or film, further interactive programs, merchandising and so on. It is crucial to obtain a reservation of the right to control such spin-offs.

Remuneration

Writers should ideally negotiate a non-returnable fee based on their usual script rates for television and a royalty share from sales and other exploitation of the product. The producer may argue for the fee to be off set in part or whole as an advance against royalties, which is standard practice in book contracts but not in television where the initial fee usually buys first television transmission with further use fees/royalties for subsequent exploitations.

In some circumstances a flat fee to buy all rights may be appropriate, where the writer's contribution is a very small part of the product.

Royalty

The appropriate royalty percentage will depend on the level of the writer's contribution in relation to the other creative elements, the number of contributors and the production costs. Producers should be encouraged to disclose full information on the production budget, marketing budget, and number of other rights holders involved, to enable writers to negotiate fair remuneration.

The Writers' Guild suggests a royalty range of 3% to 5% for major contributions, that is where the script is used through the whole electronic product (where the contribution is analogous to that of a television or film script). For other contributions, for example extensive dialogue for sections of the electronic product, a royalty of 1% to 3% is suggested.

Calculation of royalty
Royalties should ideally be based on the retail selling price, excluding VAT. Those who cannot get a royalty based on the retail price should use the price at which the product is sold to the shops. Failing this, they should argue for a share of the producer's gross receipts, or at worst a share of profits. However writers are warned that, as with films, it can be difficult to achieve actual income from a notional share of profits. The definition of profits is very important: a profit figure deducting production costs only from receipts is an ideal definition, but standard definition from producers may allow deduction of marketing and distribution costs as well.

Other clauses
Where a royalty or profit share is to be paid, it is important to agree an accounting clause which sets out how often royalty statements will be provided and payments made. You should also consider an audit clause giving you the right to inspect the producers' accounts at least once a year to check that statements are accurate.

The integrity of the writer's work

Copyright materials produced for interactive programs have moral rights attached to them but if a waiver is a condition then the writer should ensure that there are substitute clauses setting out how much of the work may be altered and preserving the right for the writer to take his or her name from the credits.

Credits

Contributors should be credited. They should agree the form and size in the contract, and ask to see examples of other products so they have an idea of how credits appear. The usual rules from film and television may not apply. The writer may be asked to waive the right of paternity. If the credits clause is satisfactory this may be appropriate but since these works are easily manipulated credit may be irretrievably lost without an assertion of the right of paternity.

Access to production and rehearsals

It is common for television contracts to include a right to attend rehearsals and editing sessions. In the case of an interactive program, the most important right may be to be consulted on the design of the electronic product during production. This will only be feasible where the writer has contributed a substantial part of the electronic product when it would be common to be involved in the development progress in any case.

Film and television programmes adapted for use in electronic products

The control of the right to make an electronic product using a film or television script in its original or adapted form will depend on the terms of the commissioning contract. In the case of direct BBC commissions, for example, the producer is granted a licence to make a television programme from the script. Interactive rights will therefore remain with the writer and must be negotiated afresh. In the case of the Producers Alliance for Cinema and Television (PACT) contracts for film or television, and all feature film contracts, copyright in the script will have been assigned and control of interactive rights will be with the producer.

When negotiating a television or film contract, where copyright is to be assigned, the writer should always try to retain some control over interactive rights just as they would for other spin-off rights.

Terms
The ideal form of licence is a licence to make and exploit one interactive program based on the script, with limits on territory and duration.

Remuneration, as with material written directly for the electronic product, is by negotiation of an advance and royalty on a guideline of 3% to 5%.

The Author's Licensing and Collecting Society (ALCS) and collective licensing

1. The future

Each week reports appear of new developments in the electronic delivery of entertainment and infotainment. ALCS believes that numerous small payments will be generated for online usage and there is a need to ensure that writers receive a just reward from every exploitation of their work. Collecting societies worldwide will have a larger role in ensuring that writers are rewarded by the digital dissemination of information.

By developing tariff structures and systems to enable permissions to be granted to multimedia publishers and producers, ALCS will be ready to respond as the digital market expands. It is essential that writers should resist pressure to accept one-off up-front payments from producers claiming that it is too difficult to make individual payments for small sums of money throughout the life of the product.

2. Research and development

ALCS is involved in researching systems that guarantee the security of writers' work when it is released onto open network systems. It is the co-ordinating partner of an ambitious three-year EC-funded project, IMPRIMATUR, Intellectual Property Rights Model and Terminology for Universal Reference. The words 'model' and 'universal' are the key. The project aims, above all, to reach a global consensus on how the creators, the publishers and producers, the IT and telecommunications industries and the user can happily co-exist. Its aim is not so much to produce proprietorial solutions as an infrastructure with international standards backed up by international law. At the same time as consensus-building, it aims to construct a networked server on which to introduce the infrastructure developing from the consensus-building process.

Further information and a brochure describing the work of IMPRIMATUR can be obtained from: IMPRIMATUR, 8 Bedford Square, London WC1B 3RA, tel: 0171-436 5578, fax: 0171-436 5579.

The IMPRIMATUR web site is: http://www.imprimatur.alcs.co.uk

Copies of *Guidelines for Writers in Electronic Publishing and Multimedia* are available from ALCS, Isis House, 74 New Oxford Street, London WC1A 1EG, tel: 0171-255 2034, fax: 0171-323 0846. (See entry under **Professional Associations**)

UK electronic publishers

Academic Press
Butterworth Heinemann UK
Cambridge University Press
Chadwyck-Healey Ltd
Dorling Kindersley Ltd
Elsevier Science Ltd
Euromonitor
HarperCollins Publishers Ltd
Helicon Publishing
Hobsons Publishing
Jane's Information Group
Macmillan Interactive Publishing

McGraw-Hill Book Co
Mosby
Thomas Nelson & Sons Ltd
Notting Hill Ltd
Oxford University Press
Penguin Books Ltd
Pitman Publishing
Radcliffe Medical Press Ltd
Random House UK Ltd
Sweet & Maxwell Ltd
Thames & Hudson Ltd

'We are very, very close to developing "small-scale, portable, total display", meaning you will carry with you, or have on your desk or in your bed for bedtime reading, the screen clearly printed. If you wish it to turn the pages at a given rate it will do so or you can choose. Above all, it will soon be online to the libraries of the world. The 14 million books of the Library of Congress will be at your fingertips, privately. It will be clearer, easier to carry, infinitely more responsive to your interests and needs than any book and we are very near to getting it right. Then, we are truly in a new world.'
Professor George Steiner

Audio Books

Abbey Home Entertainment

Warwick House, 106 Harrow Road,
London W2 1XD
☎0171 262 1012   Fax 0171 262 6020
Managing Director *Anne Miles*

Abbey were the instigators (as MSD Holdings) in the development of the spoken word. With over 20 years' experience in recording, marketing and distribution of audio, book and cassette, their catalogue includes major children's story characters such as *Thomas the Tank Engine, Rosie and Jim, Postman Pat, Rupert Bear* and *Winnie the Pooh. Specialises* in children's book/cassette packs. 80 titles in 1996. Ideas from authors and agents welcome.

Argo

See **PolyGram Spoken Word**

BBC Radio Collection

Woodlands, 80 Wood Lane, London W12 0TT
☎0181 576 2600   Fax 0181 749 0538
Owner *BBC Worldwide Publishing*
Spoken Word Publishing Director
  Sue Anstruther

ESTABLISHED in 1988 to release material from BBC Radio. *Publishes* comedy, children's, science fiction, fiction, non-fiction and sound effects. TITLES *Hancock's Half Hour; Round the Home; Alan Bennett's Diaries; Knowing Me, Knowing You; Animals of Farthing Wood*. Ideas for cassettes welcome although most releases start as BBC Radio programmes.

Bespoke Audio Ltd

Pepys Court, 84 The Chase, London SW4 0NF
☎0171 627 8777   Fax 0171 498 6420
Managing Director *Bob Nolan*

FOUNDED in 1994 by ex-**PolyGram** executive. Part of Total Records. *Publishes* and distributes for other publishers such as **Macmillan** and **HarperCollins**; biography, children's, fiction, comedy. 15 titles in 1995. AUTHORS John Cole, Patrick O'Brian, Steve Turner, Sue Townsend. Ideas from authors and agents welcome.

Canongate Audio

14 High Street, Edinburgh EH1 1TE
☎0131 557 5111   Fax 0131 557 5211

Joint Managing Directors *Jamie Byng, Hugh Andrew*

Part of **Canongate Books**. Purchased the Schiltron and Whigmaleerie lists in 1993. *Publishes* fiction, children's, humour, poetry, historical and Scottish titles. 15 titles in 1995, with a large backlist. TITLES *The Driver's Seat* Muriel Spark, read by Judi Dench; *Lanark* read by the author, Alasdair Gray; *Parahandy* Neil Munro; *Scots Quair* Lewis Grassic Gibbon; Robert Louis Stevenson titles.

Cavalcade Story Cassettes

See **Chivers Audio Books**

Champs Elysées

See under **Magazines**

Chivers Audio Books

Windsor Bridge Road, Bath, Avon BA2 3AX
☎01225 335336   Fax 01225 448005
Managing Director *Simon D. Gibbs*

Part of **Chivers Press Ltd**. *Publishes* a wide range of titles, mainly for library consumption. Fiction, autobiography, children's and crime. 216 titles in 1994. TITLES *Taken on Trust* Terry Waite; *Brideshead Revisited* Evelyn Waugh; *If Only They Could Talk* James Herriot; *The Power and the Glory* Graham Greene; *Goggle-Eyes* Anne Fine; *The Incredible Journey* Sheila Burnford.

  IMPRINTS **Chivers Audio Books, Chivers Children's Audio, Cavalcade Story Cassettes, Word-for-Word Audio Books, Sterling Audio Books.**

The Complete Listener Recorded Book Company

Field End Cottage Studios, 8 Apple Street, Oxenhope, Keighley, West Yorkshire BD22 9LT
☎01535 645983

Managing Director *James D. Gillhouley*

FOUNDED 1989. One of the largest catalogues of unabridged classic titles in Europe and the only one to include the complete novels of the Brontë sisters, Henry Fielding and Charles Dickens. TITLES *War and Peace; Anna Karenina.* Recordings of contemporary works by new authors are undertaken by special arrangement. Please write for details.

Cover To Cover Cassettes Ltd

PO Box 112, Marlborough, Wiltshire
SN8 3UG
☎01264 337725 Fax 01264 337742

Managing Director *Helen Nicoll*

Publishes classic 19th-century fiction – Jane Austen, Charles Dickens, Anthony Trollope, plus children's titles – *Fantastic Mr Fox* Roald Dahl; *Worst Witch* Jill Murphy; *Sheep-Pig* Dick King-Smith; *In Your Garden* Vita Sackville-West (book/cassette). 10 titles in 1995.

CSA Telltapes Ltd

101 Chamberlayne Road, London NW10 3ND
☎0181 960 8466 Fax 0181 968 0804

Managing Director *Clive Stanhope*

FOUNDED 1989. *Publishes* fiction, children's, short stories, poetry, travel, biographies. 12 titles in 1995. Tends to favour quality/classic/nostalgic literature for the 40+ age group. TITLES *Lamb's Tales from Shakespeare I & II; Bitter Lemons* Lawrence Durrell; *The Picture of Dorian Gray* Oscar Wilde. Ideas for cassettes welcome.

CYP Limited

The Fairway, Bush Fair, Harlow, Essex
CM18 6LY
☎01279 444707 Fax 01279 445570

Managing Director *Mike Kitson*

FOUNDED 1978. *Publishes* children's material for those under 10 years of age; educational, entertainment, licensed characters (i.e. *Mr Men; Little Miss*). Ideas for cassettes welcome.

Faber & Faber Audiobooks

3 Queen Square, London WC1N 3AU
☎0171 465 0045

Marketing Development Manager *Jonathan Tilston*

Part of **Faber & Faber** publishers. First cassettes were issued in 1994 to coincide with Poetry Day on October 6th. TITLES *Two Cures For Love – A Collection of Poems Introduced and Read by the Poet* Wendy Cope; *Readings – A Collection of Poems Introduced and Read by the Poets* Douglas Dunn, Thom Gunn, Seamus Heaney, Ted Hughes, Philip Larkin, Paul Muldoon and Tom Paulin; *The Thought-Fox and Other Poems* Ted Hughes.

Faber Penguin Audiobooks

27 Wrights Lane, London W8 5TZ
☎0171 416 3000 Fax 0171 416 3289

Publishing Manager *Jan Paterson*

A new joint venture between **Penguin Books** and **Faber & Faber**. Plans to publish 25–30 titles per year, drawing on the strength of Faber's authors. Will especially concentrate on poetry. AUTHORS include Ted Hughes, Philip Larkin, Hanif Kureishi, Sylvia Plath, T.S. Eliot.

Funny Business

See **PolyGram Spoken Word**

Golden Days of Radio

See **Hodder Headline Audio Books**

HarperCollins AudioBooks

77–85 Fulham Palace Road, London W6 8JB
☎0181 741 7070
Fax 0181 307 4813(adult)/307 4440(child.)

The Collins audio and video company was acquired in the mid-eighties but the video section was later sold. In 1990/91 HarperCollins overhauled the audio company, dividing the adult and children's tapes into two separate divisions.

ADULT DIVISION
Managing Director *Robert Williams*
Publisher *Rosalie George*

Publishes a wide range including popular and classic fiction, non-fiction, Shakespeare and poetry. 50 titles in 1995. TITLES *Honour Among Thieves* Jeffrey Archer; *The Rector's Wife* Joanna Trollope; *The Final Cut* Michael Dobbs; *Neither Here Nor There* Bill Bryson; *Heart of Danger* Gerald Seymour; *Simisola* Ruth Rendell.

CHILDREN'S:DIVISION
Publishing Director *Gail Penston*
Senior Editor *Stella Paskins*

Publishes picture books/cassettes and story books/cassettes as well as single and double tapes for children aged 2-13 years. Fiction, songs, early learning, poetry etc. 61 titles in 1995. AUTHORS Roald Dahl, C. S. Lewis, Enid Blyton, Michael Rosen, Robert Westall, Jean Ure, Nick Butterworth, Colin and Jacqui Hawkins, Judith Kerr, Jonathan Langley. Welcomes ideas for titles.

Hodder Headline Audio Books

338 Euston Road, London NW1 3BH
☎0171 873 6000 Fax 0171 873 6024

Managing Director *Rupert Lancaster*

LAUNCHED in 1994 with 50 titles. A strong list, especially for theatre, vintage radio, film tie-ins, poetry plus fiction, non-fiction, children's, religious. Approx 200 titles in 1995. AUTHORS Enid Blyton, Edwina Currie, Mick Inkpen (*Kipper* books), Stephen King, Rosamunde Pilcher,

Emma Tennant, Joanna Trollope, Terry Waite, Mary Wesley.

IMPRINT **Golden Days of Radio** series of classic vintage radio broadcasts. Welcomes ideas for cassettes.

Isis Audio Books
7 Centremead, Osney Mead, Oxford
OX2 0ES
☎01865 250333   Fax 01865 790358
Managing Director *John Durrant*
Editorial Head *Veronica Babington Smith*

Part of **Isis Publishing Ltd.** *Publishes* fiction and a few non-fiction titles. AUTHORS Virginia Andrews, Barbara Taylor Bradford, Edwina Currie, Leslie Thomas, Douglas Adams, Terry Pratchett.

Ladybird Books Ltd
Beeches Road, Loughborough, Leicestershire
LE11 2RA
☎01509 268021   Fax 01509 234672
Managing Director *Anthony Forbes Watson*

Part of the Penguin Group. Only *publishes* recordings of titles which appear on the Ladybird book list. 14 titles in 1995. TITLES *The Railway Children; Gulliver's Travels; Little Red Riding Hood; Puss in Boots.*

Laughing Stock
PO Box 408, London SW11 5TA
☎0181 944 9455   Fax 0181 944 9466
Managing Director *Colin Collino*

FOUNDED 1991. Issues a wide range of comedy cassettes from family humour to alternative comedy. 12–16 titles per year. TITLES *Red Dwarf; Shirley Valentine* (read by Willy Russell); *Rory Bremner; Peter Cook Anthology; Sean Hughes; John Bird and John Fortune.*

Listen for Pleasure
E.M.I. House, 43 Brook Green, London
W6 7EF
☎0171 605 5000   Fax 0171 605 5134
Director *Paul Holland*

Part of E.M.I. Records, the Listen for Pleasure label started in 1977 as part of Music for Pleasure. Also covers Virgin and E.M.I.. *Publishes* humour, comedy classics, children's, fiction and non-fiction, poetry. TITLES *Morecambe & Wise; The Goon Shows; The Railway Children; The Borrowers; An Evening with Johnners; The Beiderbecke Affair; All Creatures Great and Small; Under Milk Wood;*

Pride and Prejudice; Every Living Thing; Smith & Jones. Welcomes original ideas for cassettes.

Macmillan Audio Books
25 Eccleston Place, London SW1W 9NF
☎0171 881 8000   Fax 0171 881 8001
Owner *Macmillan Publishers Ltd*
Manager *Gina Rozner*

FOUNDED 1995. *Publishes* adult fiction and autobiography focusing mainly on lead book titles and releasing audio simultaneously with hardback or paperback publication. Planning to enter the children's audio market in 1997. About 25 titles per year. TITLES *With Nail* Richard E. Grant; *The Daughters of Cain* Colin Dexter; *Rose* Martin Cruz Smith; *The Seventh Scroll* Wilbur Smith.

MCI Spoken Word
36–38 Caxton Way, Watford, Hertfordshire
WD1 8UF
☎01923 255558   Fax 01923 816880
Owner *VCI Plc*
Managing Director *Peter Stack*

Established in 1993 and now a rapidly expanding publisher of a wide range of audiobooks: comedy, children's, classics, thrillers & chillers, true crime, TV programmes. 35 titles in 1994. TITLES *Inspector Morse; Barbie; Max Miller; Sherlock Holmes* (Granada TV); *The Dubliners; The Last of the Mohicans; James Bond.* Open to ideas for cassettes.

Naxos AudioBooks
H.R. House, 447 High Road, London
N12 0AF
☎0181 346 6816   Fax 0181 346 6496
Owner *HNH International, Hong Kong*
Managing Director *Nicolas Soames*

FOUNDED 1994. Part of Naxos, the classical budget CD company. *Publishes* classic and modern fiction, non-fiction, children's and junior classics, drama and poetry. 100 titles by the end of 1996. TITLES *Paradise Lost* Milton; *Ulysses* Joyce; *Kim* Kipling; *Decline and Fall of the Roman Empire* Gibbon. Ideas for cassettes welcome.

Penguin Audiobooks
27 Wrights Lane, London W8 5TZ
☎0171 416 3000   Fax 0171 416 3289
Owner *Penguin Books Ltd*
Publishing Manager *Jan Paterson*

Launched in November 1993 and has rapidly expanded since then to reflect the diversity of

Penguin Books' list. *Publishes* mostly fiction, both classical and contemporary, non-fiction and autobiography. Approx. 110 titles a year. Contemporary AUTHORS include: Dick Francis, Paul Theroux, Stephen King, Miss Reed, Barbara Vine, William Boyd, Terry MacMillan, John Mortimer.

PolyGram Spoken Word

1 Sussex Place, Hammersmith, London
W6 9XS
☎0181 910 5000   Fax 0181 910 5400

Owner *PolyGram*
General Manager *Tony Staniland*

Part of PolyGram, the Spoken Word division has been in operation for two years, publishing under the **Speaking Volumes**, **Funny Business** and **Argo** labels. *Publishes* comedy, biography, fiction, poetry and documentary titles. Approx. 50 titles in 1995. TITLES *Diaries* Alan Clark; *A Suitable Boy* Vikram Seth; *Hamlet* Richard Burton; *Immediate Action* Andy McNab; Radio One's production of *Judge Dredd*; the poetry of Pablo Neruda read by an all-star Hollywood cast. Ideas for cassettes welcome.

Random House Audiobooks

20 Vauxhall Bridge Road, London
SW1V 2SA
☎0171 973 9000   Fax 0171 233 6127

Owner *Random House UK Ltd*
Managing Director *Simon King*

The audiobooks division of Random House started early in 1991 and *publishes* fiction, non-fiction, self help and children's. 28 titles in 1995. AUTHORS include John Grisham, Stephen Fry, P. G. Wodehouse, Frederick Forsyth, Michael Caine, Michael Crichton and Anne Rice.

Reed Audio

Michelin House, 81 Fulham Road, London
SW3 6RB
☎0171 581 9393   Fax 0171 589 8419

Owner *Reed Books*
Managing Director *John Potter*
Executive Editor *Alexa Moore*

Publishes fiction, humour and non-fiction. A list of over 80 titles includes AUTHORS Roddy Doyle, Michael Palin, Molly Keane, Gary Rhodes, Bruce Chatwin, Wilbur Smith, P. J. O'Rourke.

Simon & Schuster Audio

West Garden Place, Kendal Street, London
W2 2AG
☎0171 724 7577   Fax 0171 402 0639

Audio Manager *Catherine Reed*

Simon & Schuster Audio began by distributing their American parent company's audio products. Moved on to repackaging products specifically for the UK market and in 1994 became more firmly established in this market with a huge rise in turnover. *Publishes* adult fiction, self help, business, Star Trek titles. 3 titles per month. TITLES *From Potter's Field* Patricia Cornwell; *A Thousand Acres* James Smiley; *Shipping News* E. Annie Proulx; *The Secrets of Communication* Peter Thomson; *Star Trek I, The Return* William Shatner.

Smith/Doorstop Cassettes

The Poetry Business, The Studio, Byram Arcade, Huddersfield, West Yorkshire
HD1 1ND
☎01484 434840   Fax 01484 426566

Co-directors *Peter Sansom, Janet Fisher*

Publishes poetry, read and introduced by the writer. 5 titles in 1995. AUTHORS Carol Ann Duffy, Simon Armitage, Les Murray.

Soundings

Kings Drive, Whitley Bay, Tyne & Wear
NE26 2JT
☎0191 253 4155   Fax 0191 251 0662

Managing Director *Derek Jones*

FOUNDED in 1982. *Publishes* fiction and non-fiction; crime, romance, young adults. 124 titles in 1995. Has 1100 titles recorded in their unabridged form on their list and planning to increase annual output to 150 titles. TITLES *Bees in My Bonnet* Angus McVicar; *A Ghost in Monte Carlo* Barbara Cartland; *The Upstart* Catherine Cookson; *School for Love* Olivia Manning. Ideas for cassettes welcome.

Speaking Volumes

See **PolyGram Spoken Word**

Sterling Audio Books

See **Chivers Audio Books**

Word-for-Word Audio Books

See **Chivers Audio Books**

Poetry Matters

Peter Finch

*'More and more mankind will discover that we have to turn
to poetry to interpret life for us, to console us, to sustain us.'*
Matthew Arnold

There is more of it about than I can ever remember. Bright, visible, fashionable. More books than are good for us. So many glittering magazines. The avant garde has had its forward thrust severely blunted and with perhaps the worthy exception of best-selling Pam Ayres, doggerel has had its day. The New Plain Style, so christened by *Poetry Review* editor Peter Forbes, is Britain's vital force. Poetry is where photography and dance once were, a minority art made consumer friendly. Poetry in the schools. Poetry on the Underground. Poetry on TV. It seems that if you seek to further a literary career you have to write the stuff. Irish poet wins £635,000 Nobel Prize for Literature. Terrific.

If the hype is to be believed, poetry should be as popular with the punters as soccer and it should roll out of the bookshops as fast as Delia Smith. Truth is it doesn't. Never did, never will. No one is making much money from poetry except for famous Seamus. Real poetry simply lacks the pulling power. The respectable and in recent years revamped and now pretty exciting **Poetry Society** has just reported a 50% increase in membership of which director Chris Meade is justly proud but that still only takes them to 3000 fans.

Nonetheless, things could be worse. In its own terms, poetry still rides the wave crest. With everyone from Griff Rhys Jones and the BBC to your local rhyme-a-minute tabloid joining in, William Sieghart's National Poetry Day is bigger than ever. Powered by the Colman Getty public relations consultancy Sieghart's Forward Poetry Trust's prizes, worth £10,000 annually for the best collection, £5000 for the best first book and £1000 for the best poem are presented with all the sparkle of the Booker. In media terms this kind of thing makes a mark on the world. The Poetry Society promotes Poetry for Christmas using techniques normally reserved for flogging *Reader's Digest*. Business at the **Poetry Book Society** bustles. In Swansea, Tŷ Llên, Britain's first purpose-built literature centre, gives verse a further boost when its honorary president, Jimmy Carter, declares poet Dylan Thomas the greatest writer the world has known. Goldmark Press's *Return of the Reforgotten*, a seemingly unfashionable re-run of beat heydays at the Albert Hall puts Allen Ginsberg on stage again – this time mc'd by convicted drug-smuggler Howard Marks – and pulls a 1500 audience. Access for everyone.

'Happily, the *arriviste* atmosphere of ten to fifteen years ago when seven per cent or so of English poets and literary careerists controlled at least 84 per cent of the publishing, taste-making, grant-and-prize and allied opportunities for poets, is on the wane across Britain', wrote Michael Horowitz in the *TLS*.

The new technology is mastered. With help from the BBC, the Poetry Society launches into cyberia with its poetry map on the World Wide Web while up and down the country a score of smaller operators discover the slick and inexpensively easy joy of publishing electronically. Peter Jay at **Anvil Press Poetry** will take enquiry letters by e-mail. Michael Blackburn's **Sunk Island** would prefer to download whole scripts.

The years of pressure from the concerned have finally got poetry into the education system – poets tour schools, living poets are included in the National Curriculum, the Poetry Society produces advice for teachers by the cart-load. Publishers all see this as an area of growth with **Kingfisher, Orchard, Walker Books, Penguin, Faber & Faber, Macmillan, The Bodley Head**, and others all now knocking out illustrated, reader-friendly young person's editions.

But amid all this undoubted success there are cracks to be seen. The mainstream commercial operators, once keen to boost the new money-maker, have become quietly indecisive. **Penguin** may have revived their *Modern Poets* series but take absolutely no chances with who goes in. **Sinclair-Stevenson, Hutchinson, Secker** and even long-time home for new poets **Chatto & Windus** have suspended publishing verse for the duration. *The Guardian* keen at the start to follow the *Independent*'s bold lead in using poetry daily now seems not so sure. Smaller presses, the specialists in particular, all report more unsold poetry books coming back from the shops than they had expected. The feeling is that the boom if not quite bust is certainly on the point of turn. Our labours get harder. 'Journalism is a profession but poetry, fortunately, remains a trade', said John Whitworth. Get on board now while the work is at least still there.

So how should you go about it? Join in at whatever level you want: at the *PN Review* with its insistence on the 'centrality of poetry in cultural life and on the necessity of critical engagement'; with National Poetry Day's verse marathons, poetry supermarkets and sonnets delivered by Interflora; or even with Steve Turner's enormously well-circulated Christian poetry circus which, if anything, proves that good messages can still sell. 'The poets who've gained most from the renewed interest have been those who were popular anyway, and, not surprisngly, they tend not to be post-modernists', says Peter Forbes at the usually safe *Poetry Review* but that's not the whole story. Very little in the UK is excluded. Stuffiness may well be a natural way of life (get Auberon Waugh's *The Literary Review* for more of that) but there are other approaches. If your poems *are* post-modernist fractures then try *Object Permanence* or Miles Champion's exciting new *Tongue to Boot*. Keep looking out, you'll find a slot. And don't complain that nothing rhymes any more. Much does. That revival has been rolling now for years.

Are you up to this?

See if you are ready first. Are you personally convinced that your work is up to it? If you are uncertain, then most likely that will also be the view of everyone else. Check your text for glips and blips. Rework it. Root out any clichés or the odd appearance of what Peter Sansom calls 'spirit of the age' poetry words. Do without shards, lozenges, lambent patina, stippled seagulls. If by this time your writing still sounds okay, then go ahead.

Commercial publishers

Where something can be made from it a shrinking number of conglomerate imprints still have an interest in verse. If you are a sure seller like Wendy Cope, Roger McGough or Simon Armitage you'll be here in the thick of it - sought after, considered, possibly even offered reasonable advances on your work. But if you are simply a decent poet, then you'll be on the list, if you are there at all, simply to enhance the imprint. Slim volumes are not money spinners. Those publishers who bring them out get less year after year. Their commercial poetry editors almost always have other jobs within the company and are never allowed to publish everyone they would like.

Long-term market leader, the envy of the whole business and still streets ahead of anyone else is Faber & Faber. Since the great days of T.S. Eliot, as editor, this is the imprint most poets would like to join. With their distinctive jackets and their enormous back list, Faber have twentieth-century verse sewn up. Eliot, Pound, Hughes, Heaney and Plath are all with them. Faber competitors lack such a pedigree. Promotions and marketing ploys may help to increase public awareness of verse but editor Christopher Reid, along with Jane Feaver who handles children's books, will continue to publish good poetry regardless. Faber are aware of their leading role and intend to maintain it. Sales can be enormous - Auden's *Tell Me The Truth About Love* passing 100,000 copies and Wendy Cope's *Serious Concerns* shifting 60,000. Big contemporary names include Tom Paulin, Douglas Dunn, Maurice Riordan, Simon Armitage and Paul Muldoon. 'We aim to keep up a small but steady flow of new writers along with our established authors,' says Reid. Send a brief covering letter and a sample of your writing (10-20 poems) not forgetting s.a.e. if this is where you think you'll fit in.

Robin Robertson's move from **Secker & Warburg** to **Jonathan Cape**, one of Random House's many divisions, has seen that imprint successfully revive its 60s and 70s glory days as one of the UK's great poetry outlets. Robertson expects to bring out between four and six titles annually, no anthologies, no reprints, in well-designed, distinctive editions. 'Originality and excellence are the requirements.' Michael Longley, Mark Doty, John Burnside and James Lasdun are recent successes. Worth trying? 'Yes. Look at the books on the list first. Then submit at least 30-40 poems with a covering letter and return postage.'

At **Oxford University Press**, the traditional centre of English verse, poetry editor Jacqueline Simms kicks trends by maintaining an output of ten titles annually. Thick in the mix of Keats, Milton and Pope will be found contemporary voices Sean O'Brien (winner of the Forward Prize), George Szirtes, Jo

Shapcott, Moniza Alvi, Fleur Adcock, Penelope Shuttle and Roy Fisher. Loyalty to the 24 active writers on the list comes first but the press is 'always looking for distinct, original new poets'. They've taken Tobias Hill from **The National Poetry Foundation** and discovered Alice Oswald. Are total newcomers welcome? Yes, but 'we suggest new poets get experience of seeing their poems in print first among the literary magazines. We like to see a full collection, say 30–50 poems, worked out in a book order.'

Reed's only outlet for new poetry used to be Christopher Sinclair-Stevenson's eponymous **Sinclair-Stevenson** but all that remains now are a few contractual obligations – Michael Glover, Alice Kavounas, Herbert Lomas – and then, sadly, that's that.

The Harvill Press still try to publish two or three poetry titles annually. Under poetry editor Bill Swainson, they've managed Paul Durcan, Alan Ross, Raymond Carver and Joan Kapinski. They'll look at new manuscripts 'but there is only a small chance that they will be accepted. We prefer to receive collections from established poets.'

Elsewhere the lists have gone the way of all things. **Methuen** recycle their Brecht (while adding the popular John Hegley). **Hutchinson** stick with Dannie Abse. The Orion group's **Dent** imprint, once the bolt hole for Dylan Thomas and more recently home of R.S. Thomas' selected verse, have no interest in seeing new poetry from anyone else. Secker & Warburg, and Chatto both report they are 'not taking on any poetry for the indefinite future'. In commercial terms the poetry market has slid into the swamps.

The smaller operators

Not all commercial publishing is vast and conglomerate. The Scottish family firm **Ramsay Head Press**, under editor Christine Wilson, publish Tessa Ransford. In Wales **Gwasg Gomer** do Jon Dressel, Nigel Jenkins and Chris Bendon. The **Edinburgh University Press** imprint of **Polygon**, under poetry editors Marion Sinclair and Robert Crawford, has steadily moved ahead with a policy of Scottish 'poetry for the new generation'. The press has at least a dozen poets on its lists including Thomas Clark, W.N. Herbert and Liz Lochhead and likes to pursue 'a policy of promoting new, creative writing'. Northern Ireland's general publisher, **The Blackstaff Press**, under its editor Anne Tannahill, brings out between one and two titles annually, mainly of Irish interest. Joan Newmann, Paul Durcan and Frank Ormsby are typical. Send six typewritten poems here, if this is you.

Other dabblers

Poetry in the shape of single titles dot the lists of many UK publishers but this is hardly a declaration of interest or a desire to see more. **Robert Hale** publishes

Raymond Tong, **Marion Boyars** does Robert Creeley, **Robson Books** makes money out of former boxer Vernon Scannell. Generic anthologies are always popular. **J.A. Allen** does the poetry of horses, **Headline** poetry of the countryside, **Bloomsbury** do the war poets, **Cassell** collects the poems from the Underground, **Michael Joseph** does the family, **Routledge** nets the cross-gendered, while **Pavilion** publishes love verse. It is no good sending in single poems. These presses will not wish to know. **Macmillan**, **Deutsch** and others have the occasional title but it is all tokenism. American University Presses such as **Yale**, **Ohio**, **Duke**, **Iowa** and **California** along with **W.W. Norton** do some poetry, but exclusively by Americans, so no chances there. Some specialist interests are dealt with at **Lion** (Christian verse), **Peepal Tree** (Caribbean) and **Oscars** (gay) but it isn't a lot.

Women

It would be good to report that Britain's major feminist publishing house, **Virago**, had decided to run a major poetry list but according to editor Melanie Silgardo most of the little they do anyway is now on hold. Work by poets with established reputations such as Merle Collins, Michele Roberts and Margaret Atwood will continue to appear as will collections from black American poets such as Maya Angelou. But for the average UK woman poet? Not very much. 'We're not keen to see new volumes,' said Melanie, 'send them to **Bloodaxe**.' Virago's competitor, **The Women's Press**, has little interest in poetry other than the occasional black American titles and the continued success of the work of Alice Walker.

The paperbackers

The cheap and popular end is where many poets imagine the best starting place to be. Mass-market paperback houses were founded to publish inexpensive reprints of cloth-covered originals and to a large extent they still fulfil this role. But being neither cheap nor popular, poetry does not really fit in. Check the empires of **Arrow, Minerva**, **Headline** and **Transworld**. If you discount the inspirational, you won't find a book of verse between them. **Vintage** are trying out reprints of Iain Sinclair but he is also a successful novelist. **Picador**, the upmarket paperback arm of **Macmillan**, have also ventured into new territory with their marvellous *Conductors of Chaos* anthology of elective outsiders but this is no commitment to new work. At **Penguin**, however, things have always been different. Ever innovative, the company has correctly assessed the market for both traditional and contemporary verse and has systematically and successfully filled it. Reprinting important volumes pioneered by poetry presses such as **Anvil, Carcanet** and **Bloodaxe**, originating historic and thematic anthologies, reviving classic authors and producing a multitude of translations en route,

Penguin continues to provide an almost unrivalled introduction to the world of verse. But, appearances aside, this is definitely not the place for the untried. 'We are not in the field of discovering poets,' publishing director Tony Lacey told me. 'We leave that to the specialists.' Despite this general principle, the company still originates a few titles with Craig Raine and Roger McGough serving as good examples. The main thrust, however, is still the repackaging of proven top-sellers such as James Fenton, Simon Armitage, Carol Ann Duffy and Dannie Abse backed with a programme of modern poets in translation along with larger sets from the likes of Allen Ginsberg, John Ashbery and Hugh MacDiarmid. Most poetry interest, nonetheless, has been in the revived *Penguin Modern Poets* series, which, while not hitting the bestsellers, has still managed to shift a few copies. Trios of loosely-connected poets are repackaged and issued at afforable prices. Duffy, Armitage, Eavan Boland, Fenton, Blake Morrison and others have already hit the shelves. Further volumes are expected from Scotland, Ireland, the West Country, older male practitioners along with Britain's black women plus even a volume of new youngsters. But, with the possible exception of the Sinclair/Oliver/Riley Slamdance, it is a safe selection. Up ahead lies Robert Crawford and Simon Armitage's new anthology of post-war British poetry. The future will no doubt be controversial, thank god.

The specialists

Without a doubt the real poetry presses of the UK and Ireland are now the specialists. As the commercial empires crumble so the independents blossom. A host of semi-commercial operations are now scattered across the country. They are run by genuine poetry enthusiasts whose prime concern is not so much money as the furtherance of their art. Begun as classic small presses which soon outgrow the restraints of back-bedroom offices and under-the-stairs warehousing, they emerge by stealth. Most now have national representation of some sort, with a number using *Password*, the subsidised poetry specialists (23 New Mount Street, Manchester M4 4DE), who issue a very useful catalogue. These presses have learned well how the business works. You can find them in Waterstones; you can see them in Dillons. Most (but not all) receive grant aid, without which their publishing programmes would be sunk. They are models of what poetry publishing should be – active, involving, alert, and exciting. Their numbers grow year on year. Never before have new poets been faced with so many publishing opportunities. Reports coming in from these activists tell of a slowing of interest, of failures, of bookshops making heavy returns. In contrast to their commercial fellow practitioners, who talk only of a steadying of enterprise, the specialists all seem set for seige.

For many years leaders of the pack Carcanet is by now almost indistinguishable from its trade competitors. Although no longer exclusively a publisher of verse, it still maintains a substantial interest in poetry, and has over 500 titles in print and reps in 42 countries. Managing director Michael Schmidt agrees with Auden's observation that most people who read verse read it for some reason other than the poetry. No guidance comes from our national press who offer serious criticism far less frequently than they used to. Sales of individual titles have sunk to three figures. He fights the tide with his own serious journal, *PN Review,* whose fat 100th issue a year or so back provided a splendid overview of Carcanet's style. The press concentrates on producing substantial editions which make a poet's whole *oeuvre* available alongside cheap selected poems and new titles from both the untried and the famous. Typical of their list are John Ashbery, Eavan Boland, Sophie Hannah, Les Murray, Vicki Raymond and best-seller, Elizabeth Jennings. New poets are welcome to send in material, so long as they have at least read carefully a selection of Carcanet's output and enclose the all important s.a.e.. Justin Quinn was a great success last year, Miles Champion will be next. Carcanet has an air of studied seriousness about it. 'We avoid the Technicolor and pyrotechnic media razzmatazz,' says Schmidt, adding that 'it may be time, at this cloudy *fin-de-siecle*, to declare that the field of poetry "is no longer Trojan Plain ... but Parnassus"'. At Carcanet the poets have reworked the whole Imaginary Museum.

Tony Ward's stylish **Arc Publications**, which successfully incorporates the former poetry imprint of Littlewood Arc, uses two associate editors, Michael Hulse (international) and David Morley (UK), to promote a contemporary list which increases at the rate of around eight or nine titles annually. Arc looks for innovation and diversity ignoring fashion and the 'philistine camp of market forces'. The 'renaissance' of recent times has had a positive effect on the quality of work being published, so Ward believes. His bestsellers include the ever pop-ular Ivor Cutler, E.A. Markham, Jackie Willis (a PBS choice), W.N. Herbert and John Harley Williams. Ward remains sniffy about bookshops who won't stock his product. Arc poetry gets there by other routes. Advice to contributors: 'Unsolicited material is welcome from writers whose work has appeared in poetry magazines but check the Arc list first.' Send a large s.a.e. for a catalogue.

Enitharmon Press represents quality, cares about presentation and, rare among poetry presses, has a real concern for internal design. Its books, poet/artist editions and pamphlets are produced to the highest of standards. Enitharmon has little interest in fashion, preferring 'poetry of the human spirit', which exhibits 'moral imagination'. Owner Stephen Stuart-Smith continues a policy of publishing poetry by new, established and unjustly neglected poets not only from Britain and Ireland but from many other parts of the world. David Gascoyne's *Selected Poems* sells alongside Jane Duran's Forward prize-winner *Breathe Now, Breathe.* Typical poets include Kevin Crossley-Holland, Anna Adams, Sebastian Barker and Jeremy Reed. But the times are taking their toll. 'At present, the recession is so severe that Enitharmon is not in a position to consider new work.' Help keep one of our best going: buy their books.

Peterloo Poets, run by the redoubtable Harry Chambers, represents poetry without frills, without fuss and most definitely without the avant-garde. The press aims to publish quality work by new or neglected poets, some of them late-starters, to co-publish with reputable presses abroad (Goose Lane in Canada, Storyline Press in Oregon and Lagan Press in Ireland) and to establish a Peterloo list of succeeding volumes by a core of poets of proven excellence. Chambers avoids anthologies and has finished with magazines and newsletters. The press does books and does them well. Bestsellers include U.A. Fanthorpe, John Whitworth and Dana Gioia. John Latham, Ann Drysdale, Anna Adams and John Glenday are recent additions to the list. Chambers runs his own poetry competition sponsored by Marks and Spencers (£3000 first prize) and insists that prospective contributors to his press have had at least six poems in reputable magazines. Send a full mss accompanied by a stamped envelope large enough to carry your mss back to you. Chambers currently takes three months to reply and is full until 1998.

Peter Jay's **Anvil Press** was founded in 1968 and for a long time ran as a classic alternative publisher, set up in formal opposition to the Fabers and OUPs of the poetry scene. He still sticks to an original coterie of poets and makes what personality cult he can of Harry Guest, Peter Levi, Anthony Howell and Heather Buck. 'Less is slightly better than too much,' says Jay, encapsulating Anvil's way of dealing with our nineties poetry overproduction. The press has quiet style and pays much attention to presentation both inside the book and out. Anvil's runaway bestseller is Carol Ann Duffy who also edits their useful *Anvil New Poets* anthology. Check this for a sample of the press's work. Typical poets include Michael Hamburger, James Harpur, E.A. Markham and Sue Stewart.

Seren Books (the Welsh for 'star') was an offshoot of the magazine *Poetry Wales* until 1988, when founder Cary Archard correctly perceived that poetry alone would never keep them afloat and diversified into novels, short fiction, biographies and critical texts. In receipt of significant Arts Council finance, their commitment to poetry still remains central with at least half a dozen new titles annually. 'Poetry is not in retreat, we think,' says editor Amy Wack. 'Many good new poets suddenly arriving.' Deryn Rees Jones, Tim Liardet, Leslie Norris, Tony Curtis, Robert Minhinick, R.S. Thomas and Duncan Bush are among their topsellers. When sending, Welsh authors or Welsh connections are preferred. 'Make typescript presentable and include return postage.' A good press sampler is their anthology *Burning the Bracken*. They have also published their own guide to the scene, *The Poetry Business*.

If poets once went to the commercial operators for wide distribution, they now cluster around Neil Astley's **Bloodaxe Books** for the concern, company and intelligent promotion that imprint provides. Picking up poets dropped by the commercial operators and selling on to the world's anthologists, this is certainly one of poetry's best proving grounds. Based in Newcastle upon Tyne and begun little over a decade ago, the press is unhindered by a past catalogue of classical greats or an overly regional concern. It relentlessly pursues the new. Regarded by some as garish and fast, Bloodaxe is now the UK's only real rival to the otherwise unassailable Faber. Poetry is absolutely central with a vast list as exciting, innovative and varied as anyone could wish. Astley presents the complete service from thematic anthologies, world greats, and selecteds to individual slim volumes by total newcomers. The press has its own range of excellent handbooks to the scene including Paul Hyland's *Getting Into Poetry* and Peter Sansom's *Writing Poems* along with an increasing range of critical volumes including Sean O'Brien's acclaimed assessment of contemporary British and Irish verse, *The De-regulated Muse*. Astley chastises the system for spreading media attention of the few at the critical expense of the many but admits that any attention helps sell. He reports fewer returns than his fellows but then Bloodaxe is spending more these days on marketing. Bestsellers include Peter Reading, Tony Harrison, R.S. Thomas, Brendan Keneally's best-titled book of the year, *Poetry My Arse*, along with Linda France's anthology, *Sixty Women Poets* and Jenni Couzyn's *Contemporary Women Poets*. Way out front, as expected, is their controversial decade-framing anthology *The New Poetry,* recently set for A-level. Typical recent poets include Selima Hill, Stephen Knight, Maura Dooley and Adrian Mitchell. Bloodaxe welcomes newcomers but since they receive at least 100 new collections a week, advise that you can increase your chance of an early answer by restricting yourself to sending a dozen of your best. If Bloodaxe wants to see more, they'll ask. A simple way to taste the imprint's range is to try their anthology *Poetry With An Edge*.

Coming a long way from its humble beginnings as a booklet and wild small mag publishing obsession is Rupert Loydell's commendable **Stride**. Based in the south west, the press has a hundred or so titles in print ranging from the totally unknown to the famous. Innovative poetry in small and medium size sets, alternative anthologies, criticism and interviews form the backbone. No Faber imitators in presentation but these days, certainly, slick enough. Loydell reckons that 'poetry is now in retreat from the "fashionable" tag it was lumbered with by marketing executives.' The poets he takes on need to be committed enough to sell themselves. 'Tell Stride how *you*, an author, are going to help sell the book. We're not talking money but promotion and marketing.' Bestsellers include Peter Redgrove, Jennie Fontana, Mary Plain's selection of women's poetry, Jay Ramsay's *Earth Ascending* anthology along with Stride's poetry tributes to Bob Dylan and the Beatles. Send for their lists and if you write near the edge you could find a home here.

There are other publishers who show strong signs of outgrowing their hobbyist or regional status. In Dublin, John F. Deane's **Dedalus Press** is a decade-old poetry operator with almost 100 titles on its list, mostly Irish but not invariably. Typical poets include Thomas Kinsella, Denis Delvin, John Ennis, John Jordan and Pat Boran. The imprint runs a magazine, *Tracks* and has a fine sampler in *Dedalus Irish Poets An Anthology*. Peter Fallon's County Meath-based **Gallery Press** has been around since 1970 publishing pamphlets and volumes by Irish poets such as Michael Hartnett, Gerald Dawe, Ciaron Carson, Paul Muldoon, Eilean Ni Chuilleanain, John Montague and many others. In Newcastle Peter Elfed Lewis's **Flambard Press** produces books to rival

Bloodaxe. With aid from Northern Arts the press sees a role for itself as an outlet for new or neglected writers from the north of England. Gerard Benson, Peter Mortimer, Geoffrey Holloway and Alicia Stubbersfield publish here. Also up north is Peter Sansom and Janet Fisher's **Smith/Doorstop**, the book imprint of their enterprising **The Poetry Business**, at our poetry capital, Huddersfield. They do Stanley Cook, Martin Stannard, John Lyons and others in classy Bloodaxe-clone format and have struck out successfully with a series of poets on cassette. Jill Dick's **Scottish Cultural Press** in Aberdeen is off to a fine start with a four volume annual output that includes Jenni Daiches, Gerry Cambridge and Valerie Gillies. The famous National Poetry Foundation continues their good work among the lesser knowns although getting a book by Forward prize-winner Tobias Hill certainly changes their status. Just where these publishers end and classic small presses start is getting as hard to tell as ever.

The traditional outlets

There exists a small, traditional market for new poetry, enlarged in the face of hype-driven booms, but nonetheless still a very minor component of the total scene. Poetry has a place in the national press. The *Independent* runs a daily poem (for which no one gets paid, the paper regarding it as a showcase for publishers – prospective contributors are advised to send their books – loose poems get binned), *The Guardian* features verse from time to time, as do the Sunday heavies. *The Times Literary Supplement* gives over considerable space on a regular basis, whole double page spreads devoted to the work of one poet or to a long single poem are not unusual although they have their favourites. *The London Review of Books* shows a similar interest. Mostly though, the traditional market centres around *The London Magazine*, which has the reputation for being the fastest responder in the business (you walk to the post box, mail your poems, then return home to find them rejected and waiting for you on the mat); *The Spectator, New Statesman and Society* (where Adrian Mitchell is poetry editor); Auberon Waugh's *The Literary Review*, plus the occasional spot in magazines like *The Lady* and *The Countryman* – all paying outlets, which sounds quite reassuring. Some local newspapers also consider poetry, although the chances of earning much in this market are much slighter. Try sending your work in the form of a letter to Postbag. For those interested, the magazine *Poetry Now* has published a list. But the truth is that were poetry to cease to exist overnight, then these publications would continue to publish without a flicker. Who, other than the poets, would notice?

The regional anthologies

Running in parallel with the high ground literary approach of much of the forementioned poetry publishing is an empire largely unknown to the taste-makers and ignored by the critics. Ian and Tracy Walton's distinctly ground-floor

Forward Press in Peterborough now turns over a million and a half annually by putting out more new poetry titles than the rest of the commercial business combined. Depressed with 'twenty years of not being able to enjoy poetry' because it was inevitably obscure, the couple have moved from back kitchen to factory unit in the service of 85,000 active British verse scribblers. Publishing under a variety of imprints including **Poetry Now, Arrival Press, Anchor Books** and **Triumph House**, the operation receives in excess of 100,000 submissions annually. Poets are sourced through free editorial copy in regional newspapers. 'Peterborough publishers are looking for contributions to their new poetry anthology *Poetry Now Lincolnshire & Humberside*' is a typical line. The contributors flow in their hundreds. 'It's a bit like amateur dramatics,' Ian told me, 'anyone can take part.'

The operation's success is built on its sheer approachability. Perpetuating a poetry world's Home and Away image, the Walton's and their team of editors include as many as two hundred poems in their anthologies. Costs are kept down by using in-house hi-tech printing equipment coupled to serviceable bindings. If you want to see your work, and for most contributors this is the whole *raison d'etre,* then you have to buy a copy. For many poets this will be their first appearance in book form and chances are they will want more than one. This is not a vanity operation by any means. No one is actually being ripped off nor are the publishers raking in exorbitant profits. But the literary achievement of appearing in one of these books is questionable. In mitigation it must be said, though, that for some people this will be a much-needed beginning and for others the only success they are going to get.

Ian reckons that at around 500 titles a year the limits have been reached, in the UK at least. Forward Press, with its two magazines *Poetry Now* and *Rhyme Arrival* selling just as many copies as *Poetry Review*, need to look elsewhere. Already they are cooperating with War on Want, The Samaritans, Barnardo's, Missions to Seamen and others to publish a series of charity anthologies and with their thematic collections of green-fingered, gay, mother and daughter, socialist, lottery-winning, and war poetry have filled as many gaps as there are. If *Poetry Now Young Writers - All Aboard for East Sussex* sounds like your scene then send for the Walton's catalogue (1-2 Wainman Road, Woodston, Peterborough PE2 7BU) or ring them up (01733 230759). You'll find no dubious accommodation address dealing here, but, on the other hand, few literary giants either.

The small press and the little magazine

Amateur publishing ventures have been with us for quite a long time. Virginia Woolf began the **Hogarth Press** this way, quite literally on the kitchen table. But it was not until well after the Second World War and the rise of what the Americans called the mimeo revolution that poetry magazine and pamphlet publishing really took off. Recent advances in technology have seen that revolution moved on to a considerable degree. Computer literate poets are everywhere. Publishing has been stripped of its mystery. Access to photocopiers, laser printers and desktop publishing packages are commonplace. Disposable income has gone up. Poets in growing numbers are able and willing to set up competent one-person publishing operations, turning out neat professional-looking titles on a considerable scale.

These are the small presses and the little magazines. They sell to new and often non-traditional markets rarely finding space on bookshop shelves, where they are regarded as unshiftable nuisances. Instead they go hand to hand among friends at poetry readings, creative writing classes, literary functions, via subscriptions, and are liberally exchanged among all those concerned. The question remains: is anyone out there not directly concerned with the business of poetry actually reading it? But that is another story.

Numerically, the small presses and the little magazines are the largest publishers of new poetry both in terms of range and total sales. They operate in a variety of shapes and sizes everywhere from Cardiff to Caithness and Lewes to Llandudno. The present wave of enthusiasm has thrown up a variety of support organisations to whom new poets may well direct their initial enquiries. The **Association of Little Presses** in particular, produces a useful newsletter as well as a new publications listing magazine, *PALPI*.

This country's best poetry magazines all began as classic littles. Between them *PN Review*, *Ambit*, *Agenda*, *Outposts*, *Orbis*, *Poetry Review*, *Rialto* and *Stand* do not come up to even half the circulation of journals like *Shooting Times* and *Practical Fishkeeping* – which says a lot about the way in which we value our poetry. Nonetheless, taken as a group, they will get to almost everyone who matters. In the second division in terms of kudos lie the regional or genre specialists such as *Poetry Wales*, *Lines Review*, *Poetry Ireland*, *New Welsh Review*, *Poetry Nottingham*, *Poetry Durham*, *Queer Words,* (the paperback mag of new lesbian and gay writing), *Cadmium Blue* (traditional romantic and lyrical poetry), *Psycopoetica* (psychologically based poetry), *Haiku Quarterly* and *Krax* (humorous verse). All these magazines are well produced, often with the help of grants, and all representative of a specific point of view. In Wales there is *Barddas* for poets using the strict meters and in Scotland *Lallans* for poets writing in Lowland Scots. The vast majority of small magazines, however, owe no allegiance and range from fat irregulars like *Bête Noire* and *Angel Exhaust,* quality general round-ups like *Scratch* and *Iron* (Why Iron? 'Because we hate poetry competitions. Because we've never been in the *TLS*'), to fleeting pamphlets like *The Yellow Crane* (interesting new poems), *Edible Society* (poetry, art and fresh air), *Pulsar* (poetry for pleasure), *Fat Chance* and *Rustic Rub*. Some, such as *Sepia* insist on poetry without cliché and without rhyme; *Living Poets* you get only if you have an on-line computer; while *Poetry Now* from Peterborough is run like a verse tabloid awash with stuff from totally new names.

There have been deaths. *Odyssey*, Derrick Woolf's splendid example of open-mindedness is gone, so are *Ore, Bare Bones, Joe Soap's Canoe* and *Westwords*. In their place, *Other Poetry*, *New Scottish Epoch*, *Poetic Hours*, *PPQ* (poetry on post-cards), *Red Herring*, *Blade*, *Rivet*, *Mana*, *Magma* and a host of others. Anything and everything you could want.

Among the presses there is a similar range. **Hippopotamus Press** publishes first collections and work by the neglected; Bob Cobbing's **Writers Forum** sticks to mainstream experimental; **Direction Poetry** publishes cassettes; **Dangaroo** and **Peepal Tree Press** have third world and ethnic concerns; **Katabasis** is interested in Latin American and is now expanding its English list; **Scratch**, **Staple First Editions** and **Rockingham Press** work at the edge of the mainstream; **KQBX** handles quality; **The Black Gate Press** has an interest in the Byzantine; **The Daft Lad Press** specialises in the work of Chris Challis; **The Underground Press** covers the workless valleys; **Pickpockets** does it so small you can hide a set up your sleeve; **Oscars Press** covers gay poetry; **On The Wire Press** does Christian verse; **Y Lolfa** publishes unofficial bards; **The Red Sharks Press** deals in anti-sheepist verse. For the new writer these kinds of presses are the obvious places to try first. Indeed it is where many have. Who put out T.S. Eliot's first? A small publisher. Dannie Abse, Peter Redgrove, James Fenton and Dylan Thomas, the same. R.S. Thomas, Ezra Pound and Edgar Allen Poe didn't even go that far – they published themselves.

Cash

A lot of writers new to the business are surprised to learn that their poetry will not make them much money. Being a poet is not really much of an occupation. You get better wages delivering papers. There will be the odd pound from the better heeled magazine, perhaps even as much as £40 or so from those peri-odicals lucky enough to be in receipt of a grant, but generally it will be free copies of the issues concerned, thank you letters and little more. Those with col-lections published by a subsidised, specialist publisher can expect a couple of hundred as an advance on royalties. Those using the small presses can look for-ward to a few dozen complimentary copies. The truth is that poetry itself is undervalued. You can earn money writing about it, reviewing it, lecturing on it or certainly by giving public recitations (£100 standard here, £500 if you are Tony Harrison, more if you are Ted Hughes). In fact, most things in the poetry business will earn better money than the verse itself. Expect to spend a lot on stamps and a fair bit on sample copies. Most of the time all you'll get in return is used envelopes.

Readings

Since the great Beat Generation, Albert Hall reading of 1964, there has been an ever-expanding phenomenon of poets on platforms, reading or reciting their stuff to an audience that can be anywhere between raptly attentive and fast asleep. Jaci Stephen, writing in *The Daily Mirror*, reckoned readings to be like jazz. 'Both involve a small group of people making a lot of noise, and then, just when you think it's all over, it carries on.' But I believe there can be a magic in the spoken poem. The music lives, the images echo. Yet for some writers the whole thing has devolved so far as to become a branch of the entertainment industry; for others, it is an essential aspect of what they do. Whichever way you view it, it is certainly an integral part of the business and one in which the beginner is going to need to engage sooner or later. Begin by attending and see how others manage. Watch out for local events advertised at your local library or ring your local arts board. Poets with heavy reputations can often turn out to be lousy performers while many an amateur can really shake it down. Don't expect to catch every image as you listen. Readings do not go in for total comprehension but more for glancing blows. Treat it as fun and it will be. If you are trying things yourself for the first time, make sure you've brought your books along to sell, stand upright, drop the shoulders, gaze at a spot at the back of the hall and blow.

Competitions

Poetry competitions have been the vogue for more than a decade now with the most unlikely organisations sponsoring them. The notion here is that anonymity ensures fairness. Entries are made under pseudonyms so that if your name does happen to be Miroslav Holub, then this won't help you much. Results seem to bear this out too. The big competitions run biennially by the **Arvon Foundation** with the help of commercial sponsors, or the Poetry Society's National attract an enormous entry and usually throw up quite a number of complete unknowns among the winners. And why do people bother? Cash prizes can be large – thousands of pounds – but it costs at least a pound a poem to enter, and often much more than that. If it is cash you want, then the Lottery scratch-cards are a better bet. And there has been a trend for winners to come from places like Cape Girardeau, Missouri and Tibooburra, Australia. The odds are getting longer. Who won the last Arvon? I don't remember. But if you do fancy a try then it is a pretty innocent activity. You tie up a poem for a few months and you spend a couple of pounds. Winners' tips include reading the work of the judges to see how they do it, submitting non-controversial middle-of-the-road smiling things, and doing this just before the closing date so you won't have to wait too long. Try two or three of your best. Huge wodges are costly and will only convince the judges of your insecurity. Watch the small mags for details, write to your regional arts board, check out *Quartos*, *Writer's News* or the listings in *Orbis* magazine, look on the notice board at your local library, or write for the regularly updated list from **The Poetry Library** in London (see **Poetry Organisations**).

Radio and TV

The regular slots are all on radio, naturally enough. It is so hard to make verse visually appealing. Some TV producers have tried, notably Peter Symes who produced both *Poet's News* and *Words On Film* for BBC2. Symes' approach is to avoid the illustrated poem and to concentrate instead on documentary-style collaborations between commissioned poet and film-maker. His great successes have all been with Tony Harrison although projects with Simon Armitage, Jackie Kay, Lem Sissay, Fred D'agir and others underline his open approach. 'The crucial thing,' he advises, 'is an ability to write to picture and not to rely on things the other way around.' If you have a project in mind, rather than a set of existing poems, then he would be delighted to hear from you. On Radio Four, Susan Roberts produces two regular programmes: *Poetry Please,* presented by Gareth Owen which runs listeners' requests (everything from John Donne to Carol Ann Duffy) along with features on things like Shakespeare's birthday, and *Stanza*, a late night poetry in performance slot fronted by Simon Armitage. In addition, there is *Talking Poetry*, an occasional series of readings for youngsters along with *With Great Pleasure* where prominent figures from public life choose their favourite pieces. Newcomers can try their hands at sending in but most of the slots go to the better knowns. On Radio Three, Fiona McLean produces *Best Words*, a monthly poetry magazine programme presented by Michael Rosen along with features by Simon Armitage, George Szirtes and others. She also does *Young Poets*, a series of ten-minute programmes featuring the new. Other producers such as Piers Plowright, Elizabeth Burke, Daniel Snowman and Julian May at the *Kaleidoscope* programme all put out the occasional poetry feature. Classic FM are trying verse as fillers. An enlarging but difficult market. If you are determined to put your verse on air then local radio offers better possibilities. Try sending in self-produced readings on cassette (if you are any good at it) or topical poetry which regional magazine programmes could readily use. Don't expect to be paid much.

Cyber Po

The term 'electronic media' can strike dread in the hearts of many. The newness, the difficulty, and the expense combine to make this an area to be avoided at all costs. But for those computer literate from birth there is no other way forward. In a recent Mori poll two out of three people thought the paper book would be dead within fifteen years. In its place the rapacious capacity of the CD-ROM, the enormity of Internet, the flexibility of the computer screen. In terms of communication these media are genuinely new and show every sign of lasting. And poetry has not been slow to join in. Already the entirety of English poetry published from 600 to 1900 is available from **Chadwyck-Healey** on a set of CDs (*English Poetry: The Full Text Database*) and at least one press, Sunk Island, is publishing poetry in disk form (check out their address in the listings and write for their *Electronic Poetry Pack*). The big development, however, has been in the number of poetry operators putting themselves on to the Net. When I tried sending a search-engine called Web Crawler out to hunt poetry pages it came back with a listing of more than 2000. These ranged from the University of North Carolina which provided me with colour screens of Seamus Heaney plus the poet reading from my speakers to listings of experimental poetry outlets via the Buffalo Electronic Poetry Centre, and from one-person operations in Oregon ('leave your name to say you've been') to well-arranged inter-active poetry magazines in Australia. Distance, political and geographical boundaries now mean nothing. Only language itself marks us apart. In the UK, Peter Daniels at **Poetry London** and Sean Woodward at **The Living Poets Society** (see **Poetry Organisations**.) have set up operations. As the technology gets cheaper many others are doing the same. The biggest so far is the Poetry Society who have launched its *Poetry Map* on the World Wide Web and is providing a bard's version of the cyber cafe at its new Poetry Place at Betterton Street. See the Society's entry under **Poetry Organisations** for more information.

Poetry on the Net can be changed in an instant, posted, deleted, commented upon and explained at will. To get to it is easy and, given rudimentary keyboard skills, a highly fulfilling activity. It is also as impermanent as performance and as lasting as the daily news. Who would stack it on their library shelves? Who would want to.

Starting up

Probably the best place will be locally. Find out through the library or the nearest arts board which writers groups gather in your area and attend. There you will meet others of a like mind, encounter whatever locally produced magazines there might be and get a little direct feedback on your work. 'How am I doing?' is a big question for the emerging poet and although criticism is not all that hard to come by, do not expect it from all sources. Magazine editors, for example, will rarely have the time to offer advice. It is also reasonable to be suspicious of that offered by friends and relations – they will no doubt be only trying to please. Writers groups present the best chance for poets to engage in honest mutual criticism. But if you'd prefer a more detached, written analysis of your efforts and are willing to pay a small sum, then you could apply to the service operated nationally by the Poetry Society (22 Betterton Street, London WC2H 9BU), by The Arts Council of Wales (see **Arts Councils and Regional Arts Boards**) or to one of those run on an area basis by your local arts board. There are also a number of non-subsidised critical services which you will find advertised in writers' magazines.

If you have made the decision to publish your work – and I don't suppose you'd be reading this if you hadn't – then the first thing to do is a little market research. I've already indicated how overstocked the business is with periodicals and publications, yet surprisingly you will not find many of these in your local W.H. Smith. Most poetry still reaches its public via the specialist. However, begin by reading a few newly published mainstream books. Ask at your book-seller for their recommendations. Check Waterstones or Dillons who both do a good job. Most shops these days carry a basic stock, but if you need a specialist then get hold of the Poetry Library's current list of shops with a specific interest in poetry. Enquire at the library. Try selecting a recent anthology of contempo-rary verse. To get a broad view of what's going on, not only should you read Hulse, Kennedy and Morley's Bloodaxe *The New Poetry*, but the annual *Forward Book of Poetry* (Faber); Mike Horovitz's *Grandchildren of Albion* (New Departures); Paul Beasley's *Popular Front of Contemporary Poetry* (Apples and Snakes); Bob Cobbing's *Verbi Visi Voco* (Writer's Forum); Edward Lucie Smith's Penguin *British Poetry Since 1945*; and perhaps Seamus Heaney and Ted Hughes' *The Rattle Bag* (Faber); Jeni Couzyn's *The Bloodaxe Book of Contemporary Women Poets*; Linda France's *Sixty Women Poets* (Bloodaxe); *Conductors of Chaos* edited by Iain Sinclair (Picador); William Oxley's *Completing the Picture* (Stride); *From the Other Side of the Century – A New American Poetry 1960-1990* edited by Douglas Messerli (Sun & Moon), and *Postmodern American Poetry,* a really splen-did selection edited by Paul Hoover (Norton). These last two might be harder to find but will be worth the effort. Progress to the literary magazine. Write off to a number of the magazine addresses which follow this article and ask the price of sample copies. Enquire about subscriptions. Expect to pay a little but inevitably it will not be a lot. It is important that poets read not only to famil-iarise themselves with what is currently fashionable and to increase their own facility for self-criticism, but to help support the activity in which they wish to participate. Buy – this is vital for little mags, it is the only way in which they are going to survive. Read; if it's all a mystery to you, try Tony Curtis' *How to Study Modern Poetry* (Macmillan); Peter Sansom's excellent *Writing Poems* (Bloodaxe) or my own *The Poetry Business* (Seren). How real poets actually work can be dis-covered by reading C.B. McCully's the *Poet's Voice and Craft* (Carcanet). After all this, if you still think it's appropriate, try sending in.

How to do it

Increase your chances of acceptance by following simple, standard procedure:
- Type on a single side of the paper, A4 size, single-spacing with double between stanzas exactly as you'd wish your poem to appear when printed.
- Give the poem a title, clip multi-page works together, include your name and address at the foot of the final sheet. Avoid files, plastic covers, stiffeners and fancy clips of any sort.
- Keep a copy, make a record of what you send where and when, leave a space to note reaction.

- Send in small batches – six is a good number – with a brief covering letter saying who you are. Leave justification, apology and explanation for your writers circle.
- Include a self-addressed, stamped envelope of sufficient size for reply and/or return of your work.
- Be prepared to wait some weeks for a response. Don't pester. Be patient. Most magazines will reply in the end.
- Never send the same poem to two places at the same time.
- Send your best. Work which fails to fully satisfy even the author is unlikely to impress anyone else.

Where?

Try the list which follows, sending for samples as suggested. The total market is vast – 200 or so addresses here – hundreds more in *Small Presses and Little Magazines of the UK and Ireland* (HMSO Oriel, The Friary, Cardiff – £4 including postage for the latest edition) and in *Light's List of Literary Magazines* which contains both UK and US addresses (John Light, The Lighthouse, 29 Longfield Road, Tring, Hertfordshire HP23 4DG), literally thousands and thousands worldwide in Christine Martin's *Poet's Market* (Writer's Digest Books) and Len Fulton's *Directory of Poetry Publishers* (Dustbooks) – the two main American directories. **The British Council** has also published *British Literary Periodicals – A Selected Bibliography* which covers some littles along with scholarly journals. Up to the minute information can be found in *Zene*, the small press guide, published quarterly by Andy Cox and Mark Rose at 5 Martin's Lane, Witcham, Ely, Cambridgeshire CB6 2LB.

Scams to avoid

In the world of sly schemes and scams things are changing fast. Gone are the days when a simple classified advert asking for poets to contribute to a forthcoming anthology would be enough to net the publisher a fortune. Letters to poets telling them that their work has 'unusual class and high potential' and then asking them to 'contribute forty pounds to help offset ever increasing publishing costs' are in the decline. The recent, unstinting (and if you were on the receiving end, demonic) work of the National Poetry Foundation's Johnathon Clifford has cleared many of the con men from the scene. In the firm belief that published poetry should provide its authors with free copies at least, if not an actual royalty, Clifford set about testing the many companies advertising for verse. Sending them a selection of grossly amateur items in the tradition of William McGonagall he was amazed to receive a sheaf of letters praising him as a poet of real worth, suggesting that in 'partnership' they should go right ahead and publish his shining verses and could he find his way to stumping up the odd £3000 to help pay the bills. No problem. If Clifford had been an inexperienced new writer then he might have fallen for the deal, sold the family silver and invested in what would sadly turn out to be a no-hope project where the books would languish unsold, unwanted and unread in a distant warehouse or more probably under the author's bed. Instead Clifford wrote up his experiences (*Vanity Press & The Proper Poetry Publishers* available at £6.00 from 27 Mill Road, Fareham, Hampshire PO16 0TH) and began a campaign against the vanity industry of back-street operators, accommodation addresses, and abandoned value judgements. You get published by the vanity presses because you pay and not because you are any good. His report *Vanity Publishers: The Facts and the Fiction* led to a ruling by the Advertising Standards Authority which now severely limits the future operation of such publishers. You can't advertise that which you cannot provide. Poets can once again sleep peacefully in their beds.

But not quite. Already variations and embellishments on the vanity press theme are surfacing. These include offers to put your poetry to music setting you off on the road to stardom, readings of your verse by actors with deep voices to help you break into the local radio market (there isn't one) and further requests for cash to have entries on you appear in leather-bound directories of world poets. Everyone appears, including your uncle. There are bogus competitions where entry fees bear no relation to final prize money and the advertised 'publication of winners in anthology form', often means shelling out more for what will turn out to be a badly printed potch of pusillanimity. Poets should be wary of suggestions that they have come high in the State of Florida's Laureateship Contest (or some such like) and have been awarded a framed certificate. Presentation usually occurs at a three-day festival held in one of the state's most expensive hotels. To get your bit of paper you need to stay for all three days and it is you who has to settle the bill.

In this game if anyone asks you for money then forget it. It is not the way things should be done.

The next step

Once you have placed a few poems you may like to consider publishing a booklet. There are as many small presses around as there are magazines. Start with the upmarket professionals by all means – Oxford University Press, Jonathan Cape, Faber & Faber – but be prepared for compromise. The specialists and the small presses are swifter and more open to new work.

If all else fails you could do it yourself. Blake did, so did Walt Whitman. Modern technology puts the process within the reach of us all and if you can put up a shelf, there is a fair chance you will be able to produce a book to go on it. Read my *How to Publish Yourself* (Allison & Busby), Barry Turner's *The Writer's Companion* (Macmillan) and Jonathan Zeitlyn's *Print: How You Can Do It Yourself* (Journeyman). Remember that publishing the book may be as hard as writing it but marketing and selling it is quite something else. If you are determined, have a look at Bill Godber, Robert Webb and Keith Smith's excellent *Marketing For Small Publishers* (Journeyman).

The listings

None of the lists of addresses which follow are exhaustive. Publishers come and go with amazing frequency. There will always be the brand new press on the look-out for talent and the projected magazine desperate for contributions. For up to the minute information check some of the **Organisations of Interest to Poets** in the lists which follow. Poetry has a huge market. It pays to keep your ear to the ground.

Commercial publishers carrying contemporary poetry

See main article. For addresses, see under **UK Publishers**

The specialists

See main article. For addresses, see under **UK Publishers** and **Poetry Presses**

Poetry presses

Active in Airtime See also **Active in Airtime** magazine, 53 East Hill, Colchester, Essex CO1 3QY

Acumen Publications See also **Acumen** magazine, *Patricia Oxley*, 6 The Mount, High Furzeham, Brixham, S. Devon TQ5 8QY

Agenda Editions See also **Agenda** magazine, *William Cookson & others*, 5 Cranbourne Court, Albert Bridge Road, London SW11 4PE

Aireings Press See also **Aireings** magazine, *Jean Barker*, 24 Brudenell Road, Leeds, West Yorkshire LS6 1BD

Akros Publications *Duncan Glen*, 18 Warrender Park Terrace, Edinburgh EH9 1EF

Allardyce, Barnett, Publishers See under **Small Presses**

Aloes Books *Jim Pennington & others*, 110 Mountview Road, London N4 4JH

Alun Books (includes **Goldleaf & Barn Owl Press**) *Sally Jones*, 3 Crown Street, Port Talbot, West Glamorgan SA13 1BG

Amazing Colossal Press *Maureen Richardson*, PO Box 177, Nottingham NG3 5JT

Amra Imprint *Bill Griffiths*, 21 Alfred Street, Seaham, Co. Durham SR7 7LH

Anarcho Press *Stan Trevor*, Briagha, Badninish, Dornoch, Sutherland IV25 3JB

Anchor Press See also **Poetry Now** and **Rhyme Arrival** magazines, *Ian Walton*, 1-2 Wainman Road, Woodston, Peterborough, Cambs PE2 7BU

Ankle Books 153 Gwydir Street, Cambridge CB1 2LJ

Anvil Press Poetry See under **UK Publishers**

Apparitions Press See also **Stride Publications** *Rupert Loydell*, 11 Sylvan Road, Exeter, Devon EX4 6EW

Appliance Books *Tabitha Webb*, 1 Bolton Lane, Ipswich, Suffolk 1PX 2BX

Aramby Publishing See also **Wire Poetry Magazine**, *Mal Cieslak*, 1 Alanbrooke Close, Knaphill, Surrey GU21 2RU

Arc Publications See under **UK Publishers**

Argyll Publishing Glendaruel, Argyll PA22 3AE

Arrival Press See also **Poetry Now** magazine, 1-2 Wainman Road, Woodston, Peterborough, Cambs PE2 7BU

Atlas Press See under **Small Presses**

Aural Images *Alan White*, 5 Hamilton Street, Astley Bridge, Bolton , Greater Manchester BL1 6RT

Avalanche Books *Deborah Gaye*, 125 Derricke Road, Stockwood, Bristol, Avon

Aylesford Press *D. A. Ashton*, 158 Moreton Road, Upton, Wirral, Cheshire LA9 4NZ

Bad Press *Philip Boxall*, Chisenhale Works, Chisenhale Road, London E3 5QZ

Bander-Snatch Books *Graham Holter*, 6 Highgrove, 63 Carlisle Road, Eastbourne, East Sussex BN20 7BN

The Bay Press, 7 Collingwood Terrace, Whitley Bay, North Yorks NE26 2NP

BB Books See also **Global Tapestry Journal** *Dave Cunliffe*, Springbank, Longsight Road, Copster Green, Blackburn, Lancs BB1 9EU

Bedlam Press *David Moody*, Church Green House, Old Church Lane, Pately Bridge, Harrogate, North Yorks HG3 5LZ

Beyond the Cloister *Hugh Hellicar*, Flat 1, 14 Lewes Crescent, Brighton, East Sussex

Big Little Poem Books *Robert Richardson*, 3 Park Avenue, Melton Mowbray, Leicestershire LE13 0JB

Black Cat Communications 10 Lincoln Street, Brighton, East Sussex BN2 2UH

Black Cygnet Press *A. D. Burnett*, 33 Hastings Avenue, Merry Oaks, Durham DH1 3QG

The Black Gate Press *John Spence*, 25 York Close, Cramlington, Northumberland NE23 9TN

Blackstaff Press 3 Galway Park, Dundonald BT16 0AN, N. Ireland

Blaxland Family Press *John Jarrett* 12 Matthews Road, Taunton, Somerset TA1 4NH

Bloodaxe Books see under **UK Publishers**

Blue Button Press 3 Bluecoat Buildings, Claypath, Durham DH1 1RF

Blue Cage See also **Blue Cage** magazine, 98 Bedford Road, Birkdale, Southport, Merseyside PR8 4HL

Bogle-l'ouverture Press Ltd *Valerie Bloom*, PO Box 2186, London W13 9ZQ

Bradgate Press See also **Poetry Digest** magazine *Maureen Forrest*, 28 Stainsdale Green, Whitwick, Leicestershire LE67 5PW

Brandon Book Publishers Ltd See under **Irish Publishers**

Brentham Press *Margaret Tims* 40 Oswald Road, St Albans, Herts AL1 3AW

Businesslike Publishing See under **Small Presses**

Carcanet Press See also **PN Review** and under **UK Publishers**

Carnival Press *Jill Franklin*, 32 Somerset Road, Erdington, Birmingham B23 6NG

Carnivorous Arpeggio (Press) *George Messo* 329 Beverley Road, Hull, Humberside HU5 1LD

Carr, RD & JM *R. D. & J. M. Carr*, 17 Home Farm Lane, Bury St Edmunds, Suffolk IP33 2QJ

Chapman Press See also **Chapman** magazine, *Joy Hendry*, 4 Broughton Place, Edinburgh EH1 3RX

Cheerybite Publications 45 Burton Road, Little Neston, South Wirral L64 4AE

The Chrysalis Press 11 Convent Close, Kenilworth, Warwickshire CV8 2FQ

Clocktower Press 27 Alfred Street, Stromness, Orkney KW16 3DF

Cloister Writers Press *Brenda Dimond*, 12 Milner Road, Horfield, Bristol BS7 9PQ

Cloud *Michael Thorp*, 48 Biddleston Road, Heaton, Newcastle upon Tyne NE6 5SL

Coelecanth Press *Maurice Scully*, 21 Corrovorrin Grove, Ennis, Co Clare, Eire

The Collective *John Jones*, Penlanlas Farm, Llantilio Pertholey, Y-Fenni, Gwent NP7 7HN

Commonword See also **Crocus**, *Cathy Bolton*, Cheetwood House, 21 Newton Street, Manchester M1 1FZ

Company of Poets Books Oversteps, Froude Road, Salcombe, S. Devon TQ8 8LH

The Corbie Press 57 Murray Street, Montrose, Angus DD10 8JZ

Cottage Books Publications *Patricia Batstone*, 1 Higher Mill Lane, Cullompton, Devon EX15 1AG

Crabflower Pamphlets See also **The Frogmore Papers** magazine and press, *Jeremy Page*, 42 Morehall Avenue, Folkstone, Kent CT19 4EF

Creation Books 83 Clerkenwell Road, London EC1M 5RJ

Credo Publishing *Annie Manning*, 45 Melsted Road, Boxmoor, Hemel Hempstead, Herts HP1 1SX

Crescent Moon Publishing and Joe's Press See under **Small Presses**, and **Passion** magazine

Crocus (Imprint of **Commonword**) *Cathy Bolton*, Cheetwood House, 21 Newton Street, Manchester M1 1FZ

Croftspun Publications *Catherine Gill*, Drakemyre Croft, Cairnorrie, Methlick, Ellon, Aberdeenshire AB41 0JN

Curfew Press *John Citizen*, 112 Sunnyhill Road, Streatham, London SW16 2UL

Curlew Press *P. J. Precious*, Hare Cottage, Kettlesing, Harrogate, N. Yorkshire HG3 2LB

Cwm Nedd Press *Robert King*, 16 Rhydhir, Neath Abbey, Neath, West Glamorgan SA10 7HP

ChoTriffid Books *K. V. Bailey*, 1 Val De
Mer, Alderney, Channel Islands
CN9 3YR

Daft Lad Press *Chris Challis*, 34 Leicester
Street, Leicester LE5 3YR

Damnation Publications *Kerry Sowerby*,
2 Midland Road, Leeds, West Yorks
LS6 1BQ

Dangaroo Press See also **Kunapipi** magazine,
PO Box 20, Hebden Bridge, West Yorks
HX7 5UZ

Christopher Davies (Publishers) Ltd See
under **UK Publishers**

Day Dream Press See also **Haiku
Quarterly**, *Kevin Bailey*, 39 Exmouth
Street, Swindon, Wilts SN1 3PU

Deborah Charles Publications *Bernard
Jackson*, 173 Mather Avenue, Liverpool
L18 6JZ

Dedalus Press/Peppercanister Books *John
F. Deane*, 24 The Heath, Cypress Downs,
Dublin 6, Eire

Diamond Press *G. Godbert*, 5 Berners
Mansions, 34–36 Berners Street, London
W1P 3DA

Dido Press *Diane Thomas*, 2 Pelham Street,
London SW7 2NG

Diehard Publishers *Ian King & others*,
Grindles Bookshop, 3 Spittal Street,
Edinburgh EH3 9DY

Direction Poetry Companion label to
Direction Music, *Peter Harrison*, 28 Nant y
Felin, Pentraeth, Anglesey LL75 8UY

Dissident Editions *Frederik Wolff*,
71 Ballyculter Road, Loughkeelan,
Downpatrick, Co. Down BT30 7BD

Dog and Bone Publishers 175 Queen
Victoria Drive, Scotstown, Glasgow
G12 9BP

Dragonfly Press 2 Charlton Cottages,
Barden Road, Speldhurst, Kent TN3 0LH

Dragonheart Press See also **Living Poets**
magazine, *Sean Woodward*, 11 Menin Road,
Allestree, Derby DE22 2NL

Dreadful Work Press 9 The Windses,
Upper Padley, Grindleford S30 1HY

Ellerton Press PO Box 354, Newcastle
under Lyme ST5 4NH

Embers Handpress *Roy & Eve Watkins*,
Rhiwargor, Llanddwyn, Nr Oswestry
SY10 0NE

Enitharmon Press See under **UK
Publishers**

Equinox Press Sinodum House, Shalford,
Braintree, Essex CM7 5MW

Equipage *Rod Mengham*, Jesus College,
Cambridge CB5 8BL

Eros Press See also **Interactions** magazine,
Andrew Yardwell, PO Box 250, St Helier,
Jersey JE4 8TZ, Channel Islands

Farrago Collective Press 106 High Street,
West Wickham, Kent BR4 0ND

Fatchance Press See also **Fatchance**
magazine, Elm Court, East Street,
Sheepwash, Beaworth EX21 5NL

Feather Books See under **Small Presses**

Fern Publications See also **Dandelion Arts
Magazine**, *Jacqueline Gonzalez-Marina*,
24 Frosty Hollow, East Hunsbury,
Northants NN4 0SY

57 Productions *Paul Besley*, 57 Effingham
Road, Lee Green, London SE12 8NT

Fire River Poets 19 Green Close, Holford,
Bridgwater, Somerset TA5 1SB

Firs Publications The Firs, Bryndu,
Llannon, Llanelli, Dyfed SA14 6AP

First Time Publications See also **First
Time** magazine, *Josephine Austin*, 4 Burdett
Place, George Street, Hastings, East Sussex
TN34 3ED

Five Leaves Publications *Ross Bradshaw*,
PO Box 81, Nottingham NG5 4ER

Five Seasons Press Wickton Court,
Stoke Prior, Leominster, Herefordshire
HR6 0LN

Flambard Press *Peter Elfed Lewis*, 4 Mitchell
Avenue, Jesmond, Newcastle upon Tyne
NE2 3LA

Forest Books See under **Small Presses**

Form Books *Harry Gilonis*, 42a Lowden
Road, London SE24 0BH

Forward Press/Arrival Press See also
Poetry Now and **Rhyme Arrival**
magazines, *Ian Walton*, 1–2 Wainman Road,
Woodston, Peterborough, Cambs PE2 7BU

Fox Press/Winter Sweet Press *Beryl Bron*,
Oak Tree, Main Road, Colden Common,
Nr Winchester, Hants SO21 1TL

The Frogmore Press See also **The
Frogmore Papers** magazine, *Jeremy Page*,
42 Morehall Avenue, Folkestone, Kent
CT19 4EF

Gallery Press *Peter Fallon*, Loughcrew,
Oldcastle, County Meath, Eire

Gecko Press *John Dickie*, 22 East Claremont
Street, Edinburgh EH7 4JP

Gekko Press *Anne Bailey*, 30b Stanmer
Street, Battersea, London SW11 3BG

Global Publishing Ltd PO Box 1415,
London NW6 5YW

Golgonooza Press *Brian Keeble*, 3 Cambridge
Drive, Ipswich, Suffolk IP2 9EP

Gomer Press/Gwasg Gomer See under
UK Publishers

Green Branch Press Kencot Lodge, Kencot, Lechlade, Glos GL7 3QX

Green Lantern Press 9 Milner Road, Wisbech, Cambs PE12 2LR

Grendon House Publishing See also **Christian Poetry Review** *Val Newbrook,* 67 Walsall Road, Lichfield, Staffordshire WS13 8AD

Greylag Press *Jim Vollmar,* 2 Grove Street, Higham Ferrars, Rushden, Northants NN10 8HX

Gruffyground Press *Anthony Baker,* Ladram, Sidcot, Winscombe, Somerset BS25 1PW

Hangman Books *Jack Ketch,* 2 May Road, Rochester, Kent ME1 2HY

Happy House See under **Small Presses**

Hard Pressed Poetry *Billy Mills,* 11 Watermeadow Park, Old Bawn, Tallaght, Dublin 24, Eire

Hastings Arts Pocket Press/Pickpockets *Margaret Rose,* 25 St Mary's Terrace, Hastings, East Sussex TN34 3LS

Headland Publications *Gladys Mary Coles,* Ty Coch, Galltegfa, Ruthin, Clwyd LL15 2AR

Hearing Eye *John Rety,* Box 1, 99 Torriano Avenue, London NW5 2RX

Here Now *Tom Kelly,* 69 Wood Terrace, Jarrow, Tyne & Wear NE32 5LU

Heron Press 6 Bramfield Drive, Newcastle under Lyme, North Staffs ST5 0ST

Hillside Books *Johan de Wit,* Flat 1, Sylva Court, 81 Putney Hill, London SW15 3NX

Hilltop Oress *Steve Sneyd,* 4 Nowell Place, Almondbury, Huddersfield, West Yorks HD5 9PD

Hippopotamus Press See also **Outposts Poetry Quarterly** *Roland John,* 22 Whitewell Road, Frome, Somerset BA11 4EL

Honno *Elin Ap Hywel,* Alisa Craig, Heol y Cawl, Dinas Powys, S. Glamorgan CF6 4AH

Horseshoe Publications *John Hibbert,* Box 37, Kingsley, Warrington, Cheshire WA6 8DR

Hub Editions *Colin Blundell,* 11 The Ridgway, Flitwick , Beds MK45 1DH

Hunter House – Anachoresis *J. E. Rutherford,* 36 Lisburn Street, Hillsborough, Co Down BT26 6AB

I*D Books *Clive Hopwood,* Connah's Quay Library, High Street, Connah's Quay, Deeside, Clwyd

International Concrete Poetry Archive *Paula Claire,* 11 Dale Close, Thames Street, Oxford OX1 1TU

Intimacy Books See also **Intimacy** magazine *Adam McKeown,* 4 Bower Street, Maidstone, Kent ME16 8SD

Invisible Books 75 Old Ford Road, London E2 9QD

Iron Press See also **Iron** magazine, *Peter Mortimer,* 5 Marden Terrace, Cullercoats, North Shields, Tyne & Wear NE30 4PD

Jackson's Arm Press See also **Sunk Island Review** (under **Magazines**) and **Sunk Island Publishing** (under **Small Presses**) *Michael Blackburn,* PO Box 74, Lincoln LN1 1QG

Jayol Publications 145 Saintfield Road, Lisburn, Co. Antrim BT27 6UH

Joe's Press See also **Passion** magazine and **Crescent Moon Publishing** (under **Small Presses**)

Jugglers Fingers Press See also **Uncompromising Positions** magazine, *Cheryl Wilkinson,* 92 Staneway, Leam Lane, Gateshead, Tyne & Wear NE10 8LS

Just a Tick Publishing *Mandy Coe,* 2 Dentwood Street, Liverpool L8 9SR

K. T. Publications See also **The Third Half** magazine, *Kevin Troop,* 16 Fane Close, Stamford, Lincolnshire PE9 1HG

Katabasis *Dinah Livingstone,* 10 St Martin's Close, London NW1 0HR

Kawabata Press Knill Cross House, Knill Cross, Millbrook, Nr Torpoint, Cornwall PL10 1DX

Kerin Publishers *Irene & Keith Thomas,* 29 Glan yr Afon, Ebbw Vale, Gwent NP3 5NR

Kernow Poets Press *Bill Headdon,* 41 Harries Road, Tunbridge Wells, Kent TN2 3TW

Kettleshill Press PO Box 38, Wirral, Merseyside L20 6NS

King of Hearts *Aude Gotto,* 13-15 Fye Bridge Street, Norwich, Norfolk NR3 1LJ

Klinker Zoundz *Hugh Metcalf,* 10 Malvern House, Stamford Hill Estate, London N16 6RR

The KQBX Press *James Sale & others,* 16 Scotter Road, Poverstown, Bournemouth, Dorset BH7 6LY

Kropotkin's Lighthouse Publications *Jim Huggon,* 59 Leiston Road, Knodishall, Suffolk IP17 1UQ

The Lansdowne Press 33 Lansdowne Place, Hove, East Sussex BN3 1HF

Lapwing Publications *Dennis & Rene Greig,* 1 Ballysillan Drive, Belfast BT14 8HQ

Ligden Publishers See also **Pulsar** magazine, *Jill Meredith,* 34 Linacre Close, Grange Park, Swindon, Wiltshire SN5 6DA

Lilliput Press 12 Christopher Close, Norwich, Norfolk NR1 2PQ

Lincoln Davies Publisher 14 Larkhill Lane, Freshfield, Liverpool L37 1LX

Lobby Press *Richard Tabor*, Simonburn Cottage, Sutton Montis, Yeovil, Somerset BA22 7HF

Logaston Press See under **Small Presses**

Lomond Press *R. L. Cook,* Whitecraigs, Kinnesswood, Kinross KY13 7JN

The Lymes Press *Alex Crossley*, Greenfields, Agger Hill, Finney Green, Newcastle under Lyme, Staffs ST5 6AA

Magenta *Maggie O'Sullivan*, Middle Fold Farm, Colden, Heptonstall, Hebden Bridge, West Yorks HX7 7PG

Making Waves *Anthony Selbourne*, PO Box 226, Guildford, Surrey GU3 1EW

Malfunction Press See also **Bardonni/Stopgap** magazine, *Peter E. Presford*, Rose Cottage, 3 Tram Lane, Buckley, Clwyd

Mammon Press *Fred Beake*, 12 Dartmouth Avenue, Bath, Avon BA2 1AT

Mandeville Press *Peter Scupham & others*, Old Hall, Norwich Road, South Burlingham, Norfolk NR13 4EY

The Many Press *John Welch*, 15 Norcott Road, London N16 7BJ

Marc Goldring Books PO Box 250, St Helier, Jersey, Channel Islands JE4 5PU

Marie-Anne Publications *Stephen Berridge*, Algarkirk, Abbey Lane, Aslockton, Notts NG13 9AE

Mariscat Press *Hamish White & others*, 3 Mariscat Road, Glasgow G41 4ND

Marvell Press c/o 2 Kelly Gardens, Calstock, Cornwall PL18 9SA

Maypole Editions See under **Small Presses**

Menard Press *Anthony Rudolf*, 8 The Oaks, Woodside Avenue, London N12 8AR

Microbrigade *Ulli Freer*, 74 Lodge Lane, London N12 8JJ

Morning Star Publications *Alex Finlay*, 17 Gladstone Terrace, Edinburgh EH9 1LS

Moschatel Press *Thomas A. Clarke*, Iverna Cottage, Rockness Hill, Nailsworth, Gloucester

Mr Pillow's Press See also **Apostrophe** magazine, *Diana Andersson*, 41 Canute Road, Faversham, Kent ME13 8SH

Mudfog 11 Limes Road, Linthorpe, Middlesbrough TS5 7QR

MidNAG Publications Leisure Department, Wansbeck Square, Ashington, Northumberland NE63 9XL

National Poetry Foundation See also **Pause** magazine, *Johnathon Clifford & others*, 27 Mill Road, Fareham, Hants PO16 0TH

New Albion Press *David Geall*, 42 Overhill Road, London SE22 0PH

New Departures *Michael Horowitz*, Piedmont, Bisley, Gloucestershire GL6 7BU

New Hope International *Gerald England*, 20 Werneth Avenue, Gee Cross, Hyde, Cheshire SK14 5NL

New River Project See also **Writers' Forum** and **And** magazine, *Bob Cobbing & others*, 89a Petherton Road, London N5 2QT

Next Step See also **Wits End** magazine, *Jean Turner*, 27 Pheasant Close, Winnersh, Wokingham, Berkshire RG11 5LS

North and South *Peterjon & Yasmin Skelt*, 23 Egerton Road, Twickenham, Middlesex TW2 7SL

Northern House Poets See also **Stand** magazine, 19 Haldane Terrace, Newcastle upon Tyne NE2 3AN

Northgate Books *Joseph Clancy*, PO Box 106, Aberystwyth, Dyfed SY33 3ZZ

NdA Press *Natalie D'Arbeloff*, 6 Cliff Villas, London NW1 9AL

Oasis Books See also **Oasis** magazine *Ian Robinson*, 12 Stevenage Road, London SW6 6ES

Odyssey Poets *Derrick Woolf*, Coleridge Cottage, Nether Stowey, Somerset TA5 1NQ

The Old Style Press *Frances & Nicholas McDowell*, Catchmays Court, Llandogo, Nr Monmouth, Gwent NP45 4TN

Oldtown Books/Macprint *Graham Mawhinnes*, 185 Gulladuff Road, Bellaghy, Londonderry BT45 8LW

The Oleander Press, *Philip Ward*, 17 Stansgate Avenue, Cambridge CB2 2QZ

On the Wire Press 6 Orchard Court, Beverley Road, Barnes, London SW13 0NA

Orbis Books See also **Orbis** magazine, *Mike Shields*, 199 The Long Shoot, Nuneaton, Warwickshire CV11 6JQ

Oscars Press *Peter Daniels*, BM Oscars, London WC1N 3XX

The Other Press *Frances Presley* 19b Marriott Road, London N4 3QN

Peepal Tree Press Ltd See under **Small Presses**

Pennine Pens see also **Hebden Bridge Web** *Chris Ratcliffe*, 32 Windsor Road, Hebden Bridge, West Yorkshire HX7 8LF

Pennyworth Press *Douglas Evans*, 64 Rosehill Park, Emmer Green, Reading, Berks RG4 8XF

Penygraig Community Publishing 1 Cross Street, Penygraig, Rhondda, Mid-Glamorgan

Peppercorn Books *Judith White*, 24 Cromwell Road, Ely, Cambs CB6 1AS

Pepsi Rejects *Julie Ann Devon*, 73 Manor Way, Peterlee, Co Durham SR8 5RS

Permanent Press *Robert Vas Dias*, 5B Compton Avenue, London N1 2XD

Perpetua Press 26 Norham Road, Oxford OX2 6SF

Peterloo Poets *Harry Chambers*, 2 Kelly Gardens, Calstock, Cornwall PL18 9SA

Phoenix Press *J. O. Smith*, 12 Hillside Close, Headley Down, Bordon, Hampshire GU35 9BL

Pig Press *Richard Caddel*, 7 Cross View Terrace, Durham DH1 4JY

The Piker's Pad *Ian Templeton*, Hillside Walk, Storrington, West Sussex RH20 3HL

Pikestaff Press *Robert Roberts*, Ellon House, Harpford, Sidmouth, Devon EX10 0NH

Pleasure To Be Alive 52 Cissbury Road, Tottenham, London N15

Poet and Printer *Alan Tarling*, 30 Grimsdyke Road, Hatch End, Pinner, Middlesex HA5 4PW

Poetical Histories *Peter Riley*, 27 Sturton Street, Cambridge CB1 2QG

The Poetry Bookshop *Alan Halsey*, West House, 22 Broad Street, Hay on Wye HR3 5DB

The Poetry Business *P. Sansom & others*, 51 Byram Arcade, Westgate, Huddersfield, West Yorks HD1 1ND

Poetry Life Publishing See also **Poetry Life Magazine**, *Adrian Bishop*, 14 Pennington Oval, Lymington, Hants SO41 8BQ

Poetry Wales Press See also **Seren Books** and **Poetry Wales** magazine, *Mick Felton*, First Floor, 2 Wyndham Street, Bridgend, Mid Glamorgan CF31 1EF

Polygon Books See **Edinburgh University Press** under **UK Publishers**

Polyptoton – Sea Dream Music *Keith Dixon*, 236 Sebert Road, Forest Gate, London E7 0NP

Precious Pearl Press See also **Cadmium Blue Literary Journal** magazines, *P. G. P. Thompson*, 71 Harrow Crescent, Romford, Essex RM3 7BJ

The Press Upstairs *Giles Goodland*, 360 Cowley Road, Oxford OX4 2AG

Prest Roots Press *P. E. Larkin*, 34 Alpine Court, Lower Ladyes Hill, Kenilworth, Warwickshire CV8 2GP

Pretani Press *Harris Adamson*, 78 Abbey Street, Bangor, Co. Down BT20 4JB

Priapus Press *John Cotton*, 37 Lombardy Drive, Berkhamstead, Herts HP4 2LQ

Prospero Illustrated Poets Clarion Publishing, Neatham Mill, Holybourne, Alton, Hampshire GU24 4NP

Protean Publications Flat 4, 34 Summerfield Crescent, Edgbaston, Birmingham B16 0ER

Providence Press Whitstable See also **Scriptor** magazine, *John & Lesley Dench*, 22 Plough Lane, Swalecliffe, Whitstable, Kent CT5 2NZ

Psychopoetica Publications See also **Psychopoetica** magazine, *Geoff Lowe*, Dept of Psychology, University of Hull, Hull HU6 7RX

Purple Sandpiper Press *E. Tanguy*, Misson Beau Regard, Five Oaks, Jersey, Channel Islands JE2 7GR

Pyramid Press Hawerby Hall, Hawerby, Grimsby DN36 5PX

Queenscourt Publishing *David E. Cox*, 1 Queens Court, Kenton Lane, Harrow, Middlesex HA3 8RN

Questing Beast *Luigi Squigianti*, PO Box 1147, London W3 7TZ

Race Today Publications 74 Shakespeare Road, London SE24 0PT

Ram Press *Catherine Dawson*, 42 Bradmore Park Road, London W6 0DT

Raunchland Publications *John Mingay*, 2 Henderson Street, Kingseat, by Dunfermline, Fife KY12 0TP

Raven Arts Press PO Box 1430, Finglass, Dublin 11, Eire

Reality Street Editions *Ken Edwards & others*, 4 Howard Court, Peckham Rye, London SE15 3PH

Rebec Press 79 Bronwydd Road, Carmarthen SA31 2AP

Red Candle Press See also **Candelabrum** magazine, 9 Milner Road, Wisbech, Cambs PE13 2LR

Red Sharks Press *Tôpher Mills*, 122 Clive Street, Grangetown, Cardiff CF1 7JE

Redbeck Press *David Tipton*, 24 Aireville Road, Frizinghall, Bradford, West Yorks BD9 4HH

Rialto Publications See also **The Rialto** magazine, 32 Grosvenor Road, Norwich, Norfolk NR2 2PZ

River Publishing Company, 39 Cumberland Street, London SW1V 4LU

Road Books *Judy Kravis & others*, Garravagh, Inniscarra, Co Cork, Eire

Rockingham Press *David Perman*, 11 Musley Lane, Ware, Herts SG12 7EN

Rump Books See also **Krax** magazine, *Andy Robson*, 63 Dixon Lane, Wortley, Leeds, West Yorks LS12 4RR

S. Editions *Ray Seaford*, 11 Richmond Avenue, Feltham, Middx TW14 9SG

S. A. Publishing See also **The Zone** magazine, *Tony Lee*, 13 Hazely Combe, Arreton, Isle of Wight PO30 3AJ

Salmon Poetry See **Poolbeg Press Ltd** under **Irish Publishers**

Satis *Matthew Mead*, Knoll Hill House, Ampleforth, West End, York YO6 4DU

Scottish Cultural Press PO Box 106, 11 Millburn Street, Aberdeen AB1 8ZE

Scottish Poetry Index Scottish Poetry Library, Tweedale Court, 14 High Street, Edinburgh EH1 1TE

Scratch Publications See also **Scratch** magazine, *Mark Robinson*, 9 Chestnut Road, Eaglescliffe, Stockton-on-Tees TS16 0BA

Seren Books See also **Poetry Wales Press** and **Poetry Wales** magazine, *Mick Felton*, First Floor, 2 Wyndham Street, Bridgend, Mid Glamorgan CF31 1EF

Shearsman Books See also **Shearsman** magazine, *Tony Frazer*, 47 Dayton Close, Plymouth, Devon PL6 5DX

Shell Press See also **Unicorn** magazine, *Alex Warner*, 12 Milton Avenue, Millbrook, Stalybridge, Cheshire SK15 3HB

Ship of Fools See also **Pages** magazine, *Robert Sheppard*, 239 Lessingham Avenue, London SW17 8NQ

Shoestring Press 19 Devonshire Avenue, Beeston, Nottingham NG9 1BS

SKB Books 115 Victoria Road, Mablethorpe LN12 2AL

Skoob Books Publishing Ltd See under **UK Publishers**

Slow Dancer Press *John Harvey*, Flat 2, 59 Parliament Hill, London NW3 2TB

Smith/Doorstop Books See also **The North** magazine, *Peter Sansom & others*, The Studio, Byram Arcade, Westgate, Huddersfield, West Yorks HD1 1ND

Sol Publications See also **Sol Poetry Magazine**, *Malcolm E. Wright*, 58 Malvern, Coleman Street, Southend on Sea, Essex SS2 5AD

Somniloquence Publishing *Lee Freeman & Darion Ford*, 25 Broadwater Road, Worthing, West Sussex BN14 8AD

South Manchester Poets *Dave Tarrant*, 122 Peterburgh Road, Edgeley Park, Stockport SK3 9RB

Spanner Press See also **Spanner** magazine, *Allen Fisher*, 14 Hopton Road, Hereford HR1 1BE

Spectacular Diseases See also **Spectacular Diseases** magazine, *Paul Green*, 83b London Road, Peterborough, Cambridgeshire PE2 9BS

Spike Press 57 Spencer Avenue, Earlsdon, Coventry, Warwickshire CV5 6NQ

Spineless Books *Keith Musgrove*, Owlsmead, Sutton Manderville, Salisbury, Wiltshire SP3 5NA

Spineless Press See also **Terrible Work** magazine, *Tim Allen*, 21 Overton gardens, Mannamead, Plymouth, Devon PL3 5BX

Spout Publications Birstall Library, Market Street, Birstall, Batley, West Yorks

Staple First Editions See also **Staple** magazine, Tor Cottage, 81 Cavendish Road, Matlock, Derbyshire DE4 3HD

Stingy Artist Book Co. *Bernard Hemensley*, 85 Goldcroft Road, Weymouth, Dorset DT4 0EA

Street Editions See **Reality Street Editions**

Stride Publications See also **Taxus Press**, *Rupert Loydell*, 11 Sylvlan Road, Exeter, Devon EX4 6EW

Sui Generis Publishing *Gavin Leigh*, 18e Marlborough Road, Roath, Cardiff CF2 5BX

Swan Books and Educational Services *Mrs E. O. Evans*, Sole Proprietor, Salama, 13 Henrietta Street, Swansea SA1 4HW

Swansea Poetry Workshop *Nigel Jenkins*, 124 Overland Road, Mumbles, Swansea SA3 4EU

Tabor Press *M. A. Duxbury-Hibbert*, 2 Holyhead Road, Llanerchymedd, Ynys Mon LL71 7AB

Talus Editions See also **Talus** magazine, *Hanne Bramness & others*, Dept of English, King's College, Strand, London WC2R 2LS

Taranis Books See also **West Coast Magazine** *Kenny MacKenzie*, 2 Hugh Miller Place, Edinburgh EH3 5JG

Taurus Press of Willow Dene *Paul Peter Piech*, 11 Limetree Way, Danygraig, Porthcawl, Mid Glam CF36 5AU

Taxus Press See also **Stride Publications**, 11 Sylvan Road, Exeter, Devon EX4 6EW

The Tenormen Press See also **Ostinato** magazine, *Stephen C. Middleton*, PO Box 552, London N8 7SZ

Torque Press *Peter Middleton*, 79 Welbeck Avenue, Southampton SO17 1SQ

Tracks See also **Dedalus Press** 23 The Heath, Cypress Downs, Dublin 6, Eire

Triple Cat Publishing *R. E. Field*, 3 Back Lane Cottages, Bucks Horn Oak, Farnham, Surrey GU10 4LN

Triumph House *Ian Walton*, 1-2 Wainman Road, Woodston, Peterborough, Cambs PE2 7BU

Tuba Press See also **Tuba** magazine, *Peter Ellison*, Tunley Cottage, Tunley, Nr Cirencester, Glos GL7 6LW

A Twist In The Tail *Paul Cookson*, PO Box 25, Retford, Nottinghamshire DN22 7ER

Ulsterman Pamphlets See also **The Honest Ulsterman** magazine, *Tom Clyde*, 14 Shaw Street, Belfast BT4 1PT

Underground Press *John Evans*, 9 Laneley Terrace, Maesycoed, Pontypridd, Mid Glamorgan CF37 1ER

Ure Group Press *Gary Boswell & others*, 22 Moss Lane, Parr, St Helens, Lancashire WA9 3SB

Vennel Press See also **Gairfish** magazine, *Richard Price*, 8 Richmond Road, Staines, Middlesex TW18 2AB

Ver Poets *May Badman*, 'Haycroft', 61/63 Chiswell Green Lane, St Albans, Herts AL2 3AL. (See also under **Professional Associations**)

Vigil Publications See also **Vigil** magazine, *John Howard-Greaves*, 12 Priory Mead, Bruton, Somerset BA10 0DZ

Visual Associations *Michael Weller* 3 Queen Adelaide Court, Queen Adelaide Road, London SE20 7DZ

Wanda Publications See also **Doors** and **South** magazines, Word and Action, 61 West Borough, Wimborne, Dorset BH21 1LX

Weatherlight Press *David Keefe*, 34 Cornwallis Crescent, Clifton, Bristol, Avon BS8 4PH

Welford Court Press 1 Welford Court, Leicester LE2 6ER

Wellsweep Press *John Cayley*, 1 Grove End House, 150 Highgate Road, London NW5 1PD

Westwords *Dave Woolley*, 15 Trelawney Road, Peverall, Plymouth, Devon PL3 4JS

White Adder Press 1 Forth View, Rucklaw Mains, Stenton Dunbar, East Lothian EH42 6DA

White Box Publications *James Turner*, 114 Monks Road, Exeter, Devon EX4 7BQ

Wild Goose Publications Unit 15, Six Harmony Row, Glasgow GL51 3BA

Wild Hawthorn Press *Ian Hamilton Finlay*, Little Sparta, Dunsyre, Lanark ML11 8NG

Windows Publications See also **Windows Poetry Broadsheet** *Heather Brett*, Nature Haven, Legaginney, Ballinagh, Cavan, Eire

Woodman's Press See also **Rustic Rub** magazine, *Jay Woodman*, 14 Hillfield, Selby, N. Yorkshire YO8 0ND

Words and Images See also **Dragon Fly Press**, *Charlie Bell*, 2 Charlton Cottages, Barden Road, Speldhurst, Kent TN3 0LH

Words Worth Books See also **Words Worth** magazine, *Alaric Sumner*, BM Box 4515, London WC1N 3XX

Writers Forum See also **And** magazine & **New River Project** *Bob Cobbing*, 89a Petherton Road, London N5 2QT

Writers' Own Publications *Mrs E. M. Pickering*, 121 Highbury Grove, Clapham, Bedford MK41 6DU

Wysiwyg Chapbooks *Ric Hool*, 89 Abertillery Road, Blaina, Gwent

Yorkshire Art Circus Ltd See under **Small Presses**

Young Woodchester PO Box 26, Stroud, Gloucestershire GL5 5YF

Zum Zum Books *Neil Oram*, Goshem, Bunlight, Drumnadrochit, Inverness-shire IV3 6AH

ZZZg Press *Chris Jones*, 61 Delapre Drive, Banbury, Oxon OX16 7WS

Poetry magazines

Many magazines have links with or are produced by **Poetry Presses**

Active in Airtime *Ralph Hawkins & others*, 53 East Hill, Colchester, Essex CO1 3QY

Acumen See also **Acumen Publications**, *Patricia Oxley*, 6 The Mount, Higher Furzeham, Brixham, Devon TQ5 8QY

Agenda See also **Agenda Editions** *William Cookson*, 5 Cranbourne Court, Albert Bridge Road, London SW11 4PE

Aireings See also **Aireings Press** *Jean Barker*, 3/24 Brudenell Road, Leeds LS6 1BD

Ambit *Martin Bax*, 17 Priory Gardens, London N6 5QY

Anarchist Angel *Liz Berry*, 5 Aylesford Close, Sedgley, Nr Dudley, W. Midlands DY3 3QB

And See also **Writers Forum** *Bob Cobbing & others*, 89a Petherton Road, London N5 2QT

Angel Exhaust *Andrew Duncan & others*, 27 Sturton Street, Cambridge CB1 2QC

Anthem *Howard Roake*, 36 Cyril Avenue, Bobbers Mill, Nottingham NG8 5BA

Apostrophe See also **Mr Pillow's Press** *Diana Andersson*, Orton House, 41 Canute Road, Faversham, Kent ME13 8SH

Aquarius *Eddie S. Linden*, Flat 10, Room A, 116 Sutherland Ave, Maida Vale, London W9

The Arcadian *Mike Boland*, 11 Boxtree Lane, Harrow Weald, Middlesex HA3 6JU

At Last 16 Ramsay Lane, Kincardine-on-Forth, Fife FK10 4QY

Avon Literary Intelligencer 20 Byron Place, Clifton, Bristol, Avon BS8 1JT

Axiom *Michelle Oliver*, 60 Greenfarm Road, Ely, Cardiff, South Glam CF5 4RH

The Banshee *Rachel Fones*, 16 Rigby Close, Waddon Road, Croydon CR0 4JU

Bardonni/Stopgap/Songs See also **Malfunction Press** *Peter E. Presford*, Rose Cottage, 3 Tram Lane, Buckley, Clwyd

Barfly *Jon Summers*, 96 Brookside Way, West End, Southampton SO30 3GZ

Bete Noire *John Osborne*, American Studies Dept., The University of Hull, Cottingham Road, Hull HU6 7 RX

Beyond the Brink *Ed Hackett,* PO Box 493, Sheffield S10 3YX

The Big Spoon 32 Salisbury Court, Belfast BT7 1DD

Blade *Jane Holland*, Maynrys, Glen Chass, Port St Mary, Isle of Man IM9 5PN

Blithe Spirit *Jackie Hardy*, Farnley Gate Farmhouse, Riding Mill, Northumberland NE44 6AA

Blue Cage *Paul Donnelly*, 98 Bedford Road, Birkdale, Southport, Merseyside PR8 4HL

Bogg *George Cairncross*, 31 Bellevue Street, Filey, North Yorks YO14 9HU

Bound Spiral *M. Petrucci*, Open Poetry Conventricle, 72 First Avenue, Bush Hill Park, Enfield, Middx EN1 1BW

Braquemard *David Allenby*, 20 Terry Street, Hull HU3 1UD

The Bridge *James Mawer*, 112 Rutland Street, Grimsby DN32 7NF

Brimstone Signatures *Isabel Gillard*, St Lawrence Cottage, Sellman Street, Gnosall, Stafford ST20 0EP

Brink *Alexis Kirke*, 22 Weston Park Road, Peverell, Plymouth, Devon PL3 4NU Alexisk@zeus.sc.plym.ac.uk

Butterfly & Bloomers *Maggie Allen,* 12 Wetmoor Lane, Wath-upon-Dearne, Rotherham S63 6DF

Cadmium Blue Literary Journal *Peter Geoffrey Paul Thompson*, 71 Harrow Crescent, Romford, Essex RM3 7BJ

Candelabrum Poetry Magazine See also **Red Candle Press** *M. L. McCarthy*, 9 Milner Road, Wisbech, Cambridgeshire PE13 2LR

Cascando *Emily Ormond*, PO Box 1499, London SW10 9TZ

Celtic Pen *Diarmuid O'Breaslain*, 36 Fruithill Park, Belfast B11 8GE

Cencrastus – The Curly Snake *Raymond Ross & others*, Unit 1, Abbeymount Techbase, 8 Easter Road, Edinburgh EH8 8EJ

Chapman See under **Magazines**

Christian Poetry Review See also **Grendon House Publishing** *Val Newbrook*, 67 Walsall Road, Lichfield, Staffordshire WS13 8AD

Chronicles of Disorder *Wayne Dean-Richards*, 191 Pound Road, Oldbury, Warley, West Midlands B68 8NF

City Writings *David Wright*, 47 Thornbury Avenue, Shirley, Southampton SO1 5BZ

Critical Quarterly *Brian Cox & others*, University of Strathclyde, Glasgow G1 1XH

Cuirt Review *Trish Fitzpatrick*, Galway Arts Centre, 47 Dominick Street, Galway, Eire

Cyphers *Eilean NcChuilleanain*, 3 Selskar Terrace, Ranelagh, Dublin 6, Eire

D.A.M. (Disability Arts Magazine) 11a Cleveland Avenue, Lupset Park, Wakefield, West Yorkshire WF2 8LE

Dandelion Arts Magazine See also **Fern Publications,** *Jacqueline Gonzalez-Marina*, 24 Frosty Hollow, East Hunsbury, Northants NN4 0SY

The Dark Horse *Gerry Cambridge*, 19 Cunninghamhead Estate, By Kilmarnock, Ayrshire KA3 2PY

The Darned Thing *Jean Thomas*, 24 Moore Road, Granary Way, Horsham, West Sussex RH12 1ZS

Distaff *J. Brice*, London Women's Centre, Wesley House, 4 Wild Court, Kingsway, London WC2

Dog *David Crystal*, 32b Breakspears Road, London SE4 1UW

Doors See also **Wanda Publications**, Word and Action, 61 West Borough, Wimborne, Dorset BH21 1LX

Draft 9 Wheatroyd Lane, Almondsbury, Huddersfield, West Yorkshire HD5 8XS

The Echo Room *Brendan Cleary*, 45 Bewick Court, Princess Square, Newcastle upon Tyne NE1 8HG

Eco-runes *D. O'Ruie*, 68b Fivey Road, Ballymoney BT53 8JH, N. Ireland

Edible Society *Peter Godfrey*, 10 Lincoln Street, Brighton, East Sussex BN2 2UH

Edinburgh Review See under **Magazines**

Envoi *Roger Elkin*, 44 Rudyard Road, Biddulph Moor, Stoke-on-Trent, Staffs ST8 7JN

Exile *Herbert Marr*, 8 Snow Hill, Clare, Suffolk CO10 8QF

Fatchance See also **Fatchance Press**, *Louise Hudson & others*, Elm Court, East Street, Sheepwash, Beaworthy, Devon EX21 5NL

Fire *Chris Ozzard & others*, 3 Holywell Mews, Holywell, Malvern, Worcs WR14 1LF

First Offense *T. Fletcher*, Syringa, The Street, Stodmarsh, Canterbury, Kent CT3 4BA

First Time See also **First Time Publications** *Josephine Austin*, 4 Burdett Place, George Street, Hastings, East Sussex TN34 3ED

Flaming Arrows *Leo Regan*, County Sligo V.E.C., Riverside, Sligo, Eire

Foolscap *Judi Benson*, 78 Friars Road, East Ham, London E6 1LL

Fragmente *Andrew Lawson & others*, Dept of English, University of Durham, Elvet Riverside, New Elvet, Durham DH1 3JT

Freedom Rock *Mike Coleman*, 18 Sunningdale Avenue, Sale, Cheshire M33 2PH

The Frogmore Papers See also **The Frogmore Press** *Jeremy Page*, 6 Vernon Road, London N8 0QD

Full Moon *Barbara Parkinson*, Church Road, Killybegs, Co. Donegal, Eire

Gairfish See also **Vennel Press**, *W. N. Herbert*, 34 Gillies Place, Dundee DD5 3LE

Gairm *Derek Thomson*, 29 Waterloo Street, Glasgow G2 6BZ

Global Tapestry Journal See also **BB Books** *Dave Cunliffe*, Spring Bank, Longsight Road, Copster Green, Blackburn, Lancs BB1 9EU

The Good Society Review *Mary MacGregor*, Elm Lodge, Union Place, Anstruther Easter, Fife KY10 3HQ

Granite - new verse from Cornwall *Alan M. Kent*, South View, Wheal Bull, Foxhole, St Austell, Cornwall PL26 7UA

Grille *Simon Smith*, 53 Ormonde Court, Upper Richmond Road, Putney, London SW15 5TP

Haiku Quarterly See also **Day Dream Press** *Kevin Bailey*, 39 Exmouth Street, Swindon, Wilts SN1 3PU

Handshake *John Francis Haines*, 5 Cross Farm, Station Road, Padgate, Warrington WA2 0QC

Headlock *Tony Charles*, The Old Zion Chapel, The Triangle, Somerton, Somerset TA11 6QP

Heart Throb (Formerly **People to People**) *Mike Parker*, 95 Spencer Street, Birmingham B18 6DA

Hebden Bridge Web See also **Pennine Pens** http://www.eclipse.co.uk/pens

Helicon See also **Peninsular** magazine *Shelagh Nugent*, Cherrybite Publications, Linden Cottage, 45 Burton Road, Little Neston, South Wirral L64 4AE

Hjok-Finnies Sanglines *Jim Inglis*, 8 Knockbain Road, Dingwall IV15 9NR

HU - The Honest Ulsterman See also **Ulsterman Pamphlets** press, 49 Main Street, Greyabbey, Co. Down BT22 2NF

Influences *Anthony Rollinson*, 36 Garner Street, Fratton, Portsmouth, Hants PO1 1PD

Interactions See also **Eros Press** *Diane M. Moore*, PO Box 250, St Helier, Jersey JE4 8TZ

The Interpreter's House *Merryn Williams*, 10 Farrell Road, Wootton, Bedfordshire MK43 9DU

Intimacy See also **Intimacy Books** *Adam McKeown*, 4 Bower Street, Maidstone, Kent ME16 8SD

Iota *David Holliday*, 67 Hady Crescent, Chesterfield, Derbyshire S41 0EB

Iron See also **Iron Press** *Peter Mortimer*, 5 Marden Terrace, Cullercoats, North Shields, Tyne & Wear NE30 4PD

Issue One/The Bridge *Ian Brocklebank*, 2 Tewkesbury Drive, Grimsby, South Humberside DN34 4TL

Journal of Contemporary Anglo-Scandinavian Poetry *Sam Smith*, 11 Heatherton Park, Bradford-on-Tone, Taunton, Somerset TA4 1EV

Krax See also **Rump Books** press, *Andy Robson*, 63 Dixon Lane, Wortley, Leeds, West Yorks LS12 4RR

Krino - the review *Gerald Dawe & others*, PO Box 65, Dun Laoghaire, Co. Dublin, Eire

Kunapipi See also **Dangaroo Press** *Anna Rutherford*, PO Box 20, Hebden Bridge, West Yorks HX7 5UZ

Lallans *Neil MacCullum*, 18 Redford Avenue, Edinburgh EH13 0BU

Lines Review *Tessa Ransford*, Macdonald Publishing, Edgefield Street, Loanhead, Mid Lothian EH20 9SY

The Link *David Pollard*, Brumus Management, PO Box 317, Hounslow, Middlesex TW3 2SD

Lit Up *Jeremy Rogers*, 8a Mill Street, Torrington, Devon EX38 8HQ

Living Poets – online ezine See also **Dragonheart Press** *Sean Woodward*, 11 Menin Road, Allestree, Derby DE22 2NL

London Magazine – See under **Magazines**

London Quarterly *John R. Bradley*, 63 Oakley Square, London NW1 1NJ

The Long Poem Group Newsletter *William Oxley*, 6 The Mount, Higher Furzeham, Brixham, South Devon TQ5 8QY

Magma *Laurie Smith & others*, The Stukely Press, The City Lit, Stukely Street, Drury Lane, London WC2 B 5LJ

Magpie's Nest *Bal Saini*, 176 Stoney Lane, Sparkhill, Birmingham B12 8AN

Mana *Gerait Roberts & others*, 15 Llantwit Street, Cathays, Cardiff CF2 4AJ

Modern Poetry in Translation *Daniel Weissbort*, MPT, School of Humanities, King's College, Strand, London WC2R 2LS

Mosaic *L. Williamson*, 16 Vale Close, Eastwood, Nottingham

Navis *Robert Bush & others*, 211 Bedford Hill, London SW12 9HQ

Never Bury Poetry *Bettina Jones*, 30 Beryl Avenue, Tottington, Bury, Lancs BL8 3NF

New Departures/Poetry Olympics See also **New Departures** press *Mike Horowitz*, Piedmont, Bisley, Stroud, Glos GL6 7BU

New Hope International *Gerald England*, 20 Werneth Avenue, Gee Cross, Hyde, Cheshire SK14 5NL

New Poetry Quarterly *Simon Brittan*, 5 Stockwell, Colchester, Essex CO1 1HP

New Scottish Epoch *Neil Mathers*, 57 Murray Street, Montrose, Angus DD10 8JZ

New Welsh Review See under **Magazines**

Night Dreams *Anthony Barker*, 52 Denman Lane, Huncote, Leicester LE9 3BS

Nineties Poetry *Graham Ackroyd*, 33 Lansdowne Place, Hove, East Sussex BN3 1HF

The North Also see **Smith/Doorstep** & **Poetry Business** *Peter Sansom & Janet Fisher*, The Studio, Byram Arcade, Westgate, Huddersfield, West Yorks HD1 1ND

Northlight *Anne Thomson*, 136 Byres Road, Glasgow G12 8TD

Northwords *Tom Bryan*, 68 Strathkanaird, Ullapool, Rosshire IV26 2TN

Nova Poetica 14 Pennington Oval, Lymington, Hampshire SO41 8BQ

Novocaine (Zdhu010@uk.ac.kd.cc.bay) 22 Wilderness Road, Mannamead, Plymouth, Devon PL3 4RN

O Write *Peter C. Ward*, Frankley Communty School, Pathways, New Street, Frankley, Birmingham B45 0EU

Oasis See also **Oasis Books**, *Ian Robinson*, 12 Stevenage Road, Fulham, London SW6 6ES

Object Permanence *Robin Purves & others*, 121 Menock Road, Kingspark, Glasgow G44 5SD

Orbis See also **Orbis Books** *Mike Shields*, 199 The Long Shoot, Nuneaton, Warwickshire CV11 6JQ

Ostinato – Jazz and Jazz Poetry See also **The Tenormen Press** *Stephen C. Middleton*, PO Box 522, London N8 7SZ

Other Poetry *Peter Bennet & others*, 8 Oakhurst Terrace, Benton, Newcastle upon Tyne NE12 9NY

Otter *R. Skinner*, Little Byspock, Richmond Road, Exeter, Devon

Outposts See also **Hippopotamus Press** *Roland John*, 22 Whitewell Road, Frome, Somerset BA11 4EL

Oxford Poetry *Ian Sansom & others*, Magdalen College, Oxford OX1 4AU

Oxford Quarterly Review *Ernie Hibert*, St Catherine's College, Oxford OX1 3UJ

Pages See also **Ship of Fools** press *Robert Sheppard*, 239 Lessingham Avenue, London SW17 8NQ

Paladin *Ken Morgan*, 66 Heywood Court, Tenby, Dyfed SA70 8BS

Palpi – Poetry And Little Press Info Association of Little Presses' journal, *Stan Trevor*, Briagha, Badninish, Dornoch, Sutherland IV25 3JB

Parataxis: Modernism & Modern Writing *Drew Milne*, School of English Studies, Arts Building, University of Sussex, Falmer, Brighton, East Sussex BN1 9NQ

Passion See also **Crescent Moon Publishing /Joe's Press** *Jeremy Robinson*, 18 Chaddesley Road, Kidderminster, Worcs DY10 3AD

Pause See also **National Poetry Foundation** *Helen Robinson*, 27 Mill Road, Fareham, Hants PO16 0TH

Peace and Freedom *Paul Rance*, 17 Farrow Road, Whaplode Drove, Spalding, Lincs PE12 0TS

Peer Poetry Magazine *Paul Amphlett*, 26 Arlington House, Bath Street, Bath BA1 1QN

Pen and Keyboard *David Stern*, SQR Publishing, 526 Fulham Palace Road, London SW6 6JE

The Pen Magazine *Pam Probert*, 15 Berwyn Place, Penlan, Swansea, West Glamorgan SA5 5AX

Pennine Platform *Brian Merrikin Hill*, Ingmanthorpe Hall, Farm Cottage, Wetherby, West Yorks LS22 5EQ

Peninsular See also **Helicon** magazine *Shelagh Nugent*, Cherrybite Publications, Linden Cottage, 45 Burton Road, Little Neston, South Wirral L64 4AE

Planet – the Welsh internationalist *John Barnie*, PO Box 44, Aberystwyth, Dyfed

PN Review See also **Carcanet Press** under **UK Publishers** *Michael Schmidt*, 402–406 Corn Exchange Buildings, Manchester M4 3BQ

Poetic Hours *Nicholas Clark*, 8 Dale Road, Carlton, Notts NG4 1GT

Poetry and Audience *Anthony Rowland*, School of English, University of Leeds, Leeds, West Yorks LS2 9JT

Poetry Digest *Alan Forrest,* Bradgate Press, 28 Stainsdale Green, Whitwick, Leics LE67 5PW

Poetry Durham *David Hartnett & others*, Dept of English Studies, University of Durham, Elvet Riverside, Durham DH1 3JT

Poetry Ireland Review Bermingham Tower, Upper Yard, Dublin Castle, Dublin, Eire

Poetry Life Magazine See also **Poetry Life Publishing** *Adrian Bishop,* 14 Pennington Oval, Lymington, Hants SO41 8BQ

Poetry London Newsletter *P. Daniels*, 26 Clacton Road, London E17 8AR

Poetry Manchester *Sean Boustead*, 13 Napier Street, Swinton, Manchester M27 0JQ

Poetry News *Rachel Bourke*, Poetry Society, 22 Betterton Street, London WC2H 9BU

Poetry Nottingham International *Martin Holroyd*, 39 Cavendish Road, Long Eaton, Nottingham NG10 4HY

Poetry Now See also **Arrival** and **Forward Presses** *Ian Walton*, 1-2 Wainman Road, Woodston, Peterborough, Cambs PE2 7BU

Poetry Quarterly Review See also **Odyssey Poets** *Derrick Woolf*, Coleridge Cottage, Nether Stowey, Somerset TA5 1NQ

Poetry Review *Peter Forbes*, Poetry Society, 22 Betterton Street, London WC2H 9BU

Poetry Update BM-Poetry, London WC1N 3XX

Poetry Wales See also **Seren Books** *Richard Poole*, Glan-y-Werydd, Llandanwg, Harlech LL46 2SD

The Poet's Voice Published with University of Salzburg *Fred Beake*, 12 Dartmouth Avenue, Bath, Avon BA2 1AT

Pomes *Adrian Spendlow*, 23 Bright Street, York YO2 4XS

PPQ *Peter Taylor*, PO Box 1435, London W1A 9LB

Premonitions See **Pigasus Press** under **Small Presses**

Presence *Martin Lucas*, 188 Langthorne Road, London E11 4HS

The Printer's Devil *Sean O'Brien & others*, Top Offices, 13a Western Road, Hove, East Sussex BN3 1AE

Psychopoetica See also **Psychopoetica Publications** *Geoff Lowe*, Dept. of Psychology, University of Hull, Hull HU6 7RX

Pulsar See also **Ligden Publishers** *David Pike*, 34 Lineacre, Grangepark, Swindon, Wilts SN5 6DA

Purge *Robert Hampson*, 11 Hillview Court, Hillview Road, Woking, Surrey GU22 7QN

Purple Patch *Geoff Stevens*, 8 Beaconview House, Charlemont Farm, West Bromwich B71 3PL

Plow/:/share(s) The Rectory, Castle Carrock, Carlisle CA4 9LZ

Quartos See under **Magazines**

Ramraid Extraordinaire 57 Canton Court, Canton, Cardiff CF1 9BG

The Reater *Shane Rhodes*, 1 Pilmar Lane, Roos, North Humberside HU12 0HP

Red Herring Arts Section, Central Library, The Willows, Morpeth, Northumberland NE61 1TA

The Red Shoes *Adrian Hodges*, 3 Ashfield Close, Bishops Cleeve, Cheltenham, Glos GL52 4LG

Reflections PO Box 70, Sunderland SR1 1DU

Rhyme Arrival See also **Poetry Now** magazine and **Forward Press** *Trudi Ramm*, 1-2 Wainman Road, Woodston, Peterborough, Cambs PE2 7BU

The Rialto See also **Rialto Publications** *John Wakeman & others*, 32 Grosvenor Road, Norwich, Norfolk NR2 2PZ

A Riot of Emotions *Andrew Cocker*, Dark Diamonds Pubs. PO Box HK 31, Leeds, West Yorks LS11 9XN

Rivet *Eve Catchpole & others*, 74 Walton Drive, High Wycombe, Bucks HP13 6TT

Roisin Dubh Em, 16 Gotham Street, Leicester

Rustic Rub (formerly **And What of Tomorrow**) *Jay Woodman*, 14 Hillfield, Selby, N. Yorkshire YO8 0ND

Scar Tissue *Tony Lee*, Pigasus Press, 13 Hazley Combe, Isle of Wight PO30 3AJ

Scratch See also **Scratch Publications** *Mark Robinson*, 9 Chestnut Road, Eaglescliffe, Stockton-on-Tees TS16 0BA

Scriptor See also **Providence Press Whitstable** *John & Lesley Dench*, 22 Plough Lane, Swalecliffe, Whitstable, Kent CT5 2NZ

Sepia See also **Kawabata Press** *Colin David Webb*, Knill Cross House, Nr Anderton Rd, Millbrook, Torpoint, Cornwall PL10 1DX

Shearsman See also **Shearsman Books** *Tony Frazer*, 47 Dayton Close, Plymouth, Devon PL6 5DX

Sheffield Thursday *E. A. Markham*, School of Cultural Studies, Sheffield Hallam University, 36 Collegiate Crescent, Sheffield S10 2BP

Skald *Zoe Skoulding*, 2 Park Street, Bangor, Gwynedd LL57 2AY

Smiths Knoll *Roy Blackman & others* 49 Church Road, Little Glemham, Woodbridge, Suffolk IP13 0BJ

Smoke *Dave Ward*, The Windows Project, 40 Canning Street, Liverpool L8 7NP

Sol Poetry Magazine See also **Sol Publications** *Malcolm E. Wright*, 24 Fowler Close, Southchurch, Southend-on-Sea, Essex SS1 2RD

Sound & Language 85 London Road South, Lowestoft, Suffolk NR33 0AS

South See also **Wanda Publications** Word and Action, 61 West Borough, Wimborne, Dorset BH21 1LX

Southfields *Raymond Friel & others*, 98 Gresenhall Road, Southfields, London SW18 5QJ

Spanner *Allen Fisher*, 14 Hopton Road, Hereford HR1 1BE

Spear *Jacqueline Jones*, 2 Fforest Road, Lampeter, Dyfed

Spectacular Diseases See also **Spectacular Diseases** press *Paul Green*, 83b London Road, Peterborough, Cambs PE2 9BS

Spokes *Alister & Gine Wisker*, 319a Hills Road, Cambridge CB2 2QT

Stand See also **Northern House Poets** *Jon Silkin & others*, 179 Wingrove Road, Newcastle-upon-Tyne NE4 9DA

Staple See also **Staple First Editions** *Donald Measham*, Tor Cottage, 81 Cavendish Road, Matlock, Derbyshire DE4 3HD

The Steeple *Patrick Cotter*, Three Spires Press, Killeen, Blackrock Village, Cork City, Eire

Stone Soup 37 Chesterfield Road, London W4 3HQ

Story Cellar *Sara Waddington*, 26 Cippenham Lane, Slough, Berkshire SL1 5BS

Stride See also **Stride Publications** and **Taxus Press** *Rupert Loydell*, 11 Sylvan Road, Exeter, Devon EX4 6EW

Sunk Island Review See under **Magazines** and see also **Jackson's Arm Press**

Super-Trouper *Andrew Savage*, 81 Castlerigg Drive, Burnley, Lancs BB12 8AT

Swagmag *Peter Thabit Jones*, Dan-y-Bryn, 74 Cwm Level Road, Brynhyfred, Swansea SA5 9DY

The Swansea Review, *Glyn Pursglove*, Dept of English, University College Swansea, Singleton Park, Swansea SA2 8PP

Symphony Bemerton Press, 9 Hamilton Gardens, London NW8 9PU

Tabla *Stephen James Ellis & others*, 7 Parliament Hill, London NW3 2SY

Talus See also **Talus Editions** *Marzia Balzani & others*, Dept of English, King's College, Strand, London WC2R 2LS

Tandem *Michael J. Woods*, 13 Stephenson Road, Barbourne, Worcester WR1 3EB

Target *Bryn Fortey*, 212 Caerleon Road, Newport, Gwent NP9 7GC

Tears In The Fence *David Caddy*, 38 Hod View, Stourpaine, Nr Blandford Forum, Dorset DT11 8TN

Tees Valley Writer *Derek Gregory*, 57 The Avenue, Linthorpe, Middlesborough, Cleveland TS5 6QU

10th Muse *Andrew Jordan*, 33 Hartington Road, Southampton SO2 0EW

Terrible Work See also **Spineless Press** *Tim Allen*, 21 Overston Gardens, Mannamead, Plymouth, Devon PL3 5BX

The Third Alternative *Andy Cox*, 5 St Martin's Lane, Witcham, Ely, Cambs CB4 2LB

The Third Half See also **K. T.
Publications** *Kevin Troop*, 16 Fane Close,
Stamford, Lincs PE9 1HG

Threads *Geoff Lynas*, 32 Irvin Avenue,
Saltburn, Cleveland TS12 1QH

Thumbscrew *Tim Kendall* PO Box 657,
Oxford OX2 6PH

Time Haiku *K. K. Facey*, 105 Kings Head
Hill, London E4 7JG

Tocher *Alan Bruford*, School of Scottish
Studies, 27 George Square, Edinburgh
EH8 9LD

Tongue to Boot *Miles Champion*, 5 Abbots
Court, Thackeray Street, London W8 5ES

Tops *Anthony Cooney*, Rose Cottage, 17
Hadassah Grove, Liverpool L17 8XH

Transitions 19 Queen Court, Queen Square,
London WC1N 3BB

Tuba See also **Tuba Press** *Charles Graham*,
Tunley Cottage, Tunley, Nr Cirencester,
Glos GL7 6LW

Uncompromising Positions See also
Jugglers Fingers Press *Cheryl Wilkinson*,
92 Staneway, Leam Lane, Gateshead, Tyne
& Wear NE10 8LS

Under Surveillance 60 Arnold Street,
Brighton, East Sussex BN2 2XT

Unicorn See also **Shell Press** *Alex Warner*,
12 Milton Avenue, Millbrook, Stalybridge,
Cheshire SK15 3HB

Upstart 19 Cawarden, Stantonbury, Milton
Keynes MK14 6AH

Urban Fantasy *Will Parker & others*, The Art
Hive, 34 Castle House, 1 Overton Road,
Sutton, Surrey SM2 6QE

Urthona *Chris Warren*, 19 Newmarket Road,
Cambridge CB5 8EG

Various Artists *Tony Lewis Jones*,
65 Springfield Avenue, Horfield, Bristol,
Avon BS7 9QS

Verbal Underground *Charlotte Cole*,
11 Hunter House, Junction Road, London
N19 5QE

Verse *Andrew Zawacki* University College,
Oxford

Vigil *John Howard-Greaves*, 12 Priory Mead,
Bruton, Somerset BA10 0DZ

Walking Naked *Sean Boustead*, 13 Napier
Street, Swinton, Manchester M27 3JQ

West Coast Magazine See also **Taranis
Books** *Joe Murray*, EM-DEE Productions,
Unit 7, 29 Brand Street, Glasgow
G51 1DN

Weyfarers *Margaret Palin*, Guildford Poets
Press, Hilltop Cottage, 9 White Rose Lane,
Woking, Surrey GU22 7JA

The Wide Skirt *Geoff Hattersley*, 1a Church
Street, Penistone, South Yorks S30 6AR

Windows Poetry Broadsheet See also
Windows Publications *Heather Brett &
others*, Nature Haven, Legaginney,
Ballinagh, Cavan, Eire

Wire Poetry Magazine See also **Aramby
Publishing** *Mal Cieslak*, 1 Alanbrooke
Close, Knaphill, Surrey GU21 2RU

Wits End See also **Next Step** press, *Jean
Turner*, 27 Pheasants Close, Winnersh,
Wokingham, Berks RG11 5LS

Words Worth See also **Words Worth
Books** *Alaric Sumner*, BM Box 4515,
London WC1N 3XX

Working Titles *Claire Williamson*,
5 Hillside, Clifton Wood, Bristol, Avon
BS8 4TD

Writing Women *Linda Anderson & others*,
Unit 14, Hawthorn House, Forth Banks,
Newcastle upon Tyne NE1 3SG

Yellow Crane (Formerly **The Cardiff Poet**)
Jonathan Brookes Flat 6, 23 Richmond
Crescent, Roath, Cardiff CF2 3AH

Zimmerframe Pileup *Stephen Jessener*, Loose
Hand Press, 54 Hillcrest Road,
Walthamstow, London E17 4AP

The Zone – the last word in sf See also
S. A. Publishing, *Tony Lee*, 13 Hazely
Combe, Arreton, Isle of Wight PO30 3AJ

Organisations of interest to poets

A survey of some of the societies, groups and other bodies in the UK which may be of interest to practising poets. Organisations not listed should send details of themselves to the editor, 45 Islington Park Street, London N1 1QB to facilitate inclusion in future editions.

Apples & Snakes

Unit A11, Hatcham Mews Business Centre, Hatcham Mews Park, London SE14 5QA
☎0171 639 9656

Contacts *Steve Tasane, Ruth Harrison, Julian Tipene, Ben Raikes*

A unique, independent promotional organisation for poetry and poets - furthering poetry as an innovative and popular medium and cross-cultural activity. A&S organises an annual programme of over 150 events (including their London season which actively pushes new voices), tours, residencies and festivals as well as operating a Poets-in-Education Scheme and a non-profit booking agency for poets.

The Arvon Foundation

See under **Professional Associations**

The Association of Little Presses

See under **Professional Associations**

The British Haiku Society

Sinodun, Shalford, Braintree, Essex
CM7 5HN
☎01371 851097

Secretary *David Cobb*

Formed in 1990. Promotes the appreciation and writing within the British Isles of haiku, senyru, tanka, and renga by way of tutorials, workshops, exchange of poems, critical comment and information. *Publishes* a quarterly journal, *Blithe Spirit*, and administers the annual James W. Hackett Award for haiku.

The Eight Hand Gang

5 Cross Farm, Station Road, Padgate,
Warrington WA2 0QG

Secretary *John F. Haines*

An association of British SF poets. *Publishes Handshake*, a newsletter of SF poetry and information available free in exchange for a s.a.e..

European Association for the Promotion of Poetry

European Poetry House, 'The Seven Sleepers', J.P. Minckelersstraat 168,
B-3000 Leuven, Belgium

Home of the European Poetry Library and Centre for Research, Translation and Documentation. The Association works in at least four European languages, runs the annual European Poetry Festival at Leuven and other European venues, administers the European Prize for the Translation of poetry as well as publishing bi-lingual volumes of European poets and a poetry magazine, *Letters*. Membership costs 1000BF. In 1991 the Association, with the cooperation of the Romanian Writers' Union, founded the *European Poetry and East-West Dialogue Centre 'Constantin Noica'*, located at str. Dr Ion Ratiu 2, 2400 Sibiu, Romania. The centre's principal activities are organising poetry meetings, setting up of the European Chair of Poetry (at the University of Sibiu) and publishing bi-lingual poetry volumes of poets from Central and Eastern Europe. In 1993 the Association created the *European Poetry Network* whose membership comprises 21 representative poetry centres throughout Europe.

HMSO Oriel Bookshop

The Friary, Cardiff CF1 4AA
☎01222 395548

Publishes at regular intervals *Small Presses and Little Magazines of the UK and Ireland - An Address List* (currently into its twelfth edition - £4.00 including p&p), specialises in twentieth century poetry, operates a carriage-free mail order service, hosts poetry readings and provides information on local competitions, workshops, groups and literary activities.

The Little Magazine Collection and Poetry Store

University College London, Gower Street,
London WC1E 6BT
☎0171 380 7796

Housed at University College London Library, these are the fruits of Geoffrey Soar and David

Miller's interest in UK and US alternative publishing, with a strong emphasis on poetry. The Little Magazines Collection runs to over 3500 titles mainly in the more experimental and avant-garde areas. The Poetry Store consists of over 11,000 small press items, mainly from the '60s onwards, again with some stress on experimental work. In addition, there are prints of classic earlier little magazines, from Symbolism through to the present. Anyone who is interested can consult the collections, and it helps if you have some idea of what you want to see. Bring evidence of identity for a smooth ride. The collections can be accessed by visiting the Manuscripts and Rare Books Room at University College at the above address between 10.00am and 5.00pm on weekdays. Most items are available on inter-library loans.

The Living Poets Society

Dragonheart Press, 11 Menin Road, Allestree, Derby DE22 2NL
e-mail: 1poets@drci.co.uk

President *Sean Woodward*

Established to encourage poets of any age and location to share their work through new electronic media, the Society offers inclusion in the electronic journal *Living Poets*, freely available on the Internet at http://dougal.derby.ac.uk/ 1poets. Membership is £10 per annum with reduced lifetime and junior membership. Sean Woodward also runs the Dragonheart Press which publishes poetry in a variety of formats including HTML, ASCII and Amiga Hyperbook. The annual Dragonheart Press Poetry Competition includes electronic publication as part of its prizes.

The National Convention of Poets and Small Presses/Poets and Small Press Festival

Iron Press, 5 Marden Terrace, Cullercoats, North Shields, Northumberland NE30 4PD
☎0191 253 1901

Contact *Peter Mortimer*

An accessible, some might say disorganised, weekend jamboree of writers and poetry publishers held at a different venue each year. The quasi-amateur status of the event is celebrated and it can be good fun for those with enough stamina to last out the marathon readings. There is no central organising committee - bids to host future conventions being made in person at the event itself. So far it has visited Liverpool, Hastings, Corby, Dartford, Stamford, Norwich, North Shields, Exeter, Stockton-on-Tees,

Middlesborough and Huddersfield. Write to Peter Mortimer for information on the next convention.

National Poetry Foundation

27 Mill Road, Fareham, Hampshire PO16 0TH
☎/Fax 01329 822218

The rather grand-sounding title for the charitable poetry organisation (Registered Charity No: 283032) founded by Johnathon Clifford and administered by a board of trustees from the address above. With the financial assistance of Rosemary Arthur who has so far put over £350,000 into the kitty, the NPF attempts to encourage new writers through a criticism scheme and a series of rather well produced poetry books. Subscription costs £20 which, in addition, gives members access to *Pause*, the organisation's internal magazine.

The NPF has an interest in the professional poetry recital as a fund-raising device for the furtherance of its work. Eight small mags and a number of individual poets have to date benefited from NPF financial aid. Grants are small, unrenewable and directed at that sector of the poetry community traditionally ignored by other bodies. A good history of the NPF, together with information on poetry and the poetry scene can be found in Johnathon Clifford's self-published *Metric Feet & Other Gang Members*, available from the same address.

The Northern Poetry Library

Central Library, The Willows, Morpeth, Northumberland NE61 1TA
☎01670 511156/512385 Fax 01670 518012

Membership available to everyone in Cleveland, Cumbria, Durham, Northumberland and Tyne and Wear. Associate membership available for all outside the region. Over 13,000 books and magazines for loan including virtually all poetry published in the UK since 1968. Access to English Poetry, the full text database of all English Poetry from 600 - 1900. Postal lending available too. In association with MidNag *publishes Red Herring*, a poetry magazine.

The Poetry Bookshop

Westhouse, Broad Street, Hay-on-Wye HR3 5DB
☎01497 820305

Contact *Alan Halsey*

Holds a large stock of modern and contemporary poetry - British, Irish, American, translations, concrete, etc. - mostly secondhand but including some new small press material and poetry magazines. Deals extensively by post and produces a regular catalogue.

The Poetry Book Society

PBS Freepost, Book House, 45 East Hill,
London SW18 2BR
☎0181 870 8403   Fax 0181 877 1615

Administrator *Betty Redpath*

Can't choose? This is one way to increase your reading of mainstream poetry. For an annual fee of £30, members receive quarterly a new volume of verse selected by experts and a quarterly bulletin. Members are also entitled to buy from a vast selection of PBS recommendations, all at 25% discount, to have free tickets to PBS readings and have a right to an advisory vote in any poetry prizes organised by the Society. If that's not enough, Charter Membership costing £120 will bring you 20 new books annually, while the new Associate form of membership, at £10, gives just the four bulletins and the discount offers on books. The PBS also administers the annual **T. S. Eliot Prize** for the best new collection of poetry.

The Poetry Business

The Studio, Byram Arcade, Westgate,
Huddersfield, West Yorkshire HD1 1ND
☎01484 434840   Fax 01484 426566

Administrators *Peter Sansom, Janet Fisher*

The Business runs an annual competition and organises monthly writing Saturdays. It *publishes The North* magazine and books, pamphlets and cassettes under the Smith/Doorstop imprint. Send s.a.e. for their catalogues.

Poetry Ireland

Bermingham Tower, Upper Yard, Dublin
Castle, Dublin, Republic of Ireland
☎00 353 1 6714632   Fax 00 353 1 6714634

Director *Theo Dorgan*
General Manager *Niamh Morris*

The national poetry organisation for Ireland, supported by Arts Councils both sides of the border. *Publishes* a quarterly magazine *Poetry Ireland Review* and a bi-monthly newsletter of upcoming events and competitions, as well as organising tours and readings by Irish and foreign poets and the National Poetry Competition of the Year, open to poets working in both Irish and English. Administers the Austin Clarke Library, a collection of over 6000 volumes and is Irish partner in the European Poetry Translation Network.

The Poetry Library

Royal Festival Hall, Level 5, London
SE1 8XX
☎0171 921 0943/0664/0940
Fax 0171 921 0939

Librarian *Mary Enright*

Founded by the Arts Council in 1953. A collection of 45,000 titles of modern poetry since 1912, from Georgian to Rap, representing all English-speaking countries and including translations into English by contemporary poets. Two copies of each title are held, one for loan and one for reference.

A wide range of poetry magazines and ephemera from all over the world are kept along with cassettes, records and videos for consultation, with some available for loan. There is a children's poetry section with a teacher's resource collection.

An information service compiles lists of poetry magazines, competitions, publishers, groups and workshops, which are available from the Library on receipt of a large s.a.e. It also has a noticeboard for lost quotations, through which it tries to identify lines or fragments of poetry which have been sent in by other readers.

General enquiry service available. Membership is free. Open 11.00am to 8.00pm seven days a week. Beside the Library is *The Voice Box*, a performance space especially for literature. For details of current programme ring 0171-921 0906.

Poetry London Newsletter

26 Clacton Road, London E17 8AR
Web page: http//www.rmplc.co.uk/eduweb/
sites/poetry/index.html

Contacts *Pascale Petit, Katherine Gallagher,
Peter Daniels, Tamar Yoseloff*

The UK's first online magazine for and about poetry activity in the capital. Published both as hard copy and electronically at the beginning of every term, it has three parts: new poetry by emergent and established writers, reviews, and an encyclopaedic listings section of virtually everything to do with poetry in London and fairly extensive coverage of events up and down the rest of the country. Invaluable at £12 for three issues.

Poetry submissions should be sent snail mail. Other correspondence can go e-mail to poetry@poetry.demon.co.uk. Listings data to pdaniels@easynet.co.uk or 35 Bethnal Road, London N16 7AR.

The Poetry Society
22 Betterton Street, London WC2H 9BU
☎0171 240 4810   Fax 0171 240 4818
Chairman *Bill Swainson*
Director *Chris Meade*

FOUNDED in 1909, which ought to make it venerable, the Society exists to help poets and poetry thrive in Britain. At one time notoriously strife-ridden, it has been undergoing a renaissance lately, reaching out from its Covent Garden base to promote the national health of poetry in a range of imaginative ways. Membership costs £24 for individuals and there are a range of different options available to libraries, schools, European Union members, students, etc. Current activities include:

- A quarterly magazine of new verse, views and criticism, *Poetry Review*, edited by Peter Forbes.
- A quarterly newsletter, *Poetry News*.
- Promotions, events and cooperation with Britain's many literature festivals, poetry venues and poetry publishers.
- Competitions and awards including the annual **National Poetry Competition** with a substantial first prize.
- A mss diagnosis service, *The Script*, which gives detailed reports on submissions. Reduced rates for members.
- Seminars, fact sheets, training courses, ideas packs, t-shirts.
- An education service, run in conjunction with W. H. Smith which annually puts over 1500 children in direct contact with poets. *Publishes* the excellent *Poetry Society Resources* files for primary and secondary levels, and provides specialist information and advice on all aspects of poetry in education. The special 'education' membership (schools £30) offers an additional quarterly bulletin which is a teacher's guide to the current issue of *The Poetry Review*. Recently published is *The Young Poetry Pack*, an informative and colourful guide to reading, writing and performing poetry. Many of Britain's most popular poets - including Michael Rosen, Roger McGough and Jackie Kay - contribute to the pack, offering advice and inspiration.
- A library service which assists participating libraries to become poetry friendly. A resources pack is available along with special arrangements for book purchase through library suppliers T. C. Farries. Library membership costs £40.
- A ground floor Poetry Café which provides

a space to eat, drink, read or write on the word processors provided. You can access the Internet from here or attend one of the many poetry activities going on - readings, poetry clinics, workshops or poetry lunches.

- A poetry website at http://www.bbcbc.org.uk/online/poetry. *The Poetry Map* here is a cross between a poetry magazine, an information pack and a discussion group. With full graphics, the Map contains a *Sea of Inspiration* in which float poems past and present including newly commissioned work from around the country, *The Poetry Factory* full of advice on writing and publishing, and the *Train of Thought* an online letters page.

Current developments at the Society include a Poets in Hospital programme, sponsored by Glaxo Wellcome, offering two poets placements annually.

Point
Apdo 119, E-03590 Altea, Spain
☎00 34 96 584 2350   Fax 00 34 96 584 2350
Brusselselsesteenweg 356, B-9402 Ninove, Belgium
☎00 32 54 32 4748   Fax 00 32 54 32 4660
Director *Germain Droogenbroodt*

Founded as Poetry International in 1984, Point has offices in Spain and Belgium. A multilingual publisher of contemporary verse from both established and new poets, the organisation has brought out more than 50 titles in at least eight languages, including English. Editions run the original work alongside a verse translation into Dutch made in cooperation with the poet. Point also organises an annual international poetry festival in Altea, Spain.

Quartos
BCM Writer, London WC1N 3XX

'Bi-monthly magazine for creative writers' now including a New Poets Showcase edited by Abi Hughes-Edwards. Subscription £14. Best single source of information on poetry competitions (see under **Magazines**). Runs an inexpensive critical service for poets, currently £1.50 per poem or £5 for six. Send s.a.e..

Regional Arts Boards
For a full list of addresses see **Arts Councils and Regional Arts Boards**. Most are of invaluable interest to poets as a source of infor-

mation on local activities, poetry groups, competitions, publications, readings and creative writing weekends. Many publish a magazine of their own, a number run critical services for writers. Some provide fellowships for poets, paying for school visits or for poets' workshops to be established. Service varies from region to region depending on demand and the influence and interest of the local literature officer.

Scottish Poetry Library

Tweeddale Court, 14 High Street, Edinburgh EH1 1TE
☎0131 557 2876
e-mail: spl/queries@presence.co.uk
Librarian *Penny Duce*

Freely open to the public; membership scheme £10 p.a. A comprehensive collection of work by Scottish poets in Gaelic, Scots and English, plus the work of international poets, including books, tapes, videos and magazines. Borrowing is free to all. Services include: a postal lending scheme, for which there is a small fee, and a mobile library which can visit schools and other centres by arrangement. Members receive a newsletter and support the Library, whose work includes exhibitions, bibliographies, publications, information and promotion in the field of poetry. Also available is an online catalogue and computer index to poetry and poetry periodicals.

Survivors' Poetry

Diorama Arts Centre, 34 Osnaburgh Street, London NW1 3ND
Admin *Debbie McNamara* (0171 916 5317)
Outreach *Alison Smith* (0171 916 6637)
London Events *Frank Bangay* (0171 916 0825)

Arts Council-funded literature/performance project managed by and for poets who have survived the psychiatric system. Organises regular poetry workshops and performances in London and throughout the UK. Also runs performance training workshops led by established writers. Has published two full-length anthologies of Survivors' work. Through its Outreach Project, it is currently engaged in establishing independent groups in a UK-wide network which spreads from Portsmouth to Glasgow.

Tŷ Newydd

Llanystumdwy, Cricieth, Gwynedd LL52 0LW
☎01766 522811   Fax 01766 523095
Director *Sally Baker*

Run by the Taliesin Trust, an independent, Arvon-style residential writers centre in North Wales. Programme has a strong poetry content. Fees start at £100 for weekends and £250 for week-long courses. Tutors to date have included Gillian Clarke, Wendy Cope, Roger McGough, Carol Ann Duffy, Liz Lochhead, Peter Finch and Paul Henry. See under **Writers' Courses, Circles and Workshops.**

Small Presses

Aard Press
c/o Aardverx, 31 Mountearl Gardens, London
SW16 2NL
Managing Editor *D. Jarvis, Dawn Redwood*
FOUNDED 1971. *Publishes* artists' bookworks, experimental/visual poetry, 'zines, eonist literature, topographics ephemera and international mail-art documentation. TITLES: *Eos - The Arts & Letters of Transkind* (TG & M-A 'zine); *I, Jade Green, Jade's Ladies, Jade AntiJade* (thrillers) by A. K. Ashe. AUTHORS/ARTISTS include Dawn Redwood, Petal Jeffery, Phaedra Kelly, Barry Edgar Pilcher (Eire), D. Jarvis, Y. Kumykov (Russia). No unsolicited material or proposals.
Royalties not paid. No sale-or-return deals.

ABCD
See **Allardyce, Barnett, Publishers**

Agneau 2
See **Allardyce, Barnett, Publishers**

AK Press/AKA Books
PO Box 12766, Edinburgh EH8 9YE
☎0131 555 5165   Fax 0131 555 5215
Managing Editor *Alexis McKay*
AK Press grew out of the activities of AK Distribution which distributes a wide range of radical (anarchist, feminist, etc.) literature (books, pamphlets, periodicals, magazines), both fiction and non-fiction. Long-term goal is to have some sort of high-street retail outlet for radical material. *Publishes* politics, history, situationist work, occasional fiction in both book and pamphlet form. About 12 titles a year. TITLES *Pen and the Sword* Edward W. Said; *Chronicles of Dissent* Noam Chomsky; *Some Recent Attacks* James Kelman; *Ecstatic Incisions: The Collage Art of Freddie Baer.* Unsolicited mss/proposals/synopses welcome if they fall within AK's specific areas of interest.
Royalties paid.

The Alembic Press
Hyde Farm House, Marcham, Abingdon,
Oxon OX13 6NX
☎01865 391391   Fax 01865 391322
Owner *Claire Bolton*
FOUNDED 1976. Publisher of hand-produced books by traditional letterpress methods. Short print-runs. *Publishes* bibliography, book arts

and printing, miniatures and occasional poetry. 4 titles in 1995. Book design and production service to like-minded authors wishing to publish in this manner. No unsolicited mss.

Allardyce, Barnett, Publishers
14 Mount Street, Lewes, East Sussex
BN7 1HL
☎01273 479393   Fax 01273 479393
Publisher *Fiona Allardyce*
Managing Editor *Anthony Barnett*
FOUNDED 1981. *Publishes* art, literature and music, with past emphasis on contemporary English poets. About 3 titles a year.
IMPRINTS **Agneau 2, ABCD, Allardyce Book**. TITLES *Poems* Andrea Zanzotto; *Desert Sands: The Recordings and Performances of Stuff Smith* Anthony Barnett; *The Black Heralds* César Vallejo. Unsolicited mss and synopses cannot be considered.

Amate Press
See **IKON Productions Ltd**

Anglo-Saxon Books
Frithgarth, Thetford Forest Park, Hockwold
cum Wilton, Norfolk IP26 4NQ
☎01842 828430   Fax 01842 828430
Managing Editor *Tony Linsell*
FOUNDED 1990 to promote a greater awareness of early English society and history. Originally concentrated on translations of Old English texts but has now moved on to include less academic, more popular titles. *Publishes* English history, culture, language and society before 1066. About 5 titles a year. TITLES *A Handbook of Anglo-Saxon Food; Alfred's Metres of Boethius; Spellcraft: Old English Heroic Legends.* Unsolicited mss, synopses and ideas welcome but return postage essential if material is to be returned.
Royalties paid.

Atelier Books
6 Dundas Street, Edinburgh EH3 6HZ
☎0131 557 4050   Fax 0131 557 8382
Managing Editor *Patrick Bourne*
Specialises in fine art. 1 title in 1995. Unsolicited mss, synopses and ideas for books on fine art welcome.

Atlas Press
BCM Atlas Press, London WC1N 3XX
Fax 0171 831 9489
Managing Editor *Alastair Brotchie*

FOUNDED 1983. *Publishes* prose translations from French and German and the international avant-garde. TITLES include works by authors associated with surrealism, expressionism, etc. About 15 titles a year. Interested in translations of 19th- and 20th-century writers only. Do not send unsolicited mss; write first.
Royalties paid.

Aurora Publishing
Unit 9, Bradley Fold Trading Estate, Radcliffe Moor Road, Bradley Fold, Bolton, Lancashire BL2 6RT
☎01204 370752   Fax 01204 370751
Managing Editor *Dawn Robinson*

FOUNDED 1993 as part of Aurora Enterprises Ltd. *Publishes* general and local interest titles, especially oral history and personal testimony. No poetry. About 10 titles a year. Looking to expand range and list. TITLES *Labours of Love: Personal Experiences of Childbirth; Land Army Days; 100 Years of the Manchester Ship Canal; Cotton Everywhere; The Bridgewater Canal; Rainbow's End.* Unsolicited mss, synopses and ideas welcome.
Payment Royalties or fixed fee.

AVERT
AIDS Education and Research Trust,
11 Denne Parade, Horsham, West Sussex RH12 1JD
☎01403 210202   Fax 01403 211001
Managing Editor *Annabel Kanabus*

Publishing arm of the AIDS Education and Research Trust, a national registered charity established 1986. *Publishes* books and leaflets about HIV infection and AIDS. About 3 titles a year. TITLES *AIDS: The Secondary Scene; Guidelines for Management of Children with HIV Infection.* Unsolicited mss, synopses and ideas welcome.
Royalties paid accordingly.

M. & M. Baldwin
24 High Street, Cleobury Mortimer, Near Kidderminster, Worcestershire DY14 8BY
☎01299 270110   Fax 01299 271154
Managing Editor *Dr Mark Baldwin*

FOUNDED 1978. *Publishes* local interest/history and inland waterways books. Up to 5 titles a year. TITLES *Idle Women; West Midland*

Wanderings; Canal Coins. Unsolicited mss, synopses and ideas for books welcome.
Royalties paid.

BB Books
See under **Poetry Presses**

Black Cat Books
See **Miller Publications**

The Bonaventura Press
Bagpath, Tetbury, Gloucestershire GL8 8YG
☎01453 860827   Fax 01453 860487
Managing Editor *Janet Sloss*

FOUNDED 1995 as a self-publishing venture. Synopses and ideas concerning the British connection with Menorca welcome. Shared cost publishing considered in certain circumstances. TITLES *Richard Kane, Governor of Minorca; Archive Annie or How to Survive the Mysteries of Historical Research.*

The Book Castle
12 Church Street, Dunstable, Bedfordshire LU5 4RU
☎01582 605670   Fax 01582 662431
Managing Editor *Paul Bowes*

FOUNDED 1986. *Publishes* non-fiction of local interest (Bedfordshire, Hertfordshire, Buckinghamshire, Northamptonshire, the Chilterns). 6+ titles a year. About 40 titles in print. TITLES *Chiltern Walks* series; *The Hill of the Martyr; Journeys into Bedfordshire.* Unsolicited mss, synopses and ideas for books welcome.
Royalties paid.

The Book Gallery
Bedford Road, St. Ives, Cornwall TR26 1SP
☎01736 793545
Directors *David & Tina Wilkinson*

FOUNDED 1991. *Publishes* limited edition monographs by and about writers/painters associated with the so-called Newlyn and St Ives schools of painting. Topics include Sven Berlin, Kit Barker, Arthur Caddick, Guido Morris, Leach Pottery. Ideas welcome.
Royalties not paid; flat fee.

Book-in-Hand Ltd
20 Shepherds Hill, London N6 5AH
☎0181 341 7650   Fax 0181 341 7650
Contact *Ann Kritzinger*

Print production service for self-publishers. Includes design and editing advice to give customers a greater chance of selling in the open market. Also runs an editing and reading service called **Scriptmate**.

Bookmarque Publishing
26 Cotswold Close, Minster Lovell, Oxfordshire OX8 5SX
☎01993 775179

Managing Editor *John Rose*

FOUNDED 1987. Publishing business with aim of filling gaps in motoring history of which it is said 'there are many!' *Publishes* motoring history and biography and general titles. About 8 titles a year (increasing). All design and typesetting of books done in-house. TITLES *Microcar Mania; The First Motor Racing in Britain – 1902; The History of Oxford Airport.* Unsolicited mss, synopses and ideas welcome on transport (motoring, although some aircraft/WW2 titles considered if not too large in extent). S.a.e. required for reply or return of material. No novels or similar.
Royalties paid.

Bozo
BM Bozo, London WC1N 3XX
☎01234 211606

Managing Editors *John & Cecilia Nicholson*

FOUNDED 1981. Began by producing tiny pamphlets (*Patriotic English Tracts*) and has gained a reputation for itself as one of England's foremost pamphleteers. *Publishes* historical analyses, apocalyptic rants, wry/savage humour and political 'filth'. Considerable expansion of titles is underway. No unsolicited mss, synopses or ideas.
Royalties not paid.

Brentham Press
See under **Poetry Presses**

Brinnoven
9 Thomson Green, Livingston, West Lothian EH54 8TA
☎01506 442846   Fax 01506 442846

Proprietor *William Murray*

FOUNDED 1991. *Publishes* Scottish interest titles specialising in local history, dialects, languages and traditional/folk music. About 3-5 titles a year. Unsolicited mss, synopses and ideas welcome but return postage must be included.
Royalties and fees paid.

Business Innovations Research
Tregeraint House, Zennor, St Ives, Cornwall TR26 3DB
☎01736 797061   Fax 01736 797061

Managing Director *John T. Wilson*

Publishes business books and newsletters, home

study courses, and guidebooks. Production service available to self-publishers.

Businesslike Publishing
'Bluepool', Strathoykel, Ardgay, Inverness-shire IV24 3DP
☎01549 441211

Managing Editor *Iain R. McIntyre*

FOUNDED 1989. Provides a printing and publishing service for members of the **Society of Civil Service Authors**. *Publishes* magazines, collections of poetry, short stories and Scottish history. About 8 titles a year. TITLES *From Scotland's Past; Happy Days in Rothesay; Tales of a Glasgow Childhood* - 2nd printing (non-fiction); *To Freedom Born* - 2nd printing (Doric Scots poetry); *Focus* (poetry anthology series); *Secrets of a View* (Inverness Writers' anthology); *Rhymes for no Reason* (Scots poetry). Ideas/synopses accepted. No unsolicited mss.
Royalties generally not paid but negotiable in some circumstances.

Cakebreads Publications
5a The High Street, Saffron Walden, Essex CB10 1AT
☎01799 524131

Managing Editor *Mrs Brenda Fuller*

Publishes history and Second World War nursing books. TITLES *A Nurse's War; Quiet Heroines.* No unsolicited mss.
Royalties not paid.

Chapter Two
13 Plum Lane, Plumstead Common, London SE18 3AF
☎0181 316 5389   Fax 0181 854 5963

Managing Editor *E. N. Cross*

FOUNDED 1976. Chapter Two's chief activity is the propagation of the Christian faith through the printed page. *Publishes* exclusively on Plymouth Brethren. About 12 titles a year. No unsolicited mss, synopses or ideas. Enquiries only.
Royalties not paid.

Charlewood Press
7 Weavers Place, Chandlers Ford, Eastleigh, Hampshire SO53 1TU
☎01703 261192

Managing Editors *Gerald Ponting, Anthony Light*

FOUNDED 1987. Publishes local history booklets on the Fordingbridge area, researched and written by the two partners and leaflets on local

walks. TITLES: *Breamore - A Short History & Guide; Tudor Fordingbridge; The Tragedies of the Dodingtons; Victorian Fordingbridge.* No unsolicited mss.
Royalties not paid.

The Cheverell Press

Manor Studios, Manningford Abbots, Pewsey, Wiltshire SN9 6HS
☎01672 563163   Fax 01672 564301
Managing Editor *Sarah de Larrinaga*

Publishes careers, media and performing arts. No fiction.
    IMPRINTS **The Cheverell Press, First Hand Books.** TITLES *The Guide to Drama Training in the UK 1996/7; The Guide to Careers and Training in the Performing Arts; How to Become a Working Actor.* Currently using researchers/writers on a fee basis, rather than royalties. No unsolicited mss. Started as a self-publisher and has produced a self-publishers information pack. Write for details.

Chrysalis Press

11 Convent Close, Kenilworth, Warwickshire CV8 2FQ
☎01926 855223   Fax 01926 855223
Managing Editor *Brian Buckley*

FOUNDED 1994. *Publishes* fiction, literary criticism and biography. TITLES *Two Tales; Challenge and Renewal: D.H. Lawrence and the Thematic Novel.* No unsolicited mss.
Royalties paid.

CNP Publications

Roseland, Gorran, St Austell, Cornwall
☎01726 843501   Fax 01726 843501
Managing Editor *Dr James Whetter*

FOUNDED 1975. *Publishes* poetry, political essays, local Cornish interest/biography and Celtic design. 1-2 titles a year. TITLES *An Baner Kernewek (The Cornish Banner)* – quarterly local-interest magazine; Cornish history published under the **Lyfrow Trelyspen** imprint – *Cornish Weather and Cornish People in the 17th Century; The Bodrugans: A Study of a Cornish Medieval Knightly Family.* Unsolicited mss, synopses and ideas welcome.
Royalties not paid.

The Cosmic Elk

68 Elsham Crescent, Lincoln LN6 3YS
☎01522 691146
Managing Editor *Heather Hobden*

FOUNDED 1988 to publish books, booklets, leaflets on specialised topics in science, history and the history of science at low cost. Also provides a publishing service for academic, specialised and local interests, exhibition booklets, handbooks, tutorial notes, etc.. For enquiries, phone or write with s.a.e.. TITLES *John Harrison and the Problem of Longitude; The Telescope Revolution; Law or War - the Legal Aspects of the Cuban Missile Crisis; Life and Death According to the Traditional Beliefs of the Yakuts; First Scientific Ideas on the Universe; Inside the Hampton Court Clock; History of Yakutia.*

Creation Books

93 Clerkenwell Road, London EC1R 5AR
☎0171 430 9878   Fax 0171 242 5527
Managing Editor *Peter Colebrook*

FOUNDED 1990 to publish books of extreme thought and imagination - surreal, pulp, horror, avant-garde, underground film, art. 20 titles in 1995. No unsolicited mss; all books are commissioned.
Royalties paid annually.

Crescent Moon Publishing and Joe's Press

18 Chaddesley Road, Kidderminster, Worcestershire DY10 3AD
Managing Editor *Jeremy Robinson*

FOUNDED 1988 to publish critical studies of figures such as D. H. Lawrence, Thomas Hardy, André Gide, Powys, Rilke, Piero, Bellini, Beckett, Cavafy and Robert Graves. *Publishes* literature, criticism, media, art, feminism, painting, poetry, travel, guidebooks, cinema and some fiction. New literary magazine, *Passion*, launched February 1994. Quarterly. Twice-yearly anthology of American poetry, *Pagan America*. Expansion into fiction planned over the next couple of years. About 15-20 titles per year. TITLES *Samuel Beckett Goes into the Silence; Jackie Collins and the Blockbuster Novel; Vincent Van Gogh; The Poetry of Cinema; Wild Zones: Pornography, Art and Feminism; Andrea Dworkin.* Unsolicited mss, synopses and ideas welcome but send letter first. Approach in writing only.
Royalties negotiable.

Crocus

See **Poetry Presses**

Daniels Publishing

38 Cambridge Place, Cambridge CB2 1NS
☎01223 467144   Fax 01223 467145
Publisher *Dr Victor G. Daniels*

Educational press specialising in A4 photocopiable resource packs on health and social education, study and work skills, and self development for schools, colleges, health authorities and the training market. Also educational materials for the pharmaceutical industry. Unsolicited mss, synopses and ideas welcome.

Dark Diamonds Publications
PO Box HK 31, Leeds, West Yorkshire
LS11 9XN
☎0113 2453868
Managing Editor *Andrew Cocker*

FOUNDED 1987. Member of the **Small Press Group of Great Britain**. *Publishes* 2–3 titles a year. Print runs average 1000 copies. Limited funds. Current titles: *Dark Diamonds* magazine. Journal covering social and political subjects. Mainly concerned with environmental development and human rights issues. Unsolicited articles and illustrations on the above subject matter welcome. *A Riot of Emotions* magazine features art and poetry, and carries reviews of small press publications and independent music releases. Unsolicited poetry/short story mss welcome (2000 words maximum). Also unsolicited art (b&w illustrations only) welcome. Return postage must be included with all unsolicited contributions. Unsolicited material for review also welcome. Free copy to all contributors. Contributors guidelines and current catalogue available (send s.a.e.).
Royalties not paid.

Delectus
27 Old Gloucester Street, London
WC1N 3XX
☎0181 963 0979   Fax 0181 963 0502
Contact *Michael R. Goss*

FOUNDED 1990. *Publishes* classic erotic and horror fiction. 8 titles in 1995. Unsolicited mss, synopses and ideas not welcome.
Royalties paid annually.

Diamond Press
See under **Poetry Presses**

Dog House Publications
18 Marlow Avenue, Eastbourne, East Sussex
BN22 8SJ
☎01323 729214
Managing Editor *Alexander C. Kent*

FOUNDED 1990. Publishes books and booklets on dog behaviour and related subjects. Unsolicited mss, synopses and ideas welcome but must be relevant. Mss must be practical and informed; 'we get too many doggie sob stories and poetry!' TITLES: *Dynamic Dog Psychology;*

Trance Training; Behaviour Counsellors' Handbook. Branching out into other doggie subjects, e.g. health and general new age dog care and training.
Royalties paid.

The Dragonby Press
15 High Street, Dragonby, Scunthorpe
DN15 0BE
☎01724 840645
Managing Editor *Richard Williams*

FOUNDED 1987 to publish affordable bibliography for reader, collector and dealer. About 3 titles a year. TITLES *Collins Crime Club: A Checklist*. Unsolicited mss, synopses and ideas welcome for bibliographical projects only.
Royalties paid.

Dragonfly Press
Courtyard Mews, Southover, Burwash,
East Sussex TN19 7JB
☎01435 882580
Managing Editor *C. Bell*

FOUNDED 1989. *Publishes* local history, literary fiction, poetry and how-to titles. 1–2 titles a year. TITLES *The Writer's Guide to Self-Publishing; Organisation and Time Management for Square Pegs; Common Sense for Creative Writers; Saheli Kitchen* (ethnic cookery book). No unsolicited material accepted. Commissions only.
Royalties paid where applicable.

The Edge
1 Nichols Court, Belle Vue, Chelmsford,
Essex CM2 0BS
☎01245 492561
Managing Editor *Graham Evans*

Publishes a bi-monthly magazine. Looking for 'innovative, experimental, non-mainstream science fiction, modern horror, "slipstream" or non-genre imaginative fiction'. Writers' guidelines available on request. Send s.a.e..

Education Now Publishing Cooperative Ltd
113 Arundel Drive, Bramcote Hills,
Nottingham NG9 3FQ
☎0115 9257261   Fax 0115 9257261
Managing Editors *Dr Roland Meighan, Philip Toogood*

A non-profit research and writing group set up in reaction to 'the totalitarian tendencies of the 1988 Education Act'. Its aim is to widen the terms of the debate about education and its choices. *Publishes* reports on positive educational initiatives such as flexi-schooling, mini-schooling, small schooling, home-based education and democratic schooling. 4–5 titles a year. TITLES *Skills for Self-Managed Learning* Mike Roberts; *Beyond Authoritarian School Management* Lynn Davies; *Developing Democratic Education* Clive Harber. No unsolicited mss or ideas. Enquiries only.

Royalties generally not paid.

Educational Heretics Press
113 Arundel Drive, Bramcote Hills,
Nottingham NG9 3FQ
☎0115 9257261   Fax 0115 9257261
Directors *Janet & Roland Meighan*

Non-profit venture which aims to question the dogmas of schooling in particular and education in general. TITLES *Alice Miller: The Unkind Society, Parenting and Schooling* Chris Shute; *The Freethinkers' Guide to the Educational Universe* Roland Meighan; *Compulsory Schooling Disease* Chris Shute; *John Holt: Personalised Education and the Reconstruction of Schooling* Roland Meighan. No unsolicited material. Enquiries only.

Royalties not paid but under review.

EKO Fund
Wedgwood Memorial College, Barlaston,
Staffs ST12 9DG
☎01782 372105   Fax 01782 372393
Managing Editor *Brian W. Burnett*

FOUNDED January 1996 to publish modern, lively books and magazines in and about Esperanto. Unsolicited mss, synopses and ideas welcome.

Royalties paid.

Enable Communications
PO Box 86, Coventry CV6 5ZS
☎01203 682706   Fax 01203 682706
Contact *Simon Stevens*

'Established to provide information processing and opportunity creation within the field of enablement. Primarily concentrates on providing reference material for the disability field.' TITLES *Dysability Direct; Dysability Handbook.* Unsolicited material welcome; primarily reference material required.

estamp
204 St Albans Avenue, London W4 5JU
☎0181 994 2379   Fax 0181 994 2379
Contact *Silvie Turner*

Independent publisher of fine art books on printmaking, papermaking and artists' bookmaking. Books are designed and written for artists, craftspeople and designers. TITLES *British Printmaking Studios; About Prints; Europe for Printmakers; British Artists Books; Which Paper?.* Approach in writing in first instance.

Feather Books
Fair View, Old Coppice, Lyth Bank,
Shrewsbury, Shropshire SY3 0BW
☎01743 872177
Managing Editor *Rev. John Waddington-Feather*

FOUNDED 1980 to publish writers' group work. All material has a strong Christian ethos. *Publishes* poetry (mainly, but not exclusively, religious), biography, local history. 10 titles a year. TITLES *The Quill Hedgehog Series; Feather Poets Series; Feather's Little Birthday Book Series.* No unsolicited mss, synopses or ideas. All correspondence to include s.a.e. please.

Ferry Publications
12 Millfields Close, Pentlepoir, Kilgetty,
Pembrokeshire SA68 0SA
☎01834 813991   Fax 01834 814484
Managing Editor *Miles Cowsill*

FOUNDED 1987 to publish ferry and shipping books. 3–4 titles a year. TITLES *Only Britanny Ferries, Harwich – Hoek van Holland – A 100 Years of Service.* Unsolicited mss, synopses and ideas welcome.

Royalties paid.

Field Day Publications
Foyle Arts Centre, Old Foyle College,
Lawrence Hill, Derry BT48 7NJ
☎01504 360196   Fax 01504 365419

Specialises in work of Irish interest. Pamphlets, essays, playscripts. Usually commissioned. TITLES *Revising the Rising; Field Day Anthology of Irish Writing.*

First Hand Books
See **The Cheverell Press**

Fisher Miller Publishing
11 Ramsholte Close, North Waltham,
Basingstoke, Hampshire RG25 2DG
☎01256 397482   Fax 01256 397482
Managing Editor *Janey Fisher*

ESTABLISHED 1994 as a result of enquiries from an author whose book was too esoteric to warrant publication by a commercial publisher. 'We are a service publisher, passing on the costs of publishing direct to the author to facilitate self-publishing to professional standards.' Unsolicited mss, synopses and ideas welcome. 2 titles in 1995. TITLES *The Hibiscus Years; Pika-Don* both by George Bishop.

Royalties not paid.

Fitzgerald Publishing

PO Box 804, London SE13 5JJ
☎0181 690 0597

Managing Editor *Tim Fitzgerald*
General Editor *Andrew Smith*

FOUNDED 1974. *Specialises* in scientific studies of insects and spiders. 1-2 titles a year. TITLES *Tarantulas of the USA & Mexico; Stick Insects of Europe & The Mediterranean; Baboon Spiders of Africa; Tarantula Classification and Identification Guide.* Unsolicited mss, synopses and ideas for books welcome. Also considers video scripts for video documentaries. New video documentary: *Desert Tarantulas.*

Royalties paid.

Five Leaves Publications

PO Box 81, Nottingham NG5 4ER
☎0115 9603355

Contact *Ross Bradshaw*

FOUNDED 1995 (taking over the publishing programme of Mushroom Bookshop), producing 6-8 titles a year. *Publishes* fiction, poetry, politics and Jewish Interest. TITLES *The Dybbuk of Delight: an Anthology of Jewish Women's Poetry* eds. Sonja Lyndon and Sylvia Paskin; *The Shallow Grave: a Memoir of the Spanish Civil War* Walter Gregory. No unsolicited mss; titles normally commissioned.

Royalties and fees paid.

Forest Books

20 Forest View, Chingford, London E4 7AY
☎0181 529 8470   Fax 0181 524 7890

Managing Director *Brenda Walker*
Approx. Annual Turnover £70,000

FOUNDED 1984 to promote international cultural links through publishing. *Publishes* literary translations, poetry, anthologies, fiction and plays. Particularly keen to publish works from minority languages and ethnic groups. *Specialises* in books from Eastern Europe. A number of books are published in collaboration with UNESCO. TITLES *Leaving Eden* poems by American prize-winning poet Nadya Aisenberg; *Only When the Messengers Come* dual text German/English; poems by Olly Komenda-Soentgerath, translated by Tom Beck.

Forth Naturalist & Historian

University of Stirling, Stirling, Clackmannanshire FK9 4LA
☎01259 215091   Fax 01786 464994

Also at: 30 Dunmar Drive, Alloa, Clackmannanshire FK10 2EH

Honorary Editor *Lindsay Corbett*

FOUNDED 1975 by the collaboration of Stirling University members and the Central Regional Council to promote interests and publications on central Scotland. Aims to provide a 'valuable local studies educational resource for mid-Scotland schools, libraries and people'. *Publishes* naturalist, historical and environmental studies and maps. TITLES *The Forth Naturalist & Historian from 1976* (annual publication; 1995 is Vol. 18); *Doune, Historical Notes; Doune, Postcards of the Past; Central Scotland: Land, Wildlife, People* (a new survey); *The Ochil Hills: Landscapes, Wildlife, Heritage, Walks.* In preparation: *Lure of Loch Lomond; Alloa in Days of Prosperity 1830-1914;* 1890s maps 25" to the mile - 24 of Central Scotland areas/places with historical notes. Welcomes papers, mss and ideas relevant to central Scotland. Promotes annual environment/heritage symposia - 1995 was the 21st year.

Royalties not paid.

Freedom Publishing

PO Box 4, Topsham, Exeter, Devon EX3 0YR
☎0976 213181

Proprietors *Scott and Charmiene Leland*

FOUNDED 1995. *Publishes* works connected with the topics of 'personal awakenings to truth, self-awareness and non-duality'. New authors who are not considered 'mainstream' are especially welcome. About 4 titles a year. TITLES *The Mountain Path; Araminta's Message: A Fairytale; One Year in India; I Married a Dolphin.* Unsolicited mss, synopses and ideas (with s.a.e.) welcome. Shared funding, shared profits.

The Frogmore Press

See under **Poetry Presses**

Frontier Publishing

Windetts, Kirstead, Norfolk NR15 1BR
☎01508 558174   Fax 01508 550194

Managing Editor *John Black*

FOUNDED 1983. *Publishes* travel, photography and literature. 2-3 titles a year. TITLES *Eye on the Hill: Horse Travels in Britain; Euphonics: A Poet's Dictionary of Sounds; Broken China; The*

Green Book of Poetry. No unsolicited mss; synopses and ideas welcome.
Royalties paid.

Full House Productions
12 Sunfield Gardens, Bayston Hill, Shrewsbury, Shropshire SY3 0LA
☎01743 872914

Managing Editor *Judith A. Shone*

FOUNDED 1993 by writer/producer Judith Shone in order to supply professionally written pantomime scripts to small production companies such as operatic societies, amateur dramatic societies and other performing groups – village halls etc. *Publishes* a complete low-cost 'panto-pack' consisting of scripts, posters and tickets. Future plans are to expand into publication of plays and sketches. All titles are written and published in-house. 11 titles to date; 3 planned for 1997.

Galactic Central Publications
Imladris, 25A Copgrove Road, Leeds, West Yorkshire LS8 2SP

Managing Editor *Phil Stephensen-Payne*

FOUNDED 1982 in the US. *Publishes* science fiction bibliographies. About 4 titles a year. TITLES *Gene Wolfe: Urth-Man Extraordinary; Andre Norton: Grand Master of Witch World.* All new publications originate in the UK. Unsolicited mss, synopses and ideas welcome.

Gateway Books
The Hollies, Wellow, Bath, Avon BA2 8QJ
☎01225 835127   Fax 01225 840012

Publisher *Alick Bartholomew*

FOUNDED 1983. *Publishes* mind, body and spirit, earth mysteries, alternative health. 6 titles in 1995. No unsolicited mss; synopses and ideas for books welcome but 'authors should check our list first'. No fiction, children's or poetry.
Royalties paid annually.

Geological Society Publishing House
Unit 7, Brassmill Enterprise Centre, Brassmill Lane, Bath, Avon BA1 3JN
☎01225 445046   Fax 01225 442836

Managing Editor *Mike Collins*

Publishing arm of the Geological Society which was founded in 1807. *Publishes* undergraduate and postgraduate texts in the earth sciences. 10 titles a year. Unsolicited mss, synopses and ideas welcome.
Royalties not paid.

Global Publishing Ltd
788-790 Finchley Road, Temple Fortune, London NW11 7UR
☎0181 209 1151   Fax 0181 905 5344

Chief Executive *Dr I. O. Azuonye*

FOUNDED 1993. *Publishes* contemporary issues, politics, economics, personal development, general fiction, education and humour. TITLE *If We Elect Her President in November of the Year 2000* Ikechukwu O. Azuonye. Welcomes synopses and sample chapters with return postage. Reading fee charged.
Royalties paid twice yearly.

Glosa
PO Box 18, Richmond, Surrey TW9 2AU
☎0181 948 8417

Managing Editors *Wendy Ashby, Ronald Clark*

FOUNDED 1981. *Publishes* textbooks, dictionaries and translations for the teaching, speaking and promotion of Glosa (an international, auxiliary language); also a newsletter and journal. Rapid growth in the last couple of years. TITLES *Glosa 6000 Dictionary; Introducing Euro-Glosa; Eduka-Glosa; Central Glosa; Glosa 1000 - Chinese; Glosa 1000 - Swahili Dictionary.* Spring 1994 launched *Sko-Glosa*, a new publication for and by younger students of Glosa to be distributed to schools in different countries. Also in 1994 published several fairy stories and activity pages for school children who are learning Glosa in school. Unsolicited mss and ideas for Glosa books welcome.

Gothic Press
PO Box 542, Highgate, London N6 6BG

Managing Editor *Robin Crisp*

Specialist publisher of gothic titles in quality, case editions. Non-fiction only at present. *Publishes* mysticism, supernatural, history, biography. TITLES *The Highgate Vampire; Mad, Bad and Dangerous to Know; From Satan to Christ; The Grail Church.* No unsolicited mss; synopses and ideas may be welcome.
Royalties not paid.

The Gothic Society
Chatham House, Gosshill Road, Chislehurst, Kent BR7 5NS
☎0181 467 8475   Fax 0181 295 1967

Managing Editor *Jennie Gray*

FOUNDED 1990. *Publishes* a quarterly magazine, books and supplements on Gothic and macabre subjects. History, literary criticism, reprints of forgotten texts, biography, architecture, art etc., all with a gloomy and black-hued flavour. About 8 titles a year. Synopses and ideas welcome. (Also see **Literary Societies**).

Royalties flat fee.

Grant Books

The Coach House, New Road, Cutnall Green, Droitwich, Worcestershire WR9 0PQ
☎01299 851588   Fax 01299 851446
Managing Editor *H. R. J. Grant*

FOUNDED 1978. *Publishes* golf-related titles only: course architecture, history, biography, some essays on golf course architecture, hazards etc., but no instructional material. New titles and old, plus limited editions. About 4 titles a year. TITLES *Harold H. Hilton: His Golfing Life and Times; St Andrews Night and Other Golfing Stories; Royal Cinque Ports Golf Club: A Personal Record; The Whitcombes: A Golfing Legend; The Murdoch Golf Library; Aspects of Collecting Golf Books; The Architectural Side of Golf; British Professional Golfers – A Register, 1887–1930*. Unsolicited mss, synopses and ideas welcome.

Royalties paid.

Grevatt & Grevatt

9 Rectory Drive, Newcastle upon Tyne NE3 1XT
Chairman/Editorial Head *Dr S. Y. Killingley*

FOUNDED 1981. Alternative publisher of works not normally commercially viable. Three books have appeared with financial backing from professional bodies. *Publishes* academic titles and conference reports, particularly language, linguistics and religious studies. Some poetry also. Dr Killingley is editor of the Linguistic Association's *British Linguistic Newsletter.* TITLES include *The Sanskrit Tradition in the Modern World*, a series of rewritten conference/lecture proceedings launched 1988. New title: *Sound, Speech and Silence: Selected Poems.* No unsolicited mss. Synopses and ideas should be accompanied by s.a.e..

Royalties paid annually (after the first 500 copies).

GSSE

11 Malford Grove, Gilwern, Abergavenny, Gwent NP7 0RN
☎01873 830872
Owner/Manager *David P. Bosworth*

Publishes newsletters and booklets describing classroom practice (at all levels of education and training). Ideas welcome - particularly from practising teachers, lecturers and trainers describing how they use technology in their teaching. TITLES *OLS News* (quarterly newsletter); series: *IT in the Classroom* (first title: *Databases in the Junior School*).

Royalties paid by arrangement.

Guildhall Press

41 Great James Street, Derry BT48 7DF
☎01504 364413   Fax 01504 372949
Managing Editor *Paul Hippsley*

FOUNDED 1979 to produce local history material. Government funding has helped establish the press as a community publishing house with increased output across a wider range of subjects. Interested in joint ventures with similar organisations throughout Europe to increase output and gain commercial experience. About 6 titles a year. TITLES *Seeing is Believing, Murals in Derry* Oona Woods; *Memory of Memories of Derry* Roy Clements; *Thinking Green* Dan McAllister; *Derry's Walls* Paul Hippsley; *Parade of Phantoms* Peter McCartney; *Talk of the Town* Seamus McConnell; *Derry Jail* Colm Cavanagh. Unsolicited mss, synopses and ideas welcome.

Royalties negotiable.

Happy House

3b Castledown Avenue, Hastings, East Sussex TN34 3RJ
☎01424 434778

FOUNDED 1992 as a self-publishing venture for Dave Arnold/Martin Honeysett collaboration of poetry and cartoons. TITLES *Out to Lunch; Under the Wallpaper; Before and After the Shrink.*

Haunted Library

Flat 1, 36 Hamilton Street, Hoole, Chester, Cheshire CH2 3JQ
☎01244 313685
Managing Editor *Rosemary Pardoe*

FOUNDED 1979. *Publishes* a twice-yearly ghost story magazine and booklets in the antiquarian tradition of M. R. James. The magazine publishes stories, news and articles. 2-3 titles a year. TITLE *Ghosts & Scholars.* No unsolicited mss.

Royalties not paid.

Heart of Albion Press

2 Cross Hill Close, Wymeswold, Loughborough, Leicestershire LE12 6UJ
☎01509 880725
Managing Editor *R. N. Trubshaw*

FOUNDED 1990 to publish books and booklets on the East Midlands area. *Publishes* mostly local history. About 6-8 titles a year. TITLES *Little-known Leicestershire & Rutland; User-Friendly Dictionary of Old English.* No unsolicited mss but synopses and ideas welcome.

Royalties negotiable.

Hedgerow Publishing Ltd
325 Abbeydale Road, Sheffield, South Yorkshire S7 1FS
☎0114 2554873   Fax 0114 2509400
Managing Editor *T. Hale*

FOUNDED 1988. Publisher of local interest postcards and greeting cards. Expanded into book publishing in 1990 with the emphasis on tourist-orientated material. Ideas for books relevant to the South Yorkshire and Northern Peak District areas will be considered. Interested in photographic submissions of colour transparencies of local views. Outright purchase only. Telephone *before* sending.

Royalties negotiable.

Highcliff Press
23 Avon Drive, Guisborough, Cleveland TS14 8AX
☎01287 637274
Managing Editor *Robert Sampson*

FOUNDED 1994. *Publishes* short prose and prose poems. TITLES *Possible Worlds; Possible Writings; The Sea at Le Havre-des-Pas.*

Hilmarton Manor Press
Calne, Wiltshire SN11 8SB
☎01249 760208   Fax 01249 760379
Chairman/Managing Director *Charles Baile de Laperriere*

Publishes fine art reference only. No unsolicited material. Enquiries only.

Royalties paid.

Hisarlik Press
4 Catisfield Road, Enfield Lock, Middlesex EN3 6BD
☎01992 700898   Fax 0181 292 6118
Managing Editors *Dr Jeffrey Mazo, Georgina Clark-Mazo*

FOUNDED 1991. *Publishes* academic books and journals on folklore, local history and medieval studies. 6 titles in 1995. TITLES *With Disastrous Consequences: London Disasters 1830-1917; The Maiden Who Rose From The Sea and Other Finnish Folktales; From Sagas to Society: Comparative Approaches to Early Iceland.* No unsolicited mss; synopses and ideas welcome.

Royalties paid.

Horseshoe Publications
PO Box 37, Kingsley, Warrington, Cheshire WA6 8DR
☎01928 787477 (Afternoons and evenings)
Managing Editor *John C. Hibbert*

FOUNDED 1994. Initially to publish work of Cheshire writers. Poetry, short stories and own writing. Shared cost publishing considered in certain circumstances. Reading fee on full mss £25. TITLES *One Boy's War; The Reincarnate; Windmills; The Travellers Series.* 7 titles in 1995. Unsolicited mss, synopses and ideas in the realm of commercial fiction welcome. S.a.e. for return.

IKON Productions Ltd
Manor Farm House, Manor Road, Wantage, Oxfordshire OX12 8NE
☎01235 767467   Fax 01235 767467
Publisher *Clare Goodrick-Clarke*

FOUNDED 1988. *Publishes* religion and history, heritage and countryside. Also **Amate Press** imprint. No unsolicited mss. Please write with ideas and synopses first.

Intellect Books
E.F.A.E., Earl Richards Road North, Exeter, Devon EX2 6AS
☎01392 475110   Fax 01392 475110
Publisher *Masoud Yazdani*
Assistant Publisher *Robin Beecroft*

FOUNDED 1984. *Publishes* books and journals on social implications of computing, language learning and European studies. 10 titles in 1995. TITLES *The Art and Science of Learning Languages; From Information to Knowledge; Children and Propaganda; Women in European Theatre.* Unsolicited synopses and ideas welcome.

Royalties paid.

Iolo
38 Chaucer Road, Bedford MK40 2AJ
☎01234 270175   Fax 01234 270175
Managing Director *Dedwydd Jones*

Publishes Welsh theatre-related material and campaigns for a Welsh National Theatre. SERIES *Black Books on the Welsh Theatre.* Ideas on Welsh themes welcome; approach in writing.

Ironside Books
27A Crescent Road, Rowley Park, Stafford ST17 9AL
☎01785 252625
Managing Editor *Roger Butters*

FOUNDED 1994. First publications July 1995 with plans to publish at least 6 books per year,

mostly genre fiction. TITLES *All Wind and Pistol; Murder in a Cathedral City*. Unsolicited mss and synopses (with s.a.e. for return) welcome.
Royalties paid.

JAC Publications
28 Bellomonte Crescent, Drayton, Norwich, Norfolk NR8 6EJ
☎01603 861339

Managing Editor *John James Vasco*

Publishes World War II Luftwaffe history only. TITLES *Zerstörer: The Messerschmitt 110 and its Units in 1940* John J. Vasco and Peter D. Cornwell; *Bombsights Over England* John James Vasco; *Defending the Reich* Eric Mombeek. Unsolicited mss welcome. No synopses or ideas.
Royalties paid.

Jackson's Arm Press
See **Sunk Island Publishing**

John Jones Publishing Ltd
Borthwen, Wrexham Road, Ruthin, Clwyd LL15 1DA
☎01824 707255

Managing Editor *John Idris Jones*

FOUNDED 1989. *Publishes* inexpensive books and booklets in English with a Welsh background. Interested in short, illustrated texts for the tourist and schools market. Approach in writing with s.a.e..
Royalties paid.

Katabasis
See under **Poetry Presses**

Kittiwake Press
3 Glantwymyn Village Workshops, Nr. Machynlleth, Montgomeryshire SY20 8LY
☎01650 511314   Fax 01650 511602

Managing Editor *David Perrott*

FOUNDED 1986. Owned by Perrott Cartographics. *Publishes* guidebooks only, with an emphasis on good design/production. TITLES *Western Islands Handbook; Outer Hebrides Handbook; Local Walks Guides*. Unsolicited mss, synopses and ideas welcome. Specialist cartographic and electronic publishing services available.
Royalties paid.

Lily Publications
12 Millfields Close, Kilgetty, Pembrokeshire SA68 0SA
☎01834 811895   Fax 01834 814484

Managing Editor *Miles Cowsill*

FOUNDED 1991. *Publishes* holiday guides and

specialist books. TITLES *Cardiganshire 1995/6; Brecon Beacons and Heart of Wales Guide 1995; Isle of Man 1994/5*, tourist guide to the island; *Isle of Man – A Photographic Journey*. Unsolicited mss, synopses and ideas welcome. Sister company **Lily Publications (Isle of Man) Ltd.**, PO Box 1, Portland House, Ballasalla, Isle of Man. Tel/fax 01624 823848.
Royalties paid.

Logaston Press
Logaston, Woonton, Almeley, Herefordshire HR3 6QH
☎01544 327344

Managing Editors *Andy Johnson, Ron Shoesmith*

FOUNDED 1985. *Publishes* walking guides, social history, rural issues and local history for Wales and West Midlands. 3-4 titles a year. TITLES *The Folklore of Hereford & Worcester; James Wathen's Herefordshire 1770–1820; The Prehistoric Sites of Herefordshire; Owain Glyndwr in the Marches*. Unsolicited mss, synopses and ideas welcome. Return postage appreciated.
Royalties paid.

Luath Press Ltd
Barr, Ayrshire KA26 9TN
☎01465 861636   Fax 01465 861625

Managing Editor *T. W. Atkinson*

FOUNDED 1980 to publish books of Scottish interest. *Publishes* guidebooks and books with a Scottish connection. About 6 titles a year. TITLES *Seven Steps in the Dark* (autobiography of a Scottish miner); *Mountain Days and Bothy Nights*. Unsolicited mss, synopses and ideas welcome.
Royalties paid.

Lyfrow Trelyspen
See **CNP Publications**

Madison Publishing Ltd
83 Albert Palace Mansions, Lurline Gardens, London SW11 4DH
☎0973 224536   Fax 0171 622 4679

Managing Director *Nathan Andrew Iyer*

FOUNDED 1995. *Publishes* British fiction. 1 title in 1995. TITLE *Domino Run*. No unsolicited mss. Synopses (no more than 2pp) and ideas welcome.

Madison Publishing Ltd
83 Albert Mansions, Lurline Gardens, London SW11 4DH
☎0973 224536   Fax 0171 622 4679

Managing Director *Andrew Iyer*

FOUNDED 1995. *Publishes* British fiction only. 1 title in 1995. TITLE *Domino Run* Andrew Iyer. No unsolicited material.

Royalties paid twice yearly.

Mandrake of Oxford

PO Box 250, Oxford OX1 1AP
☎01865 243671

Managing Editor *Kris Morgan*

Publishes occult, surreal, magical art, sexology, heretical and radically new ideas. 3-5 titles a year. TITLES *Shadow Matter and Psychic Phenomena* Gerhard Wassermann; *Rune Magician Trilogy* Jan Fries. No mss; send synopsis first with return postage.

Royalties paid.

Marine Day Publishers

64 Cotterill Road, Surbiton, Surrey KT6 7UN
☎0181 399 7625   Fax 0181 399 1592

Managing Editor *Stephen H. Day*

FOUNDED 1990. Part of The Marine Press Ltd. *Publishes* local history. 1 title a year. TITLES *Malden Old & New; Malden Old & New Revisited; Kingston and Surbiton Old & New; All Change.* Unsolicited synopses and ideas welcome; no mss.

Royalties not paid.

Matching Press

1 Watermans End, Matching Green, Harlow, Essex CM17 0RQ
☎01279 731308

Publisher *Patrick Streeter*

FOUNDED 1993. *Publishes* biography, autobiography, social history and fiction. Enquiries welcome.

Royalties paid.

Maypole Editions

22 Mayfair Avenue, Ilford, Essex IG1 3DQ
☎0181 252 0354

Contact *Barry Taylor*

Publisher of fiction and poetry in the main. About 3 titles a year. TITLES *Snorting Mustard; Metallum Damnantorum; Love Sonnets; X and the Glawkoid Party; No Bodyguard; Memento Mori, Cock Robin; Frog; Battle Beach.* Unsolicited mss welcome provided return postage is included. Poetry welcome for forthcoming collection. Poems should be approximately 30 lines long, broadly covering social concerns, ethnic minorities, feminist issues, romance, lyric. No politics. The annual collected anthology is designed as a small press platform for first-time poets and a permanent showcase for those already published.

Meadow Books

22 Church Meadow, Milton under Wychwood, Chipping Norton, Oxfordshire OX7 6JG
☎01993 831338

Managing Director *C. O'Neill*

FOUNDED 1990. Published a social history of hospitals. TITLES *A Picture of Health; More Pictures of Health* Cynthia O'Neill.

Mercia Cinema Society

19 Pinder's Grove, Wakefield, West Yorkshire WF1 4AH
☎01924 372748

Managing Editor *Brian Hornsey*

FOUNDED 1980 to foster research into the history of picture houses. *Publishes* books and booklets on the subject, including cinema circuits and chains. Books are often tied in with specific geographical areas. TITLES *Cinemas of Lincoln; The How to Research the History of Cinemas; Cinemas of York; Cinemas of Southampton; Cinemas of Exeter; Cinemas of Essex; Cinema Story – The Rise, Fall and Revival of Wakefield Cinemas.* Unsolicited mss, synopses and ideas.

Royalties not paid.

Meridian Books

40 Hadzor Road, Oldbury, Warley, West Midlands B68 9LA
☎0121 429 4397

Managing Editor *Peter Groves*

FOUNDED 1985 as a small home-based enterprise following the acquisition of titles from Tetradon Publications Ltd. *Publishes* local history, walking and regional guides. 4-5 titles a year. TITLES *Ridges & Valleys II: More Walks in the Midlands* Trevor Antill; *The Navigation Way: A Hundred Mile Towpath Walk* Peter Groves & Trevor Antill; New titles 1995: *The Monarch's Way, Books 1, 2 & 3* Trevor Antill. Unsolicited mss, synopses and ideas welcome if relevant. Send s.a.e. if mss is to be returned.

Royalties paid.

Merton Priory Press Ltd

7 Nant Fawr Road, Cardiff CF2 6JQ
☎01222 761544   Fax 01222 761544

Managing Director *Philip Riden*

FOUNDED 1993. *Publishes* academic and mid-market history, especially local and industrial history; also distributes for small publishers working in the same field. About 6 titles a year. Full catalogue available.

Royalties paid twice yearly.

Miller Publications

Mount Cottage, Grange Road, Saint
Michael's, Tenterden, Kent TN30 6EE
Managing Editor *Neil Miller*

FOUNDED 1994. *Publishes* horror tales 'with a
twist' – mystery, crime, comedy, suspense and
anything unusual or bizarre. IMPRINT **Black
Cat Books**. Evaluation and critique service
available for large mss. No unsolicited mss.
Send s.a.e. in the first instance for an information package.

Minimax Books Ltd

Broadgate House, Church Street,
Deeping St James, Peterborough,
Cambridgeshire PE6 8HD
☎01778 347609   Fax 01778 341198
Chairman *Bob Lavender*
Managing Director *Lynn Green*
Approx. Annual Turnover £40,000

FOUNDED in the early 1980s. *Publishes* books of
local interest, children's and history. Planning
to double the size of the list. Unsolicited mss,
synopses and ideas welcome. No academic or
technical.
Royalties paid twice yearly.

Minority Rights Group Publishing

379 Brixton Road, London SW9 7DE
☎0171 978 9498   Fax 0171 738 6265
Head of Publications *Brian Morrison*

FOUNDED in the late 1960s, MRG has offices
in many other countries and through its publications and the United Nations, works to raise
awareness of minority issues worldwide.
Publishes books, reports and educational material on minority rights. 6–8 titles a year. TITLES
*Female Genital Mutilation; The Kurds; Afro-
Latins; Burundi; North Caucasus*. Unsolicited
mss, synopses/ideas welcome.
Royalties not paid.

Morton Publishing

PO Box 23, Gosport, Hampshire
PO12 2XD
Managing Editor *Nik Morton*

FOUNDED 1994. *Publishes* fiction – genre novellas, max. 20,000 words; short story anthologies
– max. 4000 words per story. TITLES *Auguries
18* (a science fiction/fantasy/horror anthology);
A Sign of Grace Robert W. Nicholson; *Silenced
in Darkness* Robert W. Nicholson. Unsolicited
synopses and ideas for books welcome.
Royalties paid annually.

Need2Know

1–2 Wainman Road, Woodston,
Peterborough PE2 7BU
☎01733 230759   Fax 01733 230751
Managing Editor *Kerrie Pateman*

FOUNDED 1995 'to fill a gap in the market for
self-help books', Need2Know is an imprint of
Forward Press Ltd. (see under **Poetry Presses**).
Publishes self-help, reference guides for people
in difficult situations. TITLES *Make the Most of
Being a Carer; Stretch Your Money; Make the Most
of Retirement; Buying a House; Help Yourself to a
Job*. 26 titles planned for 1996. No mss.
Unsolicited synopses and ideas for books welcome in the first instance as it is important to
ensure the project fits in with the series and that
the subject is not already covered.
Payment Advance paid and six monthly payments thereafter.

New Arcadian Press

13 Graham Grove, Burley, Leeds, West
Yorkshire LS4 2NF
☎0113 2304608
Managing Editor *Patrick Eyres*

FOUNDED 1981 to publish artist-writer collab-
orations on landscape and garden themes
through *The New Arcadian Journal* (limited edi-
tion collector's items). TITLES 1990–96: *Castle
Howard; The Wentworths; A Cajun Chapbook;
Hearts of Oak; Sons of the Sea; Naumachia;
Landfall*. No unsolicited mss, synopses or ideas.
Royalties not paid.

Nimbus Press

18 Guilford Road, Leicester LE2 2RB
☎0116 2706318
Managing Editor *Clifford Sharp*

FOUNDED in 1991 to encourage churches to use
drama in worship. *Publishes* Christian and non-
religious drama. TITLES *The Cost of Living; The
End of the World Button; Provisioning and Eskimos*
David Campton. 2 titles in 1995. No unsolicited mss. Synopses and ideas for plays of less
than 25 minutes' length, suitable for production
in a church, and plays for children welcome.
Royalties paid.

Norvik Press Ltd

School of Modern Languages & European
History, University of East Anglia, Norwich,
Norfolk NR4 7TJ
☎01603 593356   Fax 01603 250599
Managing Editors *James McFarlane, Janet
Garton, Michael Robinson*

Small academic press. *Publishes* the journal *Scandinavica* and books related to Scandinavian literature. About 4 titles a year. TITLES *Literary History and Criticism* (series); *English Translations of Works of Scandinavian Literature* (series); *A Sudden Liberating Thought* Kjell Askildsen; *From Baltic Shores* ed Christopher Moseley; *Days with Diam* Svend Åge Madsen; *My Son on the Galley* Jacob Wallenberg; *A Century of Swedish Narrative* eds Sarah Death & Helena Forsås-Scott. Interested in synopses and ideas for books within its *Literary History and Criticism* series. No unsolicited mss.
Royalties paid.

Oast Books
See **Parapress Ltd**

Octave Books
See **Parapress Ltd**

Open Gate Press
51 Achilles Road, London NW6 1DZ
☎0171 431 4391   Fax 0171 431 5088
Managing Directors *Jeannie Cohen, Elisabeth Petersdorff*

FOUNDED 1989 to provide a forum for psychoanalytic social and cultural studies. *Publishes* psychology, philosophy, social sciences, politics. 5-6 titles a year. SERIES *Psychoanalysis and Society*. Synopses and ideas for books welcome.
Royalties paid twice yearly.

Oriflamme Publishing
60 Charteris Road, London N4 3AB
☎0171 281 8501   Fax 0171 281 8501
Managing Editor *Tony Allen*

FOUNDED 1982, originally to publish science fiction and fantasy but now concentrating on a range of educational textbooks, mainly English and mathematics. Some fiction and special interest also. About 7 titles a year. SERIES *The Rules of Maths; Help Yourself to English; The Rules of English*. No unsolicited mss; synopses/ideas welcome but must be brief.
Royalties paid.

Owl Press
PO Box 315, Downton, Salisbury, Wiltshire SP5 3YE
☎01243 572988   Fax 01243 572988
Managing Editors *Annie & Paul Musgrove*

FOUNDED 1990. *Publishes* humour, thrillers and books of military interest. No poetry or children's. About 10 titles a year. TITLES *David, We're Pregnant!; 101 Cartoons* Lynn Johnston; *Jungle Campaign, A Regimental Mess*. Unsolicited mss welcome provided they are accompanied by s.a.e..
Royalties paid.

Palladour Books
Hirwaun House, Aberporth, Nr. Cardigan, Dyfed SA43 2EU
☎01239 811658   Fax 01239 811658
Managing Editors *Jeremy Powell/Anne Powell*

FOUNDED 1986. Started with a twice-yearly issue of catalogues on the literature and poetry of the First World War. Occasional catalogues on Second World War poetry have also been issued. TITLES *A Deep Cry*, a literary pilgrimage to the battlefields and cemeteries of First World War British soldier-poets killed in Northern France and Flanders. No unsolicited mss.
Royalties not paid.

Parapress Ltd
12 Dene Way, Speldhurst, Tunbridge Wells, Kent TN3 0NX
☎01892 862860   Fax 01892 863861
Managing Director *Ian W. Morley-Clarke*

FOUNDED 1993. *Publishes* autobiography, biography, diaries, journals of military personnel, composers and sportsmen. Also books on local history. About 12 titles a year. Largely self-publishing. IMPRINT: **Oast Books** Literary and local guides; **Parapress** Militaria; **Octave Books** Music biographies; **Unicorn** Railway histories.

Partizan Press
816-818 London Road, Leigh on Sea, Essex SS9 3NH
☎01702 73986   Fax 01702 73986
Managing Editor *David Ryan*

Caters for the growing re-enactment and wargaming market. *Publishes* military history and local history, with particular regard to the 17th- and 18th-centuries. About 30 titles a year. TITLES *Winchester in the Civil War; Eye & Eye Witnesses; Discovery of Witchcraft*. Unsolicited mss welcome.
Royalties paid.

Paupers' Press
27 Melbourne Road, West Bridgford, Nottingham NG2 5DJ
☎0115 9815063   Fax 0115 9815063
Managing Editor *Colin Stanley*

FOUNDED 1983. *Publishes* extended essays in booklet form (about 15,000 words) on literary criticism and philosophy. About 6 titles a year. TITLES *A Report on the Violent Male* A. E. van Vogt; *Mozart's Journey to Prague: A Playscript*

Colin Wilson; *More on the Word Hoard: The Poetry of Seamus Heaney* Stephen Wade; *Proportional Representation: A Debate on the Pitfalls of our Electoral System* Gregory K. Vincent; *Sex and Sexuality in Ian McEwan's Work* Christina Byrnes; *Sex and the Intelligent Teenager* Colin Wilson. Limited hardback editions of bestselling titles. No unsolicited mss but synopses and ideas for books welcome.
Royalties paid.

Peepal Tree Press Ltd
17 King's Avenue, Leeds, West Yorkshire LS6 1QS
☎0113 2451703   Fax 0113 2468368
Managing Editor *Jeremy Poynting*

FOUNDED 1985. *Publishes* fiction, poetry, drama and academic studies. *Specialises* in Caribbean, Black British and South Asian writing. About 18 titles a year. In-house printing and finishing facilities. AUTHORS Kamau Brathwaite, Cyril Dabydeen, Beryl Gilroy, Velma Pollard, Jan Shinebourne and **Forward Poetry Prize** winner Kwame Dawes. Approach by letter with synopsis and sample chapters/poems in the first instance. Synopses and ideas for books welcome. Write or telephone for a free catalogue.
Royalties paid.

The Penniless Press
100 Waterloo Road, Ashton, Preston, Lancashire PR2 1EP
Managing Editor *Alan Dent*

Publishes quarterly magazine with literary, philosophical, artistic and political content. Prose of up to 3000 words welcome. No mss returned without s.a.e..
Payment none.

Phoenix Publications
PO Box 255, London SW16 6HA
☎0181 677 1813   Fax 0181 769 6692
Managing Editor *Dennis Sofocleous*

FOUNDED 1993. Publishes fiction, psychological dramas, horror, fantasy and New Age. Some romance considered. TITLE *Spiral Terra*. Unsolicited mss, synopses and ideas welcome.
Royalties not paid.

Pigasus Press
13 Hazely Combe, Arreton, Isle of Wight PO30 3AJ
☎01983 865668
Managing Editor *Tony Lee*

FOUNDED 1989 (formerly known as S. A. Publishing). *Publishes* science fiction and horror

short stories in magazines, genre poetry anthologies and media review newsletters. TITLES Magazines: *The Zone; Premonitions*; Newsletters: *Dragon's Breath* (monthly small press review); *Videovista* (bi-monthly review of new videos); SF poetry anthologies: *The Others Amongst Us; Millennium Blues*. Fiction and articles for SF magazines welcome. Send s.a.e. for contributor's guidelines.

Pipers' Ash Ltd
'Pipers' Ash, Church Road, Christian Halford, Chippenham, Wiltshire SN15 4BW
☎01249 720563
Managing Editor *Mr A. Tyson*

FOUNDED 1976 to publish technical manuals for computer-controlled systems. Later broadened the company's publishing activities to take in philosophy, psychology, general and science fiction, children's literature, poetry and translations. 8 titles in 1995. TITLES *Charisma; Relationships; Perceptions; Contemporary Short Stories/Science Fiction Short Stories* Val Kyrie. No unsolicited mss. Synopses and ideas welcome; 'new authors with potential will be actively encouraged'.
Royalties paid twice yearly.

Playwrights Publishing Co.
70 Nottingham Road, Burton Joyce, Nottinghamshire NG14 5AL
☎0115 9313356
Managing Editors *Liz Breeze, Tony Breeze*

FOUNDED 1990. *Publishes* one-act and full-length plays. TITLES *Birthmarks* Mark Jenkins; *Lifestyles* Silvia Vaughan; *Undercoats* Roger Pinkham. Unsolicited scripts welcome. No synopses or ideas. Reading fees: £10 one act; £20 full length.
Royalties paid.

Polymath Publishing
The Old School House, Streatley Hill, Streatley-on-Thames, Berkshire RG8 9RD
☎01491 875032   Fax 01491 875035
Owner *Charles Knevitt*

FOUNDED 1989. *Publishes* general interest and technical architecture and construction industry books, postcard books, calendars, etc., also cartoon anthologies. TITLES *From Pecksniff to the Prince of Wales: 150 Years of Punch Cartoons on Architecture, Planning and Development 1851-1991; The Responsive Office: People and Change; Seven Ages of the Architect: The Very Best of Louis Hellman 1967-92; Shelter: Human Habitats From Around the World*; re-issue of *Community*

Architecture (Penguin 1987). Synopses and ideas welcome.

Royalties negotiable.

Power Publications

1 Clayford Avenue, Ferndown, Dorset
BH22 9PQ
☎01202 875223

Contact *Mike Power*

FOUNDED 1989. *Publishes* local interest, pub walk guides and mountain bike guides. 2-3 titles a year. TITLES *Pub Walks in Cornwall/Hampshire/New Forest* (every county along the south coast); *Mountain Bike Guides to the New Forest, Hampshire, Dorset and Chilterns; Ferndown: A Look Back; Dorset Coast Path; Famous Women in Dorset*. Unsolicited mss, synopses and ideas welcome.

Royalties paid.

Praxis Books

Sheridan, Broomers Hill Lane, Pulborough,
West Sussex RH20 2DU
☎01798 873504

Proprietor *Rebecca Smith*

FOUNDED 1992. *Publishes* philosophy, paganism, reissues of Victorian fiction, general interest. 9 titles to date. TITLES *In Search of Life's Meaning* R. Matley and R. Smith; *The Poet's Kit* Katherine Knight; *A Book of Folklore* Sabine Baring-Gould; *Sussex Snippets* Becky Smith. Unsolicited mss accepted with s.a.e.. No fiction or humour. Editing service available. Shared funding, shared profits.

Previous Parrot Press

The Foundry, Church Hanborough, Nr.
Witney, Oxford OX8 8AB
☎01993 881260   Fax 01993 883080

Managing Editor *Dennis Hall*

Publishes limited editions with a strong emphasis on illustration. About 3 titles a year. TITLES *Woodcuts and Words* Rigby Graham; *Listening to the Lake* Simon Rae; *An Alphabet of Circus Skills* Pam Scott.

Pulp Faction

60 Alexander Road, London N19 3PQ
☎0171 263 2090   Fax 0171 263 2090

Managing Editor *Elaine Palmer*

Set up to encourage publication of new fiction by unknown/experimental writers. Essentially functions as a fiction magazine although in book form. First Pulp Faction to be published late 1996. Welcomes single short stories of up to 3000 words. Postage must be included for return of unused mss. Welcomes synopses and ideas for novels or short novels (from 25,000 words); also art work or graphic fiction. No telephone queries.

Royalties paid (flat fee for compilations).

QED Books

1 Straylands Grove, York YO3 0EB
☎01904 424381   Fax 01904 424381

Managing Editor *John Bibby*

Publishes and *distributes* resource guides and learning aids, including laminated posters, for mathematics and science. TITLES *Fun Maths Calendar; Maths Resource Guides; Maths and Art; Joy of Maths*. Synopses (3pp) and ideas for books welcome. QED arranges publicity for other small presses and has many contacts overseas.

Royalties by agreement.

Quay Books Exeter

Tuck Mill Cottage, Payhembury, Near
Honiton, Devon EX14 0HF
☎01404 84376

Managing Editor *Chris Smith*

FOUNDED 1990 to publish *Village Profiles*, a down-your-way type series broadcast on **BBC Radio Devon**. *Publishes* local history and general fiction by Devon authors. There are plans to expand the list. No unsolicited mss; synopses and ideas welcome but opportunities are limited at present. S.a.e. essential with submissions.

Royalties paid.

QueenSpark Books

Brighton Media Centre, 11 Jew Street,
Brighton, East Sussex BN1 1UT
☎01273 748348

A community writing and publishing group run mainly by volunteers who work together to write and produce books. Since the early 1970s they have published 40 titles: local autobiographies, humour, poetry, history and politics. Free writing workshops and groups held on a regular basis. New members welcome.

Redstone Press

7A St Lawrence Terrace, London W10 5SU
☎0171 352 1594   Fax 0171 352 8749

Managing Editor *Julian Rothenstein*

FOUNDED 1987. *Publishes* art and literature. About 5 titles a year. No unsolicited mss; synopses and ideas welcome but familiarity with Redstone's list advised in the first instance.

Royalties paid.

Rivers Oram Press

144 Hemingford Road, London N1 1DE
☎0171 607 0823   Fax 0171 609 2776

Managing Director *Elizabeth Fidlon*

FOUNDED 1990. *Publishes* radical political and social sciences. No fiction, children's or cookery. *Royalties* paid annually.

The Robinswood Press

30 South Avenue, Stourbridge, West Midlands DY8 3XY
☎01384 397475   Fax 01384 440443

Managing Editor *Christopher J. Marshall*

FOUNDED 1985. *Publishes* education, particularly remedial and Steiner-based. About 3-5 titles a year. TITLES *Waldorf Education, An Introduction; Take Time; Phonic Rhyme Time; The Extra Lesson* (exercises for children with learning difficulties); *Stories for the Festivals; Spotlight on Words; The Eden Mission.* Unsolicited mss, synopses and ideas welcome.
Royalties paid.

Romer Publications

Smith Yard, Unit 5, 29A Spelman Street, London E1 6LQ
☎0171 247 3581   Fax 0171 247 3581
Also at: PO Box 10120, NL-1001 EC, Amsterdam, The Netherlands
☎/Fax 00 31 20 6769442

Managing Editor *Hubert de Brouwer*

FOUNDED 1986. Recent expansion into children's books but main tenet remains critical reflection on origins and legitimacy of established institutions. Specialises in history, education and law. TITLES *The Children's Kosher Funbook* Rabbi L. Book; *The Decline of the House of Herod* Hubert de Brouwer; *African Mythology for Children* Impendoh Dan Iyan; *Dominic Dormouse Goes to Town* Anthony Wall. Will consider sound, coherent and quality mss, synopses or ideas appropriate to its list.
Royalties paid.

Sawd Books

Plackett's Hole, Bicknor, Sittingbourne, Kent ME9 8BA
☎01795 472262   Fax 01795 422633

Managing Editor *Susannah Wainman*

FOUNDED 1989 to supply the local interests of the people of Kent. *Publishes* local interest, cookery, gardening and general non-fiction. About 3 titles a year. No unsolicited mss; synopses and ideas welcome (include s.a.e.). No fiction.
Royalties paid.

Scottish Cultural Press

PO Box 106, Aberdeen AB9 8ZE
☎01224 583777   Fax 01224 575337

Chair/Managing Editor *Jill Dick*

FOUNDED 1992. Began publishing in 1993. *Publishes* Scottish interest titles, including cultural, local history and children's non-fiction. Pre-publication consultancy. Subscription journal management.

IMPRINTS
Scottish Cultural Press, Scottish Children's Press. TITLES *Teach Yourself Doric; John Buchan's Collected Poems* (Scottish Contemporary Poets series); *A World of Folk Tales from Multi-Cultural Scotland; A-Z Scots Words for Younger Children.* Unsolicited mss, synopses and ideas welcome provided return postage is included.
Royalties paid. Trade Counter and office: 13 Millburn Street, Aberdeen AB1 2SS

Scriptmate Editions

20 Shepherds Hill, London N6 5AH
☎0181 341 7650   Fax 0181 341 7650

Managing Editor *Ann Kritzinger*

Publishes fiction and biography. 2 titles planned for 1996. TITLES *Shooting Star - The Last of the Silent Film Stars; Victor and Adua - Since We Were Four; Echoes From the Land.* No unsolicited mss, synopses or ideas; all selections are made through **Book-in-Hand Ltd** customers (see entry).
Royalties paid.

Serif

47 Strahan Road, London E3 5DA
☎0181 981 3990   Fax 0181 981 3990

Managing Editor *Stephen Hayward*

FOUNDED 1994. *Publishes* fiction, cookery, Irish studies and modern history. TITLES *Gifts* Nuruddin Farah; *The Crowd in History* George Rudé; *The Alice B. Toklas Cookbook; The Crime Studio* Steve Aylett. Ideas and synopses welcome; no unsolicited mss.
Royalties paid.

The Sharkti Laureate

See **Precious Pearl Publications** under **Poetry Presses**

Sherlock Publications

6 Bramham Moor, Hill Head, Fareham, Hampshire PO14 3RU
☎01329 667325

Managing Editor *Philip Weller*

FOUNDED to supply publishing support to a number of Sherlock Holmes societies. *Publishes*

Sherlock Holmes studies only. About 14 titles a year. TITLES *Elementary Holmes; Alphabetically, My Dear Watson; Anonymously, My Dear Lestrade; The Annotated Sherlock Holmes Cases.* No unsolicited mss; synopses and ideas welcome.

Royalties not paid.

Silent Books Ltd
10 Market Street, Swavesey, Cambridge CB4 5QG
☎01954 232199/231000   Fax 01954 232199
Managing Director *Carole A. Green*

FOUNDED 1985. *Publishes* general art titles, gardening, cookery, community care and books for the gift market, all high quality productions. No fiction. About 12 titles a year. Unsolicited mss, synopses and ideas welcome.

Silver Link Publishing Ltd
Unit 5, Home Farm Close, Church Street, Wadenhoe, Peterborough PE8 5TE
☎01832 720440   Fax 01832 720440
Managing Editor *William Adams*

FOUNDED 1985 in Lancashire, changed hands in 1990 and now based in Northamptonshire. Small independent company specialising in nostalgia titles including illustrated books on railways, trams, ships and other transport subjects, also, under the Past and Present Publishing imprint, post-war nostalgia on all aspects of social history. TITLES: *British Railways Past and Present* series; *British Roads Past and Present* series; *British Counties, Towns and Cities Past and Present* series; *Daily Life In Britain Past and Present* series; *Classic Steam*; *Railway Heritage*; *Maritime Heritage*; *A Nostalgic Look at ...* photographic collections; *Silver Link Library of Railway Modelling.* Unsolicited synopses and ideas welcome.

Fees paid.

Spacelink Books
115 Hollybush Lane, Hampton, Middlesex TW12 2QY
☎0181 979 3148
Managing Director *Lionel Beer*

FOUNDED 1986. Named after a UFO magazine published in the 1960/70s. *Publishes* non-fiction titles connected with UFOs, Fortean phenomena and paranormal events. TITLES *The Moving Statue of Ballinspittle and Related Phenomena.* No unsolicited mss; send synopses and ideas. Publishers of *TEMS News* for the Travel and Earth Mysteries Society. Distributor of wide range of related titles and magazines.

Royalties and fees paid according to contract.

Springboard
See **Yorkshire Art Circus Ltd**

Richard Stenlake Publishing
Ochiltree Sawmill, The Lade, Ochiltree, Ayrshire KA18 2NX
☎01290 423114   Fax 01290 423114

Publishes local history, transport, Scottish, industrial and poetry. 13 titles in 1995. Unsolicited mss, synopses and ideas welcome if accompanied by s.a.e..
Royalties paid annually.

Stepney Books Publications
19 Tomlins Grove, Bow, London E3 4NX
☎0181 980 2987
Contact *Jenny Smith*

FOUNDED 1976. A community publishing project run on a part-time basis. Heavily reliant on fundraising and grants for each new publication of which there is one about every 18 months. *Publishes* history and autobiography of Tower Hamlets in London. TITLES *Memories of Old Poplar; In Letters of Gold; Outside the Gate; Children of the Green.* Unsolicited material considered but 'any publication we undertake to do can take years to get to press whilst we raise the money to fund it'.

Stone Flower Ltd
2 Horder Road, London SW6 5EE
☎0171 736 0477
Chairman *J. Norman*
Managing Director *L. G. Norman*

Publishes biography, fiction, humour and legal. 'No anthropomorphism. No hype. Some indication of literacy, please.' Unsolicited synopses and ideas welcome with return postage, *otherwise* mss only with return postage and £100 reading fee.

Royalties paid twice yearly.

Stride Publications
See under **Poetry Presses**

Sunk Island Publishing
PO Box 74, Lincoln LN1 1QG
☎01522 575660   Fax 01522 520394
Managing Editor *Michael Blackburn*

FOUNDED 1989. Publishes paperback fiction and the literary magazine, *Sunk Island Review.* TITLES *Hallowed Ground* Robert Edric; *Radio Activity* John Murray; *Winterman's Company* David Lightfoot. Also publishes poetry under the **Jackson's Arm** imprint. TITLES *Harvest* Pat

Winslow; *The Constructed Space – A Celebration of W. S. Graham* ed. Duncan & Davidson. Now publishing books on disk. TITLE *The Electronic Poetry Pack*.

Royalties by arrangement, on publication.

T.C.L. Publications
23 Castle Rise, Ridgewood, Uckfield, East Sussex TN22 5UN
☎01825 769019

Managing Editor *Duncan Haws*

FOUNDED 1966 as Travel Creatours Limited (TCL). *Publishes* nautical books only – the *Merchant Fleet* series (29 vols.). 2 titles in 1995. TITLES *White Star Line; Elder Dempster Line; Port Line with Corry, Royden, Tyser & Milburn*. Unsolicited mss welcome, 'provided they are in our standard format and subject matters'. No unsolicited synopses or ideas.

Royalties paid.

Tamarind Ltd
PO Box 296, Camberley, Surrey GU15 1QW
☎01276 683979   Fax 01276 685365

Managing Editor *Verna Wilkins*

FOUNDED 1987 to publish material in which Black children are given an unselfconscious, positive profile. *Publishes* a series of picture books and other educational material (puzzles, recipes, maps) with the emphasis on a balance between education and fun. Titles include 4 tie-ins with BBC Education. TITLE *Dave and the Tooth Fairy*. No unsolicited mss. Approach in writing.

Tarquin Publications
Stradbroke, Diss, Norfolk IP21 5JP
☎01379 384218   Fax 01379 384289

Managing Editor *Gerald Jenkins*

FOUNDED 1970 as a hobby which gradually grew and now *publishes* mathematical, cut-out models, teaching and pop-up books. Other topics covered if they involve some kind of paper cutting or pop-up scenes. 5 titles in 1995. TITLES *Make Shapes; Sliceforms; The Chemical Helix; High Fashion in Victorian Times; The Paper Jeweller; The Paper Locksmith; The Marvellous Molecule; Dragon Mobiles*. No unsolicited mss; letter with 1–2 page synopses welcome.

Royalties paid.

Tarragon Press
Moss Park, Ravenstone, Whithorn DG8 8DR
☎01988 850368   Fax 01988 850304

Director/Editorial Head *David Sumner*

FOUNDED 1987. *Publishes* medical and scientific for the layperson. About 3 titles a year.

Unsolicited mss, synopses and ideas for books welcome.

Royalties paid annually.

Tartarus Press
5 Birch Terrace, Hangingbirch Lane, Horam, East Sussex TN21 0PA
☎01435 813224

Managing Director *Raymond Russell*

FOUNDED 1987. *Publishes* fiction, short stories, essays. Also books by and about Arthur Machen. About 4 titles a year. TITLES Short story collections: *Worming the Harpy and Other Bitter Pills* Rhys Hughes; *Ritual and Other Stories* Arthur Machen; *Tales from Tartarus*. Essays: *The Secret of the Sangraal and Other Writings* Arthur Machen; *Edgar Allan Poe and Arthur Machen* Machen & Samuels. Letters: *Containing a Number of Things* Starrett & Millard.

Tickle Ltd
Tiller Court, 16 Tiller Court, London E14 8PX
☎0171 345 5135   Fax 0171 363 0136

Directors *Alexander Dury, Mark Dury*
Associate *Brian Taylor*

FOUNDED 1966 to promote children's fiction of magical and innocent quality. About 6 titles a year. Written synopses only in the first instance.

Royalties paid annually.

Travellers' Bookshop
32 St George Street, London W1R 0EA
☎0171 493 0876   Fax 0171 228 7860

Managing Editors *Lucinda Boyle, Chris Scott*

Press FOUNDED 1992 (Bookshop 1988) to publish a limited number of niche travel titles in paperback. Interested in lively, evocative or thoughtful travelogues which are exceptional to the oversubscribed travel literature field. Much less keen to publish travel guide books, but may be interested in original ideas. TITLES *Desert Biking; A Guide to Independent Motorcycling in the Sahara* (3rd edition due 1997); *Desert Travels; Motorcycle Journeys in the Sahara and West Africa*. 'We are not solely interested in motorbikes and deserts and are actively seeking typed synopses with sample chapters as part of a completed ms. We do not commission books.'

Royalties paid.

Tuckwell Press Ltd
The Mill House, Phantassie, East Linton, East Lothian EH40 3DG
☎01620 860164   Fax 01620 860164

Managing Director *John Tuckwell*

FOUNDED 1995 'out of the ashes' of Canongate

Academic. *Publishes* history, literature, ethnology, with a bias towards Scottish and academic texts. 16 titles in 1995. No unsolicited mss but synopses and ideas welcome if relevant to subjects covered.
Royalties paid annually.

Two Heads Publishing
9 Whitehall Park, London N19 3TS
☎0171 561 1606   Fax 0171 561 1607
Contact *Charles Frewin*

Independent publisher of sport, humour and guides with a London focus. Also publishes a range of cycling guides under the **Two Wheels** imprint. Synopses and ideas welcome; write in the first instance.
Royalties paid quarterly.

Tyrannosaurus Rex Press
BM Box 1129, London WC1N 3XX
☎01923 229784

Managing Editor *Dr Keith H. Seddon*

FOUNDED 1993. *Publishes* gothic, literary fiction, philosophy and religion. 1-2 titles a year. TITLES *Grim Fairy Tales; The Faceless Tarot; The Agonies of Time.* No unsolicited mss.
Royalties paid.

Underhill Press
8 Herriot Way, Thirsk, North Yorkshire YO7 1FL
☎01845 526749   Fax 01845 524347
Managing Editor *Peter Pack*

Publishing arm of the Learning Resources Development Group. Began by publishing conference and seminar proceedings but has since expanded. *Publishes* further and higher education material with particular reference to the management of learning resources; alternative systems of delivering learning; information strategy and IT in colleges; independent and distance learning; new developments in college management. 2-3 titles a year. TITLES *Product & Performance; Citing Your References; Bridging the Gap; Funding and Performance; College Learning Resources: Are They Really Worth It?.* Ideas and synopses welcome. No unsolicited mss.
Payment negotiable.

Unicorn
See **Parapress Ltd**

UNKN
Highfields, Brynymor Road, Aberystwyth, Dyfed SY23 2HX
☎01970 627337   Fax 01970 627337
Managing Editor *Niall Quinn*

Publisher *Siobhán O'Rourke*

FOUNDED 1995 originally to promote the work of writers (primarily poets) engaged in the production of experimental and marginal text - its core commitment. 1 title in 1995. TITLES *However Introduced to the Soles.* Unsolicited mss welcome. Critiques also offered.
Royalties paid.

Wakefield Historical Publications
19 Pinder's Grove, Wakefield, West Yorkshire WF1 4AH
☎01924 372748
Managing Editor *Kate Taylor*

FOUNDED 1977 by the Wakefield Historical Society to publish well-researched, scholarly works of regional (namely West Riding) historical significance. 1-2 titles a year. TITLES *Aspects of Medieval Wakefield; Landscape Gardens in West Yorkshire 1680-1880; Coal Kings of Yorkshire; The Aire and Calder Navigation; Right Royal – Wakefield Theatre 1776-1994.* Unsolicited mss, synopses and ideas for books welcome.
Royalties not paid.

Paul Watkins Publishing
18 Adelaide Street, Stamford, Lincolnshire PE9 2EN
☎01780 56793   Fax 01780 56793
Proprietor *Shaun Tyas*

Publishes non-fiction - medieval, academic, biography, nautical, local history. No fiction. 8 titles in 1995. Unsolicited mss, synopses and ideas for books welcome.
Royalties paid twice yearly.

Westwood Press
44 Boldmere Road, Sutton Coldfield, West Midlands B73 5TD
☎0121 354 5913   Fax 0121 355 6920
Managing Editor *Reg Hollins*

FOUNDED 1955 as a general printer and commenced local publication in the 1970s. *Publishes* local history of the Birmingham area only and specialised printing 'Know How' publications. TITLES *A History of Boldmere; The Book of Brum; Up the Terrace - Down Aston and Lozells.* No unsolicited mss; synopses and ideas welcome.
Royalties paid.

Whyld Publishing Co-op
Moorland House, Kelsey Road, Caistor, Lincolnshire LN7 6SF
☎01472 851374   Fax 01472 851374
Managing Editor *Janie Whyld*

Having taken over former ILEA titles on anti-sexist work with boys which would otherwise have vanished, Janie Whyld has gone on to publish a specialist list of educational materials for teachers, trainers and students, with an emphasis on equal opportunities and interpersonal skills. About 2 titles a year. Now moving into 'paperless publishing'. TITLES *Anti-Sexist Work with Boys and Young Men; Equal Opportunities in Training and Groupwork; Countering Objections to Anti-Sexist Work; Using Counselling Skills to Help People Learn; NVQs and the Assessment of Interpersonal Skills; Teaching Assertiveness in Schools and Colleges; The Essence of Yin and Yang; Multicultural Stories.* Mss, synopses/ideas which meet these requirements welcome.
Royalties nominal.

Working Books Ltd
3 Quadrant Court, Middle Street, Taunton, Somerset TA1 1SJ
☎01823 3349946   Fax 01823 3348970
Directors *E. Ephraums, G. Jones*

FOUNDED in 1983. *Publishes* highly illustrated and informative practical photography books covering conventional processes and digital imaging techniques. Due to launch motorsports imprint in 1996. About 5 titles a year. Unsolicited mss, synopsis and ideas for books welcome.
Royalties paid quarterly.

Works Publishing
12 Blakestones Road, Slaithwaite, Huddersfield, West Yorkshire HD7 5UQ
☎01484 842324   Fax 01484 842324
Managing Editor *Dave W. Hughes*

One-man operation publishing two magazines: *Works* (science fiction) and *The Modern Dance* (music review). Stories and poems welcome for *Works* but no submissions for *Modern Dance*. Unsolicited mss (with s.a.e.) welcome; no synopses/ideas. Advertising rates, single issue rates, guidelines and subscription rates are all available for an s.a.e..
Royalties not paid.

Yoffoy Publications
7 Upper Dumpton Park Road, Ramsgate, Kent CT11 7PE
☎01843 851419
Managing Editor *Frank Foy*

FOUNDED 1988. *Publishes* non-fiction and educational, plus information packs in various subject areas, including music and games. 1–2 titles a year. TITLES *Employment in Europe, A Guide; Music Network Guide* (to the music industry); *Play it Now!* (electric guitar tutor manual). Unsolicited mss, synopses and ideas welcome.

Yorkshire Art Circus Ltd
School Lane, Glass Houghton, Castleford, West Yorkshire WF10 4QH
☎01977 550401   Fax 01977 512819
Books Coordinator *Reini Schühle*
Approx. Annual Turnover £180,000

FOUNDED 1986. *Specialises* in new writing by first-time authors. *Publishes* autobiography, community books, fiction and local interest (Yorkshire, Humberside). No local history, children's, reference or nostalgia. TITLES *When Push Comes to Shove* ed. Ian Clayton; *Give Us A Job* ed. Brian Lewis; *On Earth To Make the Numbers Up* Evelyn Haythorne; *Chapati and Chips* Almas Khan; *Flood* Tom Watts. Unsolicited mss discouraged; authors should send for fact sheet in first instance. **Springboard** fiction imprint launched 1993. Write or ring for free catalogue.
Royalties paid.

UK Packagers

The Albion Press Ltd
Spring Hill, Idbury, Oxfordshire OX7 6RU
☎01993 831094　　　　Fax 01993 831982
Chairman/Managing Director *Emma Bradford*

FOUNDED 1984 to produce high-quality illustrated titles. *Commissions* illustrated trade titles, particularly children's, English literature, social history and art. About 10 titles a year. TITLES *The Arabian Nights* Sheila Moxley; *The Ocean of Story* Caroline Ness & Jacqueline Mair; *Poems for Christmas* Neil Philip & John Lawrence. Unsolicited synopses and ideas for books not welcome.

Royalties paid; fees paid for introductions and partial contributions.

Alphabet & Image Ltd
See **Marston House** under **UK Publishers**

Andromeda Oxford Ltd
11-15 The Vineyard, Abingdon, Oxfordshire OX14 3PX
☎01235 550296　　　　Fax 01235 550330
Managing Director *Mark Ritchie*
Approx. Annual Turnover £7 million

FOUNDED 1986. *Commissions* adult and junior international illustrated reference, both single volume and series. About 30 titles a year.

DIVISIONS
Adult Books *Graham Bateman* (Editorial Director); **Children's Books** *Derek Hall* (Editorial Director); **Andromeda Interactive** *Jonathan Taylor* (Managing Director). TITLES *Encyclopedia of World Geography; Cultural Atlases; Junior Science Encyclopedia; Atlas of World History; Interactive Space Encyclopedia; Complete Shakespeare; Classic Library* all on CD-ROM. Approach by letter in the first instance.

Anness Publishing Ltd
See under **UK Publishers**

Archival Facsimiles Ltd
The Old Bakery, 52 Crown Street, Banham, Norwich, Norfolk NR16 2HW
☎01953 887277　　　　Fax 01953 888361
Contact *Cris de Boos*

FOUNDED 1986. Specialist private publishers for individuals and organisations. Produces scholarly reprints for the **British Library** among others, plus high-quality limited edition publications for academic/business organisations in Europe and the USA, ranging from leather-bound folios of period print reproductions to small illustrated booklets. *Publishes* Antarctic exploration titles (about 2 a year) under the **Erskine Press** imprint. No unsolicited mss. Ideas welcome.

Royalties paid twice yearly.

AS Publishing
73 Montpelier Rise, London NW11 9DU
☎0181 458 3552　　　　Fax 0181 458 0618
Managing Director *Angela Sheehan*

FOUNDED 1987. *Commissions* children's illustrated non-fiction. No unsolicited synopses or ideas for books, but approaches welcome from experienced authors, editors and illustrators in this field.

Fees paid.

BCS Publishing Ltd
1 Bignell Park Barns, Kirtlington Road, Chesterton, Bicester, Oxon OX6 8TD
☎01869 324423　　　　Fax 01869 324385
Managing Director *Steve McCurdy*
Approx. Annual Turnover £350,000

Commissions general interest non-fiction for international co-edition market.

Belitha Press Ltd
London House, Great Eastern Wharf, Parkgate Road, London SW11 4NQ
☎0171 978 6330　　　　Fax 0171 223 4936
Editorial Director *Mary-Jane Wilkins*

FOUNDED 1980. *Commissions* children's non-fiction in all curriculum areas. About 50 titles a year. Strong on international co-edition packaging. All titles are expected to sell in at least four co-editions. TITLES *The Satellite Atlas; History's Big Mistakes; History's Heroes and Villains; Science Horizons; Magic In Art; Introducing Composers; Take It Apart; Start-Up Science; The World in the Time Of...* (8 titles exploring history and culture around the world at different times); *The World's Top Ten; Who Am I?* (a series of puzzle books for young children). No unsolicited mss. Synopses and ideas for books welcome from experienced children's writers.

Bellew Publishing Co. Ltd
See under **UK Publishers**

Bender Richardson White
PO Box 266, Uxbridge, Middlesex UB9 5BD
☎01895 832444   Fax 01895 835213

Partners *Lionel Bender, Kim Richardson, Ben White*

FOUNDED 1990 to produce illustrated non-fiction for children aged 7–14 for publishers in the UK and abroad. 15 titles in 1995. Unsolicited material not welcome.
Fees paid.

David Bennett Books Ltd
23 Albion Road, St Albans, Hertfordshire AL1 5EB
☎01727 855878   Fax 01727 864085

Managing Director *David Bennett*

FOUNDED 1989. Producer of children's books: picture and novelty books, baby gifts and non-fiction. Synopses and ideas for books welcome. No fiction or poetry.
Payment both fees and royalties.

BLA Publishing Ltd
1 Christopher Road, East Grinstead, West Sussex RH19 3BT
☎01342 318980   Fax 01342 410980

Owner *Ling Kee (UK) Ltd*

Packagers of multi-volume encyclopedias for younger readers, and information book series on various topics.
Payment varies according to contract (reference books tend to be flat fees; royalties for single author or illustrator).

Book Packaging and Marketing
3 Murswell Lane, Silverstone, Towcester, Northamptonshire NN12 8UT
☎01327 858380   Fax 01327 858380

Contact *Martin F. Marix Evans*

FOUNDED 1989. Essentially a project management service, handling books demanding close designer/editor teamwork or complicated multi-contributor administration, for publishers, business 'or anyone who needs one'. Mainly illustrated adult non-fiction including travel, historical, home reference and coffee-table books. No fiction or poetry. 3–5 titles a year. Proposals considered; and writers are often required for projects in development. TITLES *Royal College of Nursing Manual of Family Health; Pregnant and Fit; Canals of England; Contemporary Photographers*, 3rd ed.; *World War II; Nelles Guide*

to London, England and Wales; The Battles of the Somme 1916–18.

Payment Authors contract direct with client publishers; fees paid on first print usually and royalties on reprint but this depends on publisher.

Breslich & Foss Ltd
20 Wells Mews, London W1P 3FJ
☎0171 580 8774   Fax 0171 580 8784

Director *Paula Breslich*
Approx. Annual Turnover £1.5 million

Packagers of non-fiction titles only, including art, children's, crafts, gardening and health. Unsolicited mss welcome but synopses preferred. Include s.a.e. with all submissions.
Royalties paid twice yearly.

Brown Wells and Jacobs Ltd
Forresters Hall, 25–27 Westow Street, London SE19 3RY
☎0181 771 5115   Fax 0181 771 9994

Managing Director *Graham Brown*

FOUNDED 1979. *Commissions* non-fiction, novelty, pre-school and first readers, natural history and science. About 40 titles a year. Unsolicited synopses and ideas for books welcome.
Fees paid.

Calmann & King Ltd
71 Great Russell Street, London WC1B 3BN
☎0171 831 6351   Fax 0171 831 8356

Chairman *Robin Hyman*
Managing Director *Laurence King*
Approx. Annual Turnover £2.8 million

FOUNDED 1976. *Commissions* books on art, the decorative arts, design and nature. About 20 titles a year. Unsolicited synopses and ideas for books welcome.
Royalties paid twice yearly.

Cameron Books (Production) Ltd
PO Box 1, Moffat, Dumfriesshire DG10 9SU
☎01683 220808   Fax 01683 220012

Directors *Ian A. Cameron, Jill Hollis*
Approx. Annual Turnover £350,000

Commissions natural history, social history, decorative arts, fine arts including environmental art, collectors' reference, educational reference, gardening, cookery, conservation, countryside, film and design. About 6 titles a year. Unsolicited synopses and ideas for books welcome.
Payment varies with each contract.

Candle Books
See **Angus Hudson Ltd**

Chancerel International Publishers Ltd
120 Long Acre, London WC2E 9PA
☎0171 240 2811   Fax 0171 836 4186
Managing Director *W. D. B. Prowse*

FOUNDED 1976. *Commissions* educational books, and *publishes* language-teaching materials in most languages. Language teachers/writers often required as authors/consultants, especially native speakers other than English.
Payment generally by flat fee but royalties sometimes.

Philip Clark Ltd
53 Calton Avenue, Dulwich, London SE21 7DF
☎0181 693 5605   Fax 0181 299 4647
Managing Director *Philip Clark*

Founder member of the **Book Packagers Association**. *Commissions* heavily illustrated titles on a variety of subjects. TITLES include *Travellers Wine Guides* series (first edition sold over 100,000 copies in several languages; second edition due in 1997/8).
Fees paid.

Concorde House Books
See **Angus Hudson Ltd**

Roger Coote Publishing
Gissing's Farm, Fressingfield, Eye, Suffolk IP21 5SH
☎01379 588044   Fax 01379 588055
Director *Roger Goddard-Coote*

FOUNDED 1993. Packager of high-quality children's and adult non-fiction for trade, school and library markets. About 24 titles a year. No fiction.
Fees paid; no royalties.

Diagram Visual Information Ltd
195 Kentish Town Road, London NW5 8SY
☎0171 482 3633   Fax 0171 482 4932
Managing Director *Bruce Robertson*

FOUNDED 1967. Producer of library, school, academic and trade reference books. About 10 titles a year. Unsolicited synopses and ideas for books welcome.
Fees paid; no payment for sample material/ submissions for consideration.

Dorling Kindersley Ltd
See under **UK Publishers**

Eddison Sadd Editions
St Chad's House, 148 King's Cross Road, London WC1X 9DH
☎0171 837 1968   Fax 0171 837 2025
Managing Director *Nick Eddison*
Editorial Director *Ian Jackson*
Approx. Annual Turnover £3.5 million

FOUNDED 1982. Produces a wide range of popular illustrated non-fiction, with books published in 25 countries. Ideas and synopses are welcome but titles must have international appeal.
Royalties paid twice yearly; flat fees paid when appropriate.

Erskine Press
See **Archival Facsimiles Ltd**

Expert Publications Ltd
Sloe House, Halstead, Essex CO9 1PA
☎01787 474744   Fax 01787 474700
Chairman *Dr. D. G. Hessayon*

FOUNDED 1993. Produces the Expert series of books by Dr. D. G. Hessayon. TITLES *The Flowering Shrub Expert; The Greenhouse Expert; The Flower Arranging Expert; The Container Expert; The Bulb Expert*. No unsolicited material.

Angus Hudson Ltd
Concorde House, Grenville Place, Mill Hill, London NW7 4JN
☎0181 959 3668   Fax 0181 959 3678
Chairman *Angus R. M. Hudson*
Managing Director *Nicholas Jones*
Approx. Annual Turnover £2.5 million

FOUNDED 1977. Management buyout from Maxwell Communications in 1989. Leading packager of religious co-editions. *Commissions* Christian books for all ages and co-editioning throughout the world. About 60 titles in 1995.
IMPRINTS **Candle Books; Concorde House Books**. Unsolicited synopses and ideas for books welcome.
Royalties paid.

Labyrinth Publishing (UK) Ltd
32 Leighton Road, London NW5 2QE
☎0171 284 4783   Fax 0171 284 3038
Managing Director *Robert Gwyn Palmer*
Editorial Director *Geoffrey Chesler*

Packagers of illustrated non-fiction across a range of subjects from religion and mythology to psychology and self-help. Books are sold in high volume to major international publishing houses. About 10 titles a year. Synopses and ideas welcome. Authors are offered a high degree of involvement in the design and production stages.

Royalties generally flat fee.

Leading Edge Press & Publishing Ltd

Old Chapel, Burtersett, Hawes, North Yorkshire DL8 3PB
☎01969 667566   Fax 01969 667788

Chairman/Managing Director *Stan Abbott*
Approx. Annual Turnover £300,000

FOUNDED 1984. Primarily a commercial magazine/brochure/newsletter design and production house. Book production accounts for about a quarter of the company's activities. *Commissions* transport and outdoor leisure, including walking. 8–10 titles a year. Synopses and ideas for books welcome subject to prior contact by phone. The publisher encourages joint financial ventures, or sponsorship, in appropriate cases.

Royalties paid thrice yearly and/or fees.

Lennard Associates Ltd

Windmill Cottage, Mackerye End, Harpenden, Hertfordshire AL5 5DR
☎01582 715866   Fax 01582 715121

Chairman/Managing Director *Adrian Stephenson*

FOUNDED 1979. Packager and publisher of sport, humour and personality books, plus television associated titles. TITLES *Arthur's World of Cats; Go For It!* ed. Martyn Lewis; *Mike Tyson – The Release of Power* Reg Gutteridge & Norman Giller; *The Cricketers' Who's Who*; *The Whitbread Rugby World*. No unsolicited mss. IMPRINTS **Lennard Publishing, Queen Anne Press**. Acquired the latter and most of its assets in 1992.

Payment both fees and royalties by arrangement.

Lexus Ltd

205 Bath Street, Glasgow G2 4HZ
☎0141 221 5266   Fax 0141 226 3139

Managing/Editorial Director *P. M. Terrell*

FOUNDED 1980. Compiles bilingual reference, language and phrase books. About 20 titles a year. TITLES *Rough Guide Phrasebooks; Collins Italian Concise Dictionary; Harrap Study Aids; Hugo's Phrase Books; Harrap Shorter French Dictionary* (revised); *Impact Specialist Bilingual Glossaries; Oxford Student's Japanese Learner*. No unsolicited material. Books are mostly commissioned. Freelance contributors employed for a wide range of languages.

Payment generally flat fee.

Lionheart Books

10 Chelmsford Square, London NW10 3AR
☎0181 459 0453   Fax 0181 451 3681

Senior Partner *Lionel Bender*
Partner *Madeleine Samuel*
Designer *Ben White*
Approx. Annual Turnover £250,000

A design/editorial packaging team. Titles are primarily commissioned from publishers. Highly illustrated non-fiction for children aged 8–14, mostly natural history, history and general science. About 20 titles a year.

Payment generally flat fee.

Market House Books Ltd

2 Market House, Market Square, Aylesbury, Buckinghamshire HP20 1TN
☎01296 84911   Fax 01296 437073

Directors *Dr Alan Isaacs/Dr John Daintith*

FOUNDED 1970. Formerly Laurence Urdang Associates. *Commissions* dictionaries, encyclopedias and reference. About 15 titles a year. TITLES *European Culture; Concise Medical Dictionary; Brewer's 20th Century Phrase and Fable; Oxford Dictionary for Science Writers and Editors; Concise Dictionary of Business; Concise Dictionary of Finance; Bloomsbury Thesaurus; Larousse Thematica* (6 volume encyclopedia); *Collins English Dictionary; The Macmillan Encyclopedia*. Unsolicited material not welcome as most books are compiled in-house.

Fees paid.

Marshall Cavendish Books

119 Wardour Street, London W1V 3TD
☎0171 734 6710   Fax 0171 439 1423

Head of Editorial *Martin Annable*
Approx. Annual Turnover £3 million

A division of Marshall Cavendish Partworks Ltd. FOUNDED 1968. Primarily partwork material in book form but also originates its own material. Freelance editorial services sought on occasions.

Fees paid, not royalties.

Marshall Editions Ltd

170 Piccadilly, London W1V 9DD
☎0171 629 0079   Fax 0171 834 0785

Publisher *Bruce Marshall*
Editorial Director *Sophie Collins*

FOUNDED 1977. *Commissions* non-fiction, including thematic atlases, leisure, self-improvement and visual information for children. TITLES *The Human Body Explained; Revelations: The Medieval World; The Robot Zoo; The Natural History of Evolution; Your Personal Trainer*.

MM Productions Ltd
16-20 High Street, Ware, Hertfordshire
SG12 9BX
☎01920 466003   Fax 01920 466003
Chairman/Managing Director *Mike Moran*

Packager and publisher. TITLES *MM Publisher
Database; MM Printer Database* (available in UK,
European and international editions).

Oyster Books Ltd
Unit 4, Kirklea Farm, Badgworth, Axbridge,
Somerset BS26 2QH
☎01934 732251   Fax 01934 732514
Managing Director *Jenny Wood*

FOUNDED 1985. Packagers of quality books
and book/toy/gift items for children of pre-
school age to ten years. About 20 titles a year.
Most material is created in-house.
Payment usually fees.

Parke Sutton Ltd
The Old Bakery, 52 Crown Street, Banham,
Norwich, Norfolk NR16 2HW
☎01953 887277   Fax 01953 888361
Director *Crispin De Boos*

FOUNDED 1982. Produces newspapers, magazines and reference books for organisations and
training offices; and packages books for publishers. Unsolicited synopses and ideas for books
welcome. S.a.e. essential.
Royalties paid twice yearly; fees sometimes
paid rather than royalties.

Playne Books
Trefin, Haverfordwest, Dyfed SA62 5AU
☎01348 837073   Fax 01348 837063
Director *David Playne*
Editor *Gill Davies*

FOUNDED 1987. *Commissions* highly illustrated
and practical books on any subject. Currently
developing a new list for young children. Unsolicited synopses and ideas for books welcome.
Royalties paid 'on payment from publishers'.
Fees sometimes paid instead of royalties.

Mathew Price Ltd
The Old Glove Factory, Bristol Road,
Sherborne, Dorset DT9 4HP
☎01935 816010   Fax 01935 816310
Chairman/Managing Director *Mathew Price*
Approx. Annual Turnover £1 million

Commissions high-quality, full-colour picture
books and fiction for young children; also nov-

elty and non-fiction. Unsolicited synopses and
ideas for books welcome.
Fees sometimes paid instead of royalties.

Quarto Publishing
The Old Brewery, 6 Blundell Street, London
N7 9BH
☎0171 700 6700/333 0000   Fax 0171 700
4191/700 0077
Chairman *Laurence Orbach*
Approx. Annual Turnover £18 million

FOUNDED 1976. Britain's largest book packager.
Commissions illustrated non-fiction, including
painting, graphic design, visual arts, history,
cookery, gardening, crafts. *Publishes* under the
Apple imprint. Unsolicited synopses/ideas for
books welcome.
Payment flat fees paid.

Queen Anne Press
See **Lennard Associates**

Sadie Fields Productions Ltd
3D West Point, 36-37 Warple Way, London
W3 0RG
☎0181 746 1171   Fax 0181 746 1170
Directors *David Fielder/Sheri Safran*

FOUNDED 1981. Quality children's books with
international co-edition potential: pop-ups,
three-dimensional, novelty, picture and board
books, 1500 words maximum. About 30 titles
a year. Approach with preliminary letter and
sample material in the first instance. *Publishes* in
the UK under the **Tango Books** imprint.
Royalties based on a per-copy-sold rate and
paid in stages.

Salariya Book Company Ltd
25 Marlborough Place, Brighton, East Sussex
BN1 1UB
☎01273 603306   Fax 01273 693857
Managing Director *David Salariya*

FOUNDED 1989. Children's information books
– fiction, history, art, music, science, architecture, education and picture books. No unsolicited material.
Payment by arrangement.

Savitri Books Ltd
115J Cleveland Street, London W1P 5PN
☎0171 436 9932   Fax 0171 580 6330
Managing Director *Mrinalini S. Srivastava*
Approx. Annual Turnover £200,000

FOUNDED 1983. Keen to work 'very closely with
authors/illustrators and try to establish long-term

relationships with them, doing more books with the same team of people'. *Commissions* high-quality, illustrated non-fiction, crafts, New Age and nature. About 7 titles a year. Unsolicited synopses and ideas for books 'very welcome'.

Royalties 10-15% of the total price paid by the publisher.

Sheldrake Press

188 Cavendish Road, London SW12 0DA
☎0181 675 1767   Fax 0181 675 7736
Publisher *Simon Rigge*
Approx. Annual Turnover £250,000

Commissions illustrated non-fiction: history, travel, style, cookery and stationery. TITLES *The Victorian House Book; The Shorter Mrs Beeton; The Power of Steam; The Railway Heritage of Britain; Wild Britain; Wild France; Wild Spain; Wild Italy; Wild Ireland; The Kate Greenaway Baby Book.* Synopses and ideas for books welcome, but not interested in fiction.

Fees or royalties paid.

Templar Publishing

Pippbrook Mill, London Road, Dorking, Surrey RH4 1JE
☎01306 876361   Fax 01306 889097
Managing Director/Editorial Head
Amanda Wood
Approx. Annual Turnover £5 million

FOUNDED 1981. A division of The Templar Company plc. *Commissions* novelty and gift books, children's illustrated non-fiction, educational and story books, children's illustrated non-fiction. 100-175 titles a year. Synopses and ideas for books welcome.

Royalties by arrangement.

Toucan Books Ltd

Fourth Floor, 32-38 Saffron Hill, London EC1N 8BS
☎0171 404 8181   Fax 0171 404 8282
Managing Director *Robert Sackville-West*
Approx. Annual Turnover £1,400,000

FOUNDED 1985. Originally specialised in international co-editions, now focusing on fee-based editorial, design and production services to film. *Commissions* illustrated non-fiction only. About 20 titles a year. TITLES *The Earth, Its Wonders, Its Secrets; Leith's Cookery Bible; Charles II; The Complete Photography Course; Journeys into the Past* series; *People and Places.* Unsolicited synopses and ideas for books welcome. No fiction or non-illustrated titles.

Royalties twice yearly; fees paid in addition to or instead of royalties.

Touchstone Publishing Ltd

Gissing's Farm, Fressingfield, Eye, Suffolk IP21 5SH
☎01379 588044   Fax 01379 588055
Chairman/Managing Director *Roger Goddard-Coote*

FOUNDED 1989. Packager of children's non-fiction for trade, school and library markets. About 8 titles a year. No fiction, textbooks or adult material. Synopses and ideas welcome. Include s.a.e. for return.

Fees paid; no royalties.

Victoria House Publishing Ltd

4 North Parade, Bath, Avon BA1 1LF
☎01225 463401   Fax 01225 460942
Managing Director *Andrew F. Hewetson*
Approx. Annual Turnover £7.5 million

Part of the Reader's Digest Group. Trade imprint: Joshua Morris and Wishing Well. *Commissions* children's projects in novelty or interactive formats – acetate, pop-up, toy add-ons. Also religious list. About 50 titles a year.

Royalties or flat fee according to contract.

Wordwright Books

25 Oakford Road, London NW5 1AJ
☎0171 284 0056   Fax 0171 284 0041
Contact *Charles Perkins*

FOUNDED by ex-editorial people 'so good writing always has a chance with us'. *Commissions* illustrated non-fiction: social history and comment, military history, women's issues, sport. *Specialises* in military and social history, natural history, science, art, cookery, and gardening. About 4-6 titles a year. Unsolicited synopses/ideas (a paragraph or so) welcome for illustrated non-fiction.

Payment usually fees but royalties (twice-yearly) paid over a certain agreed number of copies.

Zöe Books Ltd

15 Worthy Lane, Winchester, Hampshire SO23 7AB
☎01962 851318   Fax 01962 843015
Managing Director *Imogen Dawson*
Director *Bob Davidson*

FOUNDED 1990. *Specialises* in full-colour information and reference books for schools and libraries. *Publishes* about 30 titles a year. Tends to generate own ideas but happy to hear from freelance writers and editors of information books. Does *not* publish picture books or fiction.

Fees paid.

UK Agents

★ = Member of the **Association of Authors' Agents**

The Agency (London) Ltd★
24 Pottery Lane, Holland Park, London
W11 4LZ
☎0171 727 1346   Fax 0171 727 9037

Contact *Stephen Durbridge, Sheila Lemon, Leah Schmidt, Sebastian Born, Julia Kreitman, Bethan Evans, Hilary Delamere*

FOUNDED 1995. *Handles* children's fiction, TV, film, theatre, radio scripts. No adult fiction or non-fiction. Unsolicited TV, film and radio scripts welcome. Send letter with s.a.e.. No reading fee. CLIENTS include William Boyd, Andrew Davies, Jimmy McGovern, Sam Mendes. *Commission* Home 10%; USA various.

Aitken, Stone & Wylie Ltd★
29 Fernshaw Road, London SW10 0TG
☎0171 351 7561   Fax 0171 376 3594

Contact *Gillon Aitken, Brian Stone, Antony Harwood*

FOUNDED 1984. *Handles* fiction and non-fiction. No plays or scripts unless by existing clients. Send preliminary letter, with synopsis and return postage, in the first instance. No reading fee. CLIENTS include Agatha Christie, Germaine Greer, Alan Hollinghurst, Susan Howatch, V. S. Naipul, Caryl Phillips, Piers Paul Read, Salman Rushdie, Paul Theroux. *Commission* Home 10%; US 15%; Translation 20%.

Jacintha Alexander Associates★
47 Emperor's Gate, London SW7 4HJ
☎0171 373 9258   Fax 0171 373 4374

Contact *Julian Alexander, Kirstan Romano*

FOUNDED 1981. *Handles* full-length general and literary fiction and non-fiction of all kinds. No plays, poetry, textbooks. Film and TV scripts handled for established clients only. Preliminary letter with s.a.e. essential. *Commission* Home 10-15%; US & Translation 20%. *Overseas associates* in New York, Los Angeles, Japan, and throughout Europe.

Darley Anderson Literary, TV & Film Agency★
Estelle House, 11 Eustace Road, London
SW6 1JB
☎0171 385 6652   Fax 0171 386 5571

Contact *Darley Anderson, Keith Biggs* (Crime/ Foreign Rights), *Pippa Dyson* (Film/TV scripts), *Elizabeth Wright* (Fantasy/Erotica)

Run by an ex-publisher with a sympathetic touch and a knack for spotting and encouraging talent who is known to have negotiated a £150,000 UK advance and a TV mini-series deal for one first-time novelist and a $150,000 US advance for another first-time novelist. *Handles* commercial fiction & non-fiction; also scripts for film, TV and radio. No academic books or poetry. *Special interests* Fiction: all types of thrillers and all types of women's fiction including contemporary, 20th-century romantic sagas, erotica, women in jeopardy; also crime (cosy/hard-boiled/historical), horror, fantasy, comedy and Irish novels. Non-fiction: celebrity autobiographies, biographies, 'true life' women in jeopardy, popular psychology, self-improvement, diet, health, beauty and fashion, humour/cartoons, gardening, cookery, inspirational and religious. Send letter and outline with 1-3 chapters; return postage/s.a.e. essential. CLIENTS Jane Adams, Tessa Barclay, Lee Child, Martina Cole, Joseph Corvo, Debbie Frank, Martica Heaner, Beryl Kingston, Frank Lean, Deborah McKinlay, Lesley Pearse, Allan Pease, Adrian Plass, Fred Secombe, Jane Walmsley. *Commission* Home 15%; US & Translation 20%; TV/Film/Radio 20%, *Overseas associates* Mitchell Rose Agency (New York), Renaissance-Swanson Film Agency (LA/Hollywood); and leading foreign agents throughout the world.

Anubis Literary Agency
79 Charles Gardner Road, Leamington Spa,
Warwickshire CV31 3BG
☎01926 832644   Fax 01926 832644

Contact *Steve Calcutt, Val Bissell, Maggie Heavey, Carol Scleparis*

FOUNDED 1994. Aims to target new and unpublished writers. *Handles* mainstream adult fiction, especially historical, horror, crime and women's. Especially interested in westerns. No children's books, poetry, short stories, journalism, academic or non-fiction. No unsolicited scripts; send brief (one-page) synopsis (s.a.e. essential). No reading fee. *Commission* Home 15%; USA & Translation 20%.

Yvonne Baker Associates

8 Temple Fortune Lane, London
NW11 7UD
☎0181 455 8687   Fax 0181 458 3143

Contact *Yvonne Baker*

FOUNDED 1987. *Handles* scripts for TV, theatre, film and radio. Books extremely rarely. No poetry. Approach by letter giving as much detail as possible, including s.a.e.. No reading fee. *Commission* Home 10%; US & Translation 20%.

Blake Friedmann Literary Agency Ltd★

37–41 Gower Street, London
WC1E 6HH
☎0171 631 4331   Fax 0171 323 1274

Contact *Carole Blake* (books), *Julian Friedmann* (film/TV), *Conrad Williams* (original scripts/radio)

FOUNDED 1977. *Handles* all kinds of fiction from genre to literary; a varied range of specialised and general non-fiction, plus scripts for TV, radio and film. No poetry, juvenile or science fiction unless from existing clients. *Special interests* commercial women's fiction, literate thrillers. Unsolicited mss welcome but initial letter with synopsis and first two chapters preferred. Letters should contain as much information as possible on previous writing experience, aims for the future, etc. No reading fee. CLIENTS include Gilbert Adair, Ted Allbeury, Jane Asher, Teresa Crane, Barbara Erskine, Maeve Haran, John Harvey, Ken Hom, Glenn Meade, Lawrence Norfolk, Joseph O'Connor, Michael Ridpath, Robyn Sisman, Craig Thomas. *Commission* Books: Home 15%; US & Translation 20%. Radio/TV/Film: 15%. *Overseas associates* throughout Europe, Asia and the US.

David Bolt Associates

12 Heath Drive, Send, Surrey
GU23 7EP
☎01483 721118   Fax 01483 222878

Contact *David Bolt*

FOUNDED 1983. *Handles* fiction and general non-fiction. No books for small children or verse (except in special circumstances). No scripts. *Special interests* fiction, African writers, biography, history, military, theology. Preliminary letter with s.a.e. essential. Reading fee for unpublished writers. Terms on application. CLIENTS include Chinua Achebe, David Bret, Eilis Dillon, Arthur Jacobs, James Purdy, Joseph Rhymer, Colin Wilson. *Commission* Home 10%; US & Translation 19%.

Alan Brodie Representation

211 Piccadilly, London W1V 9LD
☎0171 917 2871   Fax 0171 917 2872

Contact *Alan Brodie, Catherine King*

FOUNDED 1989. *Handles* theatre, film and TV scripts. No books. Preliminary letter and c.v. essential. No reading fee but s.a.e. required. *Commission* Home 10%; Overseas 15%.

Rosemary Bromley Literary Agency

Avington, Near Winchester, Hampshire
SO21 1DB
☎01962 779656   Fax 01962 779656

Contact *Rosemary Bromley*

FOUNDED 1981. *Handles* non-fiction. Also scripts for TV and radio. No poetry or short stories. *Special interests* natural history, leisure, biography and cookery. No unsolicited mss. Send preliminary letter with full details. Enquiries unaccompanied by return postage will not be answered. CLIENTS include Elisabeth Beresford, Linda Birch, Gwen Cherrell, Teresa Collard, estate of Fanny Cradock, Cécile Curtis, Glenn Hamilton, Jacynth Hope-Simpson, David Rees, Judy Strafford, Keith West, Ron Wilson, John Wingate. *Commission* Home 10%; US 15%; Translation 20%; Illustration 20%. ·

Felicity Bryan★

2A North Parade, Banbury Road, Oxford
OX2 6PE
☎01865 513816   Fax 01865 310055

Contact *Felicity Bryan*

FOUNDED 1988. *Handles* fiction of various types and non-fiction with emphasis on history, biography, science and current affairs. No scripts for TV, radio or theatre. No crafts, how-to, science fiction or light romance. No unsolicited mss. Best approach by letter. No reading fee. CLIENTS include John Charmley, Liza Cody, John Julius Norwich, Rosamunde Pilcher, Miriam Stoppard, Roy Strong. *Commission* Home 10%; US & Translation 20%. *Overseas associates* Lennart Sane, Scandinavia; Andrew Nurnberg, Europe; **Curtis Brown Ltd**, US.

Peter Bryant (Writers)

94 Adelaide Avenue, London SE4 1YR
☎0181 691 9085   Fax 0181 692 9107

Contact *Peter Bryant*

FOUNDED 1980. *Special interests* animation, children's fiction and TV sitcoms. Also *handles* drama scripts for theatre, radio, film and TV. No reading fee for these categories but return postage essential for all submissions. CLIENTS include Isabelle Amyes, Roy Apps, Joe Boyle, Lucy Daniel, Jimmy Hibbert, Jan Page, Ruth Silvestre, Peter Symonds. *Commission* 10%. *Overseas associates* Hartmann & Stauffacher, Germany.

Diane Burston Literary Agency
46 Cromwell Avenue, London N6 5HL
☎0181 340 6130

FOUNDED 1984. *Handles* fiction, namely women's (not romance); also crime, general fiction and non-fiction, and short stories for women's magazines. Not interested in horror, fantasy, thriller or children's. No unsolicited mss, except for short stories. Send letter with synopsis and opening chapter if possible. Reading fee charged for full reading and report. CLIENTS include Margaret James, Paula Lawrence, Richard Lazarus, Gillian Nelson, L. D. Tetlow. *Commission* Home 10%; Short Stories 15%; US 15%; Elsewhere 20%.

Bycornute Books
76A Ashford Road, Eastbourne, East Sussex BN21 3TE
☎01323 726819   Fax 01323 649053
Contact *Ayeshah Haleem*
FOUNDED 1987. *Handles* illustrated books on art, archaeology, cosmology, symbolism and metaphysics, both ancient and modern. No scripts. No unsolicited mss. Send introductory letter outlining proposal. No reading fee. *Commission* 10%.

Calderbridge Literary Agency
3 Lion Chambers, John William Street, Huddersfield, West Yorkshire HD1 1ES
☎01484 512817   Fax 01484 512817
Contact *R. Sharp, B. Malik*
FOUNDED 1995. *Handles* fiction and non-fiction – millenium, erotica, philosophy, religion; TV, film, theatre and radio scripts. No children's. No unsolicited mss; approach with letter and synopsis in the first instance. A small reading fee may be charged. *Commission* Home 10%; USA 15%.

Campbell Thomson & McLaughlin Ltd★
1 King's Mews, London WC1N 2JA
☎0171 242 0958   Fax 0171 242 2408
Contact *John McLaughlin, Charlotte Bruton*
FOUNDED 1931. *Handles* book-length mss (excluding children's, science fiction and fantasy). No plays, film scripts, articles, short stories

or poetry. No unsolicited mss. Send preliminary letter with s.a.e. in the first instance. No reading fee. *Overseas associates* Fox Chase Agency, Philadelphia; Raines & Raines, New York.

Carnell Literary Agency★
Danescroft, Goose Lane, Little Hallingbury, Hertfordshire CM22 7RG
☎01279 723626

Contact *Pamela Buckmaster*
FOUNDED 1951. *Handles* fiction and general non-fiction, specialising in science fiction and fantasy. No poetry. No scripts except from published authors. No unsolicited mss. Send preliminary letter with brief synopsis and first two chapters (include s.a.e. for acknowledgement and postage for return of material). No phone calls. *Commission* Home 10%; US & Translation 19%. Works in conjunction with agencies worldwide.

Casarotto Ramsay Ltd
National House, 60–66 Wardour Street, London W1V 3HP
☎0171 287 4450   Fax 0171 287 9128
Film/TV/Radio *Jenne Casarotto, Greg Hunt, Tracey Smith, Rachel Swann*
Stage *Tom Erhardt, Mel Kenyon*
(**Books** Handled by **Lutyens and Rubinstein**)
Took over the agency responsibilities of Margaret Ramsay Ltd in 1992, incorporating a strong client list, with names like Alan Ayckbourn, Caryl Churchill, Willy Russell and Muriel Spark. *Handles* scripts for TV, theatre, film and radio, plus general fiction and non-fiction. No poetry or books for children. No unsolicited material without preliminary letter. CLIENTS include J. G. Ballard, Edward Bond, Simon Callow, David Hare, Terry Jones, Neil Jordan, Willy Russell, David Yallop. *Commission* Home 10%; US & Translation 20%. *Overseas associates* worldwide.

Mic Cheetham Literary Agency
138 Buckingham Palace Road, London SW1W 9SA
☎0171 730 3027   Fax 0171 730 0037
Contact *Mic Cheetham*
ESTABLISHED 1994. *Handles* general and literary fiction, crime and science fiction, and non-fiction. No scripts apart from existing clients. No children's, illustrated books or poetry. No unsolicited mss. Approach in writing with publishing history, first two chapters and return postage. No reading fee. CLIENTS include: Iain

Banks, Anita Burgh, Laurie Graham, Janette Turner Hospital, Glyn Hughes, Antony Sher. *Commission* Home 10%; USA & Translation 20%. Works with **The Marsh Agency** for all translation rights.

Judith Chilcote Agency★

8 Wentworth Mansions, Keats Grove,
London NW3 2RL
☎0171 794 3717   Fax 0171 794 7431
Contact *Judith Chilcote*

FOUNDED 1990. *Handles* commercial fiction, royal books, TV tie-ins, health, beauty and fitness, cinema, self-help, popular psychology, biography and autobiography, cookery and current affairs. No academic, science fiction, children's, short stories or poetry. No unsolicited mss. Send letter with c.v., synopsis, three chapters and s.a.e. for return. No reading fee. CLIENTS include Jane Alexander, Vanessa Feltz, Jane Gordon, Teresa Gorman MP, Philippa Kennedy, Jon Snow, Douglas Thompson, Stuart White. *Commission* Home 15%; Overseas 25%. *Overseas associate* in the US, Carse Publishing Group, plus overseas agents.

Teresa Chris Literary Agency

16 Castellain Mansions, Castellain Road,
London W9 1HA
☎0171 289 0653
Contact *Teresa Chris*

FOUNDED 1989. *Handles* general, commercial and literary fiction, and non-fiction: health, business, travel, cookery, sport and fitness, gardening etc. *Specialises* in crime fiction and commercial women's fiction. No scripts. Film and TV rights handled by co-agent. No poetry, short stories, fantasy, science fiction or horror. Unsolicited mss welcome. Send query letter with sample material (s.a.e. essential) in first instance. No reading fee. CLIENTS include Prof. Eysenck, John Malcolm, Marguerite Patten. *Commission* Home 10%; US 15%; Translation 20%. *Overseas associates* Thompson & Chris Literary Agency, California; representatives in most other countries.

Serafina Clarke★

98 Tunis Road, London W12 7EY
☎0181 749 6979   Fax 0181 740 6862
Contact *Serafina Clarke, Amanda White*

FOUNDED 1980. *Handles* fiction: romance, horror, thrillers, literary; and non-fiction: travel, cookery, gardening and biography. Only deals in scripts by authors already on its books. *Special interests* gardening, history, country pursuits. No unsolicited mss. Introductory letter with synopsis (and return postage) *essential*. No reading fee. *Commission* Home 15%; US & Translation 20%. *Represents* Permanent Press, US; Second Chance Press, US.

Mary Clemmey Literary Agency★

6 Dunollie Road, London
NW5 2XP
☎0171 267 1290   Fax 0171 267 1290
Contact *Mary Clemmey*

FOUNDED 1992. *Handles* fiction and non-fiction - high-quality work with an international market. No science fiction, fantasy or children's books. TV, film, radio and theatre scripts from existing clients only. No unsolicited mss. Approach by letter giving a description of the work in the first instance. S.a.e. essential. No reading fee. CLIENTS include Paul Gilroy, Sheila Kitzinger, Ray Shell. *Commission* Home 10%; USA & Translation 20%. *Overseas Associate* Elaine Markson Literary Agency, New York.

Jonathan Clowes Ltd★

10 Iron Bridge House, Bridge Approach,
London NW1 8BD
☎0171 722 7674   Fax 0171 722 7677
Contact *Brie Burkeman*

FOUNDED 1960. Pronounced 'clewes'. Now one of the biggest fish in the pond, and not really for the untried unless they are true high-flyers. Fiction and non-fiction, plus scripts. No textbooks or children's. *Special interests* situation comedy, film and television rights. No unsolicited mss; authors come by recommendation or by successful follow-ups to preliminary letters. CLIENTS include David Bellamy, Len Deighton, Carla Lane, Doris Lessing, David Nobbs, and the estate of Kingsley Amis. *Commission* Home/US 15%; Translation 19%. *Overseas associates* **Andrew Nurnberg Associates**; Lennart Sane Agency.

Elspeth Cochrane Agency

11–13 Orlando Road, London SW4 0LE
☎0171 622 0314/4279   Fax 0171 622 5815
Contact *Elspeth Cochrane, Nicholas Turrell*

FOUNDED 1960. *Handles* fiction, non-fiction, biographies, screenplays. Subjects have included Marlon Brando, Sean Connery, Clint Eastwood, Lord Olivier. Also scripts for all media, with special interest in drama. No unsolicited mss. Preliminary letter, synopsis and s.a.e. is essential in the first instance. CLIENTS include Malcolm Needs, David Pinner, Royce Ryton, Robert Tanitch. *Commission* 12½% ('but this can change; the percentage is negotiable, as is the sum paid to the writer').

Rosica Colin Ltd
1 Clareville Grove Mews, London SW7 5AH
☎0171 370 1080   Fax 0171 244 6441
Contact *Joanna Marston*
FOUNDED 1949. *Handles* all full-length mss, plus theatre, film, television and sound broadcasting. Preliminary letter with return postage essential; writers should outline their writing credits and whether their mss have previously been submitted elsewhere. May take 3-4 months to consider full mss; synopsis preferred in the first instance. No reading fee. *Commission* Home 10%; US 15%; Translation 20%.

Combrógos Literary Agency
10 Heol Don, Whitchurch, Cardiff CF4 2AU
☎01222 623359   Fax 01222 529202
Contact *Meic Stephens*
FOUNDED 1990. *Specialises* in books about Wales or by Welsh authors, including novels, short stories, poetry, biography and general. Good contacts in Wales and London. Also editorial services, arts and media research. No unsolicited manuscripts; preliminary letter (s.a.e. essential). *Commission* 10%.

Jane Conway-Gordon★
1 Old Compton Street, London W1V 5PH
☎0171 494 0148   Fax 0171 287 9264
Contact *Jane Conway-Gordon*
FOUNDED 1982. Works in association with **Andrew Mann Ltd**. *Handles* fiction and general non-fiction, plus occasional scripts for TV/radio/theatre. No poetry or science fiction. Unsolicited mss welcome; preliminary letter and return postage preferred. No reading fee. *Commission* Home 10%; US & Translation 20%. *Overseas associates* **McIntosh & Otis, Inc.**, New York; plus agencies throughout Europe and Japan.

Rupert Crew Ltd★
1A King's Mews, London WC1N 2JA
☎0171 242 8586   Fax 0171 831 7914
Contact *Doreen Montgomery,*
  Caroline Montgomery
FOUNDED 1927. International representation, handling volume and subsidiary rights in fiction and non-fiction properties. No plays or poetry, journalism or short stories. Preliminary letter essential. No reading fee. *Commission* Home 10-15%; Elsewhere 20%.

Cruickshank Cazenove Ltd
97 Old South Lambeth Road, London SW8 1XU
☎0171 735 2933   Fax 0171 820 1081
Contact *Harriet Cruickshank*
FOUNDED 1983. *Specialises* in plays and screenplays only. No unsolicited mss. Preliminary letter with synopsis and s.a.e. essential. *Commission* Home 10%; US & Translation varies according to contract. *Overseas associates* Various.

Curtis Brown Group Ltd★
Haymarket House, 28/29 Haymarket, London SW1Y 4SP
☎0171 396 6600   Fax 0171 396 0110
Contact *Material should be addressed to the company*
Long-established literary agency, whose first sales were made in 1899. Merged with John Farquharson, forming the Curtis Brown Group Ltd in 1989. *Handles* a wide range of subjects including fiction, general non-fiction, children's and specialist, scripts for film, TV, theatre and radio. Send synopsis with covering letter and c.v. rather than complete mss. No reading fee. *Commission* Home 10%; US 20%; Translation 20%. *Overseas associates* in Australia, Canada and the US.

Judy Daish Associates Ltd
2 St Charles Place, London W10 6EG
☎0181 964 8811   Fax 0181 964 8966
Contact *Judy Daish, Sara Stroud, Deborah Harwood*
FOUNDED 1978. Theatrical literary agent. *Handles* scripts for film, TV, theatre and radio. No books. Preliminary letter essential. No unsolicited mss.

Caroline Davidson Literary Agency
5 Queen Anne's Gardens, London W4 1TU
☎0181 995 5768   Fax 0181 994 2770
Contact *Caroline Davidson, Harriet Sanders*
FOUNDED 1988. *Handles* fiction and non-fiction, including architecture, art, biography, cookery, crafts, design, fitness, gardening, history, investigative journalism, music, natural history, photography, reference, science, travel. Many highly illustrated books. First novels positively welcomed. No occult, plays or poetry. Writers should telephone or send an initial letter giving details of the project together with c.v. and s.a.e.. CLIENTS Robert Baldock, Elizabeth Bradley,

Lynda Brown, Andrew Dalby, Emma Donoghue, Willi Elsener, Anissa Helou, Paul Hillyard, Mary Hollingsworth, Tom Jaine, Bernard Lavery, Huon Mallalieu, J. P. McEvoy, Gaitri Pagrach-Chandra, Rena Salaman, Roland Vernon, S4C, the Welsh Channel Four. *Commission* US, Home, Commonwealth, Translation 12½%; occasionally more (20%) if sub-agents have to be used.

Merric Davidson Literary Agency
Oakwood, Ashley Park, Tunbridge Wells, Kent TN4 8UA
☎01892 514282   Fax 01892 514282
Contact *Merric Davidson*

FOUNDED 1990. *Handles* fiction and general non-fiction. No scripts. No children's, academic, short stories or articles. Particularly keen on contemporary fiction. No unsolicited mss. Send preliminary letter with synopsis and biographical details. S.a.e.. essential for response. No reading fee. CLIENTS include Valerie Blumenthal, Louise Doughty, Elizabeth Harris, Alison Habens, Alison MacLeod, Allis Moss, Mark Pepper. *Commission* Home 10%; US 15%; Translation 20%.

Felix de Wolfe
Manfield House, 376–378 The Strand, London WC2R 0LR
☎0171 379 5767   Fax 0171 836 0337
Contact *Felix de Wolfe*

FOUNDED 1938. *Handles* quality fiction only, and scripts. No non-fiction or children's. No unsolicited mss. No reading fee. CLIENTS include Robert Cogo-Fawcett, Brian Glover, Sheila Goff, Derek Hoddinott, Jennifer Johnston, John Kershaw, Bill MacIlwraith, Angus Mackay, Gerard McLarnon, Braham Murray, Julian Slade, Malcolm Taylor, David Thompson, Paul Todd, Dolores Walshe. *Commission* Home 12½%; US 20%.

Dorian Literary Agency
Upper Thornehill, 27 Church Street, St Marychurch, Torquay, Devon TQ1 4QY
☎01803 312095   Fax 01803 312095
Contact *Dorothy Lumley*

FOUNDED 1986. *Handles* mainstream and commercial full-length adult fiction; specialities are women's (including contemporary and sagas), crime and thrillers; horror, science fiction and fantasy. Also limited non-fiction: primarily self-help and media-related subjects; plus scripts for TV and radio. No poetry, children's, theatrical scripts, short stories, academic or technical.

Introductory letter with synopsis/outline and first chapter (with return postage) only please. No reading fee. CLIENTS include Stephen Jones, Brian Lumley, Amy Myers, Dee Williams. *Commission* Home 10%; US 15%; Translation 20-25%. Works with agents in most countries for translation.

Anne Drexl
8 Roland Gardens, London SW7 3PH
☎0171 244 9645
Contact *Anne Drexl*

FOUNDED 1988. *Handles* commercially orientated full-length mss for women's fiction, general, family sagas and crime. Ideas welcome for business-related books, how-to, DIY, hobbies and collecting. Strong interest too in juvenile fiction, including children's games, puzzles and activity books. Writers should approach with preliminary letter and synopsis (including s.a.e.). No reading fee but may ask for a contribution to admin. costs. *Commission* Home 12½%; US & Translation 20% (but varies depending on agent used).

Toby Eady Associates Ltd
9 Orme Court, London W2 4RL
☎0171 792 0092   Fax 0171 792 0879
Contact *Toby Eady, Alexandra Pringle, Victoria Hobbs*

In association with Xandra Hardie. *Handles* fiction, and non-fiction. No scripts. No unsolicited mss. Approach by letter first. No reading fee. CLIENTS include Nuha Al-Radi, Elspeth Barker, Sister Wendy Beckett, Ronan Bennett, Julia Blackburn, John Carey, Jung Chang, Bernard Cornwell, Nell Dunn, Geoff Dyer, Lucy Ellmann, Esther Freud, Kuki Gallmann, Alasdair Gray, Sean Hardie, Michael Hofmann, Tim Jeal, Rana Kabbani, Que Lei Lei, Fiona McCarthy, Karl Miller, Tim Pears, Sun Shuyun, Amir Taheri, Barbara Trapido, Hong Ying. *Commission* Home 10%; US & Translation 20%. *Overseas associates* La Nouvelle Agence; Mohr Books; The English Agency, Tokyo; Jan Michael; Rosemarie Buckman.

Eddison Pearson Literary Agents
44 Inverness Terrace, London W2 3JA
☎0171 727 9113   Fax 0171 727 9143
Contact *Clare Pearson, Tom Eddison*

FOUNDED 1995. *Handles* adult literary fiction, non-fiction and poetry; children's fiction and picture books; also TV, film, theatre and radio scripts. *Specialises* in children's books. Unsolicited mss with s.a.e welcome. Approach by letter in the first instance. No reading fee. *Commission* Home 10%; USA 12½%; Translation from 12½%.

Faith Evans Associates★

Clerkenwell House, 45 Clerkenwell Green, London EC1R 0EB

☎0171 490 2535   Fax 0171 490 4958

Contact *Faith Evans, Anne McGonigle*

FOUNDED 1987. Small, selective agency. *Handles* fiction and non-fiction. No scripts, unsolicited mss or phone enquiries. CLIENTS include Melissa Benn, Eleanor Bron, Midge Gillies, Cate Haste, Saeed Jaffrey, Helena Kennedy, Cleo Laine, Seumas Milne, Roger Mugford, Christine Purkis, Sheila Rowbotham, Lorna Sage, Marion Urch, Elizabeth Wilton, Andrea Weiss. *Commission* Home 15%; US & Translation 20%. *Overseas associates* worldwide.

John Farquharson★

See **Curtis Brown Group Ltd**

Film Rights Ltd

See **Laurence Fitch Ltd**

Laurence Fitch Ltd

483 Southbank House, Black Prince Road, Albert Embankment, London SE1 7ST

☎0171 735 8171

Contact *Laurence Fitch, Brendan Davis*

In association with Film Rights Ltd. FOUNDED 1952 (incorporating the London Play Company, FOUNDED 1922). *Handles* scripts for theatre, film, TV and radio only. No unsolicited mss. Send synopsis with sample scene(s) in the first instance. No reading fee. CLIENTS include Judy Allen, Hindi Brooks, John Chapman & Ray Cooney, John Graham, Glyn Robbins, Gene Stone, and the estate of Dodie Smith. *Commission* 10%. *Overseas associates* worldwide.

Jill Foster Ltd

3 Lonsdale Road, London SW13 9ED

☎0181 741 9410   Fax 0181 741 2916

Contact *Jill Foster, Alison Finch, Ann Foster*

FOUNDED 1976. *Handles* scripts for TV, drama and comedy. No fiction, short stories or poetry. No unsolicited mss; approach by letter in the first instance. No reading fee. CLIENTS include Colin Bostock-Smith, Jan Etherington and Gavin Petrie, Rob Gittins, Paul Hines, Julia Jones, Chris Ralling, Peter Tilbury, Susan Wilkins. *Commission* Home 12½%; US & Translation 15%.

Fox & Howard Literary Agency

4 Bramerton Street, London SW3 5JX

☎0171 352 8691   Fax 0171 352 8691

Contact *Chelsey Fox, Charlotte Howard*

FOUNDED 1992. *Handles* general non-fiction: biography, naval, military and popular history, current affairs, business, self-help, health and mind, body and spirit; educational and reference: GCSE and A-level texts. No scripts. No poetry, plays, short stories, children's, science fiction, fantasy and horror. No unsolicited mss; send letter, synopsis and sample chapter with s.a.e. for response. No reading fee. CLIENTS Sir Rhodes Boyson, Dr Graham Handley, Anthony Kemp, Bruce King, Betty Parsons, Geoffrey Regan. *Commission* Home 10%; US & Translation 20%.

French's

9 Elgin Mews South, London W9 1JZ

☎0171 266 3321   Fax 0171 286 6716

Contact *John French*

FOUNDED 1973. *Handles* fiction and non-fiction; and scripts for all media. No religious or medical books. No unsolicited mss. 'For unpublished authors we offer a reading service at £50 per mss, exclusive of postage.' Interested authors should write in the first instance. CLIENTS include Emma Allan, J. J. Duke, Becky Bell, Barry Heath, Susanna Hughes, Mal Middleton. *Commission* Home 10%.

Vernon Futerman Associates★

159a Goldhurst Terrace, London NW6 3EU

☎0171 625 9601

Fax 0171 625 9601(direct)/372 1282

Academic/Politics/Current Affairs/Show Business/Art *Vernon Futerman*

Educational *Alexandra Groom*

Fiction/TV, Film & Theatre Scripts *Guy Rose*

FOUNDED 1984. *Handles* fiction and non-fiction, including academic, art, educational, politics, history, current affairs, show business, travel, business and medicine; also scripts for film, TV and theatre. No short stories, science fiction, crafts or hobbies. No unsolicited mss; send preliminary letter with detailed synopsis and s.a.e. to Submissions Dept. 100, Richmond Hill, Richmond, Surrey TW10 6RJ. No reading fee. CLIENTS Stephen Lowe, V. Grosvenor Myer, Prof. Wu Ningkun, Judy Upton, Russell Warren Howe, Ernie Wise. *Commission* Home 12½-17½%; USA 17½-22½%; Translation 17½-25%. *Overseas associates* Brigitte Axster, Germany/Scandinavia; Lora Fountain, France.

Jüri Gabriel

35 Camberwell Grove, London SE5 8JA
☎0171 703 6186   Fax 0171 703 6186
Contact *Jüri Gabriel*

Handles quality fiction, non-fiction and scripts for film, TV and radio. Jüri Gabriel worked in television, wrote books for 20 years and is chairman of **Dedalus** publishers. No short stories, articles, verse or books for children. Unsolicited mss ('2-page synopsis and 3 sample chapters in first instance, please') welcome if accompanied by return postage and letter giving sufficient information about author's writing experience, aims etc. CLIENTS include Nigel Cawthorne, Diana Constance, James Hawes, Robert Irwin, Siân James, Mark Lloyd, David Madsen, David Miller, John Outram, Ewen Southby-Tailyour, Adisakdi Tantimedh, Dr Terence White, Herbert Williams, John Wyatt, Dr. Robert Youngson. *Commission* Home 10%; US & Translation 20%.

Eric Glass Ltd

28 Berkeley Square, London W1X 6HD
☎0171 629 7162   Fax 0171 499 6780
Contact *Janet Glass*

FOUNDED 1934. *Handles* fiction, non-fiction and scripts for publication or production in all media. No poetry. No unsolicited mss. No reading fee. CLIENTS include Marc Camoletti, Charles Dyer, Wolf Mankowitz, Jack Popplewell and the estates of Rodney Ackland, Jean Cocteau, William Douglas Home, Philip King, Robin Maugham, Beverley Nichols, Jean-Paul Sartre. *Commission* Home 10%; US 15%; Translation 20% (to include sub-agent's fee). *Overseas associates* in the US, Australia, France, Germany, Greece, Holland, Italy, Japan, Poland, Scandinavia, South Africa, Spain.

Christine Green Authors' Agent★

40 Doughty Street, London WC1N 2LF
☎0171 831 4956   Fax 0171 405 3935
Contact *Christine Green*

FOUNDED 1984. *Handles* fiction (general and literary) and general non-fiction. No scripts, poetry or children's. No unsolicited mss; initial letter and synopsis preferred. No reading fee but return postage essential. *Commission* Home 10%; US & Translation 20%.

Greene & Heaton Ltd★

37 Goldhawk Road, London W12 8QQ
☎0181 749 0315   Fax 0181 749 0318
Contact *Carol Heaton, Judith Murray*

A small agency that likes to involve itself with its authors. *Handles* fiction (no science fiction or fantasy) and general non-fiction. No original scripts for theatre, film or TV. No unsolicited mss without preliminary letter. CLIENTS include Bill Bryson, Kate Charles, Jan Dalley, Colin Forbes, P. D. James, Mary Morrissy, Conor Cruise O'Brien, William Shawcross. *Commission* Home 10%; US & Translation 20%.

Gregory & Radice Authors' Agents★

3 Barb Mews, London W6 7PA
☎0171 610 4676   Fax 0171 610 4686
Contact *Jane Gregory, Dr Lisanne Radice* (Editorial), *Pippa Dyson* (Film/TV)

FORMED 1987, incorporating the former Jane Gregory Agency established 1982. *Handles* fiction and non-fiction. *Special interest* crime, thrillers, literary and commercial fiction, politics. Particularly interested in books with potential for sales abroad and/or to film and TV. No plays, film or TV scripts, science fiction, poetry, academic or children's. No reading fee. No unsolicited mss, but preliminary letter with synopsis and first three chapters (plus return postage) welcome. *Commission* Home 15%; Newspapers 20%; US & Translation 20%; Radio/TV/Film 15%. Is well represented throughout Europe, Asia and USA.

David Grossman Literary Agency Ltd

118b Holland Park Avenue, London W11 4UA
☎0171 221 2770   Fax 0171 221 1445
Contact *Material should be addressed to the Company*

FOUNDED 1976. *Handles* full-length fiction and general non-fiction - good writing of all kinds and anything controversial. No verse or technical books for students. No original screenplays or teleplays (only works existing in volume form are sold for performance rights). Generally works with published writers of fiction only but 'truly original, well-written novels from beginners' will be considered. Best approach by preliminary letter giving full description of the work. All material must be accompanied by return postage. No approaches or submissions by fax. No unsolicited mss. No reading fee. *Commission* Rates vary for different markets. *Overseas associates* throughout Europe, Asia, Brazil and the US.

The Guidelines Partnership, Publishing Consultants & Agents
18 Pretoria Road, Cambridge CB4 1HE
☎01223 314668   Fax 01223 364619
Contact *Mr G. Black, Mrs L. Black*
FOUNDED 1986. Strong links with major publishing houses throughout the world. *Handles* educational materials, particularly study guides, for most age groups and across all subject areas, e.g. Longman GCSE and A Level Revise Guides. No fiction. Unsolicited mss only welcome subject to prior letter enclosing c.v. and s.a.e.. Approach by phone, fax or letter. No reading fee. *Commission* Home 10–15%; USA & Translation by negotiation.

Margaret Hanbury★
27 Walcot Square, London SE11 4UB
☎0171 735 7680   Fax 0171 793 0316

Represents general fiction and non-fiction. No plays, scripts, poetry, children's books, fantasy, horror. No unsolicited mss; preliminary letter with s.a.e. essential. *Commission* Home 15%; Overseas 20%.

Roger Hancock Ltd
4 Water Lane, London NW1 8NZ
☎0171 267 4418   Fax 0171 267 0705
Contact *Material should be addressed to the Company*
FOUNDED 1961. *Special interests* drama and light entertainment. Scripts only. No books. Unsolicited mss not welcome. Initial phone call required. No reading fee. *Commission* 10%.

Xandra Hardie Literary Agency
See **Toby Eady Associates Ltd**

A. M. Heath & Co. Ltd★
79 St Martin's Lane, London WC2N 4AA
☎0171 836 4271   Fax 0171 497 2561
Contact *Michael Thomas, Bill Hamilton, Sara Fisher, Sarah Molloy*
FOUNDED 1919. *Handles* fiction and general non-fiction. No scripts or poetry. Preliminary letter and synopsis essential. No reading fee. CLIENTS include Christopher Andrew, Anita Brookner, Marika Cobbold, Lesley Glaister, Graham Hancock, Hilary Mantel, Hilary Norman, Adam Thorpe, Elizabeth Walker. *Commission* Home 10–15%; US & Translation 20%; Film & TV 15%. *Overseas associates* in the US, Europe, South America, Japan.

David Higham Associates Ltd★
5–8 Lower John Street, Golden Square, London W1R 4HA
☎0171 437 7888   Fax 0171 437 1072
Scripts *Elizabeth Cree, Nicky Lund, Borra Garson*
Books *Susie Alkin-Sneath*
FOUNDED 1935. *Handles* fiction and general non-fiction: biography, history, current affairs, art, music, etc. Also scripts. Preliminary letter with synopsis essential in first instance. No reading fee. CLIENTS include John le Carré, Stephen Fry, James Herbert, Alice Walker. *Commission* Home 10%; US & Translation 20%.

Vanessa Holt Ltd★
59 Crescent Road, Leigh-on-Sea, Essex SS9 2PF
☎01702 73787/714698   Fax 01702 471890
Contact *Brenda White*
FOUNDED 1989. *Handles* general adult fiction and non-fiction. No scripts, poetry, academic or technical. *Specialises* in commercial and crime fiction. No unsolicited mss. Approach by letter in first instance, 'although agency taking on few new clients at present'; s.a.e. essential. No reading fee. *Commission* Home 10%; US & Translation 20%. *Overseas associates* in the US, Europe, South America and Japan.

Valerie Hoskins
20 Charlotte Street, London W1P 1HJ
☎0171 637 4490   Fax 0171 637 4493
Contact *Valerie Hoskins*
FOUNDED 1983. *Handles* scripts for film, theatre, TV and radio. *Special interests* feature films and TV. No unsolicited scripts; preliminary letter of introduction essential. No reading fee. CLIENTS include David Ashton, Daniel Boyle, Bryan Elsley, Matthew Graham, Kit Hesketh-Harvey, Jeff Povey, Stephen Wyatt. *Commission* Home 12½%; US 20% (maximum).

Tanja Howarth Literary Agency★
19 New Row, London WC2N 4LA
☎0171 240 5553/836 4142
Fax 0171 379 0969
Contact *Tanja Howarth*
FOUNDED 1970. Interested in taking on both fiction and non-fiction from British writers. No children's books, plays or poetry, but all other subjects considered providing the treatment is intelligent. No unsolicited mss. Preliminary letter

preferred. No reading fee. Also an established agent for foreign literature, particularly from the German language. *Commission* Home 15%; Translation 20%.

ICM

Oxford House, 76 Oxford Street, London W1N 0AX

☎0171 636 6565   Fax 0171 323 0101

Contact *Ian Amos, Sue Rodgers, Amanda Davis*

FOUNDED 1973. *Handles* film, TV and theatre scripts. No books. No unsolicited mss. Preliminary letter essential. No reading fee. *Commission* 10%. *Overseas associates* ICM, New York/Los Angeles.

Imagination

The Old Forge, 72 The Street, Ash, Kent CT3 2AA

☎01304 813378   Fax 01304 813378

Contact *Janine Gregory*

FOUNDED 1995. Television and film scripts. Full-length fiction and non-fiction. *Special interests*: drama, comedy drama, sitcom, women's fiction, historical fiction, science fiction, fantasy, horror, new age, non-fiction. No poetry or children's. No reading fee. Send synopsis, first three chapters and s.a.e. in the first instance with letter outlining career history, publishing details etc. *Commission* Home 15%; Film & TV 20%; US & Translation 20%.

IMG

Pier House, Strand on the Green, Chiswick, London W4 3NN

☎0181 233 5000   Fax 0181 233 5001

Contact *Jean Cooke (London), Julian Bach, David Chalfant (New York)*

Part of the Mark McCormack Group. Offices in New York. *Handles* celebrity books, sports-related books, commercial fiction (New York), non-fiction, how-to business books. No TV, film, radio, theatre, children's books, poetry and academic. No unsolicited mss; send letter with c.v., synopsis, three chapters and s.a.e.. CLIENTS include Ross Benson, Tony Buzan, Pat Conroy, Mark McCormack, professional sports stars, classical musicians, broadcasting personalities. *Commission* Home & USA 15%; Translation 25%.

Michael Imison Playwrights Ltd

28 Almeida Street, London N1 1TD

☎0171 354 3174   Fax 0171 359 6273

Contact *Michael Imison, Sarah McNair*

FOUNDED 1944. Michael Imison is an ex-TV director and script editor for the BBC. *Handles* plays and books based on scripts, e.g. *Yes Minister*; also film, TV, radio and theatre. No fiction or general books. *Special interest* in writers motivated primarily by writing for the theatre, and in translations, particularly from Russian and Italian. No unsolicited mss. Initial letter (plus s.a.e.) with recommendation from a known theatre professional essential. No reading fee. CLIENTS David Edgar, Dario Fo, Timberlake Wertenbaker, the Nöel Coward estate. *Commission* Home 10%; US & Translation 15%.

International Copyright Bureau Ltd

22A Aubrey House, Maida Avenue, London W2 1TQ

☎0171 724 8034   Fax 0171 724 7662

Contact *Joy Westendarp*

FOUNDED 1905. *Handles* scripts for TV, theatre, film and radio. No books. Preliminary letter for unsolicited material essential. *Commission* Home 10%; US & Translation 19%. *Overseas agents* in New York and most foreign countries.

International Scripts

1 Norland Square, London W11 4PX

☎0171 229 0736   Fax 0171 792 3287

Contact *Bob Tanner, Pat Hornsey, Jill Lawson*

FOUNDED 1979 by Bob Tanner. *Handles* all types of books and scripts for all media. No poetry or short stories. Preliminary letter required. CLIENTS include Masquerade (USA), Barricade Books (USA), Barrons (USA), Ed Gorman, Peter Haining, Julie Harris, Robert A. Heinlein, Anna Jacobs, Dean R. Koontz, Richard Laymon, Jean Moss, Mary Ryan, John Spencer, A. N. Steinberg. *Commission* Home 15%; US & Translation 20-25%. *Overseas associates* include Ralph Vicinanza, USA; Thomas Schluck, Germany; Yanez, Spain; Eliane Benisti, France.

Heather Jeeves Literary Agency★

9 Dryden Place, Edinburgh EH9 1RP

☎0131 668 3859   Fax 0131 668 3859

Contact *Heather Jeeves*

FOUNDED 1989. *Handles* general trade fiction and non-fiction, specialising in crime and cookery. Also handles historians, biographers and entertainers. Scripts for TV, film, and theatre are handled through **Casarotto Ramsay Ltd**. Not interested in academic, fantasy, science fiction, romances, poetry, short stories, sports, military history or freelance journalism. *No* unsolicited mss. Approach in the first instance in writing describing the project and professional experience. Return postage essential. No reading fee. CLIENTS include Debbie Bliss, Lindsey Davis, Elspeth Huxley, Susan Kay, Sue Lawrence, Mark Timlin. *Commission* Home 10%; US 15-20%; Translation 20%. *Overseas associates* throughout Europe and in the US.

Jane Judd Literary Agency★
18 Belitha Villas, London N1 1PD
☎0171 607 0273   Fax 0171 607 0623
Contact *Jane Judd*

FOUNDED 1986. *Handles* general fiction and non-fiction: women's fiction, crime, fantasy, thrillers, literary fiction, cookery, humour, pop/rock, biography/autobiography, investigative journalism, health, women's interests and travel. 'Looking for good sagas/women's read but not Mills & Boon-type'. No scripts, academic, gardening or DIY. Approach with letter, including synopsis, first chapter and return postage. Initial telephone call helpful in the case of non-fiction. CLIENTS include Patrick Anthony, John Brunner, Jillie Collings, John Grant, Jill Mansell, Jeremy Pascall, Lester Piggott, Jonathon Porritt. *Commission* Home 10%; US & Translation 20%.

Juvenilia
Avington, Near Winchester, Hampshire SO21 1DB
☎01962 779656   Fax 01962 779656
Contact *Rosemary Bromley*

FOUNDED 1973. *Handles* young/teen fiction and picture books; non-fiction and scripts for TV and radio. No poetry or short stories unless part of a collection or picture book material. No unsolicited mss. Send preliminary letter with full details of work and biographical outline in first instance. Preliminary letters unaccompanied by return postage will not be answered. Phone calls not advised. CLIENTS include Paul Aston, Elisabeth Beresford, Linda Birch, Denis Bond, Nicola Davies, Linda Dearsley, Terry Deary, Steve Donald, Gaye Hicyilmaz, Chris Masters, Phil McMylor, Elizabeth Pewsey, Saviour Pirotta, Kelvin Reynolds, Peter Riley, Malcolm Rose, Cathy Simpson, Margaret Stuart Barry, Keith West, Jennifer Zabel. *Commission* Home 10%; US 15%; Translation 20%; Illustration 20%.

Michelle Kass Associates★
36-38 Glasshouse Street, London W1R 5RH
☎0171 439 1624   Fax 0171 734 3394
Contact *Michelle Kass*

FOUNDED 1991. *Handles* fiction, TV, film, radio and theatre scripts. Approach by phone or explanatory letter in the first instance. No reading fee. *Commission* Home 10%; US & Translation 15-20%.

Frances Kelly★
111 Clifton Road, Kingston upon Thames, Surrey KT2 6PL
☎0181 549 7830   Fax 0181 547 0051
Contact *Frances Kelly*

FOUNDED 1978. *Handles* non-fiction, including illustrated: biography, history, art, self-help, food & wine, complementary medicine and therapies, New Age; and academic non-fiction in all disciplines. No scripts except for existing clients. No unsolicited mss. Approach by letter with brief description of work or synopsis, together with c.v. and return postage. *Commission* Home 10%; US & Translation 20%.

Paul Kiernan
13 Embankment Gardens, London SW3 4LW
☎0171 352 5562   Fax 0171 351 5986
Contact *Paul Kiernan*

FOUNDED 1990. *Handles* fiction and non-fiction, including autobiography and biography, plus specialist writers like cookery or gardening. Also scripts for TV, film, radio and theatre (TV and film scripts from book-writing clients only). No unsolicited mss. Preferred approach is by letter or personal introduction. Letters should include synopsis and brief biography. No reading fee. CLIENTS include K. Banta, Lord Chalfont, Ambassador Walter J. P. Curley, Sir Paul Fox. *Commission* Home 15%; US 20%.

Knight Features
20 Crescent Grove, London SW4 7AH
☎0171 622 1467   Fax 0171 622 1522
Contact *Peter Knight, Gaby Martin, Ann King-Hall, Carolinie Figini, Andrew Knight, Giovanna Farrell-Vinay*

FOUNDED 1985. *Handles* motor sports, cartoon books for both adults and children, puzzles, factual and biographical material, and scripts (on a very selective basis). No poetry, science fiction or cookery. No unsolicited mss. Send letter accompanied by c.v. and s.a.e. with synopsis of proposed work. Reading fee charged. CLIENTS include Michael Crozier, Frank Dickens, Christopher Hilton, Frederic Mullally. *Commission* dependent upon authors and territories. *Overseas associates* United Media, US; Auspac Media, Australia.

Cat Ledger Literary Agency★
33 Percy Street, London W1P 9FG
☎0171 436 5030   Fax 0171 631 4273
Contact *Cat Ledger*

FOUNDED 1996. *Handles* non-fiction: popular culture - film, music, sport, travel, humour, biography, politics; investigative journalism; fiction (non-genre). No scripts. No children's, poetry, fantasy, science fiction, romance. No unsolicited mss; approach with preliminary letter, synopsis and s.a.e.. No reading fee. *Commission* Home 10%; US & Translation 20%.

Barbara Levy Literary Agency★
64 Greenhill, Hampstead High Street, London NW3 5TZ
☎0171 435 9046   Fax 0171 431 2063
Contact *Barbara Levy, John Selby*

FOUNDED 1986. *Handles* general fiction, non-fiction and scripts for TV and radio. No unsolicited mss. Send detailed preliminary letter in the first instance. No reading fee. *Commission* Home 10%; US 20%; Translation by arrangement, in conjunction with **The Marsh Agency**. *US associates* Arcadia Ltd, New York.

Limelight Management
54 Marshall Street, London W1V 1LR
☎0171 734 1218   Fax 0171 287 1998
Contact *Fiona Lindsay, Linda Shanks*

FOUNDED 1991. *Handles* general non-fiction and fiction books; cookery, gardening, wine, art and crafts, health, historical and romantic. No TV, film, radio or theatre. Not interested in science fiction, short stories, plays, children's. *Specialises* in illustrated books. Unsolicited mss welcome; send preliminary letter (s.a.e. essential). No reading fee. *Commission* Home 12½%; USA & Translation 20%.

The Christopher Little Literary Agency (1979)★
48 Walham Grove, London SW6 1QR
☎0171 386 1800   Fax 0171 381 2248
Fiction/Non-fiction *Christopher Little, Patrick Walsh*
Office Manager *Bryony Evens*

FOUNDED 1979. *Handles* commercial and literary full-length fiction, non-fiction, and film/

TV scripts. *Special interests* crime, thrillers, autobiography, popular science and narrative, and investigative non-fiction. Also makes a particular speciality out of packaging celebrities for the book market and representing book projects for journalists. Rights representative in the UK for six American literary agencies. No reading fee. Send detailed letter ('giving a summary of present and future intentions together with track record, if any'), synopsis and/or first two chapters and s.a.e. in first instance. CLIENTS include Felice Arena, Simon Beckett, Marcus Berkmann, Colin Cameron, Harriet Castor, Linford Christie, Storm Constantine, Mike Dash, Frankie Dettori, Ginny Elliot, Simon Gandolfi, Brian Hall, Paula Hamilton, Damon Hill, Tom Holland, Clare Latimer, Alastair MacNeill, Sanjida O'Connell, Anna Pasternak, Samantha Phillips, A. J. Quinnell, Alvin Rakoff, Candace Robb, Peter Rosenberg, Vivienne Savory, John Spurling, David Thomas, Laura Thompson, James Whitaker, Wilbur Wright. *Commission* Home 15%; US, Translation, Motion Picture 20%.

London Independent Books
26 Chalcot Crescent, London NW1 8YD
☎0171 706 0486   Fax 0171 724 3122
Proprietor *Carolyn Whitaker*

FOUNDED 1971. A self-styled 'small and idiosyncratic' agency. *Handles* fiction and non-fiction reflecting the tastes of the proprietors. All subjects considered (except computer books and young children's), providing the treatment is strong and saleable. Scripts handled only if by existing clients. *Special interests* boats, travel, travelogues, commercial fiction. No unsolicited mss; letter, synopsis and first two chapters with return postage the best approach. No reading fee. *Commission* Home 15%; US & Translation 20%.

Clive Luhrs Publishing Services
PO Box 151, Leeds, West Yorkshire LS5 3TD
☎0113 2746701
Contact *Clive B. Luhrs*

FOUNDED 1990. *Handles* and *specialises* in railway history (British and foreign subjects), local history utilising old photographs, Russian émigré autobiography. No TV, film, radio or theatre. No unsolicited mss. Approach by letter enclosing detailed synopsis of proposed book/finished mss. S.a.e. required for initial response. Reading fee charged. *Commission* negotiable.

Lutyens and Rubinstein*

231 Westbourne Park Road, London
W11 1EB

☎0171 792 4855   Fax 0171 792 4833

Partners *Sarah Lutyens, Felicity Rubinstein*
Submissions *Anna Benn*

FOUNDED 1993. *Handles* adult fiction and non-fiction books. No TV, film, radio or theatre scripts. Unsolicited mss accepted; send introductory letter, c.v., two chapters and return postage for all material submitted. No reading fee. *Commission* Home 10%; USA & Translation 20%.

Maclean Dubois (Writers & Agents)

Hillend House, Hillend, Edinburgh EH10 7DX

☎0131 445 5885   Fax 0131 445 5898

Contact *Charles MacLean*

FOUNDED 1977. *Handles* fiction and general non-fiction. No scripts. *Specialises* in Scottish fiction and non-fiction, food and drink, historical fiction, literary fiction. Unsolicited mss will be considered. Approach by phone or in writing in the first instance for explanation of terms. Reading fee of £60 per 1000 words. *Commission* Home 10%; US 15%; Translation 20%. *Overseas associates* Lighthouse, 2 Impasse Dechêne, 37290 Boussay, France.

Andrew Mann Ltd*

1 Old Compton Street, London W1V 5PH

☎0171 734 4751   Fax 0171 287 9264

Contact *Anne Dewe, Tina Betts*

In association with **Jane Conway-Gordon**. FOUNDED 1975. *Handles* fiction, general non-fiction and film, TV, theatre, radio scripts. No unsolicited mss. Preliminary letter, synopsis and s.a.e. essential. No reading fee. *Commission* Home 10%; US & Translation 19%. *Overseas associates* various.

Manuscript ReSearch

PO Box 33, Bicester, Oxfordshire OX6 7PP

☎01869 323447   Fax 01869 324096

Contact *Graham Jenkins*

FOUNDED 1988. *Handles* fiction: thrillers, literary novels, crime and general; biographies, children's books and scripts for TV and radio. No technical, religious, science fiction, poetry or short stories unless from established clients. *Special interests* revision/rewriting scripts for selected clients. Optional criticism service available, including professional line-by-line editing and laser printing. Approach by letter with s.a.e. in first instance. No reading fee. CLIENTS include Tom Barrat, Margaritte Bell, Richard Butler, Nicholai Kollantoy, Roscoe Howells, Val Manning, Peter Pook, Kev Shannon. *Commission* Home 10%; US 20%.

Marsh & Sheil Ltd

19 John Street, London WC1N 2DL

☎0171 405 7473   Fax 0171 405 5239

Contact *Benita Edzard, Susy Behr*

FOUNDED 1985. Deals only in translation rights. Welcomes approaches from foreign literary estates and US agents seeking foreign rights representation. *Commission* Translation 10%.

The Marsh Agency*

138 Buckingham Palace Road, London
SW1W 9SA

☎0171 730 1124   Fax 0171 730 0037

Contact *Paul Marsh*

FOUNDED 1994. *Handles* translation rights only. No TV, film, radio or theatre. Not interested in anything to be sold to English language publishers. No unsolicited mss. CLIENTS include several British and American agencies and publishers. *Commission* 10%.

Judy Martin Literary Agency

138 Buckingham Palace Road, London
SW1W 9SA

☎0171 730 3779   Fax 0171 730 3801

FOUNDED 1990. *Handles* fiction and non-fiction, including humour (no gardening, cookery or children's books); plus scripts for film and TV. No plays, poetry or photography. Unsolicited mss will be considered. Include letter giving past publishing history and details of rejections, together with s.a.e. for reply or return of mss. No reading fee. *Commission* Home 15%; US & Translation 20%.

M. C. Martinez Literary Agency

60 Oakwood Avenue, Southgate, London
N14 6QL

☎0181 886 5829

Contact *Mary Caroline Martinez, Francoise Budd*

FOUNDED 1988. *Handles* high-quality fiction, children's books, arts and crafts, interior design, alternative health, DIY, cookery, travel, biography, sport and business. Also scripts for films, TV, radio and theatre. *Specialises* in fiction, children's and alternative health. No unsolicited mss. Phone call in the first instance before sending letter with synopsis; s.a.e. essential. (Possible change of address; telephone first before sending submissions.) No reading fee but may charge an admin. fee where appropriate. DTP service available. *Commission* Home 15%; US, Overseas & Translation 20%. *Overseas associates* various.

MBA Literary Agents Ltd★

45 Fitzroy Street, London W1P 5HR
☎0171 387 2076/4785   Fax 0171 387 2042
Contact *Diana Tyler, John Richard Parker, Meg Davis, Ruth Needham*

FOUNDED 1971. *Handles* fiction and non-fiction. No poetry or children's fiction. Also scripts for film, TV, radio and theatre. CLIENTS include Campbell Armstrong, Jeffrey Caine, Glenn Chandler, Neil Clarke, Maggie Furey, Valerie Georgeson, Andrew Hodges, Roy Lancaster, Paul J. McAuley, Anne McCaffrey, Anne Perry, Elspeth Sandys, Sir Roger Penrose, Iain Sinclair, Tom Vernon, Douglas Watkinson, Freda Warrington, Patrick Wright, Valerie Windsor and the estate of B. S. Johnson. No unsolicited mss. No reading fee. Preliminary letter with outline and s.a.e. essential. *Commission* Home 10%; US & Translation 20%; Theatre/TV/Radio 10%; Film 10-15%. *Overseas associates* in the US, Japan and throughout Europe. Also rights representative in the UK for the Donald Maass Agency and **Susan Schulman Agency**, New York.

Duncan McAra

30 Craighall Crescent, Edinburgh EH6 4RZ
☎0131 552 1558   Fax 0131 552 1558
Contact *Duncan McAra*

FOUNDED 1988. *Handles* fiction (thrillers and literary fiction) and non-fiction, including art, architecture, archaeology, biography, film, military, travel. Preliminary letter, synopsis and sample chapter (including return postage) essential. No reading fee. *Commission* Home 10%; Overseas by arrangement.

Bill McLean Personal Management

23B Deodar Road, London SW15 2NP
☎0181 789 8191
Contact *Bill McLean*

FOUNDED 1972. *Handles* scripts for all media. No books. No unsolicited mss. Phone call or introductory letter essential. No reading fee. CLIENTS include Dwynwen Berry, Jane Galletly, Tony Jordan, Bill Lyons, John Maynard, Glen McCoy, Michael McStay, Les Miller, Jeffrey Segal, Frank Vickery, Mark Wheatley. *Commission* Home 10%.

Eunice McMullen Children's Literary Agent Ltd

38 Clewer Hill Road, Windsor, Berkshire SL4 4BW
☎01753 830348   Fax 01753 833459
Contact *Eunice McMullen*

FOUNDED 1992. *Handles* all types of children's material from picture books to teenage fiction. Particularly interested in younger children's fiction and illustrated texts. Has a strong list of picture book author/illustrators. Send preliminary letter with s.a.e., outline and biographical details in the first instance. No unsolicited scripts. CLIENTS include Wayne Anderson, Reg Cartwright, Mark Foreman, Simon James, Graham Oakley, Sue Porter, James Riordan, Susan Winter, David Wood. *Commission* Home 10%; US 15%; Translation 20%.

Media House Literary Agents

179 King's Cross Road, London WC1X 9BZ
☎0171 833 9111   Fax 0171 833 8211
Contacts *Jennifer Chapman, Gilly Vincent*

A new, small agency not at present actively seeking clients but handling a few selected writers of original non-fiction (in particular, with film, TV and audio potential), and quality literary fiction including novellas. No poetry, children's, romantic fiction, science fiction or avant-garde works. Approach in the first instance for non-fiction with fully developed idea and at least half the complete mss. For fiction approach with full synopsis and two sample chapters. S.a.e. essential. No phone calls, please. *Commission* Home 15%; US & Europe 20%.

Richard Milne Ltd

15 Summerlee Gardens, London N2 9QN
☎0181 883 3987   Fax 0181 883 3987
Contact *R. M. Sharples, K. N. Sharples*

FOUNDED 1956. *Specialises* in drama and comedy scripts for radio, film and television. Not presently in the market for new clients as 'fully committed handling work by authors we already represent'. No unsolicited mss. *Commission* Home 10%; US 15%; Translation 25%.

William Morris Agency UK Ltd★

31-32 Soho Square, London W1V 6HH
☎0171 434 2191   Fax 0171 437 0238
Films *Stephen M. Kenis*
Television/Theatre *Jane Annakin*
Books *Stephanie Cabot*

FOUNDED 1965. Worldwide theatrical and literary agency with offices in New York, Beverly

Hills and Nashville; associates in Munich and Sydney. *Handles* theatre, TV, film and radio scripts; fiction and general non-fiction. No unsolicited material. *Commission* Film/TV/Theatre/UK Books 10%; US & Translation 20%.

Michael Motley Ltd★

42 Craven Hill Gardens, London W2 3EA
☎0171 723 2973   Fax 0171 262 4566
Contact *Michael Motley*

FOUNDED 1973. *Handles* all subjects, except short mss (e.g. journalism), poetry and original dramatic material. *Special interest* literary fiction and crime novels. Mss will be considered but must be preceded by a preliminary letter with specimen chapters and s.a.e.. No reading fee. CLIENTS include Simon Brett, Doug Nye, K. M. Peyton, Annette Roome, Barry Turner. *Commission* Home 10%; US 15%; Translation 20%. *Overseas associates* in all publishing centres.

William Neill-Hall Ltd

71 Kenley Road, London SW19 3JJ
☎0181 543 9858   Fax 0181 543 9858
Contact *William Neill-Hall*

FOUNDED 1995. *Handles* general non-fiction, cartoons, religion, academic. No TV, film, theatre or radio scripts; no fiction or poetry. *Specialises* in religion, sport, history, current affairs and humour. No unsolicited mss. Approach by phone or letter. No reading fee. CLIENTS Mark Bryant, Archbishop of Canterbury (George Carey), Jennifer Rees Larcombe, Heather Pinchen. *Commission* Home 10%; USA 15%; Translation 20%.

The Maggie Noach Literary Agency★

21 Redan Street, London W14 0AB
☎0171 602 2451   Fax 0171 603 4712
Contact *Maggie Noach*

FOUNDED 1982. Pronounced 'no-ack'. *Handles* a wide range of books including commercial, well-written fiction, general non-fiction and some children's. No scientific, academic or specialist non-fiction. No romantic fiction, poetry, plays, short stories or books for the very young. Recommended for promising young writers but *very* few new clients taken on as it is considered vital to give individual attention to each author's work. Unsolicited mss not welcome. Approach by letter (*not by telephone*), giving a brief description of the book and enclosing a few sample pages. Return postage essential. No reading fee. *Commission* Home 15%; US & Translation 20%.

Andrew Nurnberg Associates Ltd★

Clerkenwell House, 45–47 Clerkenwell Green, London EC1R 0HT
☎0171 417 8800   Fax 0171 417 8812
Directors *Andrew Nurnberg, Klaasje Mul, Sarah Nundy*

FOUNDED in the mid-1970s. *Specialises* in foreign rights, representing leading authors and agents. Branch in Moscow to provide representation for western writers in Russia and the republics of the CIS. Recently opened offices in Bucharest, Budapest, Prague, Sofia and Warsaw. *Commission* Home 15%; US & Translation 20%.

Alexandra Nye

Cauldhame Cottage, Sheriffmuir, Dunblane, Perthshire FK15 0LN
☎01786 825114
Contact *Alexandra Nye*

FOUNDED 1991. *Handles* fiction and topical non-fiction. *Special interests* literary fiction, historicals, thrillers. No children's, horror or crime. No scripts, poetry or plays. Preliminary approach by letter, with synopsis and sample chapter, preferred (s.a.e. essential for return). Reading fee for supply of detailed report on mss. CLIENTS include Dr Tom Gallagher, Harry Mehta, Robin Jenkins. *Commission* Home 10%; US 20%; Translation 15%.

David O'Leary Literary Agents

10 Lansdowne Court, Lansdowne Rise, London W11 2NR
☎0171 229 1623   Fax 0171 727 9624
Contact *David O'Leary*

FOUNDED 1988. *Handles* fiction, both popular and literary, and non-fiction. Areas of interest include thrillers, history, popular science, Russia and Ireland (history and fiction), TV drama and documentaries. No poetry or children's. No unsolicited mss but happy to discuss a proposal. Ring or write in the first instance. No reading fee. CLIENTS include James Barwick, Alexander Keegan, Jim Lusby, Roy MacGregor-Hastie, Charles Mosley, Edward Toman. *Commission* Home 10%; US 10%. *Overseas associates* Lennart Sane, Scandinavia/Spain/South America; Tuttle Mori, Japan.

Deborah Owen Ltd★

78 Narrow Street, Limehouse, London E14 8BP
☎0171 987 5119/5441   Fax 0171 538 4004
Contact *Deborah Owen, Gemma Hirst*

FOUNDED 1971. Small agency specialising in representing authors direct around the world. *Handles* international fiction and non-fiction (books which can be translated into a number of languages). No scripts, poetry, science fiction, children's or short stories. No unsolicited mss. No new authors at present. CLIENTS Amos Oz, Ellis Peters, Delia Smith, Murray Smith. *Commission* Home 10%; US & Translation 15%.

Mark Paterson & Associates★

10 Brook Street, Wivenhoe, Colchester, Essex CO7 9DS
☎01206 825433 Fax 01206 822990
Contact *Mark Paterson, Mary Swinney*

FOUNDED 1961. World rights representatives of authors and publishers handling many subjects, with specialisation in psychoanalysis and psychotherapy. CLIENTS range from Balint, Bion, Casement and Ferenczi, through to Freud and Winnicott; plus Hugh Brogan, Peter Moss and the estates of Sir Arthur Evans and Dorothy Richardson. No scripts, poetry, children's, articles, short stories or 'unsaleable mediocrity'. No unsolicited mss, but preliminary letter and synopsis with s.a.e. welcome. Reading fee may be charged. *Commission* 20% (including sub-agent's commission).

John Pawsey

60 High Street, Tarring, Worthing,
West Sussex BN14 7NR
☎01903 205167 Fax 01903 205167
Contact *John Pawsey*

FOUNDED 1981. Experience in the publishing business has helped to attract some top names here, but the door remains open for bright, new talent. *Handles* non-fiction: biography, politics, current affairs, show business, gardening, travel, sport, business and music; and fiction; will consider any well-written novel. *Special interests* sport, current affairs and popular fiction. No drama scripts, poetry, short stories, journalism or academic. Preliminary letter with s.a.e. essential. No reading fee. CLIENTS include Jonathan Agnew, Emily Bell, Dr David Lewis, David Rayvern Allen, Caroline Fabre, Elwyn Hartley Edwards, Peter Hobday, Orson Scott Card, Jon Silverman. *Commission* Home 10-15%; US & Translation 19%. *Overseas associates* in the US, Japan, South America and throughout Europe.

Maggie Pearlstine Associates Ltd★

31 Ashley Gardens, Ambrosden Avenue,
London SW1P 1QE
☎0171 828 4212 Fax 0171 834 5546
Contact *Maggie Pearlstine*

FOUNDED 1989. Small, selective agency. *Handles* commercial fiction, general and illustrated non-fiction: home and leisure, health, biography, history and politics. No children's or poetry. Deals only with scripts and short stories by existing clients. No unsolicited mss. Best approach first by letter with synopsis, sample material and s.a.e. for response. No reading fee. CLIENTS James Cox, John Drews, Mary Evans Young, Glorafilia, Prof Roger Gosden, Roy Hattersley, Prof Lisa Jardine, Charles Kennedy, Prof Nicholas Lowe, Sara Morrison, Lesley Regan, Jack Straw, Dr Thomas Stuttaford, Brian Wilson, Prof the Lord Winston, Tony Wright. Translation rights handled by **Aitken, Stone & Wylie Ltd**. *Commission* Home 12½% (fiction), 10% (non-fiction); US & Translation 20%; TV, Film & Journalism 20%.

Penman Literary Agency

185 Daws Heath Road, Benfleet, Essex SS7 2TF
☎01702 557431
Contact *Mark Sorrell*

FOUNDED 1950. Under new management since October 1993. *Handles* all types of fiction and non-fiction. No plays. Send preliminary letter, synopsis and sample chapters with s.a.e.. No reading fee. *Commission* Home 10%; Overseas 15-20%.

Peters Fraser & Dunlop Group Ltd★

503-504 The Chambers, Chelsea Harbour, Lots Road, London SW10 0XF
☎0171 344 1000 Fax 0171 352 7356/351 1756
Managing Director *Anthony Baring*
Books *Michael Sissons, Pat Kavanagh, Caroline Dawnay, Araminta Whitley, Mark Lucas, Charles Walker, Rosemary Canter*
Serial *Pat Kavanagh*
Film/TV *Anthony Jones, Tim Corrie, Norman North, Charles Walker, Vanessa Jones, St. John Donald, Gavin Knight, Rosemary Scoular*
Actors *Maureen Vincent, Ginette Chalmers, Dallas Smith*
Theatre *Kenneth Ewing, St John Donald, Nicki Stoddart*
Children's *Rosemary Canter*

FOUNDED 1988 as a result of the merger of A. D. Peters & Co. Ltd and Fraser & Dunlop, and was later joined by the June Hall Literary Agency. *Handles* all sorts of books including fiction and children's, plus scripts for film, theatre, radio and TV material. No third-rate DIY. No unsolicited mss. Prospective clients should write 'a full letter, with an account of what he/she has done and wants to do'. No reading fee. CLIENTS include Julian Barnes, Alan Bennett, A. S. Byatt, Alan Clark, Margaret Drabble, Clive James, Robert McCrum, John Mortimer, Douglas Reeman, Ruth Rendell, Anthony Sampson, Gerald Seymour, Tom Stoppard, Joanna Trollope Evelyn Waugh. *Commission* Home 10%; US & Translation 20%.

Laurence Pollinger Ltd
18 Maddox Street, London W1R 0EU
☎0171 629 9761   Fax 0171 629 9765
Contacts *Gerald J. Pollinger, Heather Chalcroft*
Negotiating Editor *Juliet Burton*
Children's Books *Lesley Hadcroft*

FOUNDED 1958. A successor of Pearn, Pollinger & Higham. *Handles* all types of books including children's. No pure science, academic or technological. Good for crime and romantic fiction. No plays. CLIENTS include the estates of H. E. Bates, W. Heath Robinson, William Saroyan, John Cowper Powys, D. H. Lawrence and other notables. Unsolicited mss welcome if preceded by letter. A contribution of £10 is requested towards editorial costs. *Commission* Home & US 15%; Translation 20%.

Murray Pollinger★
222 Old Brompton Road, London SW5 0BZ
☎0171 373 4711   Fax 0171 373 3775
Contact *Murray Pollinger, Gina Pollinger, Sara Menguc*

FOUNDED 1969. Part of the Pollinger dynasty (Murray is the youngest son of Laurence), with a particularly strong name for new writers. Securely based on serious fiction and nature and science non-fiction. *Handles* all types of general fiction, non-fiction and children's fiction. No poetry, plays or travel; no drama scripts. No unsolicited mss; writers should send a letter with synopsis and names of other agents and publishers previously approached. CLIENTS include J. M. Coetzee, Anne Fine, John Gribbin, Molly Keane, Penelope Lively, Lyall Watson, and the estate of Roald Dahl. *Commission* Home 10%; Elsewhere 20%. *Overseas associates* in all major cultural centres. See **Stop Press.**

Shelley Power Literary Agency Ltd★
Le Montaud, 24220 Berbiguières, France
☎00 33 5329 6252   Fax 00 33 5329 6254
Contact *Shelley Power*

FOUNDED 1976. Shelley Power works between London and France. This is an English agency with London-based administration/accounts office and the editorial office in France. *Handles* general commercial fiction, quality fiction, business books, self-help, true crime, investigative exposés, film and entertainment. No scripts, short stories, children's or poetry. Preliminary letter with brief outline of project (plus s.a.e.) essential. No reading fee. CLIENTS include Michael Beer, Paul Fifield, Sutherland Lyall, Shirley McLaughlin, Clive Reading, Richard Stern, Madge Swindells, Roger Wilkes. *Commission* Home 10%; US & Translation 19%.

PVA Management Limited
Hallow Park, Worcester WR2 6PG
☎01905 640663   Fax 01905 641842
Managing Director *Paul Vaughan*

FOUNDED 1978. *Handles* mainly non-fiction, plus some fiction and scripts. Please send synopsis and sample chapters together with return postage. *Commission* 15%.

Radala & Associates
17 Avenue Mansions, Finchley Road, London NW3 7AX
☎0171 794 4495   Fax 0171 431 7636
Contact *Richard Gollner, Neil Hornick, Anna Swan, Andy Marino*

FOUNDED 1970. *Handles* quality fiction, non-fiction, drama, performing and popular arts, psychotherapy, writing from Eastern Europe. Also provides editorial services, initiates in-house projects and can recommend independent professional readers if unable to read or comment on submissions. No poetry or screenplays. Prospective clients should send a shortish letter plus synopsis (maximum 2pp), first two chapters (double-spaced, numbered pages) and s.a.e. for return. *Commission* Home 10%; US 15–20%; Translation 20%. *Overseas associates* **Writers House, Inc.** (Al Zuckerman), New York; plus agents throughout Europe.

Rogers, Coleridge & White Ltd★
20 Powis Mews, London W11 1JN
☎0171 221 3717   Fax 0171 229 9084
Contacts *Deborah Rogers, Gill Coleridge, Patricia White*
Foreign Rights *Ann Warnford-Davis, Clare Loeffler*

FOUNDED 1967. *Handles* fiction, non-fiction and children's books. No poetry, plays or technical books. No unsolicited mss, please and no submissions by fax. Rights representative in UK and translation for several New York agents. *Commission* Home 10%; US 15%; Translation 20%. *Overseas associates* ICM, New York.

Hilary Rubinstein Books

61 Clarendon Road, London W11 4JE
☎0171 792 4282   Fax 0171 221 5291
Contact *Hilary Rubinstein*

FOUNDED 1992. *Handles* fiction and non-fiction, also occasional scripts for TV, film, radio and theatre. No poetry or drama. Approach in writing in the first instance. No reading fee but return postage, please. CLIENTS include Eric Lomax, Elisabeth Maxwell, Donna Williams. *Commission* Home 10%; US & Translation 20%. *Overseas associates* **Ellen Levine Literary Agency** New York; **Andrew Nurnberg Associates** (European rights).

Uli Rushby-Smith and Shirley Stewart

72 Plimsoll Road, London N4 2EE
☎0171 354 2718   Fax 0171 354 2718
Contacts *Uli Rushby-Smith, Shirley Stewart*

FOUNDED 1993. *Handles* fiction and non-fiction, commercial and literary, both adult and children's. Scripts handled in conjunction with a sub-agent. No plays, poetry or science fiction. Approach with an outline, two or three sample chapters and explanatory letter in the first instance (s.a.e. essential). No reading fee. *Commission* Home 10%; US & Translation 20%. Represents UK rights for **Curtis Brown (New York)** and Henry Holt & Co. Inc.

Rosemary Sandberg Ltd

6 Bayley Street, London WC1B 3HB
☎0171 304 4110   Fax 0171 304 4109
Contact *Rosemary Sandberg*

FOUNDED 1991. In association with **Ed Victor Ltd.** *Handles* children's picture books and novels; women's fiction (although not exclusively women's); women's interests e.g. cookery. *Specialises* in children's writers and illustrators and women's fiction. No unsolicited mss. *Commission* Home 10-15%; US 15%; Translation 15-20%.

Tessa Sayle Agency★

11 Jubilee Place, London SW3 3TE
☎0171 823 3883   Fax 0171 823 3363
Books *Rachel Calder*
Film/TV *Jane Villiers*

FOUNDED 1976 by Tessa Sayle who retired shortly before her death in 1993. *Handles* fiction: literary novels rather than category fiction; non-fiction: current affairs, social issues, travel, biographies, historical; and drama (TV, film and theatre): contemporary social issues or drama with comedy, rather than broad comedy. No poetry, children's, textbooks, science fiction, fantasy, horror or musicals. No unsolicited mss. Preliminary letter essential, including a brief biographical note and a synopsis. No reading fee. CLIENTS Books: Stephen Amidon, Peter Benson, Pete Davies, Margaret Forster, Georgina Hammick, Paul Hogarth, Mark Illis, Andy Kershaw, Phillip Knightley, Rory MacLean, Ann Oakley, Kate Pullinger, Ronald Searle, Gitta Sereny, William Styron, Mary Wesley. Drama: William Corlett, Shelagh Delaney, Marc Evans, Stuart Hepburn, John Forte, Geoff McQueen, Chris Monger, Don Shaw, Sue Townsend. *Commission* Home 10%; US & Translation 20%. *Overseas associates* in the US, Japan and throughout Europe.

Howard Seddon Associates

BM Box 1129, London WC1N 3XX
☎01923 229784   Fax 01923 229784
Contact *Dr Keith H. Seddon*

FOUNDED 1988. *Handles* full-length general and literary fiction, general non-fiction and academic. No scripts. No poetry, crime, glitzy women's, short stories, gardening, cooking or children's. *Specialises* in fantasy, gothic, horror and literary fiction; folklore, New Age, occult, philosophy, religion, social issues. No unsolicited mss. Authors come via recommendation or follow-ups to preliminary letter. Full reading and report service available. Return postage/s.a.e. essential with all enquiries. CLIENTS include Jocelyn Almond, Ravan Christchild, G. E. Vane. *Commission* Home 15%; US & Translation 20-25%.

Seifert Dench Associates

24 D'Arblay Street, London W1V 3FH
☎0171 437 4551   Fax 0171 439 1355
Contact *Linda Seifert, Elizabeth Dench*

FOUNDED 1972. *Handles* scripts for TV and film. Unsolicited mss will be read, but a letter with sample of work and c.v. (plus s.a.e.) is preferred. CLIENTS include Peter Chelsom, Tony Grisoni, Michael Radford, Stephen Volk. *Commission* Home 12½-15%. *Overseas associates* William Morris/Sanford Gross and C.A.A., Los Angeles.

The Sharland Organisation Ltd

9 Marlborough Crescent, London W4 1HE
☎0181 742 1919   Fax 0181 995 7688
Contact *Mike Sharland, Alice Sharland*

FOUNDED 1988. *Specialises* in national and international film and TV negotiations. Also negotiates multimedia, interactive TV deals and computer game contracts. *Handles* scripts for film, TV, radio and theatre; also non-fiction. Markets books for film and handles stage, radio, film and TV rights for authors. No scientific, technical or poetry. No unsolicited mss. Preliminary enquiry by letter or phone essential. *Commission* Home 15%; US & Translation 20%. *Overseas associates* various.

Vincent Shaw Associates

20 Jay Mews, Kensington Gore, London SW7 2EP
☎0171 581 8215 Fax 0171 225 1079
Contact *Vincent Shaw*

FOUNDED 1954. *Handles* TV, radio, film and theatre scripts. Unsolicited mss welcome. Approach in writing enclosing s.a.e.. No phone calls. *Commission* Home 10%; US & Translation by negotiation. *Overseas associates* Herman Chessid, New York.

Sheil Land Associates Ltd★

43 Doughty Street, London WC1N 2LF
☎0171 405 9351 Fax 0171 831 2127
Contact *Anthony Sheil, Sonia Land, Vivien Green, Robert Kirby, Simon Trewin, John Rush (film/drama/TV)*
Foreign *Benita Edzard, Susy Behr*

FOUNDED 1962. Incorporates the Richard Scott Simon Agency. *Handles* full-length general and literary fiction, biography, travel, cookery and humour, UK and foreign estates. Also theatre, film, radio and TV scripts. One of the UK's more dynamic agencies, Sheil Land represents over 270 established clients and welcomes approaches from new clients looking either to start or to develop their careers. Known to negotiate sophisticated contracts with publishers. Preliminary letter with s.a.e. essential. No reading fee. CLIENTS Peter Ackroyd, Melvyn Bragg, John Banville, Catherine Cookson, Josephine Cox, Nick Fisher, John Fowles, Susan Hill, HRH The Prince of Wales, Michael Ignatieff, John Keegan, Bernard Kops, Richard Mabey, James Roose-Evans, Eddy Shah, Tom Sharpe, Rose Tremain, John Wilsher. *Commission* Home 10%; US & Translation 20%. *Overseas associates* Georges Borchardt, Inc. (Richard Scott Simon); **Sanford J. Greenburger Associates**. UK representatives for **Farrar, Straus & Giroux, Inc**. US Film and TV representation: CAA, **H.N. Swanson**, and others.

Caroline Sheldon Literary Agency★

71 Hillgate Place, London W8 7SS
☎0171 727 9102
Contact *Caroline Sheldon*

FOUNDED 1985. *Handles* adult fiction, in particular women's, both commercial sagas and literary novels. Also full-length children's fiction. No TV/film scripts unless by book-writing clients. Send letter with all relevant details of ambitions and four chapters of proposed book (enclose large s.a.e.). No reading fee. *Commission* Home 10%; US & Translation 20%.

Jeffrey Simmons

10 Lowndes Square, London SW1X 9HA
☎0171 235 8852 Fax 0171 235 9733
Contact *Jeffrey Simmons*

FOUNDED 1978. *Handles* biography and autobiography, cinema and theatre, fiction (both quality and commercial), history, law and crime, politics and world affairs, parapsychology, sport and travel (but not exclusively). No science fiction/fantasy, children's books, cookery, crafts, hobbies or gardening. Film scripts handled only if by book-writing clients. *Special interests* personality books of all sorts and fiction from young writers (i.e. under 40) with a future. Writers become clients by personal introduction or by letter, enclosing a synopsis if possible, a brief biography, a note of any previously published books, plus a list of any publishers and agents who have already seen the mss. CLIENTS include Michael Bentine, Billy Boy, Clive Collins, Doris Collins, Euphrosyne Doxiadis, Fred Lawrence Guiles, Jim Haskins, Sanda Miller, Keith Wright. *Commission* Home 10–15%; US 15%; Translation 20%.

Simpson Fox Associates

52 Shaftesbury Avenue, London W1V 7DE
☎0171 434 9167 Fax 0171 494 2887
Contact *Georgina Capel*

ESTABLISHED 1973. *Handles* literary and commercial fiction, general non-fiction, and film/play scripts. No children's books. Approach with synopsis and sample chapter, with s.a.e., in the first instance. CLIENTS Niall Ferguson, Deborah Levy, Andrew Roberts, Peter York. *Commission* Home, US & Translation 15%.

Carol Smith Literary Agency

25 Hornton Court, Kensington High Street, London W8 7RT
☎0171 937 4874 Fax 0171 938 5323
Contact *Carol Smith*

FOUNDED 1976. *Handles* general fiction of all sorts and general non-fiction. No technical material of any kind. Submissions by invitation only. CLIENTS John Cornwell, Alexander Frater,

Sarah Harrison, Katie Stewart, Mike Wilks. *Commission* Home 10%; US & Translation 20%.

Solo Literary Agency Ltd

49-53 Kensington High Street, London
W8 5ED
☎0171 376 2166   Fax 0171 938 3165
Chairman *Don Short*
Senior Executive/Accounts *John Appleton*

FOUNDED 1978. *Handles* non-fiction. *Special interests* celebrity autobiographies, unauthorised biographies, sports and adventure stories, wildlife, nature & ecology, crime, fashion, beauty & health. Also some fiction but only from established authors. No unsolicited mss. Preliminary letter essential. CLIENTS include Nicholas Davies, Peter Essex, Uri Geller, James Oram, Betty Palko, Rick Sky. Also *specialises* in worldwide newspaper syndication of photos, features and cartoons. Professional contributors only. *Commission* Books: Home 15%; US 20%; Translation 20-30%; Journalism 50%.

Elaine Steel

110 Gloucester Avenue, London NW1 8JA
☎0181 348 0918/0171 483 2681
Fax 0181 341 9807
Contact *Elaine Steel*

FOUNDED 1986. *Handles* scripts and screenplays. No technical or academic. Initial phone call preferred. CLIENTS include Les Blair, Michael Eaton, Brian Keenan, Troy Kennedy Martin, G. F. Newman, Rob Ritchie, Snoo Wilson. *Commission* Home 10%; US & Translation 20%.

Abner Stein★

10 Roland Gardens, London SW7 3PH
☎0171 373 0456   Fax 0171 370 6316
Contact *Abner Stein*

FOUNDED 1971. *Handles* full-length fiction and general non-fiction. No scientific, technical, etc. No scripts. Send letter and outline in the first instance rather than unsolicited mss. *Commission* Home 10%; US & Translation 20%.

Micheline Steinberg Playwrights' Agent

110 Frognal, London NW3 6XU
☎0171 433 3980   Fax 0171 794 8355
Contact *Micheline Steinberg*

FOUNDED 1988. *Specialises* in plays for stage, TV, radio and film. Best approach by preliminary letter (with s.a.e.). Dramatic associate for **Laurence Pollinger Ltd**. *Commission* Home 10%; Elsewhere 15%.

Peter Tauber Press Agency

94 East End Road, London N3 2SX
☎0181 346 4165
Directors *Peter Tauber, Robert Tauber*

FOUNDED 1950. *Handles* non-fiction: hard-hitting top celebrity auto/biographies; innovative slimming books; fiction: highest-quality commercial women's fiction, thrillers and horror. No poetry, short stories, plays, children or foreign books. Please send synopsis, author c.v., first three chapters, copies of all previous rejections, a fully stamped addressed envelope, and for fiction writers, 'a non-returnable, no-obligation submission fee of £50. Failure to comply with these exact terms will result in no reply.' *Commission* 20%.

J. M. Thurley

213 Linen Hall, 162-168 Regent Street,
London W1R 5TA
☎0171 437 9545/6   Fax 0171 287 9208
Contact *Jon Thurley, Patricia Preece*

FOUNDED 1976. *Handles* all types of fiction, non-fiction, coffee-table books, etc. Also scripts for TV, film, radio and theatre. No short stories or children's illustrated books. No unsolicited mss; approach by letter in the first instance. No reading fee. *Commission* Home 10% (15% where substantial editorial/creative input involved); US & Translation 15%.

Lavinia Trevor Agency★

6 The Glasshouse, 49A Goldhawk Road,
London W12 8QP
☎0181 749 8481   Fax 0181 749 7377
Contact *Lavinia Trevor*

FOUNDED 1993. *Handles* general fiction and non-fiction. No poetry, academic or technical work. No TV, film, radio, theatre scripts. Approach with a preliminary letter and first 50-100 typewritten pages, including s.a.e.. No reading fee. *Commission* Rate by agreement with author.

Jane Turnbull★

13 Wendell Road, London W12 9RS
☎0181 743 9580   Fax 0181 749 6079
Contact *Jane Turnbull*

FOUNDED 1986. *Handles* fiction and non-fiction. No science fiction, sagas or romantic fiction. No scripts. *Specialises* in literary fiction, history, current affairs, health and diet. No unsolicited mss. Approach with letter in the first instance. No reading fee. CLIENTS include Kirsty Gunn, Penny Junor, Kevin McCloud,

Judith Wills. Translation rights handled by **Aitken, Stone & Wylie Ltd**. *Commission* Home 10%; USA & Translation 20%.

Ed Victor Ltd★
6 Bayley Street, Bedford Square, London WC1B 3HB
☎0171 304 4100   Fax 0171 304 4111
Contact *Ed Victor, Graham Greene, Maggie Phillips, Sophie Hicks*
FOUNDED 1976. *Handles* a broad range of material from Iris Murdoch to Jack Higgins, Erich Segal to Stephen Spender. Leans towards the more commercial ends of the fiction and non-fiction spectrums. No scripts, no academic. Takes on very few new writers. After trying his hand at book publishing and literary magazines, Ed Victor, an ebullient American, found his true vocation. Strong opinions, very pushy and works hard for those whose intelligence he respects. Loves nothing more than a good title auction. Preliminary letter essential, setting out very concisely and clearly what the book aims to do. No unsolicited mss. CLIENTS include Douglas Adams, Josephine Hart, Jack Higgins, Erica Jong, Iris Murdoch, Erich Segal, Will Self, Sir Stephen Spender, Fay Weldon and the estates of Raymond Chandler, and Irving Wallace. *Commission* Home 15%; US 15%; Translation 20%.

Cecily Ware Literary Agents
19C John Spencer Square, London N1 2LZ
☎0171 359 3787   Fax 0171 226 9828
Contact *Cecily Ware, Gilly Schuster, Warren Sherman*
FOUNDED 1972. Primarily a film and TV script agency representing work in all areas: drama, children's, series/serials, adaptations, comedies, etc. Also radio and occasional general fiction. No unsolicited mss or phone calls. Approach in writing only. No reading fee. *Commission* Home 10%; US 10-20% by arrangement.

Warner Chappell Plays Ltd
129 Park Street, London W1Y 3FA
☎0171 514 5236   Fax 0171 514 5201
Contact *Michael Callahan*
Formerly the English Theatre Guild, Warner Chappell are now both agents and publishers of scripts for the theatre. No unsolicited mss; introductory letter essential. No reading fee. CLIENTS include Ray Cooney, John Godber, Peter Gordon, Debbie Isitt, Arthur Miller, Sam Shepard, John Steinbeck. *Overseas representatives*

in the US, Canada, Australia, New Zealand, India, South Africa and Zimbabwe.

Watson, Little Ltd★
12 Egbert Street, London NW1 8LJ
☎0171 722 9514   Fax 0171 586 7649
Contact *Sheila Watson, Mandy Little*
Handles fiction and non-fiction. *Special interests* popular science, psychology, self-help, military history and business books. No scripts. Not interested in authors who wish to be purely academic writers. Send preliminary ('intelligent') letter rather than unsolicited synopsis. *Commission* Home 10%; US & Translation 19%. *Overseas associates* worldwide.

A. P. Watt Ltd★
20 John Street, London WC1N 2DR
☎0171 405 6774   Fax 0171 831 2154
Directors *Caradoc King, Linda Shaughnessy, Rod Hall, Lisa Eveleigh, Nick Marston, Derek Johns*
FOUNDED 1875. The oldest-established literary agency in the world. *Handles* full-length typescripts, including children's books, screenplays for film and TV, and plays. No poetry, academic or specialist works. No unsolicited mss accepted. CLIENTS include Evelyn Anthony, Quentin Blake, Martin Gilbert, Nadine Gordimer, Michael Holroyd, Garrison Keillor, Alison Lurie, Timothy Mo, Jan Morris, Michael Ondaatje, Graham Swift, and the estates of Wodehouse, Graves and Maugham. *Commission* Home 10%; US & Translation 20%. *Overseas associates* Scovil Chichak Galen Literary Agency, Inc., US.

John Welch, Literary Consultant & Agent
Milton House, Milton, Cambridge CB4 6AD
☎01223 860641   Fax 01223 440575
Contact *John Welch*
FOUNDED 1992. *Handles* military history, aviation, history, biography and some sport. No scripts for radio, TV, film or theatre. No unsolicited mss. Already has a fairly full hand of authors but still prepared to consider one or two more. Send letter with c.v., synopsis, two chapters and s.a.e. for return. Consultancy fees may apply, especially to unpublished authors. CLIENTS include Alexander Baron, Lynda Britnell, Michael Calvert, Paul Clifford, David Rooney, Norman Scarfe, David Wragg. *Commission* Home 10%; US & Translation 15%.

Dinah Wiener Ltd*

27 Arlington Road, London NW1 7ER
☎0171 388 2577   Fax 0171 388 7559
Contact *Dinah Wiener*

FOUNDED 1985. *Handles* fiction and general non-fiction: auto/biography, popular science, cookery. No scripts, children's or poetry. Approach with preliminary letter in first instance, giving full but brief c.v. of past work and future plans. Mss submitted must include s.a.e. and be typed in double-spacing. CLIENTS Catherine Alliott, T. J. Armstrong, Joy Berthoud, Malcolm Billings, Guy Burt, David Deutsch, Tania Kindersley, Dalene Matthee, Daniel Snowman, Peta Taylor, Michael Thornton, Lailan Young. *Commission* Home 15%; US & Translation 20%.

Michael Woodward Creations Ltd

Parlington Hall, Aberford, West Yorkshire LS25 3EG
☎0113 2813913   Fax 0113 2813911
Contact *Michael Woodward, Janet Woodward*

FOUNDED 1979. International Licensing company with own in-house studio. Worldwide representation. Current properties include *Teddy Tum Tum, Railway Children, Oddbods, Angel Babies, Kit 'n' Kin*. New artists should forward full-concept synopses with sample illustrations. Scripts or stories not accepted without illustration/design or concept mock-ups. No standard commission rate; varies according to contract.

Take Notice when I'm Writing for you

Who Gets Reviewed and Why

Every author expects reviews while knowing, deep down, that few are chosen. Partly it's a question of logistics. The sheer quantity of titles – 90,000 a year in Britain alone – is at least 85,000 more than the literary scouts can hope to accommodate.

Talent is relevant – up to a point. A great number of books published are not worth a second glance except by their authors' relatives. This is not to say that a bad book is automatically ignored. It all depends on what is being written about and by whom. A dismal book on a prominent royal invariably scales the heights. A dismal book *by* a prominent royal can climb any media mountain.

An easily recognisable name is always an advantage in attracting publicity. This is why established authors – even those who fail to live up to their early creativity – can rely on extensive coverage whenever they reappear in print.

Knowing the right people helps. Some time ago *The Sunday Times* ran a survey of 5000 book reviews that revealed how well-known authors connive in promoting each other's careers, setting up cliques that have a powerful influence on the publishing industry. The study, which sampled 1,200 books published in the last year, produced a detailed analysis of the 100 most reviewed books. It found that one in three of the authors of those books had also reviewed other writers on the top 100 list; they accounted for 60 out of the 650 reviews; and from there the connections spread out in all directions.

'The message,' said the *Sunday Times*, 'is clear: if you want to get ahead as a writer, find a literary "mafia" prepared to mention your name at the right parties and review your books in the "right" papers.'

Subject matter is the single most powerful determinant of review coverage. Romance and thrillers are largely ignored because there is little to be said about them except that they are good, bad or indifferent. Likewise, first novels. Biographies, on the other hand, are ideally suited to the needs of the feature writer. The number of column inches given to political memoirs, for example, is out of all proportion to their sales potential (Mrs Thatcher excepted) but literary editors do not accept this as an argument for reorganising their pages. A recently retired politician is always good for a knockabout debate which is what makes a readable feature. Whether or not the article sets off a rush to the bookshops is irrelevant.

For the most part, book reviewing is a gentler business than, say, theatre or film criticism. Raw savagery seldom intrudes in to the literary pages and nowadays there is no single book critic who is credited with the power to make or break an author. Because there are more books than there are movies or plays, criticism is diluted by its spread across a huge range of subjects. Also, literary editors tend towards books that they think deserve favour. Film and theatre critics, with fewer titles to choose from, cannot ignore the turkeys. Instead, they dispose of them speedily with an injection of vitriol.

It must be terrifying for creators of films and plays to know that success or failure can turn on the partiality of a small team of professional jurors. Simon Callow (*Being an Actor*) acknowledges that 'the verdict of four men, those who write for *The Times*, *The Guardian*, *The Sunday Times* and *The Observer*, has been crucial to any play I've ever been in, except on the fringe where *Time Out* is undisputed kingmaker'.

Naturally, resentment against this concentration of power peaks when the collective verdict on a particular work is uncompromisingly hostile. How could they be so brutish? Surely they could temper their views to show a little concern for sensitive egos? But villains transmute into heroes when they smile benignly. There is never any obligation to praise - however excessive. It feeds the ego and, more importantly, the box office. Rave reviews sell tickets. With books, no one is quite sure what is achieved by criticism, favourable or otherwise.

There is a view that book buyers seldom read reviews and that those who read reviews never buy books. It is certainly true that, say, the potboilers of Jeffrey Archer or Barbara Taylor Bradford can survive any number of snooty notices. Archer in particular is an example of an author who seems to thrive on adverse criticism. When he brings out a novel normally staid book pages assume a viciousness more characteristic of the cinema or theatre criticism. Writing in the *Sunday Times*, Nick Hornby described *Twelve Red Herrings* as '... the worst book I have ever read from cover to cover. It is dull, snobbish, ineptly written, condescending, sexist and occasionally disgraceful'. But he went on to concede that neither Archer nor his publisher would care what he thought. His faint hope was that 'sooner or later the reading public will tire of being taken for mugs, and will turn to someone who treats them like adults'. The sales for *Twelve Red Herrings* suggest that Nick Hornby has a long wait for his dream to come true.

Conversely, glowing approval from reviewers is no guarantee of a bookshop bonanza; while boosting the morale of a novelist fresh out of apprenticeship, a favourable review can do little, on its own, to delay his appearance on the remainder shelves. Could it be that the kind-heartedness shown by critics to most of the books they promote is counter-productive? Maybe book readers no longer believe what the papers say. Maybe, with *Guardian* writer James Wood, they have come to the awful realisation that 'Nobody tells the truth about contemporary literature.... That truth is too monotonous and too raw to be spoken. No critic - certainly no critic writing regularly - has a heart quite black enough to write what is true about most of the novels published this year: that they are poor, that they will not last beyond the flickering dream-life of their publication, that their writers should not have allowed them to appear, and that those writers are probably wasting their time writing at all.'

Wood sees the problem as one of 'ceaseless over-production of books, a crazy sleeplessness in which the critic is necessarily implicated'. He goes on:

> Music, art and even drama critics spend much of their time reviewing old and often venerable work. Only in literature is so much new and forgettable work endlessly produced; it is far easier to get your novel published than to have your symphony recorded by the LSO, or have your paintings exhibited at the Whitechapel. Standards are hazier in literature.

This, presumably, is why some books become bestsellers even when, on first appearance, they fail to attract the meanest notice in the national press. Peter Mayle's *A Year in Provence* was one such; so too was Sue Townsend's first excursion with Adrian Mole. Both had powerful kick-starts – the first a *Times* serialisation, the second a Radio 4 reading. Harder to explain is the phenomenon that was Alfred Wainwright, whose books on the Lakeland Fells sold a million copies without the author lifting more than his pen. According to his biographer, Hunter Davies:

> He started off self-publishing in 1955, which is like doing it in secret, then, when the *Westmoreland Gazette* took over in 1963, it was not exactly, well, dynamic. It had no publicity and no marketing department, being a little local printing firm based in Kendal. Even more amazing, it had no sales department, so no sales persons went around trying to rustle up orders. Those one million books flew till in the end he had become not just a bestselling author but a cult.

So that is the answer. Go for a strong local sale, rely on satisfied punters to spread the word and to hell with the critics. If there is sadness at being ignored by the establishment you can cry on the way to the bank.

THE GOOD ENGLISH GUIDE

English Usage in the 1990s

Compiled and written by

Godfrey Howard

This fascinating book takes English out of the
classroom and puts it in the real world.

Keep it alongside your dictionary: its 6000 entries give quick,
balanced, up-to-date answers to every question of grammar and
the use of words. And enjoy it as a celebration of English in all its
complexity, beauty, wit and poetry.

'What an achievement! Amazing what you can find out from this book.'
Fay Weldon

'Splendidly up-to-date. The Good English Guide *will
certainly be at my bedside!'*
Sue MacGregor

'A Fowler for the age.'
Keith Waterhouse *Daily Mail*

*'It could become a kind of writer's bible . . . essential
bookshelf material for every writer.'*
Writing Magazine

'One of the few books I've paid full price for over the past year!'
Publishing Director, David & Charles

Published by Macmillan, £18.99 hardback, £12.99 paperback

National Newspapers

Daily Express
Ludgate House, 245 Blackfriars Road, London
SE1 9UX
☎0171 928 8000   Fax 0171 620 1654
Owner *United Newspapers*
Editor *Richard Addis*
Circulation 1.26 million

The general rule of thumb is to approach in writing with an idea; all departments are prepared to look at an outline without commitment. Ideas welcome but already receives many which are 'too numerous to count'.
   News Editor *Alastair McCall*
   Diary Editor *John McEntee (William Hickey)*
   Features Editor *Niki Chesworth*
   Literary Editor *Belinda Harley*
   Sports Editor *David Emery*
   Planning Editor (News Desk) should be circulated with copies of official reports, press releases, etc., to ensure news desk cover at all times.
Saturday magazine **Editor** *Nigel Horne*
   Payment depends on the nature of the article accepted.

Daily Mail
Northcliffe House, 2 Derry Street,
Kensington, London W8 5TT
☎0171 938 6000   Fax 0171 937 4463
Owner *Lord Rothermere*
Editor *Paul Dacre*
Circulation 2.03 million

In-house feature writers and regular columnists provide much of the material. Photo-stories and crusading features often appear; it's essential to hit the right note to be a successful *Mail* writer. Close scrutiny of the paper is strongly advised. Not a good bet for the unseasoned. Accepts news on savings, building societies, insurance, unit trusts, legal rights, tax and small businesses.
   News Editor *Ian MacGregor*
   Diary Editor *Nigel Dempster*
   Features Editor *To be appointed*
   Sports Editor *Cameron Kelleher*
Femail *Jackie Annesley*
Weekend: Saturday supplement **Editor** *Aileen Doherty*

Daily Mirror
1 Canada Square, Canary Wharf, London
E14 5AP
☎0171 293 3000   Fax 0171 293 3409
Owner *Mirror Group Newspapers*
Editor *Piers Morgan*
Circulation 2.51 million

No freelance opportunities for the inexperienced, but strong writers who understand what the tabloid market demands are always needed.
   News Editor *Eugene Duffy*
   Diary Editor *Matthew Wright*
   Features Editor *Tina Weaver*
   Political Editor *John Williams*
   Sports Editor *David Balmforth*
   Women's Page *Jane Johnson*

Daily Record
Anderston Quay, Glasgow G3 8DA
☎0141 248 7000   Fax 0141 242 3145/6
Owner *Mirror Group Newspapers*
Editor *Terry Quinn*
Circulation 748,470

Mass-market Scottish tabloid. Freelance material is generally welcome.
   News Editor *Murray Morse*
   Features Editor *Alan Rennie*
   Education *Tom Little*
   Political Editor *Tom Brown*
   Women's Page *Julia Clarke*

Daily Sport
19 Great Ancoats Street, Manchester M60 4BT
☎0161 236 4466   Fax 0161 236 4535
Owner *Sport Newspapers Ltd*
Editor *Jeff McGowan*
Circulation 350,000

Tabloid catering for young male readership. Unsolicited material welcome; send to News Editor.
   News/Feature Editor *Neil MacKay*
   Sports Editor *Phil Smith*

Daily Star
Ludgate House, 245 Blackfriars Road, London
SE1 9UX
☎0171 928 8000   Fax 0171 922 7960
Owner *United Newspapers*
Editor *Philip Walker*

Circulation 671,508

In competition with *The Sun* for off-the-wall news and features. Freelance opportunities almost non-existent. Most material is written in-house or by regular outsiders.

News Editor *Hugh Whittow*
Features Editor *Brian Dunlea*
Entertainments *Pat Codd*
Sports Editor *Phil Rostron*
Women's Page *Karen Livermore*

The Daily Telegraph

1 Canada Square, Canary Wharf, London
E14 5DT
☎0171 538 5000   Fax 0171 538 6242

Owner *Conrad Black*
Editor *Charles Moore*
Circulation 1.27 million

Unsolicited mss not generally welcome – 'all are carefully read and considered, but only about one in a thousand is accepted for publication'. As they receive about 20 weekly, this means about one a year. Contenders should approach the paper in writing, making clear their authority for writing on that subject. No fiction.

News Editor *Martin Newland* Tip-offs or news reports from *bona fide* journalists. Must phone the news desk in first instance. Maximum 200 words. *Payment* minimum £10 (tip).

Arts Editor *Sarah Crompton*
Business Editor *Roland Gribben*
Diary Editor *David Rennie* Always interested in diary pieces; contact *Peterborough* (Diary column).
Education *John Clare*
Environment *Charles Clover*
Features Editor/Women's Page *Corinna Honan* Most material supplied by commission from established contributors. New writers are tried out by arrangement with the features editor. Approach in writing. Maximum 1500 words.
Literary Editor *John Coldstream*
Political Editor *George Jones*
Sports Editor *David Welch* Occasional opportunities for specialised items.
Payment by arrangement.

Telegraph Magazine: Saturday colour supplement. **Editor** *Emma Soames*. **Young Telegraph** (see under **Magazines**).

The European

200 Gray's Inn Road, London WC1X 8NE
☎0171 418 7777   Fax 0171 353 4386

Owner *The Barclay Brothers*
Editor *Charles Garside*

Circulation 160,511 (excl. US sales)

LAUNCHED May 1990. Three-section colour weekly aimed at a European weekend market. News and current affairs, business, sport, European affairs, society and politics, plus European arts and lifestyle section, *The European Magazine*. Freelance contributions from recognised experts in their field will be considered. First approach in writing.

News/Features *David Meilton*
Business *Tim Castle*

The European Magazine *Andrew Harvey*
Payment by arrangement.

Financial Times

1 Southwark Bridge, London SE1 9HL
☎0171 873 3000   Fax 0171 873 3076

Owner *Pearson*
Editor *Richard Lambert*
Circulation 302,175

FOUNDED 1888. Business and finance-orientated certainly, but by no means as featureless as some suppose. All feature ideas must be discussed with the department's editor in advance. Not snowed under with unsolicited contributions – they get less than any other national newspaper. Approach in writing with ideas in the first instance.

News Editor *Julia Cuthbertson*
Features Editor *John Willman*
Arts/Literary Editor *Annalena McAfee*
City/Financial Editor *Jane Fuller*
Diary Editor *Bill Hall*
Education *John Authers*
Environment *Leyla Boulton*
Political Editor *Robert Peston*
Small Businesses *Richard Gourlay*
Sports Editor *Peter Aspden*
Women's Page *Lucia van der Post*

The Guardian

119 Farringdon Road, London EC1R 3ER
☎0171 278 2332
Fax 0171 837 2114/833 8342

Owner *The Scott Trust*
Editor *Alan Rusbridger*
Circulation 401,602

Of all the nationals *The Guardian* probably offers the greatest opportunities for freelance writers, if only because it has the greatest number of specialised pages which use freelance work. But mss must be directed at a specific slot.

News Editor *Paul Webster* No opportunities except in those regions where there is presently no local contact for news stories.

Arts Editor *Claire Armitstead*
City/Financial Editor *Alex Brummer*
On Line Science, computing and technology. A major part of Thursday's paper, almost all written by freelancers. Expertise essential – but not a trade page; written for 'the interested man in the street' and from the user's point of view. Computing/communications (Internet) articles should be addressed to *Jack Schofield*; science articles to *Tim Radford*. Mss on disk or by e-mail (online@guardian.co.uk).
Diary Editor *Matthew Norman*
Education Editor *John Carvel* Expert pieces on modern education welcome. Maximum 1000 words.
Environment *John Vidal*
Features Editor *Roger Alton* Receives up to 30 unsolicited mss a day; these are passed on to relevant page editors.
Guardian Society *Malcolm Dean* Focuses on social change in the 90s – the forces affecting us, from environment to government policies. Top journalists and outside commentators on nine editorial pages.
Literary Editor *Stephen Moss*
Media Editor *John Mulholland* Approximately six pieces a week, plus diary. Outside contributions are considered. All aspects of modern media, advertising, PR, consumer trends in arts/entertainments. Background insight important. Best approach is a note, followed by phone call.
Political Editor *Mike White*
Sports Editor *Mike Averis*
Women's Page *Clare Longrigg* Now runs three days a week. Unsolicited ideas used if they show an appreciation of the page in question. Maximum 800-1000 words.

Guardian Weekend Saturday issue. **Editor** *Deborah Orr*. **The Guide** *Ben Olins*.

The Herald (Glasgow)
195 Albion Street, Glasgow G1 1QP
☎0141 552 6255　　　Fax 0141 552 2288
Owner *Caledonian Newspaper Publishing*
Editor *George McKechnie*
Circulation 106,192

The oldest national newspaper in the English-speaking world, The Herald, which dropped its 'Glasgow' prefix in February 1992, returned to Scottish hands in mid-1992 following a management buy-out and the establishment of Caledonian Newspaper Publishing. Lively, quality Scottish daily which is expanding into a national Scottish broadsheet. Approach with idea in writing or by phone in first instance.

News Editor *Colin McDiarmid*
Arts Editor *Keith Bruce*
Business Editor *Ronald Dundas*
Diary *Tom Shields*
Education *Barclay McBain*
Environment *Liz Buie*
Sports Editor *Iain Scott*
Women's Page *Jackie McGlone*

The Independent
1 Canada Square, Canary Wharf, London E14 5AP
☎0171 293 2000　　　Fax 0171 293 2435
Owner *Mirror Group Newspapers*
Editor *Andrew Marr*
Circulation 290,870

FOUNDED October 1986. The first new quality national in over 130 years. Particularly strong on its arts/media coverage, with a high proportion of feature material. Theoretically, opportunities for freelancers are good. However, unsolicited mss are not welcome; most pieces originate in-house or from known and trusted outsiders. Ideas should be submitted in writing. The newspaper runs annual travel writing awards. Details, which vary from year to year, are advertised in the paper.
News Editor *David Felton*
Features Editor *To be appointed*
Arts Editor *Mark Pappenheim*
Business Editor *Jeremy Warner*
City/Financial Editor *Peter Rodgers*
Education *Judith Judd*
Environment *Nicholas Schoon*
Literary Editor *John Walsh*
Political Editor *Tony Bevins*
Sports Editor *Paul Newman*

Independent Magazine: Saturday supplement.
Editor *Michael Watts*

Independent on Sunday
1 Canada Square, Canary Wharf, London E14 5AP
☎0171 293 2000　　　Fax 0171 293 2435
Owner *Mirror Group Newspapers*
Editor *Peter Wilby*
Circulation 321,589

FOUNDED 1986. Regular columnists contribute most material but feature opportunites exist. Approach with idea in first instance.
News Editor *Mike McCarthy*
Arts Editor *Laurence Earle*
Commissioning Editor, Features *Isabel O'Keeffe*
City/Financial Editor *To be appointed*
Environment *Geoffrey Lean*

Political Editor *Paul Routledge*
Sports Editor *Paul Newman*

International Herald Tribune

181 avenue Charles de Gaulle, 92200 Neuilly-
sur-Seine, France
☎0033 1 4143 9300   Fax 0033 1 4143 9338
Editor *John Vinocur*
Circulation 192,195

Published in France, Monday to Saturday, and
circulated in Europe, the Middle East, North
Africa, the Far East and the USA. General
news, business and financial, arts and leisure.
Use regular freelance contributors. Query letter
to features editor in first instance.
Features Editor *Katherine Knorr*
News Editor *Walter Wells*

The Mail on Sunday

Northcliffe House, 2 Derry Street,
Kensington, London W8 5TS
☎0171 938 6000   Fax 0171 937 3829
Owner *Lord Rothermere*
Editor *Jonathon Holborrow*
Circulation 2.08 million

Sunday paper with a high proportion of newsy
features and articles. Experience and judge-
ment required to break into its band of regular
feature writers.
News Editor *Jon Ryan*
City/Financial Editor *Bill Kay*
Diary Editor *Nigel Dempster*
Features Editor *Andy Bull*
Literary Editor *Paula Johnson*
Political Editor *Joe Murphy*
Sports Editor *Roger Kelly*

Night & Day: review supplement. **Editor**
Simon Kelner

You – The Mail on Sunday Magazine: colour
supplement. Many feature articles, supplied en-
tirely by freelance writers.
Editor *Dee Nolan*
Features Editor *Jane Phillimore*
Arts Editor *Liz Galbraith*

Morning Star

1-3 Ardleigh Road, London N1 4HS
☎0171 254 0033   Fax 0171 254 5950
Owner *Peoples Press Printing Society*
Editor *John Haylett*
Circulation 9,000

Not to be confused with the *Daily Star*, the
Morning Star is the farthest left national daily.
Those with a penchant for a Marxist reading of

events and ideas can try their luck, though
feature space is as competitive here as in the
other nationals.
News/Arts/Features/Women's Page
Paul Corry
Political Editor *Mike Ambrose*
Sports Editor *Amanda Kendal*

The News of the World

1 Virginia Street, London E1 9XR
☎0171 782 4000 Fax 0171 488 3262 (features)
Owner *Rupert Murdoch*
Editor *Phil Hall*
Circulation 4.69 million

Highest circulation Sunday paper. Freelance
contributions welcome. Features Department
welcomes tips and ideas. Approach by fax in
first instance with follow-up phone call.
News Editor *Alex Marunchak*
Features Editor *Ray Levine*
Literary Editor *Roy Stockdill*
Sports Editor *Mike Dunn*
Women's Page *Vicky Bubb*

Sunday Magazine: colour supplement. **Editor**
Judy McGuire. Showbiz interviews and strong
human-interest features make up most of the
content, but there are no strict rules about
what is 'interesting'. Unsolicited mss and ideas
welcome.

The Observer

119 Farringdon Road, London EC1R 3ER
☎0171 278 2332   Fax 0171 713 4250
Owner *Guardian Newspapers Ltd*
Editor *Will Hutton*
Circulation 469,412

FOUNDED 1791. Acquired by Guardian Newspapers from Lonrho in May 1993. Occupies the
middle ground of Sunday newspaper politics.
Unsolicited material is not generally welcome,
'except from distinguished, established writers'.
Receives far too many unsolicited offerings
already. No news, fiction or special page oppor-
tunities. The newspaper runs annual competi-
tions which change from year to year. Details are
advertised in the newspaper.
News Editor *Paul Dunn*
Arts Editor *Jane Ferguson*
Business Editor *Ben Laurance*
City Editor *Heather Connon*
Education *Natasha Narayan*
Features Editor *Lisa O'Kelly*
Literary Editor *Tim Adams*

Life: arts and lifestyle supplement. **Editor**
Justine Picardy.

The People

1 Canada Square, Canary Wharf, London
E14 5AP
☎0171 293 3000   Fax 0171 293 3810
Owner *Mirror Group Newspapers*
Acting Editor *Len Gould*
Circulation 2.08 million

Slightly up-market version of *The News of the World*. Keen on exposés and big-name gossip. Interested in ideas for investigative articles. Phone in first instance.
   News Editor *Danny Buckland*
   City/Financial Editor *Cathy Gunn*
   Features Editor/Women's Page *Tom Petrie*
   Political Editor *Nigel Nelson*
   Sports Editor *Ed Barry*

Yes! Magazine **Editor** *Tom Petrie*. Approach by phone with ideas in first instance.

Scotland on Sunday

20 North Bridge, Edinburgh EH1 1YT
☎0131 225 2468   Fax 0131 220 2443
Owner *The Barclay Brothers*
Editor *Brian Groom*
Circulation 90,270

Scotland's top-selling quality broadsheet. Welcomes ideas rather than finished articles.
   News Editor *William Paul*
   Features Editor *Stewart Hennessey*
   Political *Kenneth Farquharson*

Scotland on Sunday Magazine: colour supplement. **Editor** *Fiona Macleod*. Features on personalities, etc.

The Scotsman

20 North Bridge, Edinburgh EH1 1YT
☎0131 225 2468   Fax 0131 226 7420
Owner *The Barclay Brothers*
Editor *Jim Seaton*
Circulation 76,961

Scotland's national newspaper. Many unsolicited mss come in, and stand a good chance of being read, although a small army of regulars supply much of the feature material not written in-house.
   News Editor *Ian Stewart*
   City/Financial Editor *Martin Flanagan*
   Education *Graeme Wilson*
   Environment *Auslan Cramb*
   Features Editor *Alan Rennie*
   Literary Editor *Catherine Lockerbie*
   Women's Page *Gillian Glover*

Weekend **Editor** *Maggie Lennon*. Includes book reviews, travel articles, etc.

The Sun

1 Virginia Street, London E1 9XP
☎0171 782 4000   Fax 0171 488 3253
Owner *Rupert Murdoch*
Editor *Stuart Higgins*
Circulation 4.06 million

Highest circulation daily. Right-wing, populist outlook; very keen on gossip, pop stars, TV soap, scandals and exposés of all kinds. No room for non-professional feature writers; 'investigative journalism' of a certain hue is always in demand, however.
   News Editor *Glenn Goodey*
   Features Editor *Mike Ridley*
   Sports Editor *Paul Ridley*
   Women's Page *Jane Moore*

Sunday Business

3 Cavendish Square, London W1M 9HA
☎0171 468 6000   Fax 0171 436 3797
Owner *Business Newspapers UK Ltd*
Editor *Tim Rubython*

Launched April 1996. New national newspaper dedicated entirely to business. Consists of five sections: News, Money & Life, Bloomberg Trading Week, Computer Age and a colour magazine – *Business & Fortune*.
   Features/Business Editor *Bob Lea*
   Political Editor *Adrian Lithgow*

Sunday Express

Ludgate House, 245 Blackfriars Road, London
SE1 9UX
☎0171 928 8000   Fax 0171 620 1656
Owner *United Newspapers*
Editor *Sue Douglas*
Circulation 1.33 million

FOUNDED 1918. Unsolicited mss are generally welcome. Approach in writing with ideas.
   News Editor *Shan Lancaster* Occasional news features by experienced journalists only. All submissions must be preceded by ideas. 750 words.
   Features Editor *Neil Maxwell* General features (1000 words); profiles of personalities (900 words); showbiz features (1000–1500 words).
   Literary Editor *Kate Saunders*
   Sports Editor *Dean Morse*

Sunday Express Magazine: colour supplement. **Editor** *Jean Carr*. No unsolicited mss. All contributions are commissioned. Ideas in writing only.
   Payment negotiable.

Sunday Life

124–144 Royal Avenue, Belfast BT1 1EB
☎01232 264300   Fax 01232 554507
Owner *Trinity International Holdings plc*
Editor *Martin Lindsay*
Circulation 98,612

   Deputy Editor *Dave Culbert*
   Sports Editor *Jim Gracey*

Sunday Mail

Anderston Quay, Glasgow G3 8DA
☎0141 248 7000   Fax 0141 242 3145/6
Owner *Mirror Group Newspapers*
Editor *To be appointed*
Circulation 884,279

Popular Scottish Sunday paper.
   News Editor *Brian Steel*
   Features Editor *Rob Bruce*
   Political Editor *Angus McLeod*
   Women's Page *Melanie Reid*
Sunday Mail 2: weekly supplement. **Editor** *Jeanette Harkess*.

Sunday Mirror

1 Canada Square, Canary Wharf, London
E14 5AP
☎0171 293 3000   Fax 0171 293 3939
Owner *Mirror Group Newspapers*
Acting Editor *Jim Cassidy*
Circulation 2.49 million

Receives anything up to 100 unsolicited mss weekly. In general terms, these are welcome, though the paper patiently points out it has more time for contributors who have taken the trouble to study the market. Initial contact in writing preferred, except for live news situations. No fiction.
   News Editor *Chris Boffey* The news desk is very much in the market for tip-offs and inside information. Contributors would be expected to work with staff writers on news stories.
   City/Financial Editor *Diane Boliver*
   Features Editor *Clive Nelson* 'Anyone who has obviously studied the market will be dealt with constructively and courteously.' Cherishes its record as a breeding ground for new talent.
   Sports Editor *Bill Bradshaw*
Sunday Mirror Magazine: colour supplement. **Editor** *Kate Bravery*.

Sunday Post

2 Albert Square, Dundee DD1 9QJ
☎01382 223131   Fax 01382 201064
Owner *D. C. Thomson & Co. Ltd*

Editor *Russell Reid*
Circulation 904,504

The highest circulation Scottish Sunday paper. Contributions should be addressed to the editor.
   News Editor *Iain MacKinnon*

Sunday Post Magazine: monthly colour supplement. **Editor** *Maggie Dun*.

Sunday Sport

19 Great Ancoats Street, Manchester
M60 4BT
☎0161 236 4466   Fax 0161 236 4535
Owner *David Sullivan*
Editor *Jon Wise*
Circulation 284,280

FOUNDED 1986. Sunday tabloid catering for a particular sector of the male 18–35 readership. As concerned with 'glamour' (for which, read: 'page 3') as with human interest, news, features and sport. Regular short story competition (maximum 1000 words). Unsolicited mss are welcome; receives about 90 a week. Approach should be made by phone in the case of news and sports items, by letter for features. All material should be addressed to the news editor.
   News Editor *Mark Harris* Off-beat news, human interest, preferably with photographs.
   Features Editor *Mark Harris* Regular items: glamour, showbiz and television, as well as general interest.
   Sports Editor *Marc Smith* Hard-hitting sports stories on major soccer clubs and their personalities, plus leading clubs/people in other sports. Strong quotations to back up the news angle essential.
   Payment negotiable and on publication.

Sunday Telegraph

1 Canada Square, Canary Wharf, London
E14 5DT
☎0171 538 5000   Fax 0171 513 2504
Owner *Conrad Black*
Editor *Dominic Lawson*
Circulation 655,963

Right-of-centre quality Sunday paper (meaning it has the least tendency to bend its ear to the scandals of the hour). Traditionally formal, it has pepped up its image to attract a younger readership. Unsolicited material from untried writers is rarely ever used. Contact with idea and details of track record.
   News Editor *Chris Anderson*
   City/Financial Editor *Neil Bennett*
   Features Editor *Rebecca Nicolson*

Arts Editor *John Preston*
Literary Editor *Miriam Gross*
Diary Editor *Sunny Tucker*
Sports Editor *Colin Gibson*
Women's Page *Rebecca Nicolson*
Sunday Telegraph Magazine Rebecca Tyrrel

The Sunday Times
1 Pennington Street, London E1 9XW
☎0171 782 5000   Fax 0171 782 5658
Owner *Rupert Murdoch*
Editor *John Witherow*
Circulation 1.28 million

FOUNDED 1820. Tendency to be anti-establishment, with a strong crusading investigative tradition. Approach the relevant editor with an idea in writing. Close scrutiny of the style of each section of the paper is strongly advised before sending mss. No fiction. All fees by negotiation.

News Editor *Mark Skipworth* Opportunities are very rare.

News Review Editor *Martin Ivens* Submissions are always welcome, but the paper commissions its own, uses staff writers or works with literary agents, by and large. The features sections where most opportunities exist are *Style & Travel* and *The Culture*.

Arts Editor *David Mills*
Economics Editor *David Smith*
Education *Cathy Scott-Clark*
Environment *Jonathan Leake*
Literary Editor *Geordie Greig*
Sports Editor *Nick Pitt*
Style Editor *Jeremy Langmead*

Sunday Times Magazine: colour supplement. **Editor** *Robin Morgan*. No unsolicited material. Write with ideas in first instance.

The Times
1 Pennington Street, London E1 9XN
☎0171 782 5000   Fax 0171 488 3242
Owner *Rupert Murdoch*
Editor *Peter Stothard*
Circulation 674,802

Generally right (though columns/features can range in tone from diehard to libertarian). *The Times* receives a great many unsolicited offerings. Writers with feature ideas should approach by letter in the first instance. No fiction.

News Editor *James McManus*
Arts Editor *Richard Morrison*
Business/City/Financial Editor
    Lindsay Cook
Diary Editor *Andrew Yates*
Education *John O'Leary*
Environment *Nick Nuttall*
Executive Features Editor *Brian MacArthur*
Deputy Literary Editor *Erica Wagner*
Political Editor *Phil Webster*
Sports Editor *David Chappell*

Weekend Times **Editor** *Jane Owen*

The Times Magazine: Saturday supplement. **Editor** *Nicholas Wapshott*

Wales on Sunday
Thomson House, Havelock Street, Cardiff
CF1 1WR
☎01222 223333   Fax 01222 342462
Owner *Trinity International Holdings plc*
Editor *Robin Fletcher*
Circulation 59,311

LAUNCHED 1989. Tabloid with sports supplement. Does not welcome unsolicited mss.

News Editor *Mark Hindle*
Features/Women's Page *Mike Smith*
Sports Editor *Mark Dawson*

Freelance Rates – Newspapers

Freelance rates vary enormously. The following minimum rates, negotiated by the **National Union of Journalists**, should be treated as guidelines. Most work can command higher fees from employers whether or not they have NUJ agreements. It is up to freelancers to negotiate the best deal they can.

National Newspapers and News Agencies

Words

(A premium of 50% should be added to all the rates listed below for exclusive coverage.)

Home news: £21+ per 200 words or part thereof
Foreign news: £21+ per 100 words
City and business news: £21+ per 100 words
Sports match reports: Minimum £63.

Sunday Papers

Features: £210–315+ per 1000 words
Reviews: £157.50–200+ per 1000 words

National Daily Papers

Features: £168–210+ per 1000 words
Reviews: £157.50–183.75+ per 1000 words
Listings: £131.25–157.50+ per 1000 words
Gazette: £199.50+ per 1000 words

Diary paragraphs: Gossip column items, art reviews and notices: these attract a higher fee than the minimum per word since they are of restricted length. Lead items – about £105, others £47.25.

Photographic Fees

National papers day rate: £136.50, half-day: £84 (some papers may work on an assignment rate rather than half-day rates).
Studio or location work or commissions requiring special equipment/techniques (e.g. aerial): £682.50 per day.
Black and White reproduction fees for one British use only in a national newspaper:

Up to (sq in)	20	20–30	30–50	50–80	Over 80
Minimum	£71.40	£80.85	£91.35	£105	by negotiation

Colour reproduction fees: by negotiation.
Cover and front page: 50% extra.
Photographs ordered and accepted but not used: at least £71.40.
Print fee: at least £6.30.

Cartoons and Illustrations

Cartoon size: 1 column £94.50, thereafter subject to individual negotiation.
Colour: Double the above rate. (All rates quoted are for one-time British use.)

Colour Supplements

Words

Rates are high. Commissioning editors will pay by 1000 words or by the page.
A fee should not be less than £262.50+ for up to 1000 words.

Photographic Fees

Commissioned work : about £294 a day plus expenses; £168 per half-day.
Studio work: £682.50
Colour reproduction fees:

Up to:	¼ page	½ page	¾ page	full page
Minimum	£178.50	£244.65	£288.75	£346.50

Cartoons, Illustrations, Crosswords

Should be at least double the national newspaper rate.

Crosswords

Under 15x15: at least £96.60; 15x15 and upwards: at least £111.30.

Provincial Newspapers (England & Wales)

Words

Minimum News Lineage Rate Weekly newspapers: £1.60 for up to and including
10 lines; 15.7p per line thereafter. Daily, evening and Sunday newspapers:
£2.79 for up to and including 10 lines; 25p per line thereafter.

Minimum Feature Rate (for features submitted on spec.) Weekly newspapers:
£1.76 for up to and including 10 lines; 17p per line thereafter. Daily, evening
and Sunday newspapers: £3.09 for up to and including 10 lines; 25p per line
thereafter.

Commissioned features Vary from paper to paper, taking into account, when
negotiating, circulation (including the area), plus advertising revenue per page.

Photographic Reproduction Fees

Black and White	*Daily/Evening/Sunday*	*Freesheet/Weekly*
Up to 10 sq in	£19.43	£13.65
Over 10 and up to 50 sq in	£25.20	£16.28
Over 50 and up to 80 sq in	£38.33	£25.20
Over 80 and up to 150 sq in	by negotiation	by negotiation

Colour: Daily newspapers minimum rate of £25.70 for colour pictures of less than 8 sq in which do not exceed single column width. For other colour pictures, minimum fees will be as for black and white above, plus 25% subject to a minimum rate of £30.19 for daily and Sunday papers, £20.21 for weeklies.

Cartoons
Single Frame: at least £49.88
Feature Strip (up to 4 frames): £91.35
Crosswords: at least £56.70

Provincial Newspapers (Scotland)

Words
Minimum News and Sport Lineage Rate At least 20.8p per line, subject to a minimum payment of £2.57 for each contribution. Copy used as a front page lead: at least 41.7p a line.
Minimum Feature Rate At least £76.86 per 1000 words.

Photography
Black and White Commissioned: £22.31; submitted: £21.26
Colour By negotiation.

Regional Newspapers

Regional newspapers are listed in alphabetical order under town. Thus the *Evening Standard* appears under 'L' for London; the *Lancashire Evening Post* under 'P' for Preston.

Aberdeen
Evening Express (Aberdeen)
PO Box 43, Lang Stracht, Mastrick, Aberdeen AB9 8AF
☎01224 690222　　　　Fax 01224 699575
Owner *Northcliffe Newspapers Group Ltd*
Editor *Geoff Teather*
Circulation 67,742

Circulates in Aberdeen and the Grampian region. Local, national and international news and pictures, family finance and property news. Unsolicited mss welcome 'if on a controlled basis'.
　News Editor *Yvonne Flynn* Freelance news contributors welcome.
　Features Editor *Raymond Anderson* Women, fashion, showbiz, health, hobbies, property – anything will be considered on its merits.
　Sports Editor *Alan Brown*
　Women's Page *Karen Grant*
　Payment £30–60.

The Press and Journal
PO Box 43, Lang Stracht, Mastrick, Aberdeen AB9 8AF
☎01224 690222　　　　Fax 01224 663575
Owner *Northcliffe Newspapers Group Ltd*
Editor *Derek Tucker*
Circulation 107,138

Circulates in Aberdeen, Grampians, Highlands, Tayside, Orkney, Shetland and the Western Isles. A well-established regional daily which is said to receive more unsolicited mss a week than the *Sunday Mirror*. Unsolicited mss are nevertheless welcome; approach in writing with ideas. No fiction.
　News Editor *David Knight* Wide variety of hard or off-beat news and features relating especially, but not exclusively, to the North of Scotland.
　Sports Editor *Jim Dolan*
　Women's Page *Kate Yuill*
　Payment by arrangement.

Aylesford
Kent Today
Messenger House, New Hythe Lane, Larkfield, Aylesford, Kent ME20 6SG
☎01622 717880　　　　Fax 01622 715225
Owner *Kent Messenger Group*
Editor *C. Stewart*
Circulation 24,148

Assistant Editor (Production) *Shane Jarvis*
　Community Editor *David Jones*
　Sports Editor *Mike Rees*
　Women's Page *Jane Millington*
　Business Editor *Trevor Sturgess*

Barrow in Furniss
North West Evening Mail
Abbey Road, Barrow in Furness, Cumbria LA14 5QS
☎01229 821835　　　　Fax 01229 840164
Owner *CN Group Ltd*
Editor *Donald Martin*
Circulation 20,673

All editorial material should be addressed to the editor.
　Features Editor *Bill Myers*.
　Sports Editor *Leo Clarke*.

Basildon
Evening Echo
Newspaper House, Chester Hall Lane, Basildon, Essex SS14 3BL
☎01268 522792　　　　Fax 01268 282884
Owner *Westminster Press*
Editor *Bob Dimond*
Circulation 51,899

Relies almost entirely on staff and regular outside contributors, but will consider material sent on spec. Approach the editor in writing with ideas. Although the paper is Basildon-based, its largest circulation is in the Southend area.

Bath
The Bath Chronicle
33/34 Westgate Street, Bath, Avon BA1 1EW
☎01225 444044   Fax 01225 445969
Owner *Westminster Press (Media in Wessex)*
Editor *David Gledhill*
Circulation 17,720

Local news and features especially welcomed.
   Deputy Editor *John McCready*
   News Editor *Paul Wiltshire*
   Features Editor *Andrew Knight*
   Sports Editor *Neville Smith*

Belfast
Belfast Telegraph
Royal Avenue, Belfast BT1 1EB
☎01232 264000   Fax 01232 554506
Owner *Trinity International Holdings plc*
Editor *Edmund Curran*
Circulation 133,132

Weekly business supplement.
   Deputy Editor *Nick Garbutt*
   News/Features Editor *Janet Devlin*
   Sports Editor *Sammy Hamill*
   Business Editor *Martina Purdy*

The Irish News
113/117 Donegall Street, Belfast BT1 2GE
☎01232 322226   Fax 01232 337505
Owner *Irish News Ltd*
Editor *Tom Collins*
Circulation 44,967

All material to appropriate editor (phone to check), or to the news desk.
   Deputy Editor *Noel Doran*
   Head of Content *Ben Webster, Fiona McGarry*
   Arts Editor *Colin McAlpin*
   Sports Editor *Stephen O'Reilly*
   Women's Page *Ann Molloy*

Ulster News Letter
46-56 Boucher Crescent, Belfast BT12 6QY
☎01232 680000   Fax 01232 664412
Owner *Century Newspapers Ltd*
Editor *Geoff Martin*
Circulation 33,753

Supplements: *Farming Life* (weekly); *Shopping News; Belfast Newsletter.*
   Deputy Editor *Mike Chapman*
   Assistant Editor *Billy Kennedy*
   News Editor *Harry Robinson*
   Features Editor *Geoff Hill*
   Sports Editor *Brian Millar*
   Fashion & Lifestyle/Property Editor
     Sandra Chapman

Birmingham
Birmingham Evening Mail
28 Colmore Circus, Queensway, Birmingham B4 6AX
☎0121 236 3366   Fax 0121 233 0271
Owner *Midland Independent Newspapers plc*
Editor *Ian Dowell*
Circulation 197,532

Freelance contributions are welcome, particularly topics of interest to the West Midlands and Women's Page pieces offering original and lively comment.
   News Editor *Norman Stinchcombe*
   Features Editor *Paul Cole*
   Women's Page *Briony Jones*

Birmingham Post
28 Colmore Circus, Queensway, Birmingham B4 6AX
☎0121 236 3366 Fax 0121 233 0271/625 1105
Owner *Midland Independent Newspapers plc*
Editor *Nigel Hastilow*
Circulation 26,090

One of the country's leading regional newspapers. Freelance contributions are welcome. Topics of interest to the West Midlands and pieces offering lively, original comment are particularly welcome.
   News Editor *Chris Russon*
   Features Editor *Peter Bacon*
   Women's Page *Ros Dodd*

Sunday Mercury (Birmingham)
28 Colmore Circus, Birmingham B4 6AZ
☎0121 236 3366   Fax 0121 625 1105
Owner *Birmingham Post & Mail Ltd*
Editor *Peter Whitehouse*
Circulation 144,707

   News Editor *Bob Haywood*
   Features Editor *Stefan Bartlett*
   Sports Editor *Roger Skidmore*

Blackburn
Lancashire Evening Telegraph
Newspaper House, High Street, Blackburn, Lancashire BB1 1HT
☎01254 678678   Fax 01254 680429
Owner *Reed Northern Newspapers Ltd*
Editor *Peter Butterfield*
Circulation 45,381

News stories and feature material with an East Lancashire flavour (a local angle, or written by

local people) welcome. Approach in writing with an idea in the first instance. No fiction.
News/Features/Women's Page Editor *Nick Nunn*

Blackpool
Evening Gazette (Blackpool)
PO Box 20, Preston New Road, Blackpool, Lancashire FY4 4AU
☎01253 839999   Fax 01253 766799
Owner *United Newspapers*
Managing Editor *Philip Welsh*
Circulation 44,578

Unsolicited mss welcome in theory. Approach in writing with an idea. Supplements: *Monday Green* (sport); *Eve* (women, Tuesday); *Wheels* (motoring, Wednesday); *Property* (Thursday); *Sevendays* (entertainment & leisure, Saturday).
Head of Content *Ian Hamilton*
Sports Editor *Tony Durkin*

Bolton
Bolton Evening News
Newspaper House, Churchgate, Bolton, Lancashire BL1 1DE
☎01204 522345   Fax 01204 365068
Owner *To be confirmed*
Editor *Andrew Smith*
Circulation 43,806

Business, children's page, travel, local services, motoring, fashion and cookery.
News Editor *Melvyn Horrocks*
Features Editor/Women's Page *Angela Kelly*

Bournemouth
Evening Echo
Richmond Hill, Bournemouth, Dorset BH2 6HH
☎01202 554601   Fax 01202 292115
Owner *Southern Newspapers plc*
Editor *Gareth Weekes*
Circulation 46,808

FOUNDED 1900. Has a strong features content and invites specialist articles, particularly on unusual and contemporary subjects but only with a local angle. Supplements: business, gardening, family matters, motoring. Regular features on weddings, property, books, local history, green issues, the Channel coast. All editorial material should be addressed to the **News Editor** *Andy Bissell*.
Payment on publication.

Bradford
Telegraph & Argus (Bradford)
Hall Ings, Bradford, West Yorkshire BD1 1JR
☎01274 729511   Fax 01274 723634
Owner *Bradford & District Newspapers*
Editor *Perry Austin-Clarke*
Circulation 57,213

No unsolicited mss – approach in writing with samples of work. No fiction.
Head of Content *Rob Irvine* Local features and general interest. Showbiz pieces. 600–1000 words (maximum 1500).
Sports Editor *Peter Rowe*
Women's Editor *Sharon Dale*

Brighton
Evening Argus
Argus House, Crowhurst Road, Hollingbury, Brighton, East Sussex BN1 8AR
☎01273 544544   Fax 01273 505703
Owner *Southern Publishing (Westminster Press) Ltd*
Editor *Chris Fowler*
Circulation 64,264
News Editor *Claire Byrd*
Sports Editor *Chris Giles*
Women's Page *Winifred Blackmore*

Bristol
Evening Post
Temple Way, Bristol, Avon BS99 7HD
☎0117 9260080   Fax 0117 9279568
Owner *Bristol Evening Post plc*
Editor *Adrian Faber*
Circulation 84,521

Unsolicited mss welcome; receives about a dozen a week. Approach in writing with ideas.
News Editor *Rob Stokes*
Features Editor *Matthew Shelley*
Sports Editor *Chris Bartlett*

Western Daily Press
Temple Way, Bristol, Avon BS99 7HD
☎0117 9260080   Fax 0117 9290971
Owner *Bristol United Press Ltd*
Editor *Ian Beales*
Circulation 60,451
News Editor *Steve Hughes*
Features Editor *Jane Riddiford*
Sports Editor *Bill Beckett*
Women's Page *Lynda Cleasby*

Burton-upon-Trent
Burton Mail
65-68 High Street, Burton upon Trent,
Staffordshire DE14 1LE
☎01283 512345   Fax 01283 510075/515351
Owner *Burton Daily Mail Ltd*
Editor *Brian Vertigen*
Circulation 20,030

Fashion, health, wildlife, environment, nostalgia,
financial/money (Monday); consumer, motoring
(Tuesday); women's world, rock (Wednesday);
property (Thursday); motoring, farming, what's
on (Friday); what's on, leisure (Saturday).
  News/Features Editor *Andrew Parker*
  Sports Editor *Rex Page*
  Women's Page *Corry Adger*

Cambridge
Cambridge Evening News
Winship Road, Milton, Cambridge CB4 6PP
☎01223 434434   Fax 01223 434415
Owner *Cambridge Newspapers Ltd*
Editor *Robert Satchwell*
Circulation 41,906

News Editor *John Conlon*
  Sports Editor *Mike Finnis*
  Women's Page *Angela Singer*

Cardiff
South Wales Echo
Thomson House, Cardiff CF1 1XR
☎01222 223333   Fax 01222 583624
Owner *Trinity International Holdings plc*
Editor *Keith Perch*
Circulation 77,618

Circulates in South and Mid Glamorgan and
Gwent.
  News Editor *Jeremy Clifford*
  Features Editor *Martin Wells*
  Sports Editor *Terry Phillips*

The Western Mail
Thomson House, Havelock Street, Cardiff
CF1 1WR
☎01222 223333   Fax 01222 583652
Owner *Trinity International Holdings plc*
Editor *Neil Fowler*
Circulation 64,172

Circulates in Cardiff, Merthyr Tydfil, Newport,
Swansea and towns and villages throughout
Wales. Mss welcome if of a topical nature, and
preferably of Welsh interest. No short stories or
travel. Approach in writing to the editor. 'Usual
subjects already well covered, e.g. motoring,
travel, books, gardening. We look for the
unusual.' Maximum 1000 words. Opportunities
also on women's page. Supplements: *Television
Wales; Arena; Welsh Homes; Country and Farming;
Business; Sport.*
  Head of News & Features *Alan Edmunds*
  Sports Editor *Mark Tattersall*

Carlisle
News & Star
Newspaper House, Dalston Road, Carlisle,
Cumbria CA2 5UA
☎01228 23488   Fax 01228 512828
Owner *Cumbrian Newspaper Group Ltd*
Editor *Keith Sutton*
Circulation 26,795

  News Editor *Mark Brown*
  Head of Content *Steve Johnston*
  Sports Editor *John Nicholson*
  Women's Page *Jane Loughran*

Cheltenham
Gloucestershire Echo
1 Clarence Parade, Cheltenham,
Gloucestershire GL50 3NZ
☎01242 526261   Fax 01242 578395
Owner *Northcliffe Newspapers Group Ltd*
Editor *Anita Syvret*
Circulation 26,387

All material, other than news, should be
addressed to the editor.
  News Editor *Chris Bishop*

Chester
Chronicle Newspapers (Chester)
Chronicle House, Commonhall Street,
Chester CH1 2BJ
☎01244 340151   Fax 01244 340165
Owner *Trinity International Holdings plc*
Editor-in-Chief *Bob Adams*

All unsolicited feature material will be considered.

Colchester
Evening Gazette (Colchester)
Oriel House, 43-44 North Hill, Colchester,
Essex CO1 1TZ
☎01206 761212   Fax 01206 769523
Owner *Essex County Newspapers*
Editor *Martin McNeill*
Circulation 29,525

Unsolicited mss not generally used. Relies

heavily on regular contributors.

News Editor *Irene Kettle*
Features Editor *Iris Clapp*

Coventry
Coventry Evening Telegraph

Corporation Street, Coventry CV1 1FP
☎01203 633633   Fax 01203 550869

Owner *Midland Independent Newspapers*
Editor *Dan Mason*
Circulation 83,838

Unsolicited mss are read, but few are published. Approach in writing with an idea. No fiction. All unsolicited material should be addressed to the editor. Maximum 600 words for features.

News Editor *Peter Mitchell*
Features Editor *Paul Simoniti*
Sports Editor *Roger Draper*
Women's Page *Barbara Argument*
Payment negotiable.

Darlington
The Northern Echo

Priestgate, Darlington, Co. Durham DL1 1NF
☎01325 381313   Fax 01325 380539

Owner *North of England Newspapers*
Editor *David Flintham*
Circulation 72,499

FOUNDED 1870. Freelance pieces welcome but telephone first to discuss submission.

News Editor *Tony Metcalf* Interested in reports involving the North-east or North Yorkshire. Preferably phoned in.
Features Editor *Chris Lloyd* Background pieces to topical news stories relevant to the area. Must be arranged with the features editor before submission of any material.
Business Editor *Colin Tapping*
Sports Editor *Kevin Dinsdale*
Payment and length by arrangement.

Derby
Derby Evening Telegraph

Northcliffe House, Meadow Road, Derby DE1 2DW
☎01332 291111   Fax 01332 253027

Owner *Northcliffe Newspapers Group Ltd*
Editor *Mike Lowe*
Circulation 63,478

Weekly business supplement.

News Editor *Kevin Booth*
Features Editor/Women's Page *Stephanie Smith*

Sports Editor *Steve Nicholson*
Motoring Editor *Bob Maddox*

Devon
Herald Express

See under *Torquay*

Doncaster
The Doncaster Star

40 Duke Street, Doncaster, South Yorkshire DN1 3EA
☎01302 344001   Fax 01302 329072

Owner *Sheffield Newspapers Ltd*
Editor *Lynne Fletcher*
Circulation 7,916

All editorial material to be addressed to the editor.

Sports Editor *Steve Hossack*
Women's Page *Janet Makinson*

Dundee
The Courier and Advertiser

80 Kingsway East, Dundee DD4 8SL
☎01382 223131   Fax 01382 454590

Owner *D. C. Thomson & Co. Ltd*
Editor *Adrian Arthur*
Circulation 103,768

Circulates in Dundee, Tayside, Fife and parts of Central and Grampian. Features welcome on a wide variety of subjects, not solely of local/Scottish interest. Two pages devoted to features each weekend, supplied by freelancers and in-house. Finance, insurance, agriculture, EU topics, motoring, women, modern homes. Only rule of thumb is to keep it short. Maximum 500 words.

News Editor *Steve Bargeton*
Features Editor/Women's Page *Shona Lorimer*
Sports Editor *Graham Dey*

Evening Telegraph & Post

80 Kingsway East, Dundee DD4 8SL
☎01382 223131   Fax 01382 454590

Owner *D. C. Thomson & Co. Ltd*
Editor *Alan Proctor*
Editor *Harold Pirie*
Circulation 35,584

Circulates in Tayside, Dundee and Fife. All material should be addressed to the editor.

East Anglia
East Anglian Daily Times

See under *Ipswich*

Eastern Daily Press
See under *Norwich*

Edinburgh
Evening News
20 North Bridge, Edinburgh EH1 1YT
☎0131 225 2468   Fax 0131 225 7302
Owner *European Press Holdings Ltd*
Editor *John C. McGurk*
Circulation 86,102

FOUNDED 1873. Circulates in Edinburgh, Fife, Central and Lothian. Coverage includes: lifestyle and entertainments (daily); motoring column (Friday); gardening, computers, book reviews, DIY, historical memories, shopping, fashion, nature, show business, and *The Doctor* (health). Unsolicited feature material welcome. Approach the appropriate editor by telephone.
   News Editor *Simon Reynolds*
   Features Editor *Helen Martin* Weekender magazine supplement of broad general/historical interest. Occasional Platform pieces (i.e. sounding off, topical or opinion pieces). Maximum 1000 words.
   Sports Editor *Paul Greaves*
   Payment NUJ/house rates.

Exeter
Express & Echo
Heron Road, Sowton, Exeter, Devon
EX2 7NF
☎01392 442211
Fax 01392 442294/442287 (editorial)
Owner *Express & Echo Publications Ltd*
Editor *Rachael Campey*
Circulation 30,812

Weekly supplements: *Business Week; Property Echo; Wheels; Weekend Echo.*
   News Editor *Mike Beard*
   Features Editor/Women's Page *Sue Kemp*
   Sports Editor *Jerry Charge*

Glasgow
Evening Times
195 Albion Street, Glasgow G1 1QP
☎0141 552 6255   Fax 0141 553 1355
Owner *Caledonian Publishing*
Editor *John D. Scott*
Circulation 136,036

Circulates in the Strathclyde region. Supplement: *Evening Times Sport.*
   News Editor *Ally McLaws*
   Features Editor *Russell Kyle*
   Sports Editor *David Stirling*
   Women's Page *Marian Pallister*

The Herald (Glasgow)
See **National Newspapers**

Gloucester
The Citizen
St John's Lane, Gloucester GL1 2AY
☎01452 424442   Fax 01452 307238
Owner *Northcliffe Newspapers Group Ltd*
Editor *Spencer Feeney*
Circulation 37,087

All editorial material to be addressed to the **News Editor** *Chris Hill.*

Gloucestershire Echo
See under *Cheltenham*

Greenock
Greenock Telegraph
2 Crawfurd Street, Greenock PA15 1LH
☎01475 726511   Fax 01475 783734
Owner *Clyde & Forth Press Ltd*
Editor *Ian Wilson*
Circulation 20,618

Circulates in Greenock, Port Glasgow, Gourock, Kilmacolm, Langbank, Bridge of Weir, Inverkip, Wemyss Bay, Skelmorlie, Largs. Unsolicited mss considered 'if they relate to the newspaper's general interests'. No fiction. All material to be addressed to the editor or the **News Editor** *David Carnduff.*

Grimsby
Grimsby Evening Telegraph
80 Cleethorpe Road, Grimsby, N. E. Lincs
DN31 3EH
☎01472 359232   Fax 01472 358859
Owner *Northcliffe Newspapers Group Ltd*
Editor *Peter Moore*
Circulation 71,167

Sister paper of the *Scunthorpe Evening Telegraph.* Unsolicited mss generally welcome. Approach in writing. No fiction. Monthly supplement: *Business Telegraph.* All material to be addressed to the **News Editor** *S. P. Richards.* Particularly welcome hard news stories – approach in haste by telephone.
   Special Publications Editor *B. Farnsworth*

Guernsey
Guernsey Evening Press & Star
Braye Road, Vale, Guernsey, Channel Islands
GY1 3BW
☎01481 45866   Fax 01481 48972
Owner *Guernsey Press Co. Ltd*
Editor *Graham Ingrouille*

Circulation 15,891

Special pages include children's and women's interest, gardening and fashion.

News Editor *Dave Edmonds*
Sports Editor *John Le Poidevin*
Women's Page *Jo Porter*

Halifax
Evening Courier

PO Box 19, Halifax, West Yorkshire HX1 2SF
☎01422 365711   Fax 01422 330021

Owner *Johnston Press Plc*
Editor *Edward Riley*
Circulation 31,731

News Editor *John Kenealy*
Features Editor *William Marshall*
Sports Editor *Ian Rushworth*
Women's Page *Diane Crabtree*

Hartlepool
Mail (Hartlepool)

Clarence Road, Hartlepool TS24 8BU
☎01429 274441   Fax 01429 869024

Owner *Northeast Press Ltd*
Editor *Christopher Cox*
Circulation 26,254

Deputy Editor *Harry Blackwood*
News Editor *Phillip Hickey*
Features Editor *Bernice Saltzer*
Sports Editor *Neil Watson*
Women's Page *Margaret O'Rourke*

Huddersfield
Huddersfield Daily Examiner

Queen Street South, Huddersfield, West Yorkshire HD1 2TD
☎01484 430000   Fax 01484 423722

Owner *Trinity International Holdings plc*
Editor *John Williams*
Editor *Richard Mallinson*
Circulation 37,694

Home improvement, home heating, weddings, dining out, motoring, fashion, services to trade and industry.

News Editor *Neil Atkinson*
Features Editor *Andrew Flynn*
Sports Editor *John Gledhill*
Women's Page *Hilarie Stelfox*

Hull
Hull Daily Mail

Blundell's Corner, Beverley Road, Hull, North Humberside HU3 1XS
☎01482 327111   Fax 01482 584353

Owner *Northcliffe Newspapers Group Ltd*
Editor *Michael Wood*
Circulation 89,156

News/Features Editor *Michelle Lalor*
Sports Editor *Chris Harvey*
Women's Page *Jo Davison*

Ipswich
East Anglian Daily Times

30 Lower Brook Street, Ipswich, Suffolk IP4 1AN
☎01473 230023   Fax 01473 225296

Owner *Eastern Counties Newspaper Group*
Editor *Malcolm Pheby*
Circulation 47,463

FOUNDED 1874. Unsolicited mss generally not welcome; three or four received a week and almost none are used. Approach in writing in the first instance. No fiction. Supplement: *Anglia Business Scene*; plus specials: Property and industry in East Anglia; and Look at the Land.

News Editor *Robyn Bechelet* Hard news stories involving East Anglia (Suffolk, Essex particularly) or individuals resident in the area are always of interest.

Features Editor *Derek Clements* Mostly in-house, but will occasionally buy in when the subject is of strong Suffolk/East Anglian interest. Photo features preferred (extra payment). Special advertisement features are regularly run. Some opportunities here. Maximum 1000 words.

Sports Editor *Tony Garnett*
Women's Page *Cathy Brown*

Evening Star

30 Lower Brook Street, Ipswich, Suffolk IP4 1AN
☎01473 230023   Fax 01473 225296

Owner *Eastern Counties Newspaper Group*
Editor *Terry Hunt*
Circulation 30,391

Deputy Editor *Nigel Pickover*
Sports Editor *Mike Horne*

Jersey
Jersey Evening Post

PO Box 582, Jersey, Channel Islands JE4 8XQ
☎01534 611611   Fax 01534 611622

Owner *Jersey Evening Post Ltd*
Editor *Chris Bright*
Circulation 23,194

Special pages: gardening, motoring, farmers and growers, property, boating, computer and office, young person's (16-25), women, food and drink, personal finance, rock and classical reviews.

News Editor *Sue Le Ruez*
Features Editor *Rob Shipley*
Sports Editor *Ron Felton*

Kent
Kent Messenger
See under *Maidstone*

Kent Today
See under *Aylesford*

Kettering
Evening Telegraph
Northfield Avenue, Kettering, Northamptonshire NN16 9TT
☎01536 81111   Fax 01536 85983
Owner *EMAP*
Editor *David Rowell*
Circulation 36,500

Business Telegraph (weekly); *Guide* supplement (Thursday/Saturday), featuring TV, gardening, videos, films, eating out; two monthly supplements, *Home & Garden* and *Car Driver*.
News Editor *Helen O'Neill*
Business Editor *Tony Bacon*
Sports Editor *Ian Davidson*

Lancashire
Lancashire Evening Post
See under *Preston*

Lancashire Evening Telegraph
See under *Blackburn*

Leamington
Leamington Spa Courier
32 Hamilton Terrace, Leamington Spa, Warwickshire CV32 4LY
☎01926 888222   Fax 01926 451690
Owner *Central Counties Newspapers*
Editor *Martin Lawson*
Circulation 13,410

One of the Leamington Spa Courier Series which also includes the *Warwick Courier* and *Kenilworth Weekly News*. Unsolicited feature articles considered, particularly matter with a local angle. Telephone with idea first.
News Editor *Mark Sanderson*

Leeds
Yorkshire Evening Post
Wellington Street, Leeds, West Yorkshire LS1 1RF
☎0113 2432701   Fax 0113 2388536
Owner *Yorkshire Post Newspapers Ltd*
Editor *Christopher Bye*
Circulation 101,810

Evening sister of the *Yorkshire Post*.
News Editor *Richard Spencer*
Features Editor *Anne Pickles*
Sports Editor *Ian Ward*
Women's Page *Carmen Bruegmann*

Yorkshire Post
Wellington Street, Leeds, West Yorkshire LS1 1RF
☎0113 2432701   Fax 0113 2388537
Owner *Yorkshire Post Newspapers Ltd*
Editor *Tony Watson*
Circulation 76,771

A serious-minded, quality regional daily with a generally conservative outlook. Three or four unsolicited mss arrive each day; all will be considered but initial approach in writing preferred. All submissions should be addressed to the editor. No fiction.
Assistant Editor (News) *John Furbisher*
Features Editor *Mick Hickling* Open to suggestions in all fields (though ordinarily commissioned from specialist writers).
Sports Editor *Bill Bridge*
Women's Page *Jill Armstrong*

Leicester
Leicester Mercury
St George Street, Leicester LE1 9FQ
☎0116 2512512   Fax 0116 2530645
Owner *Northcliffe Newspapers Group Ltd*
Editor *Nick Carter*
Circulation 114,420

News Editor *Simon Orrell*
Features Editor *Mark Clayton*

Lincoln
Lincolnshire Echo
Brayford Wharf East, Lincoln LN5 7AT
☎01522 525252   Fax 01522 545759
Owner *Northcliffe Newspapers Group Ltd*
Editor *Cliff Smith*
Circulation 30,124

Best buys, holidays, motoring, dial-a-service, restaurants, sport, leisure, home improvement, women's page, record review, gardening corner, stars. All editorial material to be addressed to the **Assistant Editor** *Mike Gubbins*.

Liverpool
Daily Post
PO Box 48, Old Hall Street, Liverpool
L69 3EB
☎0151 227 2000   Fax 0151 236 4682
Owner *Liverpool Daily Post & Echo Ltd*
Editor *Alastair Machray*
Circulation 71,879

Unsolicited mss welcome. Receives about six a day. Approach in writing with an idea. No fiction. Local, national/international news, current affairs, profiles – with pictures. Maximum 800–1000 words.
   Features Editor *Mark Davies*
   Sports Editor *Len Capeling*
   Women's Page *Margaret Kitchen*

Liverpool Echo
PO Box 48, Old Hall Street, Liverpool
L69 3EB
☎0151 227 2000   Fax 0151 236 4682
Owner *Liverpool Daily Post & Echo Ltd*
Editor *John Griffith*
Circulation 160,861

One of the country's major regional dailies. Unsolicited mss welcome; initial approach with ideas in writing preferred.
   News Editor *Tony Storey*
   Features Editor *Janet Tansley* Maximum 1000 words.
   Sports Editor *Ken Rogers*
   Women's Editor *Sue Lee*

London
Evening Standard
Northcliffe House, 2 Derry Street, London
W8 5EE
☎0171 938 6000   Fax 0171 937 2648
Owner *Lord Rothermere*
Editor *Max Hastings*
Circulation 534,066

Long-established evening paper, serving Londoners with both news and feature material. Genuine opportunities for London-based features. Produces a weekly colour supplement, *ES The Evening Standard Magazine*.
   Deputy Editor *Peter Boyer*
   Associate Editor (Features) *Nicola Jeal*
   News Editor *Stephen Clackson*
   Features Editor *Bernice Davison*
   Sports Editor *Michael Herd*
   Editor, *ES Adam Edwards*

Maidstone
Kent Messenger
6 & 7 Middle Row, Maidstone, Kent
ME14 1TG
☎01622 695666   Fax 01622 757227
Owner *Kent Messenger Group*
Editor *Ron Green*
Circulation 42,000

Very little freelance work is commissioned.

Manchester
Manchester Evening News
164 Deansgate, Manchester M60 2RD
☎0161 832 7200   Fax 0161 834 3814
Owner *Manchester Evening News Ltd*
Editor *Michael Unger*
Circulation 180,620

One of the country's major regional dailies. Initial approach in writing preferred. No fiction. *Property* (Tuesday); holiday feature (Saturday); *Lifestyle* (Friday).
   News Editor *Lisa Roland*
   Features Editor *Diane Robinson* Regional news features, personality pieces and showbiz profiles considered. Maximum 1000 words.
   Sports Editor *Neville Bolton*
   Women's Page *Diane Cooke*
   Payment based on house agreement rates.

Middlesbrough
Evening Gazette
Borough Road, Middlesbrough, Cleveland
TS1 3AZ
☎01642 245401   Fax 01642 232014
Owner *Trinity International Holdings plc*
Editor *Ranald Allan*
Circulation 69,000

Special pages: business, motoring, home, computing.
   News Editor *Tony Beck*
   Features Editor *Alan Sims*
   Sports Editor *Allan Boughey*
   Women's Page *Kathryn Armstrong*
   Crime *Damian Bates*
   Environment *Iain Laing*
   Consumer *Julia Paul*
   Health *Amanda Todd*
   Councils *Sandy McKenzie*

Mold
Evening Leader
Mold Business Park, Wrexham Road, Mold,
Clwyd CH7 1XY
☎01352 707707   Fax 01352 752180

Owner *North Wales Newspapers*
Editor *Reg Herbert*
Circulation 30,976

Circulates in Wrexham, Clwyd, Deeside and Chester. Special pages/features: motoring, travel, arts, women's, children's, photography, local housing, information and news for the disabled, music and entertainment.
Features Page *Jeremy Smith*
News Editor *David Metcalf*
Women's Page *Gail Cooper*
Sports Editor *Allister Syme*

Newcastle
Evening Chronicle

Thomson House, Groat Market, Newcastle upon Tyne, Tyne & Wear NE1 1ED
☎0191 232 7500   Fax 0191 232 2256
Owner *Trinity International Holdings plc*
Editor *Neil Benson*
Circulation 118,360

Receives a lot of unsolicited material, much of which is not used. Family issues, gardening, pop, fashion, cooking, consumer, films and entertainment guide, home improvements, motoring, property, angling, sport and holidays. Approach in writing with ideas.
News Editor *David Bourn*
Features Editor *Jane Pikett* Limited opportunities due to full-time feature staff. Maximum 1000 words.
Sports Editor *Paul New*
Women's Interests *Kay Jordan*

The Journal

Thomson House, Groat Market, Newcastle upon Tyne, Tyne & Wear NE1 1ED
☎0191 232 7500   Fax 0191 232 2256
Owner *Trinity International Holdings plc*
Editor *To be appointed*
Circulation 55,373

Daily platforms include farming and business. Monthly full-colour business supplement: *The Journal Northern Business Magazine.*
News/Features Editor *Tom Patterson*
Sports Editor *Nick Crockford*
Women's Editor *Jennifer Wilson*
Agricultural Editor *David Leach*
Arts & Entertainment Editor *David Whetstone*
Environmental Editor *Tony Henderson*

Sunday Sun

Thomson House, Groat Market, Newcastle upon Tyne, Tyne & Wear NE1 1ED
☎0191 232 7500   Fax 0191 230 0238

Owner *Trinity International Holdings plc*
Editor *Chris Rushton*
Circulation 124,975

All material should be addressed to the appropriate editor (phone to check), or to the editor.
Head of Content *Carole Watson*
Sports Editor *David Lamont*

Newport
South Wales Argus

Cardiff Road, Maesglas, Newport, Gwent NP9 1QW
☎01633 810000   Fax 01633 462202
Owner *South Wales Argus Ltd*
Editor *Gerry Keighley*
Circulation 33,816

Circulates in Newport, Gwent and surrounding areas.
News Editor *Jeremy Flye*
Features Editor/Women's Page *Lesley Williams*
Sports Editor *Carl Difford*

North of England
The Northern Echo

See under *Darlington*

Northampton
Chronicle and Echo

Upper Mounts, Northampton NN1 3HR
☎01604 231122   Fax 01604 233000
Owner *Northampton Mercury Co. Ltd*
Editor *Mark Edwards*
Circulation 29,672

Unsolicited mss are 'not necessarily unwelcome but opportunities to use them are rare'. Some three or four arrive weekly. Approach in writing with an idea. No fiction. Supplements: *Sports Chronicle* (Monday); *Business Chronicle* (Tuesday); *Property Chronicle* (Wednesday); women's page, music page (Thursday); motoring (Friday).
Head of Content *Peter Clarke*
Features Editor/Women's Page *Ruth Supple*
Sports Editor *Steve Pitts*

Northern Ireland
Belfast Telegraph

See under *Belfast*

The Irish News

See under *Belfast*

Sunday Life (Belfast)
See **National Newspapers**

Norwich
Eastern Daily Press
Prospect House, Rouen Road, Norwich,
Norfolk NR1 1RE
☎01603 628311   Fax 01603 612930
Owner *Eastern Counties Newspapers*
Editor *Peter Franzen*
Circulation 78,198

Unsolicited mss welcome. Approach in writing with ideas. News (if relevant to Norfolk), and features up to 900 words. Other pieces by commission only. Supplements: what's on (daily); employment (twice-weekly); motoring (weekly); business (weekly); property pages (weekly); women's interests (monthly); arts focus (monthly); plus agriculture, horse and rider, boating, golf and wildlife.
> **News Editor** *Paul Durrant*
> **Features Editor** *Colin Chinery*
> **Sports Editor** *David Thorpe*
> **Women's Page** *Sarah Hardy*

Evening News
Prospect House, Rouen Road, Norwich,
Norfolk NR1 1RE
☎01603 628311   Fax 01603 612930
Owner *Eastern Counties Newspapers*
Editor *Bob Crawley*
Circulation 39,689

Includes special pages on local property, motoring, children's page, pop, fashion, arts, entertainments and TV, gardening, local music scene, home and family.
> **Assistant Editor** *Roy Strownger*
> **Deputy Editor** *Celia Sutton*
> **Features Editor** *Derek James*

Nottingham
Evening Post Nottingham
Forman Street, Nottingham NG1 4AB
☎0115 9482000   Fax 0115 9644027
Owner *Northcliffe Newspapers Group Ltd*
Editor *Graham Glen*
Circulation 100,000

Unsolicited mss welcome. Send ideas in writing. Supplements: *Car Buyer* (thirteen issues a year); business, holidays and travel supplements; financial, employment and consumer pages.
> **News Editor** *Elaine Pritchard*
> **Head of Content** *Jon Grubb* Good local

interest only. Maximum 800 words. No fiction.
> **Sports Editor** *Mick Hollan*

Newport
Evening Telegraph
See under *Tunbridge Wells*

Oldham
Evening Chronicle
PO Box 47, Union Street, Oldham,
Lancashire OL1 1EQ
☎0161 633 2121   Fax 0161 627 0905
Owner *Hirst Kidd & Rennie Ltd*
Editor *Philip Hirst*
Circulation 34,666

'We welcome the good but not the bad.' Motoring, food and wine, women's page, business page.
> **News Editor** *Mike Attenborough*
> **Women's Page** *Ralph Badham*

Oxford
Oxford Mail
Osney Mead, Oxford OX2 0EJ
☎01865 244988   Fax 01865 243382
Owner *Oxford & County Newspapers*
Editor *Chris Cowley*
Circulation 32,346

Unsolicited mss are considered but a great many unsuitable offerings are received. Approach in writing with an idea, rather than by phone. No fiction. All fees negotiable.
> **News Editor** *Andy Chatfield*
> **Features Editor** *Annette Nix* Any features of topical or historical significance. Maximum 800 words.
> **Sports Editor** *Stuart Earp*
> **Women's Page** *Fiona Tarrant*

Paisley
Paisley Daily Express
14 New Street, Paisley PA1 1YA
☎0141 887 7911   Fax 0141 887 6254
Owner *Scottish & Universal Newspapers Ltd*
Editor *Norman Macdonald*
Circulation 8,270

Circulates in Paisley, Linwood, Renfrew, Johnstone, Elderslie, Raiston and Barrhead. Unsolicited mss welcome only if of genuine local (Paisley) interest. The paper does not commission work, and will consider submitted material. Maximum 1000-1500 words. All submissions to the editor.

Features Editor/Women's Page *Anne Dalrymple*
Sports Editor *Matthew Vallance*

Plymouth
Evening Herald
17 Brest Road, Derriford Business Park, Derriford, Plymouth, Devon PL6 5AA
☎01752 765500   Fax 01752 765527
Owner *Northcliffe Newspapers Group Ltd*
Editor *Alan Cooper*
Circulation 55,036

All editorial material to be addressed to the editor or the **News Editor** *Anthony Abbott.*

Sunday Independent
Burrington Way, Plymouth, Devon PL5 3LN
☎01752 777151   Fax 01752 780680
Owner *Southern Newspapers plc*
Editor *Anna Jenkins*
Circulation 40,844

Fashion, what's on, gardening, computers, DIY, business, motors and motorcycles, furniture, food and wine, out and about, property, photography, hobbies, health and beauty, kitchens. All editorial should be addressed to the editor.

Western Morning News
17 Brest Road, Derriford Business Park, Derriford, Plymouth, Devon PL6 5AA
☎01752 765500   Fax 01752 765535
Owner *Northcliffe Newspapers Group Ltd*
Editor *Barrie Williams*
Circulation 50,556

Unsolicited mss welcome, but best to telephone features editor first. Special pages include a motoring supplement, West country matters, books, antiques, lifestyle and arts.

News Editor *Philip Bowern*
Features Editor *Janet Wooster* Mostly local interest, 600-800 words. Must be topical.
Sports Editor *Rick Cowdery*
All other editorial material to be addressed to the editor.

Portsmouth
The News
The News Centre, Hilsea, Portsmouth, Hampshire PO2 9SX
☎01705 664488   Fax 01705 673363
Owner *Portsmouth Printing & Publishing Ltd*
Editor *Geoffrey Elliott*

Circulation 76,348

Unsolicited mss not generally welcome. Approach by letter.
News Editor *Mark Acheson*
Features Editor *Rachel Hughes* General subjects of SE Hants interest. Maximum 600 words. No fiction.
Sports Editor *Colin Channon* Sports background features. Maximum 600 words.
Women's Page *Rachel Hughes*

Preston
Lancashire Evening Post
Olivers Place, Eastway, Fulwood, Preston, Lancashire PR2 9ZA
☎01772 254841   Fax 01772 880173
Owner *United Newspapers Publications Ltd*
Editor *Neil Hodgkinson*
Circulation 53,760

Unsolicited mss are not generally welcome; many are received and not used. All ideas in writing to the editor.

Reading
Evening Post
Tessa Road, Reading, Berkshire RG1 8NS
☎0118 9575833   Fax 0118 9599363
Owner *Guardian Media Group*
Editor *Kim Chapman*
Circulation 22,456

Unsolicited mss welcome; one or two received every day. Fiction rarely used. Interested in local news features, human interest, well-researched investigations. Special sections include women's page (Monday & Thursday); motoring and motorcycling (Tuesday); business (Wednesday); gardening (Friday); rock music (Friday); children's page (Friday); travel (Friday).

Features Editor *Kate Magee*
News Editor *Mark Hoey* Topical subjects, particularly of Thames Valley interest. Maximum 800 words.
Women's Page *Kate Magee*

Scarborough
Scarborough Evening News
17-23 Aberdeen Walk, Scarborough, North Yorkshire YO11 1BB
☎01723 363636   Fax 01723 354092
Owner *Yorkshire Regional Newspapers Ltd*
Editor *David Penman*
Circulation 16,939

Special pages include property (Monday);

motoring (Tuesday/Friday).
News Editor *Chris Nixon*
Motoring *Dennis Sissons*
Sports Editor *Charles Place*
All other material should be addressed to the editor.

Scotland
Daily Record (Glasgow)
See **National Newspapers**

Scotland on Sunday (Edinburgh)
See **National Newspapers**

The Scotsman (Edinburgh)
See **National Newspapers**

Sunday Mail (Glasgow)
See **National Newspapers**

Sunday Post (Dundee)
See **National Newspapers**

Scunthorpe
Scunthorpe Evening Telegraph
Doncaster Road, Scunthorpe, N. E. Lincs
DN15 7RE
☎01724 843421   Fax 01724 853495
Owner *Northcliffe Newspapers Group Ltd*
Editor *P. L. Moore*
Circulation 24,574

All correspondence should go to the news editor.
Assistant Editor *D. H. Stephens*
News Editor *Simon Drury*

Sheffield
The Star
York Street, Sheffield, South Yorkshire
S1 1PU
☎0114 2767676   Fax 0114 2725978
Owner *Sheffield Newspapers Ltd*
Editor *Peter Charlton*
Circulation 102,749

Unsolicited mss not welcome, unless topical and local.
Joint News Editors *Bob Westerdale/Alison Hurndall* Contributions only accepted from freelance news reporters if they relate to the area.
Features Editor *Jim Collins* Very rarely require outside features, unless on specialised subject.
Sports Editor *Derek Fish*
Women's Page *Fiona Firth*
Payment negotiable.

Shropshire
Shropshire Star
See under *Telford*

South Shields
Gazette
Chapter Row, South Shields, Tyne & Wear
NE33 1BL
☎0191 455 4661   Fax 0191 456 8270
Owner *Northeast Press Ltd*
Editor *Phillip Hickey*
Circulation 24,177

News Editor *Chris Storey*
Sports Editor *John Cornforth*
Women's Page *Joy Yates*

Southampton
The Southern Daily Echo
Newspaper House, Test Lane, Redbridge, Southampton, Hampshire SO16 9JX
☎01703 424777   Fax 01703 424770
Owner *Southern Newspapers Ltd*
Editor *Patrick Fleming*
Circulation 60,028

Unsolicited mss 'tolerated'. Approach the editor in writing with strong ideas; staff supply almost all the material.

Stoke on Trent
Evening Sentinel
Sentinel House, Etruria, Stoke on Trent, Staffordshire ST1 5SS
☎01782 289800   Fax 01782 280781
Owner *Staffordshire Sentinel Newspapers Ltd*
Editor *Sean Dooley*
Circulation 95,334

Weekly sports final supplement. All material should be sent to the **News Editor** *Michael Wood*.

Sunderland
Sunderland Echo
Echo House, Pennywell, Sunderland, Tyne & Wear SR4 9ER
☎0191 534 3011   Fax 0191 534 5975
Owner *North East Press Ltd*
Editor *Ian Holland*
Circulation 58,529

All editorial material to be addressed to the news editor.

Swansea
South Wales Evening Post
Adelaide Street, Swansea, West Glamorgan
SA1 1QT
☎01792 650841   Fax 01792 469665
Owner *Northcliffe Newspapers Group Ltd*
Editor *George Edwards*
Circulation 66,566

Circulates throughout South West Wales.
  News Editor *Jonathan Isaacs*
  Sports Editor *David Evans*

Swindon
Evening Advertiser
100 Victoria Road, Swindon, Wiltshire
SN1 3BE
☎01793 528144   Fax 01793 542434
Owner *Media in Wessex*
Editor *Kevin Mochrie*
Circulation 25,595

Copy and ideas invited. 'All material must be
strongly related or relevant to the town of
Swindon, borough of Thamesdown or the
county of Wiltshire.' Little scope for freelance
work. Fees vary depending on material.
  Head of Content *Pauline Leighton*
  Sports Editor *Alan Johnson*
  Women's Page *Shirley Mathias*

Telford
Shropshire Star
Ketley, Telford, Shropshire TF1 4HU
☎01952 242424   Fax 01952 254605
Owner *Shropshire Newspapers Ltd*
Editor *Andy Wright*
Circulation 94,160

No unsolicited mss; approach the editor with
ideas in writing in the first instance. No news
or fiction.
  News Editor *Sarah-Jane Smith*
  Features Editor *Alun Owen* Limited opportunities; uses mostly in-house or syndicated
material. Maximum 1200 words.
  Sports Editor *Peter Byram*
  Women's Page *Kim Bennett*

Torquay
Herald Express
Harmsworth House, Barton Hill Road,
Torquay, Devon TQ2 8JN
☎01803 213213   Fax 01803 313093
Owner *Northcliffe Newspapers Group Ltd*
Editor *J. C. Mitchell*

Circulation 29,609

Drive scene, property guide, Monday sports,
special pages, rail trail, Saturday surgery, nature
and conservation column, Saturday children's
page. Supplements: *Curriculum*, *Gardening*,
Healthcare News (all quarterly); *Visitors Guide*
and *Antiques & Collectables* (fortnightly); *Devon
Days Out* (every Saturday in summer and at
Easter and May Bank Holidays). Unsolicited
mss generally not welcome. All editorial material should be addressed to the editor in writing.

Wales
South Wales Argus
See under *Newport*

South Wales Echo
See under *Cardiff*

South Wales Evening Post
See under *Swansea*

Wales on Sunday
See **National Newspapers**

Western Mail
See under *Cardiff*

West of England
Express & Echo
See under *Exeter*

Western Daily Press
See under *Bristol*

Western Morning News
See under *Plymouth*

Weymouth
Dorset Evening Echo
57 St Thomas Street, Weymouth, Dorset
DT4 8EU
☎01305 784804   Fax 01305 760387
Owner *Southern Newspapers plc*
Editor *Michael Woods*
Circulation 21,386

Farming, by-gone days, films, arts, showbiz,
brides, teens page, children's page, and video.
  News Editor *Paul Thomas*
  Sports Editor *Jack Wyllie*

Wolverhampton
Express & Star
Queen Street, Wolverhampton, West
Midlands WV1 3BU
☎01902 313131   Fax 01902 319721
Owner *Midlands News Association*

Editor *Warren Wilson*
Circulation 204,231

> **Deputy Editor** *Richard Ewels*
> **News Editor** *David Evans*
> **Features Editor** *Garry Copeland*
> **Sports Editor** *Steve Gordos*
> **Women's Page** *Shirley Tart*

Worcester
Evening News

Berrow's House, Hylton Road, Worcester
WR2 5JX
☎01905 748200   Fax 01905 429605

Owner *Reed Midland Newspapers Ltd*
Editor *Andrew Martin*
Circulation 23,588

Pulse pop page (Thursday/Friday/Saturday);
leisure (Wednesday); property (Thursday).
Weekly supplements: *Midweek News*; *Motoring
News*; *Weekend News and Entertainment*.

> **News Editor** *Linda Jones*
> **Features Editor/Women's Page** *Mark
>   Higgitt*
> **Sports Editor** *Paul Ricketts*

York
Yorkshire Evening Press

PO Box 29, 76–86 Walmgate, York
YO1 1YN
☎01904 653051   Fax 01904 612853

Owner *York & County Press*
Editor *Elizabeth Page*
Circulation 43,634

Unsolicited mss not generally welcome, unless
submitted by journalists of proven ability.
Business Press Pages (Monday); *Women's Press
Extra* (monthly section); *Property Press*
(Thursday); *8 Days* leisure and entertainments
supplement (Saturday).

> **News Editor** *Claire Timms*
> **Picture Editor** *Martin Oates*
> **Sports Editor** *Martin Jarred*
> *Payment* negotiable.

Yorkshire
Yorkshire Evening Post

See under *Leeds*

Yorkshire Post

See under *Leeds*

Life + 70
The basics of copyright

In that perverse way that bureaucrats have of concentrating on the least important aspects of life, those artful men of Brussels have now decided that the customary British copyright of life plus 50 years should be extended to match the customary German copyright of life plus 70 years.

The extra 20 years belong to the current owner of the copyright or, in the case of a recently expired copyright, to the last owner. If you are currently working on the biography of a well-known literary figure who was out but is now back in to copyright, don't worry. The current wisdom is that you will still be able to quote freely. The owner of a revived copyright cannot prevent publication or grant exclusive licences though there may be an obligation to pay 'whatever royalty or fee is reasonable' for extensive quotes.

Copyright boundaries

Copyright applies to all written work, unpublished as well as published. For works not published during the author's lifetime, the period of copyright runs from the date of publication. For a published work of joint authorship, protection extends from the end of the year of the death of the author who dies last.

In most books a copyright notice appears on one of the front pages. In its simplest form this is the symbol © followed by the name of the copyright owner and the year of first publication. The assertion of copyright may be emphasised by the phrase 'All rights reserved', and in case there are any lingering doubts the reader may be warned that 'No part of this publication may be reproduced or transmitted in any form or by any means without permission'.

But this is to overstate the case. It is perfectly legitimate for a writer to quote from someone else's work for 'purposes of criticism or review' as long as 'sufficient acknowledgement' is given. What he must not do is to lift 'a substantial part'. In one case, four lines from a thirty-two line poem were held to amount to 'a substantial part'. On the other hand, even a 'substantial' quotation from a copyright work may be acceptable if a student or critic is engaged in 'fair dealing with a literary work for the purposes of research or music study'.

Some years ago the Society of Authors and the Publishers Association stated that they would usually regard as 'fair dealing' the use of a single extract of up to 400 words, or a series of extracts (of which none exceeds 300 words) to a total of 800 words from a prose work, or of extracts to a total of 40 lines from a poem, provided that this did not exceed a quarter of the poem.

Titles and trademarks

Technically, there is no copyright in a title. But where a title is inseparable from the work of a particular author, proceedings for 'passing off' are likely to be successful. Everything depends on the nature of the rival works, the methods by which they are exploited and the extent to which the title is essentially distinctive.

The singularity of letters

The copyright status of a letter is something of a curiosity. The actual document belongs to the recipient, but the copyright remains with the writer and after his or her death, to the writer's estate. This has caused difficulty for some biographers who have assumed that it is the owners of letters who are empowered to give permission to quote from them. This only applies if the writer has assigned copyright.

Copyright in lectures and speeches

The pre-1988 rule was unnecessarily complicated and depended, for example, on whether the lecturer was speaking from prepared notes. Now, even if a speaker talks without notes, copyright exists in a lecture as soon as it is recorded (in writing or otherwise) but not until then. The copyright belongs to the person who spoke the words, whether or not the recording was made by, or with the permission of, the speaker.

Copyright on ideas

Writers trying to sell ideas should start on the assumption that it is almost impossible to stake an exclusive claim. So much unsolicited material comes the way of publishers and script departments, duplication of ideas is inevitable.

Frequent complaints of plagiarism have led publishers and production companies to point out the risks whenever they acknowledge an unsolicited synopsis or script, warning correspondents, 'it is often the case that we are currently considering or have already considered ideas that may be similar to your own'.

The fact is that to succeed in an action for infringement of copyright on an idea or on the bare bones of a plot, the copying of 'a combination or series of dramatic events' must be very close indeed. Proceedings have failed because incidents common to two works have been stock incidents or revolving around stock characters common to many works. Furthermore, as copyright is not a monopoly, it is a perfectly good defence if a later author can show that he had no knowledge of an earlier author's work.

The best way of protecting ideas, says solicitor Carolyn Jennings, is to 'get any-one who sees your work to sign a letter confirming that they will not disclose the ideas behind your work to anyone else, and will not use those ideas except by arrangement with you'. The catch, as Ms Jennings readily concedes is that 'it is very difficult to get broadcasters or film companies to sign such a letter'. In a highly competitive, fast-moving industry, it is likely that many synopses or scripts based on similar ideas are floating around though created entirely independently.

Minimum security is in refusing to discuss ideas before they are written down. If there is still a worry that a proposal could end up in the wrong hands, copy the manuscript, send it to yourself by registered post, then deposit the package and dated receipt at a bank or other safe place. At least then no one can fault your memory on essential details.

Copyright in photographs

Copyright in photographs taken on or after 1st August 1989 belongs to the pho-tographer, unless they were taken in the course of employment.

Permissions

A quotation of a 'substantial' extract from a copyright work or for any quotation of copyright material, however short, for an anthology must be approved by the publishers of the original work.

It is in the author's interest to deal with permissions as early as possible. Last-minute requests just before a book goes to press can lead to embarrassing diffi-culties if fees are too high or if permission is refused.

Anthology and quotation rates

The Society of Authors and the Publishers Association have recently revised their recommendations for 'basic minimum fees' for quotation and anthology use of copyright material.

Prose

The suggested rate is £95–£115 per 1,000 words for world rights. The rate for the UK and Commonwealth or the USA alone is usually half of the world rate. For an individual country (e.g. Canada, Australia or New Zealand): one quarter of the world rate.

Where an extract is complete in itself (e.g. a chapter or short story) publishers sometimes charge an additional fee at half the rate applicable for 1,000 words.

Further information

A booklet entitled *The Law of Copyright and Rights in Performances* is available from The British Copyright Council, Copyright House, 29–33 Berners Street, London W1P 4AA.

For any queries on copyright contact: The Department of Trade and Industry, Intellectual Property Policy Directorate, Copyright Enquiries, Room 4/5, Hazlitt House, 45 Southampton Buildings, London WC2A 1AR (Tel: 0171 438 4778).

Magazines

Abraxas

57 Eastbourne Road, St Austell, Cornwall
PL25 4SU
☎01726 64975

Owner *Paul Newman*
Editors *Paul Newman, Geoffrey Lee Cooper*

FOUNDED 1991. QUARTERLY incorporating the *Colin Wilson Newsletter*. Aims at being a periodical, but sometimes turns out to be a spasmodical. Unsolicited mss welcome after a study of the magazine – initial approach by phone or letter preferred.

Features Essays, translations and reviews. Recent issues have had Colin Wilson remembering R.D. Laing and appraising the work of Jacques Derrida and Michel Foucault; Paul Newman on *Little Grey Gropers from Mars* or 'Close Encounters of a Fourth Kind', and Ted Brown appraising 'Frozen Atlantis'. *Abraxus* also welcomes provocative, lively articles on little-known literary figures (e.g. David Lindsay/E. H. Visiak/Laura Del Rivo/P. D. Ouspensky/ Brocard Sewell) and new slants on psychology, existentialism and ideas. Maximum length 2000 words. *Payment* nominal if at all.

Fiction One story per issue. Favours compact, obsessional stories – think of writers like Kafka, Borges or Wolfgang Borchert – of not more than 2000 words.

Poetry Double-page spread – slight penchant for the surreal but open to most styles – has published D. M. Thomas, Zofia Ilinksa, Kenneth Steven and John Ellison.
Payment free copy of magazine.

Acclaim

PO Box 101, Tunbridge Wells, Kent
TN4 8YD
☎01892 511322   Fax 01892 514282

Owner/Editor *Merric Davidson*

FOUNDED 1992. BI-MONTHLY. Short story digest, with emphasis on shortlisted entries from the annual **Ian St James Award**. Not interested in poetry, plays, sketches or children's material; the magazine is devoted solely to the short story. No unsolicited mss. Approach with ideas only, by phone or in writing.

News Anything at all that is solely connected with the writing of short stories.

Features As above for news, plus articles by writers on tricks of the trade, etc. Maximum 2000 words.

Reviews Of short story collections only.
Payment negotiable/nothing for news items.

Accountancy

40 Bernard Street, London WC1N 1LD
☎0171 833 3291   Fax 0171 833 2085

Owner *Institute of Chartered Accountants in England and Wales*
Editor *Brian Singleton-Green*
Circulation 72,146

FOUNDED 1889. MONTHLY. Written ideas welcome.

Features *Brian Singleton-Green* Accounting/tax/business-related articles of high technical content aimed at professional/managerial readers. Maximum 2000 words.
Payment by arrangement.

Accountancy Age

32-34 Broadwick Street, London W1A 2HG
☎0171 316 9000   Fax 0171 316 9250

Owner *VNU Business Publications*
Editor *Andrew Pring*
Circulation 70,000

FOUNDED 1969. WEEKLY. Unsolicited mss welcome. Ideas may be suggested in writing provided they are clearly thought out.

Features *Adrian Murdoch* Topics right across the accountancy, business and financial world. Maximum 2000 words.
Payment negotiable.

Active Life

Aspen Specialist Media, Christ Church, Cosway Street, London NW1 5NJ
☎0171 262 2622   Fax 0171 706 4811

Owner *Aspen Specialist Media*
Editor *Helene Hodge*

FOUNDED 1990. BI-MONTHLY magazine aimed at over 50s. General consumer interests including travel, finance, property and leisure. Opportunities for freelancers in all departments, including fiction. Approach in writing with synopsis of ideas. Authors' notes available on receipt of s.a.e..

Acumen

See under **Poetry, Little Magazines**

African Affairs

Dept of Politics, University of Reading, Whiteknights, PO Box 218, Reading, Berkshire RG6 2AA

☎01734 318501   Fax 01734 753833

Owner *Royal African Society*
Editors *Peter Woodward, David Killingray*
Circulation 2250

FOUNDED 1901. QUARTERLY learned journal publishing articles on contemporary developments on the African continent. Unsolicited mss welcome.

Features Should be well researched and written in a style that is immediately accessible to the intelligent lay reader. Maximum 8000 words.

Payment up to £40 per 1000 words for non-academics; no payment for academics.

Air International

PO Box 100, Stamford, Lincolnshire PE9 1XQ

☎01780 55131   Fax 01780 57261

Owner *Key Publishing Ltd*
Editor *Malcolm English*

FOUNDED 1971. MONTHLY. Civil and military aircraft magazine. Unsolicited mss welcome but initial approach by phone or in writing preferred.

Airforces Monthly

PO Box 100, Stamford, Lincolnshire PE9 1XQ

☎01780 55131   Fax 01780 57261

Owner *Key Publishing Ltd*
Editor *David Oliver*
Circulation 33,000

FOUNDED 1988. MONTHLY. Modern military aircraft magazine. Unsolicited mss welcome but initial approach by phone or in writing preferred.

Amateur Film and Video Maker

Church House, 102 Pendlebury Road, Swinton, Manchester M27 4BFJ

☎0161 794 0771   Fax 0161 728 5308

Owner *Film Maker Publications*
Editor *Mrs Liz Donlan*
Circulation 2600

FOUNDED in the 1930s. BI-MONTHLY magazine of the Institute of Amateur Cinematographers. Reports news and views of the Institute. Unsolicited mss welcome but all contributions are unpaid.

Amateur Gardening

Westover House, West Quay Road, Poole, Dorset BH15 1JG

☎01202 680586   Fax 01202 674335

Owner *IPC Magazines Ltd*
Editor *Graham Clarke*
Circulation 66,475

FOUNDED 1884. WEEKLY. New contributions are welcome provided that they have a professional approach. Of the twenty unsolicited mss received each week, 90% are returned as unsuitable. All articles/news items are supported by colour pictures (which may or may not be supplied by the author).

Features Topical and practical gardening articles. Maximum 800 words.

News Compiled and edited in-house generally.

Payment negotiable.

Amateur Golf

129A High Street, Dovercourt, Harwich, Essex CO12 3AX

☎01255 507526   Fax 01255 508483

Publisher *Fore Golf Publications Ltd*
Editor *Paul Baxter*
Circulation 13,000

MONTHLY journal of the English Golf Union. UK coverage of amateur golf interests, club events and international matches. Unsolicited mss considered. Approach with ideas in writing or by phone.

Features *John Lelean* Golf course management, new developments and equipment, golf holidays, profiles and general amateur golf concerns. Maximum 2000 words.

Amateur Photographer

King's Reach Tower, Stamford Street, London SE1 9LS

☎0171 261 5100   Fax 0171 261 5404

Owner *IPC Magazines Ltd*
Group Editor *Keith Wilson*
Circulation 35,796

WEEKLY. For the competent amateur with a technical interest. Freelancers are used but writers should be aware that there is ordinarily no use for words without pictures.

Amateur Stage

83 George Street, London W1H 5PL

☎0171 486 1732   Fax 0171 224 2215

Owner *Platform Publications Ltd*
Editor *Charles Vance*

Some opportunity here for outside contributions. Topics of interest include amateur pre-mières, technical developments within the amateur forum and items relating to landmarks or anniversaries in the history of amateur societies. Approach in writing only (include s.a.e for return of mss).

No payment.

Ambit
See under **Poetry, Little Magazines**

The American
114-115 West Street, Farnham, Surrey GU9 7HL
☎01252 713366   Fax 01252 724951
Owner *British American Newspapers Ltd*
Editor *David J. Williams*
Circulation 15,000

FOUNDED 1976. FORTNIGHTLY community newspaper for US citizens resident in the UK and as such requires a strong American angle in every story. 'We are on the look-out for items on business and commerce, diplomacy and international relations, defence and 'people' stories.' Maximum length 'five minutes read'. First approach in writing with samples of previous work.

Payment 'modest but negotiable'.

Amiga Format
30 Monmouth Street, Bath, Avon BA1 2AP.
☎01225 442244   Fax 01225 318740
Owner *Future Publishing*
Editor *Nick Veitch*
Circulation 75,854

FOUNDED 1988. MONTHLY. Specialist computer magazine dedicated to Commodore Amiga home computers, offering reviews, features and product information of specific interest to Amiga users. Unsolicited material welcome. Contact by phone with ideas.

News *Steve McGill* Amiga-specific exclusives and product information. Length 500-1000 words.

Features *Nick Veitch* Computer-related features (i.e. CD-ROMs, games, virtual reality) with Amiga-specific value. Maximum 10,000 words.

Special Pages *Graeme Sandiford* Hardware and software reviews. Maximum 3000 words.

Payment £100 per 1000 words.

Animal Action
Causeway, Horsham, West Sussex RH12 1HG
☎01403 264181   Fax 01403 241048
Owner *RSPCA*

Editor *Michaela Miller*
Circulation 70,000

BI-MONTHLY. RSPCA youth membership magazine. Articles (pet care, etc.) are written in-house. Good-quality animal photographs welcome.

Antique and New Art
10-11 Lower John Street, London W1R 3PE
☎0171 434 9180   Fax 0171 287 3828
Owner *Antique Publications*
Editor-in-Chief *Alistair Hicks*
Managing Editor *Victoria O'Brien*
Circulation 22,000

FOUNDED 1986. QUARTERLY. Amusing coverage of antiques and art. Unsolicited mss not welcome. Approach by phone or in writing in the first instance. Interested in freelance contributions on international art news items.

The Antique Collector
7 St John's Road, Harrow, Middlesex HA1 2EE
☎0181 863 2020   Fax 0181 863 2444
Owner *Orpheus Publications*
Editor *Susan Morris*
Circulation 15,000

FOUNDED 1930. SIX ISSUES YEARLY. Opportunities for freelance features. Submit ideas in writing. Acceptance depends primarily on how authoritative and informative they are. Topical and controversial material is always welcome. Maximum 2000 words with high quality illustrations in colour.

Payment £250 for a major feature (1500 words).

The Antique Dealer and Collectors' Guide
PO Box 805, Greenwich, London SE10 8TD
☎0181 691 4820   Fax 0181 691 2489
Owner *Statuscourt Ltd*
Publisher *Philip Bartlam*
Circulation 12,500

FOUNDED 1946. MONTHLY. Covers all aspects of the antiques and fine art worlds. Unsolicited mss welcome.

Features Practical but readable articles on the history, design, authenticity, restoration and market aspects of antiques and fine art. Maximum 2000 words. *Payment* £76 per 1000 words.

News *Philip Bartlam* Items on events, sales, museums, exhibitions, antique fairs and markets. Maximum 300 words.

Apollo Magazine

1 Castle Lane, London SW1E 6DR
☎0171 233 6640   Fax 0171 630 7791

Owner *Paul Z. Josefowitz*
Editor *Robin Simon*

FOUNDED 1925. MONTHLY. Specialist articles on art and antiques, exhibition and book reviews, exhibition diary, information on dealers and auction houses. Unsolicited mss welcome. Interested in specialist, usually new research in fine arts, architecture and antiques. Approach in writing. Not interested in crafts or practical art or photography.

Aquarist & Pondkeeper

Caxton House, Wellesley Road, Ashford, Kent TN24 8ET
☎01233 636349   Fax 01233 631239

Owner *M. J. Publications Ltd*
Editor *Dick Mills*
Circulation 20,000

FOUNDED 1924. MONTHLY. Covers all aspects of aquarium and pondkeeping: conservation, herpetology (study of reptiles and amphibians), news, reviews and aquatic plant culture. Unsolicited mss welcome. Ideas should be submitted in writing first.

Features Good opportunities for writers on any of the above topics or related areas. 1500 words (maximum 2500), plus illustrations. 'We have stocks in hand for up to two years, but new material and commissioned features will be published as and when relevant.' Average lead-in 4–6 months.

News Very few opportunities.

Architects' Journal

151 Rosebery Avenue, London EC1R 4QX
☎0171 505 6700   Fax 0171 505 6701

Owner *EMAP Architecture*
Editor *Paul Finch*
Circulation 18,000

WEEKLY trade magazine dealing with all aspects of the industry. No unsolicited mss. Approach in writing with ideas.

Architectural Design

42 Leinster Gardens, London W2 3AN
☎0171 402 2141   Fax 0171 723 9540

Owner *Academy Group Ltd*
Editor *Maggie Toy*
Circulation 12,000

FOUNDED 1930. BI-MONTHLY. Theoretical architectural magazine. Unsolicited mss not generally welcome. Copy tends to come from experts in the field.

The Architectural Review

151 Rosebery Avenue, London EC1R 4QX
☎0171 505 6725   Fax 0171 505 6701

Owner *EMAP Architecture*
Editor *Peter Davey*
Circulation 20,000

MONTHLY trade magazine dealing with all aspects of the industry. No unsolicited mss. Approach in writing with ideas.

Arena

Block A, Exmouth House, Pine Street, London EC1R 0JL
☎0171 837 7270   Fax 0171 837 3906

Owner *Wagadon Ltd/Condé Nast Publications*
Editor *Peter Howarth*

Style and general interest magazine for men. Intelligent feature articles and profiles, plus occasional fiction.

Features Fashion, lifestyle, film, television, politics, business, music, media, design, art, architecture and theatre.

Payment £200–250 per 1000 words.

Art & Craft

Villiers House, Clarendon Avenue, Leamington Spa, Warwickshire CV32 5PR
☎01926 887799   Fax 01926 883331

Owner *Scholastic Ltd*
Editor *Sian Morgan*
Circulation 23,000

FOUNDED 1936. MONTHLY aimed at a specialist market – the needs of primary school teachers and pupils. Ideas and synopses considered for commission.

Features The majority of contributors are primary school teachers with good art and craft skills and familiar with the curriculum.

News Handled by in-house staff. No opportunities.

Art Monthly

Suite 17, 26 Charing Cross Road, London WC2H 0DG
☎0171 240 0389   Fax 0171 240 0389

Owner *Britannia Art Publications*
Editor *Patricia Bickers*
Circulation 4000

FOUNDED 1976. TEN ISSUES YEARLY. News and features of relevance to those interested in modern and contemporary visual art. Unsolicited mss welcome. Contributions should be addressed to the editor, accompanied by an s.a.e.

Features Alongside exhibition reviews: usually 750-1000 words and almost always commissioned. Interviews and articles of up to 1500 words on art theory, individual artists, contemporary art history and issues affecting the arts (e.g. funding and arts education). Book reviews of 750-1000 words.

News Brief reports (250-300 words) on art issues.

Payment negotiable.

The Art Newspaper
27-29 Vauxhall Grove, London SW8 1SY
☎0171 735 3331   Fax 0171 735 3332
Owner *Umberto Allemandi & Co. Publishing*
Editor *Laura Suffield*
Circulation 30,000

FOUNDED 1990. MONTHLY. Broadsheet format with up-to-date information on the international art market, news, museums, exhibitions, archaeology, conservation, books and current debate topics. Length 250-2000 words. No unsolicited mss. Approach with ideas in writing. Commissions only.

Payment £120 per 1000 words.

The Artist
Caxton House, 63-65 High Street, Tenterden, Kent TN30 6BD
☎0158076 3673   Fax 0158076 5411
Owner *Irene Briers*
Editor *Sally Bulgin*
Circulation 17,500

FOUNDED 1931. MONTHLY.

Features *Sally Bulgin* Art journalists, artists, art tutors and writers with a good knowledge of art materials are invited to write to the editor with ideas for practical and informative features about art, materials, techniques and artists.

Artscene
Dean Clough Industrial Park, Halifax, West Yorkshire HX3 5AX
☎01422 322527   Fax 01422 322518
Owner *Yorkshire and Humberside Arts*
Editor *Victor Allen*
Circulation 25,000

FOUNDED 1973. MONTHLY. Listings magazine for Yorksire and Humberside. No unsolicited mss. Approach by phone with ideas.

Features Profiles of artists (all media) and associated venues/organisers of events of interest. Topical relevance vital. Maximum length 1500 words. *Payment* £100 per 1000 words.

News Artscene strives to bring journalistic values to arts coverage – all arts 'scoops' in the region are of interest. Maximum length 500 words. *Payment* £100 per 1000 words.

Asian Times
See **Caribbean Times/Asian Times**

Audit
19 Rutland Street, Cork, Republic of Ireland
☎00 353 21313855   Fax 00 353 21313496
Editor *Ken Ebbage* (01438 840770)
Circulation 1000

BI-MONTHLY with a specialist, professional readership and world-wide circulation. Features tend to be commissioned. Approach in writing with ideas. Maximum 3000 words. No unsolicited mss. *Payment* £250.

The Author
84 Drayton Gardens, London SW10 9SB
☎0171 373 6642
Owner *The Society of Authors*
Editor *Derek Parker*
Manager *Kate Pool*
Circulation 6000

FOUNDED 1890. QUARTERLY journal of **The Society of Authors**. Unsolicited mss not welcome.

Autocar
38-42 Hampton Road, Teddington, Middlesex TW11 0JE
☎0181 943 5013   Fax 0181 943 5653
Owner *Haymarket Magazines Ltd*
Editor *Michael Harvey*
Circulation 84,159

FOUNDED 1895. WEEKLY. All news stories, features, interviews, scoops, ideas, tip-offs and photographs welcome.

Features *Gavin Conway*
News *Julian Rendell*
Payment from £175 per 1000 words/negotiable.

Baby Magazine
The Publishing House, Highbury Station Road, Islington, London N1 1SE
☎0171 226 2222   Fax 0171 359 5225
Owner *Highbury House Communications*
Editor *Natasha Mekie*

TEN ISSUES ANNUALLY. For parents-to-be and parents of children up to five years old. No unsolicited mss.

Features Send synopsis of feature with covering letter in the first instance. Unsolicited material is not returned.

Back Brain Recluse (BBR)
PO Box 625, Sheffield S1 3GY
Owner *Chris Reed*
Editor *Chris Reed*
Circulation 3000

International speculative fiction magazine providing opportunity for new writers. 'We strongly recommend familiarity with our guidelines for contributors, and with recent issues of *BBR*, before any material is submitted.' All correspondence must be accompanied by s.a.e. or international reply coupons.
Payment £5 per 1000 words.

Badminton
Connect Sports, 14 Woking Road, Cheadle Hulme, Cheshire SK8 6NZ
☎0161 486 6159/0171 938 7399 (editorial)
Fax 0161 486 6159

Owner *Mrs S. Ashton*
Editor *William Kings*

BI-MONTHLY. Specialist badminton magazine, with news, views, product information, equipment reviews, etc. Unsolicited material will be considered. Approach the editor by phone with an idea.

Features *William Kings* Open to approaches and likes to discuss ideas in the first instance. Interested in badminton-related articles on health, fitness, psychology, clothing, accessories, etc.
Payment £60.

Balance
British Diabetic Association, 10 Queen Anne Street, London W1M 0BD
☎0171 323 1531   Fax 0171 637 3644
Owner *British Diabetic Association*
Editor *Maggie Gibbons*
Circulation 150,000

FOUNDED 1935. BI-MONTHLY. Unsolicited mss are not accepted. Writers may submit a brief proposal in writing. Only topics relevant to diabetes will be considered.

Features *Maggie Gibbons* Medical, diet and lifestyle features written by people with diabetes or with an interest and expert knowledge in the field. Most general features are based on experience or personal observation. Max. 1500 words.
Payment NUJ rates.

News *Maggie Gibbons* Short pieces about activities relating to diabetes and the lifestyle of diabetics. Maximum 150 words.

Young Balance *Jackie Mace* Any kind of article written by those under 18 and with personal experience of diabetes. *Payment* varies.

The Banker
149 Tottenham Court Road, London W1P 9LL
☎0171 896 2507   Fax 0171 896 2586
Owner *Pearson Professional*
Editor *Stephen Timewell*
Circulation 14,520

FOUNDED 1926. MONTHLY. News and features on banking, finance and capital markets worldwide.

BBC Gardeners' World Magazine
Woodlands, 80 Wood Lane, London W12 0TT
☎0181 576 2000   Fax 0181 576 3986
Owner *BBC Worldwide Publishing*
Editor *Adam Pasco*
Circulation 320,000

FOUNDED 1991. MONTHLY. Gardening advice, ideas and inspiration. No unsolicited mss. Approach by phone or in writing with ideas.

BBC Good Food
Woodlands, 80 Wood Lane, London W12 0TT
☎0181 576 2000   Fax 0181 576 3825
Owner *BBC Worldwide Publishing*
Editor *Mitzie Wilson*
Circulation 401,054

FOUNDED 1989. MONTHLY food and drink magazine with television and radio links. No unsolicited mss.

BBC Homes & Antiques
Woodlands, 80 Wood Lane, London W12 0TT
☎0181 576 3490   Fax 0181 576 3867
Owner *BBC Worldwide Publishing*
Editor *Judith Hall*
Circulation 120,063

FOUNDED 1993. MONTHLY traditional home interest magazine with a strong bias towards antiques and collectables. Opportunities for freelancers are limited; most features are commissioned from regular stable of contributors. No fiction, health and beauty, fashion or general showbusiness. Approach with ideas by phone or in writing.

Features *Judith Hall* At-home features: inspirational houses - people-led items. Pieces commissioned on recce shots and cuttings. Guidelines available on request. Celebrity features: 'at homes or favourite things' – send cuttings of relevant published work. Max. 1500 words.

Special Pages Regular feature on memories of childhood homes. Max. 800 words.

Payment negotiable.

BBC Music Magazine

Room A1004, Woodlands, 80 Wood Lane, London W12 0TT

☎0181 576 3283   Fax 0181 576 3292

Owner *BBC Worldwide Publishing*
Editor *Fiona Maddocks*
Circulation 325,660 (worldwide)

FOUNDED 1992. MONTHLY. All areas of classical music. Not interested in unsolicited material. Approach with ideas only, by fax or in writing.

BBC Vegetarian Good Food

Woodlands, 80 Wood Lane, London W12 0TT

☎0181 576 3767   Fax 0181 576 3825

Owner *BBC Worldwide Publishing*
Editor *Mary Gwynn*
Circulation 78,000

FOUNDED 1992. MONTHLY magazine containing recipes, health and environment features. Unsolicited mss not welcome. Approach in writing with ideas.

BBC Wildlife Magazine

Broadcasting House, Whiteladies Road, Bristol, Avon BS8 2LR

☎0117 973 8402   Fax 0117 946 7075

Owner *BBC Worldwide Publishing*
Editor *Rosamund Kidman Cox*
Circulation 132,717

FOUNDED 1963 (formerly *Wildlife*, née *Animals*). MONTHLY. Unsolicited mss not welcome.

Competition The magazine runs an annual competition for professional and amateur writers with a first prize of £1000 (see entry under **Prizes**).

Features Most features commissioned from writers with expert knowledge of wildlife or conservation subjects. Unsolicited mss are usually rejected. Maximum 3500 words. *Payment* £120–350.

News Most news stories commissioned from known freelancers. Maximum 800 words. *Payment* £40–100.

Bedfordshire Magazine

50 Shefford Road, Meppershall, Bedfordshire SG17 5LL

☎01462 813363

Owner *White Crescent Press*
Editor *Betty Chambers*
Circulation 2400

FOUNDED 1947. QUARTERLY. Unsolicited material welcome on Bedfordshire. No general interest articles. Approach by phone or in writing in the first instance.

Features History, biography, natural history and arts. Nothing in the way of consumer features.

News Very little.

Fiction Occasional stories and poems of county interest only.

Special Pages Primarily historical material on Bedfordshire. Maximum 1500 words.

Payment nominal.

Bee World

18 North Road, Cardiff CF1 3DY

☎01222 372409   Fax 01222 665522

Owner *International Bee Research Association*
Editor *Dr P. A. Munn*
Circulation 1700

FOUNDED 1919. QUARTERLY. High-quality factual journal, including peer-reviewed articles, with international readership. Features on apicultural science and technology. Unsolicited mss welcome. It is recommended that authors write to the Editor for guidelines before submitting mss.

Bella

H. Bauer Publishing, Shirley House, 25-27 Camden Road, London NW1 9LL

☎0171 284 0909   Fax 0171 485 3774

Owner *H. Bauer Publishing*
Editor-in-Chief *Jackie Highe*
Circulation 1.2 million

FOUNDED 1987. WEEKLY. General interest women's magazine. Contributions welcome.

Features *Sharon Bexley* Maximum 1200–1400 words. Send s.a.e. for guidelines.

Fiction *Linda O'Byrne* Maximum 1200–3000 words. Send s.a.e. for guidelines.

Payment about £300 per 1000 words/varies.

Best

Portland House, Stag Place, London SW1E 5AU

☎0171 245 8700   Fax 0171 245 8825

Owner *G & J (UK)*
Editor *Dennis Neeld*
Circulation 664,972

FOUNDED 1987. WEEKLY women's magazine and stablemate of the magazine *Prima*. Multiple features, news, short stories on all topics of interest to women. Important for would-be contributors to study the magazine's style which differs from many other women's weeklies. Approach in writing with s.a.e.

Features Maximum 1500 words. No unsolicited mss.

Fiction 'Five-Minute Story' slot; unsolicited mss accepted. Maximum 1400 words. *Payment* £100.

Best of British

Ian Beacham Publishing, 200 Eastgate, Deeping St James, Peterborough, Cambridgeshire PE6 8RD
☎01738 347003   Fax 01738 347003
Owner *Choice Publications (EMAP)*
Editor *Ian Beacham*

FOUNDED 1994. BI-MONTHLY magazine celebrating all things British, both past and present. Study of the magazine is advised in the first instance. All preliminary approaches should be made in writing.

The Big Issue

Fleet House, 57-61 Clerkenwell Road, London EC1M 5NP
☎0171 418 0418   Fax 0171 418 0428
Owner *The Big Issue*
Editor-in-Chief *A. John Bird*
Editor *Joanne Mallabar*
Deputy Editor *Steve Chamberlain*
Circulation 108,526

FOUNDED 1991. WEEKLY. A campaigning and general interest magazine with a bias towards social issues such as homelessness. Regional editions are also produced in Manchester, Newcastle, Ireland, Scotland and Wales.

Features On London life and getting the most out of the Capital on little money; streetlife human-interest features and social issues. Only one or two freelance features carried in each issue usually, so it is best to approach the deputy editor with an idea in the first instance, either by phone or in writing. Max. 1400 words. *Payment* £150 for 1000 words (main feature) but the majority of work is donated to help the homeless (a percentage of the proceeds from sales goes directly to the homeless).

News *Lucy Johnston* Hard-hitting social injustice-orientated stories, with the emphasis on London. *No payment.*

Fiction Must be written by homeless people. Not interested otherwise.

Special Pages Finance, sport, arts, etc. Reviews and news. Max. 300 words. *No payment.*

Birds

The Lodge, Sandy, Bedfordshire SG19 2DL
☎01767 680551   Fax 01767 692365
Owner *Royal Society for the Protection of Birds*
Editor *R. A. Hume*
Circulation 504,000

QUARTERLY magazine which covers not only wild birds but also wildlife and related conservation topics. No interest in features on pet birds or 'rescued' sick/injured/orphaned ones. Mss or ideas welcome. On the look-out for photo features (colour transparencies) from photographers. Especially interested in unusual bird behaviour. 'No captive birds, please.'

Birdwatch

310 Bow House, 153-159 Bow Road, London E3 2SE
☎0181 983 1855   Fax 0181 983 0246
Owner *Solo Publishing*
Editor *Dominic Mitchell*
Circulation 20,000

FOUNDED 1991. MONTHLY high-quality magazine featuring illustrated articles on all aspects of birds and birdwatching, especially in Britain. No unsolicited mss. Approach in writing with synopsis of 100 words maximum.

Features *Dominic Mitchell* Unusual angles/personal accounts, if well-written. Articles of an educative or practical nature suited to the readership. Maximum 2000-3000 words.

Fiction *Dominic Mitchell* Very little opportunity although occasional short story published. Maximum 1500 words.

News *Tim Harris* Very rarely use external material.

Payment £40 per 1000 words.

Black Beauty & Hair

Hawker Consumer Publications Ltd, 13 Park House, 140 Battersea Park Road, London SW11 4NB
☎0171 720 2108   Fax 0171 498 3023
Owner *Hawker Consumer Publications Ltd*
Editor *Irene Shelley*
Circulation 21,323

QUARTERLY with two annual specials: Bridal issue in March, hairstyle book in October. Black beauty and fashion magazine with emphasis on humorous but authoritative articles relating to clothes, hair, lifestyle, sexual politics, women's interests, etc. Unsolicited contributions welcome.

Features Beauty and fashion pieces welcome from writers with a sound knowledge of the Afro-Caribbean beauty scene plus bridal features. Minimum 1000 words.
Payment £85 per 1000 words.

Boat International
5-7 Kingston Hill, Kingston upon Thames, Surrey KT2 7PW
☎0181 547 2662   Fax 0181 547 1201
Owner *Edisea Ltd*
Editor *Nicholas Jeffery*
Circulation 24,000

FOUNDED 1983. MONTHLY. Unsolicited mss welcome. Approach with ideas in writing and s.a.e.
Features Maximum 2000 words.
News Maximum 300 words.
Payment £100 per 1000 words.

Book and Magazine Collector
43-45 St. Mary's Road, London W5 5RQ
☎0181 579 1082   Fax 0181 566 2024
Owner *John Dean*
Editor *Crispin Jackson*
Circulation 12,000

FOUNDED 1984. MONTHLY. Contains articles about collectable authors/publications/subjects. Unsolicited mss welcome – but write first. Must be bibliographical and include a full bibliography and price guide. Not interested in purely biographical features. Approach in writing with ideas.
Features Maximum length 4000 words.
Payment £30 per 1000 words.

The Book Collector
20 Maple Grove, London NW9 8QY
☎0181 200 5004   Fax 0181 200 5004
Owner *The Collector Ltd*
Editor *Nicolas J. Barker*
FOUNDED 1950. QUARTERLY magazine containing matters of bibliographical interest.

Bookdealer
Suite 34, 26 Charing Cross Road, London WC2H 0DH
☎0171 240 5890   Fax 0171 379 5770
Editor *Barry Shaw*
WEEKLY trade paper which acts almost exclusively as a platform for people wishing to buy or sell rare/out-of-print books. Eight-page editorial only; occasional articles and book reviews by regular freelance writers.

Books
43 Museum Street, London WC1A 1LY
☎0171 404 0304   Fax 0171 242 0762
Editor *Liz Thomson*
Circulation 130,000

Formerly *Books and Bookmen*. Consumer magazine dealing chiefly with features about authors and reviews of books. Carries few commissioned pieces.
Payment negotiable.

Books in Wales
See **Llais Llyfrau**

The Bookseller
12 Dyott Street, London WC1A 1DF
☎0171 420 6000   Fax 0171 836 6381
Owner *J. Whitaker & Sons Ltd*
Editor *Louis Baum*

Trade journal of the publishing and book trade – the essential guide to what is being done to whom. Trade news and features, including special features, company news, publishing trends, etc. Unsolicited mss rarely used as most writing is either done in-house or commissioned from experts within the trade. Approach in writing first.
Features *Jenny Bell*
News *Jason Cowley*

Boyz
See **The Pink Paper**

Brides and Setting Up Home
Vogue House, Hanover Square, London W1R 0AD
☎0171 499 9080   Fax 0171 460 6369
Owner *Condé Nast Publications Ltd*
Editor *Sandra Boler*
Circulation 64,263

BI-MONTHLY. Much of the magazine is produced in-house, but a good, relevant feature on cakes, jewellery, music, flowers, etc. is always welcome. Maximum 1000 words. Prospective contributors should telephone with an idea in the first instance.

British Birds
Fountains, Park Lane, Blunham, Bedford MK44 3NJ
☎01767 640025   Fax 01767 640025
Owner *British Birds Ltd*
Editor *Dr J. T. R. Sharrock*
Circulation 10,000

FOUNDED 1907. MONTHLY ornithological magazine published by non-profit-making company. Features annual *Reports on Rare Birds in Great Britain*, bird news from official national correspondents throughout Europe and sponsored competitions for Bird Photograph of the Year, Bird Illustrator of the Year and Young Ornithologists of the Year. Unsolicited mss welcome from ornithologists only.

Features Well-researched, original material relating to Western Palearctic birds welcome. Maximum 6000 words.

News *Bob Scott/Wendy Dickson* Items ranging from conservation to humour. Maximum 200 words.

Payment only for photographs, drawings and paintings.

British Chess Magazine

The Chess Shop, 69 Masbro Road, London W14 OLS
☎0171 603 2877   Fax 0171 371 1477
Owner *Murray Chandler*
Editor *Murray Chandler*

FOUNDED 1881. MONTHLY. Emphasis on tournaments, the history of chess and chess-related literature. Approach in writing with ideas. Unsolicited mss not welcome unless from qualified chess experts and players.

British Medical Journal

BMA House, Tavistock Square, London WC1H 9JR
☎0171 387 4499   Fax 0171 383 6418
Owner *British Medical Association*
Editor *Professor Richard Smith*

No market for freelance writers.

British Philatelic Bulletin

Royal Mail, Royal London House, Finsbury Square, London EC2A 1NL
Owner *Royal Mail*
Editor *J. R. Holman*
Circulation 40,000

FOUNDED 1963. MONTHLY. News and features on British stamps, postmarks, postal history and services; exhibition reports, book reviews. Unsolicited mss considered.

Features On British stamps or postal history. Non-British stamps are mentioned only in articles on stamp design or thematic collecting. Maximum 2000 words but longer articles may be serialised. *Payment £30 per 1000 words.*

News Short items on British philatelic events. *No payment.*

British Railway Modelling

The Maltings, West Street, Bourne, Lincolnshire PE10 9PH
☎01778 393313   Fax 01778 394748
Owner *Warners Group Holdings Plc*
Editor *David Brown*
Assistant Editor *Alan Burrows*
Circulation 17,594

FOUNDED 1993. MONTHLY. A general magazine for the practising modeller. Unsolicited mss welcome. Interested in features on quality models, from individual items to complete layouts. Approach in writing.

Features articles on practical elements of the hobby, e.g. locomotive construction, kit conversions etc. Layout features and articles on individual items which represent high standards of the railway modelling art. Maximum length 6000 words (single feature). *Payment* up to £35 per published page.

News news and reviews containing the model railway trade, new products etc. Maximum length 1000 words. *Payment* up to £35 per published page.

Broadcast

33–39 Bowling Green Lane, London EC1R 0DA
☎0171 505 8014   Fax 0171 505 8050
Owner *EMAP Business Communications*
Editor *Mike Jones*
Circulation 11,200

FOUNDED 1960. WEEKLY. Opportunities for freelance contributions. Write to the relevant editor in the first instance.

Features *Mark McNulty* Any broadcasting issue. Maximum 1500 words.

News *Jacey Lamerton* Broadcasting news. Maximum 400 words.

Payment £180 per 1000 words.

Brownie

17–19 Buckingham Palace Road, London SW1W 0PT
☎0171 834 6242   Fax 0171 828 8317
Owner *The Guide Association*
Editor *Marion Thompson*
Circulation 30,000

FOUNDED 1962. MONTHLY. Aimed at Brownie members aged 7–10, plus an 8-page pull-out section for Rainbow Guides aged 5–7.

Articles Crafts and simple make-it-yourself items using inexpensive or scrap materials.

Features Of general interest (500–600 words).

Fiction Brownie content an advantage. No adventures involving unaccompanied children in dangerous situations – day or night. Maximum 1000 words.

Payment £40 per 1000 words pro rata.

Building

Builder House, 1 Millharbour, London E14 9RA

☎0171 560 4141   Fax 0171 560 4004

Owner *The Builder Group*
Editor *Peter Bill*
Circulation 23,000

FOUNDED 1842. WEEKLY. Features articles on aspects of the modern building industry. Unsolicited mss are not welcome but freelancers with specialist knowledge of the industry are often used.

Features Focus on the modern industry. No building history required. Maximum 1000 words.

News Maximum 300 words.

Payment by arrangement.

The Burlington Magazine

14–16 Duke's Road, London WC1H 9AD

☎0171 388 1228   Fax 0171 388 1230

Owner *The Burlington Magazine Publications Ltd*
Editor *Caroline Elam*

FOUNDED 1903. MONTHLY. Unsolicited contributions welcome on the subject of art history provided they are previously unpublished. All preliminary approaches should be made in writing.

Exhibition Reviews Usually commissioned, but occasionally unsolicited reviews are published if appropriate. Maximum 1000 words.

Articles Maximum 4500 words. *Payment* £100 (maximum).

Shorter Notices Maximum 2000 words. *Payment* £50 (maximum).

Business Brief

PO Box 582, Five Oaks, St Saviour, Jersey JE4 8XQ

☎01534 25517   Fax 01534 38889

Owner *Michael Stephen Publishers*
Editor *Harry McRandle*
Circulation 4,100

FOUNDED 1989. MONTHLY magazine covering business developments in the Channel Islands and how they affect the local market. Interested in business-orientated articles only – 800 words maximum.

Payment £7 per 100 words.

Business Life

Haymarket House, 1 Oxendon Street, London SW1Y 4EE

☎0171 925 2544   Fax 0171 839 4508

Owner *Premier Magazines*
Editor *Sandra Harris*
Editorial Assistant *Catherine Flanagan*
Circulation 193,000

MONTHLY. Glossy business travel magazine with few opportunities for freelancers. Distributed on BA European routes, TAT and Deutsche BA only. Unsolicited mss not welcome. Approach with ideas in writing only.

Business Traveller

Compass House, 22 Redan Place, London W2 4SZ

☎0171 229 7799   Fax 0171 229 9441

Owner *Perry Publications*
Editor *Gillian Upton*
Circulation 55,386

MONTHLY. Consumer publication. Opportunities exist for freelance writers but unsolicited contributions tend to be 'irrelevant to our market'. Would-be contributors advised to study the magazine first. Approach in writing with ideas.

Payment varies.

Camcorder User

57–59 Rochester Place, London NW1 9JU

☎0171 485 0011   Fax 0171 482 6269

Owner *W. V. Publications*
Editor *Christine Morgan*
Circulation 23,850

FOUNDED 1988. MONTHLY magazine dedicated to camcorders, with features on creative technique, shooting advice, new equipment, accessory round-ups and interesting applications on location. Unsolicited mss, illustrations and pictures welcome. *Payment* negotiable.

Campaign

174 Hammersmith Road, London W6 7JP

☎0171 413 4036   Fax 0171 413 4507

Owner *Haymarket Publishing Ltd*
Editor *Stefano Hatfield*
Circulation 15,813

FOUNDED 1968. WEEKLY. Lively magazine serving the advertising and related industries. Freelance contributors are best advised to write in the first instance.

Features Articles of 1500–2000 words.

News Relevant news stories of up to 300 words.

Payment negotiable/£35–50 for news.

Camping and Caravanning

Greenfields House, Westwood Way,
Coventry, Warwickshire CV4 8JH
☎01203 694995   Fax 01203 694886

Owner *Camping and Caravanning Club*
Editor *Peter Frost*
Circulation 121,576

FOUNDED 1901. MONTHLY. Interested in journalists with camping and caravanning knowledge. Write with ideas for features in the first instance.

Features Outdoor pieces in general, plus items on specific regions of Britain. Maximum 1200 words. Illustrations to support text essential.

Camping Magazine

5 Sun Street, Lewes, East Sussex
BN7 2QB
☎01273 477421

Owner *Garnett Dickinson Publishing*
Editor *John Lloyd*

FOUNDED 1961. MONTHLY magazine with features on walking and camping. Aims to reflect this enjoyment by encouraging readers to appreciate the outdoors and to pursue an active camping holiday, whether as a family in a frame tent or as a lightweight backpacker. Articles that have the flavour of the camping lifestyle without being necessarily expeditionary or arduous are always welcome. Study of the magazine is advised in the first instance. Ideas welcome. Contact editor by phone before sending mss.
Payment negotiable.

Canal and Riverboat

c/o Burrows Design Works,
Jonathan Scott Hall, Thorne Road, Norwich,
Norfolk NR1 1UH
☎01603 623856   Fax 01603 623856

Owner *A. E. Morgan Publications Ltd*
Editor *Chris Cattrall*
Circulation 26,000

Covers all aspects of waterways, narrow boats and cruisers. Contributions welcome. Make initial approach in writing.

Features *Chris Cattrall* Waterways, narrow boats and motor cruisers, cruising reports, practical advice, etc. Unusual ideas and personal comments are particularly welcome. Maximum 2000 words. *Payment* around £50 per page.

News *Chris Cattrall* Items of up to 300 words welcome on the Inland Waterways System, plus photographs if possible. *Payment* £15.

Car Mechanics

Kelsey Publishing, 77 High Street,
Beckenham, Kent BR3 1AN
☎0181 658 3531   Fax 0181 650 8035

Owner *Kelsey Publishing*
Editor *Peter Simpson*
Circulation 35,000

MONTHLY. Practical guide to DIY, maintenance and repair of post-1978 cars. Unsolicited mss, preferably with good-quality colour prints or transparencies, welcome 'at sender's risk'. Ideas preferred. Approach by phone.

Features Good, technical, entertaining and well-researched material welcome.
Payment by arrangement.

Caravan Life

The Maltings, West Street, Bourne,
Lincolnshire PH10 9PH
☎01778 391166   Fax 01778 394748

Editor *Stuart Craig*

FOUNDED 1987. Magazine for experienced caravanners and enthusiasts providing practical and useful information and product evaluation. Opportunities for caravanning, relevant touring and travel material with good-quality colour photographs.

Caravan Magazine

Link House, Dingwall Avenue, Croydon,
Surrey CR9 2TA
☎0181 686 2599Fax 0181 781 6044/760 0973

Owner *Link House Magazines Ltd*
Editor *Barry Williams*
Circulation 23,834

FOUNDED 1933. MONTHLY. Unsolicited mss welcome. Approach in writing with ideas. All correspondence should go direct to the editor.

Features Touring with strong caravan bias and technical/DIY features. Maximum 1500 words.
Payment by arrangement.

Caribbean Times/Asian Times

3rd Floor, Tower House, 141-149 Fonthill Road, London N4 3HF
☎0171 281 1191   Fax 0171 263 9656

Owner *Arif Ali*
Editor *Arif Ali*

Two WEEKLY community papers for the Asian, African and Caribbean communities in Britain. *Caribbean Times* has a circulation of 22,500 and was founded in 1981; *Asian Times* was founded two years later and has a circulation of 33,000. Interested in general, local and international issues relevant to these communities. Approach in writing with ideas for submission.

Carmarthenshire Life

21 High Street, Haverford West,
Pembrokeshire SA61 2BW
☎01437 768828   Fax 01437 760926

Owner *United Provincial Newspapers*
Editor *Alison Heighton*

FOUNDED 1995. MONTHLY county magazine with articles on local history, issues, characters, off-beat stories with good colour or b&w photographs. No country diaries, short stories or poems. Most articles are commissioned from known freelancers but 'always prepared to consider ideas from new writers'. No mss. Send cuttings of previous work (published or not) and synopsis to the editor.

Cars and Car Conversions Magazine

Link House, Dingwall Avenue, Croydon,
Surrey CR9 2TA
☎0181 686 2599   Fax 0181 781 6042

Owner *Link House Magazines Ltd*
Editor *Steve Bennett*
Circulation 46,537

FOUNDED 1965. MONTHLY. Unsolicited mss welcome but prospective contributors are advised to make initial contact by telephone.
Features Technical articles on current motorsport and unusual sport-orientated road cars. Length by arrangement. *Payment* negotiable.

Cat World

10 Western Road, Shoreham by Sea,
West Sussex BN43 5WD
☎01273 462000   Fax 01273 455994

Owner *D. M. & J. H. Colchester*
Editor *Joan Moore*
Circulation 19,000

FOUNDED 1981. MONTHLY. Unsolicited mss welcome but initial approach in writing preferred.
Features Lively, first-hand experience features on every aspect of the cat. Breeding features and veterinary articles by acknowledged experts only. Maximum 1000 words. *Payment* £35 per 1000 words.
News Short, concise, factual or humorous items concerning cats. Maximum 100 words. *Payment* £5.
Poems Maximum 50 words. *Payment* £7.50.

Catch

Albert Square, Dundee DD1 9QJ
☎01382 223131   Fax 01382 200880

Owner *D. C. Thomson & Co. Ltd*
Editor *Jacquie Fraser*
Assistant Editor *Nicola Gilray Scott*
General Features *Michelle Simpson*
Beauty *Susan Jamieson*
Health *Joanna Scott*

FOUNDED 1990. MONTHLY magazine for young women aged 16–19; typical reader viewed as 17 and single. Works towards a much broader editorial base than *Looks*, going beyond the beauty and personality profile pages, and aims to bridge the gap between magazines like *Just Seventeen* and titles for the older woman.

Catholic Herald

Lamb's Passage, Bunhill Row, London
EC1Y 8TQ
☎0171 588 3101   Fax 0171 256 9728

Editor *To be appointed*
Deputy Editor *Piers McGrandle*
Literary Editor *Damian Thompson*
Circulation 22,000

Interested not only in straight Catholic issues but also in general humanitarian matters, social policies, the Third World, the arts and books. *Payment* by arrangement.

Certified Accountant

19 Rutland Street, Cork, Republic of Ireland
☎00 353 21313 855   Fax 00 353 21313 496

Editor *Brian O'Kane*
Circulation 59,000

MONTHLY. Specialist, professional readership with worldwide circulation. Unsolicited mss welcome though most features tend to be commissioned. Make initial contact in writing. No fiction.
Features Maximum 1750 words. *Payment* £135 per 1000 words.

Challenge

Revenue Buildings, Chapel Road, Worthing,
West Sussex BN11 1BQ
☎01903 214198   Fax 01903 217663

Owner *Challenge Publishing*
Editor *Donald Banks*
Circulation 80,000

FOUNDED 1958. MONTHLY Christian newspaper which welcomes contributions. Send for copy of writers' guidelines in the first instance.
Fiction Short children's stories. Maximum 600 words.

News Items of up to 500 words (preferably with pictures) 'showing God at work', and human interest photo stories. 'Churchy' items not wanted. Stories of professional sportsmen who are Christians always wanted but check first to see if their story has already been used.

Women's Page Relevant items of interest welcome.

Payment negotiable.

Champs-Elysées
119 Altenburg Gardens, The Conservatory, Bakery Place, London SW11 1JQ
☎0171 738 9323   Fax 0171 738 0707
Owner *Wes Green*
European Editor *David Ralston*

FOUNDED 1984. MONTHLY audio magazine for advanced speakers of French, German, Italian and Spanish issued in two parts: Part One is an hour-long programme (original stories, interviews and songs) in one of the above languages on cassette; Part Two is a booklet comprising a complete transcript with a glossary of difficult words plus features in English relating to topics covered on the tape. Interested in receiving ideas for unusual, well-researched stories for a sophisticated and well-educated readership.

Features European culture and travel. 1500 words maximum. *Payment* £200 per 1000 words. Approach in writing in the first instance.

Chapman
4 Broughton Place, Edinburgh EH1 3RX
☎0131 557 2207   Fax 0131 556 9565
Owner *Joy M. Hendry*
Editor *Joy M. Hendry*
Circulation 2000

FOUNDED 1970. QUARTERLY. Scotland's quality literary magazine. Features poetry, short works of fiction, criticism, reviews and articles on theatre, politics, language and the arts. Unsolicited material welcome if accompanied by s.a.e.. Approach in writing unless discussion is needed. Priority is given to full-time writers.

Features *Joy Hendry* Topics of literary interest, especially Scottish literature, theatre, culture or politics. Maximum 5000 words.

Fiction *Joy Hendry* Short stories, occasionally novel extracts if self-contained. Maximum 6000 words. *Payment* £15 per 1000 words.

Special Pages *Joy Hendry* Poetry, both UK and non-UK in translation (mainly, but not necessarily, European). *Payment* £8 per published page.

(*Payment* can be had in each category in equivalent copies at discount rate.)

Chapter One
See **Alliance of Literary Societies**

Chat
King's Reach Tower, Stamford Street, London SE1 9LS
☎0171 261 6565   Fax 0171 261 6534
Owner *IPC Magazines Ltd*
Editor *Ms Terry Tavner*
Circulation 580,000

FOUNDED 1985. WEEKLY general interest women's magazine. Unsolicited mss considered (about 100 received each week). Approach in writing with ideas. Not interested in contributors 'who have never bothered to read *Chat* and don't therefore know what type of magazine it is'.

Features *Karen Swayne* Human interest and humour. Max. 1000 words. *Payment* up to £250 maximum.

Fiction *Shelley Silas* Max. 1,000 words.

Cheshire Life
2nd Floor, Oyston Mill, Strand Road, Preston, Lancashire PR1 8UR
☎01772 722022   Fax 01772 736496
Owner *Life Magazines*
Editor *Patrick O'Neill*
Circulation 11,000

FOUNDED 1934. MONTHLY. Homes, gardens, personalities, business, farming, conservation, heritage, books, fashion, arts, science – anything which has a Cheshire connection somewhere.

Child Education
Villiers House, Clarendon Avenue, Leamington Spa, Warwickshire CV32 5PR
☎01926 887799   Fax 01926 883331
Owner *Scholastic Ltd*
Editor *Gill Moore*
Circulation 61,000

FOUNDED 1923. MONTHLY magazine aimed at nursery, pre-school playgroup, infant and first teachers. Articles from teachers, relating to education for 4–7-year age group, are welcome. Maximum 1700 words. Approach in writing with synopsis. No unsolicited mss.

Choice
Apex House, Oundle Road, Peterborough, Cambridgeshire PE2 9NP
☎01733 555123   Fax 01733 898487
Owner *EMAP/Bayard Presse*
Editor *Sue Dobson*

Circulation 120,000

MONTHLY full-colour, lively and informative magazine for people aged 50 plus which helps them get the most out of their lives, time and money after full-time work.

Features Real–life stories, hobbies, interesting (older) people, British heritage and countryside, involving activities for active bodies and minds, health, competitions. Unsolicited mss read (s.a.e. for return of material); write with ideas and copies of cuttings if new contributor. No phone calls, please.

Rights/News All items affecting the magazine's readership are written by experts. Areas of interest include pensions, state benefits, health, money, property, legal, and caring for elderly relatives.

Payment by arrangement.

Christian Herald

See **New Christian Herald**

Church Music Quarterly

151 Mount View Road, London N4 4JT
☎0181 341 6408   Fax 0181 340 0021
Owner *Royal School of Church Music*
Editor *Trevor Ford*
Associate Editor *Marianne Barton*
Circulation 13,700

QUARTERLY. Contributions welcome. Telephone in the first instance.

Features *Trevor Ford* Articles on Church music or related subjects considered. Maximum 2000 words.

Payment £60 per page.

Church of England Newspaper

10 Little College Street, London SW1P 3SH
☎0171 976 7760   Fax 0171 976 0783
Owner *Parliamentary Communications Ltd*
Editor *Colin Blakely*
Circulation 11,600

FOUNDED 1828. WEEKLY. Almost all material is commissioned but unsolicited mss are considered. Some fiction and poetry, but rarely.

Features *Andrew Carey* Preliminary enquiry essential. Maximum 1200 words.

News *Emma Watkins* Items must be sent promptly and should have a church/Christian relevance. Maximum 200-400 words.

Payment by negotiation.

Church Times

33 Upper Street, London N1 0PN
☎0171 359 4570   Fax 0171 226 3073
Owner *Hymns Ancient & Modern*

Editor *Paul Handley*
Circulation 38,990

FOUNDED 1863. WEEKLY. Unsolicited mss considered.

Features *Paul Handley* Religious topics. Max. 1600 words. *Payment* £100 per 1000 words.

News *Paul Handley* Occasional reports (commissions only) on out-of-London events.

Payment by arrangement.

Classic Boat

Link House, Dingwall Avenue, Croydon, Surrey CR9 2TA
☎0181 686 2599   Fax 0181 781 6535
Owner *Boating Publications Ltd*
Editor *Robin Gates*
Circulation 14,611

FOUNDED 1987. MONTHLY. Traditional boats and classic yachts old and new; maritime history. Unsolicited mss, particularly if supported by good photos, are welcome. Sail and power boat pieces considered. Approach in writing with ideas. Interested in well-researched stories on all nautical matters. Cruising articles welcome. No fiction or poetry. Contributor's notes available (s.a.e.).

Features Boatbuilding, boat history and design, events, yachts and working boats. Material must be well-informed and supported where possible by good-quality or historic photos. Maximum 3000 words. Classic is defined by excellence of design and construction – the boat need not be old and wooden! *Payment* £75–100 per published page.

News Discarded famous classic boats, events, boatbuilders, etc. Maximum 500 words. *Payment* according to merit.

Classic Cars

Kings Reach Tower, Stamford Street, London SE1 9LS
☎0171 261 5858   Fax 0171 261 6731
Owner *EMAP National*
Editor *Robert Coucher*
Circulation 81,845

FOUNDED 1973. MONTHLY classic car magazine containing entertaining and informative articles about old cars and associated personalities.

Classical Guitar

Olsover House, 43 Sackville Road, Newcastle upon Tyne NE6 5TA
☎0191 276 0448   Fax 0191 276 1623
Owner *Ashley Mark Publishing Co.*
Editor *Colin Cooper*
FOUNDED 1982. MONTHLY.

Features *Colin Cooper* Usually written by staff writers. Maximum 1500 words. *Payment* by arrangement.

News *Thérèse Wassily Saba* Small paragraphs and festival concert reports welcome. *No payment.*

Reviews *Chris Kilvington* Concert reviews of up to 250 words. Approach in writing.

Classical Music

241 Shaftesbury Avenue, London WC2H 8EH
☎0171 333 1742   Fax 0171 333 1769

Owner *Rhinegold Publishing Ltd*
Editor *Keith Clarke*

FOUNDED 1976. FORTNIGHTLY. A specialist magazine using precisely targeted news and feature articles aimed at the music business. Most material is commissioned but professionally written unsolicited mss are occasionally published. Freelance contributors may approach in writing with an idea but should familiarise themselves beforehand with the style and market of the magazine.

Payment negotiable.

Classical Piano

241 Shaftesbury Avenue, London WC2H 8EH
☎0171 333 1724   Fax 0171 333 1769

Owner *Rhinegold Publishing*
Editor *Jessica Duchen*
Circulation 11,000

FOUNDED 1993. BI-MONTHLY magazine containing features, profiles, technical information, news, reviews of interest to those with a serious amateur or professional concern with pianos or their playing. Unsolicited mss occasionally accepted but no unsolicited reviews, artist profiles or musical analysis. Freelance material should be well-written, legible and pertain to the piano at a high level. Approach with ideas in writing.

Climber

7th Floor, The Plaza Tower, East Kilbride, Glasgow G74 1LW
☎01355 246444   Fax 01355 263013

Owner *Caledonian Magazines Ltd*
Editor *Tom Prentice*
Circulation 16,000

FOUNDED 1962. MONTHLY. Unsolicited mss welcome (they receive about ten a day). Ideas welcome.

Features Freelance features are accepted on climbing, mountaineering and hill-walking in the UK and abroad, but the standard of writing must be extremely high. Maximum 2000

words. *Payment* negotiable.

News No freelance opportunities as all items are handled in-house.

Clothing World Magazine

578 Kingston Road, Raynes Park, London SW20 8DR
☎0181 540 8381   Fax 0181 540 8388

Owner *Company Clothing Information Services Ltd*
Editor *Carole Bull*
Circulation 6000

A leading source of technical and business information for the UK's sophisticated clothing industry. Unsolicited mss welcome on any aspect of the design, manufacture and distribution of clothing.

Club International

2 Archer Street, London W1V 7HE
☎0171 734 9191   Fax 0171 734 5030

Owner *Paul Raymond*
Editor *Robert Swift*
Circulation 180,000

FOUNDED 1972. MONTHLY. Features and short humorous items in the style of *Viz, Private Eye*, etc.

Features Maximum 1000 words.
Shorts 200–750 words.
Payment negotiable.

Coin News

Token Publishing Ltd, PO Box 14, Honiton, Devon EX14 9YP
☎01404 45414   Fax 01404 45313

Owner *J. W. Mussell and Carol Hartman*
Editor *J. W. Mussell*
Circulation 10,000

FOUNDED 1964. MONTHLY. Contributions welcome. Approach by phone in the first instance.

Features Opportunity exists for well-informed authors 'who know the subject and do their homework'. Maximum 2500 words.

Payment £20 per 1000 words.

Combat and Militaria

Castle House, 97 High Street, Colchester, Essex CO1 1TH
☎01206 540621   Fax 01206 564214

Owner *Maze Media Ltd*
Editor *James Marchington*

MONTHLY publication about military affairs. Unsolicited mss and photographs welcome on any current military matters.

Payment by agreement.

Commerce Magazine

Station House, Station Road, Newport
Pagnell, Milton Keynes MK16 0AG
☎01908 614477   Fax 01908 616441

Owner *Holcot Press Group*
Group Editor *Steve Brennan*
Circulation 35,000

MONTHLY. Ideas welcome. Approach by phone
or in writing first.

Features *Isabelle Morgan* By-lined articles
frequently used. Generally 750–800 words with
photos.

News Handled in-house.

Special Pages Throughout the year – media
and marketing; building and construction;
finance and professional; office update.

No payment.

Company

National Magazine House, 72 Broadwick
Street, London W1V 2BP
☎0171 439 5000   Fax 0171 439 5117

Owner *National Magazine Co. Ltd*
Editor *Fiona McIntosh*
Circulation 305,000

MONTHLY. Glossy women's magazine appealing
to the independent and intelligent young
woman. A good market for freelancers: 'We
look for great newsy features relevant to young
British women'. Keen to encourage bright, new,
young talent, but uncommissioned material is
rarely accepted. Feature outlines are the only
sensible approach in the first instance. Maximum
1500–2000 words. Features to *Rachel Loos*.

Payment £250 per 1000 words.

Company Clothing Magazine

Willowbrook House, The Green, Leire,
Lutterworth, Leicestershire LE17 5HL
☎010455 202088   Fax 010455 202692

Owner *Company Clothing Information*
  Services Ltd
Editor *Carole Bull*
Circulation 12,000

Only UK magazine dedicated to the corporate
clothing industry. Unsolicited mss welcome on
any aspect of business clothing and workwear.

Complete Car

Compass House, 22 Redan Place, London
W2 4SZ
☎0171 229 7799   Fax 0171 229 7846

Owner *Perry Motorpress Ltd*
Editor-in-Chief *Wolfgang Koenig*

Circulation 60,000

FOUNDED 1994. MONTHLY car magazine.
Unsolicited mss are rarely, if ever, used.
Prospective contributors are advised to make
initial approach in writing 'once they have read
the magazine from cover to cover at least once'.

Computer Weekly

Quadrant House, The Quadrant, Sutton,
Surrey SM2 5AS
☎0181 652 3122   Fax 0181 652 8979

Owner *Reed Business Publishing*
Editor *Helena Sturridge*
Circulation 120,000

FOUNDED 1966. Freelance contributions welcome.

Features *David Evans* Always looking for
good new writers with specialised industry
knowledge. Previews and show features on
industry events welcome. Maximum 2000
words.

News *Karl Schneider* Some openings for
regional or foreign news items. Maximum 300
words.

Payment Up to £50 for stories/tips.

Computing, The IT Newspaper

32–34 Broadwick Street, London W1A 2HG
☎0171 316 9158   Fax 0171 316 9160

Owner *VNU Business Publications Ltd*
Editor *Dr Jerry Sanders*
Circulation 114,000

WEEKLY newspaper.

Features *Janine Milne*
News *Bill Boyle*
Unsolicited mss *Linda Leung*

Unsolicited technical articles welcome.
Please enclose s.a.e. for return.

Payment Technical notes: £60; book
reviews: £30; feature articles: £170 per 1000
words; news leads (leading to story): £30; fully
researched story: £60 per 350 words.

Contemporary Review

Cheam Business Centre, 14 Upper Mulgrave
Road, Cheam, Surrey SM2 7AZ
☎0181 643 4846   Fax 0181 241 7507

Owner *Contemporary Review Co. Ltd*
Editor *Dr Richard Mullen*

FOUNDED 1866. MONTHLY. One of the first
periodicals to devote considerable space to the
arts. Covers a wide spectrum of interests, including home affairs and politics, literature and the
arts, history, travel and religion. No fiction.
Maximum 3000 words.

Literary Editor *Betty Abel* Monthly book section with reviews which are generally commissioned.

Payment £5 per page.

Cosmopolitan

National Magazine House, 72 Broadwick Street, London W1V 2BP

☎0171 439 5000   Fax 0171 439 5016

Owner *National Magazine Co. Ltd*
Editor *Mandi Norwood*
Circulation 456,131

MONTHLY. Designed to appeal to the mid-twenties, modern–minded female. Popular mix of articles, with emphasis on relationships and careers, and hard news. Known to have a policy of not considering unsolicited mss but always on the look-out for 'new writers with original and relevant ideas and a strong voice'. Send short synopsis of idea. All would-be writers should be familiar with the magazine.

Payment about £200 per 1000 words.

Cotswold Life

7 Ambrose Street, Cheltenham, Gloucestershire GL50 8LQ

☎01242 226373   Fax 01242 516320

Owner *Beshara Press*
Editor *John Drinkwater*
Circulation 10,000

FOUNDED 1968. MONTHLY. News and features on life in the Cotswolds. Most news written in-house but contributions welcome for features.

Features Interesting places and people, reminiscences of Cotswold life in years gone by, and historical features on any aspect of Cotswold life. Approach in writing in the first instance. Maximum 1500-2000 words.

Payment by negotiation after publication.

Country

Hill Crest Mews, London Road, Baldock, Hertfordshire SG7 6JN

☎01462 490206   Fax 01462 893565

Owner *The Country Gentlemen's Association*
Editor *Barry Turner*
Circulation 25,000

FOUNDED 1893. MONTHLY. The magazine of the Country Gentlemen's Association. News and features covering rural events, countryside, leisure, heritage, homes and gardens. Ideas and sample material welcome; approach in writing in the first instance.

Payment by negotiation.

Country Garden & Smallholding

Broad Leys Publishing Company, Buriton House, Station Road, Newport, Saffron Walden, Essex CB11 3PL

☎01799 540922   Fax 01799 541367

Owner *D. and K. Thear*
Editor *Helen Sears*
Circulation 28,000

FOUNDED 1975. MONTHLY journal dealing with practical country living. Unsolicited mss welcome; around 30 are received each week. Articles should be detailed and practical, based on first-hand knowledge and experience about aspects of small farming and country living.

Country Homes and Interiors

King's Reach Tower, Stamford Street, London SE1 9LS

☎0171 261 6451   Fax 0171 261 6895

Owner *Home Interest Group/IPC Magazines Ltd*
Acting Editor *Caroline Suter*
Circulation 115,000

FOUNDED 1986. MONTHLY. The best approach for prospective contributors is with an idea in writing as unsolicited mss are not welcome.

Features *Dominic Bradbury* Monthly personality interviews of interest to an intelligent, affluent readership (women and men), aged 25–44. Maximum 1200 words. Also hotel reviews, leisure pursuits and weekending pieces in England and abroad. Length 750 words.

Houses *Rebecca Duke* Country-style homes with excellent design ideas. Length 1000 words.

Payment negotiable.

Country Life

King's Reach Tower, Stamford Street, London SE1 9LS

☎0171 261 7058   Fax 0171 261 5139

Owner *IPC Magazines Ltd*
Editor *Clive Aslet*
Circulation 42,066

Features which relate to the countryside, wildlife, rural events, sports and pursuits, and are of interest to well-heeled country dwellers, are welcome. Strong informed material rather than amateur enthusiasm. 'No responsibility can be taken for transparencies/artwork submitted.'

Payment from £120 per 1000 words.

Country Living

National Magazine House, 72 Broadwick Street, London W1V 2BP

☎0171 439 5000   Fax 0171 439 5093

Owner *National Magazine Co. Ltd*

Editor *Susy Smith*
Circulation 182,311

Magazine aimed at country dwellers and town dwellers who love the countryside. Covers people, conservation, wildlife, houses (gardens and interiors) and country businesses. No unsolicited mss.

Payment negotiable.

Country Origins

PO Box 4, Nairn IV12 4HU
☎01667 454441   Fax 01667 454401
Owner *David St John Thomas*
Editor *Hilary Gray*

FOUNDED 1995. QUARTERLY magazine offering a factual look at yesterday's countryside, incorporating family history. No unsolicited mss.

Country Sports

59 Kennington Road, London SE1 7PZ
☎0171 928 4742   Fax 0171 620 1401
Owner *British Field Sports Society*
Editor *Graham Downing*
Circulation 84,000

FOUNDED 1996. QUARTERLY magazine on country sports and conservation issues. No unsolicited mss.

Country Walking

Bretton Court, Bretton, Peterborough, Cambridgeshire PE3 8DZ
☎01733 264666   Fax 01733 261984
Owner *EMAP Plc*
Editor *Lynne Maxwell*
Circulation 40,065

FOUNDED 1987. MONTHLY magazine containing walks, features related to walking and things you see, country crafts, history, nature, photography etc, plus pull-out walks guide containing 28 routes every month. Very few unsolicited mss accepted. An original approach to subjects welcomed. Not interested in book or gear reviews, news cuttings or poor-quality pictures. Approach by phone with ideas.

Features *Lynne Maxwell* reader's story (maximum 1000 words). Health-related features (500-1000 words).

Special Pages *Heather Turley* 'Down your way' section walks. Accurately and recently researched walk and fact file. Points of interest along the way and pictures to illustrate. Please contact for guidelines (unsolicited submissions not often accepted for this section).

Payment not negotiable.

Country-Side

BNA, 48 Russell Way, Higham Ferrers, Northamptonshire NN10 8EJ
☎01933 314672   Fax 01933 314672
Owner *British Naturalists' Association*
Editor *Dr D. Applin*
Circulation *c.* 9,000

FOUNDED 1905. BI-MONTHLY. Conservation and natural history magazine. Unsolicited mss and ideas for features welcome on conservation, environmental and natural history topics. Approach in writing with ideas. Maximum 1400 words.

Payment £50 (with pictures).

The Countryman

Sheep Street, Burford, Oxon OX18 4LH
☎01993 822258   Fax 01993 822703
Owner *Link House Magazines Limited*
Editor *Christopher Hall*
Circulation 50,000

FOUNDED 1927. SIX ISSUES YEARLY. Unsolicited mss with s.a.e. welcome; about 120 received each week. Contributors are strongly advised to study the magazine's content and character in the first instance. Approach in writing with ideas.

The Countryman's Weekly

Yelverton, Devon PL20 7PE
☎01822 855281   Fax 01822 855372
Publisher *Vic Gardner*
Editor *Jayne Willcocks*

FOUNDED 1982. WEEKLY. Unsolicited material welcome.

Features On any country sports topic. Maximum 1000 words.

Payment rates available on request.

The Countrysider's Magazine

PO Box 4, Nairn IV12 4HU
☎01667 454441   Fax 01667 454401
Owner *David St John Thomas*
Editor *Hilary Gray*

FOUNDED 1994 (formerly *Country Talk*). QUARTERLY magazine which celebrates the real living, working countryside.

Features *From Our Correspondent* items from 50 to a maximum of 500 words. Contributors' notes available. Approach in writing in the first instance. In general, unsolicited mss not welcome as 'we have far more material than we can use at present'.

County

70-72 St Mark's Road, Maidenhead,
Berkshire SL6 6DW
☎01628 789444   Fax 01628 789396

Owner *Mr and Mrs Watts*
Editor *Mrs Ashlyn Watts*
Circulation 50,000

FOUNDED 1986. QUARTERLY lifestyle magazine featuring homes, interiors, gardening, fashion and beauty, motoring, leisure and dining. Welcome unsolicited mss. All initial approaches should be made in writing.

The Cricketer International

Third Street, Langton Green, Tunbridge Wells, Kent TN3 0EN
☎01892 862551   Fax 01892 863755

Owner *Ben G. Brocklehurst*
Editor *Peter Perchard*
Circulation 40,000

FOUNDED 1921. MONTHLY. Unsolicited mss considered. Ideas in writing only. No initial discussions by phone. All correspondence should be addressed to the editor.

Cumbria

Dalesman Publishing Co. Ltd, Stable Courtyard, Broughton Hall, Skipton, North Yorkshire BD23 3AE
☎01756 701381   Fax 01756 701326

Owner *Dalesman Publishing Co. Ltd*
Editor *Terry Fletcher*
Circulation 15,300

FOUNDED 1951. MONTHLY. County magazine of strong regional and countryside interest only. Unsolicited mss welcome. Maximum 1000 words. Approach in writing or by phone with feature ideas.

Cycle Sport

King's Reach Tower, Stamford Street, London SE1 9LS
☎0171 261 5588   Fax 0171 261 5758

Owner *IPC Magazines Ltd*
Editor *Andrew Sutcliffe*
Circulation 22,956

Magazine dedicated to professional cycle racing.

Cycling Today

67-71 Goswell Road, London EC1V 7EN
☎0171 410 9410   Fax 0171 410 9440

Owner *Stonehart Group*
Editor *Jerome Smail*
Circulation 20,800

Previously *New Cyclist*. MONTHLY general interest cycling magazine. Unsolicited feature proposals welcome. Not interested in personal accounts such as how you began cycling.

Features Almost any cycling subject. Touring pieces with high-quality transparencies. Submissions welcomed from writers and illustrators with specialist knowledge: e.g. sports medicine, bike mechanics. NB it may take them some time to reply. Maximum 2000 words.

Cycling Weekly

King's Reach Tower, Stamford Street, London SE1 9LS
☎0171 261 5588   Fax 0171 261 5758

Owner *IPC Magazines Ltd*
Editor *Andrew Sutcliffe*
Circulation 38,134

FOUNDED 1891. WEEKLY. All aspects of cycle sport covered. Unsolicited mss and ideas for features welcome. Approach in writing with ideas. Fiction rarely used.

Features Cycle racing, technical material and related areas. Maximum 2000 words. Most work commissioned but interested in seeing new work. *Payment* £60-100 per 1000 words (quality permitting).

News Short news pieces, local news, etc. Maximum 300 words. *Payment* £15 per story.

The Dalesman

Stable Courtyard, Broughton Hall, Skipton, North Yorkshire BD23 3AE
☎01756 701381   Fax 01756 701326

Owner *Dalesman Publishing Co. Ltd*
Editor *Terry Fletcher*
Circulation 55,000

FOUNDED 1939. Now the biggest-selling regional publication of its kind in the country. MONTHLY magazine with articles of specific Yorkshire interest. Unsolicited mss welcome; receive approximately ten per day. Initial approach in writing preferred. Maximum 2000 words. *Payment* negotiable.

Dance & Dancers

214 Panther House, 38 Mount Pleasant, London WC1X 0AP
☎0171 837 2711   Fax 0171 837 2711

Owner *Dance & Dancers Ltd*
Editor *John Percival*

FOUNDED 1950. MONTHLY magazine covering ballet and modern dance throughout the world. Some opportunity here for 'good writers with good knowledge of dance', but preliminary discussion is strongly advised. *Payment* nominal.

Dance Theatre Journal

Laban Centre for Movement & Dance, Laurie Grove, London SE14 6NH

☎0181 692 4070   Fax 0181 694 8749

Owner *Laban Centre for Movement & Dance*
Editor *Ann Nugent*

FOUNDED 1982. QUARTERLY. Interested in features on every aspect of the contemporary dance scene, particularly issues such as the funding policy for dance, critical assessments of choreographers' work and the latest developments in the various schools of contemporary dance. Unsolicited mss welcome. Length 1000–3000 words.

Payment varies 'according to age and experience'.

The Dancing Times

Clerkenwell House, 45–47 Clerkenwell Green, London EC1R 0EB

☎0171 250 3006   Fax 0171 253 6679

Owner *The Dancing Times Ltd*
Editor *Mary Clarke*

FOUNDED 1910. MONTHLY. Freelance suggestions welcome from specialist dance writers and photographers only. Approach in writing.

Darts World

9 Kelsey Park Road, Beckenham, Kent BR3 6LH

☎0181 650 6580   Fax 0181 650 2534

Owner *World Magazines Ltd*
Editor *A. J. Wood*
Circulation 24,500

Features Single articles or series on technique and instruction. Max. 1200 words.
Fiction Short stories with darts theme of no more than 1000 words.
News Tournament reports and general or personality news required. Max. 800 words.
Payment negotiable.

Dateline Magazine

23 Abingdon Road, London W8 6AL

☎01869 324100   Fax 01869 324529

Owner *John Patterson*
Editor *Peter Bennett/Nicky Boult*
Circulation 23,000

FOUNDED 1976. MONTHLY magazine for single people. Unsolicited mss welcome.

Features Anything of interest to, or directly concerning, single people. Max. 2500 words.
News Items required at least six weeks ahead. Max. 2500 words.
Payment from £45 per 1000 words; £10 per illustration/picture used (black & white preferred at present).

David Hall's Coarse Fishing Magazine

69 Temple Street, Rugby, Warwickshire CV21 3TB

☎01788 535218   Fax 01788 541845

Owner *Chrisreel Ltd*
Editor *John Hunter*
Circulation 50,000

FOUNDED 1985. MONTHLY. Unsolicited mss welcome but initial approach by phone or in writing preferred.

Features Any general coarse angling interest accepted. Length 1000–2000 words.
Reviews Product reviews welcome.
Payment variable.

Day by Day

Woolacombe House, 141 Woolacombe Road, Blackheath, London SE3 8QP

☎0181 856 6249

Owner *Loverseed Press*
Editor *Patrick Richards*
Circulation 24,000

FOUNDED 1963. MONTHLY. News commentary and digest of national and international affairs, with reviews of the arts (books, plays, art exhibitions, films, opera, musicals) and county cricket reports among regular slots. Unsolicited mss welcome (s.a.e. essential). Approach in writing with ideas. Contributors are advised to study the magazine in the first instance.

News *Ronald Mallone* Interested in themes connected with non-violence and social justice only. Maximum 600 words.
Features No scope for freelance contributions here.
Fiction *Michael Gibson* Very rarely published.
Poems *Michael Gibson* Short poems in line with editorial principles considered. Maximum 20 lines.
Payment negotiable.

Decanter

Priory House, 8 Battersea Park Road, London SW8 4BG

☎0171 627 8181   Fax 0171 738 8688

Editor *Jonathan Goodall*
Circulation 32,000

FOUNDED 1975. Glossy wines and spirits magazine. Unsolicited material welcome but an advance telephone call is appreciated. No fiction.

News/Features All items and articles should concern wines, spirits, food and related subjects.

Derbyshire Life and Countryside

Heritage House, Lodge Lane, Derby
DE1 3HE
☎01332 347087   Fax 01332 290688
Owner *B. C. Wood*
Editor *Vivienne Irish*
Circulation 11,824

FOUNDED 1931. MONTHLY county magazine for Derbyshire. Unsolicited mss and photographs of Derbyshire welcome, but written approach with ideas preferred.

Descent

51 Timbers Square, Roath, Cardiff,
South Glamorgan CF2 3SH
☎01222 486557   Fax 01222 486557
Owner *Ambit Publications*
Editor *Chris Howes*
Assistant Editor *Judith Calford*

FOUNDED 1969. BI-MONTHLY magazine for cavers and mine enthusiasts. Submissions welcome from freelance contributors who can write accurately and knowledgeably on any aspect of caves, mines or underground structures.

Features General interest articles of under 1000 words welcome, as well as short foreign news reports, especially if supported by photographs/illustrations. Suitable topics include exploration (particularly British, both historical and modern), expeditions, equipment, techniques and regional British news. Maximum 2000 words.

Payment on publication according to page area filled.

Desire

192 Clapham High Street, London
SW4 7UD
☎0171 627 5155   Fax 0171 627 5808
Owner *Red Sky Publishing Ltd*
Editor *Ian Jackson*

FOUNDED 1994. Published alternate months. Britain's first erotic magazine for both women and men, celebrating sex and sensuality with a mix of articles, columns, features, reviews, fiction and poetry.

Features 1500–3000 words.
Fiction 1500–2800 words.
Send s.a.e. for contributors' guidelines and rates.

Director

Mountbarrow House, Elizabeth Street,
London SW1W 9RB
☎0171 730 8320   Fax 0171 235 5627
Editor *Stuart Rock*
Circulation 40,000

1991 Business Magazine of the Year. Published by The Director Publications Ltd. for the members of the Institute of Directors. Wide range of features from political and business profiles and management thinking to employment and financial issues. Also book reviews. Regular contributors used. Send letter with synopsis/published samples rather than unsolicited mss. Strictly no 'lifestyle' writing.

Payment negotiable.

Dirt Bike Rider (DBR)

PO Box 100, Stamford, Lincolnshire PE9 1XQ
☎01780 55131   Fax 01780 57261
Owner *Key Publishing Ltd*
Editor *Roddy Brooks*
Circulation 33,000

FOUNDED 1981. MONTHLY. Off-road dirt bikes (motor-cross, endurance, trial and trail). Interested in personality features.

Disability Now

12 Park Crescent, London W1N 4EQ
☎0171 636 5020   Fax 0171 436 4582
Publisher *SCOPE* (Formerly *The Spastics Society*)
Editor *Mary Wilkinson*
Circulation 35,000

FOUNDED 1984. MONTHLY. Leading publication for disabled people in the UK, reaching those with a wide range of physical disabilities, as well as their families, carers and relevant professionals. No unsolicited material but freelance contributions welcome. Approach in writing.

Features Covering new initiatives and services, personal experiences and general issues of interest to a wide national readership. Max. 1200 words. Disabled contributors welcomed.

News Maximum 500 words.

Special Pages Possible openings for cartoonists.

Payment by arrangement.

Disabled Driver

DDMC, Cottingham Way, Thrapston,
Northamptonshire NN14 4PL
☎01832 734724   Fax 01832 733816
Owner *Disabled Drivers' Motor Club*
Circulation 14,500 plus

BI-MONTHLY publication of the Disabled Drivers' Motor Club. Includes information for members, members' letters. Approach in writing with ideas. Unsolicited mss welcome.

Dog World

9 Tufton Street, Ashford, Kent TN23 1QN
☎01233 621877   Fax 01233 645669
Owner *Dog World Ltd*
Editor *Simon Parsons*
Circulation 30,210

FOUNDED 1902. WEEKLY newspaper for people who are seriously interested in pedigree dogs. Unsolicited mss occasionally considered but initial approach in writing preferred.

Features Well-researched historical items or items of unusual interest concerning dogs. Maximum 1000 words. Photographs of unusual 'doggy' situations often of interest. *Payment* up to £50.

News Freelance reports welcome on court cases and local government issues involving dogs.

Fiction Very occasionally.

Dragon's Breath

See **Pigasus Press** under **Small Presses**

The Ecologist

Agriculture House, Bath Road, Sturminster Newton, Dorset DT10 1DU
☎01258 473476   Fax 01258 473795
Owner *Ecosystems Ltd*
Co-Editors *Nicholas Hildyard, Sarah Sexton*
Circulation 9000

FOUNDED 1970. BI-MONTHLY. Unsolicited mss welcome but initial approach in writing preferred.

Features Contents tend to be academic, but accessible to the general reader, looking at the social, political, economic and gender aspects of environmental and related issues. Writers are advised to study the magazine for style. Maximum 5000 words.
Payment £20 per 1000 words.

The Economist

25 St James's Street, London SW1A 1HG
☎0171 830 7000   Fax 0171 839 2968
Owner *Pearson/individual shareholders*
Editor *Bill Emmott*
Circulation 620,000

FOUNDED 1843. WEEKLY. Worldwide circulation. Approaches should be made in writing to the editor. No unsolicited mss.

Edinburgh Review

22 George Square, Edinburgh EH8 9LF
☎0131 650 4218   Fax 0131 662 0053
Owner *Polygon Books*
Editors *Gavin Wallace, Robert Alan Jamieson*
Circulation 1500

FOUNDED 1969. TWICE YEARLY. Articles and fiction on Scottish and international literary, cultural and philosophical themes. Unsolicited contributions are welcome (1600 are received each year), but prospective contributors are strongly advised to study the magazine first. Allow up to three months for a reply.

Features Interest will be shown in accessible articles on philosophy and its relationship to literature or visual art.

Fiction Scottish and international. Maximum 6000 words.

Electrical Times

Quadrant House, The Quadrant, Sutton, Surrey SM2 5AS
☎0181 652 3115   Fax 0181 652 8972
Owner *Reed Business Publishing*
Editor *Steve Hobson*
Circulation 13,000

FOUNDED 1891. MONTHLY. Aimed at electrical contractors, designers and installers. Unsolicited mss welcome but initial approach preferred.

Elle

20 Orange Street, London WC2H 7ED
☎0171 957 8383   Fax 0171 930 0184
Owner *EMAP Elan Publications*
Editor *Marie O'Riordan*
Circulation 202,000

FOUNDED 1985. MONTHLY glossy. Prospective contributors should approach the relevant editor in writing in the first instance, including cuttings.

Features Max. 2000 words.

News/Insight Short articles on current/cultural events with an emphasis on national, not London-based, readership. Max. 500 words.
Payment about £250 per 1000 words.

Embroidery

PO Box 42B, East Molesley, Surrey KT8 9BB
☎0181 943 1229   Fax 0181 977 9882
Owner *Embroiderers' Guild*
Editor *Maggie Grey*
Circulation 14,500

FOUNDED 1933. QUARTERLY. Features articles on embroidery techniques, historical and foreign embroidery, and specific artists' work with illustrations. Also reviews. Unsolicited mss welcome. Maximum 1000 words.

Payment negotiable.

Empire

Mappin House, 4 Winsley Street, London W1N 7AR

☎0171 436 1515   Fax 0171 637 7031

Owner *EMAP Metro Publications*
Editor *Mark Salisbury*

FOUNDED 1989. Launched at the Cannes Film Festival. MONTHLY guide to the movies which aims to cover the world of films in a 'comprehensive, adult, intelligent and witty package'. Although most of *Empire* is devoted to films and the people behind them, it also looks at the developments and technology behind television and video. Wide selection of in-depth features and stories on all the main releases of the month, and reviews of over 100 films and videos. Contributions welcome but must approach in writing first.

Features Short, behind-the-scenes features on films.

Payment by agreement.

En Voyage

PO Box 582, St Saviour, Jersey, Channel Islands JE4 8XQ

☎01534 25517   Fax 01534 38889

Owner *Michael Stephen Publishers*
Editor *Harry McRandle*
Circulation 40,000

Channel Islands magazine published every four months. Features Aurigny Airline news, business articles, humorous pieces, celebrity profiles and general topics. No unsolicited material. Approach with ideas by telephone in the first instance.

The Engineer

30 Calderwood Street, London SE18 6QH

☎0181 855 7777   Fax 0181 316 3040

Owner *Miller Freeman*
Editor *To be appointed*
Circulation 38,000

FOUNDED 1856. News magazine for engineers and their managers.

Features Most outside contributions are commissioned but good ideas are always welcome. Maximum 2000 words.

News Some scope for specialist regional freelancers, and for tip-offs. Maximum 500 words.

Techscan Technology news from specialists, and tip-offs. Maximum 500 words.

Payment by arrangement.

ES (Evening Standard magazine)

See under **Regional Newspapers**

Escape: The Career and Lifestyle Magazine

Clarendon Court, Over Wallop, Stockbridge, Hampshire SO20 8HU

☎0126 4782298

Owner *Weavers Press Publishing Ltd*
Editor *Paul King*

SIX ISSUES YEARLY. Articles, news, features, reviews, personal experience and information for anyone who wants to change jobs and get into a new career or self-employment. Also articles on how to improve one's Quality of Life. Send letter outlining proposal in the first instance. Length 700–1700 words. No work considered unless accompanied by s.a.e..

Payment £20 per 1000 words.

Esquire

National Magazine House, 72 Broadwick Street, London W1V 2BP

☎0171 439 5000   Fax 0171 439 5067

Owner *National Magazine Co. Ltd*
Editor *Rosie Boycott*
Circulation 111,000

FOUNDED 1991. MONTHLY. Quality men's general interest magazine. No unsolicited mss or short stories.

Essentials

King's Reach Tower, Stamford Street, London SE1 9LS

☎0171 261 6970   Fax 0171 261 5262

Owner *IPC Magazines*
Editor *Sue James*
Circulation 365,000

FOUNDED 1988. MONTHLY women's interest magazine. Unsolicited mss (not originals) welcome if accompanied by s.a.e.. Initial approach in writing preferred. Prospective contributors should study the magazine thoroughly before submitting anything.

Features *Sarah Barbour* Maximum 2000 words (double-spaced on A4).

Payment negotiable, but minimum £100 per 1000 words.

Essex Countryside

Griggs Farm, West Street, Coggeshall, Essex CO6 1NT

☎01376 562578   Fax 01376 562578

Owner *Market Link Publishing Ltd*
Editor *Andy Tilbrook*

Circulation 15,000

FOUNDED 1952. MONTHLY. Unsolicited material of Essex interest welcome. No general interest material.

Features Countryside, culture and crafts in Essex. Maximum 1500 words.

Payment £40.

European Medical Journal

PO Box 30, Barnstaple, Devon EX32 9YU

Owner *Dr Vernon Coleman*
Editor *Dr Vernon Coleman*
Circulation 21,000

FOUNDED 1991. OCCASIONAL critical medical review published simultaneously in English and German. Approach in writing after careful study of journal.

Eventing

King's Reach Tower, Stamford Street,
London SE1 9LS
☎0171 261 5388   Fax 0171 261 5429

Owner *IPC Magazines Ltd*
Editor *Kate Green*

FOUNDED 1984. MONTHLY. Specialist horse trials magazine. Opportunities for freelance contributions.

Payment NUJ rates.

Evergreen

PO Box 52, Cheltenham, Gloucestershire
GL50 1YQ
☎01242 577775   Fax 01242 222034

Editor *R. Faiers*
Circulation 75,000

FOUNDED 1985. QUARTERLY magazine featuring articles and poems about Britain. Unsolicited contributions welcome.

Features Britain's natural beauty, towns and villages, nostalgia, wildlife, traditions, odd customs, legends, folklore, crafts, etc. Length 250–2000 words.

Payment £15 per 1000 words; poems £4.

Everywoman

9 St Alban's Place, London N1 0NX
☎0171 704 8440/359 5496   Fax 0171 226 9448

Editor *Lorna Russell*
Circulation 15,000

Feminist magazine providing general news and features geared towards women's interests in current affairs and practical concerns, such as health, employment and relationships, rather than traditional consumer lifestyle pursuits. No short stories, please. Contributors must study the magazine, show an understanding of its point of view, and indicate which section submissions are intended for. Approach in writing with a synopsis, not by phone.

Executive Travel

Church Street, Dunstable, Bedfordshire
LU5 4HB
☎01582 695097   Fax 01582 695095

Owner *Reed Travel Group*
Editor *Mike Toynbee*
Circulation 43,378

FOUNDED 1979. MONTHLY. Aimed specifically at frequent corporate travellers.

The Expatriate

175 Vauxhall Bridge Road, London
SW1V 1ER
☎0171 233 8595   Fax 0171 233 8718

Owner *FMI Publishers*
Editor *Vera Madan*
Circulation 2000

FOUNDED 1977. MONTHLY. Serves the expatriate community. Unsolicited mss welcome.

Features Special features on working in particular countries, and international travel. Also psychological problems for spouses, education difficulties, pensions, investment and taxation features, health matters.

News Information on special facilities for expatriates, e.g. mail-order presents, financial services, relocation agents, etc.

The Face

3rd Floor, Block A, Exmouth House, Pine Street, London EC1R 0JL
☎0171 837 7270   Fax 0171 837 3906

Owner *Wagadon Ltd*
Editor *Richard Benson*
Fashion Editor *Ashley Heath*
Circulation 100,000

FOUNDED 1980. Magazine of the style generation, concerned with who's what and what's cool. Profiles, interviews and stories. No fiction. Acquaintance with the 'voice' of *The Face* is essential before sending mss on spec.

Features *Ekow Eshun/Ashley Heath* New contributors should write to the features editor with their ideas. Maximum 3000 words.

Payment £150 per 1000 words.
Diary No news stories.

Family Circle

King's Reach Tower, Stamford Street,
London SE1 9LS
☎0171 261 5000   Fax 0171 261 5929
Owner *IPC Magazines Ltd*
Editor *Gilly Batterbee*
Circulation 286,494

FOUNDED 1964. THIRTEEN ISSUES YEARLY.
Little scope for freelancers as most material is
produced in-house. Unsolicited material is
rarely used, but it is considered. Prospective
contributors are best advised to send written
ideas to the relevant editor.
    Fashion and Beauty *Janine Steggles*
    Food and Drink *Sally Mansfield*
    Features *Emma O'Reilly* Very little outside
work commissioned. Maximum 2500–3000
words.
    Fiction *Dee Remmington* Short stories of
1000–1500 words.
    Home *Caroline Rodrigues*
    Payment not less than £100 per 1000 words.

Family Tree Magazine

61 Great Whyte, Ramsey, Huntingdon,
Cambridgeshire PE17 1HL
☎01487 814050
Owner *J.M. & M. Armstrong & Partners*
Editorial Director J.M. Armstrong
Circulation 38,000

FOUNDED 1984. MONTHLY. News and features
on matters of genealogy. Unsolicited mss considered. Keen to receive articles about unusual
sources of genealogical research. Not interested
in own family histories. Approach in writing
with ideas. All material should be addressed to
Michael Armstrong.
    Features Any genealogically related subject.
Maximum 3000 words. No puzzles or fictional
articles.
    Payment £20 per 1000 words (news and fea-
tures).

Fancy Fowl & Turkeys

Andover Road, Highclere, Newbury,
Berkshire RG15 9PH
☎01635 253239   Fax 01635 254146
Owner *Fancy Fowl Publications Ltd*
Editor *Shirley Murdoch*
Circulation 3000

FOUNDED 1981. Two publications, one specialising in rare poultry and waterfowl, the other in
commercial turkey production. *Fancy Fowl*
MONTHLY catering for those interested in keeping and exhibiting rare and pure breeds of poultry and waterfowl. Interested in news (maximum

300 words) and features (maximum 800 words)
in line with the magazine's content. *Payment*
£30 per 1000 words. *Turkeys* BI-MONTHLY aiming to deal with all aspects of turkey breeding,
growing, processing and marketing at an international level. Specialist technical information from
qualified contributors will always be considered.
Length by arrangement. No unsolicited mss.
Approach in writing with ideas, or by phone.
Payment £70 per 1000 words.

Farmers Weekly

Quadrant House, Sutton, Surrey SM2 5AS
☎0181 652 4911   Fax 0181 652 4005
Owner *Reed Business Publishing*
Editor *Stephen Howe*
Circulation 98,268

WEEKLY. 1996 Business Magazine of the Year.
For practising farmers. Unsolicited mss considered.
    Features A wide range of material relating
to farmers' problems and interests: specific sections on arable and/or livestock farming, farm
life, practical and general interest, machinery
and business.
    News General interest farming news.
    Payment negotiable.

Farming News

Miller Freeman, 30 Calderwood Street,
London SE18 6QH
☎0181 855 7777   Fax 0181 854 6795
Owner *Miller Freeman Farming Press Ltd*
Editor *Donald Taylor*
Circulation 74,000

News and features of direct concern to the
industry.

Fast Car

Berwick House, 8-10 Knoll Rise, Orpington,
Kent BR6 0PS
☎01689 874025   Fax 01689 896847
Owner *Security Publications*
Editor *Danny Morris*
Circulation 60,000

FOUNDED 1987. MONTHLY. Concerned with
the modification of road and race vehicles,
with technical data and testing results. No kit-
car features, race reports or road-test reports of
standard cars.
    Features Innovative ideas in line with the
magazine's title. Generally about five pages in
length.
    News Any item in line with magazine's
title. Copy should be as concise as possible.
    Payment negotiable.

The Field

King's Reach Tower, Stamford Street,
London SE1 9LS
☎0171 261 5198   Fax 0171 261 5358
Owner *IPC Magazines*
Editor *J. Young*

FOUNDED 1853. MONTHLY magazine for those who are serious about the British countryside and its pleasures. Unsolicited mss (and transparencies) welcome but initial approach should be made in writing.

Features Exceptional work on any subject concerning the countryside. Most work tends to be commissioned.

Payment varies.

Film Review

Visual Imagination Ltd, 9 Blades Court,
Deodar Road, London SW15 2NU
☎0181 875 1520   Fax 0181 875 1588
Owner *Visual Imagination Ltd*
Editor *David Richardson*
Circulation 50,000

MONTHLY. Reviews, profiles, interviews and special reports on films. Unsolicited material considered.

First Down

The Spendlove Centre, Enstone Road,
Charlbury, Oxford OX7 3PQ
☎01608 811266   Fax 01608 811380
Owner *Independent UK Sports Publishing*
Editor *Neil Rowlands*
Circulation 25,000

FOUNDED 1986. WEEKLY American football tabloid paper. Features and news.

Fishkeeping Answers

Bretton Court, Bretton, Peterborough,
Cambridgeshire PE3 8DZ
☎01733 264666   Fax 01733 265515
Owner *EMAP Apex Publications Ltd*
Managing Editor *Steve Windsor*
Editor *Karen Youngs*
Circulation 20,000

FOUNDED 1992. MONTHLY. Concerned with all aspects of keeping fish. Unsolicited mss, synopses and ideas welcome. Approach by phone or in writing with ideas. No fiction.

Features Specialist answers to specific fishkeeping problems, breeding, plants, health, etc; aquatic plants and ponds; plus coldwater fish, marine and tropical, and herptiles. 1500 words. Quality fish photographs welcome.

Flight International

Quadrant House, The Quadrant, Sutton,
Surrey SM2 5AS
☎0181 652 3882   Fax 0181 652 3840
Owner *Reed Business Publishing*
Editor *Allan Winn*
Circulation 60,000

FOUNDED 1909. WEEKLY. International trade magazine of the aerospace industry, including civil, military and space. Unsolicited mss considered. Commissions preferred – phone with ideas and follow up with letter. E-mail, modem and disc submissions encouraged.

Features *Forbes Mutch* Technically informed articles and pieces on specific geographical areas with international appeal. Analytical, in-depth coverage required, preferably supported by interviews. Maximum 1800 words.

News *Andrew Chuter* Opportunities exist for news pieces from particular geographical areas on specific technical developments. Maximum 350 words.

Payment NUJ rates.

Flora International

46 Merlin Grove, Eden Park, Beckenham,
Kent BR3 3HU
☎0181 658 1080
Owner *Maureen Foster*
Editor *Russell Bennett*
Circulation 15,000

FOUNDED 1974. BI-MONTHLY magazine for flower arrangers and florists. Unsolicited mss welcome. Approach in writing with ideas. Not interested in general gardening articles.

Features Fully illustrated, preferably with b&w photos or illustrations/colour transparencies. Flower arranging, flower gardens and flowers. Floristry items written with practical knowledge and well illustrated are particularly welcome. Maximum 2000 words.

Profiles/Reviews Personality profiles and book reviews.

Payment £40 per 1000 words.

FlyPast

PO Box 100, Stamford, Lincolnshire PE9 1XQ
☎01780 55131   Fax 01780 57261
Owner *Key Publishing Ltd*
Editor *Ken Delve*
Circulation 41,742

FOUNDED 1981. MONTHLY. Historic aviation, mainly military, Second World War period up to c.1970. Unsolicited mss welcome.

Folk Roots

PO Box 337, London N4 1TW
☎0181 340 9651   Fax 0181 348 5626

Owner *Southern Rag Ltd*
Editor *Ian A. Anderson*
Circulation 14,000

FOUNDED 1979. MONTHLY. Features on folk and roots music, and musicians. Maximum 3000 words.

Football Monthly

Prosport Media, Suite 108, Vanguard House, Dewsbury Road, Leeds, West Yorkshire LS11 5DD
☎0113 2443417   Fax 0113 2346243

Owner *Prosport Media*
Editor *Steven Angelsey*
Circulation 34,000

FOUNDED 1951. MONTHLY football magazine. Features, interviews and historical items. Approach the editor in writing with ideas in the first instance.

For Women

Portland Publishing, 4 Selsdon Way, London E14 9EL
☎0181 538 8969   Fax 0181 987 0756

Circulation 60,000

FOUNDED 1992. MONTHLY magazine of women's general interest – celebrity interviews, beauty, health and sex, erotic fiction and erotic photography. No homes and gardens articles. Approach in writing in the first instance.

Features Relationships and sex. Maximum 2500 words. *Payment* £150 per 1000 words.

Fiction Erotic short stories. Maximum 2000 words. *Payment* £125 total.

Fortean Times: The Journal of Strange Phenomena

PO Box 2409, London NW5 4NP
☎0171 485 5002   Fax 0171 485 5002

Owners/Editors *Bob Rickard/Paul Sieveking*
Circulation 50,000

FOUNDED 1973. MONTHLY Accounts of strange phenomena and experiences, curiosities, mysteries, prodigies and portents. Unsolicited mss welcome. Approach in writing with ideas. No fiction, poetry, rehashes or politics.

Features Well-researched and referenced material on current or historical mysteries, or first-hand accounts of oddities. Maximum 3000 words, preferably with good relevant photos/illustrations.

News Concise copy with full source references essential.
Payment negotiable.

Foundation: The Review of Science Fiction

c/o Dept. of History, University of Reading, Whiteknights, Reading, Berkshire RG6 6AA
☎0118 9263047

Owner *Science Fiction Foundation*
Editor *Dr Edward James*

THRICE-YEARLY publication devoted to the critical study of science fiction.
Payment None.

France Magazine

France House, Digbeth Street, Stow-on-the-Wold, Gloucestershire GL54 1BN
☎01451 831398   Fax 01451 830869

Owner *France Magazine Ltd*
Editor *Philip Faiers*
Circulation 60,000

FOUNDED 1989. QUARTERLY magazine containing all things of interest to Francophiles – in English. No unsolicited mss. Approach with ideas in writing.

Freelance Market News

Cumberland House, Lissadell Street, Salford, Manchester M6 6GG
☎0161 702 8225   Fax 0161 745 8865

Editor *Saundrea Williams*
Circulation 2200

MONTHLY. News and information on the freelance writers' market, both inland and overseas. Includes market information on competitions, seminars, courses, overseas openings, etc. Short articles (700 words maximum). Unsolicited contributions welcome.
Payment £15-£20 per 1000 words.

Freelance Writing & Photography

Clarendon Court, Over Wallop, Stockbridge, Hampshire SO20 8HU
☎0126 4782298

Owner *Weavers Press Publishing Ltd*
Editor *Paul King*

Articles, features, reviews, interviews, competitions, tips, hints, market news for the freelance writer and photographer. 300-1800 words. No work considered unless accompanied by s.a.e.. Ideas in writing preferred in first instance.
Payment £20 per 1000 words.

The Freelance

NUJ, Acorn House, 314 Gray's Inn Road,
London WC1X 8DP
☎0171 278 7916   Fax 0171 278 1812

BI-MONTHLY published by the **National Union of Journalists**. Contributions welcome.

Garden Answers

Apex House, Oundle Road, Peterborough,
Cambridgeshire PE2 9NP
☎01733 898100   Fax 01733 898433

Owner *EMAP Apex Publications Ltd*
Managing Editor *Adrienne Wild*
Circulation 117,565

FOUNDED 1982. MONTHLY. 'It is unlikely that unsolicited manuscripts will be used, as articles are usually commissioned and must be in the magazine style.' Prospective contributors should approach the editor in writing. Interested in hearing from gardening writers on any subject, whether flowers, fruit, vegetables, houseplants or greenhouse gardening.

Garden News

Apex House, Oundle Road, Peterborough,
Cambridgeshire PE2 9NP
☎01733 898100   Fax 01733 898433

Owner *EMAP Apex Publications Ltd*
Editor *Jim Ward*
Circulation 100,838

FOUNDED 1958. Britain's biggest-selling gardening WEEKLY. News and advice on growing flowers, fruit and vegetables, plus colourful features on all aspects of gardening for the committed gardener. News and features welcome, especially if accompanied by photos or illustrations. Contact the editor before submitting any material.

The Garden, Journal of the Royal Horticultural Society

Apex House, Oundle Road, Peterborough,
Cambridgeshire PE2 9NP
☎01733 898100   Fax 01733 890657

Owner *The Royal Horticultural Society*
Editor *Ian Hodgson*
Circulation 193,584

FOUNDED 1866. MONTHLY journal of the Royal Horticultural Society. Covers all aspects of the art, science and practice of horticulture and garden making. 'Articles must have depth and substance'; approach by letter with a synopsis in the first instance.

Gardens Illustrated

John Brown Publishing Ltd, The Boathouse,
Crabtree Lane, London SW6 6LU
☎0171 470 2400   Fax 0171 381 3930

Owner *John Brown Publishing Ltd*
Editor *Rosie Atkins*
Circulation 46,000

FOUNDED 1993. BI-MONTHLY. 'Britain's fastest growing garden magazine' with a world-wide readership. The focus is on garden design, with a strong international flavour. Unsolicited mss are rarely used and it is best that prospective contributors approach the editor with ideas in writing, supported by photographs.

Gay Times

Worldwide House, 116–134 Bayham Street,
London NW1 0BA
☎0171 482 2576   Fax 0171 284 0329

Owner *Millivres Ltd*
Editor *David Smith*
Circulation 57,000

Covers all aspects of gay life, plus general interest likely to appeal to the gay community, art reviews and news. Redesigned in May 1996 for a completely new look. Regular freelance writers used. Unsolicited contributions welcome.
Payment negotiable.

Get Active Magazine

Centre for Fitness, 41 Overstone Road,
Hammersmith, London W6 0AD
☎0181 741 0215   Fax 0181 748 7812

Owner *Artonia Ltd*
Editor *Lydia Campbell*
Circulation 50,000

FOUNDED 1992. BI-MONTHLY for people who lead an active life. Unsolicited mss, synopses and ideas welcome. Approach in writing with ideas. No fiction or any material not related to fitness, health and an active lifestyle.

Features Across a wide range of interests: health, nutrition, fitness, beauty, activities (active ones such as hiking, biking or scuba diving!), etc. Maximum 1000 words.

News Club reviews and developments of interest to those engaged in an active lifestyle.

Special Pages Items relating to personal improvement towards an active lifestyle.
Payment £150 per 1000 words.

Gibbons Stamp Monthly

Stanley Gibbons, 5 Parkside, Ringwood,
Hampshire BH24 3SH
☎01425 472363   Fax 01425 470247

Owner *Stanley Gibbons Holdings plc*

Editor *Hugh Jefferies*
Circulation 22,000

FOUNDED 1890. MONTHLY. News and features. Unsolicited mss welcome. Make initial approach in writing or by telephone to avoid disappointment.

Features *Hugh Jefferies* Unsolicited material of specialised nature and general stamp features welcome. Maximum 3000 words but longer pieces can be serialised. *Payment* £20–50 per 1000 words.

News *Michael Briggs* Any philatelic news item. Maximum 500 words. *No payment.*

Girl About Town
9 Rathbone Street, London W1P 1AF
☎0171 636 6651   Fax 0171 255 2352

Owner *Independent Magazines*
Editor-in-Chief *Bill Williamson*
News/Style Pages *Dee Pilgrim*
Circulation 100,000

FOUNDED 1972. Free WEEKLY magazine for women aged 16 to 26. Unsolicited mss may be considered. No fiction.

Features Standards are 'exacting'. Commissions only. Some chance of unknown writers being commissioned and unsolicited material is considered. Maximum 1200 words.

News Some, including film, music, fashion and beauty. Maximum 200 words.
Payment negotiable.

Golf Monthly
King's Reach Tower, Stamford Street, London SE1 9LS
☎0171 261 7237   Fax 0171 261 7240

Owner *IPC Magazines Ltd*
Editor *Colin Callander*
Circulation 87,021

FOUNDED 1911. MONTHLY. Player profiles, golf instruction, general golf features and columns. Not interested in instruction material from outside contributors. Unsolicited mss welcome. Approach in writing with ideas.

Features Maximum 1500–2000 words.
Payment by arrangement.

Golf Weekly
Bretton Court, Bretton, Peterborough, Cambridgeshire PE3 8DZ
☎01733 264666   Fax 01733 267198

Owner *EMAP Pursuit Ltd*
Editor *Bob Warters*
Circulation 20,000

FOUNDED 1890. WEEKLY. Unsolicited material welcome from full-time journalists only. For features, approach in writing in first instance; for news, fax or phone.

Features Maximum 1500 words.
News Maximum 300 words.
Payment negotiable.

Golf World
Advance House, 37 Millharbour, London E14 9TX
☎0171 538 1031   Fax 0171 538 4106

Owner *EMAP Pursuit Ltd*
Editor *David Clarke*
Circulation 92,122

FOUNDED 1962. MONTHLY. No unsolicited mss. Approach in writing with ideas.

Good Food Retailing
Stanstead Publications, Edwards House, 2 Alric Avenue, New Malden, Surrey KT3 4JN
☎0181 336 0558   Fax 0181 336 0672

Owner *Robert Farrand*
Editor *Robert Farrand*
Circulation 4200

FOUNDED 1980. TEN ISSUES YEARLY. Serves the speciality food retail trade. Small budget for freelance material.

Good Holiday Magazine
91 High Street, Esher, Surrey KT10 9QD
☎01372 468140   Fax 01372 470765

Editor *John Hill*
Circulation 100,000

FOUNDED 1985. QUARTERLY aimed at better-off holiday-makers rather than travellers. Worldwide destinations including Europe and domestic. Any queries regarding work/commissioning must be in writing. Copy must be precise and well-researched – the price of everything from coffee and tea to major purchases are included along with exchange rates, etc. *Payment* negotiable.

Good Housekeeping
National Magazine House, 72 Broadwick Street, London W1V 2BP
☎0171 439 5000   Fax 0171 439 5591

Owner *National Magazine Co. Ltd*
Editor-in-Chief *Pat Roberts Cairns*
Circulation 518,435

FOUNDED 1922. MONTHLY glossy. No unsolicited mss. Write with ideas in the first instance to the appropriate editor.

Features *Hilary Robinson* Most work is commissioned but original ideas are always welcome. Send short synopsis, plus relevant cuttings, showing previous examples of work published. No unsolicited mss.

Fiction *Hilary Robinson* No unsolicited mss.

Entertainment *Hilary Robinson* Three pages of reviews and previews on film, television, theatre and art.

Good Ski Guide
91 High Street, Esher, Surrey KT10 9QD
☎01372 468140   Fax 01372 470765
Editor *John Hill*
Circulation 40,000

FOUNDED 1976. QUARTERLY. Unsolicited mss welcome from writers with a knowledge of skiing and ski resorts. Prospective contributors are best advised to make initial contact in writing as ideas and work need to be seen before any discussion can take place.
Payment negotiable.

GQ
Vogue House, Hanover Square, London W1R 0AD
☎0171 499 9080   Fax 0171 495 1679
Owner *Condé Nast Publications Ltd*
Editor *Angus Mackinnon*
Commissioning Editor *Jessamy Calkin*
Circulation 128,000

FOUNDED 1988. MONTHLY. No unsolicited material. Phone or write with an idea in the first instance.

Gramophone
177-179 Kenton Road, Harrow, Middlesex HA3 0HA
☎0181 907 4476   Fax 0181 907 0073
Owner *General Gramophone Publications Ltd*
Editor *James Jolly*
Circulation 65,941

Classical music magazine, of which 95% is reviews. At any time they are using around 50 regular freelance writers, who provide classical music reviews and, on occasion, features or interviews. Reviewing is the starting place on the magazine, however. Submit samples of published work to the editor.

Granta
2-3 Hanover Yard, Noel Road, London N1 8BE
☎0171 704 9776   Fax 0171 704 0474
Editor *Ian Jack*
Deputy Editor *Ursula Doyle*

QUARTERLY magazine of new writing, including fiction, autobiography, politics, history and reportage published in paperback book form. Highbrow, diverse and contemporary, with a thematic approach. Unsolicited mss (including fiction) considered. A lot of material is commissioned. Important to read the magazine first to appreciate its very particular fusion of cultural and political interests. No reviews. No poetry.
Payment negotiable.

The Great Outdoors
See **TGO**

Guardian Weekend
See under **National Newspapers (The Guardian)**

Guiding
17-19 Buckingham Palace Road, London SW1W 0PT
☎0171 834 6242   Fax 0171 828 8317
Owner *The Guide Association*
Editor *Nora Warner*
Circulation 31,000

FOUNDED 1914. MONTHLY. Unsolicited mss welcome provided topics relate to the movement and/or women's role in society. Ideas in writing appreciated in first instance.

Features Topics that can be useful in the Guide programme, or special interest features with Guide link. Maximum 1200 words.

News Guide activities. Max. 100–150 words.

Special Pages Outdoor activity, information pieces, Green issues. Max. 1200 words.
Payment £70 per 1000 words.

Hair
King's Reach Tower, Stamford Street, London SE1 9LS
☎0171 261 6975   Fax 0171 261 7382
Owner *IPC Magazines Ltd*
Editor *Annette Dennis*
Circulation 168,500

FOUNDED 1980. BI-MONTHLY hair and beauty magazine. No unsolicited mss, but always interested in good photographs. Approach with ideas in writing.

Features *Jacki Wadeson/Sharon Christal* Fashion pieces on hair trends. Max. 1000 words.
Payment negotiable.

Hairflair
4th Floor, 27 Maddox Street, London W1R 9LE
☎0171 493 3533   Fax 0171 499 6686
Owner *Hairflair Publishing Ltd*
Editor *Joani Walsh*

Circulation 62,930

FOUNDED 1982. MONTHLY. Original and interesting hair-related features written in a young, lively style to appeal to a readership aged 16–35 years. Unsolicited mss not welcome, but as the magazine is expanding new ideas are encouraged. Write to the editor.

Features Hair and beauty. Max. 1000 words. *Payment* negotiable.

Harpers & Queen

National Magazine House, 72 Broadwick Street, London W1V 2BP
☎0171 439 5000   Fax 0171 439 5506

Owner *National Magazine Co. Ltd*
Editor *Fiona Macpherson*
Circulation 86,500

MONTHLY. Up-market glossy combining the Sloaney and the streetwise. Approach in writing (not phone) with ideas.

Features *Anthony Gardner/Samantha Weinberg* Ideas only in the first instance.

Fiction *Heather Hodson* Only literary fiction welcome. Maximum 3000 words.

News Snippets welcome if very original. *Payment* negotiable.

Health & Fitness Magazine

Nexus Media, Nexus House, Azalea Drive, Swanley, Kent BR8 8HY
☎01322 660070   Fax 01322 615636

Owner *Nexus Media*
Editor *Sharon Walker*
Circulation 65,000

FOUNDED 1983. MONTHLY. Will consider ideas; approach in writing in the first instance.

Health Education

MCB University Press, 60-62 Toller Lane, Bradford, West Yorkshire BD8 9BY
☎01274 777700   Fax 01274 785200/785201

Owner *MCB University Press*
Editor *Sharon Kingman*
Circulation 2000

FOUNDED 1992. SIX ISSUES YEARLY. Health education magazine with a strong emphasis on schools and young people. Professional readership. Most work is commissioned. Ideas considered.

Health Shopper

The Old Auction Mart, Station Approach, Godalming, Surrey GU7 1EU
☎01483 860116   Fax 01483 860938

Owner *Nigel Cross*

Editor *Nigel Cross*
Circulation 75,000

FOUNDED 1977. BI-MONTHLY. Unsolicited mss welcome only if related to the specialised interests of the magazine in encouraging a healthy lifestyle and increased awareness of alternative therapies. Prospective contributors are advised to make their first approach in writing.

Hello!

Wellington House, 69-71 Upper Ground, London SE1 9PQ
☎0171 334 7404   Fax 0171 334 7412

Owner *Hola!* (Spain)
Editor *Maggie Koumi*
Circulation 452,103

WEEKLY. Owned by a Madrid-based publishing family, Hello! has grown faster than any other British magazine since its launch here in 1988 and continues to grow despite the recession. The magazine is printed in Madrid, with editorial offices both there and in London. Major colour features plus regular b&w news and local-interest pages. Although much of the material is provided by regulars, good proposals do stand a chance. Approach with ideas in the first instance. No unsolicited mss.

Features Interested in personality-based features, often with a newsy angle, and exclusive interviews from generally unapproachable personalities.

Payment by arrangement.

Here's Health

20 Orange Street, London WC2H 7ED
☎0171 957 8383   Fax 0171 930 4637

Owner *EMAP Elan Publications*
Editor *Annabel Goldstaub*
Circulation 42,000

FOUNDED 1956. MONTHLY. Full-colour magazine dealing with alternative medicine, nutrition, natural health, wholefoods, supplements, organics and the environment. Prospective contributors should bear in mind that this is a specialist magazine with a pronounced bias towards alternative/complementary medicine, using expert contributors on the whole.

Features Length varies.
Payment negotiable.

Heritage

4 The Courtyard, Denmark Street, Wokingham, Berkshire RG40 2AZ
☎01734 771677   Fax 01734 772903

Owner *Bulldog Magazines*
Editor *Sian Ellis*

Circulation 70,000

FOUNDED 1984. BI-MONTHLY. Unsolicited mss welcome. Interested in complete packages of written features with high-quality transparencies – words or pictures on their own also accepted. Not interested in poetry, fiction or non-British themes. Approach in writing with ideas.

Features on historical themes and people, British villages, tours, towns, castles, gardens, traditions, crafts, historical themes and people. Maximum length 1200-1500 words. *Payment* approx. £100 per 1000 words.

News Small pieces – usually picture stories in Diary section. Limited use. Maximum length 100–150 words. *Payment* £20.

Heritage Scotland
5 Charlotte Square, Edinburgh
EH2 4DU
☎0131 243 9386   Fax 0131 243 9309
Owner *National Trust for Scotland*
Editor *Peter Reekie*
Circulation 140,660

FOUNDED 1983. QUARTERLY magazine containing heritage/conservation features. No unsolicited mss.

Hi-Fi News & Record Review
Link House, Dingwall Avenue, Croydon,
Surrey CR9 2TA
☎0181 686 2599   Fax 0181 781 6046
Owner *Link House Magazines Ltd*
Editor *Steve Harris*
Circulation 25,000

FOUNDED 1956. MONTHLY. Write in the first instance with suggestions based on knowledge of the magazine's style and subject. All articles must be written from an informed technical or enthusiast viewpoint.

Music *Christopher Breunig*
Payment negotiable, according to technical content.

High Life
Haymarket House, 1 Oxendon Street,
London SW1Y 4EE
☎0171 925 2544   Fax 0171 839 4508
Owner *Premier Magazines*
Editor *William Davis*
Circulation 295,000

FOUNDED 1973. MONTHLY glossy. British Airways in-flight magazine. Almost all the content is commissioned. No unsolicited mss. Few opportunities for freelancers.

Home & Country
104 New Kings Road, London SW6 4LY
☎0171 731 5777   Fax 0171 736 4061
Owner *National Federation of Women's Institutes*
Editor *Amber Tokeley*
Circulation 87,774

FOUNDED 1919. MONTHLY. Official full-colour journal of the Federation of Women's Institutes, containing articles on a wide range of subjects of interest to women. Strong environmental country slant with crafts and cookery plus gardening appearing every month. Unsolicited mss, photos and illustrations welcome.

Payment by arrangement.

Home & Family
Mary Sumner House, 24 Tufton Street,
London SW1P 3RB
☎0171 222 5533   Fax 0171 222 1591
Owner *MU Enterprises Ltd*
Editor *Margaret Duggan*
Circulation 85,826

FOUNDED 1976. QUARTERLY. Unsolicited mss considered. No fiction or poetry.

Features Family life, social problems, marriage, Christian faith, etc. Maximum 1000 words.
Payment modest.

Home Words
See **Hymns Ancient & Modern Ltd** under **UK Publishers**

Homebrew Supplier
304 Northridge Way, Hemel Hempstead,
Hertfordshire HP1 2AB
☎01442 67228   Fax 01442 67228
Owner *Homebrew Publications*
Editor *Evelyn Barrett*
Circulation 1500

FOUNDED 1960. QUARTERLY trade magazine. Unsolicited mss welcome.

Homebrew Today
304 Northridge Way, Hemel Hempstead,
Hertfordshire HP1 2AB
☎01442 67228   Fax 01442 67228
Owner *Homebrew Publications*
Editor *Evelyn Barrett*
Circulation 150,000

FOUNDED 1986. QUARTERLY. Articles on all aspects of home brewing and the use of home-made wine in cooking, etc. Unsolicited mss welcome.

Homes & Gardens

King's Reach Tower, Stamford Street,
London SE1 9LS
☎0171 261 5678   Fax 0171 261 6247

Owner *IPC Magazines Ltd/Reed Publishing*
Editor *Julia Watson*
Circulation 173,806

FOUNDED 1919. MONTHLY. Almost all published articles are specially commissioned. No fiction or poetry. Best to approach in writing with an idea.

Horse & Pony Magazine

Bretton Court, Bretton, Peterborough,
Cambridgeshire PE3 8DZ
☎01733 264666   Fax 01733 261984

Owner *EMAP Pursuit Publications*
Editor *Andrea Oakes*
Circulation 58,570

Magazine for young (aged 10–16) owners and 'addicts' of the horse. Features include pony care, riding articles and celebrity pieces. Some interest in freelancers but most feature material is produced by staff writers.

Horse and Hound

King's Reach Tower, Stamford Street,
London SE1 9LS
☎0171 261 6315   Fax 0171 261 5429

Owner *IPC Magazines Ltd*
Editor *Arnold Garvey*
Circulation 70,000

WEEKLY. The oldest equestrian magazine on the market, now re-launched with modern make-up and colour pictures throughout. Contains regular veterinary advice and instructional articles, as well as authoritative news and comment on fox hunting, international showjumping, horse trials, dressage, driving and cross-country riding. Also weekly racing and point-to-points, breeding reports and articles. The magazine includes junior sections for the Pony Club. Regular books and art reviews, and humorous articles and cartoons are frequently published. Plenty of opportunities for freelancers. Unsolicited contributions welcome.

Now also publishes a sister monthly publication, *Eventing*, which covers the sport of horse trials comprehensively.

Payment NUJ rates.

Horse and Rider

Haslemere House, Lower Street, Haslemere,
Surrey GU27 2PE
☎01428 651551   Fax 01428 653888

Owner *D. J. Murphy (Publishers) Ltd*

Editor *Alison Bridge*
Circulation 40,527

FOUNDED 1949. MONTHLY. Adult readership, largely horse-owning. News and instructional features, which make up the bulk of the magazine, are almost all commissioned. New contributors and unsolicited mss are occasionally used. Approach the editor in writing with ideas.

Horticulture Week

60 Waldegrave Road, Teddington, Middlesex
TW11 8LG
☎0181 943 5719   Fax 0181 943 5673

Owner *Haymarket Magazines Ltd*
Editor *Vicky Browning*
Circulation 11,200

FOUNDED 1841. WEEKLY. Specialist magazine involved in the supply of business-type information. No unsolicited mss. Approach in writing in first instance.

Features No submissions without prior discussion. *Payment* negotiable.

News *Guy Campos* Information about horticultural businesses – nurseries, garden centres, landscapers and parks departments in the various regions of the UK. No gardening stories.

House & Garden

Vogue House, Hanover Square, London
W1R 0AD
☎0171 499 9080   Fax 0171 629 2907

Owner *Condé Nast Publications Ltd*
Editor *Susan Crewe*
Circulation 161,218

Most feature material is produced in-house but occasional specialist features are commissioned from qualified freelancers, mainly for the interiors or wine and food sections.

Features *Liz Elliot* Suggestions for features, preferably in the form of brief outlines of proposed subjects, will be considered.

House Beautiful

National Magazine House, 72 Broadwick
Street, London W1V 2BP
☎0171 439 5000   Fax 0171 439 5595

Owner *National Magazine Co. Ltd*
Editor *Caroline Atkins*
Circulation 325,398

FOUNDED 1989. MONTHLY. Lively magazine offering sound, practical information and plenty of inspiration for those who want to make the most of where they live. Over 100 pages of easy-reading editorial. Regular features about decoration, DIY and home finance.

House Buyer
96 George Lane, South Woodford, London
E18 1AD
☎0181 532 9299   Fax 0181 532 9329
Owner *Dalton's Weekly Plc*
Editor *Con Crowley*
Circulation 18,000

FOUNDED 1955. MONTHLY magazine with features and articles for house buyers, including retirement homes, mortgage information, etc. A 32-page section includes details of over 200,000 new homes throughout the UK. Unsolicited mss will neither be read nor returned.

ID Magazine
Universal House, 251–255 Tottenham Court Road, London W1P 0AE
☎0171 813 6170   Fax 0171 813 6179
Owner *Levelprint*
Editor *Avril Mair*
Circulation 45,000

FOUNDED 1980. MONTHLY lifestyle magazine for both sexes aged 16–24. Very hip. 'We are always looking for freelance writers with new or unusual ideas.' A different theme each issue (past themes have been Green politics, taste, films, sex, love and loud dance music) means it is advisable to discuss feature ideas in the first instance.

Ideal Home
King's Reach Tower, Stamford Street,
London SE1 9LS
☎0171 261 6474   Fax 0171 261 6697
Owner *IPC Magazines Ltd*
Editor-in-chief *Sally O'Sullivan*
Circulation 226,316

FOUNDED 1920. MONTHLY glossy. Unsolicited feature articles are welcome if appropriate to the magazine (one or two are received each week). Prospective contributors wishing to submit ideas should do so in writing to the editor. No fiction.
Features Furnishing and decoration of houses, kitchens or bathrooms; interior design, soft furnishings, furniture and home improvements, lifestyle, etc. Length to be discussed with editor.
Payment negotiable.

The Illustrated London News
20 Upper Ground, London SE1 9PF
☎0171 928 2111   Fax 0171 620 1594
Owner *James Sherwood*
Editor *Alison Booth*
Circulation 47,547

FOUNDED 1842. Although the *ILN* covers issues concerning the whole of the UK, its emphasis remains on the capital and its life. Travel, wine, restaurants, events, cultural and current affairs are all covered but the magazine now only publishes the occasional special issue. There are few opportunities for freelancers but all unsolicited mss are read (receives about 20 a week). The best approach is with an idea in writing. Particularly interested in articles relating to events and developments in contemporary London, and about people working in the capital. All features are illustrated, so ideas with picture opportunities are particularly welcome.

Image Magazine
Upper Mounts, Northampton NN1 3HR
☎01604 231122   Fax 01604 233000
Owner *Northampton Mercury Co.*
Editor *Peter Hall*
Circulation 8,500

FOUNDED 1905. MONTHLY general interest regional magazine. No unsolicited mss. Approach by phone or in writing with ideas. No fiction.
Features Local issues, personalities, businesses, etc., of Northamptonshire, Bedfordshire, Buckinghamshire interest. Max. 500 words. *Payment* £60.
News No hard news as such, just monthly diary column.
Other Regulars on motoring, fashion, lifestyle, sport, travel, history, and picture files. Maximum 500 words. *Payment* £60.

In Britain
Haymarket House, 1 Oxendon Street,
London SW1Y 4EE
☎0171 925 2544   Fax 0171 976 1088
Owner *Premier Magazines*
Editor *Andrea Spain*
Circulation 40,000

MONTHLY. Travel magazine of the British Tourist Authority. Articles vary from 1000 to 1500 words. Approach in writing with ideas and samples – not much opportunity for unsolicited work.

The Independent Magazine
See under **National Newspapers (The Independent)**

Infusion
16 Trinity Churchyard, Guildford, Surrey
GU1 3RR
☎01483 62888   Fax 01483 302732
Publisher *Bond Clarkson Russell*

Editor *Lorna Swainson*
Circulation 800,000

FOUNDED 1986. THREE ISSUES YEARLY. Sponsored by the Tea Council. Features women's general interest, health, leisure and all subjects related to tea. All editorial features are commissioned. Approach with ideas only in writing.

Interzone: Science Fiction & Fantasy

217 Preston Drove, Brighton, East Sussex
BN1 6FL
☎01273 504710
Owner *David Pringle*
Editor *David Pringle*
Circulation 10,000

FOUNDED 1982. MONTHLY magazine of science fiction and fantasy. Unsolicited mss are welcome 'only from writers who have a knowledge of the magazine and its contents'. S.a.e. essential for return.
    Fiction 2000–6000 words. *Payment* £30 per 1000 words.
    Features Book/film reviews, interviews with writers and occasional short articles. Length by arrangement. *Payment* negotiable.

Investors Chronicle

Greystoke Place, Fetter Lane, London
EC4A 1ND
☎0171 405 6969   Fax 0171 405 5276
Owner *Pearson Professional*
Editor *Ceri Jones*
Surveys Editor *Christina Nordenstahl*
Circulation 64,000

FOUNDED 1861. WEEKLY. Opportunities for freelance contributors in the survey section only. All approaches should be made in writing. Over forty surveys are published each year on a wide variety of subjects, generally with a financial, business or investment emphasis. Copies of survey list and synopses of individual surveys are obtainable from the surveys editor.
    Payment from £100.

Jane's Defence Weekly

Sentinel House, 163 Brighton Road,
Coulsdon, Surrey CR5 2NH
☎0181 700 3700   Fax 0181 763 1007
Owner *Jane's Information Group*
Publishing Director *Robert Hutchinson*
Editor *Carol Reed*
Circulation 25,827

FOUNDED 1984. WEEKLY. No unsolicited mss.

Approach in writing with ideas in the first instance.
    Features Current defence topics (politics, strategy, equipment, industry) of worldwide interest. No history pieces. Max. 2000 words. *Payment* minimum £100 per 1000 words.

Jazz Journal International

1-5 Clerkenwell Road, London
EC1M 5PA
☎0171 608 1348   Fax 0171 608 1292
Owner *Jazz Journal Ltd*
Editor-in-Chief *Eddie Cook*
Circulation 12,000

FOUNDED 1948. MONTHLY. A specialised jazz magazine, mainly for record collectors, principally using expert contributors whose work is known to the editor. Unsolicited mss not welcome, with the exception of news material (for which no payment is made). It is not a gig guide, nor a free reference source for students.

Jersey Now

Michael Stephen Publishers,
PO Box 582, Five Oaks, St Saviour,
Jersey, Channel Islands JE4 8XQ
☎01534 25517   Fax 01534 38889
Owner *Michael Stephen Publishers*
Managing Editor *Harry McRandle*
Circulation 10,000

FOUNDED 1984. SEASONAL lifestyle magazine with features on homes, leisure, motoring, fashion, beauty, health, local issues and travel. No fiction. No unsolicited mss. Approach by phone in the first instance.

Jewish Chronicle

25 Furnival Street, London
EC4A 1JT
☎0171 405 9252   Fax 0171 405 9040
Owner *Kessler Foundation*
Editor *Edward J. Temko*
Circulation 50,000

Unsolicited mss welcome if 'the specific interests of our readership are borne in mind by writers'. Approach in writing, except for urgent current news items. No fiction. Maximum 1500 words for all material.
    Features *Gerald Jacobs*
    Leisure/Lifestyle *Alan Montague*
    Home News *Barry Toberman*
    Foreign News *Joseph Millis*
    Supplements *Angela Kiverstein*
    Payment negotiable.

Jewish Quarterly

PO Box 2078, London W1A 1JR
☎0171 629 5004(admin)/0181 361 6372(edit)
Fax 0181 361 6372

Publisher *Jewish Literary Trust Ltd*
Editor *Elena Lappin*

FOUNDED 1953. QUARTERLY illustrated magazine featuring Jewish literature and fiction, politics, art, music, film, poetry, history, dance, community, autobiography, Hebrew, Yiddish, Israel and the Middle East, Judaism, interviews, Zionism, philosophy and holocaust studies. Features a major books and arts section. Unsolicited mss welcome but letter or phone call preferred in first instance.

Johnny Miller 96 Not Out

9 Whitehall Park, Highgate, London N19 3TS
☎0171 561 1606   Fax 0171 561 1607

Owner *Two Heads Publishing*
Editor *Tim Lezard*
Circulation 9000

MONTHLY cricket magazine styled as 'the essential word on cricket today'. Welcome approaches from potential contributors who have something new and, preferably, humorous to say about cricket today.

The Journal Magazines (Norfolk, Suffolk, Cambridgeshire)

The Old Eagle, Market Place, Dereham, Norfolk NR19 2AP
☎01362 699699   Fax 01362 699606

Owner *Hawksmere Plc*
Editor *Pippa Bastin*
Circulation 7000 each

FOUNDED 1990. MONTHLY magazines covering items of local interest – history, people, conservation, business, places, food and wine, fashion, homes and sport.
    Features 750 words maximum, plus pictures. Approach the editor by phone with ideas in the first instance
    Payment £75.

Just Seventeen

20 Orange Street, London WC2H 7ED
☎0171 957 8383   Fax 0171 930 5728

Owner *EMAP Elan Publications*
Acting Editor *Fiona Gibson*
Circulation 265,000

FOUNDED 1983. WEEKLY. Top of the mid-teen market, with news, articles and fiction of interest to girls aged 12–18. Ideas are sought in all areas. Prospective contributors should send ideas to the relevant editorial department, then follow up with a phone call.
    Beauty *Jessie Cartner-Morley*
    Features *Piers Wenger*
    Fiction *Joanna Briscoe* Max. 2000 words.
    Music *Kate Hodges*
    News *Sophie Davies*
    Payment by arrangement.

Kennel Gazette

Kennel Club, 1-5 Clarges Street, Piccadilly, London W1Y 8AB
☎0171 493 6651   Fax 0171 495 6162

Owner *Kennel Club*
Editor *Charles Colborn*
Circulation 10,000

FOUNDED 1873. MONTHLY concerning dogs and their breeding. Unsolicited mss welcome.
    Features Maximum 2500 words.
    News Maximum 500 words.
    Payment £70 per 1000 words.

Kent Life

Dateam House, Tovil Hill, Maidstone, Kent ME15 6QS
☎01622 687031   Fax 01622 757646

Editor *Roderick Cooper*
Publisher *Dateam Publishing*
Circulation 10,000

FOUNDED 1962. MONTHLY. Strong Kent interest plus fashion, food, books, wildlife, motoring, property, sport, interiors with local links. Unsolicited mss welcome. Interested in anything with a genuine Kent connection. No fiction or non-Kentish subjects. Approach in writing with ideas. Maximum length 1500 words.
    Payment negotiable.

Keyboard Review

Alexander House, Forehill, Ely, Cambridgeshire CB7 4AF
☎01353 665577   Fax 01353 662489

Owner *Music Maker Publications*
Editor *Sam Molineaux*
Circulation 18,000

FOUNDED 1985. MONTHLY. Broad-based keyboard magazine, covering organs, pianos, keyboards, synthesisers, MIDI keyboard, add-ons such as samplers and modules, and their players. Approach by phone or in writing with ideas.
    Features *Richard Fairhurst* Interviews with keyboard players and instrument reviews. Maximum 3000 words.
    News *Beck Laxton* Brief items on keyboard world. Maximum 400 words.
    Payment negotiable.

The Lady

39-40 Bedford Street, Strand, London
WC2E 9ER
☎0171 379 4717   Fax 0171 497 2137

Owner *T. G. A. Bowles*
Editor *Arline Usden*
Circulation 66,000

FOUNDED 1885. WEEKLY. Unsolicited mss are accepted provided they are not on the subject of politics or religion, or on topics covered by staff writers, i.e. fashion and beauty, health, cookery, household, gardening, finance and shopping.

Features Well-researched pieces on British and foreign travel, historical subjects or events; interviews and profiles and other general interest topics. Maximum 1000 words for illustrated articles; 900 words for one-page features; 450 words for first-person 'Viewpoint' pieces. All material should be addressed to the editor. *Payment* £60 per 1000 words printed.

Photographs supporting features may be supplied as colour transparencies or b&w prints. *Payment* £14–18 per picture used.

Land Rover World Magazine

Link House, Dingwall Road, Croydon, Surrey
CR9 2TA
☎0181 686 2599   Fax 0181 781 6042

Owner *Link House Magazines Ltd*
Editor *Alan Kidd*
Circulation 30,000

FOUNDED 1993. MONTHLY. Incorporates *Practical Land Rover Monthly*. Unsolicited mss welcome, especially if supported by high-quality illustrations. Best, however, to make initial contact by letter or telephone.

Features *Alan Kidd* All articles with a Land Rover theme of interest. Potential contributors are strongly advised to examine previous issues before starting work. *Payment* negotiable.

Learning Resources Journal

11 Malford Grove, Gilwern, Abergavenny,
Gwent NP7 0RN
☎01873 830872

Owner *Learning Resources Development Group*
Editor *David P. Bosworth*
Circulation 600

THRICE-YEARLY publication on the organisation of resources in schools and colleges, which aims to enhance learning in general. Unsolicited mss welcome. Interested in descriptions of classroom/lab/workshop practice and in new resource sources such as telelink/satellite communication; the application of educational technology to the learning situation; European outlooks, etc. Maximum 2500 words (news pieces 100 words). Ideas should be discussed with the editor – sample copy available. *No payment.*

Liberal Democrat News

4 Cowley Street, London SW1P 3NB
☎0171 222 7999   Fax 0171 222 7904

Owner *Liberal Democrats*
Editor *David Boyle*

FOUNDED 1988. WEEKLY. As with the political parties, this is the result of the merger of *Liberal News* (1946) and *The Social Democrat* (1981). Political and social topics of interest to party members and their supporters. Unsolicited contributions welcome.

Features Maximum 800 words.
News Maximum 350 words.
No payment.

Lincolnshire Life

County Life Ltd, PO Box 81, Lincoln
LN1 1HD
☎01522 527127   Fax 01522 560035

Publisher *A.L. Robinson*
Executive Editor *Jez Ashberry*
Circulation 10,000

FOUNDED 1961. MONTHLY county magazine featuring geographically relevant articles. Maximum 1000-1500 words. Contributions supported by three or four good-quality photographs are always welcome. Approach in writing. *Payment* varies.

The List

14 High Street, Edinburgh EH1 1TE
☎0131 558 1191   Fax 0131 557 8500

Owner *The List Ltd*
Publisher *Robin Hodge*
Editor *Kathleen Morgan*
Circulation 14,000

FOUNDED 1985. FORTNIGHTLY. Arts and events guide covering Glasgow and Edinburgh. Interviews and profiles of people working in film, theatre, music and the arts. Maximum 1200 words. Not interested in anything not related to the arts or to life in Central Scotland. No unsolicited mss. Phone with ideas. News material tends to be handled in-house. *Payment* £80.

Literary Review

51 Beak Street, London W1R 3LF
☎0171 437 9392   Fax 0171 734 1844
Owner *Namara Group*
Editor *Auberon Waugh*
Circulation 15,000

FOUNDED 1979. MONTHLY. Publishes book reviews (commissioned), features and articles on literary subjects. Prospective contributors are best advised to contact the editor in writing. Unsolicited mss not welcome. Runs a monthly competition, the Literary Review Grand Poetry Competition, on a given theme. Open to subscribers only. Details published in the magazine.
Payment varies.

Living France

Gairnside House, Gate End, Northwood, Middlesex HA6 3QG
☎01923 828100   Fax 01923 836572
Editor *Clive Graham-Ranger*

FOUNDED 1989. MONTHLY. For Francophiles and people wishing to buy property in France. No unsolicited mss except perhaps for readers' page material. Approach in writing with an idea.

Llais Llyfrau/Books in Wales

Cyngor Llyfrau Cymru/Welsh Books Council, Castell Brychan, Aberystwyth, Dyfed SY23 2JB
☎01970 624151   Fax 01970 625385
Owner *Cyngor Llyfrau Cymru/Welsh Books Council*
Editors *R. Gerallt Jones, Katie Gramich, Lorna Herbert*

FOUNDED 1961. QUARTERLY bilingual magazine containing articles of relevance to the book trade in Wales plus reviews of new books and comprehensive lists of recent titles. A complete section devoted to children's books appears every quarter. No unsolicited mss. All initial approaches should be made in writing.
Features *R. Gerallt Jones* (Welsh)/*Katie Gramich* (English) Each edition features a writer's diary in Welsh and English, plus articles on books, publishing, the media etc. Most items commissioned. Articles on the literature of Wales are welcome, in either language.
Special pages *Lorna Herbert* Children's Books section – latest Welsh-language and Welsh-interest books reviewed.
Payment £30 maximum.

Logos

5 Beechwood Drive, Marlow, Buckinghamshire SL7 2DH
☎01628 477577   Fax 01628 477577
Owner *Whurr Publishers Ltd*
Editor *Gordon Graham*
Associate Editor *Betty Cottrell Graham*

FOUNDED 1990. QUARTERLY. Aims to 'deal in depth with issues which unite, divide, excite and concern the world of books,' with an international perspective. Each issue contains 6-8 articles of between 3500-7000 words. Hopes to establish itself as a forum for contrasting views. Suggestions and ideas for contributions are welcome, and should be addressed to the editor. 'Guidelines for Contributors' available. Contributors write from their experience as authors, publishers, booksellers, librarians, etc. A share of the royalties goes to a trust fund for causes connected with the book.
No payment.

London Magazine

30 Thurloe Place, London SW7 2HQ
☎0171 589 0618
Owner *Alan Ross*
Editor *Alan Ross*
Deputy Editor *Jane Rye*
Circulation 4500

FOUNDED 1954. BI-MONTHLY paperback journal providing an eclectic forum for literary talent, thanks to the dedication of Alan Ross. *The Times* once said that '*London Magazine* is far and away the most readable and level-headed, not to mention best value for money, of the literary magazines'. Today it boasts the publication of early works by the likes of William Boyd, Graham Swift and Ben Okri among others. The broad spectrum of interests includes art, memoirs, travel, poetry, criticism, theatre, music, cinema, short stories and essays, and book reviews. Unsolicited mss welcome; s.a.e. essential. About 150-200 unsolicited mss are received weekly.
Fiction Maximum 5000 words.
Payment £100 maximum.
Annual Subscription £28.50 or $67.

London Review of Books

28 Little Russell Street, London WC1A 2HN
☎0171 404 3336   Fax 0171 404 3337
Owner *LRB Ltd*
Editor *Mary-Kay Wilmers*
Circulation 21,717

FOUNDED 1979. FORTNIGHTLY. Reviews, essays

and articles on political, literary, cultural and scientific subjects. Also poetry. Unsolicited contributions welcome (approximately 50 received each week). No pieces under 2000 words. Contact the editor in writing. Please include s.a.e.

Payment £100 per 1000 words; poems £50.

Looking Good
7 Cheyne Walk, Northampton NN1 5PT
☎01604 602345   Fax 01604 602249
Owner *Herald Newspapers Ltd*
Publisher *Alison Panter*
Circulation 12,500

FOUNDED 1984. MONTHLY county lifestyle magazine of Northamptonshire. Contributions are not required as all work is done in-house.

Looks
20 Orange Street, London WC2H 7ED
☎0171 957 8383   Fax 0171 930 4091
Owner *EMAP Women's Group Magazines*
Editor *Wendy Rigg*
Circulation 231,000

MONTHLY magazine for young women aged 15–22, with emphasis on fashion, beauty and hair, as well as general interest features, including celebrity news and interviews, giveaways, etc. Freelance writers are occasionally used in all areas of the magazine. Contact the editor with ideas.

Payment varies.

Loving Holiday Special
PO Box 435A, Surbiton, Surrey KT6 6YT
Owner *Perfectly Formed Publishing Ltd*
Editor *Jo Pink*
Circulation 40,000

ANNUAL. Unclichéd love stories for women under 30. Story lengths 1000–4000 words. Write for a style guide before putting pen to paper.

Machine Knitting Monthly
PO Box 1479, Maidenhead, Berkshire SL6 8YX
☎01628 783080   Fax 01628 33250
Owner *Machine Knitting Monthly Ltd*
Editor *Sheila Berriff*

FOUNDED 1986. MONTHLY. Unsolicited mss considered 'as long as they are applicable to this specialist publication. We have our own regular contributors each month but we're always willing to look at new ideas from other writers.' Approach in writing in first instance.

Management Today
22 Lancaster Gate, London W2 3LY
☎0171 413 4566   Fax 0171 413 4138
Owner *Management Publications Ltd*
Editor *Charles Skinner*
Circulation 103,000

General business topics and features. Ideas welcome. Send brief synopsis to the editor.

Payment about £300 per 1000 words.

Map Collector
48 High Street, Tring, Hertfordshire HP23 5BH
☎01442 891004   Fax 01442 827712
Owner *Valerie G. Scott*
Editor *Valerie G. Scott*
Circulation 2500

FOUNDED 1977. QUARTERLY magazine dedicated to the history of cartography and study of early maps. Articles, book reviews, news items and guide to prices. Not interested in modern mapping.

Features Articles on early maps particularly welcome. Maximum 2500 words.

News Events and exhibitions of early maps. Maximum 300 words.

Payment NUJ rates.

marie claire
2 Hatfields, London SE1 9PG
☎0171 261 5240   Fax 0171 261 5277
Owner *European Magazines Ltd*
Editor *Juliet Warkentin*
Circulation 455,109

FOUNDED 1988. MONTHLY. An intelligent glossy magazine for women, with strong international features and fashion. No unsolicited mss. Approach with ideas in writing. No fiction.

Features *Lorraine Butler* Detailed proposals for feature ideas should be accompanied by samples of previous work.

Marketing Week
St Giles House, 50 Poland Street, London W1V 4AX
☎0171 439 4222   Fax 0171 434 1439
Owner *Centaur Communications*
Editor *Stuart Smith*
Circulation 38,000

WEEKLY trade magazine of the marketing industry. Features on all aspects of the business, written in a newsy and up-to-the-minute style. Approach with ideas in the first instance.

Features *John Rees*
Payment negotiable.

Match

Bretton Court, Bretton, Peterborough,
Cambridgeshire PE3 8DZ
☎01733 260333   Fax 01733 465206

Owner *EMAP Pursuit Publications*
Editor *Chris Hunt*
Circulation 140,296

FOUNDED 1979. Popular WEEKLY football
magazine aimed at 10-15-year-olds. Most
material is generated in-house by a strong news
and features team. Some freelance material
used if suitable, apart from photographs. No
submissions without prior consultation with
editor, either by phone or in writing.
     Features/News Good and original material
is always considered. Maximum 500 words.
     Payment negotiable.

Matrix

See **British Science Fiction Association**
under **Professional Associations**

Mayfair

2 Archer Street, Piccadilly Circus, London
W1V 7HE
☎0171 734 9191   Fax 0171 734 5030

Owner *Paul Raymond Publications*
Editor *Steve Shields*
Circulation 331,760

FOUNDED 1966. THIRTEEN ISSUES YEARLY.
Unsolicited material accepted if suitable to the
magazine. Interested in features and humour
aimed at men aged 20-30. For style, length,
etc., writers are advised to study the magazine.

Mayfair Times

102 Mount Street, London W1X 5HF
☎0171 629 3378   Fax 0171 629 9303

Owner *Mayfair Times Ltd*
Editor *Stephen Goringe*
Circulation 20,000

FOUNDED 1985. MONTHLY. Features on
Mayfair of interest to both residential and commercial readers. Unsolicited mss welcome.

Medal News

Token Publishing Ltd, PO Box 14, Honiton,
Devon EX14 9YP
☎01404 831878   Fax 01404 831895

Owners *J. W. Mussell, Carol Hartman*
Editor *Diana Birch*
Circulation 2500

FOUNDED 1989. MONTHLY. Unsolicited material welcome but initial approach by phone or
in writing preferred.

     Features Only interested in articles from
well-informed authors 'who know the subject
and do their homework'. Max. 2500 words.
     Payment £20 per 1000 words.

Media Week

33-39 Bowling Green Lane, London
EC1R 0DA
☎0171 505 8341   Fax 0171 505 8363

Owner *EMAP Media*
Editor *Susannah Richmond*
Circulation 14,694

FOUNDED 1986. WEEKLY trade magazine. UK
and international coverage on all aspects of
commercial media. No unsolicited mss.
Approach in writing with ideas.

Melody Maker

King's Reach Tower, Stamford Street,
London SE1 9LS
☎0171 261 6229   Fax 0171 261 6706

Owner *IPC Magazines Ltd*
Editor *Allan Jones*
Circulation 61,781

WEEKLY. Freelance contributors used on this
tabloid magazine competitor of the *NME*.
Opportunities exist in reviewing and features.
     Features *Paul Lester* A large in-house team,
plus around six regulars, produce most feature
material.
     Reviews *Saron O'Connell* (Live), *Everett True*
(Albums) Sample reviews, whether published
or not, welcome on pop, rock, soul, funk, etc.
     Payment negotiable.

Metropolitan

19 Victoria Avenue, Didsbury, Manchester
M20 2GY
☎0161 434 6290

Publishers *John Ashbrook, Elizabeth Baines,
     Ailsa Cox*
Editors *Elizabeth Baines, Ailsa Cox*
Circulation 1500

FOUNDED 1993. BI-ANNUAL magazine devoted
to the short story, with the occasional novel
extract (usually of a forthcoming novel), author
interview or cultural commentary. In its first year
recognised by *The Sunday Times* as one of 'the
livelier literary magazines'. A platform for new
talent alongside names such as Colum McCann,
Carl Tighe, Moy McCrory and Livi Michael.
     Features Usually commissioned, but open
to proposals. Approach in writing with idea,
c.v. and s.a.e..
     Fiction Stories of high literary standard
engaging with contemporary issues. Unsolici-

ted mss welcome. S.a.e. essential. Maximum length 6000 words (2,500 ideal).

No poetry please.

Payment negotiable (depending on grants). Annual subscription £7.

MiniWorld Magazine

Link House, Dingwall Road, Croydon, Surrey CR9 2TA
☎0181 686 2599   Fax 0181 781 6042
Owner *Link House Magazines Ltd*
Editor *Monty Watkins*
Circulation 45,000

FOUNDED 1992. MONTHLY car magazine devoted to the Mini. Unsolicited material welcome but prospective contributors are advised to make initial contact by phone.

Features Restoration, tuning tips, technical advice and sporting events. Readers' cars and product news. Length by arrangement.

Payment negotiable.

Mizz

King's Reach Tower, Stamford Street, London SE1 9LS
☎0171 261 6319   Fax 0171 261 6032
Owner *IPC Magazines Ltd*
Editor *Jeanette Baker*
Circulation 193,700

FOUNDED 1985. FORTNIGHTLY magazine for the 14–19-year-old girl: 'a useful rule of thumb is to write for a 16-year-old'. Freelance articles welcome on real life, human interest stories and emotional issues. All material should be addressed to the features editor.

Features *Julie Burniston* Approach in writing, with synopsis, for feature copy; send sample writing with letter for general approach. No fiction.

The Modern Dance

See under **Small Presses (Works Publishing)**

Modern Machine Knitting

PO Box 1479, Maidenhead, Berkshire SL6 8YX
☎01628 783080   Fax 01628 33250
Owner *Modern Knitting Ltd*
Editor *Anne Smith*

FOUNDED 1951. MONTHLY. Any article related to machine knitting considered. The magazine has its own specialist writers each month but unsolicited mss or ideas in writing are welcome.

Features Around thirty pages of magazine including illustrations, diagrams, etc.

Payment negotiable.

Mojo

Mappin House, 4 Winsley Street, London W1N 7AR
☎0171 436 1515   Fax 0171 637 4925
Owner *EMAP-Metro*
Editor *Mat Snow*
Circulation 52,000

FOUNDED 1993. MONTHLY magazine containing features, reviews and news stories about rock music and its influences. Receives about five mss per day.

Features *Jin Irvin* Amateur writers discouraged except as providers of source material, contacts, etc. *Payment* negotiable.

News All verifiable, relevant stories considered. *Payment* approx. £150 per 1000 words.

Reviews Write to News Editor with relevant specimen material. *Payment* approx. £150 per 1000 words.

Moneywise

Berkeley Magazines Ltd, 10 Old Bailey, London EC4M 7NB
☎0171 409 5274   Fax 0171 409 5261
Owner *Reader's Digest Association*
Editor *Matthew Vincent*
Circulation 130,239

FOUNDED 1990. MONTHLY. Unsolicited mss with s.a.e. welcome but initial approach in writing preferred.

More!

20 Orange Street, London WC2H 7ED
☎0171 957 8383   Fax 0171 930 4637
Owner *EMAP Elan Publications*
Editor *Tony Cross*
Circulation 427,713

FOUNDED 1988. FORTNIGHTLY women's magazine aimed at the working woman aged 18–24. Features on sex and relationships plus news. Most items are commissioned; approach features editor with idea. Prospective contributors are strongly advised to study the magazine's style before submitting anything.

Mother and Baby

Victory House, Leicester Place, London WC2H 7BP
☎0171 437 9011   Fax 0171 434 0656
Owner *EMAP Elan Publications*
Editor *Sharon Parsons*
Circulation 112,201

FOUNDED 1956. MONTHLY. Unsolicited mss welcome, about practical baby and childcare. Personal 'viewpoint' pieces are considered.

Approaches may be made by telephone or in writing.

Motor Boat and Yachting

King's Reach Tower, Stamford Street,
London SE1 9LS
☎0171 261 5333   Fax 0171 261 5419

Owner *IPC Magazines Ltd*
Editor *Alan Harper*
Circulation 20,331

FOUNDED 1904. MONTHLY for those interested in motor boats and motor cruising.

Features *Alan Harper* Cruising features and practical features especially welcome. Illustrations (mostly colour) are just as important as text. Max. 3000 words. *Payment* £100 per 1000 words or by arrangement.

News *Dennis O'Neill* Factual pieces. Max. 200 words. *Payment* up to £50 per item.

Motorcaravan & Motorhome Monthly (MMM)

14 Eastfield Close, Andover, Hampshire
SP10 2QP
Fax 01264 324794

Owner *Sanglier Publications Ltd*
Editor *Penny Smith*
Circulation 23,569

FOUNDED 1966. MONTHLY. 'There's no money in motorcaravan journalism but for those wishing to cut their first teeth...' Unsolicited mss welcome if relevant, but ideas in writing preferred in first instance.

Features Caravan site reports – contact the editor for questionnaire. Maximum 500 words.

Travel Motorcaravanning trips (home and overseas). Maximum 2000 words.

News Short news items for miscellaneous pages. Maximum 200 words.

Fiction Must be motorcaravan-related and include artwork/photos if possible. Maximum 2000 words.

Special pages DIY – modifications to motorcaravans. Maximum 1500 words.

Owner Reports Contributions welcome from motorcaravan owners. Contact the Editor for requirements. Maximum 2000 words.

Payment varies.

Ms London

7-9 Rathbone Street, London W1V 1AF
☎0171 636 6651   Fax 0171 255 2352

Owner *Independent Magazines*
Editor-in-Chief *Bill Williamson*
Editor *Cathy Howes*
Circulation 120,000

FOUNDED 1968. WEEKLY. Aimed at working women in London, aged 18-35. Unsolicited mss must be accompanied by s.a.e.. Because the magazine is purely London-orientated, there is a real bias towards London-based writers who are in touch with the constantly changing trends and attitudes of the capital.

Features Content is varied and ambitious, ranging from stage and film interviews to fashion, careers, relationships, homebuying and furnishing. Approach with ideas first and sample of published writing. Material should be London-angled, sharp and fairly sophisticated in content. Maximum 1500 words. *Payment* about £125 per 1000 words.

News Handled in-house but follow-up feature ideas welcome.

Music Week

Miller Freeman Entertainment, Ludgate House,
245 Blackfriars Road, London SE1 9UR
☎0171 620 3636   Fax 0171 401 8035

Owner *Miller Freeman Entertainment*
Editor-in-Chief *Steve Redmond*
Managing Editor *Selina Webb*
Circulation 13,900

WEEKLY. Britain's only weekly music business magazine also includes dance industry title *Record Mirror*. No unsolicited mss. Approach in writing with ideas.

Features *Selina Webb* Analysis of specific music business events and trends. Maximum 2000 words.

News Music industry news only. Maximum 350 words.

Musical Option

2 Princes Road, St Leonards on Sea, East Sussex TN37 6EL
☎01424 715167   Fax 01424 712214

Owner *Musical Option Ltd*
Editor *Denby Richards*
Circulation 5000

FOUNDED 1877. QUARTERLY with free supplement in intervening months. Classical music content, with topical features on music, musicians, festivals, etc., and reviews (concerts, festivals, opera, ballet, jazz, CDs, CD-Roms, videos, books and music). International readership. No unsolicited mss; commissions only. Ideas always welcome though; approach by phone. It should be noted that topical material has to be submitted six months prior to events. Not interested in review material, which is already handled by the magazine's own regular team of contributors.

Payment Negotiable.

Musical Times
79 Macaulay Square, London SW4 0RU
☎0171 627 3688   Fax 0171 622 1317
Owner *The Musical Times Publications Ltd*
Editor *Antony Bye*
FOUNDED 1844. Scholarly journal with a practical approach to its subject. Unsolicited mss will occasionally be considered.
Payment negotiable.

My Guy Magazine
PO Box 435a, Surbiton, Surrey KT6 6YT
☎0181 255 3151   Fax 0181 390 5832
Owner *Perfectly Formed Publishing*
Editor *Frank Hopkinson*
Circulation 45,000
FOUNDED 1977. MONTHLY teen magazine for girls and boys. No freelance contributions.

My Weekly
80 Kingsway East, Dundee DD4 8SL
☎01382 464276   Fax 01382 452491
Owner *D. C. Thomson & Co. Ltd*
Editor *Harrison Watson*
Circulation 434,031
A traditional women's WEEKLY. D.C. Thomson has long had a policy of encouragement and help to new writers of promise. Ideas welcome. Approach in writing.
Features Particularly interested in human interest pieces (1000–1500 words) which by their very nature appeal to all age groups.
Fiction Three stories a week, ranging in content from the emotional to the off-beat and unexpected. 2000–4000 words. Also serials.
Payment negotiable.

The National Trust Magazine
36 Queen Anne's Gate, London SW1H 9AS
☎0171 222 9251   Fax 0171 222 5097
Owner *The National Trust*
Editor *Sarah-Jane Forder*
Circulation 2.2 million
FOUNDED 1968. THRICE-YEARLY. Conservation of historic houses, coast and countryside in the UK. No unsolicited mss. Approach in writing with ideas.

Natural World
20 Upper Ground, London SE1 9PF
☎0171 805 5555   Fax 0171 805 5911
Publishers *Illustrated London News Group on behalf of The Wildlife Trusts*
Editor *Linda Bennett*
Circulation 150,000

FOUNDED 1981. THRICE-YEARLY. Unsolicited mss welcome if of high quality and relevant to ideals of the magazine. Ideas in writing preferred. No poetry.
Features Popular but accurate articles on British wildlife and the countryside, particularly projects associated with the local wildlife trusts. Maximum 1500 words. *Payment* £150 per 1000 words.
News Interested in national wildlife conservation issues, particularly those involving local nature conservation or wildlife trusts. Maximum 300 words.

The Naturalist
c/o University of Bradford, Bradford, West Yorkshire BD7 1DP
☎01274 384212   Fax 01274 384231
Owner *Yorkshire Naturalists' Union*
Editor *Prof. M. R. D. Seaward*
Circulation 5000
FOUNDED 1875. QUARTERLY. Natural history, biological and environmental sciences for a professional and amateur readership. Unsolicited mss welcome. Particularly interested in material – scientific papers – relating to the north of England.
No payment.

Nature
Porters South, 4–6 Crinan Street, London N1 9XW
☎0171 833 4000
Owner *Macmillan Magazines Ltd*
Editor *Philip Campbell*
Circulation 55,438
Covers all fields of science, with articles and news on science policy only. No features. Little scope for freelance writers.

Needlecraft
30 Monmouth Street, Bath, Avon BA1 6LH
☎01225 442244   Fax 01225 462986
Owner *Future Publishing*
Editor *Rebecca Bradshaw*
Circulation 74,095
FOUNDED 1991. MONTHLY. Needlework projects with full instructions covering cross-stitch, needlepoint, embroidery, patchwork quilting and lace. Will consider ideas or sketches for projects covering any of the magazine's topics. Initial approaches should be made in writing.
Features on the needlecraft theme. Discuss ideas before sending complete mss. Maximum 1000 words.
Technical pages on 'how to' stitch, use

different threads, etc. Only suitable for experienced writers.
Payment negotiable.

New Beacon
224 Great Portland Street, London W1N 6AA
☎0171 388 1266   Fax 0171 388 0945
Owner *Royal National Institute for the Blind*
Editor *Ann Lee*
Circulation 6000

FOUNDED 1917. MONTHLY. Published in print, braille and on tape. Unsolicited mss welcome. Approach with ideas in writing. Personal experiences by writers who have a visual impairment (partial sight or blindness), and authoritative items by professionals or volunteers working in the field of visual impairment welcome. Maximum 1500 words.
Payment £30 per 1000 words.

New Christian Herald
Herald House, 96 Dominion Road,
Worthing, West Sussex BN14 8JP
☎01903 821082   Fax 01903 821081
Owner *Herald House Ltd*
Editor *Russ Bravo*
Circulation 30,000

WEEKLY. Evangelical, inter-denominational Christian newspaper intended for adults with families. News, bible-based comment and incisive features. Contributors' guidelines available.
Payment Herald House rates.

New Humanist
Bradlaugh House, 47 Theobald's Road,
London WC1X 8SP
☎0171 430 1371   Fax 0171 430 1271
Owner *Rationalist Press Association*
Editor *Jim Herrick*
Circulation 3000

FOUNDED 1885. QUARTERLY. Unsolicited mss welcome. No fiction.
Features Articles with a humanist perspective welcome in the following fields: religion (critical), humanism, human rights, philosophy, current events, literature, history and science. 2000–4000 words. *Payment* nominal, but negotiable.
Book reviews 750–1000 words, by arrangement with the editor.

New Impact
Anser House, PO Box 1448, Marlow, Bucks
SL7 3HD
☎01628 481581   Fax 01628 481581
Owner *D. E. Sihera*
Editor *Elaine Sihera*

Circulation 10,000

FOUNDED 1993. BI-MONTHLY. Promotes training enterprise and diversity from a minority ethnic perspective. Unsolicited mss welcome. Interested in training, arts, features, personal achievement, small business features, profiles or personalities especially for a multicultural audience. Not interested in anything unconnected to training or business. Approach in writing with ideas. Promotes the British Diversity Awards each November.
News Local training/business features – some opportunities. Maximum length 250 words. *Payment* negotiable.
Features Original, interesting pieces with a deliberate multicultural/equal opportunity focus. Personal/professional successes and achievements welcome. Maximum length 1500 words. *Payment* negotiable.
Fiction Short stories, poems – especially from minority writers. Maximum length 1500 words. *Payment* negotiable.
Special Pages Interviews with personalities – especially Asian, Afro-Caribbean. Maximum length 1200 words. *Payment* negotiable.

New Internationalist
55 Rectory Road, Oxford OX4 1BW
☎01865 728181   Fax 01865 793152
Owner *New Internationalist Trust*
Co-Editors *Vanessa Baird, Chris Brazier, David Ransom, Nikki van der Gaag*
Circulation 70,000

Radical and broadly leftist in approach, but unaligned. Concerned with world poverty and global issues of peace and politics, feminism and environmentalism, with emphasis on the Third World. Difficult to use unsolicited material as they work to a theme each month and features are commissioned by the editor on that basis. The way in is to send examples of published or unpublished work; writers of interest are taken up. Unsolicited material for shorter articles could be used in the magazine's regular *Update* section.

New Moon Magazine
28 St Albans Lane, London NW11 7QE
☎0181 731 8031   Fax 0181 381 4033
Owner *New Moon Publishing*
Editor *Matthew Kalman*
Circulation 8000

FOUNDED 1990. MONTHLY Jewish magazine covering arts, entertainment, politics, religion, and relationships for an audience that is mostly aged 20–40 and single. No fiction or poetry.

Features *Victoria Stagg Elliott* Opportunities exist primarily with celebrity interviews and general features. Not many opportunities for outside contributors but 'always open to a good idea'. Maximum 4000 words. Approach with ideas in writing in the first instance.

Payment by arrangement.

New Musical Express

Floor 25, King's Reach Tower, Stamford Street, London SE1 9LS
☎0171 261 6472   Fax 0171 261 5185
Owner *IPC Magazines Ltd*
Editor *Steve Sutherland*
Circulation 118,755

Britain's best-selling musical WEEKLY. Free-lancers used, but always for reviews in the first instance. Specialisation in areas of music (or film, which is also covered) is a help.

Reviews: Books *Stephen Dalton* **Film** *Stephen Dalton* **LPs** *John Robinson* **Live** *Ted Kessler*. Send in examples of work, either published or specially written samples.

New Scientist

King's Reach Tower, Stamford Street, London SE1 9LS
☎0171 261 5000   Fax 0171 261 6464
Owner *IPC Magazines Ltd*
Editor *Alun Anderson*
Circulation 116,000

FOUNDED 1956. WEEKLY. No unsolicited mss. Approach in writing or by phone with an idea.

Features *Jeremy Webb* Commissions only, but good ideas welcome. Max. 3500 words.

News *Stephanie Pain* Mostly commissions, but ideas for specialist news, particularly from academics and specialist writers, are welcome. Max. 1000 words.

Reviews *Maggie McDonald* Reviews are commissioned.

Forum *Richard Fifield* Unsolicited material welcome if of general/humorous interest and related to science. Max. 1000 words.

Payment £200+ per 1000 words.

New Statesman and Society

Foundation House, Perseverance Works, 38 Kingsland Road, London E2 8DQ
☎0171 739 3211   Fax 0171 739 9307
Owner *Geoffrey Robinson*
Editor *Ian Hargreaves*
Deputy Editor *Paul Anderson*
Circulation 25,000

WEEKLY magazine, the result of a merger (May 1988) of *New Statesman* and *New Society*.

Coverage of news, book reviews, arts, current affairs, politics and social reportage. Unsolicited contributions with s.a.e. will be considered. No short stories.

Literary *Boyd Tonkin*
Arts *Marina Benjamin*

New Welsh Review

Chapter Arts Centre, Market Road, Cardiff CF5 1QE
☎01222 665529   Fax 01222 665529
Owner *New Welsh Review Ltd*
Editor *Robin Reeves*
Circulation 1000

FOUNDED 1988. QUARTERLY Welsh literary magazine, published in English. Welcomes material of literary and cultural interest to Welsh readers and those with an interest in Wales. Approach in writing in the first instance.

Features Max. 3000 words. *Payment* £15 per 1000 words.

Fiction Max. 5000 words. *Payment* £60 average.

News Max. 400 words. *Payment* £5–£15.

New Woman

20 Orange Street, London WC2H 7ED
☎0171 957 8383   Fax 0171 930 7246
Owner *Hachette/EMAP Magazines Ltd*
Editor *Eleni Kyriacou*

MONTHLY women's interest magazine – a 'self-indulgent, informative and intelligent' read. Main topics of interest include men, sex, love, health, careers, beauty and fashion. Uses mainly established freelancers but unsolicited ideas submitted in synopsis form will be considered.

Features/News *Linda Bird* Articles must be original and look at subjects or issues from a new or unusual perspective.

Beauty *Jan Masters*
Fashion *Corinna Kitchen*

News From the Centre (NFC)

See **The National Small Press Centre** under **Professional Associations**

19

King's Reach Tower, Stamford Street, London SE1 9LS
☎0171 261 6410   Fax 0171 261 7634
Owner *IPC Magazines Ltd*
Editor *April Joyce*
Circulation 203,000

MONTHLY women's magazine aimed at 16-20-year-olds. A little different from the usual teen magazine mix: *19* are now aiming for a 50/50 balance between fashion/lifestyle aspects and newsier, meatier material, e.g. women in prison, boys, abortion, etc.. 40% of the magazine's feature material is commissioned, ordinarily from established freelancers. 'But we're always keen to see bold, original, vigorous writing from people just starting out.'

Features *Lysane Currie* Approach in writing with ideas.

North East Times

Tattler House, Beech Avenue, Fawdon, Newcastle upon Tyne NE3 4LA
☎0191 284 4495   Fax 0191 285 9606
Owner *Chris Robinson (Publishing) Ltd*
Editor *Chris Robinson*
Circulation 10,000

MONTHLY county magazine incorporating *Newcastle Life.* No unsolicited mss. Approach with ideas in writing. Not interested in any material that is not applicable to ABC1 readers.

The North

See **Poetry, Little Magazines**

Nursing Times

Porters South, 4–6 Crinan Street, London N1 9SQ
☎0171 843 4600   Fax 0171 843 4633
Owner *Macmillan Magazines Ltd*
Editor *Jane Salvage*
Circulation 78,511

A large proportion of *Nursing Times'* feature content is from unsolicited contributions sent on spec. Pieces on all aspects of nursing and health care, both practical and theoretical, written in a lively and contemporary way, are welcome. Commissions also.

Payment varies/NUJ rates apply to commissioned material from union members only.

Office Secretary

Brookmead House, Thorney Leys Business Park, Witney, Oxfordshire OX8 7GE
☎01993 775545
Owner *Trade Media Ltd*
Editor *Danusia Hutson*
Circulation 60,000

FOUNDED 1986. QUARTERLY. Features articles of interest to secretaries and personal assistants aged 25–60. No unsolicited mss.

Features Informative pieces on current affairs, health, food, fashion, hotel, travel, motoring, office and employment-related topics. Length 1000 words.

Payment by negotiation.

OK! Weekly

The Northern & Shell Tower, City Harbour, London E14 9GL
☎0171 987 6262   Fax 0171 515 6650
Owner *Richard Desmond*
Editor *Richard Barber*
Circulation 200,000

FOUNDED 1996. WEEKLY celebrity-based magazine. Approach with ideas in writing in the first instance.

The Oldie

45–46 Poland Street, London W1V 4AU
☎0171 734 2225   Fax 0171 734 2226
Owner *Oldie Publications Ltd*
Editor *Richard Ingrams*
Circulation 45,000

FOUNDED 1992. MONTHLY general interest magazine with a strong humorous slant for the older person.

OLS (Open Learning Systems) News

11 Malford Grove, Gilwern, Abergavenny, Gwent NP7 0RN
☎01873 830872   Fax 01873 830872
Owner *David P. Bosworth*
Editor *David P. Bosworth*
Circulation 800

FOUNDED 1980. QUARTERLY dealing with the application of open, flexible, distance learning and supported self-study at all educational/training levels. Interested in open-access learning and the application of educational technology to learning situations. Case studies particularly welcome. Not interested in theory of education alone, the emphasis is strictly on applied policies and trends.

Features Learning programmes (how they are organised); student/learner-eye views of educational and training programmes with an open-access approach. Approach the editor by phone or in writing.

No payment for 'news' items. Focus items will negotiate.

Opera

1A Mountgrove Road, London N5 2LU
☎0171 359 1037   Fax 0171 354 2700
Owner *Opera Magazine Ltd*
Editor *Rodney Milnes*
Circulation 11,500

FOUNDED 1950. MONTHLY review of the current opera scene. Almost all articles are commissioned and unsolicited mss are not welcome. All approaches should be made in writing.

Opera Now
241 Shaftesbury Avenue, London WC2H 8EH
☎0171 333 1740   Fax 0171 333 1769
Owner *Rhinegold Publishing Ltd*
Editor-in-Chief *Graeme Kay*
Deputy Editor *Rachel Connolly*

FOUNDED 1989. BI-MONTHLY. News, features and reviews for those interested in opera. No unsolicited mss. All work is commissioned. Approach with ideas in writing.

Options
King's Reach Tower, Stamford Street, London SE1 9LS
☎0171 261 5000   Fax 0171 261 7344
Owner *IPC Magazines Ltd*
Editor *Maureen Rice*
Circulation 169,000

'Invest in yourself' is the motto of this women's magazine with an emphasis on practical and self-help articles. Almost all material is written by a regular team of freelancers, but new writers are encouraged.
Payment about £250 per 1000 words.

Orbis
See under **Poetry, Little Magazines**

Parents
Victory House, Leicester Place, London WC2H 7BP
☎0171 437 9011   Fax 0171 434 0656
Owner *EMAP Elan Publications*
Editor *Julia Goodwin*
Circulation 70,000

FOUNDED 1976. MONTHLY. Features commissioned from outside contributors. Approach with ideas. Age span: from pregnancy to four years.

Paris Transcontinental
Institut des Pays Anglophones, Sorbonne Nouvelle, 5 rue de l'Ecole de Médicine, Paris, France 75006
☎00 33 1 69018635
Owner *Claire Larrière*
Editor-in-chief *Claire Larrière*
Editors *Devorah Goldberg, Albert Russo*
Circulation 550

FOUNDED 1990. BI-ANNUAL. French magazine which publishes original short stories in English from around the world. No poetry, non-fiction or artwork. All themes. A good style, originality and strength. The magazine purports to be a forum for writers of excellent stories whose link is the English language and the short story. Length 2500–4500 words. Original short stories only. No translations: stories must be written in English. Stories should be submitted along with a few lines about yourself and your work (about 100 words only) and must be accompanied by International Reply Coupons
Payment two copies of the magazine.

PCW Plus
30 Monmouth Street, Bath, Avon BA1 2BW
☎01225 442244   Fax 01225 446019
Owner *Nick Alexander*
Editor *Andrew Chapman*
Circulation 10,000

FOUNDED 1986. MONTHLY. Unsolicited contributions welcome but initial approach in writing preferred.
Features *Martin Le Poidevin* 'We will welcome any interesting feature-length articles on writing but must involve reference to PCW. Good illustrations preferred as well.' Maximum 2000 words.
Case in Point Regular feature on original uses to which people have put their Amstrad PCWs. Good illustrations important. Maximum 1600 words.
Payment negotiable.

Pembrokeshire Life
21 High Street, Haverford West, Pembrokeshire SA61 2BW
☎01437 768828   Fax 01437 760926
Owner *United Provincial Newspapers*
Editor *Alison Heighton*

FOUNDED 1991. MONTHLY county magazine with articles on local history, issues, characters, off-beat stories with good colour or b&w photographs. No country diaries, short stories, poems. Most articles are commissioned from known freelancers but 'always prepared to consider ideas from new writers'. No mss. Send cuttings of previous work (published or not) and synopsis to the editor.

Penthouse
Northern & Shell Tower, 4 Selsdon Way, City Harbour, London E14 9GL
☎0171 987 5090   Fax 0171 987 0756
Owner *Northern & Shell plc*
Editor *Derek Botham*
Editorial Director *Paul Ashford*

Managing Editor *Jonathan Richards*
Circulation 102,421

FOUNDED 1965. THIRTEEN ISSUES YEARLY. No fiction.

Features *Stewart Meagher* Unsolicited mss welcome, 'but most of those we do receive are unsuitable because the authors haven't looked at the magazine'. First approach by phone or in writing with ideas. Maximum 3500 words. Must have a fairly long-term appeal. *Payment* negotiable 'but generally pretty good'.

News *Stewart Meagher* Limited opportunities for unsolicited material.

The People's Friend

80 Kingsway East, Dundee DD4 8SL
☎01382 462276/223131   Fax 01382 452491
Owner *D. C. Thomson & Co. Ltd*
Editor *Sinclair Matheson*
Circulation 520,000

The *Friend* is basically a fiction magazine, with two serials and several short stories each week. FOUNDED in 1869, it has always prided itself on providing 'a good read for all the family'. All stories should be about ordinary, identifiable characters with the kind of problems the average reader can understand and sympathise with. 'We look for the romantic and emotional developments of characters, rather than an over-complicated or contrived plot. From time to time we can also use a romantic/mystery/adventure/period-type story.'

Short Stories Can vary in length from 1000 words or less to as many as 4000.

Serials Long-run serials of 10-15 instalments or more preferred. Occasionally shorter.

Articles Short fillers welcome.

Payment on acceptance.

Period House

7 St Johns Road, Harrow, Middlesex
HA1 2EE
☎0181 863 2020   Fax 0181 863 2444
Owner *Cornelius Bohane*
Editor *Laura Goodhart*
Circulation 25,000-35,000

FOUNDED 1991. MONTHLY on the pleasures and perils of period house ownership. Freelance opportunities for articles on relevant renovation and period topics. Approach by phone or in writing in the first instance.

Features 'Lots of opportunities for competent writers well-versed in the period house and garden world.' Case study ideas on renovated houses always welcome. Maximum 1000 words. *Payment* variable.

Period Living & Traditional Homes

Victory House, 14 Leicester Place, London
WC2H 7BP
☎0171 208 3245   Fax 0171 434 0656
Owner *EMAP Elan*
Editor *Clare Weatherall*
Circulation 50,561

FOUNDED 1992. Formed from the merger of *Period Living* and *Traditional Homes*. Covers interior decoration in a period style, period house profiles, traditional crafts, renovation of period properties, antiques and profiles of collectors.

Features *Dominique Coughlin*

Payment varies according to length/type of article.

The Philosopher

BM Box 1129, London WC1N 3XX
☎01923 229784   Fax 01923 229784
Owner *The Philosophical Society of Great Britain*
Editor *Dr Keith H. Seddon*
Associate/Reviews Editor *Dr Keith H. Seddon*

FOUNDED 1913. BI-ANNUAL journal of the Philosophical Society of Great Britain. Analytical philosophy in the Anglo-American tradition. Wide range of interests, but leaning towards articles that present philosophical investigation which is relevant to the individual and to society in our modern era. Accessible to the non-specialist. Will consider articles and book reviews. No 'new age' philosophy, pseudo-science, amateur essays on 'philosophy of life'. Notes for Contributors available; send s.a.e.. As well as short philosophical papers, will accept:

News about lectures, conventions, philosophy groups. Ethical issues in the news. Maximum 1000 words.

Reviews of philosophy books (maximum 600 words); discussion articles of individual philosophers and their published works (maximum 2000 words)

Payment free copies.

Picture Postcard Monthly

15 Debdale Lane, Keyworth, Nottingham
NG12 5HT
☎0115 9374079   Fax 0115 9376197
Owners *Brian & Mary Lund*
Editor *Brian Lund*
Circulation 4300

FOUNDED 1978. MONTHLY. News, views, clubs, diary of fairs, sales, auctions, and well-researched postcard-related articles. Might be interested in general articles supported by postcards. Unsolicited mss welcome. Approach by phone or in writing with ideas.

Pilot
The Clock House, 28 Old Town, Clapham, London SW4 0LB
☎0171 498 2506   Fax 0171 498 6920
Owner/Editor *James Gilbert*
Circulation 31,427

FOUNDED 1968. MONTHLY magazine for private plane pilots. No staff writers; the entire magazine is written by freelancers – mostly regulars. Unsolicited mss welcome but ideas in writing preferred. Perusal of any issue of the magazine will reveal the type of material bought.

Features *James Gilbert* Many articles are unsolicited personal experiences/travel accounts from pilots of private planes; good photo coverage is very important. Maximum 5000 words. *Payment* £100–700 (first rights). Photos £25 each.

News *Mike Jerram* Contributions need to be as short as possible. See *Pilot Notes* in the magazine.

The Pink Paper
72 Holloway Road, London N7 8NZ
☎0171 296 6210   Fax 0171 296 0026
Owner *Chronos Group*
Editor *Paul Clements*
Circulation 55,000

FOUNDED 1987. WEEKLY. National newspaper for lesbians and gay men covering politics, social issues, health, the arts and all areas of concern to the lesbian/gay community. Incorporates *Boyz*. Unsolicited mss welcome. Initial approach by phone with an idea preferred. Interested in profiles, reviews, in-depth features and short news pieces.

News Maximum 300 words.
Listings/Arts & Reviews (Max. 200 words)**/ Books** *Tim Teeman*

Boyz
  Editor *Simon Gage*
  Listings, Bars & Clubs *David Hudson*
  Editorial Assistant *Nick Kynaston*
  Album & Single Reviews *Tim Teeman*
  Payment by arrangement.

Plays and Players
Northway House, 1379 High Road, London N20 9LP
☎0181 343 8515   Fax 0181 446 1410
Owner *Mineco Designs*
Editor *Sandra Rennie*
Circulation 9500

Theatre MONTHLY which publishes a mixture of news, reviews, reports and features on all aspects of the theatre. Rarely uses unsolicited material but writers of talent are taken up. Almost all material is commissioned.

PN Review
See under **Poetry, Little Magazines**

Poetry Ireland Review
See under **Poetry, Little Magazines**

Poetry Review
See under **Poetry, Little Magazines**

Poetry Wales
See under **Poetry, Little Magazines**

The Polish Gazette (Gazeta)
PO Box 1945, Edinburgh EH4 1AB
☎0131 315 2002
Owner *Gazeta Ltd*
Editor *Maria Rayska*

FOUNDED 1995. QUARTERLY. The only English language publication in the UK for the Polish community, friends of Poland, and businesses dealing with Poland. Approach in writing with ideas for articles.

Features *Tony Keniston* travel, business, autobiography. 600 words maximum.

News *Maria Rayska* general, local and international news of interest to the Polish community in Britain, Poland, exhibitions and events, etc.

Payment by arrangement.

Pony
D.J. Murphy (Publishers) Ltd, Haslemere House, Lower Street, Haslemere, Surrey GU27 2PE
☎01428 651551   Fax 01428 653888
Owner *D. J. Murphy (Publishers) Ltd*
Editor *Janet Rising*
Circulation 38,000

FOUNDED 1948. Lively MONTHLY aimed at 10–16-year-olds. News, instruction on riding, stable management, veterinary care, interviews. Approach in writing with an idea.

Features welcome. Maximum 900 words.

News Written in-house. Photographs and illustrations (serious/cartoon) welcome.

Payment £65 per 1000 words.

Popular Crafts
Nexus House, Boundary Way, Hemel Hempstead, Hertfordshire HP2 7ST
☎01442 66551   Fax 01442 66998
Owner *Nexus Special Interests*

Editor *Charlotte Coward-Williams*
Circulation 32,000

FOUNDED 1980. MONTHLY. Covers crafts of all kinds. Freelance contributions welcome – copy needs to be lively and interesting. Approach in writing with an outline of idea.

Features Project-based under the following headings: Homecraft; Needlecraft; Popular Craft; Kidscraft; News and Columns. Any craft-related material including projects to make, with full instructions/patterns supplied in all cases; profiles of crafts people and news of craft group activities or successes by individual persons; articles on collecting crafts; personal experiences and anecdotes; readers' homes.
Payment on publication.

PR Week

174 Hammersmith Road, London W6 7JP
☎0171 413 4529   Fax 0171 413 4509
Owner *Haymarket Business Publications Ltd*
Editor *Stephen Farish*
Circulation 20,000

FOUNDED 1984. WEEKLY. Contributions accepted from experienced journalists. Approach in writing with an idea.
Features *Kate Nicholas*
News *Steve Bevan*
Payment £170 per 1000 words.

Practical Boat Owner

Westover House, West Quay Road, Poole, Dorset BH15 1JG
☎01202 680593   Fax 01202 674335
Owner *IPC Magazines*
Editor *Rodger Witt*
Circulation 52,000

FOUNDED 1967. MONTHLY magazine of practical information for cruising boat owners. Receives about 1500 mss per year. Interested in hard facts about gear, equipment, pilotage from experienced yachtsmen.

Features technical articles about maintenance, restoration, modifications to cruising boats, power and sail up to 45ft, or reader reports on gear and equipment. European pilotage articles and cruising guides. Approach in writing with synopsis in the first instance.
Payment negotiable.

Practical Caravan

60 Waldegrave Road, Teddington, Middlesex TW11 8LG
☎0181 943 5784   Fax 0181 943 5798
Owner *Haymarket Magazines Ltd*
Editor *Ally Watson*

Deputy Editor *John Rawlings*
Circulation 50,011

FOUNDED 1964. MONTHLY. Contains caravan reviews, travel features, investigations, products, park reviews. Unsolicited mss welcome on travel relevant only to caravanning/touring vans. No motorcaravan or static van stories. Approach with ideas by phone.

Features *John Rawlings* must refer to caravanning, towing. Written in friendly, chatty manner. Features with pictures/transparencies preferred (to include caravans where possible). Maximum length 2000 words. *Payment* £110 per 1000 words.

Special Pages Caravan park reviews, geared towards touring facilities and use. Should be accompanied by photos. Maximum length 700 words per park. *Payment* £80 per 1000 words.

Practical Fishkeeping

Bretton Court, Bretton, Peterborough, Cambridgeshire PE3 8DZ
☎01733 264666   Fax 01733 465353
Owner *EMAP Pursuit Publishing Ltd*
Managing Editor *Steve Windsor*
Circulation 39,000

MONTHLY. Practical articles on all aspects of fishkeeping. Unsolicited mss welcome. Approach in writing with ideas. Quality photographs of fish always welcome. No fiction or verse.

Practical Gardening

Apex House, Oundle Road, Peterborough, Cambridgeshire PE2 9NP
☎01733 898100   Fax 01733 898433
Owner *EMAP Apex Publications Ltd*
Editor *Andrew Blackford*
Circulation 73,349

FOUNDED 1960. MONTHLY aimed at broad-based readership of relatively knowledgeable gardeners and enthusiasts. Unsolicited mss will be considered but there are few acceptances out of the 200 or so received each year. Careful study of the magazine's content and market is essential.

Features Pieces on real-life gardens, particularly those with an unusual angle, welcome, provided they are in keeping with the magazine's style. Emphasis on creative planting schemes and features – but also on the people *behind* the gardens. Maximum 1200 words. *Practical Gardening* is not a how-to publication, but aims to offer creative ideas and inspiration.
Payment from £120 per 1000 words.

Practical Parenting

King's Reach Tower, Stamford Street,
London SE1 9LS
☎0171 261 5058   Fax 0171 261 6542

Owner *IPC Magazines Ltd*
Editor-in-Chief *Jayne Marsden*
Circulation 109,788

FOUNDED 1987. MONTHLY. Practical advice on
pregnancy, birth, babycare and childcare up to
five years. Submit ideas in writing with synopsis
or send mss on spec. Interested in feature articles
of up to 3000 words in length, and in readers'
experiences/personal viewpoint pieces of
between 750–1000 words. Humorous articles on
some aspect of parenthood may also stand a
chance. All material must be written for the
magazine's specifically targeted audience and in-
house style. *Payment* negotiable.

Practical Photography

Apex House, Oundle Road, Peterborough,
Cambridgeshire PE2 9NP
☎01733 898100   Fax 01733 894472

Owner *EMAP Apex Publications Ltd*
Editor *Martyn Moore*
Circulation 85,000

MONTHLY. All types of photography, particularly technique-orientated pictures. No unsolicited mss. Preliminary approach may be made
by telephone. Always interested in new ideas.

Features Anything relevant to the world of
photography, but not 'the sort of feature produced by staff writers'. Features on technology
and humour are two areas worth exploring.
Bear in mind that there is a three-month lead-
in time. Maximum 2000 words.

News Only 'hot' news applicable to a
monthly magazine. Maximum 400 words.
Payment varies.

Practical Wireless

Arrowsmith Court, Station Approach,
Broadstone, Dorset BH18 8PW
☎01202 659910   Fax 01202 659950

Owner *P.W. Publishing*
Editor *Rob Mannion*
Circulation 27,000

FOUNDED 1932. MONTHLY. News and features
relating to amateur radio, radio construction
and radio communications. Unsolicited mss welcome and guidelines available (send s.a.e.).
Approach by phone with ideas in the first
instance. Copy should be supported where possible by artwork, either illustrations, diagrams or
photographs.
Payment £54–70 per page.

Practical Woodworking

Boundary Way, Hemel Hempstead,
Hertfordshire HP2 7ST
☎01442 66551   Fax 01442 66636

Owner *Nexus Special Interests Ltd*
Editor *Nick Hunton*
Circulation 41,000

FOUNDED 1965. MONTHLY. Contains articles
relating to woodworking – projects, techniques,
new products, tips, letters etc. Unsolicited mss
welcome. No fiction. Approach with ideas in
writing or by phone.

News Anything related to woodworking.
Payment £60 per published page.

Features Projects, techniques etc. *Payment*
£60 per published page.

Prediction

Link House, Dingwall Avenue, Croydon,
Surrey CR9 2TA
☎0181 686 2599   Fax 0181 781 1159

Owner *Link House Magazines Ltd*
Editor *Jo Logan*
Circulation 35,000

FOUNDED 1936. MONTHLY. Covering astrology and occult-related topics. Unsolicited
material in these areas welcome (about 200–
300 mss received every year).

Astrology Pieces, ranging from 800–2000
words, should be practical and of general interest. Charts and astro data should accompany
them, especially if profiles.

Features *Jo Logan* Articles on mysteries of
the earth, alternative medicine, psychical/ occult
experiences and phenomena are considered.
800–2000 words. *Payment* £25–75.

News & Views Items of interest to readership welcome. Maximum 300 words. *No payment.*

Premonitions

See **Pigasus Press** under **Small Presses**

Press Gazette

33–39 Bowling Green Lane, London
EC1R 0DA
☎0171 505 8000   Fax 0171 505 8220

Owner *EMAP Media*
Editor *Roy Farndon*
Circulation 8,754

WEEKLY magazine containing news, features
and analysis of all areas of journalism, print and
broadcasting. Unsolicited mss welcome, interested in profiles of magazines, broadcasting
companies and news agencies, personality profiles, technical and current affairs relating to the

world of journalism. No vague, trite and ill-directed pieces; we serve a professional market which requires professional reading. Approach with ideas by phone, fax or in writing.

Prima

Portland House, Stag Place, London
SW1E 5AU
☎0171 245 8700   Fax 0171 630 5509
Owner *Gruner & Jahr (UK)*
Editor *Lindsay Nicholson*
Circulation 557,338

FOUNDED 1986. MONTHLY women's magazine.

Features Coordinator *Diana Cambridge* Mostly practical and written by specialists, or commissioned from known freelancers. Unsolicited mss not welcome.

Private Eye

6 Carlisle Street, London W1V 5RG
☎0171 437 4017   Fax 0171 437 0705
Owner *Pressdram*
Editor *Ian Hislop*
Circulation 190,000

FOUNDED 1961. FORTNIGHTLY satirical and investigative magazine. Prospective contributors are best advised to approach the editor in writing. News stories and feature ideas are always welcome, as are cartoons. All jokes written in-house.

Payment in all cases is 'not great', and length of piece varies as appropriate.

Prospect

4 Bedford Square, London WC1B 3RA
☎0171 255 1281   Fax 0171 255 1279
Owner *Prospect Publishing Limited*
Editor *David Goodhart*
Circulation 20,000

FOUNDED1995. MONTHLY. Essays, reviews and research on current/international affairs and cultural issues. No news features. No unsolicited mss. Approach in writing with ideas in the first instance.

Psychic News

Clock Cottage, Stansted Hall, Stansted, Essex
CM24 8UD
☎01279 817050   Fax 01279 817051
Owner *Psychic Press 1995 Ltd*
Editor *Julie Stretton*
Circulation 15,000

FOUNDED 1932. *Psychic News* is the world's only WEEKLY spiritualist newspaper. It covers subjects such as psychic research, hauntings, ghosts, poltergeists, spiritual healing, survival after death, and paranormal gifts. Unsolicited material considered.

Publishing News

43 Museum Street, London WC1A 1LY
☎0171 404 0304   Fax 0171 242 0762
Editor *Fred Newman*

WEEKLY newspaper of the book trade. Hardback and paperback reviews and extensive listings of new paperbacks and hardbacks. Interviews with leading personalities in the trade, authors, agents and features on specialist book areas.

Punch

Trevor House, 100 Brompton Road, London
SW3 1ER
☎0171 225 6846   Fax 0171 225 6845
Owner *Liberty Publishing*
Editor *Peter McKay*

Originally FOUNDED in 1841, this WEEKLY humorous magazine RELAUNCHES in September 1996. Ideas are welcome; approach in writing in the first instance.
Payment negotiable.

Q

Mappin House, 4 Winsley Street, London
W1N 7AR
☎0171 436 1515   Fax 0171 323 0680
Owner *EMAP Metro Publications*
Editor *Andrew Collins*
Circulation 214,225

FOUNDED 1986. MONTHLY. Glossy aimed at educated rock music enthusiasts of all ages. Few opportunities for freelance writers. Unsolicited mss are strongly discouraged. Prospective contributors should approach in writing only.

Quartos Magazine

BCM Writer, 27 Old Gloucester Street,
London WC1N 3XX
☎01559 371108
Owner/Editor *Suzanne Ruthven*
Circulation 1500

FOUNDED 1987. BI-MONTHLY. Contains practical 'nuts and bolts' advice on creative writing. Unsolicited mss welcome on non-fiction. Interested in lively, original articles on writing in its broadest sense. Approach with ideas in writing. No material returned unless accompanied by s.a.e.

News Writers' workshops, courses, circles

etc. Competitions, new writing books. Maximum length 200 words. *Payment* none.

Features Any interesting writing features including interviews with writers. Maximum length 1000 words. *Payment* £20 per 1000 words.

Poetry Both short and long unpublished poems, provided they are original and interesting. No 'therapeutic/confessional poems and those which meander without rhyme or reason'. Short critique service offered: £1.50 per poem or £5 for a collection of six poems, plus s.a.e.. Material should be addressed to The Poetry Editor.

Fiction None – although a regular readers' competition provides the fiction in each issue. Maximum length 1000 words. *Payment* £10 prize and publication.

Special Pages: *Vellum* indulges the literary-minded by featuring old favourites from Marlowe and Johnson to Machen and Orwell. Maximum 1000 words. *Payment* £20 per 1000 words.

QWF (Quality Women's Fiction)
80 Main Street, Linton, Nr Swadlincote, Derbyshire DE12 6QA
☎01283 761042

Editor *Jo Good*

QUARTERLY small press magazine FOUNDED in 1994 as a show-case for the best in women's short story writing – original, thought-provoking, with forthright female characters. Features two regular article slots: *Against All Odds* and *A Guided Tour Around the New Man*. Will only consider stories that are previously unpublished and of less than 3000 words; articles must be less than 500 words. Include covering letter and brief biography with mss. Also runs a script appraisal service. For further details, contact the editor at the above address.

Radio Times
Woodlands, 80 Wood Lane, London W12 0TT
☎0181 576 3120   Fax 0181 576 3160

Owner *BBC Worldwide Ltd*
Editor *Nicholas Brett*
Executive Editor *Sue Robinson*
Circulation 1,464,392

WEEKLY. UK's leading broadcast listings magazine. The majority of material is provided by freelance and retained writers, but the topicality of the pieces means close consultation with editors is essential. Very unlikely to use unsolicited material. Detailed BBC, ITV, Channel 4 and satellite television and radio listings are accompanied by feature material relevant to the week's output.

Payment by arrangement.

RAIL
Apex House, Oundle Road, Peterborough, Cambridgeshire PE2 9NP
☎01733 898100 ext. 6949   Fax 01733 894472

Owner *EMAP Apex Publications*
Managing Editor *Nigel Harris*
Circulation 36,018

FOUNDED 1981. FORTNIGHTLY magazine dedicated to modern railway. News and features, and topical newsworthy events. Unsolicited mss welcome. Approach by phone with ideas. Not interested in personal journey reminiscences. No fiction.

Features By arrangement with the editor. Traction-related subjects of interest. Maximum 2000 words. *Payment* varies/negotiable.

News Any news item welcomed. Maximum 500 words. *Payment* varies (up to £100 per 1000 words).

The Railway Magazine
King's Reach Tower, Stamford Street, London SE1 9LS
☎0171 261 5533/5821   Fax 0171 261 5269

Owner *IPC Magazines Ltd*
Editor *Nick Pigott*
Circulation 35,187

FOUNDED 1897. MONTHLY. Articles, photos and short news stories of a topical nature, covering modern railways, steam preservation and railway history, welcome. Maximum 2000 words, with sketch maps of routes, etc., where appropriate. Unsolicited mss welcome. Maximum 2000 words.

Payment negotiable.

Rambling Today
1–5 Wandsworth Road, London SW8 2XX
☎0171 582 6878   Fax 0171 587 3799

Owner *Ramblers' Association*
Editor *Annabelle Birchall*
Circulation 85,000

QUARTERLY. Official magazine of the Ramblers' Association, available to members only. Unsolicited mss welcome. S.a.e. required for return.

Features Freelance features are invited on any aspect of walking in Britain and abroad. Length 900–1300 words, preferably with good photographs. No general travel articles.

Reader's Digest
Berkeley Square House, Berkeley Square,
London W1X 6AB
☎0171 629 8144   Fax 0171 408 0748
Owner *Reader's Digest Association Ltd*
Editor-in-Chief *Russell Twisk*
Circulation 1.6 million

In theory, a good market for general interest features of around 2500 words. However, 'a tiny proportion' comes from freelance writers, all of which are specially commissioned. Toughening up its image with a move into investigative journalism. Opportunities exist for short humorous contributions to regular features – 'Life's Like That', 'Humour in Uniform'. Issues a helpful booklet called 'Writing for Reader's Digest' available by post at £2.50. *Payment* £150.

Record Collector
43–45 St Mary's Road, Ealing, London
W5 5RQ
☎0181 579 1082   Fax 0181 566 2024
Owner *Johnny Dean*
Editor *Peter Doggett*

FOUNDED 1979. MONTHLY. Detailed, well-researched articles welcome on any aspect of record collecting or any collectable artist in the field of popular music (1950s–90s), with complete discographies where appropriate. Unsolicited mss welcome. Approach with ideas by phone. *Payment* negotiable.

Red Wing
151 Mill Road, Hamilton, Lanarkshire
ML3 8JA
☎01698 457431
Editor *Paul Nicoll*
Editor *Stephen Mungall*

FOUNDED 1995. QUARTERLY independent, radical left-wing magazine with short stories, poetry, philosophy, news review, art, political and cultural analysis. Unsolicited mss 'very welcome'; approach in writing in the first instance.
Features *S. Mungall/P. Nicoll* 1500 words maximum.
News *P. Nicoll* 1000 words maximum.
Fiction *S. Mungall* 1000 words maximum.
Poetry *J. Briggs*
Political *G. Hayes*
Payment none.

Reincarnation International
Phoenix Research Publications, PO Box 26,
London WC2H 9LP
☎0171 240 3956   Fax 0171 379 0620
Publisher *Reincarnation International Ltd*

Editor *Roy Stemman*
Circulation 3000

QUARTERLY. The only publication in the world dealing with all aspects of reincarnation – from people who claim to recall their past lives spontaneously to the many thousands who have done so through hypnotic regressions. It also examines reincarnation in the light of various religious beliefs and the latest discoveries about the mind and how it works.

Report
ATL, 7 Northumberland Street, London
WC2N 5DA
☎0171 930 6441   Fax 0171 930 1359
Owner *Association of Teachers and Lecturers*
Editor *Nick Tester*
Circulation 150,000

FOUNDED 1978. EIGHT ISSUES YEARLY during academic terms. Contributions welcome. All submissions should go directly to the editor. Articles should be no more than 800 words and must be of practical interest to the classroom teacher and F. E. lecturers.

Resident Abroad
Greystoke Place, Fetter Lane, London
EC4A 1ND
☎0171 405 6969   Fax 0171 242 0263
Owner *Financial Times*
Editor *William Essex*
Circulation 17,919

FOUNDED 1979. MONTHLY magazine aimed at British expatriates. Unsolicited mss considered, if suitable to the interests of the readership.
Features Up to 1200 words on finance, property, employment opportunities and other topics likely to appeal to readership, such as living conditions in countries with substantial British expatriate populations. No 'lighthearted looks' at anything.
Fiction Rarely published, but exceptional, relevant stories (no longer than 1000 words) might be considered.
Payment £150 per 1000 words for good pieces from expatriate or former expatriate writers drawing on actual experience.

Riding
2 West Street, Bourne, Lincolnshire
PE10 9NE
☎01778 393747   Fax 01778 425453
Owner *Riding Magazine Ltd*
Editor *Amanda Stevenson*

Aimed at an adult, horse-owning audience.

Most of the writers on *Riding* are freelance with the emphasis on non-practical and lifestyle-orientated features. New and authoritative writers always welcome.

Payment negotiable.

Right Now!
BCM Right, London WC1N 3XX
Owner *Right Now!*
Editor *Derek Turner*
Circulation 1200

FOUNDED 1993. QUARTERLY right-wing conservative commentary. Welcomes well-documented disputations, news stories and elegiac features about British heritage ('the more politically incorrect, the better!'). No fiction and poems, although exceptions may be made. Approach in writing in the first instance.

No payment.

Risqué
2 Caversham Street, London SW3 4AH
☎0171 351 4995   Fax 0171 351 4995
Owner *Rockzone Ltd*
Editor *Leonard Holdsworth*
Circulation 85,000

FOUNDED 1991. MONTHLY. Elegant international magazine for men, covering all men's interests. Unsolicited ideas welcome, but not complete mss at first. Maximum 3500 words.

Payment negotiable.

Rouge
46 Frostic Walk, London E1 5LT
☎0171 377 9426   Fax 0171 377 9426
Owner *Breakaway Publications Ltd.*
Editor *Roger Evans*

FOUNDED 1989. QUARTERLY. News, features and reviews for lesbians, gay men and bisexuals, with a focus on sexual politics, HIV and AIDS and safer sex. Politics rather than lifestyle. Unsolicited features of up to 1700 words welcome.

Payment by arrangement.

Rugby News & Monthly
7-9 Rathbone Street, London W1P 1AF
☎0171 436 3331   Fax 0171 436 3332
Owner *Independent Magazines Ltd*
Editor *Richard Bath*
Circulation 25,000

FOUNDED 1987 and incorporated *Rugby Monthly* magazine in July 1994. Contains news, views and features on the UK and the world rugby scene, with special emphasis on clubs,

schools, fitness and coaching. Welcomes unsolicited material.

Rugby World
23rd Floor, King's Reach Tower, Stamford Street, London SE1 9LS
☎0171 261 6830   Fax 0171 261 5419
Owner *IPC Magazines Ltd*
Editor *Alison Kervin*
Circulation 42,135

MONTHLY. Features of special rugby interest only. Unsolicited contributions welcome but s.a.e. essential for return of material. Prior approach by phone or in writing preferred.

Saga Magazine
The Saga Building, Middelburg Square, Folkestone, Kent CT20 1AZ
☎01303 711523   Fax 01303 712699
Owner *Saga Publishing Ltd*
Editor *Paul Bach*
Circulation 601,851

FOUNDED 1984. TEN ISSUES YEARLY. '*Saga Magazine* sets out to celebrate the role of older people in society. It reflects their achievements, promotes their skills, protects their interests, and campaigns on their behalf. A warm personal approach, addressing the readership in an up-beat and positive manner, required.' It has a hard core of celebrated commentators/writers (e.g. Clement Freud) as regular contributors and there is limited scope for well-written features – good-quality, colour transparencies enhance acceptance chances. Subjects of interest include achievement, hobbies, finance, food, wine, social comment, motoring, fitness, diet, etc. Length 1000–1200 words (maximum 1600).

Sailplane and Gliding
281 Queen Edith's Way, Cambridge CB1 4NH
☎01223 247725   Fax 01223 413793
Owner *British Gliding Association*
Editor *Gillian Bryce-Smith*
Circulation 8400

FOUNDED 1930. BI-MONTHLY for gliding enthusiasts. A specialist magazine with very few opportunities for freelancers. *No payment.*

Sainsbury's The Magazine
20 Upper Ground, London SE1 9PD
☎0171 633 0266   Fax 0171 401 9423
Owner *New Crane Publishing*
Editor *Michael Wynn Jones*

Food Editor *Delia Smith*
Circulation 325,000

FOUNDED 1993. MONTHLY featuring a main core of food and cookery, health, beauty, fashion, home, gardening, travel and news. No unsolicited mss. Approach in writing with ideas only in the first instance.

The Salisbury Review

33 Canonbury Park South, London
N1 2JW
☎0171 226 7791   Fax 0171 354 0383
Owner *Claridge Press*
Editor *Roger Scruton*
Managing Editor *Merrie Cave*
Circulation 1700

FOUNDED 1982. QUARTERLY magazine of conservative thought. Editorials and features from a right-wing viewpoint. Unsolicited material welcome.
Features Maximum 4000 words.
Reviews Maximum 1000 words.
No payment.

Scotland on Sunday Magazine

See under **National Newspapers (Scotland on Sunday)**

The Scots Magazine

2 Albert Square, Dundee DD1 9QJ
☎01382 223131   Fax 01382 322214
Owner *D. C. Thomson & Co. Ltd*
Editor *John Methven*
Circulation 70,000

FOUNDED 1739. MONTHLY. Covers a wide field of Scottish interests ranging from personalities to wildlife, climbing, reminiscence, history and folklore. Outside contributions welcome; 'staff delighted to discuss in advance by letter'.

The Scottish Farmer

The Plaza Tower, The Plaza, East Kilbride
G74 1LW
☎013552 46444   Fax 013552 63013
Owner *Caledonian Magazines Ltd*
Editor *Alasdair Fletcher*
Circulation 23,086

FOUNDED 1893. WEEKLY. Farmer's magazine covering most aspects of Scottish agriculture. Unsolicited mss welcome. Approach with ideas in writing.
Features *Alasdair Fletcher* Technical articles on agriculture or farming units. 1000–2000 words.

News *John Duckworth* Factual news about farming developments, political, personal and technological. Maximum 800 words.
Weekend Family Pages Rural and craft topics.
Payment £10 per 100 words; £25 per photo.

Scottish Field

Special Publications, Royston House,
Caroline Park, Edinburgh EH5 1QJ
☎0131 551 2942   Fax 0131 551 2938
Owner *Oban Times*
Editor *Archie Mackenzie*

FOUNDED 1903. MONTHLY. Scotland's quality lifestyle magazine. Unsolicited mss welcome but writers should study the magazine first.
Features Articles of general interest on Scotland and Scots abroad with good photographs or, preferably, colour slides. Approx 1000 words.
Payment negotiable.

Scottish Golfer

The Cottage, 181A Whitehouse Road,
Edinburgh EH14 6BY
☎0131 339 7546   Fax 0131 339 1169
Owner *Scottish Golf Union*
Editor *Martin Dempster*
Circulation 30,000

FOUNDED MID-1980s. MONTHLY. Features and results, in particular the men's events. No unsolicited mss. Approach in writing with ideas.

Scottish Home & Country

42A Heriot Row, Edinburgh EH3 6ES
☎0131 225 1934   Fax 0131 225 8129
Owner *Scottish Women's Rural Institutes*
Editor *Stella Roberts*
Circulation 16,000

FOUNDED 1924. MONTHLY. Scottish or rural-related issues. Unsolicited mss welcome but reading time may be from 2–3 months. Commissions are rare and tend to go to established contributors only.

Scottish Rugby Magazine

11 Dock Place, Leith, Edinburgh
EH6 6LU
☎0131 554 0540   Fax 0131 554 0482
Owner *Hiscan Ltd*
Editor *Kevin Ferrie*
Circulation 19,200

FOUNDED 1990. MONTHLY. Features, club profiles, etc. Approach in writing with ideas.

Scouting Magazine

Baden Powell House, Queen's Gate, London
SW7 5JS
☎0171 584 7030   Fax 0171 590 5103
Owner *The Scout Association*
Editor *David Easton*
Circulation 30,000

MONTHLY magazine for adults connected to
or interested in the Scouting movement.
Interested in Scouting-related features only.
No fiction. *Payment* by negotiation.

Screen

The John Logie Baird Centre, University of
Glasgow, Glasgow G12 8QQ
☎0141 330 5035   Fax 0141 307 8010
Owner *The John Logie Baird Centre*
Editors *Annette Kuhn, John Caughie, Simon
    Frith, Norman King, Karen Lury, Jackie Stacey*
Editorial Assistant *Caroline Beven*
Circulation 1500

QUARTERLY academic journal of film and television studies for a readership ranging from
undergraduates to media professionals. There
are no specific qualifications for acceptance of
articles. Straightforward film reviews are not
normally published. Check the magazine's style
and market in the first instance.

Screen International

33–39 Bowling Green Lane, London
EC1R 0DA
☎0171 505 8080   Fax 0171 505 8117
Owner *EMAP Business Communications*
Editor *Boyd Farrow*

International trade paper of the film, video and
television industries. Expert freelance writers
are occasionally used in all areas. No unsolicited mss. Approach with ideas in writing.
    Features *Mike Goodridge*
    Payment negotiable on NUJ basis.

Sea Breezes

Units 28–30, Spring Valley Industrial Estate,
Braddan, Isle of Man IM2 2QS
☎01624 626018   Fax 01624 661655
Owner *Print Centres*
Editor *Captain A. C. Douglas*
Circulation 14,500

FOUNDED 1919. MONTHLY. Covers virtually
everything relating to ships and seamen. Unsolicited mss welcome; they should be thoroughly researched and accompanied by relevant
photographs. No fiction, poetry, or anything
which 'smacks of the romance of the sea'.

Features Factual tales of ships, seamen and
the sea, Royal or Merchant Navy, sail or
power, nautical history, shipping company histories, epic voyages, etc. Length 1000–4000
words. 'The most readily acceptable work will
be that which shows it is clearly the result of
first-hand experience or the product of extensive and accurate research.'
    Payment £9 per page (about 640 words).

She Magazine

National Magazine House, 72 Broadwick
Street, London W1V 2BP
☎0171 439 5000   Fax 0171 439 5350
Owner *National Magazine Co. Ltd*
Editor *Alison Pylkkanen*
Circulation 256,689

Glossy MONTHLY for the thirtysomething
woman and modern mother, addressing her
needs as an individual, a partner and a parent.
Talks to its readers in an intelligent, humorous
and sympathetic way. Features should be about
1500 words long. Approach with ideas in writing. No unsolicited material.
    Payment NUJ rates.

Shoot Magazine

King's Reach Tower, Stamford Street,
London SE1 9LS
☎0171 261 6287   Fax 0171 261 6019
Owner *IPC Magazines Ltd*
Editor *David C. Smith*
Circulation 147,000

FOUNDED 1969. WEEKLY football magazine.
No unsolicited mss. Present ideas for news, features or colour photo-features to the editor by
telephone.
    Features Hard-hitting, topical and off-beat.
Length 400–1000 words.
    News Items welcome, especially exclusive
gossip and transfer speculation. Maximum 150
words.
    Payment NUJ rates (negotiable for exclusive
material).

Shooting and Conservation (BASC)

Marford Mill, Rossett, Wrexham, Clwyd
LL12 0HL
☎01244 570881   Fax 01244 571678
Owner *The British Association for Shooting and
    Conservation (BASC)*
Editor *Mike Barnes*
Circulation 111,000

QUARTERLY. Unsolicited mss welcome.

Features/Fiction Good articles and stories on shooting, conservation and related areas are always sought. Maximum 1500 words.
Payment negotiable.

Shooting Times & Country Magazine

King's Reach Tower, Stamford Street, London SE1 9LS
☎0171 261 6180   Fax 0171 261 7179
Owner *IPC Magazines*
Editor *John Gregson*
Circulation 36,108

FOUNDED 1882. WEEKLY. Covers shooting, fishing and related countryside topics. Unsolicited mss considered. Maximum 1100 words.
Payment negotiable.

Shropshire Magazine

77 Wyle Cop, Shrewsbury, Shropshire SY1 1UT
☎01743 362175
Owner *Leopard Press Ltd*
Editor *Pam Green*

FOUNDED 1950. MONTHLY. Unsolicited mss welcome but ideas in writing preferred.
Features Personalities, topical items, historical (e.g. family) of Shropshire; also general interest: homes, weddings, antiques, food, holidays, etc. Maximum 1000 words.
Payment negotiable but modest.

Sight & Sound

British Film Institute, 21 Stephen Street, London W1P 1PL
☎0171 255 1444   Fax 0171 436 2327
Owner *British Film Institute*
Editor *Philip Dodd*

FOUNDED 1932. MONTHLY. Topical and critical articles on international cinema, with regular columns from the USA and Europe. Length 1000-5000 words. Relevant photographs appreciated. Also book, film and video release reviews. Unsolicited material welcome. Approach in writing with ideas.
Payment by arrangement.

The Sign

See **Hymns Ancient & Modern Ltd** under **UK Publishers**

Ski Survey

118 Eaton Square, London SW1W 9AF
☎0171 245 1033   Fax 0171 245 1258
Owner *Ski Club of Great Britain*

Editor *Gill Williams*
Circulation 21,093

FOUNDED 1903. FIVE ISSUES YEARLY. Features from established ski writers only.

The Skier and The Snowboarder Magazine

48 London Road, Sevenoaks, Kent TN13 1AP
☎01732 743644   Fax 01732 743647
Owner *Hollander Publishing Ltd*
Editor *Frank Baldwin*
Circulation 30,000

SEASONAL. From September to May. SIX ISSUES YEARLY. Outside contributions welcome.
Features Various topics covered, including race reports, resort reports, fashion, equipment update, dry slope, school news, new products, health and safety. Crisp, tight, informative copy of 1000 words or less preferred.
News All aspects of skiing news covered.
Payment negotiable.

Slimming

Victory House, 14 Leicester Place, London WC2H 7BP
☎0171 437 9011   Fax 0171 434 0656
Owner *EMAP Elan Publications*
Editor *Christine Michael*
Circulation 161,000

FOUNDED 1969. TEN ISSUES YEARLY. Leading magazine about slimming, diet and health. Opportunities for freelance contributions on general health (diet-related); psychology related to health and fitness; celebrity interviews. It is best to approach with an idea in writing.
Payment negotiable.

Smallholder

Hook House, Wimblington March, Cambridgeshire PE15 0QL
☎01354 741182   Fax 01354 741182
Owner *Smallholder Publications*
Editor *Liz Wright*
Circulation 18,000

FOUNDED 1982. MONTHLY. Outside contributions welcome. Send for sample magazine and editorial schedule before submitting anything. Follow up with samples of work to the editor so that style can be assessed for suitability. No poetry or humorous but unfocused personal tales.
Features New writers always welcome, but must have high level of technical expertise –

'not textbook stuff'. Length 750-1500 words.

News All agricultural and rural news welcome. Length 200-500 words.

Payment negotiable ('but modest').

Smash Hits

Mappin House, Winsley Street, London
W1N 7AR
☎0171 436 1515 Fax 0171 636 5792

Owner *EMAP Metro Publications*
Editor *Kate Thornton*
Circulation 302,048

FOUNDED 1979. FORTNIGHTLY. Top of the mid-teen market. Unsolicited mss are not accepted, but prospective contributors may approach in writing with ideas.

Snooker Scene

Cavalier House, 202 Hagley Road, Edgbaston, Birmingham B16 9PQ
☎0121 454 2931 Fax 0121 452 1822

Owner *Everton's News Agency*
Editor *Clive Everton*
Circulation 16,000

FOUNDED 1971. MONTHLY. No unsolicited mss. Approach in writing with an idea.

Somerset Magazine

23 Market Street, Crewkerne, Somerset
TA18 7JU
☎01460 78000 Fax 01460 76718

Owner *Smart Print Publications Ltd*
Editor *Roy Smart*
Circulation 6000

FOUNDED 1990. MONTHLY magazine with features on any subject of interest (historical, geographical, arts, crafts) to people living in Somerset. Length 1000-1500 words, preferably with illustrations. Unsolicited mss welcome but initial approach in writing preferred.

Payment negotiable.

The Source

19 Cumberland Street, Edinburgh EH3 6RT
☎0131 556 8673 Fax 0131 556 8673

Owner *Source Publishing*
Editors *Andrew Kelly, Corene Lemaitre*

FOUNDED 1985. QUARTERLY magazine of new fiction, journalism, poetry and art. Will consider short stories, topical articles and poetry. No genre fiction. Approach with complete mss only.

Features Articles on arts controversies and literary debates. 2000 words maximum.

News Analysis and critical overviews of top-

ical events. 2000 words maximum.

Fiction Dynamic, imaginative, risk-taking fiction. Potential contributors are advised to study the magazine in the first instance. 3000 words maximum.

Real Life Metropolitan life from a personal point of view. 2000 words maximum.

Payment by arrangement.

The Spectator

56 Doughty Street, London
WC1N 2LL
☎0171 405 1706 Fax 0171 242 0603

Owner *The Spectator (1828) Ltd*
Editor *Frank Johnson*
Circulation 55,087

FOUNDED 1828. WEEKLY political and literary magazine. Prospective contributors should write in the first instance to the relevant editor. Unsolicited mss welcome, but over twenty are received every week and few are used.

Arts *Elizabeth Anderson*
Books *Mark Amory*
Payment nominal.

Sport Magazine

The Sports Council, 16 Upper Woburn Place, London WC1H 0QP
☎0171 388 1277 Fax 0171 383 0273

Owner *The Sports Council*
Editor *Louise Fyfe*
Circulation 15000

FOUNDED 1949. BI-MONTHLY. Covering sports development, policies and politics, plus new ideas and innovations in the world of sport. Approach by phone with ideas.

News/Features On any of the areas mentioned above. Features should be 750–1000 words.

Payment £100 per 1000 words.

The Sporting Life

1 Canada Square, Canary Wharf, London
E14 5AP
☎0171 293 3029 Fax 0171 293 3758

Owner *Mirror Group Newspapers Ltd*
Editor *Tom Clarke*
Circulation 95,181

DAILY newspaper of the horse-racing world. Always on the look-out for specialised, well-informed racing writers – not necessarily established sports writers. No unsolicited mss. Phone or write with an idea in first instance. 'The talented will be taken up and used again.'

Associate Editor/Features *Alastair Down*

Springboard – Writing To Succeed

30 Orange Hill Road, Prestwich, Manchester M25 1LS
☎0161 773 5911
Owner/Editor *Leo Brooks*
Circulation 200

FOUNDED 1990. QUARTERLY. *Springboard* is not a market for writers but a forum from which they can find encouragement and help. Provides articles, news, market information, competition/folio news directed at helping writers to achieve success. Free to subscribers: a copy of *The Curate's Egg* – a collection of poetry submitted.

Staffordshire Life

The Publishing Centre, Derby Street, Stafford ST16 2DT
☎01785 257700   Fax 01785 253287
Owner *The Staffordshire Newsletter*
Editor *Philip Thurlow-Craig*
Circulation 16,000

FOUNDED 1982. BI-MONTHLY county magazine devoted to Staffordshire, its surroundings and people. Contributions welcome. Approach in writing with ideas.
Features Maximum 1200 words.
Fashion Copy must be supported by photographs.
Payment NUJ rates.

Stage and Television Today

47 Bermondsey Street, London SE1 3XT
☎0171 403 1818   Fax 0171 403 1418
Owner *The Stage Newspaper Ltd*
Editor *Brian Attwood*
Circulation 42,000

FOUNDED 1880. WEEKLY. No unsolicited mss. Prospective contributors should write with ideas in the first instance.
Features Preference for middle-market, tabloid-style articles. 'Puff pieces', PR plugs and extended production notes will not be considered. Maximum 800 words.
News News stories from outside London are always welcome. Maximum 300 words.
Payment £100 per 1000 words.

Stand Magazine

See under **Poetry, Little Magazines**

Staple Magazine

See under **Poetry, Little Magazines**

Stone Soup

37 Chesterfield Road, London W4 3HQ
☎0181 742 7554   Fax 0181 742 7554
Editors *Igor Klikovac, Ken Smith*
Associate Editors *Srdja Pavlović, Vesna Domany-Hardy*
Circulation 2000

THRICE-YEARLY international literary magazine for new writing – mainly poetry and theory. Edited by English poet Ken Smith and Bosnian poet Igor Klikovac, the magazine is printed in English and languages of former Yugoslavia. Also interested in publishing writing in all European languages. Mss should be sent in duplicate, preferably on disc; s.a.e. essential for return of material.

Storm

120 Clarendon Road, London W11 1SA
Editor *Joanna Labon*

FOUNDED 1990. Supported by the Arts Council and founded in response to the fall of the Berlin Wall in 1989, to publish prose fiction (short stories and extracts from novels) from Eastern Europe. *Storm* is not somewhere for new or beginner writers to send their work, and unsolicited mss are not welcome.

The Strad

7 St. John's Road, Harrow, Middlesex HA12 2EE
☎0181 863 2020   Fax 0181 863 2444
Owner *Orpheus Publications Ltd*
Editor *Brian Yule*
Circulation 12,000

FOUNDED 1890. MONTHLY for classical string musicians, makers and enthusiasts. Unsolicited mss welcome.
Features Profiles of string players, composers, luthiers and musical instruments. Maximum 2000 words.
News/Reviews *Joanna Pieters, Juliette Barber.*
Payment £100 per 1000 words.

Student Outlook

87 Kirkstall Road, London SW2 4HE
☎0181 671 7920
Owner *I. J. Hensall*
Editor *D. Patton*
Circulation 80,000

FOUNDED 1990. THRICE-YEARLY (one for each academic term). Student-related topics across a broad range of interests, including music, film, books, 'Campus News' and 'Planet News' (politics from a green perspective). Unsolicited mss welcome from both students and ex-students who are not long out of student life.

Payment £50 per two-page feature. Shorter pieces by negotiation. As a pilot project, both 'Campus News' and 'Planet News' are on the Internet and during this phase mss are welcome, preferably on disc, but no payment offered.

Suffolk and Norfolk Life

Barn Acre House, Saxtead Green, Suffolk IP13 9QJ
☎01728 685832   Fax 01728 685842
Owner *Today Magazines Ltd*
Editor *Kevin Davis*
Circulation 17,000

FOUNDED 1989. MONTHLY. General interest, local stories, historical, personalities, wine, travel, food. Unsolicited mss welcome. Approach by phone or in writing with ideas. Not interested in anything which does not relate specifically to East Anglia.

Features *Kevin Davis* Maximum 1500 words, with photos.

News *Kevin Davis* Maximum 1000 words, with photos.

Special Pages *Sue Wright* Study the magazine for guidelines. Maximum 1500 words.

Payment £25 (news); £30 (other).

Suffolk Countryside

Griggs Farm, West Street, Coggeshall, Essex CO6 1NT
☎01376 562578   Fax 01376 562578
Owner *Market Link Publishing*
Editor *Andy Tilbrook*

FOUNDED 1995. MONTHLY. Unsolicited material of Suffolk interest welcome. No general interest material.

Features Countryside, culture and crafts in Suffolk. Maximum 1500.

Payment £40.

Sunday Express Magazine

See under **National Newspapers (Sunday Express)**

Sunday Magazine

See under **National Newspapers (News of the World)**

Sunday Mail Magazine

See under **National Newspapers (Sunday Mail, Glasgow)**

Sunday Mirror Magazine

See under **National Newspapers (Sunday Mirror)**

Sunday Post Magazine

See under **National Newspapers (Sunday Post, Glasgow)**

Sunday Times Magazine

See under **National Newspapers (The Sunday Times)**

Sunk Island Review

Sunk Island Publishing, PO Box 74, Lincoln LN1 1QG
☎01522 575660   Fax 01522 520394
Owner *Sunk Island Publishing*
Editor *Michael Blackburn*
Circulation 1000

FOUNDED 1989. BI-ANNUAL magazine containing new short stories, novel extracts, poetry, some articles and reviews, also translations. Unsolicited mss welcome. Seeking new creative writing. No horror, romance, religious writing. No maximum length. Approach with ideas in writing.

Payment on publication by arrangement.

Superbike Magazine

Link House, Dingwall Avenue, Croydon, Surrey CR9 2TA
☎0181 686 2599   Fax 0181 781 1164
Editor *Grant Leonard*
Circulation 40,000

FOUNDED 1977. MONTHLY. Dedicated to all that is best and most exciting in the world of high-performance motorcycling. Unsolicited mss, synopses and ideas welcome.

Surrey County Magazine

PO Box 154, South Croydon, Surrey CR2 0XA
☎0181 657 8568   Fax 0181 657 8568
Owner *Datateam Publishing*
Editor *Theo Spring*
Circulation 9500

FOUNDED 1970. MONTHLY. County matters for Surrey dwellers. News, views, history and comment. Interested in product information for an A/AB readership. Unsolicited mss welcome. Approach by phone or in writing with ideas.

Sussex Life

30-32 Teville Road, Worthing, West Sussex BN11 1UG
☎01903 218719   Fax 01903 820193
Owner *Sussex Life Ltd*
Editor *Trudi Linscer*

Circulation 35,000

FOUNDED 1965. MONTHLY. Sussex and general interest magazine. Interested in investigative, journalistic pieces relevant to the area and celebrity profiles. No historical pieces. Unsolicited mss, synopses and ideas in writing welcome. Maximum 500 words.

Payment £15 per 500 words.

Swimming Times

Harold Fern House, Derby Square, Loughborough, Leicestershire LE11 0AL
☎01509 234433   Fax 01509 235049

Owner *Amateur Swimming Association*
Editor *P. Hassall*
Circulation 20,000

FOUNDED 1923. MONTHLY about competitive swimming and associated subjects. Unsolicited mss welcome.

Features Technical articles on swimming, water polo, diving or synchronised swimming. Length and payment negotiable.

The Tablet

1 King Street Cloisters, Clifton Walk, London W6 0QZ
☎0181 748 8484   Fax 0181 748 1550

Owner *The Tablet Publishing Co Ltd*
Editor *John Wilkins*
Circulation 18,759

FOUNDED 1840. WEEKLY. Quality international Roman Catholic magazine featuring articles of interest to concerned laity and clergy. Unsolicited material welcome (1500 words) if relevant to magazine's style and market. All approaches should be made in writing.

Payment from about £50.

Take a Break

Shirley House, 25–27 Camden Road, London NW1 9LL
☎0171 284 0909   Fax 0171 284 3778

Owner *H. Bauer*
Editor *John Dale*
Circulation 1.3 million

FOUNDED 1990. WEEKLY. True-life feature magazine. Approach with ideas in writing.

News/Features Always on the look-out for good, true-life stories. Maximum 1200 words. *Payment* negotiable.

Fiction Sharp, succinct stories which are well told and often with a twist at the end. All categories, provided it is relevant to the magazine's style and market. Maximum 1000 words. *Payment* negotiable.

Talking Business

237 Kennington Lane, London SE11 5QY
☎0171 582 0536   Fax 0171 582 4917

Owner *Square One Publishing Ltd*
Editor *Peter Dean*
Circulation 6,500

FOUNDED 1994. MONTHLY. News, reviews, features and charts covering the expanding audiobooks market. Interested in considering business-oriented material and personality profiles. Approach in writing in the first instance.

The Tatler

Vogue House, Hanover Square, London W1R 0AD
☎0171 499 9080   Fax 0171 409 0451

Owner *Condé Nast Publications Ltd*
Editor *Jane Procter*
Circulation 80,373

Up-market glossy from the Condé Nast stable. New writers should send in copies of either published work or unpublished material; writers of promise will be taken up. The magazine works largely on a commission basis: they are unlikely to publish unsolicited features, but will ask writers to work to specific projects.

Features *Harriet Lane*

The Tea Club Magazine

PO Box 221, Guildford, Surrey GU1 3YT
☎01483 562888   Fax 01483 302732

Publisher *Bond Clarkson Russell*
Editor *Lorna Swainson*

FOUNDED 1992 by The Tea Council. THRICE YEARLY. Specialist focus on tea and tea-related topics. All editorial features are commissioned. Approach with ideas only.

Tees Valley Writer

See under **Poetry, Little Magazines**

Telegraph Magazine

See under **National Newspapers (The Daily Telegraph)**

TGO (The Great Outdoors)

The Plaza Tower, East Kilbride, Glasgow G74 1LW
☎01355 246444   Fax 01355 263013

Owner *Caledonian Magazines Ltd*
Editor *Cameron McNeish*
Circulation 22,000

FOUNDED 1978. MONTHLY. Deals with walking, backpacking and countryside topics. Unsolicited mss are welcome.

Features Well-written and illustrated items on relevant topics. Maximum 2000 words. Colour photographs only please.

News Short topical items (or photographs). Maximum 300 words.

Payment £100–200 for features; £10–20 for news.

Theologia Cambrensis

Church in Wales Centre, Woodland Place, Penarth, Cardiff CF64 2EX

☎01222 705278   Fax 01222 712413

Owner *The Church in Wales*
Editor *Dr John Herbert*

FOUNDED 1988. THRICE YEARLY. Concerned exclusively with theology and news of theological interest. Includes religious poetry, letters and book reviews (provided they have a scholarly bias). No secular material. Unsolicited mss welcome. Approach in writing with ideas.

The Third Alternative

5 Martins Lane, Witcham, Ely, Cambridgeshire CB6 2LB

☎01353 777931

Owner *TTA Press*
Editor *Andy Cox*

FOUNDED 1993. Quarterly magazine of horror, fantasy, science fiction and slipstream fiction, plus poetry, features and art. Publishes talented newcomers alongside award-winning authors. Unsolicited mss welcome if accompanied by s.a.e. or International Reply Coupons. Guidelines are available but potential contributors are also advised to study the magazine.

This England

PO Box 52, Cheltenham, Gloucestershire GL50 1YQ

☎01242 577775   Fax 01242 222034

Owner *This England Ltd*
Editor *Roy Faiers*
Circulation 180,000

FOUNDED 1968. QUARTERLY, with a strong overseas readership. Celebration of England and all things English: famous people, natural beauty, towns and villages, history, traditions, customs and legends, crafts, etc. Generally a rural basis, with the 'Forgetmenots' section publishing readers' recollections and nostalgia. Up to one hundred unsolicited pieces received each week. Unsolicited mss/ideas welcome. Length 250–2000 words.

Payment £25 per 1000 words.

Time

Brettenham House, Lancaster Place, London WC2E 7TL

☎0171 499 4080   Fax 0171 322 1230

Owner *Time Warner, Inc.*
Editor *Barry Hillenbrand* (London Bureau Chief)
Circulation 5.46 million

FOUNDED 1923. WEEKLY current affairs and news magazine. There are no opportunities for freelancers on *Time* as almost all the magazine's content is written by staff members from various bureaux around the world. No unsolicited mss.

Time Out

Universal House, 251 Tottenham Court Road, London W1A 1BZ

☎0171 813 3000   Fax 0171 813 6001

Publisher *Tony Elliott*
Editor *Dominic Wells*
Circulation 110,500

FOUNDED 1968. WEEKLY magazine of news and entertainment in London.

Features *Elaine Paterson* 'Usually written by staff writers or commissioned, but it's always worth submitting an idea by phone if particularly apt to the magazine.' Max. 2500 words.

News *Tony Thompson* Despite having a permanent team of staff news writers, sometimes willing to accept contributions from new journalists 'should their material be relevant to the issue'.

Payment £164 per 1000 words.

The Times Educational Supplement Scotland

37 George Street, Edinburgh EH2 2HN

☎0131 220 1100   Fax 0131 220 1616

Owner *Times Supplements Ltd*
Editor *Willis Pickard*
Circulation 6000

FOUNDED 1965. WEEKLY. Unsolicited mss welcome.

Features Articles on education in Scotland. Maximum 1200 words.

News Items on education in Scotland. Maximum 600 words.

Payment NUJ rates for NUJ members.

The Times Educational Supplement

Admiral House, 66–68 East Smithfield, London E1 9XY

☎0171 782 3000   Fax 0171 782 3200

Owner *News International*
Editor *Patricia Rowan*

Circulation 137,287

FOUNDED 1910. WEEKLY. New contributors are welcome and should phone with ideas for news or features; write for reviews.

Arts and Books *Heather Neill*

Media & Resources *Gillian Macdonald* Unsolicited reviews are not accepted. Anyone wanting to review should write, sending examples of their work and full details of their academic and professional background to either the literary editor or the media and resources editor. Maximum 1200 words.

Opinion *Patricia Rowan* 'Platform': a weekly slot for a well-informed and cogently argued viewpoint. Maximum 1200 words. 'Second Opinion': a shorter comment on an issue of the day by somebody well placed to write on the subject. Maximum 700 words.

Further Education *Ian Nash* Includes college management.

Primary *Diane Hofkins*

School Management *Bob Doe* Weekly pages on practical issues for school governors and managers. Maximum 1000 words.

Features *Sarah Bayliss* Longer articles on contemporary practical subjects of general interest to the *TES* reader. Maximum 1000-1500 words; longer or multi-part features are rarely accepted.

Extra *Joyce Arnold* Subjects covered include: science, travel, music, modern languages, home economics, school visits, primary education, history, geography, mathematics, health, life skills, environmental education, technology, special needs. Articles should relate to current educational practice. Age-range covered is primary to sixth form. Maximum 1000-1300 words. *Payment* by arrangement.

Update a monthly magazine section devoted to Primary (*Diane Hofkins*); Computers/IT (*Merlin John*); School management (*Bob Doe*); or FE (*Ian Nash*).

The Times Higher Education Supplement

Admiral House, 66-68 East Smithfield, London E1 9XY

☎0171 782 3000   Fax 0171 782 3300/1

Owner *News International*
Editor *Auriol Stevens*
Circulation 27,000

FOUNDED 1971. WEEKLY. Unsolicited mss are welcome but most articles and *all* book reviews are commissioned. 'In most cases it is better to write, but in the case of news stories it is all right to phone.'

Books *Andrew Robinson*

Features *Sian Griffiths* Most articles are commissioned from academics in higher education.

News *Clare Sanders-Smith* Freelance opportunities very occasionally.

Science *Kam Patel/Aisling Irwin*

Science Books *Andrew Robinson*

Foreign *David Jobbins*

Payment NUJ rates.

The Times Literary Supplement

Admiral House, 66-68 East Smithfield, London E1 9XY

☎0171 782 3000   Fax 0171 782 3100

Owner *News International*
Editor *Ferdinand Mount*
Circulation 33,000

FOUNDED 1902. WEEKLY review of literature. Contributors should approach in writing and be familiar with the general level of writing in the *TLS*.

Literary Discoveries *Alan Jenkins*

Poems *Mick Imlah*

News *Ferdinand Mount* News stories and general articles concerned with literature, publishing and new intellectual developments anywhere in the world. Length by arrangement.

Payment by arrangement.

Titbits

2 Caversham Street, London SW3 4AH

☎0171 351 4995   Fax 0171 351 4995

Owner *Sport Newspapers Ltd*
Editor *Leonard Holdsworth*
Circulation 150,000

FOUNDED 1895. MONTHLY. Consumer magazine for men covering show business and general interests. Unsolicited mss and ideas in writing welcome. Maximum 3000 words. News, features, particularly photofeatures (colour), and fiction.

Payment negotiable.

To & Fro

17 Grove Park, Waltham Road, White Waltham, Maidenhead, Berkshire SL6 3LW

☎01628 829815   Fax 01628 829816

Owner/Editor *Anne Smith*

FOUNDED 1978. BI-MONTHLY. Specialist machine knitting magazine. Interested in material related to machine knitting only. Unsolicited mss and ideas welcome. Contact the editor in writing in the first instance.

Today's Golfer

Bretton Court, Bretton, Peterborough,
Cambridgeshire PE3 8DZ
☎01733 264666   Fax 01733 267198

Owner *EMAP Pursuit Publishing*
Editor *Neil Pope*
Deputy Editor *Steve Carr*

FOUNDED 1988. MONTHLY. Golf instruction,
features, player profiles and news. Unsolicited
mss welcome. Approach in writing with ideas.
Not interested in instruction material from
outside contributors.

Features/News *Kevin Brown* Opinion,
player profiles and general golf-related features.

Today's Runner

Bretton Court, Bretton, Peterborough,
Cambridgeshire PE3 8DZ
☎01733 264666   Fax 01733 267198

Owner *EMAP Pursuit Publishing Ltd*
Editor *Victoria Tebbs*
Circulation 30,000

FOUNDED 1985. MONTHLY. Instructional articles on running, fitness, and lifestyle, plus run-
ning-related activities and health.

Features Specialist knowledge an advantage. Opportunities are wide, but approach
with idea in first instance.

News Opportunities for people stories,
especially if backed up by photographs.

Top Santé Health and Beauty

Presse Publishing, 17 Radley Mews,
Kensington, London W8 6JP
☎0171 938 3033   Fax 0171 938 5464

Owner *Presse Publishing*
Editor *Jane Garton*
Circulation 155,788

FOUNDED 1993. MONTHLY magazine covering
all aspects of health and beauty. Unsolicited
mss not generally accepted. Not interested in
anything except health and beauty. Approach
in writing with ideas.

Tourism Times

Michael Stephen Publishers, PO Box 582,
Five Oaks, St Saviour, Jersey JE4 8XQ
☎01534 25517   Fax 01534 38889

Owner *The Guiter Group*
Editor *Sarah Scriven*
Circulation 5000

FOUNDED 1993. BI-ANNUAL travel trade newspaper of the Jersey Tourist industry. Contributions from travel experts welcome; interesting
tourism stories which relate to the Channel

Islands – 1000 words maximum. Approach by
phone in the first instance.

Townswoman

Media Associates, 8 Capitol House, Heigham
Street, Norwich, Norfolk NR2 4TE
☎01603 616005   Fax 01603 767397

Owner *Townswomen's Guilds*
Editor *Moira Eagling*
Circulation 32,000

FOUNDED 1933. MONTHLY. No unsolicited
mss. Few opportunities as in-house editorial staff
are strong.

Traditional Homes

See **Period Living & Traditional Homes**

Trail Walker

Bretton Court, Bretton, Peterborough,
Cambridgeshire PE3 8DZ
☎01733 264666   Fax 01733 261984

Owner *EMAP Pursuit Publishing Ltd*
Editor *David Ogle*
Circulation 30,642

FOUNDED 1990. MONTHLY. Gear reports,
where to walk and practical advice for the hill-
walker and long distance walker. Approach by
phone or in writing in the first instance.

Features *David Ogle* Very limited requirement for overseas articles, 'written to our style'.
Ask for guidelines. Max. 2000 words.

Big requirement for guided walks articles.
Specialist writers only. Ask for guidelines. Max.
750–2000 words (depending on subject).

Payment £60 per 1000 words.

Traveller

45–49 Brompton Road, London SW3 1DE
☎0171 581 4130   Fax 0171 581 1357

Owner *I. M. Wilson*
Editor *Caroline Brandenburger*
Circulation 35,359

FOUNDED 1970. QUARTERLY. Unsolicited mss/
ideas welcome.

Features Six colour features per issue –
copy must be accompanied by good-quality
colour transparencies. Articles welcome on off-
beat cultural or anthropological subjects.
Western Europe rarely covered. No general
travel accounts. Maximum 2000 words.

Payment £125 per 1000 words.

Trout Fisherman

Bretton Court, Bretton, Peterborough,
Cambridgeshire PE3 8DZ
☎01733 264666   Fax 01733 263294

Owner *EMAP Pursuit Publications*
Editor *Chris Dawn*
Circulation 46,241

FOUNDED 1977. MONTHLY instructive magazine on trout fishing. Most of the articles are
commissioned, but unsolicited mss and quality
colour transparencies welcome.
Features Maximum 2500 words.
Payment varies.

True

112 Old Street, London EC1V 9BP
☎0171 336 6886   Fax 0171 336 7447
Owners *Claude Grunitzky/Sunita Olympio*
(True Ltd)
Editors *Claude Grunitzky, Sunita Olympio*
Circulation 39,000

FOUNDED 1995. MONTHLY urban music and
style magazine with a strong emphasis on hip
hop, soul and jungle culture. Interested in seeing urban news features, original, offbeat and
black music profiles and features. Approach in
writing in the first instance.
News *Will Ashon*
Fiction *Claude Grunitzky*
Fashion *Karen Binns.*

Turkeys

See **Fancy Fowl**

TV Times

King's Reach Tower, Stamford Street,
London SE1 9LS
☎0171 261 5000   Fax 0171 261 7777
Owner *IPC Magazines*
Editor *Liz Murphy*
Circulation 998,617

FOUNDED 1968. WEEKLY magazine of listings
and features serving the viewers of independent
television, BBC, satellite and radio. Almost no
freelance contributions used, except where the
writer is known and trusted by the magazine.
No unsolicited contributions.

Twinkle

2 Albert Square, Dundee DD1 2QJ
☎01382 223131 ext. 4149 Fax 01382 322214
Owner *D. C. Thomson & Co. Ltd*
Editor *David Robertson*
Circulation 65,000

FOUNDED 1968. WEEKLY magazine for 5–7-
year-olds. Mainly picture stories but some text-
based pieces. Will consider unsolicited material
but would-be contributors are advised to study
the magazine first. 500–600 words maximum
for text-based stories.

Ulster Tatler

39 Boucher Road, Belfast BT12 6UT
☎01232 681371   Fax 01232 381915
Owner/Editor *Richard Sherry*
Circulation 10,000

FOUNDED 1965. MONTHLY. Articles of local
interest and social functions appealing to
Northern Ireland's ABC1 population.
Welcomes unsolicited material; approach by
phone or in writing in the first instance.
Features *Noreen Dorman* Maximum 1500
words. *Payment* £50.
Fiction *Richard Sherry* Maximum 3000
words. *Payment* £150.

The Universe

St James's Buildings, Oxford Street,
Manchester M1 6FP
☎0161 236 8856   Fax 0161 236 8530
Owner *Gabriel Communications Ltd*
Editor *Joe Kelly*
Circulation 90,000

Occasional use of new writers, but a substantial
network of regular contributors already exists.
Interested in a very wide range of material: all
subjects which might bear on Christian life. Fiction not normally accepted. *Payment* negotiable.

Vector

See **British Science Fiction Association**
under **Professional Associations**

The Vegan

Donald Watson House, 7 Battle Road, St
Leonards on Sea, East Sussex TN37 7AA
☎01424 427393   Fax 01424 717064
Owner *Vegan Society*
Editor *Richard Farhall*
Circulation 5000

FOUNDED 1944. QUARTERLY. Deals with the
ecological, ethical and health aspects of vegan-
ism. Unsolicited mss welcome. Maximum
2000 words.
Payment negotiable.

Verbatim, The Language Quarterly

PO Box 199, Aylesbury, Buckinghamshire
HP20 2HY
☎01296 395880
Editor *Laurence Urdang*
Circulation 25,000

FOUNDED 1974. QUARTERLY. Authors are
urged to review a copy of the periodical before
submitting anything. Sample copy and writers'

guidelines available on request. Unsolicited mss welcome. Approach in writing with ideas. No phone calls.

Features Any aspect of words and language and the way they are used. Max. 1500 words.

Payment negotiable/up to £200 for full-length article.

Veteran Car

Jessamine Court, 15 High Street, Ashwell, Hertfordshire SG7 5NL

☎01462 742818   Fax 01462 742997

Owner *The Veteran Car Club of Great Britain*
Editor *Elizabeth Bennett*
Circulation 1500

FOUNDED 1938. BI-MONTHLY magazine which exists primarily for the benefit of members of The Veteran Car Club of Great Britain. It is concerned with all aspects of the old vehicle hobby – events, restoration, history, current world news, legislation, etc., relating to pre-1919 motor cars. Most professional writers who contribute to the magazine are Club members. No budget for paid contributions.

Vintage Homes

PhD Publishing, Navestock Hall, Navestock, Essex RM4 1HA

☎01708 370380/370053

Owner *PhD Publishing*
Editor *David Hoppit*

FOUNDED 1996. ANNUAL publication covering everything you need to know about planning and building your own home, including interior design and garden landscaping; also bespoke house builders.

Vintage Times

PhD Publishing, Navestock Hall, Navestock, Essex RM4 1HA

☎01708 370380/370053

Owner *PhD Publishing*
Editor *David Hoppit*
Circulation 48,000

FOUNDED 1994. QUARTERLY lifestyle magazine 'for over-40s who have not quite given up hope of winning Wimbledon'. Preliminary approach by phone or in writing with ideas.

Vogue

Vogue House, Hanover Square, London W1R 0AD

☎0171 499 9080   Fax 0171 408 0559

Owner *Condé Nast Publications Ltd*
Editor *Alexandra Shulman*

Circulation 186,162

Condé Nast Magazines tend to use known writers and commission what's needed, rather than using unsolicited mss. Contacts are useful.

Features *Eve MacSweeney* Upmarket general interest rather than 'women's'. Good proportion of highbrow art and literary articles, as well as travel, gardens, food, home interest and reviews. No fiction.

The Voice

370 Coldharbour Lane, London SW9 8PL

☎0171 737 7377   Fax 0171 274 8994

Owner *Vee Tee Ay Media Resources*
Editor *Annie Stewart*
Circulation 50,060

FOUNDED 1982. WEEKLY newspaper, particularly aimed at the black British community. Copy for consideration welcome but 'publication is not guaranteed'. Initial approach in writing preferred. Opportunities in both features and news – especially from the regions.

Payment from £100 per 1000 words/negotiable.

The War Cry

101 Queen Victoria Street, London EC4P 4EP

☎0171 236 5222   Fax 0171 236 3491

Owner *The Salvation Army*
Editor *Captain Charles King*
Circulation 80,000

FOUNDED 1879. WEEKLY magazine containing Christian comments on current issues. Unsolicited mss welcome if appropriate to contents. No fiction or poetry. Approach by phone with ideas.

News relating to Christian Church or social issues. Maximum length 500 words. *Payment* £20 per article.

Features Magazine-style articles of interest to the 'man/woman-in-the-street'. Maximum length 500 words. *Payment* £20 per article.

The Water Gardener

9 Tufton Street, Ashford, Kent TN23 1QN

☎01233 621877   Fax 01233 645669

Owner *Dog World Publishing*
Editor *Peter McHoy*
Circulation 22,506

FOUNDED 1994. Nine issues per year. Everything relevant to water gardening. Will consider in-depth features on aspects of the subject; write with idea in the first instance. Maximum 2000 words.

Payment by negotiation.

Waterways World

Kottingham House, Dale Street, Burton on Trent, Staffordshire DE14 3TD
☎01283 564290   Fax 01283 561077

Owner *Waterway Productions Ltd*
Editor *Hugh Potter*
Circulation 21,683

FOUNDED 1972. MONTHLY magazine for inland waterway enthusiasts. Unsolicited mss welcome, provided the writer has a good knowledge of the subject. No fiction.

Features *Hugh Potter* Articles (preferably illustrated) are published on all aspects of inland waterways in Britain and abroad, including recreational and commercial boating on rivers and canals.

News *Regan Milnes* Maximum 500 words.
Payment £37 per 1000 words.

Waymark

Woodlands, West Lane, Sutton in Craven, Keighley, West Yorkshire BD20 7AS
☎01535 637957   Fax 01535 637576

Editor *Stephen Jenkinson*
Circulation 500

FOUNDED 1986. QUARTERLY journal of the Institute of Public Rights of Way Officers. Glossy, colour in-house magazine for countryside access managers in England and Wales, employed in both the public and private sectors.

News Most produced in-house but some opportunities for original/off-beat items. Maximum 300 words.

Features Countryside, environment, politics, local government, IT-users with special needs, pressure/special interest groups, training, personal safety, natural history, mapping, local history and archive research. Maximum 1000 words.

Special Pages Cartoons or brief humorous items on an access or countryside/environmental theme welcome. Send ideas in writing with s.a.e. initially.
Payment negotiable, up to £25.

Wedding and Home

King's Reach Tower, Stamford Street, London SE1 9LS
☎0171 261 7471   Fax 0171 261 7459

Owner *IPC Magazines Ltd*
Editor *Christine Prunty*
Circulation 44,500

BI-MONTHLY for women planning their wedding, honeymoon and first home. Most features are written in-house or commissioned

from known freelancers. Unsolicited mss are not welcome, but approaches may be made in writing.

Weekly News

Albert Square, Dundee DD1 9QJ
☎01382 223131   Fax 01382 201390

Owner *D. C. Thomson & Co. Ltd*
Editor *David Hishmurgh*
Circulation 365,000

WEEKLY. Newsy, family-orientated magazine designed to appeal to the busy housewife. 'We get a lot of unsolicited stuff and there is great loss of life among them.' Usually commissions, but writers of promise will be taken up. Series include showbiz, royals and television. No fiction.
Payment negotiable.

West Lothian Life

Ballencrieff Cottage, Ballencrieff Toll, Bathgate, West Lothian EH48 4LD
☎01506 632728   Fax 01506 632728

Owner *Pages Editorial & Publishing Services*
Editor *Susan Coon*

QUARTERLY county magazine for people who live, work or have an interest in West Lothian. Includes three or four major features (1500 words) on successful people, businesses or initiatives. A local walk takes up the centre spread. Regular articles by experts on collectables, property, photography, cookery and local gardening, plus news items, letters and a competition. Freelance writers used exclusively for main features. Phone first to discuss content and timing.
Payment by arrangement.

What Car?

38–42 Hampton Road, Teddington, Middlesex TW11 0JE
☎0181 943 5944   Fax 0181 943 5959

Owner *Haymarket Motoring Publications Ltd*
Editor *Mark Payton*
Circulation 135,787

MONTHLY. The car buyer's bible, *What Car?* concentrates on road test comparisons of new cars, news and buying advice on used cars, as well as a strong consumer section. Some scope for freelancers. Testing is only offered to the few, and general articles on aspects of driving are only accepted from writers known and trusted by the magazine. No unsolicited mss.
Payment negotiable.

What Hi-Fi?
60 Waldegrave Road, Teddington, Middlesex
TW11 8LG
☎0181 943 5000   Fax 0181 943 5798
Owner *Haymarket Magazines Ltd*
Publishing Editor *Rahiel Nasir*
Circulation 73,906

FOUNDED 1976. MONTHLY. Features on hi-fi
and new technology. No unsolicited contributions. Prior consultation with the editor essential.
  Features General or more specific on hi-fi
and new technology pertinent to the consumer
electronics market.
  Reviews Specific product reviews. All
material is now generated by in-house staff.
Freelance writing no longer accepted.

What Investment
3rd Floor, 4-8 Tabernacle Street, London
EC2A 4LU
☎0171 638 1916   Fax 0171 638 3128
Owner *Charterhouse Communications*
Editor *Keiron Root*
Circulation 37,000

FOUNDED 1983. MONTHLY. Features articles
on a variety of savings and investment matters.
Unsolicited mss welcome. All approaches
should be made in writing.
  Features Length 1200-1500 words (maximum 2000).
  Payment NUJ rates minimum.

What Mortgage
4-8 Tabernacle Street, London EC2A 4LU
☎0171 638 1916   Fax 0171 638 3128
Owner *Charterhouse Communications*
Editor *Nia Williams*
Circulation 30,000

FOUNDED 1982. MONTHLY magazine on property purchase, choice and finance. Unsolicited
mss welcome; prospective contributors may
make initial contact either by telephone or in
writing.
  Features Up to 1500 words on related topics are considered. Particularly welcome are
new angles, new ideas or specialities relevant to
mortgages.
  Payment £150 per 1000 words.

What's New in Building
Miller Freeman House, 30 Calderwood Street,
London SE18 6QH
☎0181 855 7777   Fax 0181 316 3169
Owner *Miller Freeman plc*
Editor *Mark Pennington*

Circulation 31,496

MONTHLY. Specialist magazine covering new
products for building. Unsolicited mss not generally welcome. The only freelance work available is rewriting press release material. This is
offered on a monthly basis of 25-50 items of
about 150 words each.
  Payment £5.25 per item.

What's new in Farming
Miller Freeman House, 30 Calderwood Street,
London SE18 6QH
☎0181 855 7777 ext. 5070 Fax 0181 854 6795
Owner *Miller Freeman plc*
Managing Editor *Donald Taylor*
Circulation 48,500

FOUNDED 1977. Published eight times a year.
The magazine is primarily a guide to new agricultural products, with features covering the
application of new technology. All copy is
written in-house or by established freelance
contributors.
  Features Articles on relevant agricultural
topics. Maximum 2000 words.
  Payment negotiable.

What's New in Interiors
Miller Freeman House, 30 Calderwood Street,
London SE18 6QH
☎0181 855 7777   Fax 0181 316 3169
Owner *Miller Freeman plc*
Editor *Mark Pennington*
Circulation 22,000

FOUNDED 1981. QUARTERLY. Aimed at interior designers, architects and specifiers. Make
initial contact in writing or by telephone.
  Features New product information only.
Maximum 80 words for each product item.

What's On in London
180-182 Pentonville Road, London N1 9LB
☎0171 278 4393   Fax 0171 837 5838
Owner *E. G. Shaw*
Editor *Michael Darvell*
Circulation 40,000

FOUNDED 1935. WEEKLY entertainment-based
guide and information magazine. Features, listings and reviews. Always interested in well-thought-out and well-presented mss. Articles
should have London/Home Counties connection, except during the summer when they can
be of much wider tourist/historic interest, relating to unusual traditions and events. Approach
the editor by telephone in the first instance.
  Features *Graham Hassell*

Art *Ria Higgins*
Cinema *David Clark*
Pop Music *Danny Scott*
Classical Music *Michael Darvell*
Theatre *Neil Smith*
Events *Chris Murray*
Payment by arrangement.

Wine

Quest Magazines Ltd., 652 Victoria Road,
South Ruislip, Middlesex HA4 0SX
☎0181 842 1010   Fax 0181 841 2557

Owner *Wilmington Publishing*
Editor *Susan Low*
Circulation 35,000

FOUNDED 1983. MONTHLY. No unsolicited mss.
News/Features Wine, food and food/
wine-related travel stories. Prospective contributors should approach in writing.

Wisden Cricket Monthly

6 Beech Lane, Guildford, Surrey GU2 5ES
☎01483 32573/570358   Fax 01483 33153

Owner *Wisden Cricket Magazines Ltd*
Editor *David Frith*
Circulation 42,000

FOUNDED 1979. MONTHLY. Very few uncommissioned articles are used, but would-be contributors are not discouraged. Approach in
writing. *Payment* varies.

Woman

King's Reach Tower, Stamford Street,
London SE1 9LS
☎0171 261 5000   Fax 0171 261 5997

Owner *IPC Magazines Ltd*
Editor *Carole Russell*
Circulation 795,400

Long-running, popular women's magazine
which boasts a readership of over 2.5 million.
No unsolicited mss. Most work commissioned.
Approach with ideas in writing.
Features *Mandie Appleyard* Maximum 1250
words.
Books *Gillian Carter*

Woman and Home

King's Reach Tower, Stamford Street,
London SE1 9LS
☎0171 261 5000   Fax 0171 261 7346

Owner *IPC Magazines Ltd*
Editor *Orlando Murrin*
Circulation 395,000

FOUNDED 1926. MONTHLY. Prospective contributors are advised to write with ideas, includ-

ing photocopies of other published work or
details of magazines to which they have contributed. S.a.e. essential for return of material.
Most freelance work is specially commissioned.

Woman's Journal

King's Reach Tower, Stamford Street,
London SE1 9LS
☎0171 261 6220   Fax 0171 261 7061

Owner *IPC Magazines Ltd*
Editor *Deirdre Vine*
Circulation 166,412

MONTHLY. Original, entertaining feature ideas
welcome, with samples of previous work.
Features *Jane Dowdeswell* Major features are
generally commissioned, but new fresh ideas
on all subjects welcome. Maximum 2000
words. *Payment* negotiable.
Design and Homes *Sue Price*
Fashion *Alex Parnell*
Food *Katie Stewart*
Health *Cherry Maslen*

Woman's Own

King's Reach Tower, Stamford Street,
London SE1 9LS
☎0171 261 5474   Fax 0171 261 5346

Owner *IPC Magazines Ltd*
Editor *Keith McNeill*
Circulation 774,265

WEEKLY. Prospective contributors should contact the features editor *in writing* in the first
instance before making a submission.
Features *Keith Richmond*
Fiction No unsolicited fiction. Annual
short story competition. Maximum 3500
words.

Woman's Realm

King's Reach Tower, Stamford Street,
London SE1 9LS
☎0171 261 5000   Fax 0171 261 5326

Owner *IPC Magazines Ltd*
Editor *Kathy Watson*
Deputy Editor *Linda Belcher*
Circulation 390,548

FOUNDED 1958. WEEKLY. Some scope here for
freelancers. Write to the appropriate editor in
the first instance.
Features Interested in human-interest
ideas/articles, dramatic emotional stories,
strong adventure and chillmng ghost/supernat-
ural stories. Plus real-life stories with a difference. *Payment* NUJ rates.
Fiction Two short stories used every week,
a one-pager (up to 1200 words), plus a longer

one (2500 words). Unsolicited mss no longer accepted.

Woman's Weekly
King's Reach Tower, Stamford Street,
London SE1 9LS
☎0171 261 5000   Fax 0171 261 6322
Owner *IPC Magazines Ltd*
Editor *Olwen Rice*
Circulation 782,261

Mass-market women's WEEKLY.

Features *Frances Quinn* Focus on strong human interest and inspirational stories, film and television personalities, as well as light, entertaining stories and family features of interest to women of 35 upwards. Freelancers used regularly, but tend to be experienced magazine journalists.

Fiction *Gaynor Davies* Short stories 1500–5000 words; serials 12,000–30,000 words. Guidelines for serials: 'a strong romantic emotional theme with a conflict not resolved until the end'; short stories allow for more variety.

Woodworker
Nexus House, Boundary Way, Hemel Hempstead, Hertfordshire HP2 7ST
☎01442 66551   Fax 01442 66998
Owner *Nexus Special Interests*
Editor *Paul Richardson*
Circulation 45,000

FOUNDED 1901. MONTHLY. Contributions welcome; approach with ideas in writing.

Features Articles on woodworking with good photo support appreciated. Maximum 2000 words. *Payment* £40–60 per page.

News Stories and photos (b&w) welcome. Maximum 300 words. *Payment* £10–25 per story.

Working Titles
See under **Poetry, Little Magazines**

Works Magazine
See under **Small Presses (Works Publishing)**

World Fishing
Royston House, Caroline Park, Edinburgh EH5 1QJ
☎0131 551 2942   Fax 0131 551 2938
Owner *The Oban Times Ltd*
Editor *Martin Gill*
Circulation 5746

FOUNDED 1952. MONTHLY. Unsolicited mss welcome; approach by phone or in writing with an idea.

News/Features Technical or commercial nature relating to commercial fishing industry worldwide. Maximum 1000 words.
Payment by arrangement.

World of Bowls
22–26 Market Road, London N7 9PW
☎0171 607 8585   Fax 0171 700 1408
Owner *HBP Ltd*
Editor *Keith Hale*
Circulation 40,000

MONTHLY on all aspects of flat green bowling. Welcome personality pieces. No tuition articles. Approach in writing in the first instance.

Features Unusual, off-the-wall bowling features. Maximum 1000 words.

News Hard news stories. Maximum 200 words. *Payment* by negotiation.

The World of Interiors
Condé Nast Publications, Vogue House, Hanover Square, London W1R 0AD
☎0171 499 9080   Fax 0171 493 4013
Owner *Condé Nast Publications Ltd*
Editor *Min Hogg*
Circulation 71,407

FOUNDED 1981. MONTHLY. Best approach by phone or letter with an idea, preferably with reference snaps or guidebooks.

Features *Sarah Howell* Most feature material is commissioned. 'Subjects tend to be found by us, but we are delighted to receive suggestions of houses unpublished elsewhere, and would love to find new writers.'

World Soccer
King's Reach Tower, Stamford Street, London SE1 9LS
☎0171 261 5737   Fax 0171 261 7474
Owner *IPC Magazines Ltd*
Editor *Keir Radnedge*
Circulation 60,000

FOUNDED 1960. MONTHLY. Unsolicited material welcome but initial approach by phone or in writing preferred. News and features on world soccer.

Writers' Monthly
29 Turnpike Lane, London N8 0EP
☎0181 342 8879   Fax 0181 347 8847
Owner *The Writer Ltd*
Editor *Alan Williams*

FOUNDED 1984. MONTHLY. For writers and aspiring writers. 'Publishers and agents use the magazine to find new writers and help them publish their works.' Articles on writing for television, theatre, radio, newspapers and magazines. Regular features include publisher/ agency profile, poets' press, author interviews, regular short story and poetry competitions. Unsolicited mss from new and established writers welcome.

Features On any aspect of writing. Maximum 2200 words.

Payment negotiable.

Xenos
29 Prebend Street, Bedford MK40 1QN
☎01234 349067

Editor *Stephen Copestake*

FOUNDED 1990. BI-MONTHLY. Science fiction, fantasy, horror, occult, humour, mystery and suspense short story digest. Devoted to a very wide definition of 'fantasy'. 'We favour an optimistic emphasis.' No purely romantic stories, blood and gore, or pornographic/experimental material. Length 2000–10,000 words. All stories printed are evaluated by readers and their comments are printed in the 'Evaluations' section of the subsequent issue. All submissions receive free and prompt analysis by the editor, plus suggestions for revision if appropriate. All submissions must be accompanied by s.a.e. or IRC and be well presented. Annual competition with cash prizes (closing date May 31st). Single issue £3.45; annual subscription £16.50.

Yachting Monthly
King's Reach Tower, Stamford Street, London SE1 9LS
☎0171 261 6040   Fax 0171 261 7555

Owner *IPC Magazines Ltd*
Editor *Geoff Pack*
Circulation 41,390

FOUNDED 1906. MONTHLY magazine for yachting enthusiasts. Unsolicited mss welcome, but many are received and not used. Prospective contributors should make initial contact in writing.

Features *Paul Gelder* A wide range of features concerned with maritime subjects and cruising under sail; well-researched and innovative material always welcome, especially if accompanied by colour transparencies. Maximum 2750 words.

Payment £90–£110 per 1000 words.

Yachting World
King's Reach Tower, Stamford Street, London SE1 9LS
☎0171 261 6800   Fax 0171 261 6818

Owner *IPC Magazines Ltd*

Editor *Andrew Bray*
Circulation 32,500

FOUNDED 1894. MONTHLY with international coverage of yacht racing, cruising and yachting events. Will consider well researched and written sailing stories. Preliminary approaches should be by phone for news stories and in writing for features.

Payment by arrangement.

Yes Magazine
See under **National Newspapers (The People)**

You – The Mail on Sunday Magazine
See under **National Newspapers (The Mail on Sunday)**

You and Your Wedding
Silver House, 31–35 Beak Street, London W1R 3LD
☎0171 437 2998 (editorial)Fax 0171 287 8655

Owner *AIM Publications Ltd*
Editor *Carole Hamilton*
Circulation 55,000

FOUNDED 1985. QUARTERLY. Anything relating to weddings, setting up home, and honeymoons. No unsolicited mss. Ideas may be submitted in writing only. No phone calls.

Young Telegraph
346 Old Street, London EC1V 9NQ
☎0171 613 3376   Fax 0171 613 3372

Editor *Damian Kelleher*
Circulation 1.25 million

FOUNDED 1990. WEEKLY colour supplement for 8–12-year-olds. Unsolicited mss and ideas in writing welcome.

Features *Kitty Melrose* Usually commissioned. Any youth-orientated material. Maximum 500 words.

News *Richard Mead* Short, picture-led articles always welcome. Maximum 80 words.

Payment by arrangement.

Your Garden Magazine
IPC Magazines Ltd., Westover House, West Quay Road, Poole, Dorset BH15 1JG
☎01202 680603   Fax 01202 674335

Owner *IPC Magazines Ltd*
Editor *Michael Pilcher*
Circulation 99,399

FOUNDED 1993. MONTHLY full colour glossy for all gardeners. Welcome good, solid gardening advice that is well written. Receive approx 50 mss per month but only 5% are accepted. Always approach in writing in the first instance.

Features *Michael Pilder* Good gardening features, preferably with a new slant. Small gardens only. Maximum 1000 words. Photographs welcome.

Payment negotiable.

Yours Magazine

Apex House, Oundle Road, Peterborough, Cambridgeshire PE2 9NP
☎01733 555123　　　　Fax 01733 898487

Owner *Choice Publications - Bayard Presse*
Editor *Neil Patrick*
Circulation 211,460

FOUNDED 1973. MONTHLY. Aimed at a readership aged 55 and over.

Features Best approach by letter with outline in first instance. Maximum 1000 words.

News Short, newsy items of interest to readership welcome. Length 300-500 words.

Fiction One or two short stories used in each issue.

Payment negotiable.

ZENE

5 Martins Lane, Witcham, Ely, Cambridgeshire CB6 2LB
☎01353 777931

Owner *TTA Press*
Editor *Andy Cox*

FOUNDED 1994. Features detailed contributors' guidelines of international small press and semi-professional publications, plus varied articles, news, views, reviews and interviews.

Features Unsolicited articles, maximum 2000 words, welcome on any aspect of small press publishing: market information, writing, editing, illustrating, interviews and reviews. All genres.

The Zone

See **Pigasus Press** under **Small Presses**

Freelance Rates – Magazines

Freelance rates vary enormously. The following guidelines are minimum rates negotiated by the **National Union of Journalists**. Most work can command higher fees from employers whether or not they have NUJ agreements. It is up to freelancers to negotiate the best deal they can.

The following NUJ grouping is according to the prosperity of the publication (i.e. based on advertising rates per page):

Group A (over £5000 per page of advertising)
Accountancy Age, Bella, Best, Chat, Company, Cosmopolitan, Country Living, Elle, GQ, Harpers & Queen, Hello!, Ideal Home, Just Seventeen, Looks, Melody Maker, More!, Options, Prima, Q, Radio Times, Reader's Digest, Vogue, Woman, Woman's Own, Woman's Realm, Woman's Weekly, Woman and Home.

Group B (£3000 to £5000 per page of advertising)
Arena, Business Life, Choice, Computer Weekly, Computing, Director, The Economist, Essentials, marie claire, Marketing Week, Mother and Baby, New Scientist, Time Out, Yours.

Group C (£1500 to £3000 per page of advertising)
Accountancy, Country Life, Executive Travel, Home & County, Mizz, New Statesman & Society, Parents, Tatler, TES, The Universe, Wedding and Home.

Group D (£500 to £1500 per page of advertising)
Everywoman, Gay Times, Nursing Times, The Lady, Practical Photography.

Group E (no advertising or less than £500 per page)
Ethnic newspapers and magazines, The Pink Paper, The Big Issue.

Words

These figures (rounded off to the nearest £) are the minimum rates which should be paid by magazines in these groups.

	Features (per 1000 words)	News (per 100 words)	Research/production/ reporting/sub-editing/ picture research (per day)
Group A	negotiable	negotiable	£126
Group B	£247	£24	£115
Group C	£211	£21	£110
Group D	£152	£16	£105
Group E	£126	£15	£ 94

The fee for working as an editor should be at least £131 per day.

Photographic Fees

Commission fees are based on day rates (over 4 hours) and half-day rates (up to 4 hours). Rates are for one use only. Most companies recognise that commission fees are payment for time and will therefore pay reproduction fees on top. Where freelancers are paid over and above the minimum commission fees outlined below this may not apply. Reproduction fees are based on A4 pages, black and white, one British use only. The fees listed are intended as a minimum.

Commission fees

	day	half-day
Group A	£257	£151
Group B	£210	£128
Group C	£189	£116
Group D	£173	£ 99
Group E	£162	£ 89

Reproduction fees

Up to:	¼ page	½ page	¾ page	full page
Group A	£89	£131	£160	£262+
Group B	£78	£109	£144	£199
Group C	£63	£ 91	£128	£178
Group D	£57	£ 78	£109	£147
Group E	£47	£ 53	£ 84	£113

Colour: By negotiation
Cover: 50% extra.
Studio/location work and specialist assignments: £682 per day.

Cartoons

	Group A	Group B & C	Group D & E
Minimum fee	£ 89	£72	£57
Feature strip	£110	£96	£89

Illustrations

Payment at not less than the appropriate rate for photographs. Colour and cover rates should be agreed by negotiation but should not be less than double the above rates. All rates quoted are for one British use only.

News Agencies

AP Dow Jones
10 Fleet Place, London EC4M 7RB
☎0171 832 9105   Fax 0171 832 9101

Everything is generated in-house. No unsolicited material.

Associated Press News Agency
12 Norwich Street, London
EC4A 1BP
☎0171 353 1515/353 6323(News)/353 4731
Fax (Photos) 0171 353 8118

Material is either generated in-house or by regulars. Hires the occasional stringer. No unsolicited mss.

National News Press and Photo Agency
109 Clifton Street, London
EC2A 4LD
☎0171 417 7707   Fax 0171 216 4111

All press releases welcomed. Most work is ordered or commissioned. Coverage includes courts, tribunals, conferences, general news, etc - words and pictures - as well as PR.

PA News Ltd
292 Vauxhall Bridge Road, London SW1V 1AE
☎0171 963 7000

No unsolicited mss. They will be returned unread with an apology. Most material is produced in-house though occasional outsiders may be used. A phone call to discuss specific material may lead somewhere 'but this is rare'.

Press & Pictures
Hercules Road, London SE1 7DU
☎0171 261 8484   Fax 0171 928 7652

Material generally commissioned. No unsolicited mss.

Reuters Ltd
85 Fleet Street, London EC4P 4AJ
☎0171 250 1122

No unsolicited mss.

Solo Syndication Ltd
49-53 Kensington High Street, London
W8 5ED
☎0171 376 2166   Fax 0171 938 3165

FOUNDED 1978. *Specialises* in world-wide newspaper syndication of photos, features and cartoons. Professional contributors only.

National and Regional Television

BBC Television

Television Centre, Wood Lane, London
W12 7RJ
☎0181 743 8000
Managing Director, Network TV *Will Wyatt*
Controller, BBC1 *Alan Yentob*
Controller, BBC2 *Michael Jackson*
Head of Features *Anne Morrison*
Head of Purchased Programmes *June Dromgoole*

The principal divisions within BBC TV (excluding News and Current Affairs, Education, and Religious Broadcasting, which operate as separate directorates within the BBC) are: Children's Programmes; Documentaries; Drama Group; Entertainment Group; Music & Arts; Science & Features; Sport & Events Group. Address given if different from above.

CHILDREN'S PROGRAMMES
Head of Children's Programmes *Anna Home*
Executive Producer, Drama *Richard Callanan*
Executive Producer, Entertainment *Chris Pilkington*
Executive Producer, Factual Programmes *Eric Rowan*
Editor, Blue Peter *Lewis Bronze*
Producer, Grange Hill *Stephen Andrew*
Producer, Jackanory *Maggie Barbour*
Editor, Live & Kicking *Christopher Bellinger*
Editor, Newsround *Nick Heathcote*

DOCUMENTARIES
White City, 201 Wood Lane, London
W12 7TS
☎0181 752 5252   Fax 0181 752 6060
Head of Documentaries *Paul Hamann*
Editor, Inside Story *Olivia Lichtenstein*
Editor, Modern Times *Stephen Lambert*
Editor, Reputations *Janice Hadlow*
Editor, Timewatch *Laurence Rees*

DRAMA GROUP
Head of Drama Group *To be appointed*
Head of Feature Film *Mark Shivas*
Head of Serials *Michael Wearing*
Head of Series *Chris Parr*
Head of Single Drama *George Faber*
Executive Producer, Performance *Simon Curtis*

Development Executive, Independents *Jenny Killick*

ENTERTAINMENT GROUP
Fax 0181 743 2457
Head of Entertainment Group *Chris Pye*
Head of Comedy *Geoffrey Perkins*
Head of Light Entertainment *Michael Leggo*
Head of Comedy Entertainment *Jon Plowman*
Head of Independent Production *Kevin Lygo*
Editor, Comedy Development *Rosie Bunting*

MUSIC AND ARTS
Fax 0181 740 0883
Head of Music & Arts *Kim Evans*
Head of Music Programmes *Avril MacRory*
Editor, Arts Features *Keith Alexander*
Series Editor, Omnibus *Nigel Williams*
Series Editor, Arena *Anthony Wall*
Head of Development/Editor, Books & Special Projects *Roland Keating*

SCIENCE AND FEATURES
201 Wood Lane, London W12 7RJ
☎0181 752 6178
Head of Science & Features *Jana Bennett*
Editor, Tomorrow's World *Edward Briffa*
Editor, Horizon *John Lynch*
Editor, QED *Lorraine Heggess*

SPORT AND EVENTS GROUP
Head of Sport & Events Group *Jonathan Martin*
Editor, Match of the Day/Sportsnight *Niall Sloane*
Editor, Grandstand *David Gordon*

BBC News and Current Affairs

BBC Television Centre, Wood Lane, London
W12 7RJ
☎0181 743 8000

News and current affairs broadcasting across television and radio were unified as a single operation in 1987.

Managing Director, News and Current Affairs *Tony Hall*
Head of Weekly News & Current Affairs *Mark Damazer*

Managing Editor, Weekly Programmes
  Tim Suter
Head of News Programmes *Peter Bell*
Managing Editor, News Programmes *John Morrison*
Head of Political Programmes *Samir Shah*
Head of News Gathering, News & Current Affairs *Chris Cramer*
Editor, Foreign Affairs Unit *John Simpson*
Editor, Business & Economics Unit *Peter Jay*
News Editor, Breakfast News *Tim Orchard*
News Editor, One O'Clock News *Jon Barton*
News Editor, Six O'Clock News *Nikki Clarke*
News Editor, Nine O'Clock News *Malcolm Balen*
News Editor, Newsnight *Peter Horrocks*
Editor, Public Eye *Mark Wakefield*
Editor, Panorama *Steve Hewlett*
Editor, The Money Programme *Jane Ellison*
Editor, On the Record *David Jordan*
Editor, Ceefax *Claire Prosser*
Head of Subtitling *Ruth Griffiths*

Ceefax
Room 7013, Television Centre, Wood Lane, London W12 7RJ
☎0181 576 1801

The BBC's main news and information service, broadcasting hundreds of pages on both BBC1 and BBC2. It is on the air at all times when transmitters are broadcasting.

Subtitling
Room 1468, BBC White City, Wood Lane, London W12 7RJ
☎0181 752 7054/0141 330 2345 ext. 2128

A rapidly expanding service (approx 40% of total BBC output is subtitled including all news bulletins) available via Ceefax page 888. Units based in both London and Glasgow.

BBC Educational Directorate
BBC White City, 201 Wood Lane, London W12 7TS
☎0181 752 5252

Director of Education *Jane Drabble*
Head of Educational Policy & Services
  Lucia Jones
Head of Editorial, Educational Publishing
  Sarah Dann
Head of Commissioning, Schools Programmes *Frank Flynn*
Head of Commissioning, Education for Adults *Glenwyn Benson*

Head of Open University Production Centre *Colin Robinson* (Walton Hall, Milton Keynes, MK7 6BH. ☎01908 655544 Fax 01908 376324)
Managing Editor, The Learning Zone & BBC Focus *Paul Gerhardt*(Woodlands, 80 Wood Lane, London W12 0TT. ☎0181 743 5588)

The educational programme-making and publishing activities of the BBC were brought together in 1993 under the aegis of the education directorate. This incorporates radio and television broadcasting of school programmes, education for adults, Open University and the new Market Development division which produces a range of multimedia products and promotion activity. The BBC produces audio and visual material on behalf of and in partnership with the Open University. The Learning Zone broadcasts education, training and information programmes from midnight to 7.00am during the week. BBC Focus assists non-profit making organisations to make and broadcast their own programmes on education, information and training.

BBC Religious Broadcasting
New Broadcasting House, PO Box 27, Oxford Road, Manchester M60 1SJ
☎0161 200 2020   Fax 0161 244 3183
Head of Religious Broadcasting *Rev. Ernest Rea*

Regular programmes for television include *This is the Day; Songs of Praise; Everyman; Heart of the Matter.* Radio output includes *Good Morning Sunday; Sunday Half-hour; Thought for the Day; Choral Evensong; Pause for Thought; Seeds of Faith.*

BBC Regional Broadcasting
The BBC Regional Broadcasting Directorate consists of BBC Northern Ireland, BBC Scotland, BBC Wales, Midlands & East Region, North Region, South Region, all with an autonomous management structure, making local, regional and network programmes.

BBC Northern Ireland
Broadcasting House, 25-27 Ormeau Avenue, Belfast BT2 8HQ
☎01232 338000

Controller *Patrick Loughrey*
Head of Programmes *Anna Carragher*
Head of News & Current Affairs *Tony Maddox*

Editor, Current Affairs *Andrew Colman*
Managing Editor, General Programmes
Paul Evans
Head of TV Drama *Robert Cooper*
Political Editor *Jim Dougal*
Chief Producer, Features *Charlie Warmington*
Chief Producer, Current Affairs *Michael
Cairns*
Chief Producer, Sport *Terry Smith*
Chief Producer, Agriculture *Veronica Hughes*
Chief Producer, Music & Arts *Ian Kirk-Smith*
Chief Producer, Youth & Community
Fedelma Harkin
Chief Producer, Education *Michael McGowan*
Chief Producer, Religion *Bert Tosh*

Regular programmes include *PK Tonight; Inside
Ulster; 29 Bedford Street* and *Country Times*. Religious, educational, news & current affairs programming across both TV and radio comes
under the aegis of separate directorates within
the BBC. See individual entries in this section
for each.

BBC Scotland

Broadcasting House, Queen Margaret Drive,
Glasgow G12 8DG
☎0141 339 8844

Controller *John McCormick*
Head of Television *Colin Cameron*
**Head of Bi-Media News, Current Affairs
& TV Sport** *Kenneth Cargill*
Head of Arts *John Archer*
Head of Arts & Entertainment *Mike Bolland*
Head of Drama *Andrea Calderwood*
Head of Gaelic & Features *Ken MacQuarrie*
**Head of Education & Religious
Broadcasting** *Andrew Barr*

Headquarters of BBC Scotland with opt-out
stations based in Aberdeen, Dundee, Edinburgh
and Inverness. Regular programmes include the
nightly *Reporting Scotland* plus *Friday Sportscene;
Frontline Scotland* and *Landward* (bi-monthly
farming news).

Aberdeen
Broadcasting House, Beechgrove Terrace,
Aberdeen AB9 2ZT
☎01224 625233

News, plus some features, but most programmes are made in Glasgow.

Dundee
Nethergate Centre, 66 Nethergate, Dundee
DD1 4ER
☎01382 202481
News only.

Edinburgh
Broadcasting House, Queen Street, Edinburgh
EH2 1JF
☎0131 469 4200

All programmes made in Glasgow.

Inverness
7 Culduthel Road, Inverness 1V2 4AD
☎01463 221711
News only.

BBC Wales

Broadcasting House, Llandaff, Cardiff CF5 2YQ
☎01222 572888   Fax 01222 552973

Controller *Geraint Talfan Davies*
Head of Programmes (Welsh Language)
Gwynn Pritchard
Head of Programmes (English Language)
Dai Smith
Head of News & Current Affairs *Aled Eurig*
Head of Drama *Karl Francis*
Series Producer, Pobol y Cwm *Cliff Jones*
Head of Sport *Arthur Emyr*
Head of Factual Programmes *John Geraint*

Headquarters of BBC Wales, with regional television centres in Bangor and Swansea. All Welsh
language programmes are transmitted by **S4C**
and produced in Cardiff or Swansea. Regular
programmes include *Wales Today; Wales on
Saturday;* and *Pobol y Cwm* (Welsh-language
drama series).

Bangor
Broadcasting House, Meirion Road, Bangor,
Gwynedd LL57 2BY
☎01248 370880   Fax 01248 351443

Head of Production *Marian Wyn Jones*
News only.

Swansea
Broadcasting House, 32 Alexandra Road,
Swansea, West Glamorgan SA1 5DZ
☎01792 654986   Fax 01792 468194

Senior Producer *Geraint Davies*

BBC Midlands & East

Broadcasting Centre, Pebble Mill Road,
Birmingham B5 7QQ
☎0121 414 8888   Fax 0121 414 8634

Head of Broadcasting *Nigel Chapman*
Head of Network Television *Rod Natkiel*
Head of Television Drama *Tony Virgo*
Head of Local Programmes *Adrian Van
Klaveren*
Editor, News & Current Affairs *Peter Lowe*

Managing Editor, Network Television, Daytime and Lifestyle Programmes *Stephanie Silk*
Managing Editor, Network Television Leisure & Countryside Programmes *John King*

Home of the Pebble Mill Studio. Regular programmes include *Midlands Today* and *The Midlands Report*. Output for the network includes: *The Clothes Show; Telly Addicts; Top Gear; Good Morning Anne and Nick; Gardener's World; Kilroy*. Openings exist for well-researched topical or local material.

BBC Midlands & East serves opt-out stations in Nottingham and Norwich.

BBC East Midlands (Nottingham)
East Midlands Broadcasting Centre, York House, Mansfield Road, Nottingham NG1 3JA
☎0115 9550500

Head of Local Programmes *Richard Lucas*

Local news programmes such as *East Midlands Today*

BBC East (Norwich)
St Catherine's Close, All Saint's Green, Norwich, Norfolk NR1 3ND
☎01603 619331   Fax 01603 667865

Head of Centre *Arnold Miller*
Editor, News & Current Affairs *David Holdsworth*

Regular slots include *Look East* (regional magazine) and *Matter of Fact*.

BBC North
New Broadcasting House, Oxford Road, Manchester M60 1SJ
☎0161 200 2020

Head of Broadcasting *Colin Adams*
Head of Youth & Entertainment Features *John Whiston*
Editor, News & Current Affairs *Richard Porter*

Headquarters of BBC North, incorporating the former North East and North West divisions. Leeds and Newcastle continue to make their own programmes, each having its own head of centre. Regular programmes include *Rough Guides; The Travel Show; Great Railway Journeys; Red Dwarf; Mastermind.*

Leeds
Broadcasting Centre, Woodhouse Lane, Leeds, West Yorkshire LS2 9PX
☎01132 441188

Head of Centre *Martin Brooks*

Editor, News & Current Affairs *Jon Williams*
Regional Political Editor *Geoff Talbott*
Series Producer, Close Up North *Ian Lundall*

Newcastle upon Tyne
Broadcasting Centre, Barrack Road, Newcastle Upon Tyne NE99 2NE
☎0191 232 1313

Head of Centre *Olwyn Hocking*
Editor, News and Current Affairs/News Editor, Look North *Ian Cameron*
Producers, Look North *Iain Williams, Brid Fitzpatrick, Andrew Lambert, Fiona MacBeth*
Producer, North of Westminster *Michael Wild*

BBC South
Broadcasting House, Whiteladies Road, Bristol, Avon BS8 2LR
☎0117 9732211

Head of Broadcasting *John Shearer*
Head of Television Features *Jeremy Gibson*
Head of Natural History Unit *Alastair Fothergill*
Editor, The Natural World *John Sparks*

BBC South incorporates BBC West (Bristol), BBC South (Southampton), BBC South West (Plymouth), and BBC South East (Elstree), each with its own head of centre. Bristol is the home of the BBC's Natural History Unit, producing programmes like *Wildlife on One; The Natural World; Watch Out*; and *The Really Wild Show*. BBC South produces a wide range of television features for regional programming across its four centres, such as *999; Lifesavers; Men's Health; Antiques Roadshow; 10x10; Under the Sun; Floyd.*

BBC West (Bristol)
(address/telephone number as above)
Head of Local Programmes, West *John Conway*
Editor, West Political Unit *Paul Cannon*

BBC South (Southampton)
Broadcasting House, Havelock Road, Southampton, Hampshire SO14 7PU
☎01703 226201

Head of Centre, South *Nigel Kay*
Editor, News & Current Affairs *Andy Griffee*

BBC South West (Plymouth)
Broadcasting House, Seymour Road, Mannamead, Plymouth, Devon PL3 5BD
☎01752 229201

Head of Centre, South West *Roy Roberts*
Editor, News *Roger Clark*
Editor, Current Affairs *Simon Willis*

BBC South East (Elstree)
Elstree Centre, Clarendon Road,
Borehamwood, Hertfordshire WD6 1JF
☎0181 953 6100

Head of Centre, South East *Michele Romaine*
Editor, Newsroom South East *Guy Pelham*
Editor, First Sight *Alison Rooper*

The regional broadcasting centres produce little more than news, being supplied with programmes from BBC West at Bristol.

Independent Television
Anglia Television

Anglia House, Norwich, Norfolk NR1 3JG
☎01603 615151   Fax 01603 631032

London office: 48 Leicester Square, London WC2H 7FB
☎0171 321 0101   Fax 0171 930 8499

Managing Director *Malcolm Wall*
Controller of News *Mike Read*
Director of Programmes *Graham Creelman*

Anglia Television is a major producer of programmes for the ITV network and Channel 4, including *Gardens Without Borders, Food Guide, The Time ... The Place*, and the *Survival* wildlife documentaries, Britain's best-selling programme export. A wide range of peak-time drama includes the P. D. James murder mysteries.

Border Television plc

Television Centre, Durranhill, Carlisle, Cumbria CA1 3NT
☎01228 25101   Fax 01228 41384

Chairman & Chief Executive *James Graham OBE*
Head of Programmes *Neil Robinson*

Border's programming concentrates on documentaries rather than drama. Most scripts are supplied in-house but occasionally there are commissions. Apart from notes, writers should not submit written work until their ideas have been fully discussed.

Carlton UK Television

101 St Martin's Lane, London WC2N 4AZ
☎0171 240 4000   Fax 0171 240 4171

Chairman *Nigel Walmsley*
Chief Executive *Clive Jones*
Managing Director, Carlton Broadcasting *Colin Stanbridge*

Carlton UK Television comprises four separate entities: Carlton Broadcasting, which is responsible for the ITV licence for London and the South East, with programmes produced by independent companies; **Central Broadcasting** (see entry); **Carlton UK Productions** (see under **Film, TV and Video Producers**); Carlton UK Sales which sells airtime and sponsorship for both broadcasters. Also runs two facilities operations: The Television House in Nottingham, supplying studios and related services and Carlton 021, the largest commercial operator of Outside Broadcast Services in Europe.

Central Broadcasting

Central House, Broad Street, Birmingham B1 2JP
☎0121 643 9898   Fax 0121 616 1531

Chairman *Leslie Hill*
Managing Director *Rod Henwood*

Part of **Carlton UK Television**. Responsible for the ITV licence for East, West and South Midlands. Regular programmes include *Central Weekend; Tuesday Specials; Crime Stalker*.

Channel 4

124 Horseferry Road, London SW1P 2TX
☎0171 396 4444   Fax 0171 306 8353

Chief Executive *Michael Grade*
Director of Programmes *John Willis*
Controller, Factual Programmes *Karen Brown*
Head of Drama *David Aukin*
Controller, Arts & Entertainment *Stuart Cosgrove*
COMMISSIONING EDITORS
Independent Film & Video (Acting Editor) *Robin Gutch*
Documentaries *Peter Moore*
News & Current Affairs *David Lloyd*
Entertainment *Seamus Cassidy*
Sport *Mike Miller*
Youth *David Stevenson*
Multicultural Programmes *Farrukh Dhondy*
Religion & Features *Peter Grimsdale*
Head of Purchased Programmes *Mairi MacDonald*

When Channel 4 started broadcasting as a national TV channel in November 1982, it was the first new TV service to be launched in Britain for 18 years. Under the 1981 Broadcasting Act it was required to cater for tastes and audiences not previously served by the other broadcast channels, and to provide a suitable proportion of educational programmes. Channel 4 does not make any of its own programmes; they are commissioned from the independent production companies, from the ITV sector, or co-produced with other organisations. The role of the commissioning editors is to sift through proposals for programmes and see interesting projects through to broadcast. Regulated by the ITC.

Channel 5 Broadcasting Ltd

Cavendish House, 128-134 Cleveland Street, London W1P 5DN
☎0171 911 0055   Fax 0171 916 6556

Chief Executive *Ian Ritchie*
Director of Programmes *Dawn Airey*
Controller of Children's Programmes
  Nick Wilson
Controller of Features & Arts *Michael Attwell*
Controller of News, Current Affairs &
  Documentaries *Ian Gardam*

Channel 5 Broadcasting Ltd, led by Greg Dyke of Pearson TV, won the franchise for Britain's third commercial terrestrial television station in 1995 with a bid of £22.02 million. Described by Dyke as as 'kind of younger ITV', the station comes on air in January 1997 with a programme of soap operas five nights weekly, current affairs, mainstream drama and entertainment.

Channel Television

The Television Centre, La Pouquelaye, St Helier, Jersey, Channel Islands JE1 3ZD
☎01534 816816   Fax 01534 816817
Also at: The TV Centre, St George's Place, St Peter Port, Guernsey
☎01481 723451

Managing Director *John Henwood*
Director of Television *Michael Lucas*

The teen soap *Island* produced by Channel Television for Children's ITV was the company's first drama commission and was filmed exclusively on location in the Channel Islands. Previous commissions for ITV and Ch4 have included documentaries, factual series and animation programmes.

GMTV

The London Television Centre, Upper Ground, London SE1 9TT
☎0171 827 7000   Fax 0171 827 7001

Managing Director *Christopher Stoddart*
Director of Programmes *Peter McHugh*
Managing Editor *John Scammell*

Winner of the national breakfast television franchise. Jointly owned by LWT, Scottish Television, Carlton Television, The Guardian and Manchester Evening News, and Disney. GMTV took over from TV-AM on 1 January 1993, with live programming from 6 am to 9.25 am. Regular news headlines, current affairs, topical features, showbiz and lifestyle, sports and business, quizzes and competitions, travel and weather reports. More family-orientated than its predecessor, with a softer approach altogether to news and less time given over to City news.

Grampian Television plc

Queen's Cross, Aberdeen AB9 2XJ
☎01224 846846   Fax 01224 846800

Director of Programmes/Head of
  Documentaries & Features *George W.*
  Mitchell, MA
Head of News & Current Affairs *Alistair*
  Gracie
Head of Gaelic *Robert Kenyon*

Extensive regional news and reports including farming, fishing and sports, interviews and leisure features, various light entertainment, Gaelic and religious programmes, and live coverage of the Scottish political, economic and industrial scene. Serves the area stretching from Fife to Shetland. Regular programmes include *Gaelic News; Criomagan* (Gaelic Diary); and *Reflections*.

Granada Television

Granada TV Centre, Quay Street, Manchester M60 9EA
☎0161 832 7211   Fax 0161 953 0283
London office: Stornoway House, 13 Cleveland Row, London SW1A 1GG
☎0171 451 3000

Joint Managing Directors *Jules Burns,*
  Andrea Wonfor
Director of Production *Max Graesser*
Head of Factual Programming *Ian McBride*
Head of Features *James Hunt*
Controller of Drama *Gub Neal*
Executive Producer, Drama Serials
  Carolyn Reynolds
Head of Current Affairs &
  Documentaries *Charles Tremayme*
Controller of Entertainment & Comedy
  Andy Harries
Head of Music *Iain Rousham*

Opportunities for freelance writers are not great but mss from professional writers will be considered. All mss should be addressed to the head of scripts. Regular programmes include *Coronation Street; World in Action;* and *This Morning*.

HTV Group plc

Television Centre, Culverhouse Cross, Cardiff CF5 6XJ
☎01222 590590   Fax 01222 599108

Chief Executive *Christopher Rowlands*
Group Director of Broadcasting *Ted George*

Managing Director, Programmes *Stephen Matthews*
Controller of Children's & Family Programmes (Wales & West) *Dan Maddicott*

HTV (Wales)
(address/telephone number as above)
Deputy Director of Broadcasting *Menna Richards*

HTV (West)
Television Centre, Bath Road, Bristol, Avon BS4 3HG
☎0117 9778366   Fax 0117 9722400
Director of Programmes *Jeremy Payne*
The company produces and develops a wide range of programmes in all genres for national and international markets. Strong local programming in West & Wales. Scripts welcome, particularly from writers who live or work in the regions. Regular programmes include *Soccer Sunday; Fair's Fair* (consumer programme); *The Really Helpful Programme* and *Wales This Week*.

ITN (Independent Television News Ltd)

200 Gray's Inn Road, London WC1X 8XZ
☎0171 833 3000
Editor-in-Chief *Richard Tait*
Editor, ITN Programmes for ITV *Nigel Dacre*
Provider of the main national and international news for ITV and Channel 4. Programmes on ITV: *Lunchtime News; Early Evening News; News at Ten; ITN Morning News*, plus regular news summaries, and three programmes a day at weekends. Programmes on Channel 4: in-depth news analysis programmes, including *Channel 4 News* and *The Big Breakfast News*. ITN also provides the news, sport and business news for *ITN's World News*, the first international English-language news programme. Regulated by the ITC.

LWT (London Weekend Television)

The London Television Centre, Upper Ground, London SE1 9LT
☎0171 620 1620
Chief Operating Officer *Charles Allen*
Managing Director *Steve Morrison*
Director of Programmes *David Liddiment*
Controller of Entertainment *Nigel Lythgoe*
Controller of Drama *Sally Head*
Controller of Arts *Melvyn Bragg*

Controller of Factual and Regional Programmes *Simon Shaps*
Makers of current affairs, entertainment and drama series such as *Blind Date, Surprise Surprise, The Knock, London's Burning*; also *The South Bank Show* and *Jonathan Dimbleby*. Provides a large proportion of ITV's drama and light entertainment, and also BSkyB and Channel 4.

Meridian Broadcasting

Television Centre, Southampton, Hampshire SO14 0PZ
☎01703 222555   Fax 01703 335050
London office: 48 Leicester Square, London WC2H 7LY
☎0171 839 2255
Chief Executive *Roger Laughton*
Director of Broadcasting, M&I *Richard Platt*
Director of Programmes and Production *Mary McAnally*
Controller of Drama *Simon Lewis*
Controller of Children's Programmes *Richard Morss*
Controller of News, Sport & Current Affairs *Jim Raven*
All network and most regional output is usually commissioned from independent producers and programming is bound by the ITC guidelines which insist upon news, current affairs, children's and religious programming across a wide range of tastes. Regular programmes include: *Meridian Tonight; The Pier* (arts/entertainment); *Countryways*.

S4C

Parc Ty Glas, Llanishen, Cardiff CF4 5GG
☎01222 747444   Fax 01222 754444
Chief Executive *Huw Jones*
Director of Programmes *Deryk Williams*
The Welsh 4th Channel, established by the Broadcasting Act 1980, is responsible for a schedule of Welsh and English programmes on the Fourth Channel in Wales. Known as S4C, the service is made up of about 30 hours per week of Welsh language programmes and more than 85 hours of English language output from Channel 4. Ten hours a week of the Welsh programmes are provided by the BBC; the remainder are purchased from HTV and independent producers. Drama, comedy and documentary are all part of S4C's programming.

Scottish Television

Cowcaddens, Glasgow G2 3PR
☎0141 300 3000   Fax 0141 300 3030

London office: 20 Lincoln's Inn Field, London
WC2A 3ED
☎0171 446 7000   Fax 0171 446 7010

Director of Broadcasting Blair Jenkins
Controller of Drama Robert Love
Controller of Entertainment Sandy Ross
Controller of Factual Entertainment
Eamonn O'Neil
Head of News, Sport & Current Affairs
Scott Ferguson

An increasing number of STV programmes such as Taggart and Doctor Finlay are now networked nationally. Programme coverage includes drama, religion, news, sport, outside broadcasts, special features, entertainment and the arts, education and Gaelic programmes. Produces many one-offs for ITV and Channel 4.

Teletext Ltd

101 Farm Lane, Fulham, London SW6 1QJ
☎0171 386 5000   Fax 0171 386 5002

Managing Director Peter Van Gelder
Editor Graham Lovelace

On 1 January 1993 Teletext Ltd took over the electronic publishing service, previously the domain of Oracle, servicing both ITV and Channel 4. Transmits a wide range of news pages and features, including current affairs, sport, TV listings, weather, travel, holidays, finance, games, competitions, etc. Provides a regional service to each of the ITV regions.

Tyne Tees Television

Television Centre, Newcastle upon Tyne
NE1 2AL
☎0191 261 0181   Fax 0191 261 2302

London office: 15 Bloomsbury Square,
London WC1A 2LJ
☎0171 405 8474   Fax 0171 242 2441

Managing Director John Calvert
Director of Broadcasting Peter Moth
Head of Current Affairs &
Documentaries Peter Mitchell
Head of Young People's Programmes
Lesley Oakden
Head of Entertainment Christine Williams
Head of Training & Community Affairs
Annie Wood
Head of Sport Roger Tames
Controller of News Graeme Thompson

Programming covers religion, politics, news and current affairs, regional documentaries, business, entertainment, sport and arts. Regular programmes include The Dales Diary; Tyne Tees News; Tonight and Around the House (politics).

UTV (Ulster Television)

Havelock House, Ormeau Road, Belfast
BT7 1EB
☎01232 328122   Fax 01232 246695

Controller of Programming A. Bremner
Head of Factual Programmes Michael Beattie
News Editor Rob Morrison
Director of Outside Broadcasts Robert
Lamrock
Director of Gardening/Heritage Ruth
Johnston

Regular programmes on news and current affairs, sport, education, music, light entertainment, arts, politics and health.

Westcountry Television Ltd

Western Wood Way, Langage Science Park,
Plymouth, Devon PL7 5BG
☎01752 333333   Fax 01752 333444

Chief Executive Stephen Redfarn
Director of News & Sport Richard Myers
Director of Programmes Jane McCloskey

Came on air in 1 January 1993. News, current affairs, documentary and religious programming. Regular programmes include Westcountry Live; Westcountry Focus; Westcountry Showcase; Anybody Out There?; My Story.

Yorkshire Television

The Television Centre, Leeds, West Yorkshire
LS3 1JS
☎0113 2438283   Fax 0113 2445107

London office: 15 Bloomsbury Square,
London WC1A 2LJ
☎0171 312 3700   Fax 0171 242 2441

Group Managing Director & Chief
Executive of Yorkshire Television Bruce
Gyngell
Group Controller, Factual Programmes
Chris Bryer
Group Controller, Drama Keith Richardson
Head of News & Current Affairs Ali Rashid
Group Controller, Entertainment David
Reynolds
Head of Sport Robert Charles
Head of Religion Pauline Duffy
Head of Children's Patrick Titley
Controller of Education Chris Jelley

Drama series, film productions, studio plays and

long-running series like *Emmerdale* and *Heartbeat*. Always looking for strong writing in these areas, but prefers to find it through an agent. Documentary/current affairs material tends to be supplied by producers; opportunities in these areas are rare but adaptations of published work as a documentary subject are considered. Light entertainment comes from an already well-established circle of professionals in this area which is difficult to infiltrate. In theory opportunity exists within series, episode material. Best approach is through a good agent.

Cable and Satellite Television
Asianet
Elliott House, Victoria Road, London
NW10 6NY
☎0181 930 0930   Fax 0181 930 0546
Chief Executive *Dr Banad Viswanath*
Managing Director *Deepak Viswanath*

Broadcasting since September 1994, Asianet transmits entertainment to the Asian community 24 hours a day in English, Hindi, Gujarati, Punjabi, Bengali and Urdu.

Channel One Television Ltd
60 Charlotte Street, London W1P 2AX
☎0171 209 1234   Fax 0171 209 1235
Also at: The Television Centre, Bath Road, Bristol, Avon BS4 3HG
☎0117 9722551   Fax 0117 9722492
Managing Director *Julian Aston*
Director of Programming *Nick Pollard*

Owned by Daily Mail & General Trust plc. 24-hour, news-led channel.

CNN International (CNNI)
CNN House, 19–22 Rathbone Place, London
W1P 1DF
☎0171 637 6739   Fax 0171 637 6738
Acting Managing Director *Randy Freedman*
Bureau Chief *Charles Hoff*

Owned by Turner Broadcasting System Inc. World-wide, 24-hour international television news network, transmitted from the USA and adapted for a European audience. Live coverage of world events, global business reports, sport, in-depth features, weather, etc via satellite.

European Business News (EBN)
10 Fleet Place, London EC4M 7RB
☎0171 653 9300   Fax 0171 653 9333
Managing Director *Michael Connor*

24-hour European financial and corporate news broadcasting.

Live TV
24th Floor, One Canada Square, Canary Wharf, London E14 5AP
☎0171 293 3900   Fax 0171 293 3820
Managing Director *Kelvin MacKenzie*
Head of Programming *Nick Ferrari*

24-hour cable channel with an emphasis on upbeat and lively entertainment and information programming. Owned by Mirror Group Newspapers.

Maxat Ltd
200 Gray's Inn Road, London WC1X 8XZ
☎0171 430 4400   Fax 0171 430 4321
Chief Executive *Julian Costley*

European satellite providing sports, news-gathering and uplink services to, for example, the BBC, ITN, ABC, NBC, MTV and UK Gold.

MTV Europe (Music Television)
Hawley Crescent, London NW1 8TT
☎0171 284 7777   Fax 0171 284 7788
President, International *William Roedy*

ESTABLISHED 1987. Europe's 24-hour music and youth entertainment channel, available on cable and via satellite. Transmitted from London in English across Europe.

Sky Television plc (BSkyB)
6 Centaurs Business Park, Grant Way, Isleworth, Middlesex TW7 5QD
☎0171 705 3000   Fax 0171 705 3030
Chief Executive & Managing Director
    Sam Chisholm
Head of Programming *David Elstein*

The ten-channel British Sky Broadcasting group (owned by News International, Chargeurs, Granada and Pearson) broadcasts via Astra satellite, cable TV operators and SMATV in the UK and Ireland.

Sky Movies
24-hours of blockbuster action, comedy, horror and adventure films.

The Movie Channel
24-hours of motion pictures with a film première every day.

Sky Movies Gold
Described as a film treasure-trove of some of the best-loved films of all time. Includes The Disney Channel.

Sky Sports/Sky Sports 2/Sky Sports Gold
Dedicated to a UK audience with an emphasis on live coverage of major sports events, British and international football, Test cricket, boxing, tennis and snooker.

SKY MULTI-CHANNELS PACKAGE:

Sky One (general family entertainment channel); **Sky News** (24-hour news); **Sky Travel** (holiday information); **Sky Soap** (American soaps); **TLC Europe** (home and family interests, DIY, cookery, etc); **Nickelodeon** (children's channel); **Bravo** (classic television); **The Discovery Channel** (adventure, travel, nature, history and technology explored); **CMT Europe** (country music); **TCC** (children's television from around the world); **The Family Channel** (family entertainment); **UK Gold** (vintage BBC and Thames TV programmes); **QVC** (24-hour shopping channel); **UK Living** (women's channel); **MTV** (music television); **VH1** (classic hit music); **The Sci-Fi Channel** (science fiction and fact, fantasy and classic horror); **EBN** (European business news; **Paramount Television** (tv favourites/comedy); **The History Channel**.

NBC Super Channel
4th Floor, 3 Shortlands, Hammersmith, London W6 8BX
☎0181 600 6600   Fax 0181 600 6119
President & Managing Director *Roger L. Ogden*
Director of Programming *Suzette Knittl*

Launched in 1987 and relaunched under NBC ownership in 1993. 24-hour European broadbased news, information and entertainment service in English (with occasional programmes and advertisements in Dutch and German).

UK Living/UK Gold
The Quadrangle, 180 Wardour Street, London W1V 4AE
☎0171 306 6100   Fax 0171 306 6101
Chief Executive *Bruce Steinberg*
Programme Director, UK Living *Liz Howell*
Programme Director, UK Gold *Steve Ireland*

UK Living broadcasts from 6.00 am to midnight daily. Women's magazine programmes, gameshows, soaps and films. UK Gold broadcasts from 6.00 am to 2.00 am daily. Vintage drama and light entertainment programmes.

National and Regional Radio

BBC and Independent

BBC Radio

Broadcasting House, London W1A 1AA
☎0171 580 4468   Fax 0171 636 9786

Managing Director, Network Radio *To be appointed*
Controller, Radio 1 *Matthew Bannister*
Controller, Radio 2 *James Moir*
Controller, Radio 3 *Nicholas Kenyon*
Controller, Radio 4 *Michael Green*
Controller, Radio 5 Live *Jenny Abramsky*

Radio output for religious and educational broadcasting comes under the aegis of separate directorates established to handle both TV and radio output in these areas. See entries **BBC Religious Broadcasting** and **BBC Educational Directorate** (incorporating Schools Programmes and Education for Adults) under **BBC Television**. It is anticipated that the Education for Adults series *Writers Weekly*, produced by Clare Csonka, will be broadcast in the autumn. Radio 1 is the popular music-based station. Radio 2 broadcasts popular light entertainment with celebrity presenters. Radio 3 is devoted mainly to classical and contemporary music, while Radio 4 is the main news and current affairs station. It broadcasts a wide range of other programmes such as consumer matters, wildlife, science, gardening, etc., and produces the bulk of drama, comedy, serials and readings. Radio 5 Live, which won the 1996 Sony Radio Award for UK Station of the Year, is the 24-hour news and sport station which replaced Radio 5 in March 1994.

DRAMA

Head of Drama, Network Radio *Caroline Raphael*
Editor, Single Plays & Readings *Jeremy Mortimer*
Editor, Series & Serials *Marilyn Imrie*
Editor, Readings *Paul Kent*

Caroline Raphael, Head of Drama reports that they are 'keen to commission more comedy, more women and more work from writers from ethnic minorities in both the play and serial slots.' Writers interested in dramatising extant work should always check with the chief producer of Series and Serials to ensure that it has not already been done, or is not already being considered.

All mss should be sent to the appropriate chief producer of either Single Plays or Series & Serials, or to the editor of Readings. The response time is approximately 3–4 months. Plays are commissioned twice a year as part of a commissioning cycle. Drama slots include: *Classic Serial; Playhouse; The Monday Play; Thursday Afternoon Play; Thirty Minute Play; Saturday Playhouse; Book at Bedtime; The Late Book; The Archers.* Plays for Radio 4 take about one year – eighteen months to reach production though the schedules remain flexible enough to allow for adjustments. Radio 3 is mainly committed to classics and new works from established writers.

LIGHT ENTERTAINMENT & COMEDY

Head of Light Entertainment *Jonathan James-Moore*
Script Editor *Paul Schlesinger*

Virtually every comic talent in Britain got their first break writing one-liners for topical comedy weeklies like Radio 4's *Week Ending* and Radio 2's *The News Huddlines* (currently paying about £8 for a 'quickie' - one- or two-liners - and £20 per minute for a sketch - but these are usually commissioned). Comedy writers say it is easier to get a radio pilot launched than a TV pilot, but then TV pays ten times as much as radio. Ideas welcome. Regular programmes include *The News Quiz; Just a Minute; I'm Sorry I Haven't a Clue; The Movie Quiz; Brain of Britain; King Street Junior* (comedy drama); *Quote ... Unquote.*

SPORT & OUTSIDE BROADCASTS

Head of Sport & Outside Broadcasts *Bob Shennan*
Sports Editor *Andy Gilles*

Sports news and commentaries across Radio 1, 4 and 5 Live, with the majority of output on Radio 5 Live (regular programmes include *Sports Report* and *6-0-6* (presented by David Mellor).

MAGAZINE PROGRAMMES

Head of Magazine Programmes *Dave Stanford*
Editor, Factual Entertainment *Ian Gardhouse*
Editor, Face the Facts *Graham Ellis*
Editor, You and Yours *Huw Marks*
Joint Editors, Woman's Hour *Clare Selerie, Sally Feldman*

Regular programmes include *Midweek; You and Yours; Face the Facts; Call Nick Ross; The Food*

Programme; Desert Island Discs; Any Questions.
There are also programmes for the handicapped:
Does He Take Sugar?; and for the blind: *In Touch.*
Contributions to existing series considered.

ARTS, SCIENCE & FEATURES
Head of Arts, Science & Features *Anne
Winder*
Editor, Arts *John Boundy*
Editor, Documentary Features *Richard
Bannerman*
Editor, Topical Features *Sharon Banoff*
Editor, Science *Deborah Cohen*

Incorporates Radio 3's *Nightwaves;* *Blue Skies*;
Radio 4's *Pick of the Week; Kaleidoscope* (arts
review and features); *Medicine Now; Science Now,*
and Radio 5 Live's *Gut Reaction; Chain Reaction*
and *Acid Test.* Written ideas for 20-minute talks
or 45-minute documentaries welcome.

MUSIC
Head of Radio 3 Music *Dr John Evans*
Head of Radio 2 Music *Bill Morris*
Head of Radio 1 Music *Trevor Dann*

Regular programmes include *Music in Mind;
Composer of the Week; In Tune* (music, arts,
interviews); *Impressions* (jazz magazine).

BBC News and Current Affairs
(Radio)

Broadcasting House, London W1A 1AA
☎0171 580 4468

Managing Director, Radio & Television
Tony Hall
**Head of News Programmes, News &
Current Affairs** *Peter Bell*
**Head of Political Programmes, News &
Current Affairs** *Samir Shah*
Head of News Gathering *Chris Carner*
Editor, Radio News Programmes *Steve
Mitchell*
Editor, General News Service *Dave Dunford*
Foreign Editor *Vin Ray*
Home Editors *Nikki Clarke, Peter Mayne*

BBC Radio news and current affairs broadcasting comes under the aegis of BBC News &
Current Affairs, a directorate established in
1987 to unify news and current affairs across
both radio and television.

PROGRAMME EDITORS
Today *Roger Mosey*
**The World at One/The World This
Weekend** *Kevin Marsh*
PM *Margaret Budy*
The World Tonight *Anne Koch*
Editor, Radio 1 News *Ian Parkinson*

Deputy Head of Weekly Programmes
Anne Sloman

Contributions from outside writers to existing
series welcome.

BBC World Service

PO Box 76, Bush House, Strand, London
WC2B 4PH
☎0171 240 3456   Fax 0171 379 6729
Managing Director *Sam Younger*
**Editor, World Service News & Current
Affairs** *Bob Jobbins*
Head, English Programmes *Alastair Lack*

The World Service broadcasts in English and 41
other languages (Macedonian is the latest to be
added to the list). The English service is round-
the-clock, with news and current affairs as the
main component. The BBC World Service is
financed by a grant-in-aid voted by Parliament
and by Foreign and Commonwealth Office contracts for services, amounting to around £178
million for 1996/97. With 140 million regular
listeners, excluding any estimate for countries
where research has not been possible, it reaches a
bigger audience than its five closest competitors
combined. Coverage includes world business,
politics, people/events/opinions, topical and
development issues, the international scene,
developments in science, technology and medicine, health matters, farming, sport, religion,
music, the media, the arts. Regular Sunday programmes include *Play of the Week* (classic/con-
temporary drama) and *Short Story* (unpublished
stories by listeners living outside Britain).

If you have an idea for a feature programme
or series, please direct your query in the first
instance to: Radio News Features (0171 257
2203) or Radio Arts Features (0171 257 2961).

BBC Radio Nan Gaidheal
See **BBC Radio Scotland**

BBC Radio Northern Ireland

Broadcasting House, 25–27 Ormeau Avenue,
Belfast BT2 8HQ
☎01232 338000

Controller, Northern Ireland *Patrick Loughrey*
Senior Producer, Radio Drama *Pam Brighton*
Editor, Current Affairs *Andrew Colman*

Local stations: Radio Foyle and Radio Ulster
(see **Local Radio**).

BBC Radio Scotland

Broadcasting House, Queen Margaret Drive,
Glasgow G12 8DG
☎0141 338 8844

Broadcasting House, 5 Queen Street,
Edinburgh EH2 1JF
☎0131 469 4200
Broadcasting House, Beechgrove Terrace,
Aberdeen AB9 2ZT
☎01224 625233
Broadcasting House, Inverness, 7 Culduthel
Road, Inverness IV2 4AD
☎01463 221711
Controller, Scotland *John McCormick*
Head of Radio *James Boyle*
Editor, News *Robin Wyllie*
Editor, Glasgow *Neil Fraser*
Editor, Edinburgh *Allan Jack*
Editor, Aberdeen *Andrew Jones*
Editor, Radio Nan Gaidheal *Ishbel MacLennan*
Editor, Programme Development *Mike
Shaw*
Senior Producer, Drama *Hamish Wilson*
Editor, Sport *Douglas Wernham*

Produces a full range of news and current affairs
programmes, plus comedy, documentaries,
drama, short stories, talks and features. The emphasis is on speech-based programmes, reflecting
Scottish culture. BBC Radio Scotland provides a
national radio service, primarily from its centres
in Glasgow, Edinburgh, Inverness and Aberdeen, and represents Scottish culture in the UK.
Radio Nan Gaidheal, the Gaelic radio service,
broadcasts about 32 hours per week and is used
at both national and regional levels. The main
production centre is at 52 Church Street,
Stornoway, Isle of Lewis PA87 2LS, Tel 01851
705000 (general and youth programmes). Regular programmes broadcast by BBC Radio
Scotland include *Good Morning Scotland; Speaking
Out* (topical); *Travel Time; Mr Anderson's Fine
Tunes* and *Travelling Folk*. Community stations:
Highland, Selkirk, Dumfries, Orkney and Shetland (see **Local Radio**).

BBC Wales

Broadcasting House, Llandaff, Cardiff
CF5 2YQ
☎01222 572888   Fax 01222 552973
Broadcasting House, 32 Alexandra Road,
Swansea, West Glamorgan SA1 5DZ
☎01792 654986   Fax 01792 468194
Broadcasting House, Meirion Road, Bangor,
Gwynedd LL57 2BY
☎01248 370880   Fax: 01248 351443
Controller, Wales *Geraint Talfan Davies*
Head of Programmes (English) *Dai Smith*
Head of Programmes (Welsh) *Gwynn
Pritchard*

Editor, Radio Wales *Nick Evans*
Editor, Radio Cymru *Aled Glynne-Davies*
**Head of News/Current Affairs (TV &
Radio)** *Aled Eurig*

Two national radio services now account for
nearly 200 hours of programmes per week.
Radio Wales transmits a wide mix of output in
the English language, whilst Radio Cymru
broadcasts a comprehensive range of programmes in Welsh. Regular programmes include
Good Morning Wales; Rush Hour and *Bore Nwydd*.

BFBS (British Forces Broadcasting Service)

Bridge House, North Wharf Road, London
W2 1LA
☎0171 724 1234
Controller of Programmes *Charly Lowndes*

Classic FM

Academic House, 24–28 Oval Road, London
NW1 7DQ
☎0171 284 3000   Fax 0171 713 2630
Chief Executive *John Spearman*
Programme Controller *Michael Bukht*
Head of News *Clare Carson*

Classic FM, Britain's first independent national
commercial radio station, started broadcasting
in September 1992. It plays accessible classical
music 24 hours a day and broadcasts news,
weather, travel, business information, charts,
music and book event guides, political/
celebrity/general interest talks, features and
interviews. Classic has gone well beyond its
expectations, attracting 4.7 million listeners a
week.

Talk Radio UK

76 Oxford Street, London W1N 0TR
☎0171 636 1089   Fax 0171 636 1053
Managing Director *Travis Baxter*
Director of Programmes *Jason Bryant*
News Editor *Bob Farrer*

LAUNCHED in February 1995, Talk Radio is
the third national commercial radio station.
Broadcasts 24 hours a day with a mix of news,
opinions, entertainment, weather, traffic and
sport based on studio topical interviews,
celebrity chat and 'the views of the Great
British listening audience'.

Virgin Radio

1 Golden Square, London W1R 4DJ
☎0171 434 1215   Fax 0171 434 1197
Chief Executive *David Campbell*

Managing Director *John Pearson*
Programme Director *Mark Story*

Britain's second national commercial station launched April 1993 whose slogan is 'Classic tracks and today's best music'. Rock and pop from the '60s to the present day with a target audience of 20–45-year-olds.

BBC Local Radio

BBC Regional Broadcasting

Henry Wood House, 3 & 6 Langham Place, London W1A 1AA
☎0171 580 4468

Managing Director *Ronald Neil*

There are 38 local BBC radio stations in England transmitting on FM and medium wave. These present local news, information and entertainment to local audiences and reflect the life of the communities they serve. They have their own newsroom which supplies local bulletins and national news service. Many have specialist producers. A comprehensive list of programmes for each is unavailable and would soon be out of date. For general information on programming, contact the relevant station direct.

BBC Radio Aberdeen
See **BBC Radio Scotland**

BBC Radio Berkshire
See **Thames Valley FM**

BBC Radio Bristol
PO Box 194, Bristol, Avon BS99 7QT
☎0117 9741111   Fax 0117 9732549

Managing Editor *Michael Hapgood*

Wide range of feature material used.

BBC Radio Cambridgeshire
PO Box 96, 104 Hills Road, Cambridge CB2 1LD
☎01223 259696   Fax 01223 460832

Managing Editor *Nigel Dyson*
Assistant Editor, Programmes *Gerald Main*

Short stories are broadcast occasionally. Scripts from listeners within Cambridgeshire are considered but there is no payment.

BBC Radio Cleveland
Broadcasting House, PO Box 95FM, Middlesbrough, Cleveland TS1 5DG
☎01642 225211   Fax 01642 211356

Managing Editor *David Peel*

Assistant Editor *John Ogden*

Material used is almost exclusively local to Cleveland, Co. Durham and North Yorkshire, and written by local writers. Contributions welcome for *House Call* (Saturdays 1.05–2 pm, presented by Bill Hunter). Poetry and the occasional short story are included.

BBC Radio Cornwall
Phoenix Wharf, Truro, Cornwall TR1 1UA
☎01872 75421   Fax 01872 75045

News Editor *Pauline Causey*

On air from 1983 serving Cornwall and the Isles of Scilly. The station broadcasts a news/talk format 18 hours a day on 103.9/95.2 FM. Chris Blount's afternoon programme includes interviews with local authors and arts-related features on Cornish themes.

BBC Coventry & Warwickshire
25 Warwick Road, Coventry CV1 2WR
☎01203 559911   Fax 01203 520080

Managing Editor *Peter Davies*
Senior Editor *Conal O'Donnell*

News, current affairs, public service information and community involvement, relevant to its broadcast area: Coventry and Warwickshire. Occasionally uses the work of local writers, though cannot handle large volumes of unsolicited material. Any material commissioned will need to be strong in local interest and properly geared to broadcasting.

BBC Radio Cumbria
Annetwell Street, Carlisle, Cumbria CA3 8BB
☎01228 592444   Fax 01228 511195

Managing Editor *John Watson*

Few opportunities for writers apart from *Write Now*, a weekly half-hour regional local writing programme, shared with Radio Merseyside, Radio GMR Talk and Radio Lancashire. Contact *Jenny Collins* on 0151-708 5500.

BBC Radio Derby
PO Box 269, Derby DE1 3HL
☎01332 361111   Fax 01332 290794

Managing Editor *Mike Bettison*

News and information (the backbone of the station's output), local sports coverage, daily magazine and phone-ins, minority interest, Asian and West Indian weekly programmes.

BBC Radio Devon
PO Box 5, Broadcasting House, Seymour Road, Plymouth, Devon PL1 1XT
☎01752 260323   Fax 01752 234599

Managing Editor *Bob Bufton*

Short stories – up to 1000 words from local authors only – used weekly on the Sunday afternoon show (2.05-3.30 pm) and on Friday's *Late Night Sou' West* (10.05pm-midnight). Contact *Debbie Peers*.

BBC Radio Scotland (Dumfries)

Elmbank, Lover's Walk, Dumfries DG1 1NZ
☎01387 268008   Fax 01387 252568

News Editor *Willie Johnston*
Senior Producer *Glenn Cooksley*

Previously Radio Solway. The station mainly outputs news bulletins (four daily). Recent changes have seen the station become more of a production centre with programmes being made for Radio Scotland as well as BBC Radio 2 and 5 Live. Freelancers of a high standard, familiar with Radio Scotland, should contact the producer.

BBC Essex

198 New London Road, Chelmsford, Essex CM2 9XB
☎01245 262393   Fax 01245 492983

Managing Editor *Margaret Hyde*

Provides no regular outlets for writers but mounts special projects from time to time; these are well publicised on the air.

BBC Radio Foyle

8 Northland Road, Londonderry BT48 7JT
☎01504 378600   Fax 01504 378666

Station Manager *Jim Sheridan*
News Editor *Poilin Ni Chiarain*
Arts/Book Reviews *Frank Galligan, Stephen Price, Colum Arbuckle*
Features *Michael Bradley, Marie Louise Kerr, Danny Kelly*

Radio Foyle broadcasts about seven hours of original material a day, seven days a week to the north west of Northern Ireland. Other programmes are transmitted simultaneously with Radio Ulster. The output ranges from news, sport, and current affairs to live music recordings and arts reviews. Provides programmes as required for Radio Ulster and the national networks and also provides television input to nightly BBC NI News Magazine programme.

BBC Radio Gloucestershire

London Road, Gloucester GL1 1SW
☎01452 308585   Fax 01452 306541

Managing Editor *To be appointed*

News and information covering the large variety of interests and concerns in Gloucester-shire. Leisure, sport and music, plus African-Caribbean and Asian interests. Short stories encouraged from local authors. Mss should last 5-6 minutes on air and should be sent to the Managing Editor.

BBC GLR

PO Box 94.9, 35c Marylebone High Street, London W1A 4LG
☎0171 224 2424   Fax 0171 487 2908

Managing Editor *Steve Panton*
Acting Assistant Editor (News) *Martin Shaw*
Assistant Editor (General Programmes) *Jude Howells*

Greater London Radio was launched in 1988. It broadcasts news, information, travel bulletins, sport and rock music to Greater London and the Home Counties.

BBC GMR Talk

PO Box 951, Manchester M60 1SD
☎0161 200 2000   Fax 0161 228 6110 (admin)

Managing Editor *Karen Hannah*
Contacts *Alison Butterworth, Sally Wheatman*

Programmes of interest to writers are: *GM Arts*, a weekly arts and events programme on a Thursday evening, 6.30-7.30pm; and James H. Reeve's afternoon programme, Monday to Friday 1.00pm to 4.00pm, includes coverage of leisure, entertainment and arts. *Write Now*, a weekly half-hour regional local writing programme is shared with Radio Merseyside, Radio Cumbria and Radio Lancashire. Contact *Jenny Collins* on 0151-708 5500. GMR Talk is predominately a talk station and often carries interviews with new, as well as established, local writers.

BBC Radio Guernsey

Commerce House, Les Banques, St Peter Port, Guernsey, Channel Islands GY1 2HS
☎01481 728977   Fax 01481 713557

Managing Editor *Bob Lloyd-Smith*

BBC Hereford & Worcester

Hylton Road, Worcester WR2 5WW
☎01905 748485   Fax 01905 748006

Also at: 43 Broad Street, Hereford HR4 9HH
Tel 01432 355252 Fax 01432 356446
Managing Editor *Eve Turner*
Senior Producer (Programme) *Denzil Dudley*

Interested in short stories, plays or dramatised documentaries with a local flavour.

BBC Radio Scotland (Highland)

Broadcasting House, 7 Culduthel Road,
Inverness IV2 4AD
☎01463 720720   Fax 01463 236125

Station Manager *Ishbel MacLennan*

Also see **BBC Radio Scotland**.

BBC Radio Humberside

9 Chapel Street, Hull, North Humberside
HU1 3NU
☎01482 323232   Fax 01482 226409

Managing Editor *John Lilley*
Assistant Editor *Barry Stephenson*

Occasionally broadcasts short stories by local
writers and holds competitions for local amateur authors and playwrights.

BBC Radio Jersey

18 Parade Road, St Helier, Jersey, Channel
Islands JE2 3PL
☎01534 870000   Fax 01534 832569

Station Manager *Bob Lloyd-Smith*
News Editor *Cathy Kier*

Local news, current affairs and community
items.

BBC Radio Kent

Sun Pier, Chatham, Kent ME4 4EZ
☎01634 830505   Fax 01634 830573

Managing Editor *David Farwig*

Occasional commissions are made for local interest documentaries and other one-off programmes.

BBC Radio Lancashire

Darwen Street, Blackburn, Lancashire
BB2 2EA
☎01254 262411   Fax 01254 680821

Managing Editor *Steve Taylor*

Journalism-based radio station, interested in
interviews with local writers. Also *Write Now*, a
weekly half-hour regional local writing programme, shared with Radio Cumbria, Radio
Merseyside and Radio GMR Talk. Contact
Jenny Collins on 0151-708 5500.

BBC Radio Leeds

Broadcasting House, Woodhouse Lane, Leeds,
West Yorkshire LS2 9PN
☎0113 2442131   Fax 0113 2420652

Acting Managing Editor *Ashley Peatfield*

One of the country's biggest local radio stations,
BBC Radio Leeds was also one of the first, coming on air in the 1960s as something of an experi-

mental venture. The emphasis is on speech, with
a comprehensive news, sport and information
service as the backbone of its daily output.

BBC Radio Leicester

Epic House, Charles Street, Leicester LE1 3SH
☎0116 2516688 Fax 0116 2513632 (Management)/2511463 (News)

Managing Editor *Liam McCarthy*
Station Manager *Jeremy Robinson*

The first local station in Britain. Concentrates
on speech-based programmes in the morning
and on a music/speech mix in the afternoon.
Leicester runs a second station (on AM) for the
large Asian community.

BBC Radio Lincolnshire

PO Box 219, Newport, Lincoln LN1 3XY
☎01522 511411   Fax 01522 511726

Managing Editor *David Wilkinson*
Assistant Editor *Mike Curtis*

Unsolicited material considered only if locally
relevant. Maximum 1000 words: straight narrative preferred, ideally with a topical content.

BBC Radio Manchester

See **BBC GMR Talk**

BBC Radio Merseyside

55 Paradise Street, Liverpool L1 3BP
☎0151 708 5500   Fax 0151 794 0988

Acting Managing Editor *Mick Ord*

Write Now, a weekly 25-minute regional writers'
programme, is produced at Radio Merseyside
and also broadcast on BBC Radio Cumbria,
Radio GMR Talk and Radio Lancashire. Short
stories (maximum 1200 words), plus poetry and
features on writing. Contact *Jenny Collins* on
0151-708 5500.

BBC Radio Newcastle

Broadcasting Centre, Newcastle upon Tyne
NE99 1RN
☎0191 232 4141   Fax 0191 232 5082

Station Manager *Tony Fish*
Assistant Editor *Andrew Hartley*

'We welcome short stories of about 10 minutes
duration for consideration for broadcast in our
afternoon programme. We are *only* interested
in stories by local writers.' Afternoon programme producer: *Sarah Miller*.

BBC Radio Norfolk

Norfolk Tower, Surrey Street, Norwich,
Norfolk NR1 3PA
☎01603 617411   Fax 01603 633692

Assistant Editors *Jill Bennett, David Clayton*

Good local material welcome for features/documentaries, but must relate directly to Norfolk.

BBC Radio Northampton

Broadcasting House, Abington Street,
Northampton NN1 2BH
☎01604 239100   Fax 01604 230709

Managing Editor *Claire Paul*
Assistant Editor *Mike Day*

No literary outlets although books of local interest are reviewed on air occasionally.

BBC Radio Nottingham

PO Box 222, Nottingham NG1 3HZ
☎0115 9550500   Fax 0115 9550501

Editor, News & Programmes *Peter Hagan*
Assistant Editors *Nick Brunger, Paula Boys-Stones*

Rarely broadcasts scripted pieces of any kind but interviews with authors form a regular part of the station's output.

BBC Radio Scotland (Orkney)

Castle Street, Kirkwall KW15 1DF
☎01856 873939   Fax 01856 872908

Senior Producer *John Fergusson*

Regular programmes include *Around Orkney; Farmyard Impressions; Moot Point.*

BBC Radio Oxford

See **Thames Valley FM**

BBC Radio Scotland (Selkirk)

Municipal Buildings, High Street, Selkirk
TD7 4BU
☎01750 21884   Fax 01750 22400

Senior Producer *Carol Wightman*

Formerly BBC Radio Borders. Produces weekly travel and holiday programme *The Case for Packing.*

BBC Radio Sheffield

60 Westbourne Road, Sheffield S10 2QU
☎0114 2686185   Fax 0114 2664375

Managing Editor *Barry Stockdale*
Assistant Editor *Everard Davy*

During the early part of 1995, Radio Sheffield broadcast a series of short stories by writers in Yorkshire and Humberside.

BBC Radio Scotland (Shetland)

Brentham House, Lerwick, Shetland ZE1 0LR
☎01595 694747   Fax 01595 694307

Senior Producer *Mary Blance*

Regular programmes include *Good Evening Shetland.*

BBC Radio Shropshire

2-4 Boscobel Drive, Shrewsbury, Shropshire
SY1 3TT
☎01743 248484   Fax 01743 271702

Managing Editor *Barbara Taylor*
Assistant Editor *Eric Smith*

Unsolicited literary material very rarely used, and then only if locally relevant.

BBC Radio Solent

Broadcasting House, Havelock Road,
Southampton, Hampshire SO14 7PW
☎01703 631311   Fax 01703 339648

Managing Editor *Chris Van Schaick*

BBC (Radio) Somerset Sound

14 Paul Street, Taunton, Somerset TA1 3PF
☎01823 252437   Fax 01823 332539

Senior Producer *Richard Austin*

Informal, speech-based programming, with strong news and current affairs output and regular local-interest features, including local writing. Poetry and short stories on *Sheelagh Leigh-Ewers* programme.

BBC Southern Counties Radio

Broadcasting Centre, Guildford, Surrey
GU2 5AP
☎01483 306306   Fax 01483 304952

Managing Editor *Mark Thomas*
Senior Producer, Newsgathering *Roger Mahony*

Formerly known as BBC Radio Sussex and Surrey.

BBC Radio Stoke

Cheapside, Hanley, Stoke on Trent,
Staffordshire ST1 1JJ
☎01782 208080   Fax 01782 289115

Managing Editor *To be appointed*
Assistant Editors *Mervyn Gamage, Chris Ramsden*

Emphasis on news, current affairs and local topics. Music represents one third of total output. Unsolicited material of local interest is welcome – send to an assistant editor.

BBC Radio Suffolk

Broadcasting House, St Matthews Street,
Ipswich, Suffolk IP1 3EP
☎01473 250000   Fax 01473 210887

Managing Editor *Ivan Howlett*

Assistant Editors *Kevin Burch*

Strongly speech-based, dealing with news, current affairs, community issues, the arts, agriculture, commerce, travel, sport and leisure. Programmes often carry interviews with writers.

BBC Radio Sussex and Surrey
See **BBC Southern Counties Radio**

Thames Valley FM
269 Banbury Road, Oxford OX2 7DW
☎01865 311444   Fax 01865 311996
Managing Editor *Steve Egginton*

Formed from a merger of BBC Radio Berkshire and BBC Radio Oxford. No opportunities at present as the outlet for short stories has been discontinued for the time being.

BBC Three Counties Radio
PO Box 3CR, Hastings Street, Luton,
Bedfordshire LU1 5XL
☎01582 441000   Fax 01582 401467
Managing Editor *David Robey*
Assistant Editor *Jeff Winston*

Encourages freelance contributions from the community across a wide range of radio output, including interview and feature material. The station *very* occasionally broadcasts drama. Stringent local criteria are applied in selection. Particularly interested in historical topics (five minutes maximum).

BBC Radio Ulster
Broadcasting House, Ormeau Avenue, Belfast
BT2 8HQ
☎01232 338000   Fax 01232 338800
Head of Programmes *Anna Carragher*
Senior Producer, Radio Drama *Pam Brighton*

Programmes broadcast from 6.30 am–midnight weekdays and from 8.00 am–midnight at weekends. Radio Ulster has won six Sony awards in recent years. Programmes include: *Good Morning Ulster, Gerry Anderson, Talkback, All Arts and Parts, Inside Politics.*

BBC Radio Wales in Clwyd
The Old School House, Glanrafon Road,
Mold, Clwyd CH7 1PA
☎01352 700367   Fax 01352 759821
Senior Broadcast Journalist *Tracy Cardwell*
Producers, Factual Programmes *Gavin McCarthy, Jane Morris*

Broadcasts regular news bulletins Monday to Friday and until lunchtime on Saturday, and *Borderlines Magazine*, produced by Jane Morris, a network programme on Wednesday afternoons (2–3pm).

BBC Radio WCR
See **BBC Radio WM/WCR**

BBC Wiltshire Sound
Broadcasting House, Prospect Place, Swindon,
Wiltshire SN1 3RW
☎01793 513626   Fax 01793 513650
Managing Editor *Sandy Milne*

Regular programmes include: *Wake Up Wiltshire; Wiltshire Today; Wiltshire at One.*

BBC Radio WM/WCR
PO Box 206, Birmingham B5 7SD
☎0121 414 8484   Fax 0121 472 3174
Managing Editor *Peter Davies*
Senior Producer, Programmes *Tony Wadsworth*

This is a news and current affairs station with no interest in short stories or plays.

BBC Radio York
20 Bootham Row, York YO3 7BR
☎01904 641351   Fax 01904 610937
Managing Editor *Geoff Sargieson*
Assistant Editor *Jane Sampson*

A daily outlet for short stories, provided they are either set locally (i.e. North Yorkshire) or have some other local relevance.

Independent Local Radio

Amber Radio
PO Box 4000, Norwich, Norfolk
NR3 1DB
☎01603 630621   Fax 01603 666353

Part of East Anglian Radio plc. Broadcasts classic songs and easy listening; national and local news.

96.3 Aire FM/Magic 828
PO Box 2000, 51 Burley Road, Leeds, West
Yorkshire LS3 1LR
☎0113 2452299   Fax 0113 2421830
Programme Director *Jim Hicks*

Music-based programming. 96.3 Aire FM caters for the 15-40-year-old listener while Magic 828 aims at the 35-55 age group with classic oldies of the sixties and seventies.

Beacon Radio/WABC

267 Tettenhall Road, Wolverhampton,
West Midlands WV6 0DQ
☎01902 757211   Fax 01902 745456

Programme Director, Beacon Radio *Peter Wagstaff*

Programme Director, WABC *Dave Myatt*

No outlets for unsolicited literary material at present.

Radio Borders

Tweedside Park, Tweedbank, Galashiels
TD1 3TD
☎01896 759444   Fax 01896 759494

Programme Controller *Rod Webster*
Head of News *Craig Williams*

Breeze

See **Essex FM**

Radio Broadland

St Georges Plain, 47-49 Colegate, Norwich,
Norfolk NR3 1DB
☎01603 630621   Fax 01603 666252

Programme Director *Mike Stewart*

Part of East Anglian Radio plc. Popular music programmes only.

96.4 BRMB-FM/ 1152 XTRA-AM

Radio House, Aston Road North,
Birmingham B6 4BX
☎0121 359 4481   Fax 0121 359 1117

Programme Controller, BRMB *Francis Currie*
Programme Controller, XTRA *Steve Marsh*
News Editor *Nicole Pullman*

Music-based stations; no outlets for writers.

Brunel Classic Gold/ GWR FM (West)

PO Box 2020, Bristol, Avon BS99 7SN
☎0117 9843201   Fax 0117 9843202

GWR FM (West): PO Box 2000, Bristol BS99 7SN ☎0117 9843200 Fax 0117 9843202

Programme Controller, Brunel Classic Gold *Jana Rangooni*
Programme Controller, GWR FM (West) *Dirk Antony*

Very few opportunities. Almost all material originates in-house. Part of the GWR Group plc.

Capital FM/Capital Gold

Euston Tower, London NW1 3DR
☎0171 608 6080   Fax 0171 387 2345

Head of News & Talks *David Hedges*

Britain's largest commercial radio station. Main outlet is news and showbiz programme each weekday evening at 7 pm called *The Way It Is*. This covers current affairs, showbiz, features and pop news, aimed at a young audience. The vast majority of material is generated in-house.

Central FM

PO Box 103, Stirling FK7 7JY
☎01786 451188   Fax 01786 461883

Managing Director *Grant Millard*

Broadcasts music, sport and local news to Central Scotland 24 hours a day.

Century Radio

Century House, PO Box 100, Church Street,
Gateshead NE8 2YY
☎0191 477 6666   Fax 0191 477 5660

Programme Controller *John Simons*

Music, talk, news and interviews, 24 hours a day.

CFM

PO Box 964, Carlisle, Cumbria CA1 3NG
☎01228 818964   Fax 01228 819444

Programme Controller *Alex Rowland*
News Editor *Gill Garston*

Music, news and information station.

Cheltenham Radio

Radio House, PO Box 99, Cheltenham,
Gloucestershire GL53 7YX
☎01242 261555   Fax 01242 261666

Programme Controller *Tony Peters*

Music-based programmes, broadcasting 24 hours a day.

Chiltern FM/Chiltern Supergold

Chiltern Road, Dunstable, Bedfordshire
LU6 1HQ
☎01582 666001   Fax 01582 661725

Programme Controller, FM *Mark Collins*
Programme Controller, Supergold *Willie Morgan*

Part of the GWR Group plc. Music-based programmes, broadcasting 24 hours a day.

City FM/Radio City Gold

PO Box 194, 8-10 Stanley Street, Liverpool
L1 6AF
☎0151 227 5100   Fax 0151 471 0330

Managing Director *Lynne Wood*
Programme Controller, City FM *Tony McKenzie*

Programme Controller, City Gold *Gerry Phillips*

Opportunities for writers are very few and far between as this is predominantly a music station.

Radio Clyde/Clyde 1 FM/Clyde 2

Clydebank Business Park, Clydebank G81 2RX
☎0141 306 2272   Fax 0141 306 2265
Director *Alex Dickson, OBE,AE,FIMgt*

Radio Clyde and the IBA, together with **The Society of Authors** and **The Writers' Guild**, launched a major new commissioning scheme for radio drama in 1989. The aim was to create a regular strand of specially produced plays for independent radio stations. Members of the Society or Guild were asked to submit outlines for previously unsubmitted work towards a one-hour production for radio - preference for contemporary themes, and no special emphasis on Scottish works. Accepted outlines led to full-length script commissions for production at Radio Clyde's drama department. Few opportunities outside of this now as programmes usually originate in-house or by commission. All documentary material is made in-house. Good local news items always considered.

Coast FM

41 Conwy Road, Colwyn Bay, Clwyd LL28 5AB
☎01492 534555   Fax 01492 534248
Programme Director *Terry Underhill*
Programme Controller *Kevin Howard*

Programmes include an hour of Welsh language items each weekday. Broadcasts 24 hours a day.

Cool FM

See **Downtown Radio**

Downtown Radio/Cool FM

Newtownards, Co. Down, Northern Ireland BT23 4ES
☎01247 815555   Fax 01247 815252
Programme Head *John Rosborough*

Downtown Radio first ran a highly successful short story competition in 1988, attracting over 400 stories. The competition is now an annual event and writers living within the station's transmission area are asked to submit material during the winter and early spring. The competition is promoted in association with Eason Shops. For further information, write to *Derek Ray* at the station.

Essex FM/Breeze

Radio House, Clifftown Road, Southend on Sea, Essex SS1 1SX
☎01702 333711   Fax 01702 345224
Programme Controller, Essex FM/Breeze *Paul Chantler*

No real opportunities for writers' work as such, but will often interview local authors of published books. Contact *Heather Bridge* (Programming Secretary) in the first instance.

Forth FM/Max AM

Forth House, Forth Street, Edinburgh EH1 3LF
☎0131 556 9255   Fax 0131 558 3277
Director of Programming *Tom Steele*
News Editor *David Johnston*

News stories welcome from freelancers. Max AM, launched 1990, is aimed at the 35+ age group. Although music-based, it includes a wide range of specialist general interest programmes.

Fortune 1458

PO Box 1458, Quay West, Trafford Park, Manchester M17 1FL
☎0161 872 1458   Fax 0161 872 0206
Head of Programming *Simon Wynne*

Music-based programmes, 24 hours a day.

Fox FM

Brush House, Pony Road, Cowley, Oxford OX4 2XR
☎01865 871000
Fax 01865 748721/871009 (news)
Managing Director *Phil Angell*
Head of News *Joanne Coburn*

Backed by an impressive list of shareholders including the Blackwell Group of Companies. No outlet for creative writing; however, authors soliciting book reviews should contact *David Freeman* at the station.

Galaxy 101

Broadcast Centre, Portland Square, Bristol, Avon BS2 8RZ
☎0117 9240111   Fax 0117 9245589
Programme Controller *Simon Dennis*

Music and news, 24 hours a day.

GEM AM

29-31 Castle Gate, Nottingham NG1 7AP
☎0115 9527000   Fax 0115 9527003
Station Director *Chris Hughes*

Part of the GWR Group plc. Music and news.

Gemini Radio FM/AM

Hawthorn House, Exeter Business Park,
Exeter, Devon EX1 3QS
☎01392 444444   Fax 01392 444433

Programme Controller (FM) *Kevin Kane*
Programme Controller (AM) *Mike Allen*

Took over the franchise previously held by
DevonAir Radio in January 1995. Part of
Orchard Media Group. Occasional outlets for
poetry and short stories on the AM wavelength.
Contact *Mike Allen*.

Great North Radio (GNR)

See **Metro FM**

Great Yorkshire Gold

900 Herries Road, Sheffield, South Yorkshire
S6 1RH
☎0114 2852121   Fax 0114 2853159

Programme Controller *Paul Carrington*

Music, news and features, 24 hours a day.

GWR FM (East)

PO Box 2000, Swindon, Wiltshire SN4 7EX
☎01793 440300   Fax 01793 440302

Programme Controller *Scott Williams*

Music-based programmes, 24 hours a day. See
also **Brunel Classic Gold/GWR FM (West)**.

Hallam FM

Radio House, 900 Herries Road, Sheffield
S6 1RH
☎0114 2853333   Fax 0114 2853159

Programme Director *Steve King*

Heart FM

1 The Square, 111 Broad Street, Birmingham
B15 1AS
☎0121 626 1007   Fax 0121 696 1007

Managing Director *Phil Riley*
Programme Director *Paul Fairburn*

Commenced broadcasting in September 1994.
Music, regional news and information.

102.7 Hereward FM/Classic Gold 1332 AM

PO Box 225, Queensgate Centre,
Peterborough, Cambridgeshire PE1 1XJ
☎01733 460460   Fax 01733 281445

Programme Controller, Hereward FM
 Adrian Cookes
Programme Controller, Classic Gold *Rob Jones*

Not usually any openings offered to writers as

all material is compiled and presented by in-
house staff.

Horizon Radio

Broadcast Centre, Crownhill, Milton Keynes,
Buckinghamshire MK8 0AB
☎01908 269111   Fax 01908 564893

Programme Controller *Steve Fountain*

Part of the GWR Group plc. Music and news.

Invicta FM/Invicta Supergold

PO Box 100, Whitstable, Kent
CT5 3QX
☎01227 772004   Fax 01227 771558

Programme Controller *Sandy Beech*

Music-based station, serving listeners in the
South East.

Isle of Wight Radio

Dodnor Park, Newport, Isle of Wight
☎01983 822557   Fax 01983 821690

Programme Director *Andy Shier*

Part of the GWR Group plc, Isle of Wight
Radio is the island's only radio station broadcasting local news, music and general entertainment.

Key 103

See **Piccadilly Gold**

Leicester Sound FM

Granville House, Granville Road, Leicester
LE1 7RW
☎0116 2561300   Fax 0116 2561305

Station Director *Carlton Dale*
Programme Controller *Colin Wilsher*
News Editor *Peter Beame*

Predominantly a music station. Very occasionally, unsolicited material of local interest – 'targeted at our particular audience' – may be
broadcast.

London News 97.3 FM/ London News Talk 1152 AM

72 Hammersmith Road, London
W14 8YE
☎0171 973 1152   Fax 0171 371 2199

Programme Director (FM) *Nick Wheeler*
Programme Director (AM) *Charles Golding*

Took over from LBC early in October 1994.
London News 97.3 FM – 24-hour rolling news
station; London News Talk 1152 AM – phone-
in and conversation station.

Magic 828

See **96.3 Aire FM**

Marcher Gold

Marcher Sound Ltd., The Studios, Mold Road, Wrexham, Clwyd LL11 4AF
☎01978 752202   Fax 01978 759701

Programme Controller *Kevin Howard*

Occasional features and advisory programmes. Hour-long Welsh language broadcasts are aired weekdays at 6.00 pm.

Max AM

See **Forth FM**

Mercia FM/Mercia Classic Gold

Mercia Sound Ltd., Hertford Place, Coventry CV1 3TT
☎01203 868200   Fax 01203 868202

Station Director *Ian Rufus*
Programme Controller *Steve Dawson*

Mercury FM/Mercury Extra AM

Broadfield House, Brighton Road, Crawley, West Sussex RH11 9TT
☎01293 519161   Fax 01293 560927

Programme Controller *John Brocks*

Mercury FM is predominantly music. Mercury Extra AM broadcasts 50% music, 50% speech.

Metro FM/
Great North Radio (GNR)

Swalwell, Newcastle upon Tyne NE99 1BB
☎0191 420 0971 (Metro)/420 3040 (GNR)
Fax 0191 488 9222

Programme Director, Metro *Giles Squire*
Programme Controller, GNR *Jim Brown*

Very few opportunities for writers, but phone-in programmes may interview relevant authors.

Moray Firth Radio

PO Box 271, Scorgvie Place, Inverness IV3 6SF
☎01463 224433   Fax 01463 243224

Programme Controller *Thomas Prag*
Book Reviews *May Marshall*

Book reviews every Monday afternoon at 2.20 pm. Also fortnightly arts programme called *The North Bank Show* which features interviews with authors, etc.

Northants FM/Supergold

Broadcast Centre, The Enterprise Park, Broughton Green Road, Northampton NN1 2HW
☎01604 792411   Fax 01604 721934

Programme Controller *Terry Doyle*

Music and news, 24 hours a day.

NorthSound Radio

45 King's Gate, Aberdeen AB2 6BL
☎01224 632234   Fax 01224 633282

Programme Controller *Fiona Stalker*

Features and music programmes 24 hours a day.

Ocean FM/South Coast Radio

Whittle Avenue, Segensworth West, Fareham, Hampshire PO15 5PA
☎01489 589911   Fax 01489 589453

Programme Controller *Steve Power*
News Editor *Karen Woods*

Music-based programming only.

Orchard FM

Haygrove House, Shoreditch, Taunton, Somerset TA3 7BT
☎01823 338448   Fax 01823 321044

Programme Controller *Phil Easton*
News Editor *Lyndsey Ashwood*.

Music-based programming only.

Piccadilly Gold/Key 103

127–131 The Piazza, Piccadilly Plaza, Manchester M1 4AW
☎0161 236 9913   Fax 0161 228 1503

Programme Director *John Dash*

Music-based programming only.

Plymouth Sound FM/AM

Earl's Acre, Alma Road, Plymouth, Devon PL3 4HX
☎01752 227272   Fax 01752 670730

Programme Controllers *Allen Fleckney*(FM), *Peter Greig* (AM)

Music-based station. No outlets for writers.

Premier Radio

Glen House, Stag Place, London SW1E 5AG
☎0171 233 6705   Fax 0171 233 6706

Head of Programming *Shane Huntley*

Formerly London Christian Radio. Broadcasts programmes that reflect the beliefs and values of the Christian faith 24 hours a day.

The Pulse

Forster Square, Bradford, West Yorkshire BD1 5NE
☎01274 731521   Fax 01274 307774

Programme Director *Steve Martin*

The Pulse broadcasts news on the hour and a late night phone-in, but is principally a music-based station. Provides the **Great Yorkshire Gold** service on its AM transmitters (see entry).

Q103.FM
PO Box 103, Vision Park, Chivers Way,
Histon, Cambridge CB4 4WW
☎01223 235255   Fax 01223 235161
Station Director *Alistair Wayne*
Part of GWR Group plc. Music and news.

RAM FM
Market Place, Derby DE1 3AA
☎01332 292945   Fax 01332 292229
Programme Controller *Dick Stone*
Part of the GWR Group plc. Music-programming only.

Red Dragon FM/Touch AM
Radio House, West Canal Wharf, Cardiff
CF1 5XJ
☎01222 384041   Fax 01222 384014
Programme Controller *Phil Roberts*
News Editor *Andrew Jones*
Music-based programming only.

Red Rose Gold/Rock FM
PO Box 301, St Paul's Square, Preston,
Lancashire PR1 1YE
☎01772 556301   Fax 01772 201917
Programme Director *Mark Matthews*
Music-based stations. No outlets for writers.

Sabras Sound
Radio House, 63 Melton Road, Leicester
LE4 6PN
☎0116 2610666   Fax 0116 2667776
Programme Controller *Don Kotak*
Programmes for the Asian community, broadcasting 24 hours a day.

Scot FM
Number 1 Shed, Albert Quay, Leith,
Edinburgh EH6 7DN
☎0131 554 6677   Fax 0131 554 2266
Also at: Anderston Quay, Glasgow G3 8DA
☎0141 204 1003 Fax 0141 204 1067
Managing Director *Bob Christie*
Head of Talk *Ken McRobb*
Commenced broadcasting in September 1994 to the central Scottish region. Music and talk shows, sport and phone-ins.

Severn Sound FM/
Severn Sound Supergold
67 Southgate Street, Gloucester GL1 2DQ
☎01452 423791
Fax 01452 529446/423008 (news)

Station Director *Penny Holton*
Programme Controller *Andy Westgate*
Part of the GWR Group plc. Music and news.

SGR FM 97.1/96.4
Alpha Business Park, Whitehouse Road,
Ipswich, Suffolk IP1 5LT
☎01473 461000   Fax 01473 741200
Programme Director *Mike Stewart*
Head of Presentation *Mark Pryke*
Features Producer *Nigel Rennie*

Signal Cheshire
Regent House, 1st Floor, Heaton Lane,
Stockport, Cheshire SK4 1BX
☎0161 480 5445   Fax 0161 474 1806
Programme Director *John Evington*
Programme Co-ordinator *Neil Cossar*
Strong local flavour to programmes. Part of the Signal Network.

Signal One/Signal Gold/Signal Stafford
Studio 257, Stoke Road, Stoke on Trent,
Staffordshire ST4 2SR
☎01782 747047   Fax 01782 744110
Programme Director *John Evington*
Head of News *Paul Sheldon*
Music-based station. No outlets for writers. Part of the Signal Network.

Sound Wave
See **Swansea Sound 1170 M/Wave**

South Coast Radio
See **Ocean FM**

South West Sound FM
See **West Sound Radio**

Southern FM
PO Box 2000, Brighton, East Sussex BN41 2SS
☎01273 430111   Fax 01273 430098
Programme Controller *Steve Power*
News Manager *Phil Bell*
Music, news, entertainment and competitions.

Spectrum International
Endeavour House, Brent Cross, London
NW2 1JT
☎0181 905 5000   Fax 0181 209 1029
Managing Director *Wolfgang Bucci*
Programme Controller *Angela Borgnana*
Minority community programmes across a broad spectrum of groups: Afro-Caribbean, Asian, Arabic, Chinese, Greek, Irish, Italian, Jewish,

Persian, Spanish. Appropriately targeted news/magazine items and book reviews will receive consideration.

Spire FM

City Hall Studios, Malthouse Lane, Salisbury, Wiltshire SP2 7QQ
☎01722 416644   Fax 01722 415102

Station Director *Ian Axton*

Music, news current affairs, quizzes and sport. Won the Sony Award for the best local radio station in 1994.

Sun. City 103.4

PO Box 1034, Sunderland, Tyne & Wear SR1 3YZ
☎0191 567 3333   Fax 0191 567 0777

Station Manager *Bruce Davidson*

Music-based programmes only.

Sunrise FM

Sunrise House, 30 Chapel Street, Bradford, West Yorkshire BD1 5DN
☎01274 735043   Fax 01274 728534

Programme Controller, Chief Executive & Chairman *Usha Parmar*

Programmes for the Asian community in Bradford. Part of the Sunrise Radio Group.

Sunshine 855

South Shropshire Communications Ltd., Sunshine House, Waterside, Ludlow, Shropshire SY8 1GS
☎01584 873795   Fax 01584 875900

Station Manager & Programme Controller *Mark Edwards*

Music, news and information broadcast 24 hours a day.

Swansea Sound 1170 M/Wave/Sound Wave

Victoria Road, Gowerton, Swansea, West Glamorgan SA4 3AB
☎01792 893751   Fax 01792 898841

Head of Programmes *Rob Pendry*
Head of News *Lynn Courtney*

Interested in a wide variety of material, though news items must be of local relevance. An explanatory letter, in the first instance, is advisable.

Tay FM/Radio Tay AM

Radio Tay Ltd., PO Box 123, Dundee DD1 9UF
☎01382 200800   Fax 01382 593252

Managing Director *Sandy Wilkie*

Programme Director *Ally Ballingall*

Wholly owned subsidiary of Scottish Radio Holdings. Unsolicited material is assessed. Short stories and book reviews of local interest are welcome. Send to the programme controller.

TFM Radio

Yale Crescent, Stockton-on-Tees, Cleveland TS17 6AA
☎01642 615111   Fax 01642 674402

Programme Controller *Graham Ledger*

Music, sport and information, 24 hours a day.

Touch AM

See **Red Dragon FM**

TRENT FM

29-31 Castlegate, Nottingham NG1 7AP
☎0115 9527000   Fax 0115 9527003

Station Director *Chris Hughes*

Part of the GWR Group plc.

2CR-FM (Two Counties Radio)

5-7 Southcote Road, Bournemouth, Dorset BH1 3LR
☎01202 294881   Fax 01202 299314

Programme Controller *Paul Allen*

Wholly owned subsidiary of the GWR Group. Serves Dorset and Hampshire. All reviews/topicality/press releases to The Producer, Morning Crew, 2CRFM at the above address. *The 2CRFM Breakfast Show* focuses on any material that touches the lives of our listeners.

2-Ten FM/Classic Gold 1431

PO Box 210, Reading, Berkshire RG31 7RZ
☎0118 9254400   Fax 0118 9254456

Programme Controller *Andrew Phillips*

A subsidiary of the GWR Group plc. Music-based programming.

Viking FM

Commercial Road, Hull, North Humberside HU1 2SA
☎01482 325141   Fax 01482 218650/587067

Managing Director *Dee Ford*
Programme Controller *Phil White*
News Co-ordinator *Stephen Edwards*
Features Producer *Paul Bromley*

Viva! 963AM

Golden Rose House, 26 Castlereagh Street, London W1H 6DJ
☎0171 706 9963   Fax 0171 706 8585

Managing Director *Richard Wheatly*

Music and speech broadcasting 24 hours a day.

WABC
See **Beacon Radio**

Wessex FM
Radio House, Trinity Street, Dorchester,
Dorset DT1 1DJ
☎01305 250333   Fax 01205 250052

Programme Manager *Roger Kennedy*

Music, local news, information and features.
These include motoring, cooking, reviews of
theatre, cinema, books, videos, local music.
Expert phone-ins on gardening, antiques, pets,
legal matters, DIY and medical issues.

West Sound Radio/
South West Sound FM
Radio House, 54 Holmston Road, Ayr
KA7 3BE
☎01292 283662
Fax 01292 283665/262607 (news)

Programme Controller, News Editor
  Gordon McArthur

Radio Wyvern
PO Box 22, 5-6 Barbourne Terrace,
Worcester WR1 3JZ
☎01905 612212

Managing Director *Norman Bilton*
Programme Controller *Stephanie Denham*

Independent company, not part of any larger
group. *Very* occasionally, a local writer may be
commissioned to produce something of interest to the Wyvern audience.

Radio XL 1296 AM
KMS House, Bradford Street, Birmingham
B12 0JD
☎0121 753 5353   Fax 0121 753 3111

Programme Director *Tony Inchley*

Asian broadcasting for the West Midlands, 24
hours a day.

1152 XTRA-AM
See **96.4 BRMB-FM**

Freelance Rates – Broadcasting

Freelance rates vary enormously. The following guidelines are minimum rates negotiated by the **National Union of Journalists**. Most work can command higher fees from employers whether or not they have NUJ agreements. It is up to freelancers to negotiate the best deal they can.

BBC

Radio News Reports (excluding local radio, including External Services): £38.01 for up to two minutes (domestic news broadcasts) and up to three minutes; £8.50 for each minute thereafter.

Television News Reports (including regional): £46.72 for up to two minutes; £11.55 for each minute thereafter.

Radio (excluding local): £70.35 for up to two minutes; £14.70 for each minute thereafter.

Radio (local): £18.90 for up to two minutes; £6.93 for each minute thereafter.

News Copy: £11.45 (network); £8.50 non–network.

Commissioned Sports Results: £3.15 per result.

Still Photographers (commission rates): £49.88 (half-day); £99.75 (full day).

Still Fees (black and white or colour): £37.17 for a single picture or first picture in a series: second use £18.59; third or subsequent use £12.39. Where a series is provided on the same event: £18.59 for first use of the second picture; £12.39 for first use of third and subsequent use.

Day and half-day rates Category one (reporters in network regional television and radio): £107 a day; £53.55 half-day. Category two (experienced broadcast journalists): £84.53 a day; £42.26 half-day. Category three (junior reporters in local radio): £72.98 a day; £36.49 half-day.

Radio talks and features

Interviews

Up to five minutes:	£48
Five to ten minutes:	negotiable
Ten to fifteen minutes:	£64
Fifteen minutes and over:	negotiable
Script and read:	£18.50 per minute

Script only: £14.40 per minute
Illustrated talks: £14.80 per minute
Linked interviews: one interview £77; two interviews: £100

Features/documentaries
Up to seven minutes: £171.50; £24.50 per minute thereafter.

Talks
Contributions for one national region (Scotland, Wales or Northern Ireland) may be contracted at two-thirds of the rates above.

Independent radio

News Copy Ordered or submitted, and broadcast by the station: £7.64 per item.

News Reports (Voice) For a report or talk on tape or broadcast by a freelancer: £20.62 for first two minutes; £6.87 per minute thereafer. *Day Rates* £71.81 a day (over 4 hours and up to 8); £35.91 half-day (up to 4 hours).

Sports Ordered match coverage, including previews, flashes and summaries: £36.71; ordered calls for running reports and additional telephone fee: £13.87; result only service: £2.99.

Tip offs £7.86 for each tip off supplied and used.

Travelling and out-of-pocket expenses are generally paid.

ITV Association

News
Report or *Talk* Recorded on tape/film, or broadcast: not less than £51.68

Sports Copy Not recorded or broadcast by the freelancer: not less than £12.08, with payment for results only £5.37.

News Copy Not recorded or broadcast by the freelancer: not less than £10.45.

Ordered Assignments Ordered reports or talks shall be paid for even if not used; in such cases the minimum rate shall be paid.

Daily engagements Day rate: £108.15; half-day: £59.85.

Commission fee for photographers to take still photographs For an assignment taking up to a day: £108.15. For an assignment taking up to half a day: £59.85.

The above items do not include travelling and out-of-pocket expenses.

Stills
Black and white and colour: First use: £33.44; second use: £16.12; third and subsequent use: £9.71.

For a series of pictures First use: £70.02; second use: £32.29; third and subsequent use: £21.53. Travel and out-of-pocket expenses shall be paid in addition.
Tip offs £18.27 for each tip off supplied and used.

Research

TV organisations which hire freelancers to research programme items should pay on a day rate which reflects the value of the work and the importance of the programme concerned.

Presentation

In all broadcast media, presenters command higher fees than news journalists. There is considerable variation in what is paid for presenting programmes and videos, according to their audience and importance. Day rates with television companies are usually about £161 a day.

Radio drama

A beginner in radio drama should receive at least £37.82 per minute for a sixty-minute script. For an established writer – one who has three or more plays to his credit – the minimum rate per minute is £57.58.
Fees for dramatisations range from 65–85% of the full drama rate, depending on the degree of original material and dialogue.
An attendance payment of £33.87 per production is paid to established writers.

Television drama

For a sixty-minute teleplay, the BBC will pay an established writer £7170 and a beginner £4551. The corresponding figures for ITV are £8168 for the established writer, £5803 for a writer new to television but with a solid reputation in other literary areas.
Day rates for attendance at read-throughs and rehearsals is £65 for the BBC and £69 for ITV.

Feature films

An agreement between **The Writers' Guild** and **PACT** allows for a minimum guaranteed payment to the writer of £31,200 on a feature film with a budget in excess of £2 million; £19,000 on a budget from £750,000 to £2 million; £14,000 on a budget below £750,000.

Film, TV and Video Producers

Absolutely Productions Ltd
6–7 Fareham Street, London W1V 3AH
☎0171 734 9824　　　Fax 0171 734 8284
Executive Producer *Miles Bullough*

TV and radio production company specialising in comedy and entertainment. OUTPUT *Absolutely* Series 1–4 (Ch4); *mr don and mr george* (Ch4); *Squawkietalkie* (comedy wildlife programme for Ch4); *In Montreal Just for Laughs* (Radio 1 documentary).

Action Time Ltd
Wrendal House, 2 Whitworth Street West, Manchester M1 5WX
☎0161 236 8999　　　Fax 0161 236 8845
Chairman *Stephen Leahy*
Director of Programming *Trish Kinane*

Major producers and licensers of TV quiz and game entertainment shows such as *Body Heat; You've Been Framed; Catchphrase; Backdate; Jeopardy; Spellbound; Raise the Roof; Stars in Their Eyes*. Action Time has co-production partners in Germany, Holland, Ireland, Russia, Spain, Sweden and Wales.

Alomo
See **SelecTV plc**

Amy International Productions
2A Park Avenue, Wraysbury, Middlesex TW19 5ET
☎01784 483131　　　Fax 01784 483812
Contact *Simon MacCorkindale, Susan George*

Makers of drama for film and TV. OUTPUT *Stealing Heaven; That Summer of White Roses; The House that Mary Bought*. In development: *Manimal; Lucan; The Liaison; Such a Long Journey; Dragon Under the Hill*.

Anglia TV Entertainment
48 Leicester Square, London WC2H 7FB
☎0171 389 8555　　　Fax 0171 930 8499
Managing Director *Vernon Lawrence*
Controller of Drama *Simon Lewis*
Head of Drama Development *Sue Hogg*

Television drama. RECENT OUTPUT P. D. James' *A Mind To Murder* (TV movie); Jilly Cooper's *Riders* and *The Man Who Made Husbands Jealous* (both 3-part dramas); P. D. James' *Original Sin* (3-part drama); Agatha Christie's *The Pale Horse* (TV movie).

Antelope (UK) Ltd
2 Bloomsbury Place, London WC1A 2QA
☎0171 209 0099　　　Fax 0171 209 0098
Managing Director *Mick Csáky*
Head of Non-Fiction *Krishan Arora*
Production Manager *Alison Havell*

Film, television and video productions for drama, documentary and corporate material. OUTPUT *The Pier* (weekly arts and entertainment programme); *Placido Domingo* (ITV); *Baden Powell – The Boy Man; Howard Hughes – The Naked Emperor* (Ch4 'Secret Lives' series); *Hiroshima*. No unsolicited mss – 'we are not reading any new material at present'.

Apex Television Production & Facilities Ltd
Button End Studios, Harston, Cambridge CB2 5NX
☎01223 872900　　　Fax 01223 873092
Contact *Bernard Mulhern*

Video producer: drama, documentary, commercials and corporate. Largely corporate production for a wide range of international companies. Many drama-based training programmes and current-affairs orientated TV work. No scripts. All work is commissioned against a particular project.

Arena Films Ltd
2 Pelham Road, London SW19 1SX
☎0181 543 3990　　　Fax 0181 540 3992
Producer *David Conroy*

Film and TV drama. Scripts with some sort of European connection or tie-in particularly welcome. Open-minded with regard to new writing.

AVC Eclipse Ltd
Walters Farm Road, Tonbridge, Kent TN9 1QT
☎01732 365107　　　Fax 01732 362600
Contact *Brian Adams*

Practitioners in audio and visual communications. *Specialises* in corporate videos, conferences, PR events and award ceremonies, safety, sales and marketing, and training.

Humphrey Barclay Productions
See **Essential Film & TV Productions Ltd**

Michael Barratt Ltd
Profile House, 5-7 Forlease Road, Maidenhead, Berkshire SL6 1RP
☎01628 770800   Fax 01628 770144
Contact *Michael Barratt*

Corporate and educational video, and TV programmes. Also a wide range of publishing work including company newspapers, brochures and training manuals. Unsolicited scripts and ideas welcome 'if they are backed by commercial realism – like sources of funding for development. However, straightforward notification of availability, special writing skills, contact addresses, etc, will find a place in the company records'. Also trades as MBL Publishing Ltd.

Bazal Productions
See **Broadcast Communications**

Beckmann Communications Ltd
Britannia House, 1 Glenthorne Road, London W6 0LF
☎0181 748 9898   Fax 0181 748 4250
Contact *David Willoughby*

London office of Isle of Man-based company. Video and television documentary. OUTPUT *Heritage Europe* (travel series); *Maestro* (12-part series on classical composers); *Wars in Peace* (co-production with ITN). One-page proposals considered. No scripts.

Behr Cinematography
22 Redington Road, London NW3 7RG
☎0171 794 2535   Fax 0171 794 2535
Contact *Arnold Behr, Betty Burghes*

Documentary, educational, corporate film and/or video, often for voluntary organisations. No actors, except for voice-overs. No unsolicited mss. S.a.e. appreciated from applicants needing a reply.

Paul Berriff Productions Ltd
The Chestnuts, Woodfield Lane, Hessle, North Humberside HU13 0EW
☎01482 641158   Fax 01482 649692
Contact *Paul Berriff, Janice Kearns*

Television documentary. OUTPUT *Rescue* (13-part documentary for ITV); *M25: The Magic Roundabout* ('First Tuesday'); *Animal Squad*

Undercover (Ch4); *Evidence of Abuse* (BBC1 'Inside Story'); *Lessons of Darkness* (BBC2 'Fine Cut'); *The Nick* (Ch4 series); *Confrontation on E Wing* (BBC 'Everyman').

BFI Production
29 Rathbone Street, London W1P 1AG
☎0171 636 5587   Fax 0171 580 9456
Head of Production *Ben Gibson*

Part of the **British Film Institute**. Produces a range of projects from short films and videos to feature-length films, acting as producer and co-investor. Feature treatments or screenplays are accepted for consideration, generally low-budget and innovative. Unsolicited mss have a two-month turnaround period. OUTPUT includes *Madagascar Skin; Loaded; 3 Steps to Heaven*. Runs a New Directors Scheme (advertised annually).

Martin Bird Productions
Saucelands Barn, Coolham, Horsham, West Sussex RH13 8QG
☎01403 741620   Fax 01403 741647
Contact *Alastair Martin-Bird*

Makers of film and video specialising in programmes covering equestrianism and the countryside. No unsolicited scripts, but always looking for new writers who are fully acquainted with the subject.

Black Coral Productions Ltd
PO Box 33, Woodford Green, Essex IG9 6DB
☎0181 281 0401   Fax 0181 504 3338
Contacts *Lazell Daley, Signet Kirby*

Producers of drama, documentary and corporate material for video and television. Committed to the development of new writing. Runs a monthly television/radio writers' workshop in central London and offers a script evaluation service for which a fee is payable. Runs the following courses: *Writing for TV/Radio Drama - Foundation; Writing for TV Series - Intermediate; Writing for Radio Drama - Intermediate*. TV Intermediate courses carry 50% concessionary places.

Blue Heaven Productions Ltd
45 Leather Lane, London EC1N 7TJ
☎0171 404 4222   Fax 0171 404 4266
Contact *Graham Benson, Christine Benson*

Television drama and documentary. OUTPUT *The Ruth Rendell Mysteries; Crime Story: Dear Roy, Love Gillian; Ready When You Are* (two series for Meridian Regional). Scripts considered but treatments or ideas preferred in the first instance. New writing encouraged.

Bond Clarkson Russell Ltd

16 Trinity Churchyard, Guildford, Surrey
GU1 3RR
☎01483 62888   Fax 01483 302732

Contact *Peter Bond, Chris Russell, Nigel Mengham*

Corporate literature, film, video and multimedia producer of a wide variety of material, including conference videos, for blue-chip companies in the main. No scripts. All work is commissioned.

Matt Boney Associates

Woodside, Holdfast Lane, Grayswood,
Haslemere, Surrey GU27 2EU
☎01428 656178

Contact *Matt Boney*

Writer/director for video and television: commercials, documentaries, skiing and travel. No unsolicited mss.

Box Clever Productions

The Maples Centre, 144 Liverpool Road,
London N1 1LA
☎0171 619 0606   Fax 0171 700 2248

Contact *Claire Walmsley*

Broadcast TV, film and video documentaries, specialising in social and current affairs. Sister company of Boxclever Communication Training, specialising in media interview skills. OUTPUT documentaries for BBC and Ch4; corporate videos for the European Commission, public sector and voluntary organisations. No unsolicited scripts; outlines and proposals only.

British Lion Screen Entertainment Ltd

Pinewood Studios, Iver, Buckinghamshire
SL0 0NH
☎01753 651700   Fax 01753 656391

Chief Executive *Peter R. E. Snell*

Film production. OUTPUT has included *A Man for All Seasons; Treasure Island; Turtle Diary; Lady Jane; The Crucifer of Blood; Death Train.* No unsolicited mss. Send synopses only.

Broadcast Communications

48 Bedford Square, London WC1B 3DP
☎0171 255 2551   Fax 0171 580 8101

Chief Executive *Tom Barnicoat*

Head of Broadcasting *Frances Whitaker*
Head of Corporate *Angela Law*

Television division of *The Guardian Media Group.* One of Britain's largest independent producers, responsible for more than 700 hours of programmes a year, for the BBC, ITV, Channel 4 and BSkyB. It has six programme production companies, all wholly owned. These are: Initial Film and Television; Bazal Productions; Connaught Films; Business Television; Lomond Television; and Hawkshead. OUTPUT spans drama, music, entertainment and factual programmes.

Business Television

See **Broadcast Communications**

Caledonian Television Ltd

Caledonian House, Phoenix Crescent,
Strathclyde Business Park, Strathclyde
ML4 3UJ
☎01698 845522   Fax 01698 845811

Contact *Russell Galbraith, Jock Brown*

Film, video and TV: documentary and corporate. Send preliminary letter in the first instance.

Caravel Film Techniques Ltd

The Great Barn Studios, Cippenham Lane,
Slough, Berkshire SL1 5AU
☎01753 534828   Fax 01753 571383

Contact *Nick See*

Film, video and TV: documentary, commercials and corporate. OUTPUT Promos for commercial TV, documentaries BBC & ITV, sales and training material for corporate blue chip companies. No unsolicited scripts. Prepared to review mostly serious new writing.

Carlton UK Productions

35–38 Portman Square, London W1H 9FH
☎0171 486 6688   Fax 0171 486 1132

Director of Programmes *Andy Allan*
Director of Drama & Co-production
  Jonathan Powell
Controller of Entertainment and Comedy
  John Bishop
Controller of Factual Programmes *Steve Clark*

Makers of independently produced TV drama for ITV. OUTPUT *She's Out; Kavanagh QC; Morse; Boon; Gone to the Dogs; The Guilty; Tanamera; Soldier, Soldier; Seekers; Sharpe; Peak Practice, Cadfael, Faith.* 'We try to use new writers on established long-running series.' Scripts welcome from experienced writers and agents only.

Carnival (Films & Theatre) Ltd

12 Raddington Road, Ladbroke Grove,
London W10 5TG
☎0181 968 0968/1818/1717
Fax 0181 968 0155/0177

Film *Brian Eastman*
Theatre *Andrew Welch*

Film, TV and theatre producers. OUTPUT Film: *Firelight* (Hollywood Pictures/Wind Dancer Productions); *Shadowlands* (Savoy/Spelling); *In Hitler's Shadow* (Home Box Office); *Under Suspicion* (Columbia/Rank/LWT); *Wilt* (Rank/ LWT); *Whoops Apocalypse* (ITC). Television: *Poirot* (LWT); *Bugs* (BBC); *Anna Lee* (LWT); *All or Nothing At All* (LWT); *Head Over Heels* (Carlton); *The Big Battalions* (Ch4); *Jeeves & Wooster* I–IV (Granada); *Traffik* (Ch4); *Forever Green* (LWT); *Porterhouse Blue* (Ch4); *Blott on the Landscape* (BBC). Theatre: *What a Performance; Juno & the Paycock; Murder is Easy; Misery; Ghost Train; Map of the Heart; Shadowlands; Up on the Roof.*

Cartwn Cymru

Screen Centre, Llantrisant Road, Cardiff
CF5 2PH
☎01222 575999   Fax 01222 575919

Contact *Naomi Jones*

Animation production company. OUTPUT *Toucan 'Tecs* (YTV/S4C) for ITV children's network; *Funnybones* (S4C/BBC); *Turandot: the Animated Opera*, operavox series (S4C/BBC). In production: *Moses, Elijah, David* and *Saul in The Old Testament - the animated version; The Jesus Story* (S4C).

Pearl Catlin Associates

Production Centre, The Clock House,
Summersbury Drive, Shalford, Guildford,
Surrey GU4 8JQ
☎01483 567932   Fax 01483 302646

Contact *Pearl Catlin, Peter Yolland, Paul Bernard*

Film and video: drama, documentary, children's, feature films. Interested in creative ideas for all kinds of programmes.

CCC Wadlow Productions Ltd

47 Dean Street, London W1V 5HL
☎0171 287 0833   Fax 0171 434 4278

Head of Productions *Sarah Dent*

Film and video, multimedia and graphic design: corporate and commercials. CLIENTS include Bovis; Camelot; De La Rue plc; Del Monte Foods International; East Midlands Electricity; Hill & Norton; Knowlton; Lloyds of London; Nationwide Building Society; P&O; Saatchi & Saatchi; Samaritans. 'We are very keen to hear from new writers, but please send c.v.s rather than scripts.'

Celador Productions Ltd

39 Long Acre, London WC2E 9JT
☎0171 240 8101   Fax 0171 836 1117

Contact *Paul Smith, Nic Phillips*

Primarily light entertainment programming for all broadcast television and radio channels, including game shows, variety, documentaries and sitcoms. OUTPUT *Talking Telephone Numbers; Everybody's Equal; The Hypnotic World of Paul McKenna; The South Bank Show - Cliff Richard; Schofield's TV Gold* (all for ITV); *Canned Carrott; Carrott's Commercial Breakdown; The Detectives; Auntie's Bloomers; Gibberish; Digging The Dancing Queens* (all for BBC); *Classic Country* (BSB) and Sky TV's London link for the Oscar Awards.

Central Office of Information Film & Video

Hercules Road, London SE1 7DU
☎0171 261 8667   Fax 0171 261 8776

Contact *Geoff Raison*

Film, video and TV: drama, documentary, commercials, corporate and public information films. OUTPUT includes government commercials and corporate information, plus a monthly magazine for overseas use. No scripts. New writing commissioned as required.

Channel X Communications Ltd

First Floor, 22 Stephenson Way, London
NW1 2HD
☎0171 387 3874   Fax 0171 387 0738

Contact *Alan Marke, Mike Bolland*

FOUNDED 1986 by Jonathan Ross and Alan Marke to develop Ross's first series *The Last Resort.* Now producing comedy series and documentary. Actively developing narrative comedy and game shows. OUTPUT *Unpleasant World of Penn & Teller; XYZ; Jo Brand - Through The Cakehole; Sean's Show; The Smell of Reeves & Mortimer; Fantastic Facts; One for the Road; Funny Business; Shooting Stars.*

Charisma Films Ltd

14–15 Vernon Street, London W14 0RJ
☎0171 603 1164   Fax 0171 603 1175

Contact *James Atherton*

Film and TV (limited). Scripts from experienced writers only.

Chatsworth Television Ltd

97-99 Dean Street, London W1V 5RA
☎0171 734 4302   Fax 0171 437 3301
Head of Drama Development *Stephen Jeffrey-Poulter*

Drama and light entertainment TV producers. All unsolicited drama scripts will be considered. Mainly interested in contemporary, factually based or comedy drama material, but *not* sitcoms. S.a.e. must accompany *all* submissions.

Childsplay Productions Ltd

8 Lonsdale Road, London NW6 6RD
☎0171 328 1429   Fax 0171 328 1416
Contact *Kim Burke*

Television: drama, children's (not pre-school) and educational. OUTPUT includes *Streetwise; All Change; Picture Box; Miles Better; Eye of the Storm; Pirates.* Some unsolicited work accepted but *telephone to discuss first.*

Cinexsa Film Productions Ltd

209 Manygate Lane, Shepperton, Middlesex TW17 9ER
☎01932 225950   Fax 01932 225950
Contact *Mrs J. Wright*

Film, video and TV production for drama, documentary, commercials and corporate. CLIENTS BMA, British Telecom, charities.

Circus Films

See **Elstree (Production) Co. Ltd.**

Claverdon Films Ltd

28 Narrow Street, London E14 8DQ
☎0171 702 8700   Fax 0171 702 8701
Contact *Mike Bluett, Tony Palmer*

Film and TV: drama and documentary. OUTPUT *Menuhin; Maria Callas; Testimony; In From the Cold; Pushkin; England, My England* (by John Osborne); *Kipling.* Unsolicited material is read, but please send a written outline first.

The Clear Picture Co.

Folds Head Farm, Calver, Nr Sheffield S30 1XJ
☎01433 631086   Fax 01433 631050
Contact *Shaun Gilmartin, Judy Laybourn*

Television documentaries, sport and corporate programmes. OUTPUT includes programmes for Carlton Television, Central Television, YTV and Sky Sports. No drama. 'We use in-house writers on most projects. However, we do occasionally use freelance talent from across a range of skills.'

Cleveland Productions

5 Rainbow Court, Oxhey, Near Watford, Hertfordshire WD1 4RP
☎01923 254000   Fax 01923 254000
Contact *Michael Gosling*

Film and video production for documentary and commercials. Tape slide and multi-track recording facilities available. Also stills photography.

Tony Collingwood Productions Ltd

See **Convergence Productions Ltd**

Compass Film Productions Ltd

175 Wardour Street, London W1V 3FB
☎0171 734 8115   Fax 0171 439 6456
Contact *Simon Heaven, Heather Simms*

Specialists since 1974 in documentary, educational and promotional programmes for TV and corporate clients. OUTPUT *Violent Lives; A Door to Understanding; Cardboard Citizens* (all for Ch4); *Last Chance Hotel* (BBC); *Behind the Mask* (BBC '40 Minutes'); *Loneliness Week* (BBC Wales).

Complete Communications

Communications House, Garsington Road, Cowley, Oxford OX4 2NG
☎01865 384004/383073   Fax 01865 749854
Contact *A. M. Black, Ms C. Richman, Ms V. Andrews*

Video production for corporate, commercial and documentary work, plus satellite/business production. No unsolicited mss. Samples of work are kept on file. Freelancers used.

Connaught Films

See **Broadcast Communications**

Convergence Productions Ltd/ Tony Collingwood Productions Ltd

Unit 10, The Chandlery, 50 Westminster Bridge Road, London SE1 7QY
☎0171 721 7531   Fax 0171 721 7533
Producers *Christopher O'Hare, Terence Clegg*
Development Director *Helen Stroud*

Film and TV. Convergence Productions produces live action, drama documentaries; Tony Collingwood Productions specialises in children's animation. OUTPUT Convergence: *Coral Browne: Caviar to the General* (Ch4 documentary); *On the Road Again* (8-part documentary series for BBC and Discovery Channel UK); a documentary on Harry S. Truman; *The Last Executioner* (feature film developed with the support of the European Script Fund). Collingwood: *RARG* (award-winning animated film); two series of *Captain Zed and the Zee Zone* (ITV); *Daisy-Head Mayzie* (Dr Seuss animated series for Turner Network and Hanna-Barbera); *Oscar's Orchestra* (13-part animated series for BBC and Time Warner); *Dennis and Gnasher* (13-episode animated series for HIT Entertainment and D.C. Thomson). Programmes in development include 60-minute programme for Ch4's 'Witness' *Better Dead Than Gay* and a half-hour documentary for Ch4's 'Without Walls' *The True Story of Marco Polo*.

Creative Channel Ltd

Channel TV, Television Centre, La Pouquelaye, St Helier, Jersey, Channel Islands JE1 3ZD
☎01534 68999   Fax 01534 59446
Managing Director *Gordon de Ste Croix*

Part of the Channel Television Group. Producers of TV commercials and corporate material: information, promotional, sales, training and events coverage. OUTPUT *Exploring Guernsey* and *This is Jersey* (video souvenir travel guides); *The Original Passenger Picture Show* (magazine programme screened on UK buses); promotional videos for all types of businesses in the Channel Islands and throughout Europe; plus over 300 commercials a year. No unsolicited mss; new writing/scripts commissioned as required. Interested in hearing from local writers resident in the Channel Islands.

Creative Film Makers Ltd

Pottery Lane House, 34A Pottery Lane, London W11 4LZ
☎0171 229 5131   Fax 0171 229 4999
Contact *Michael Seligman, Nicholas Seligman*

Corporate and sports documentaries, commercials and television programmes. OUTPUT *The World's Greatest Golfers*, plus various corporate and sports programmes for clients like Nestlé, Benson & Hedges, Wimpey, Bouygues. 'Always open to suggestions but have hardly ever received unsolicited material of any value.' Keen nevertheless to encourage new writers.

Creative Film Productions

68 Conway Road, London N14 7BE
☎0181 447 8187   Fax 0181 886 3054
Contact *Phil Davies*

OUTPUT Animation: *Joey* (Ch4). Drama: *Billy* (ITV); *Baby Love* (feature). Documentary: short series about food (BBC). Corporate: *A Little Time* for Parkinson's Disease Society.

The Creative Partnership

13 Bateman Street, London W1V 5TB
☎0171 439 7762   Fax 0171 437 1467
Contact *Christopher Fowler, Jim Sturgeon*

Producers of commercials and marketing campaigns for feature films. OUTPUT includes campaigns for *Pulp Fiction; The Lion King; Goldeneye; Trainspotting*. No scripts. 'We train new writers in-house, and find them from submitted c.v.s. All applicants must have previous commercial writing experience.'

Cricket Ltd

1 Lower James Street, London W1R 3PN
☎0171 287 4848   Fax 0171 413 0654
Creative Director *Andrew Davies*
Head of Production (Film & Video)
  Jonathan Freer

'Communications solutions for business clients wishing to influence targeted external and internal audiences.' Film and video, live events and conferences, print and design, and business television.

Croft Television and Graphics Ltd

Croft House, Progress Business Centre, Whittle Parkway, Slough SL1 6DQ
☎01628 668735   Fax 01628 668791
Contact *Keith Jones, Terry Adlam*

Producers of video and TV for drama, documentary, commercials, corporate, training and children's educational programmes. Also any form of visual communication and entertainment. Unsolicited scripts welcome but write first with synopsis. Fresh and creative new writing encouraged.

Cromdale Films Ltd

12 St Paul's Road, London N1 2QN
☎0171 226 0178
Contact *Ian Lloyd*

Film, video and TV: drama and documentary. OUTPUT *The Face of Darkness* (feature film); *Drift to Dawn* (rock music drama); *The Overdue Treatment* (documentary); *Russia, The Last Red Summer* (documentary). Initial phone call advised before submission of scripts.

Crown Business Communications Ltd

United House, 9 Pembridge Road, London W11 3JY
☎0171 727 7272   Fax 0171 727 9940
Contact *Nicky Havelaar*

Leading producers of videos, conferences and multi-media programmes for business. Interested in talented scriptwriters with experience in the field of business.

CVG Television
1 Sutton Street, Birmingham B1 1PE
☎0121 622 1337   Fax 0121 622 3080
Contact *Sally Murcutt*

Video and TV: drama, documentary and corporate, predominantly for charity organisations. Programmes target the whole age spectrum, and cover topical and moral issues from a Christian perspective.

Dancetime Ltd
See **Table Top Productions**

Dareks Production House
58 Wickham Road, Beckenham, Kent BR3 2RQ
☎0181 658 2012   Fax 0181 658 2012
Contact *David Crossman*

Independent producers of corporate and broadcast television.

Dibgate Productions Ltd
Studio 4, Parkstead Lodge, 31 Upper Park Road, London NW3 2UL
☎0171 722 5634
Contact *Nicholas Parsons*

Documentary and travel films; plus comedy shorts for cinema and television. OUTPUT has included *A Fair Way to Play; Mad Dogs and Cricketers; Relatively Greek; Viva Menorca; Terribly British.*

Directors Video Company
Unit 4B-5B, Askew Crescent, Chiswick, London W12 9DP
☎01276 66444
Contact *Frances Jacobs, Tony Barton*

Corporate video; drama and documentary. OUTPUT Mostly corporate identity programmes, recruitment and new product launches. Writers 'with new ideas and showreels of video scripts' are particularly welcome.

Diverse Productions Limited
Gorleston Street, London W14 8XS
☎0171 603 4567   Fax 0171 603 2148
Contact *Rita Shamia*

Broadcast television production with experience in news, current affairs, documentaries,

training and education, religion, consumer and graphics-based programming. Now also developing drama, children's and entertainment series. OUTPUT *The Pulse; Checkout; Europe Express; African Footsteps; Mind Field; The Experimenter* and many single documentaries.

Drake A-V Video Ltd
89 St Fagans Road, Fairwater, Cardiff CF5 3AE
☎01222 560333   Fax 01222 554909
Contact *Ian Lewis*

Corporate A-V film and video, mostly promotional, training or educational. Scripts in these fields welcome.

The Drama House Ltd
1 Hertford Place, London W1P 5RS
☎0171 388 9140   Fax 0171 388 3511
Contact *Gwynneth Lloyd, Jack Emery*

Television producers. OUTPUT *Breaking the Code* (BBC1); *Witness Against Hitler* (BBC1); *Suffer the Little Children* (BBC2 'Stages'); *A Curse on the House of Windsor* (Ch4 'Without Walls' drama-documentary); *Call to Prayer* (BBC1 4-part documentary series). Scripts welcome. Interested in developing contacts with new and established writers.

Charles Dunstan Communications Ltd
42 Wolseley Gardens, London W4 3LS
☎0181 994 2328   Fax 0181 994 2328
Contact *Charles Dunstan*

Producers of film, video and TV for documentary and corporate material. OUTPUT *Renewable Energy* for broadcast worldwide in *Inside Britain* series; National Power Annual Report Video *The Electric Environment*. No unsolicited scripts.

Eagle and Eagle Ltd
15 Marlborough Road, London W4 4EU
☎0181 995 1884   Fax 0181 995 5648
Contact *Robert Eagle, Catharine Alen-Buckley*

Film, video and TV: drama, documentary and children's programmes. Broadcast work includes programmes on aviation, psychology, medicine, education and arts. No unsolicited scripts.

East Anglian Productions
Studio House, 21-23 Walton Road, Frinton on Sea, Essex CO13 0AA
☎01255 676252   Fax 01255 850528
Contact *Ray Anderson*

Film, video and TV: drama and documentary,

children's television, comedy, commercials and corporate. Interested in comedy too. Scripts welcome. Keen to encourage new writing.

Edinburgh Film & Video Productions

Nine Mile Burn, by Penicuik, Midlothian EH26 9LT

☎01968 672131   Fax 01968 672685

Contact R. Crichton

Film, TV drama and documentary. OUTPUT Sara; Moonacre; Torch; Silent Mouse; The Curious Case of Santa Claus; The Stamp of Greatness. No unsolicited scripts at present.

Elstree (Production) Co. Ltd

Shepperton Studios, Studios Road, Shepperton, Middx TW17 0QD

☎01932 572680/1   Fax 01932 572682

Produces feature films and TV drama/situation comedy. OUTPUT Prospects (Euston Films/Ch4); Rude Health (Ch4); Othello (BBC); Great Expectations (Disney Channel); Porgy & Bess (with Trevor Nunn); Old Curiosity Shop (Disney Channel/RHI); London Suite (NBC/Hallmark). Recently established Circus Films with Trevor Nunn for feature film projects, the first being Twelfth Night (Renaissance).

Enigma Productions Ltd

13–15 Queen's Gate Place Mews, London SW7 5BG

☎0171 581 0238   Fax 0171 584 1799

Head of Development Jane Wittekind

Backed by Warner Bros. OUTPUT Memphis Belle (true story of an American B-17 bomber crew in Second World War); Meeting Venus (a comedy about a multinational opera company); Bill Forsyth's Being Human; War of the Buttons (children's film). In development: Fade Out (drama set in Prague in the 1940s); Shackleton (true story of the Antarctic explorer); Serenade (musical romantic comedy); The Scarlet Pimpernel. Unsolicited submissions accepted only from a recognised agent or motion picture lawyer.

The Entertainment Partnership

(incorporating Entertainment Productions & People)

305 Gray's Inn Road, London WC1X 8QF

☎0171 713 1234   Fax 0171 713 1741

Chief Executive Tony Fitzpatrick

Video and TV productions for documentary,

corporate and factual entertainment. OUTPUT Take That and Party; Pop Goes Summer; Music from the Bridge/Music from the Circus; Dance into Fitness; The Common Sense Guide to Pregnancy. Unsolicited scripts welcome. Information on and work from new writers welcome in any field.

Essential Film & TV Productions Ltd

5 Anglers Lane, London NW5 3DG

☎0171 482 1992   Fax 0171 485 4287

Creative Director Christopher Skala

TV situation comedy and drama. OUTPUT Surgical Spirit (Granada); Porkpie (Ch4); Agony Again (BBC).

Farnham Film Company Ltd

34 Burnt Hill Road, Lower Bourne, Farnham, Surrey GU10 3LZ

☎01252 710313   Fax 01252 725855

Contact Ian Lewis

Television and film: children's drama and documentaries. Unsolicited mss welcome. 'Always looking for new material which is commercially viable.'

Farrant Partnership

91 Knatchbull Road, London SE5 9QU

☎0171 733 0711   Fax 0171 738 5224

Contact James Farrant

Corporate video productions.

Filmit Productions

2 Tunstall Road, London SW9 8BN

☎0171 738 4175   Fax 0171 738 3787

Contact John Samson

Television documentaries and corporate work. OUTPUT A Polite Enquiry; The Gulf Between Us; Loyalty on the Line; Who Let Our Children Die (all documentaries for Ch4); Free for All; Speak Out (Ch4 series). Unsolicited scripts welcome. Keen to discover and nurture new writing talent.

First Creative Group Ltd

The Stables, Mellings Farm, Benson Lane, Catforth, Preston, Lancashire PR4 0HY

☎01772 690450   Fax 01772 690964

Contact M. Mulvihill

Film, video and TV productions for documentary and corporate material. Unsolicited scripts welcome. Open to new writing.

First Information Group

Knightsbridge House, 197 Knightsbridge,
London SW7 1RB
☎0171 393 3000   Fax 0171 393 3033
Contact *Michael Rodd*

Multi-media for business and industry including video, computer and on-line services. No unsolicited material but always interested in c.v.s and personal profiles.

Fitting Images Ltd

Alfred House, 127A Oatlands Drive,
Weybridge, Surrey KT13 9LB
☎01932 840056   Fax 01932 858075
Managing Director *Sue Fleetwood*

Promotional, training, medical/pharmaceutical; contacts from experienced writers of drama and comedy welcome. We are also interested in broadcast projects.

Flashback Communication Ltd

25 Greenhead Street, Glasgow G40 1ES
☎0141 554 6868   Fax 0141 554 6869
Contact *Chris Attkins*

Video and TV producers: drama, documentary, corporate, training and education, and sell-throughs. OUTPUT includes dramatised training videos and TV programmes or inserts for the ITV network, BBC and stations worldwide. Proposals considered; no scripts. New talent encouraged. Interested in fresh ideas and effective style.

Flicks Films Ltd

101 Wardour Street, London W1V 3TD
☎0171 734 4892   Fax 0171 287 2307
Managing Director/Producer *Terry Ward*

Film and video: children's animated series and specials. OUTPUT *The Mr Men; Little Miss; Bananaman; The Pondles; Junglies; Nellie the Elephant; See How They Work With Dig and Dug.* Scripts specific to their needs will be considered. 'Always willing to read relevant material.'

Focus Films Ltd

The Rotunda Studios, Rear of 116–118
Finchley Road, London NW3 5HT
☎0171 435 9004/5   Fax 0171 431 3562
Contact *David Pupkewitz, Lisa Disler, Malcolm Kohill*

Film and TV producers. Drama OUTPUT *CrimeTime* (European Script Fund Award, medium-budget feature thriller); *Diary of a*

Sane Man (experimental feature for Ch4); *Othello* (Ch4 drama). Projects in development include *Sweet Bananas* (Feature – ESF Award); *Johnny Riff; Chastity Brogan - US Marshal* (both features). No unsolicited scripts.

Folio Productions

60 Charlotte Street, London W1P 2AX
☎0171 240 5389   Fax 0171 436 3117
Contact *Charles Thompson*

Film, TV and video: documentary and corporate work. OUTPUT includes programmes for *Dispatches, Cutting Edge, Secret History* and *Black Bag* (Ch4); plus a 7-part commando series for ITV. Scripts and ideas welcome, including work from new writers.

Forge Productions Ltd

14 Ceylon Road, London W14 0PY
☎0171 602 1867   Fax 0171 602 1867
Contact *Ralph Rolls*

Video and TV: documentary and promotions for campaigns. OUTPUT includes *Everyman: Celtic Britain* for BBC1; religious programmes for the BBC, including four programmes on Islamic communities in the UK; 13-part TV series on the paranormal for European 'Discovery'; *Kaleidoscope* feature for Radio 4. New writers encouraged but no unsolicited mss.

Mark Forstater Productions Ltd

Suite 66, 124–128 Barlby Road, London
W10 6BL
☎0181 964 1888   Fax 0181 960 9819
Production *Mark Forstater*

Active in the selection, development and production of material for film and TV. OUTPUT *Monty Python and the Holy Grail; The Odd Job; The Grass is Singing; Xtro; Forbidden; Separation; The Fantasist; Shalom Joan Collins; The Silent Touch; Grushko; The Wolves of Willoughby Chase; Between the Devil and the Deep Blue Sea; Doing Rude Things.* No unsolicited mss.

Friday Productions Ltd

23a St. Leonards Terrace, London SW3 4QG
☎0171 730 0608   Fax 0171 730 0608
Contact *Georgina Abrahams*

Film and TV productions for drama material. OUTPUT *Goggle Eyes; Harnessing Peacocks; The December Rose.* No unsolicited scripts. New writing encouraged especially from under-represented groups.

Gala International Ltd
222 Kensal Road, London W10 5BN
☎0181 969 4502   Fax 0181 969 5337

Producer *David Lindsay*

Corporate videos, including product documentaries and sales promotion material. Unsolicited scripts welcome. New writing encouraged.

John Gau Productions
Burston House, 1 Burston Road, Putney,
London SW15 6AR
☎0181 788 8811   Fax 0181 789 0903

Contact *John Gau*

Documentaries and series for TV, plus corporate video. OUTPUT includes *Assignment Adventure* (Ch4); *Korea* series (BBC1); *Reaching for the Skies* (BBC2); *Voyager* (Central); *The Power and The Glory* (BBC2); *The Team – A Season With McLaren* (BBC2); *The Great Outdoors* (Ch4); *Lights, Camera, Action!: A Century of the Cinema* (ITV network); *The Triumph of the Nerds* (Ch4).

Noel Gay Television
6th Floor, 76 Oxford Street, London
W1N 0AT
☎0171 412 0400   Fax 0171 412 0300

Contact *Charles Armitage*

The association with Noel Gay (agency/management and music publishing) makes this one of the most securely financed independents in the business. Recent OUTPUT and confirmed productions for 1997: *I-Camcorder* (Ch4); *10%ers – Series 2* (Carlton/ITV); *Call Up the Stars* (BBC1); *Smeg Outs* (BBC video); *Les Bubb* (BBC Scotland); *Red Dwarf - Series 7&8; Red Dwarf Christmas Special* (BBC); *Making of Red Dwarf* (BBC video); *Dave Allen* (ITV). Joint ventures and new companies include a partnership with Odyssey, a leading Indian commercials, film and TV producer, and international networks; a joint venture with Reed Consumer Books to develop book and magazine ideas for film, video and television, and the Noel Gay Motion Picture Company, whose 1996 credits include *Trainspotting* with Ch4 and Figment Films, and *Killer Tongue*, a co-production with Iberoamericana. Other associate NGTV companies are Grant Naylor Productions, Rose Bay Film Productions, Sidewinder, Picture That, Pepper Productions and Jane Davies Casting.

Geofilms Ltd
12 Thame Lane, Culham, Oxford OX14 3DS
☎01235 555422   Fax 01235 530581

Contact *Ms. Martine Benoit*

Film, video and TV productions for documentary, corporate and education material. OUTPUT *Equinox: The Bermuda Triangle; Dispatches: Power Connection* (Ch4); *Horizon: Magma Chamber; Antenna: Hot Ice* (BBC2); also training programmes for the Resource Industry. Unsolicited scripts welcome relating to earth sciences and the environment.

Goldcrest Films and Television Ltd
65-66 Dean Street, London W1V 6PL
☎0171 437 8696   Fax 0171 437 4448

Chief Executive Officer *John Quested*

FOUNDED in the late 70s. Formerly part of the Brent Walker Leisure Group but independent since 1990 following management buy-out led by John Quested. The company's core activities are film production and worldwide distribution. Scripts via agents only.

The Good Film Company
2nd Floor, 14-15 D'Arblay Street, London
W1V 3FP
☎0171 734 1331   Fax 0171 734 2997

Contact *Yanina Barry*

Commercials and pop videos. CLIENTS include Hugo Boss, Cadbury's, Wella, National Express Coaches, Camel Cigarettes, Tunisian Tourist Board. Unsolicited mss welcome.

Carol Gould Productions Plc
9 Cedric Chambers, Northwick Close,
London NW8 8JH
☎0171 266 1953   Fax 0171 266 1954

Contact *Carol Gould*

Up and running since late 1993, Carol Gould Productions produces television/film documentary and drama. Projects in development include a feature film *A Twig From the Cherry Orchard*; and two drama series: *Spitfire Girls* (published as a novel September, 1995); and *Hot Shots*. No unsolicited mss. Write or call with ideas in the first instance.

Granada Film
36 Golden Square, London W1R 4AH
☎0171 494 6388   Fax 0171 494 6360

Contact *Pippa Cross, Tessa Gibbs*

Films and TV films. OUTPUT *My Left Foot; Jack & Sarah; August* (features); *Some Kind of Life* (TV). No unsolicited scripts. Supportive of new writing but often hard to offer real help as Granada are developing mainstream commercial projects which usually requires some status in talent areas.

Grasshopper Enterprises Ltd

50 Peel Street, London W8 7PD
☎0171 229 1181   Fax 0171 229 2070
Contact *Joy Whitby*

Children's programmes and adult drama. No unsolicited mss.

Green Umbrella Ltd

The Production House, 147A St Michaels Hill, Bristol, Avon BS2 8DB
☎0117 9731729   Fax 0117 9467432

Television documentary makers. OUTPUT includes episodes for *The Natural World* and *Wildlife on One*. Unsolicited scripts relating to natural history subjects are welcome.

Reg Grundy Productions (GB) Ltd

Grundy House, 1 Bargehouse Crescent, 34 Upper Ground, London SE1 9PD
☎0171 928 8942   Fax 0171 928 8417

Television: drama and light entertainment. OUTPUT Game shows: *Celebrity Squares; Going for Gold; Small Talk; Pot of Gold; Man O Man.* Factual: *How Do They Do That?; Eureka!*

Howard Hall

6 Foster Road, Abingdon, Oxfordshire OX14 1YN
☎01235 533981/0860 775438
Fax 01235 533981
Contact *Howard Hall*

Film, video and TV: drama, documentary, commercials and corporate programmes. OUTPUT includes drama training programmes, satellite programmes, commercials, and programmes for broadcast channels. Scripts welcome. 'Always looking for new writers. We need a store of good writers in different fields of work.' Howard Hall has written two books: *Corporate Video Directing* (Focal Press) and *Careers in Film and Video* (**Kogan Page**).

Hammer Film Productions Ltd

Millennium Studios, Elstree Way, Borehamwood, Hertfordshire WD6 1SF
☎0181 207 4011   Fax 0181 905 1127
Contact *Roy Skeggs, Graham Skeggs*

Feature films. No unsolicited scripts.

Hammerwood Film Productions

110 Trafalgar Road, Portslade, East Sussex BN41 1GS
☎01273 277333   Fax 01273 822247
Contact *Ralph Harvey, Karen King, Ray Collins*

Film, video and TV drama. In development: *Sacre Bleu* and *Operation Pandora*. 1996 projects: *Sawney Beane* and *The Last of the Hapsburgs* – 52-part TV series (co-production with Imperial Productions); Boadicea (co-production with Pan-European Group). Most material is written in-house. 'We do not have the time to read scripts but will always read 2-3-page synopses/plot outlines. Anything of interest will be followed up.' Hammerwood is also a distributor with a stock of 5000 movies and TV programmes.

Hand Pict Productions Ltd

4 Picardy Place, Edinburgh EH1 3JT
☎0131 558 1543   Fax 0131 556 0792
Contact *George Cathro*

Television production for drama and documentary material. OUTPUT *The Ken Fine Show* (6-part series for Scottish Television); *Face Value* (Ch4); *Et in Stadia Ego* ('Without Walls', Ch4); *Blood Ties* (arts documentary for BBC Wales); *Blackfish* (current affairs for Ch4); *The Boat Band* (BBC). Unsolicited scripts welcome but pressure of work and programmes in production can lead to delays in response. Encourages new writing.

HandMade Films Ltd

15 Golden Square, London W1R 3AG
☎0171 434 3132   Fax 0171 434 3143

Feature films. OUTPUT has included *Mona Lisa; The Missionary; Time Bandits; Withnail and I; The Lonely Passion of Judith Hearne; The Raggedy Rawney; Checking Out; How To Get Ahead in Advertising; Nuns on the Run.* New projects for release in 1996 include *Intimate Relations* and *Sweet Angel Mine.* No unsolicited mss at present.

Hartswood Films Ltd

Shepperton Studios, Shepperton, Middlesex TW17 0QD
☎01932 572294   Fax 01932 572299
Contact *Beryl Vertue, Elaine Cameron*

Film and TV production for drama and light entertainment. OUTPUT *Men Behaving Badly* (BBC, previously Thames); *Is It Legal?* (Carlton); *The English Wife* (Meridian); *A Woman's Guide to Adultery* (Carlton); *My Good Friend* (ITV); *Code Name Kyril* (HTV). No unsolicited scripts. New writing read if recommended by agents.

Hat Trick Productions Ltd

10 Livonia Street, London W1V 3PH
☎0171 434 2451   Fax 0171 287 9791
Contact *Denise O'Donoghue*

Television programmes. OUTPUT includes *A*

Very Open Prison; Clive Anderson Talks Back; Confessions; Drop the Dead Donkey; Eleven Men Against Eleven; Father Ted; Game On; Have I Got News For You; Room 101; The Peter Principle; Whose Line is it Anyway?.

Hawthornden Films

Cambridge Court, Cambridge Road, Frinton on Sea, Essex CO13 9HN
☎01255 676381   Fax 01255 676381
Contact *Timothy Foster*

Active in European film co-production in the Netherlands, France and Italy. Mainstream connections in the USA. Also documentaries.

Head to Head Communication Ltd

The Hook, Fiveways Business Centre, Plane Tree Crescent, Feltham, Middlesex TW13 7AQ
☎0181 893 7766   Fax 0181 893 2777
Contact *Bob Carson*

Producers of business and corporate communication programmes and events.

Jim Henson Productions Ltd

30 Oval Road, Camden, London NW1 7DE
☎0171 428 4000   Fax 0171 428 4001
Contact *Angus Fletcher*

Feature films and TV: family entertainment and children's. OUTPUT *Gulliver's Travels; Babe; The Muppet Christmas Carol; Labyrinth; The Witches* (films); *Dinosaurs* (ABC); *The Muppet Show* (ITV); *The Storyteller* (Ch4); *The Secret Life of Toys* (BBC); *The Animal Show* (BBC). Scripts via agents only.

Hightimes Productions Ltd

5 Anglers Lane, London NW5 3DG
☎0171 482 5202   Fax 0171 485 4254
Contact *A. C. Mitchell, A. Humphreys*

Television comedies. OUTPUT *Trouble in Mind* (situation comedy, 9 episodes LWT); *Me & My Girl* (situation comedy, 5 series, LWT package); *The Zodiac Game* (game show, 2 series, Anglia package); *Guys 'n' Dolls* (light entertainment, 13 episodes, BSB). Unsolicited scripts welcome. New writing encouraged where possible.

Philip Hindin

66 Melbourne Way, Bush Hill Park, Enfield, Middlesex EN1 1XQ
☎0181 366 2978   Fax 0181 363 7523
Contact *P. Hindin*

Producer of quiz-panel game shows for TV

and theatre. No unsolicited material but always interested in new ideas/writing. Comedy material – revue style, blackout sketches in vaudeville style considered.

Holmes Associates

38–42 Whitfield Street, London W1P 5FR
☎0171 813 4333   Fax 0171 637 9024
Contact *Andrew Holmes, Alison Carter*

Prolific originators, producers and packagers of documentary, drama and music television and films. OUTPUT has included *The Shadow of Hiroshima* (Ch4 'Witness'); *The House of Bernarda Alba* (Ch4/WNET/Amaya); *Piece of Cake* (drama mini-series for LWT); *Well Being* and *Signals* (Ch4); *The Cormorant* (BBC/Screen 2); *John Gielgud Looks Back* (Ch4); *Four Up Two Down* and *Rock Steady* (Ch4); *Timeline* (with MPT, TVE Spain & TRT Turkey). Unsolicited scripts will be considered.

Hourglass Pictures Ltd

117 Merton Road, Wimbledon, London SW19 1ED
☎0181 540 8786   Fax 0181 542 6598
Director *Martin Chilcott*

Film and video: documentary, drama and commercials. OUTPUT includes television science documentaries; public relations material for government and industrial bodies; health and social issues for the World Health Organisation; product promotion for pharmaceutical companies. Open to new writing.

Hourglass Productions Limited

Television: 4 The Heights, London SE7 8JH
☎0181 858 6870   Fax 0181 858 6870
Film: Charlton House, Charlton Road, London SE7 8RE ☎0181 319 8949
Managing Director *John Walsh*
Head of Finance *David Walsh*
Head of Development *Maura Walsh*

Award-winning producers of drama, documentary and music promos. OUTPUT *Ray Harryhausen: Movement Into Life* (Oscar-winner, BBC); *The Comedy Store* (BBC); *Sceptic & The Psychic* (Ch4 drama); *The Sleeper* (BBC); *The Frozen Four* (BBC film). Co-production partners with D L Taffner Entertainment. 'We often lecture to writers looking to sell their mss. With Ch4's 'Short & Curlies' season of drama one-off shorts we hope to inject an element of first timers, competing for slots.' Prefers to receive mss through agents but will read unsolicited material.

Hubner Video & Film Ltd
79 Dean Street, London W1V 5MA
☎0171 439 4060   Fax 0171 287 1072
Contact *Martin Hubner, Christine Fontaine*

Film commercials, corporate videos and documentaries, and feature film scripts. CLIENTS Associated Newspapers, Gateway Supermarkets, De Beers Diamonds, Bentalls, British Gas, IBM, Nat West, Audi, Parkfield/Ford (USA). Unsolicited scripts or outlines for feature films and documentaries welcome. Material is read and discussed before being forwarded if promising to TV/film companies or agents for production packaging.

Alan Hydes Associates
East Royd House, Woodlands Drive,
Apperley Bridge, West Yorkshire BD10 0PA
☎0113 2503467   Fax 0113 2503467
Contact *Alan Hydes*

Film, video and TV: drama and corporate work, including children's TV programmes, promotional, recruitment and security films for the Halifax Building Society. Also news agency facilities for national press and television. No unsolicited scripts. Interested in new ideas for conversion to drama.

Icon Films
56 Kingsdown Parade, Bristol, Avon BS6 5UQ
☎0117 9248535   Fax 0117 9240386
Contact *Harry Marshall*

Film and TV documentaries. OUTPUT *The Elephant Men* (WNET/Ch4); *The Living Edens – Bhutan, The Last Shangri La* (ABC/Kome); *Tiger!* (Turner); *In the Realm of the Dragon; Joanna Lumley in Bhutan* (both for BBC); *Lost Civilisations – Tibet* (Time Life for NBC). Open-minded to new writing. Scripts welcome.

Ideal Image Ltd
Cherrywood House, Crawley Down Road,
Felbridge, Surrey RH19 2PP
☎01342 312566   Fax 01342 312566
Contact *Alan Frost*

Producers of documentary and drama for film, video, TV and corporate clients. OUTPUT *The Devils' Year* (documentary on the Red Devils); *Just Another Friday* (corporate drama). Scripts welcome.

In Video Productions Ltd
16 York Place, Edinburgh EH1 3EP
☎0131 557 2151   Fax 0131 557 5465
Contact *Jamie Swinton*

Film, video and TV production for documentary, commercials, corporate and title sequences material. Unsolicited scripts welcome.

INCA (Independent Communications Associates) Ltd
20–28 Dalling Road, London W6 0JB
☎0181 748 0160   Fax 0181 748 3114
Managing Director *William Woollard*

Television documentary and corporate work. OUTPUT includes science, technology and medical documentaries for programmes such as *Equinox* and *Horizon*; also educational, current affairs, music, arts and light entertainment. Proposals for documentary programmes or series welcome. Positive policy towards new writing.

Independent Image Ltd
33–34 Soho Square, London W1V 6DP
☎0171 292 4300   Fax 0171 292 4299
Joint Managing Directors *Tom Kinninmont, David Wickham*

Film, video and TV productions for drama, documentary, commercials and corporate material. OUTPUT *Hostage* (TV/feature film); *More Than a Game* (8-part documentary series on sport). Unsolicited scripts welcome but write first. Positive view on new writing: 'good track record of using new writers'. Has some involvement with The Annual Young Playwrights Course run by the Scottish Youth Theatre.

Initial Film and Television
See **Broadcast Communications**

Interesting Television Ltd
Oakslade Studios, Station Road, Hatton,
Warwickshire CV35 7LH
☎01926 843777
Senior Producer *John Pluck*

Producers of broadcast television documentaries and feature series on film and video for ITV and BBC TV. Currently looking towards cable, satellite and home video to broaden its output. Ideas for television documentaries particularly welcome. Send a treatment in the first instance, particularly if the subject is 'outside our area of current interest'. OUTPUT has included television programmes on heritage, antiques, gardening, science and industry; also projects on heritage, health and sports for the home video front.

ISIS Productions Ltd
14–15 Vernon Street, London W14 0RG
☎0171 602 0959   Fax 0171 603 0644
Production Coordinator *Farne Sinclair*

Formed in 1991, Isis Productions maintains an association with **Oxford University Press**, handling and packaging material published by them. Current: *Classic Albums* (major 8-part series on the making of classic rock albums, co-produced with Daniel Television, BBC and NCRV). OUTPUT *Dido and Aeneas* (BBC2/Thirteen WNET/ZDF-Arte/NVC Arts); *Ivy's Genes* (documentary for Ch4 'Inside Out' series); *The Score* (classical music magazine series, co-produced with After Image for BBC2); *Mine Eyes Have Seen the Glory* (3-part documentary series, co-produced with Cutting Edge/WTTW Chicago); *Teenage Health Freak* (Ch4 comedy drama, co-produced with Limelight). *Short* outlines and treatments of unsolicited scripts welcome. Would like to see new writing.

Kanthi TV

Cowburn House, Latchley Plain, Cornwall PL18 9AY
☎01822 833627   Fax 01822 834493
Contact *Kanthi Ford*

Video and TV: drama, documentary, corporate and commercials. OUTPUT *People Games; Home from Home*; and news coverage. Unsolicited scripts and ideas welcome. Keen to support new writing.

Kay Communications Ltd

Gauntley Court Studios, Gauntley Court, Nottingham NG7 5HD
☎0115 9781333   Fax 0115 9783734
Contact *John Alexander*

Makers of industrial video programmes and training programmes. Scripts written in-house. No unsolicited mss.

King Rollo Films Ltd

Dolphin Court, High Street, Honiton, Devon EX14 8LS
☎01404 45218   Fax 01404 45328
Contact *Clive Juster*

Film, video and TV: children's animated series. OUTPUT *Mr Benn; King Rollo; Victor & Maria; Towser; Play-It-Again; The Adventures of Spot; Not Now, Bernard; The Hill and the Rock; Two Can Toucan; The Sad Story of Veronica Who Played the Violin; Elmer; I Want a Cat; Oscar Got the Blame; Super Dooper Jezebel; I'm Coming to Get You; I Want My Potty; The Adventures of Ric; It's Fun to Learn With Spot; Art; Buddy & Pip; Spot's Magical Christmas; Fred; Philipp; Jakob.* Generally work from existing published material 'although there will always be the odd exception'. Proposals or phone calls in the first instance. No scripts.

Kingfisher Television Productions Ltd

The Television House, Lenton Lane, Nottingham NG7 2NA
☎0115 9645262   Fax 0115 9645263
Contact *Tony Francis*
Broadcast television production.

Koninck

175 Wardour Street, London W1V 3AB
☎0171 734 4943   Fax 0171 494 0405
Contact *Keith Griffiths*

Film and TV: drama and documentary. OUTPUT includes projects with directors like Jan Svankmajer, the Brothers Quay, G. F. Newman, Chris Petit and Patrick Keiller. 'We try to promote new talent and develop work by young writers new to the screen and experienced writers looking for new and imaginative ways to express their ideas.'

Lagan Pictures Ltd

7 Rugby Court, Agincourt Avenue, Belfast BT7 1PN
☎01232 326125
Producer/Director *Stephen Butcher*
Producer *Alison Grundle*

Film, video and TV: drama, documentary and corporate. OUTPUT *A Force Under Fire* (Ulster TV). In development: one-off and series drama, documentaries and dramatised documentaries. 'We are always interested in hearing from writers originating from or based in Northern Ireland or anyone with, preferably unstereotypical, projects relevant to Northern Ireland. We do not have the resources to deal with unsolicited mss, so please phone or write with a brief treatment/synopsis in the first instance.'

Landseer Film and Television Productions Ltd

140 Royal College Street, London NW1 0TA
☎0171 485 7333   Fax 0171 485 7573
Contact *Kate Greening*

Film and video production: documentary, drama, music and arts, children's and current affairs. OUTPUT *Winter Dreams* (BBC2); *Sunny Stories - Enid Blyton* (Arena); *J. R. R. Tolkien* (Tolkien Partnership); *Kenneth MacMillan at 60* (BBC); *Discovering Delius* (Delius Trust); *Should Accidentally Fall* (BBC/Arts Council); *Nobody's Fool* ('South Bank Show' on Danny Kaye for LWT); *Mister Abbott's Broadway* ('Omnibus' BBC).

Helen Langridge Associates
75 Kenton Street, London WC1N 1NN
☎0171 833 2955   Fax 0171 837 2836

Managing Directors *Helen Langridge, Mike Wells*

Film, video and TV: drama, music videos and commercials.

Lawson Productions Ltd
Newton Park, Wicklow, Co Wicklow
Republic of Ireland
☎00 353 404 69497   Fax 00 353 404 69092

Contact *Sarah Lawson*

Film and TV: drama and comedy. OUTPUT has included *That's Love* (UK and US); *Home to Roost* (US version); *The Dawning* with Anthony Hopkins; *Life After Life* (ITV) with George Cole; *Natural Lies* (BBC); *Seekers* (ITV). No unsolicited mss unless via agents, but always interested in new talent.

Lightarama Ltd
12a Wellfield Avenue, London N10 2EA
☎0181 444 8315   Fax 0181 444 8315

Contact *Alexis Key*

Video and TV production for commercials and corporate material and also special effects (lighting). OUTPUT Mercedes Benz training programme; Renault UK training programme; British Gas special effects; Discovery Channel, new idents, lighting effects; Video London Sound Studios Ltd; French to English translation of French Natural History series; IPSEN International Ltd, brochure and communication consultancy. No unsolicited scripts but c.v.s welcome. Interested in new and creative ideas.

Lilyville Productions Ltd
7 Lilyville Road, London SW6 5DP
☎0171 371 5940   Fax 0171 736 9431

Contact *Tony Cash*

Drama and documentaries for TV. OUTPUT *Poetry in Motion* (series for Ch4); *South Bank Show: Ben Elton & Vanessa Redgrave*; *Musique Enquête* (drama-based French language series, Ch4); *Landscape and Memory* (arts documentary series for the BBC); Jonathan Miller's production of the *St Matthew Passion* for the BBC. Scripts with an obvious application to TV may be considered. Interested in new writing for documentary programmes.

Limelight
3 Bromley Place (off Conway Street), London
W1P 5HB
☎0171 255 3939   Fax 0171 436 4334

Head of Television *Sally Woodward*
Managing Director *Adam Whittaker*
Contact *James Christie-Miller*

Film, music video and TV drama and commercials. OUTPUT *Hear My Song; Teenage Mutant Ninja Turtles I* (feature films); *Teenage Health Freak I & II* (TV series); *ReBoot* (animated TV series). New writing encouraged. Scripts welcome.

Little Dancer Ltd
Avonway, Naseby Road, London
SE19 3JJ
☎0181 653 9343   Fax 0181 653 9343

Contact *Robert Smith, Sue Townsend*

Television and cinema, both shorts and full-length features.

Living Tape Productions
See **Videotel Productions**

Lomond Television
See **Broadcast Communications**

Lucida Productions
1st Floor, 53 Greek Street, London
W1V 5LR
☎0171 437 1140   Fax 0171 287 5335

Contact *Paul Joyce*

Television and cinema: arts, adventure, current affairs, documentary, drama and music. OUTPUT has included *Motion and Emotion: The Films of Wim Wenders 1989; Dirk Bogarde – By Myself; Sam Peckinpah - Man of Iron; The Making of Naked Lunch; Kris Kristofferson – Pilgrim; Wild One: Marlon Brando; Reel Women*. Currently in production with documentaries for Cinefile 4. Unsolicited scripts welcome.

Main Communications
City House, 16 City Road, Winchester,
Hampshire SO23 8SD
☎01962 870680   Fax 01962 870699

Contact *Eben Wilson*

Multimedia marketing, communications, electronic and publishing company for film, video and TV: drama, documentary and commercials. OUTPUT includes marketing communications, educational, professional and managerial distance learning, documentary programmes for broadcast TV and children's material. Interested in proposals for television programmes, and in ideas for video sell-throughs, interactive multimedia and business information texts and programming.

Malone Gill Productions Ltd

Canaletto House, 39 Beak Street, London
W1R 3LD
☎0171 287 3970   Fax 0171 287 8146

Contact *Georgina Denison*

Mainly documentary but also some drama. OUTPUT *Vermeer* ('South Bank Show'); *Highlanders* (ITV); *Storm Chasers* (Ch4); *Nature Perfected* (Ch4); *The Feast of Christmas* (Ch4); *The Buried Mirror: Reflections on Spain and the New World* by Carlos Fuentes (BBC2/ Discovery Channel); *Nomads* (Ch4/ITEL), Bronze medal winner, New York Film Festival 1991 and first in the 11th Rencontres Internationales de l'Environnement et de la Nature, Paris 1992. Approach by letter with proposal in the first instance.

Mike Mansfield Television Ltd

5–7 Carnaby Street, London
W1V 1PG
☎0171 494 3061   Fax 0171 494 3057

Contact *Hilary Stewart*

Television for BBC, ITV network and Ch4. OUTPUT includes *Animal Country; Just a Minute; The James Whale Show; The Exchange; The Entertainers; HRH the Princess of Wales Concert of Hope; Cue the Music; Helter Skelter.*

Bill Mason Films Ltd

Orchard House, Dell Quay, Chichester,
West Sussex PO20 7EE
☎01243 783558

Contact *Bill Mason*

Film and video: documentaries only. OUTPUT *The Daimler Benz Story; The History of Motor Racing; The History of the Motor Car.* No need for outside writing; all material is written in-house. The emphasis is on automotive history.

Maverick Television

The Custard Factory, Gibb Street,
Birmingham B9 4AA
☎0121 771 1812   Fax 0121 771 1550

Contact *Tony Steyger, Jonnie Turpie*

FOUNDED 1994. High quality and innovative Hi-8 programming in both documentary and drama. Now expanding into light entertainment and more popular drama. OUTPUT includes *Going for a Song* (antiques panel game, BBC1); *Blazed* (Ch4 drama); *Trade Secrets* (BBC2); *Video Diaries* (BBC1); *Wingnut and the Sprog* (Ch4 drama); *Michelle's Story* (a Comic Relief special, BBC1).

Maya Vision Ltd

43 New Oxford Street, London WC1A 1BH
☎0171 836 1113   Fax 0171 836 5169

Contact *Rebecca Dobbs*

Film and TV: drama and documentary. OUTPUT *Saddam's Killing Fields* (for 'Viewpoint', Central TV); *3 Steps to Heaven* (feature film for BFI/Ch4); *A Place in the Sun* (drama for Ch4/Arts Council); *Barcelona* (for 'Omnibus', BBC1); *North of Vortex* (drama for Ch4/Arts Council); *Out* (several pieces for Ch4's lesbian and gay series). No unsolicited material; commissions only.

Media Set

Unit 8A, Intec 2, Wade Road, Basingstoke,
Hampshire RG24 8NE
☎01256 50022   Fax 01256 50046

Contact *Paul Friend*

Broadcast and corporate television production company. Scripts and ideas for development welcome, including treatments for interactive television and multimedia.

MediSci Healthcare Communications

Stoke Grange, Fir Tree Avenue, Stoke Poges,
Buckinghamshire SL2 4NN
☎01753 516644   Fax 01753 516965

Contact *Peter Fogarty, Caroline Witts, Christine Lowe*

Corporate: medical programmes and training packages for health care professionals. Health care ideas welcome. No unsolicited mss.

Melendez Films

33 Gresse Street, London W1P 1PN
☎0171 323 2311   Fax 0171 323 2331

Contact *Steven Melendez, Graeme Spurway*

Independent producers working with TV stations. Animated films aimed mainly at a family audience, produced largely for the American market, and prime-time network broadcasting. Also develops and produces feature films (eight so far). OUTPUT has included *Peanuts* (half-hour TV specials); *The Lion, the Witch and the Wardrobe; Babar the Elephant* (TV specials); *Dick Deadeye or Duty Done*, a rock musical based on Gilbert & Sullivan operettas; and a video of fairytales *Happily Ever After; Jules Feiffer Series.* Always interested in new ideas. 'Three of the above walked in through the door.' No scripts. Typed outlines/treatments welcome. Enclose s.a.e. for return.

Melrose Film Productions

16 Bromells Road, London
SW4 0BL
☎0171 627 8404   Fax 0171 622 0421

Contact *Alison Roux*

Producers of generic management and staff training films, and interactive programmes.

Mentorn Films

138-140 Wardour Street, London
W1V 3AV
☎0171 287 4545   Fax 0171 287 3728

Contact *Tom Gutteridge, Tom Needham*

FOUNDED in 1985 by ex-BBC arts producer Tom Gutteridge. Producer of successful peak-time show *Challenge Anneka* and Emmy award-winning drama *The Bullion Boys*. Co-producer of Gerry Anderson's *Space Precinct*. Film, video and television: cinema, documentary, drama, music and arts.

Mersey Television Company Ltd

Campus Manor, Childwall Abbey Road, Liverpool L16 0JP
☎0151 722 9122   Fax 0151 722 1969

Contact *Donna Smith*

The best known of the independents in the North of England. Makers of television programmes: drama and fiction serials for popular consumption only. OUTPUT *Brookside; Hollyoaks; And the Beat Goes On* (all for Ch4).

MMW Productions Ltd

26 Woodsford Square, London
W14 8DP
☎0171 602 0657   Fax 0171 602 0657

Contact *Max Morgan-Witts*

Film, video and TV: drama, documentary, corporate and sell-through videos. Literary: joint-author 10 non-fiction books including re-published *Voyage of the Damned; Enola Gay; Guernica*.

MNV

8 Dereham Road, Hingham, Norfolk
NR9 4HU
☎01953 851067/0973 222843
Fax 01953 851067

Contact *Michael Norman*

Video production: corporate, training and communications. Also video publishing and conference television. No unsolicited mss but interested in new writers.

Alan More Films

Suite 205-206, Pinewood Studios,
Pinewood Road, Iver, Buckinghamshire
SL0 0NH
☎01753 656789   Fax 01753 656844

Contact *Alan More, Judith More*

Film, video and TV: documentary, commercials and corporate. No scripts. No need of outside writers.

The Morrison Company

302 Clive Court, Maida Vale, London
W9 1SF
☎0171 289 7976   Fax 0171 289 7976

Contact *Don Morrison*

Film and video: drama, documentary and commercials. Unsolicited mss welcome.

Mosaic Pictures Ltd

2nd Floor, 8-12 Broadwick Street, London
W1V 1FH
☎0171 437 6514/3769   Fax 0171 494 0595

Contact *Colin Luke*

Makers of film for television.

Newgate Company

13 Dafford Street, Larkhall, Bath, Avon
BA1 6SW
☎01225 318335

Contact *Jo Anderson*

A commonwealth of established actors, directors and playwrights, Newgate originally concerned itself solely with theatre writing (at the Bush, Stratford, Roundhouse, etc.) However, in the course of development, several productions have fed into a list of ongoing drama for BBC TV/Ch4. Now looking to develop this co-production strand for film and television projects with other 'Indies'.

Northlight Productions Ltd

The Media Village, Grampian Television,
Queen's Cross, Aberdeen AB9 4XJ
☎01224 646460   Fax 01224 646450

Contact *Robert Sproul-Cran*

Film, video and TV: drama, documentary and corporate work. OUTPUT ranges from high-end corporate fund-raising videos for the National Museum of Scotland to *Anything But Temptation*, a feature film currently in development, and *Calcutta Chronicles* (5-part documentary series for Ch4). Scripts welcome. Has links with EAVE (European Audio-Visual Entrepreneurs) and Media 95.

Open Media

Ground Floor, 9 Leamington Road Villas,
London W11 1HS
☎0171 229 5416   Fax 0171 221 4842

Contact *Alice Kramers, Sebastian Cody*

Broadcast television: OUTPUT *After Dark; The
Secret Cabaret; James Randi Psychic Investigator;
Opinions; Is This Your Life?; Don't Quote Me;
Brave New World; The Talking Show.*

Open Mind Productions

6 Newburgh Street, London W1V 1LH
☎0171 437 0624   Fax 0171 434 9256

Directors *Chris Ellis, Roland Tongue*

Video and TV production, including documentary and educational. OUTPUT *Investigating
Britain* (BBC); *Living Proof* (Ch4); *The
Geography Programme: Images of the Earth* (for
BBC Schools TV); *Eureka: The Earth in Space;
Geography, Start Here: The Local Network; Rat-a-
tat-tat; One Last Lie* (for Ch4 Schools). No
unsolicited material. Currently developing
children's drama series. 'We are a small company interested in programmes that reflect our
name. We want to produce more drama and
multi-media resources.' Chris Ellis, a writer
himself, is a guest lecturer on scriptwriting with
BBC TV Training and the London Media
Workshop.

Original Film & Video Productions Ltd

Greek Court, 14A Old Compton Street,
London W1V 5PE
☎0171 734 9721   Fax 0171 437 1782

Contact *Boyd Catling*

Corporate film and video: commercials, broadcast TV and video publishing. Unsolicited mss
welcome. Some writing is commissioned by
clients themselves and some is originated in-
house.

Orpheus Productions

6 Amyand Park Gardens, Twickenham,
Middlesex TW1 3HS
☎0181 892 3172   Fax 0181 892 4821

Contact *Richard Taylor*

Television documentaries and corporate work.
OUTPUT has included programmes for BBC
Current Affairs, Music and Arts, and the
African–Caribbean Unit as well as documen-
taries for the Shell Film Unit and Video Arts.
Unsolicited scripts are welcomed with caution.
'We have a preference for visually stirring doc-
umentaries with quality writing of the more

personal and idiosyncratic kind, not straight
reportage.'

Ovation Productions

Osprey House, 10 Little Portland Street,
London W1N 5DF
☎0171 637 8575   Fax 0171 580 5686

Contact *John Plews*

Corporate video and conference scripts.
Unsolicited mss not welcome. 'We talk to new
writers from time to time.'

Oxford Scientific Films Ltd

Lower Road, Long Hanborough, Oxfordshire
OX8 8LL
☎01993 881881   Fax 01993 882808

10 Poland Street, London W1V 3DE
☎0171 494 0720   Fax 0171 287 9125

Managing Director *Karen Goldie-Morrison*

Established independent media company with
specialist knowledge and expertise in award-
winning natural history films and science-based
programmes. Film, video and TV: documentaries, TV commercials, multimedia, and educational films. Scripts welcome. Operates an
extensive stills and film footage library specialising in wildlife and special effects (see **Picture
Libraries**).

Pace Productions Ltd

12 The Green, Newport Pagnell,
Buckinghamshire MK16 0JW
☎01908 618767   Fax 01908 617641

Contact *Chris Pettit*

Film and video: drama, documentary, corporate and commercials.

Pacesetter Productions Ltd

New Barn House, Leith Hill Lane, Ockley,
Surrey RH5 5PH
☎01306 621433   Fax 0171 732 5911

Contact *Adele Spencer, Ronnie Spencer*

Film and video producers of drama, documen-
tary and corporate work. OUTPUT *History of the
Telephone; Pictures from the Past; The Wheatfield;
Merchant of Wood Street* (the latter two feature
films in development). CLIENTS include British
Telecom, British Gas, Midland Bank, Lloyds
Bank. No unsolicited scripts.

Barry Palin Associates Ltd

143 Charing Cross Road, London
WC2H 0EE
☎0171 439 0039   Fax 0171 494 1305

Contact *Barry Palin*

Film, video and TV production for drama, documentary, commercials and corporate material. OUTPUT *Harmfulness of Tobacco* Anton Chekhov short story – BAFTA Best Short Film Award-winner (Ch4); Corporate: Kraft Jacobs Suchard. Unsolicited scripts welcome. New writing encouraged.

Paper Moon Productions
Wychwood House, Burchetts Green Lane, Littlewick Green, Nr. Maidenhead, Berkshire SL6 3QW
☎01628 829819   Fax 01628 822428
Contact *David Haggas*
Television and video: medical and health education documentaries. OUTPUT includes *Shamans and Science*, a medical documentary examining the balance between drugs discovered in nature and those synthesised in laboratories. Unsolicited scripts welcome. Interested in new writing 'from people who really understand television programme-making'.

Parallax Pictures Ltd
7 Denmark Street, London WC2H 8LS
☎0171 836 1478   Fax 0171 497 8062
Contact *Sally Hibbin*
Feature films/television drama. OUTPUT *Riff-Raff; Bad Behaviour; Raining Stones; Ladybird, Ladybird; I.D.; Land and Freedom; The Englishman Who Went up a Hill But Came Down a Mountain; Bliss.*

Philip Partridge Productions Ltd
The High Street, South Woodchester, Nr Stroud, Glos. GL5 5EL
☎01453 872743   Fax 01453 872743
Contact *Phil Partridge*
Film and TV producers for drama and comedy material. OUTPUT *Once Upon a Time in the North* Tim Firth six 30-minute comedies on film (BBC1). Unsolicited scripts welcome 'providing writers are patient while they're read'. Particularly interested in developing new writing with writers who are totally committed.

PBF Motion Pictures
The Little Pickenhanger, Tuckey Grove, Ripley, Surrey GU23 6JG
☎01483 225179   Fax 01483 224118
Contact *Peter B. Fairbrass*
Film, video and TV: drama, documentary, commercials and corporate. Also televised chess series and chess videos. OUTPUT *Grandmaster Chess* (in association with Thames TV); *Glue Sniffing; RN*

Special Services; Nightfrights (night-time TV chiller series). CLIENTS include GEC-Marconi, Coca Cola, MoD, Marks & Spencer, various government departments, British Consulate. No scripts; send one-page synopsis only in the first instance. Good scripts which relate to current projects will be followed up, otherwise not, as PBF do not have the time to reply to proposals which do not interest them. Only good writing stands a chance.

Pelicula Films
7 Queen Margaret Road, Glasgow G20 6DP
☎0141 945 3333   Fax 0141 946 8345
Contact *Mike Alexander*
Television producers. Makers of drama documentaries and music programmes for Ch4 and the BBC. OUTPUT *As an Eilean (From the Island); Gramsci; Down Home; Scapa Flow 1919; The Jazz Apple; The Land of Europe.*

Pentagon Communications
Anchor House, The Maltings, Hull, Humberside HU1 3HA
☎01482 226298   Fax 01482 226245
Contact *Jon Levy*
Mainly corporate; also TV documentary, drama and commercials. Unsolicited mss welcome.

Penumbra Productions Ltd
21A Brondesbury Villas, London NW6 6AH
☎0171 328 4550   Fax 0171 328 3844
Contact *H. O. Nazareth*
Film, video, TV and radio: drama, documentary and information videos on health, housing, arts and political documentaries. OUTPUT includes *Repomen* (Cutting Edge, Ch4); *Doctors and Torture* (Inside Story, BBC); *Bombay & Jazz* (BBC2); *Awaaz* (information video in eight languages for Kings Fund/Manchester Council for Community Relations); *When Shura Met Hobie* (BBC Radio 3). In development: *Slave Brides* (for TV/cinema). Film treatments, drama proposals and documentary synopses welcome. Keen to assist in the development of new writing but only interested in social issue-based material.

PHI Television Ltd
Wood Farm, Peasenhall, Suffolk IP17 2HG
☎01728 660252   Fax 01728 660306
Contact *David Holmans*
Television drama, games and light entertainment. OUTPUT *Operation Julie; Treasure Hunt;*

Bullseye; Jangles. No scripts in the first instance. Send one-page outlines only.

Picture Palace Films Ltd
53A Brewer Street, London W1R 3FD
☎0171 734 6630   Fax 0171 734 8574
Contact *Malcolm Craddock*

Leading independent producer of TV drama. OUTPUT *Sharpe's Rifles* (11 x 2-hour films for Central TV); *Little Napoleons* (4-part comedy drama for Ch4); *The Orchid House* (4-part drama series for Ch4); numerous episodes for *Eurocops; Tandoori Nights; 4 Minutes; When Love Dies; Ping Pong* (feature film).

Phil Pilley Productions
Ferryside, Felix Lane, Shepperton, Middlesex TW17 8NG
☎01932 246455   Fax 01932 246455
Contact *Phil Pilley*

Programmes for TV and video, mainly sports, including documentaries for the BBC, ITV, Ch4 and the US. Also books, newspapers and magazine features, mainly sports. Unsolicited ideas and synopses welcome.

Planet 24 Ltd
The Planet Building, Thames Quay, 195 Marsh Wall, London E14 9SG
☎0171 345 2424   Fax 0171 345 9400
Executive Producer/Managing Director
   Charles Parsons

Television and radio producers of light entertainment, comedy and music programmes. OUTPUT TV: *The Big Breakfast; The Word; The Messiah* (live recording); *Hotel Babylon; Gaytime TV; Delicious*. Radio: *Entertainment Superhighway; Straight Up; Rock Wives; Pulp*. Unsolicited scripts welcome.

Platinum Film & TV Production Ltd
79 Islip Street, London NW5 2DL
☎0171 916 9091   Fax 0171 916 5238
Contact *Terry Kelleher*

Television documentaries, including drama-documentary. OUTPUT *South Africa's Black Economy* (Ch4); *Murder at the Farm* (Thames TV); *The Biggest Robbery in the World* (major investigative true-crime drama-documentary for Carlton TV). Scripts and treatments welcome.

Portman Productions
105 Ladbroke Grove, London W11 1TG
☎0171 468 3400   Fax 0171 468 3499

Head of Development *Katherine Butler*
Cinema and television drama. Synopses in the first instance, please.

Premiere Productions Ltd
16 Castello Avenue, London SW15 6EA
☎0181 785 2933   Fax 0181 780 1684
Contact *Peter Fudakowski*

Film and video: drama and corporate, including dramatised training videos. Currently looking for feature film scripts, with Anglo/American/East European themes. Preference for stories with humour. No horror or sci-fi. Please enclose a list of previous submissions and return postage.

Primetime plc
Seymour Mews House, Seymour Mews, Wigmore Street, London W1H 9PE
☎0171 935 9000   Fax 0171 935 1992
Contact *Richard Price, Simon Willock*

Television distribution and packaging, plus international co-productions. OUTPUT *An Evening with Sir Peter Ustinov; Porgy and Bess* (BBC, Homevale, Greg Smith); *Re:Joyce* (BBC); *The CIA* (BBC/A&E/NRK); *José Carreras - A Life* (LWT); *Othello* (BBC); *Ustinov on the Orient Express* (A&E/CBC/NOB/JMP); *Ethan Frome* (American Playhouse). Works closely with associated US company, Primetime Entertainment. No unsolicited scripts.

Prometheus Productions
Maughanby Farm, Little Salkeld, Penrith, Cumbria CA10 1NP
☎01768 898334   Fax 01768 897084
Contact *Clem Shaw*

Film and TV: drama and documentary. OUTPUT Documentaries: *Cutting Edge; Encounters* (Ch4); *Secret History*. Drama: *Batman Can't Fly* (BBC Screen 2); *Conchies; State Control; Foreign Affairs* (feature film). Keen to seek out, encourage and promote new writing. Scripts via agents welcome.

Red Lion Communications Ltd
76 Cleveland Street, London W1P 5DS
☎0171 323 4540   Fax 0171 323 0263
Contact *Mike Kilcooley*

Video producers: commercials, training and corporate work, including product launch videos, in-house training, open learning, multimedia programmes, etc. 'We are always on the look-out for new, well thought through ideas for broadcast.'

Red Rooster Film and Television Entertainment

29 Floral Street, London WC2E 9DP
☎0171 379 7727   Fax 0171 379 5756

Contact *Linda James*

Film and TV drama. OUTPUT *The Sculptress; Crocodile Shoes; Body & Soul; The Life and Times of Henry Pratt; Smokescreen.* No unsolicited scripts. Encourages new writers; 'recommend that they find an agent'.

Renaissance Vision

15 Capitol House, Heigham Street, Norwich, Norfolk NR2 4TE
☎01603 767272   Fax 01603 768163

Contact *B. Gardner*

Video: full range of corporate work (training, sales, promotional, etc.). Producers of educational and special-interest video publications. Willing to consider good ideas and proposals.

Richmond Films & Television Ltd

5 Dean Street, London W1V 5RN
☎0171 734 9313   Fax 0171 287 2058

Contact *Sandra Hastie*

Film and TV: drama, comedy and children's. OUTPUT *Press Gang; The Lodge.* Scripts welcome provided they are accompanied by explanatory note with regard to where they have been submitted previously and the response they received, plus a list of credits. A treatment or synopsis must be included. 'We are quite prepared to use new writers if they are good.'

Roberts & Wykeham Films

7 Barb Mews, Hammersmith, London W6 7PA
☎0171 602 4897   Fax 0171 602 3016

Contact *S. Wykeham*

Television documentaries and packaging. OUTPUT *The Late Late Show* 1988-1996 (post-production package for Ch4); Ch4 'Dispatches': *Trail of Red Mercury; Mandela's Nuclear Nightmare;* BBC 'Everyman': *Road Back to Hell.* No unsolicited scripts.

Rose Bay Film Productions

6th Floor, 76 Oxford Street, London W1N 0AT
☎0171 412 0400   Fax 0171 412 0300

Contact *Matthew Steiner, Simon Usiskin*

Film and TV production for drama, entertainment and documentary. Unsolicited scripts welcome.

Saffron Productions Ltd

Craigs End, Stambourne, Halstead, Essex CO9 4NQ
☎01440 785200   Fax 01440 785775

Contact *Victor Pemberton, David Spenser*

Film and TV production for drama and documentary. OUTPUT *Omnibus* Arts documentaries (BBC) (Emmy Award Winners); *Keys of the Kingdom* 4 x 60 mins drama series (BBC); *Our Family* 3 x 90 mins drama series (BBC); *The Animated Dickens* 6 x 30 mins series. Also a variety of other programmes. Unsolicited scripts welcome. Keen to promote new writers and experienced writers of any age.

Sands Films

119 Rotherhithe Street, London SE16 4NF
☎0171 231 2209   Fax 0171 231 2119

Contact *Richard Goodwin, Christine Edzard*

Film and TV drama. OUTPUT *Little Dorrit; The Fool; As You Like It; A Dangerous Man; The Long Day Closes; A Passage to India.* In development: *Buddenbrooks.* No unsolicited scripts.

Scala Productions

39-43 Brewer Street, London W1R 3FD
☎0171 734 7060   Fax 0171 437 3248

Contact *Stephen Woolley, Nik Powell, Elisabeth Karlsen, Amanda Posey, Finola Dwyer*

Production company set up by ex-Palace Productions Nik Powell and Steve Woolley, who have an impressive list of credits including *Company of Wolves; Absolute Beginners; Mona Lisa; Scandal; Crying Game; Backbeat; Hollow Reed; Neon Bible.* Projects in development: *Jonathan Wild; Dead Heart; Mort; The Lost Son; Wise Children.*

Schwops Productions

34 Ashton Road, Luton, Bedfordshire LU1 3QE
☎01582 412622   Fax 01582 412095

Contact *Maureen Brown*

Video producer of drama, documentary and corporate material. Areas of interest include music, travel, ballet, medical and training material. Also distribution, facilities, duplication, and sell-through videos. Open-minded to new writing. Scripts welcome.

Scope Picture Productions Ltd

Keppie House, 147 Blythswood Street, Glasgow G2 4EN
☎0141 332 7720   Fax 0141 332 1049

TV Commercials *Sharon Fullarton*

Corporate *Bill Gordon*

Corporate film and video; broadcast documentaries and sport; TV commercials. Unsolicited mss, realistic scripts/ideas welcome.

Screen First Ltd

The Studios, Funnells Farm, Down Street, Nutley, East Sussex TN22 3LG
☎01825 712034/5   Fax 01825 713511
Contact *M. Thomas, P. Madden*

Television dramas, documentaries, arts and animation programmes. OUTPUT *Secret Passions* series I, II, III, IV (presenting new animation for Ch4). Developing major drama series and animation special. No unsolicited scripts.

Screen Ventures Ltd

49 Goodge Street, London
W1P 1FB
☎0171 580 7448   Fax 0171 631 1265
Contact *Christopher Mould, David Chambers*

Film and TV sales and production: documentary, music videos and drama. OUTPUT *Woodstock Diary; Vanessa Redgrave* (LWT 'South Bank Show'); *Mojo Working; Burma: Dying for Democracy* (Ch4); *Genet* (LWT 'South Bank Show'); *Dani Dares* (Ch4 series on strong women).

Securicor Communication & Media Services

15 Carshalton Road, Sutton, Surrey
SM1 4LE
☎0181 770 7000   Fax 0181 722 2672
Contact *Paul Fahey, Gill Arney*

Television producers of drama, documentary and corporate material. OUTPUT includes promotional, information and training videos for the Securicor Group and selected clients. Also audio, print design and production. Unsolicited scripts are sometimes welcome.

SelecTV plc

45 Foubert's Place, London
W1V 2DN
☎0171 434 3060   Fax 0171 494 1421

Comprising Alomo, Clement/La Frenais and WitzEnd Productions. Producers of television drama and comedy. OUTPUT *Pie In the Sky; Goodnight Sweetheart; Birds of a Feather; Love Hurts; Lovejoy; The New Statesman; Tracey Ullman: A Class Act; Over the Rainbow.* Scripts not welcome unless via agents but new writing is encouraged.

Seventh House Films

1 Hall Farm Place, Bawburgh, Norwich, Norfolk NR9 3LW
☎01603 749068   Fax 01603 749069
Contact *Clive Dunn, Angela Rule*

Documentary for film, video and TV. OUTPUT *A Pleasant Terror* (life and ghosts of M. R. James); *Piano Pieces* (musical excursion exploring different aspects of the piano); *Rockin' the Boat* (memories of pirate radio); *White Knuckles* (on the road with a travelling funfair); *King Romance* (life of Henry Rider Haggard); *A Drift of Angels* (three women and the price of art); *Bare Heaven* (the life and fiction of L. P. Hartley); *A Swell of the Soil* (life of Alfred Munnings); *Light Out of the Sky* (the art and life of Edward Seago). 'We welcome programme proposals with a view to collaborative co-production. Always interested in original and refreshing expressions for visual media.'

Sianco Cyf

Tŷr Drindod, y Sgwâr, Porthaethwy, Gwynedd LL59 5EE
☎01248 715005   Fax 01248 715006
Contact *Siân Teifi*

Children's, youth and education programmes. Children's drama.

Signals, Essex Media Centre

21 St Peter's Street, Colchester, Essex
CO1 1EW
☎01206 560255   Fax 01206 369086
Coordinator *Caroline Norbury*

Promotion and documentary work for the voluntary and arts sectors. Specialists in media education projects. No unsolicited mss.

Siriol Productions

3 Mount Stuart Square, Butetown, Cardiff
CF1 6RW
☎01222 488400   Fax 01222 485962
Contact *Andrew Offiler*

Animated series, mainly for children. OUTPUT includes *The Hurricanes; Tales of the Toothfairies; Billy the Cat,* as well as the feature films, *Under Milkwood* and *The Princess and the Goblin.* Write with ideas and sample script in the first instance.

Skyline Film & TV Productions Ltd

PO Box 8210, London W4 1WH
☎0181 741 4500   Fax 0181 995 2117
Contact *Mairi Bett*

Television programmes, educational, drama and feature films. Suppliers of programmes to all major broadcasters. Always interested in new ideas/talent; written submissions only, please.

Sleeping Giant Films
56-58 Clerkenwell Road, London
EC1M 5PX
☎0171 490 5060   Fax 0171 490 5060
Contact *Harriet Pacaud*

Documentary film producer. OUTPUT includes *Kirkby's Kingdom*, the story of a Yorkshire smallholder whose land is threatened by property developers. Interested in original ideas with strong visual potential on environmental, natural history, arts and cultural themes. No fiction-based material. Happy to look at documentary ideas. Commentary writers used.

Smith & Watson Productions
The Gothic House, Fore Street, Totnes,
South Devon TQ9 5EH
☎01803 863033   Fax 01803 864219
Contact *Chris Watson, Nick Smith*

Film, video and TV: documentaries, drama, party political broadcasts (for the Liberal Democrats), and commercials. In production: *The Lads* (ITV series). Unsolicited mss welcome. Interested in new writing.

Solo Vision Ltd
49-53 Kensington High Street, London
W8 5ED
☎0171 376 2166   Fax 0171 938 3165
Contact *Don Short*

Video and TV: documentary, game shows, and corporate work. OUTPUT *Starmate* (the astrology game); *Surrogate Grandmother* (documentary, LWT/Cable USA); plus video packaging.

Specific Films
25 Rathbone Street, London
W1P 1AG
☎0171 580 7476   Fax 0171 494 2676
Contact *Michael Hamlyn, Melanie Claus*

FOUNDED 1976. Currently working on *My Entire Life* – a feature film co-produced by PolyGram and the AFFC. OUTPUT includes *The Adventures of Priscilla, Queen of the Desert* a full-length feature film co-produced with Latent Image (Australia) and financed by PolyGram and AFFC; *U2 Rattle and Hum* (full-length feature film – part concert film/part cinema verité documentary); and numerous pop promos for major international artists.

Spectel Productions Ltd
184 Alcester Road South, Kings Heath,
Birmingham B14 6DE
☎0121 443 5958   Fax 0121 443 5958
Contact *David Webster*

Film and video: documentary and corporate; also video publishing. No unsolicited scripts.

Spellbound Productions Ltd
90 Cowdenbeath Path, Twyford Street,
London N1 0LG
☎0171 278 0052   Fax 0171 278 0052
Contact *Paul Harris*

Film and television drama. OUTPUT includes *Leave to Remain* for 'Film on 4'. Unsolicited scripts welcome. Please enclose s.a.e. for return of material. Keen to support and encourage new writing.

SPI 1980 Ltd
27 Old Gloucester Street, London
WC1N 3XX
☎0171 435 1007
Contact *Victor Schonfeld*

Drama, arts, current affairs, documentary, films for TV and cinema. OUTPUT includes *It's a Boy!; MoneyLove; Shattered Dreams, Picking Up the Pieces; The Animals Film; Courage Along the Divide; And I Don't Have to Do the Dishes.* Send a brief letter prior to submission of unsolicited material.

'Spoken' Image Ltd
The Design Centre, 44 Canal Street,
Manchester M1 3WD
☎0161 236 7522   Fax 0161 236 0020
Contact *Geoff Allman, Steve Jones, Steve Foster, Phil Griffin*

Film, video and TV production for documentary and corporate material. Specialising in high-quality brochures and reports, exhibitions, conferences, film and video production for broadcast, industry and commerce. Unsolicited scripts welcome. Interested in educational, and historical new writing, mainly for broadcast programmes.

Stephens Kerr Ltd
Braycrest House, 8-12 Camden High Street,
London NW1 0JH
☎0171 916 2124   Fax 0171 916 2125
Contact *Eleanor Stephens*

Film, video and TV: drama and documentary. OUTPUT *Sex Talk; Love Talk; Men Talk; The*

Love Weekend (all for Ch4); *Nights; Food File.* Unsolicited scripts welcome. Keen to support new writing.

Straight Forward Film & Television Productions Ltd
Crescent Studios, 18 High Street, Holywood, Co. Down BT18 9AD
☎01232 427697   Fax 01232 422289
Contact *Moya Neeson, John Nicholson, Ian Kennedy*

Video and TV: documentary and corporate work. OUTPUT *Close to Home* (Ch4 documentary); *Greenfingers* (BBC/RTE gardening series); *Places Apart* (BBC Northern Ireland); plus various corporates for local industry which are handled by the sister company Morrow Communications. Unsolicited scripts welcome. New work in drama and documentary fields welcome, particulary if with a strong Irish theme, contemporary or historical.

Strawberry Productions Ltd
36 Priory Avenue, London W4 1TY
☎0181 994 4494   Fax 0181 742 7675
Contact *John Black*

Film, video and TV: drama and documentary; corporate and video publishing.

Supervision (West) Ltd
26-27 West Street, Horsham, West Sussex RH12 1PB
☎01403 274488   Fax 01403 269264
Contact *Charles Marriott, Teresa Reed*

Film, video and TV: drama, documentary, corporate, sell-through videos, and commercials, including radio. Unsolicited scripts welcome. New writing supported if good.

Swanlind Communication
The Wharf, Bridge Street, Birmingham B1 2JR
☎0121 616 1701   Fax 0121 616 1520
Managing Director *Peter Stack*

Producer of business television and internal communication strategies.

Table Top Productions
1 The Orchard, Chiswick, London W4 1JZ
☎0181 742 0507   Fax 0181 742 0507
Contact *Alvin Rakoff*

TV and film. OUTPUT *Paradise Postponed* (TV mini-series); *A Voyage Round My Father; The First Olympics 1896; Dirty Tricks.* No unsolicited mss. Also Dancetime Ltd.

Talisman Films Ltd
5 Addison Place, London W11 4RJ
☎0171 603 7474   Fax 0171 602 7422
Contact *Alan Shallcross*

Drama for film and TV: developing the full range of drama – TV series, serials and single films, as well as theatric features. 'We will only consider material submitted via literary agents.' Interested in supporting and encouraging new writing.

TalkBack Productions
36 Percy Street, London W1P 0LN
☎0171 323 9777   Fax 0171 637 5105
Managing Director *Peter Fincham*

Independent TV production company set up in 1981 by comedians Mel Smith and Griff Rhys Jones. Specialises in comedy, comedy drama and drama; also corporate and training films. OUTPUT *Smith and Jones; Murder Most Horrid; Bonjour la Classe; Demob; The Day Today; Paris; Knowing Me Knowing You with Alan Patridge; Milner; Loose Talk; In Search of Happiness; They Think It's All Over.*

Tandem TV & Film Ltd
10 Bargrove Avenue, Hemel Hempstead, Hertfordshire HP1 1QP
☎01442 61576   Fax 01442 219250
Contact *Barbara Page*

Film and video production for drama, documentary and corporate material, including dramatised health and safety programmes for training; series of five-minute programmes for television, corporate programmes for various companies. Specialises in construction and civil engineering films, and Christian programming. Writers are usually commissioned. Welcomes new writing.

Teamwork Productions
Gate House, Walderton, Chichester, West Sussex PO18 9ED
☎01705 631384/0378 776640
Contact *Rob Widdows*

Video and TV producer of documentary, corporate and commercial work. OUTPUT includes motor racing coverage, motor sport productions and corporate motor sport videos. Good ideas will always be considered. No scripts.

Telemagination Ltd
41 Buckingham Palace Road, London SW1W 0PP
☎0171 828 5331   Fax 0171 828 7631

Contact *John M. Mills*

Producers of television animation. OUTPUT includes *The Animals of Farthing Wood*, 39 half-hour episodes for children's television. Original animated adult and comedy sitcoms for TV. Unsolicited outlines welcome either in writing or by phone. No new writings considered unless the outlines have been discussed first.

Televideo Productions

Sovereign House, 3–7 Sidney Street, Sheffield, South Yorkshire S1 4RG
☎0114 2491500   Fax 0114 2491505
Contact *Graham King*

Video and television: TV news and sports coverage, documentary and corporate work; sell-through videos (distributed on own label). OUTPUT includes *The Premier Collection* (football club videos); varied sports coverage for cable, satellite and terrestrial broadcasters plus a wide range of corporate work from drama-based material to documentary.

Teliesyn

Helwick House, 19 David Street, Cardiff CF1 2EH
☎01222 667556   Fax 01222 667546
Director of Production *Carmel Gahan*

Film and video: produces drama, documentary, music and social action in English and Welsh. Celtic Film Festival, BAFTA Cymru, Grierson and Indie award winner. OUTPUT *Branwen* (90 minute feature film for S4C); *Reel Truth* (drama doc series on the history of early film for S4C and Ch4); *Subway Cops and the Mole Kings* (Ch4); *Dragon's Song* (music series for schools, Ch4); *Codi Clawr Hanes II* (a second drama-documentary series on women's history for S4C). Will consider unsolicited mss only if accompanied by synopsis and c.v. Encourages new writing wherever possible, in close association with a producer.

Tern Television Productions Ltd

73 Crown Street, Aberdeen AB1 2EX
☎01224 211123   Fax 01224 211199
74 Victoria Crescent Road, Glasgow G12 9JN
☎ 0141 337 2892
Contact *David Strachan, Gwyneth Hardy, Nick Ibbotson*

Broadcast, video, corporate and training. Specialises in religious and factual entertainment. Currently developing drama. Unsolicited mss welcome.

Thames Television Ltd

Broom Road, Teddington Lock, Middlesex TW11 9NT
☎0181 614 2800
Managing Director *Mike Phillips*
Controller of Production *Keith Mosedale*
Head of Drama *Antony Root*
Head of Entertainment *John Fisher*

UK's largest independent and distribution company. OUTPUT includes *The Bill; This is Your Life; Strike it Lucky; Take Your Pick; Wish You Were Here?*

Theatre of Comedy Co.

See **Theatre Producers**

Huw Thomas & Associates

17 Brunswick Gardens, London W8 4AS
☎0171 727 9953   Fax 0171 727 9931
Contact *Anne E. Thomas*

Video and TV: documentary and corporate; also media training. CLIENTS include Lloyd's of London, Nestlé, Morgan Crucible. No unsolicited scripts.

Tiger Aspect Productions

5 Soho Square, London W1V 5DE
☎0171 434 0672   Fax 0171 287 1448
Contact *Charles Brand*

Television producers for documentary programmes, drama and comedy – variety, sitcom and comedy drama. OUTPUT *Mr Bean; The Thin Blue Line; The Vicar of Dibley; Our Man In (Series 1 & 2); Sean Hughes is Thirtysomehow; Harry Enfield and Chums; The Village; Just for Laughs; Paul Merton's Life of Comedy; Heroes and Villains.* Unsolicited mss read but a higher priority is given to work submitted through agents. Writers submitting work on spec. should bear in mind that when the volume of material is heavy, it can take up to three months to respond. Writers are advised to submit a brief c.v. with scripts.

Tonfedd

Uned 33, Cibyn, Caernarfon, Gwynedd LL55 2BD
☎01286 676800   Fax 01286 676466
Contact *Hefin Elis*

Light entertainment, music.

Alan Torjussen Productions Ltd

17 Heol Wen, Cardiff CF4 6EG
☎01222 624669   Fax 01222 624669
Contact *Alan Torjussen*

Film, video and TV production for drama, documentary, commercials and corporate material. Particularly interested in all types of documentary, education, schools and drama. Background includes work in the Welsh language. Unsolicited scripts welcome, particularly if about Wales by Welsh writers (includes Welsh language scripts). Also original ideas for comedy and documentary/dramas.

Touch Productions Ltd
3rd Floor, 14–18 Heddon Street, London W1R 8DP
☎0171 287 5520   Fax 0171 437 3675
Contact *Will Aslett*

Main output consists of human-interest documentaries. OUTPUT network documentaries including programmes for *Inside Story*, *Cutting Edge*, *Modern Times*, *QED*, *Dispatches*, and *Short Stories*.

Transatlantic Films Production and Distribution Company
184 Kensington Church Street, London W8 4DP
☎0171 727 0132   Fax 0171 603 5049
Contact *Revel Guest*

Producers of TV documentaries. OUTPUT *Greek Fire* 10 x 30 mins on Greek culture (Ch4); *Four American Composers* 4 x 1 hour (Ch4); *The Horse in Sport* 8 x 1 hour (Ch4); *A Year in the Life of Placido Domingo*. No unsolicited scripts. Interested in new writers to write 'the book of the series', e.g. for *Greek Fire* and *The Horse in Sport*, but not usually drama script writers.

Turning Point Productions
Pinewood Studios, Pinewood Road, Iver Heath, Buckinghamshire SL0 0NH
☎01753 630666   Fax 01753 650855
Contact *Adrian Bate*

Television drama producer. OUTPUT includes *Red Fox* (mini-series for LWT). No unsolicited scripts. Very keen to nurture new writing talent though.

TurnOver Titles
c/o Media Set, Unit 8A, Intec 2, Wade Road, Basingstoke, Hampshire RG24 8NE
☎01256 50022   Fax 01256 50046
Contact *Paul Friend*

A television and film production company. Looking to produce and develop original scripts and ideas for big and small screen. Mainly interested in sitcoms and drama series, also radical and cult ideas for low budget programming. Write in the first instance, please.

Twentieth Century Fox Productions Ltd
Twentieth Century House, 31–32 Soho Square, London W1V 6AP
☎0171 437 7766   Fax 0171 434 2170

London office of the American giant.

Two Four Productions Ltd
Quay West Studios, Old Newnham, Plymouth, Devon PL7 5BH
☎01752 345424   Fax 01752 344244
Managing Director *Charles Wace*
Senior Producer *Charles Boydell*

Video and television: drama, documentary, commercials and corporate. OUTPUT includes *Close to Home: Journey for Life* (current affairs for Ch4); *The West at Work* (business magazine for Westcountry Television); *Great Westerners* (documentary for HTV) and *The Church in Crisis* (current affairs programme for BBC2 South West). Currently in production are *On the Moor* (a 6-part documentary filmed inside Dartmoor Prison); *HMP Dartmoor* (ITV network); *Soul Mates* and *The Right Thing* (two 13-part series for satellite television); and *Westcountry Focus* (a series of weekly business programmes for Westcountry Television). Ideas welcome.

Two Plus Two Videographics
6 Lake End Court, Bath Road, Taplow, Maidenhead, Berkshire SL6 0JQ
☎01628 668099/77   Fax 01628 668055
Contact *Barry Tyler*

Producers of corporate, training, and promotional videos. Most work is done for blue chip companies. Unsolicited scripts welcome 'but we don't want to be swamped especially with "follow up" phone calls'.

Two Sides TV Ltd
53A Brewer Street, London W1R 3FD
☎0171 439 9882   Fax 0171 287 2289
Managing Director *Catherine Robins*

Broadcast TV including children's programmes such as *The Adventures of Captain Zeelig* for ITV. Always looking for fresh new children's writing with a humorous edge. Also documentaries ('Equinox', 'Under the Sun') for Ch4 and BBC.

UBA Ltd

6 Cambridge Street, London SW6 2EE
☎0171 371 0160   Fax 0171 384 3181
Contact *Peter Shaw*

Quality feature films and TV for an international market. OUTPUT *Windprints; The Lonely Passion of Judith Hearne* (co-production with **HandMade Films Ltd**); *Taffin; Castaway; Turtle Diary.* In development: *Hunting the Devil; A Witch in New York; Sweeney Todd; Leo, The Magnificent; The Honeytrap; Kinder Garden; Keep the Aspidistra Flying; Paul Robeson.* Prepared to commission new writing whether adapted from another medium or based on a short outline/treatment. Concerned with the quality of the script (*Turtle Diary* was written by Harold Pinter) and breadth of appeal. 'Exploitation material' not welcome.

United International Pictures (UK)

Mortimer House, 37–41 Mortimer Street,
London W1A 2JL
☎0171 636 1655   Fax 0171 636 4118

UK office of American giant; distributes for Paramount.

United Media Ltd

68 Berwick Street, London W1V 3PE
☎0171 287 2396   Fax 0171 287 2398
Contact *Mr N. Mackie*

Film, video and TV: drama. OUTPUT *To the Lighthouse* (TV movie with BBC); *Jamaica Inn* (HTV mini-series); *The Krays* (feature film with Fugitive/Rank). Unsolicited scripts welcome but synopses preferred in the first instance. 'We encourage new writing if we see commercially orientated talent.'

Upstream Presentation Ltd

Ridings House, 66 Alma Road, Windsor,
Berkshire SL4 3EZ
☎01753 858895   Fax 01753 864123
Contact *Peter Wrigglesworth, Nick Woollard*

Film, video and TV: documentary and corporate, plus conferences and live events. Upstream provides a broad range of business communication services for major European clients, covering employee communications, sales promotion, corporate image and video news releases. Also sell-through video production. 'We welcome writers from advertising and broadcast who seek opportunities in the corporate sector.'

Vanson Productions

2 Cairns Way, London SW11 1ES
☎0171 223 1919/801 7020   Fax 0171 924 4072
Contact *Yvette Vanson*

Film, video and TV: drama and arts documentaries. OUTPUT *Making Advances* (BBC1), a five part series on sexual harassment at work presented by Emma Freud; *How Low Can You Go?* (Ch4 'Critical Eye'); *Law Matters* (Granada 'This Morning'); *Presumed Guilty* (BBC1 'Inside Story'). Supportive of new writing.

Vera Productions

30–38 Dock Street, Leeds, West Yorkshire
LS10 1JF
☎0113 2428646   Fax 0113 2451238
Contact *Alison Garthwaite, Catherine Mitchell*

Video: drama, documentary, corporate, promotional, training and campaigning material. OUTPUT *There's More to Drugs Than Dying; Children Who Foster; I Want to be an Astronaut; Video 28* (celebration and record of lesbians' response to Section 28 of the Local Government Bill); *International Women's Day; Gender on the Timetable.* Unsolicited mss welcome from women only. New writers welcome.

Video Arts (Production) Ltd

Dumbarton House, 68 Oxford Street, London
W1N 0LH
☎0171 637 7288   Fax 0171 580 8103
Contact *Margaret Tree*

Film and video, CDi and CD-ROM: training, corporate and educational.

Video Enterprises

12 Barbers Wood Road, High Wycombe,
Buckinghamshire HP12 4EP
☎01494 534144 (mobile: 0831 875216)
Fax 01494 534144
Contact *Maurice R. Fleisher*

Video and TV, mainly corporate: business and industrial training, promotional material and conferences. No unsolicited material 'but always ready to try out good new writers'.

Video Newsreels

Church Cottage, Ruscombe, Nr Twyford,
Berkshire RG10 9UB
☎01734 321123   Fax 01734 321333
Contact *Gerry Clarke*

Corporate video production: sales and training. OUTPUT has included staff-training videos for

British Airways and Midland Bank. Unsolicited mss welcome.

Video Presentations
PO Box 281, Wimbledon, London
SW19 3DD
☎0181 542 7721   Fax 0181 243 0855
Contact *John Holloway*

Corporate video. CLIENTS include the Post Office, IBM, British Gas, Freemans, Eastern Electricity.

Videoplus Communications
3 Braunfels Walk, Craven Road, Newbury, Berkshire RG14 5NQ
☎01635 37653   Fax 01635 37653
Contact *Mike Spencer*

Video: corporate, sales, training, promotional and documentary. CLIENTS include the Reader's Digest Association, Radio Rentals, Hewlett Packard, Safeway, GE Capital and Black & Decker.

Videotel Productions/ Living Tape Productions
Ramillies House, 1–2 Ramillies Street, London W1V 1DF
☎0171 439 6301   Fax 0171 437 0731
Contact *Robert Wallace*

Film, video and TV of a broadly educational nature but not exclusively so. Unsolicited mss welcome in the education and training fields only. 'We would like to support new writers who can put up with the ego-bashing they are likely to get from industrial and commercial sponsors.' OUTPUT has included *Oceans of Wealth* (British Gas, DTI & Ch4); *Response to Marine Chemical Spills* (for industrial consortium); *Dealing with Violence and Aggression at Work* (NHS, THF); *Defence against Drug Traffickers* (SKULD); *Alcohol, Beware!* (Mobil); *Responsible Chemical Manufacturing* (consortium of chemical companies); *Hospital Security* (NAHAT); *The Office* (BBC/EBS Trust); *More than Meets the Eye* (DOH, EBS Trust).

Brian Waddell Productions Ltd
Strand Studios, 5/7 Shore Road, Holywood, Co. Down BT18 9HX
☎01232 427646   Fax 01232 427922
Contacts *Brian Waddell, Maureen Gallagher*

Producers of a wide range of television programmes in leisure activities, the arts, music, children's, comedy, travel/adventure and documentaries. Currently developing several drama projects. Interested in encouraging new writers, particularly within Ireland.

Wall to Wall Television
8–9 Spring Place, London
NW5 3ER
☎0171 485 7424   Fax 0171 267 5292
Contact *Jane Root, Alex Graham*

Documentary, features and drama. OUTPUT includes *Statement of Affairs* (Carlton TV); *You, Me & It*; *Slice of Life*; *Big Science* (BBC); *Baby It's You*; *Sophie's Meat Course* (Ch4). Material is produced in-house; occasional outside ideas accepted. Continued expansion means more opportunities for writers.

The Walnut Partnership
Crown House, Armley Road, Leeds, West Yorkshire LS12 2EJ
☎0113 2456913   Fax 0113 2439614
Contact *Geoff Penn*

A film and video production company specialising in business communication.

Warner Sisters Film & TV Ltd
Canelot Studios, 222 Kensal Road, London W10 5BN
☎0181 960 3550   Fax 0181 960 3880
Chief Executives *Lavinia Warner, Jane Wellesley, Anne-Marie Casey, Dorothy Viljoen*

FOUNDED 1984. Drama, comedy and documentary. TV and feature films. OUTPUT includes *Selling Hitler*; *Rides*; *Life's a Gas*; *She-Play*; *A Village Affair*; *Dangerous Lady*; *Dressing for Breakfast*; *The Spy that Caught a Cold*; *The Bite*. Developing a wide range of TV and feature projects.

Wave Communication Group
Wave Studios, 12 Park Street, Lytham, Lancashire FY8 5LU
☎01253 796399   Fax 01253 794532
Contact *Roy Turner*

Corporate film and video, including sell-throughs, sponsored, tourism-based programmes, and technical and specialist videograms. OUTPUT *England's North Country*; *Why Thermal Storage*; *Just Two Drops*; *Safe Isolation of Chemical Plant*. Unsolicited scripts not normally welcome. Keen to support new writing talent. 'We welcome contact with new writers whom we assess on track record or sample writing.'

Western Eye Business Television

Easton Business Centre, Felix Road, Easton,
Bristol, Avon BS5 0HE
☎0117 9415854   Fax 0117 9415899
Contact *Steve Spencer*

Corporate video production for Royal Mail,
Motorola, HNE Healthcare, British Airways,
and various charities. Uses freelance writers.
Unsolicited scripts not usually accepted.

Michael White Productions Ltd

48 Dean Street, London W1V 5HL
☎0171 734 7707   Fax 0171 734 7727
Contact *Michael White*

High–output company whose credits include
Widow's Peak; White Mischief; Nuns on the Run
(co–production with **HandMade Films Ltd**);
The Comic Strip Series. Also theatre projects,
including *Fame; Me and Mamie O'Rourke; She
Loves Me; Crazy for You*. Contributions are
passed by Michael White to a script reader for
consideration.

White City Films

79 Sutton Court Road, Chiswick, London
W4 3EQ
☎0181 994 6795/4856   Fax 0181 995 9379
Contact *Aubrey Singer*

Film producers. OUTPUT has included *The
Restoration of the Sistine Chapel* (NTV); *The
Witness of the Long March* (Ch4); *Return to
Saigon; Return to Peking; Joseph Needham, FRS
FBA*. No unsolicited scripts.

Maurice Winnick Associates Ltd

66 Melbourne Way, Bush Hill Park, Enfield,
Middlesex EN1 1XQ
☎0181 366 2978   Fax 0181 363 7523

Producers of quiz–panel game shows for TV
and theatre. No unsolicited material but always
interested in new ideas/writing.

WitzEnd Productions

See **SelecTV plc**

WLS International Limited

Suite 6, Camelot Court, Alverton Street,
Penzance, Cornwall TR18 2QN
☎01736 331833   Fax 01736 331822/62437
Contact *Claire Welsh, Philip Morris*

Film and TV production for dramas and commercials. OUTPUT ranging from Korean commercials to features, both national and international. Has a growing list of overseas clients.

Unsolicited scripts welcome. New writing
'always welcome'.

Wolfhouse Productions Ltd

13–15 Northgate, Heptonstall, West
Yorkshire HX7 7ND
☎01422 844595
Contact *Jay Jones*

Most recent productions are medical documentaries such as an investigation into diabetes control sponsored by Bayer Diagnostics, collaborative literary and cultural projects such as *The Boys
From Savoy* with David Glass, and corporates for
clients such as South Yorkshire Supertram and
Datacolor International. Interested in ideas,
scripts and possible joint development for broadcast, sell-through and experimental arts.

The Word Business

56 Leyborne Park, Kew, Richmond, Surrey
TW9 3HA
☎0181 948 8346   Fax 0181 948 8346
Contact *John Mabbett*

Copywriter, scriptwriter, producer of corporate video material, generally low-budget projects. No unsolicited scripts. Writing is handled
in-house.

Workhouse Television

Granville House, St Peter Street, Winchester,
Hampshire SO23 8BP
☎01962 863449   Fax 01962 841026
Television Manager *Carol Wade*

Video and TV: documentary, light entertain-
ment, magazine programmes and corporate
work. OUTPUT *Dear Nick* (ITV); *Lifeschool A-Z*
(BBC); *Big Day Out* (BBC); *Parents Talking;
DIY; Cash in Hand* (The Learning Channel);
Time Off; Tale of Three Seaside Towns (Meridian);
Mastercraft (WestCountry TV); *Wizadora* (net-
work). Corporate clients include BZW,
Barclays, Price Waterhouse, Nuclear Electric.

Working Title Films Ltd

Oxford House, 76 Oxford Street, London
W1N 9FD
☎0171 307 3000   Fax 0171 307 3001/2/3
Co–Chairmen (Films) *Tim Bevan, Eric Fellner*
Head of Development (Films) *Debra Hayward*
Development Executive (Films) *Natascha
    Wharton*
Television *Simon Wright*

Affiliated to PolyGram Filmed Entertainment.
Feature films, TV drama; also family/children's
entertainment and TV comedy. OUTPUT

Films: *Fargo; Dead Man Walking; Loch Ness; French Kiss; Four Weddings and a Funeral; The Hudsucker Proxy; The Tall Guy; A World Apart; Wish You Were Here; My Beautiful Laundrette.* Television: *Zig and Zag's Million Quid Vid; The Borrowers I & II; Armisted Maupin's Tales of the City; News Hounds; Echoes.* No unsolicited mss at present, but keen to encourage new writing nevertheless.

Worldview Pictures

35 Inkerman Road, London NW5 3BT
☎0171 916 4696   Fax 0171 916 1091
Contact *Stephen Trombley, Bruce Eadie*

Documentaries and series for television, plus theatrical. OUTPUT *Raising Hell: The Life of A.J. Bannister; The Execution Protocol* (both for Discovery/BBC/France 2); *Drancy: A Concentration Camp in Paris; The Lynchburg Story* (both for Discovery/Ch4/France 2).

Worldwide Television News

The Interchange, Oval Road, London NW1 7EP
☎0171 410 5200   Fax 0171 413 8302
Contact *Gerry O'Reilly*

Video and TV: documentary, news, features, sport and entertainment. OUTPUT *Earthfile* (weekly environmental series); *Roving Report* (weekly current affairs series); *Earth Works* (children's environmental series); *Crime International* (reality-based crime show); plus many one-off specials. Unsolicited material welcome.

Wortman Productions UK

48 Chiswick Staithe, London W4 3TP
☎0181 994 8886
Producer *Neville Wortman*

Film, video and TV production for drama, documentary, commercials and corporate material. OUTPUT *House in the Country* John Julius Norwich (ITV series); *Ellington* (Jazz series); *'C'm on to My House* (TV feature series); *Theatre* (CD-ROM); *Celebration Theatre Company for the Young - The Winter's Tale.* Send outline treatments 2–3 pages and s.a.e. and a couple of pages of dialogue if appropriate. Open to new writing.

Zenith Productions Ltd

43–45 Dorset Street, London W1H 4AB
☎0171 224 2440   Fax 0171 224 3194
Script Executive *Ming Ho*

Feature films and TV. OUTPUT Films: Hal Hartley's *Amateur*, Nicole Holofcener's *Walking and Talking.* Television: *Inspector Morse; Hamish MacBeth; Rhodes; Bodyguards.* No unsolicited scripts.

The Zoom Production Company

102 Dean Street, London W1V 5RA
☎0171 434 3895   Fax 0171 734 2751
Managing Director *Mark Bergin*

Film and video production for corporate clients. Full spectrum of corporate communications in both public and private sectors.

Theatre Producers

Aba Daba

30 Upper Park Road, London NW3 2UT
☎0171 722 5395   Fax 0171 722 5395

Contact *Aline Waites, Robin Hunter*

Plays and satirical pantomimes performed at venues like the Water Rats, Underneath the Arches and the Canal Café in London. The company writes all its own material but would be happy to consider some of the great piles of unsolicited mss they receive, were it not for the fact that there is absolutely no money available for outsiders.

Actors Touring Company

Alford House, Aveline Street, London SE11 5DQ
☎0171 735 8311Fax 0171 735 1031 attn ATC

Artistic Director *Nick Philippou*

'Actors Touring Company turn European classics into modern masterpieces.' ATC produces new versions of either lesser-known plays by well-known writers (eg *The Modern Husband* by Henry Fielding) or seminal plays by writers unknown in the UK (eg *Celestina* by Ferdinand de Rojas). Collaborations with writers are based on adaptation and/or translation work and unsolicited mss will only be considered in this category. 'We endeavour to read mss but do not have the resources to do so quickly.' As a small-scale company, all plays must have a cast of six or less.

Almeida Theatre Company

Almeida Street, Islington, London N1 1TA
☎0171 226 7432   Fax 0171 704 9581

Artistic Directors *Ian McDiarmid, Jonathan Kent*

FOUNDED 1980. Now in its eighth year as a full-time producing theatre, presenting a year-round theatre and music programme in which international writers, composers, performers, directors and designers are invited to work with British artists on challenging new and classical works. Previous productions: *Butterfly Kiss; The Rules of the Game; Medea; No Man's Land; The Rehearsal; Bajazet; Galileo; Moonlight; The School for Wives; Hamlet.* No unsolicited mss: 'our producing programme is very limited and linked to individual directors and actors'.

Alternative Theatre Company Ltd

Bush Theatre, Shepherds Bush Green, London W12 8QD
☎0171 602 3703   Fax 0171 602 7614

Literary Manager *Joanne Reardon*

FOUNDED 1972. Trading as The Bush Theatre. Produces about six new plays a year (principally British) and hosts up to four visiting companies also producing new work: 'we are a writer's theatre.' Previous productions: *Kiss of the Spiderwoman* Manuel Puig; *More Light* Snoo Wilson; *Raping the Gold* Lucy Gannon; *Handful of Stars* Billy Roche; *Boys Mean Business* Catherine Johnson; *The Pitchfork Disney* Philip Ridley; *Phoenix* Roy MacGregor; *Democracy* John Murrell; *Beautiful Thing* Jonathan Harvey; *Killer Joe* Tracy Letts. Scripts are read by a team of associates, then discussed with the management, a process which takes about three months. The theatre offers a small number of commissions, recommissions to ensure further drafts on promising plays, and a guarantee against royalties so writers are not financially penalised even though the plays are produced in a small house.

Annexe Theatre Company Ltd

The Quadrangle Business Centre, Ruchill Street, Glasgow G20 9PX
☎0141 945 4444   Fax 0141 945 4358

Artistic Director *Paula MacGee*
Associate Director *Wendy Seager*
Administrator *Doreen McArdle*
Literary Manager *Chris Ballance*

FOUNDED 1986. Touring productions, weekend play readings and workshops for writers. Interested in considering new work from writers based in Scotland only. Writers' pack available. All scripts are read and reports given; writers are encouraged through re-writes, one-to-one meetings; playwrights with potential are invited to join the company's Development Programme. In 1995, Annexe staged a major Scottish tour of a new play that had evolved through the Development Programme.

Yvonne Arnaud Theatre

Millbrook, Guildford, Surrey GU1 3UX
☎01483 440077   Fax 01483 64071

Contact *James Barber*

New work always considered. Credits include: *Otherwise Engaged* Simon Gray; *Communicating Doors* Alan Ayckbourn; *The Weekend* Michael Palin; *Indian Ink* Tom Stoppard; *Home* David Storey; *Cellmates* Simon Gray.

Birmingham Repertory Theatre
Broad Street, Birmingham B1 2EP
☎0121 236 6771   Fax 0121 236 7883
Artistic Director *Bill Alexander*
Associate Directors *Gwenda Hughes, Tony Clark*
Literary Manager *Ben Payne*
The Birmingham Repertory Theatre aims to provide a platform for the best work from new writers from both within and beyond the West Midlands region along with a programme which also includes classics and 'discovery' plays. The Rep is committed to a policy of integrated casting and to the production of new work which reflects the diversity of modern experience. The commissioning of new plays takes place across the full range of the theatre's activities: in the Main House, the Studio (which is a dedicated new writing space) and the touring work of the Youth, Community and Education Department. 'Writers are advised that the Rep is very unlikely to produce an unsolicited script. We usually assess unsolicited submissions on the basis of whether it indicates a writer with whom the theatre may be interested in working. Writers are encouraged to become acquainted with the work of the theatre through activities such as Repwriters (the writers' group attached to the theatre) or through attending performances before submitting unsolicited scripts. Writers are welcome to send details of rehearsed readings and productions as an alternative means of introducing the theatre to their work. The theatre also maintains close links with *Stagecoach* (the regional writers' training agency) and the **MA in Playwriting Studies** at the University of Birmingham.'

Black Theatre Co-op
8 Bradbury Street, London N16 8JN
☎0171 249 9150   Fax 0171 275 9440
Artistic Director *Felix Cross*
FOUNDED 1978. Plays to a mixed audience, approximately 65% female. Usually tours nationally twice a year. 'Committed in the first instance to new writing by Black British writers and work which relates to the Black culture and experience throughout the Diaspora, although anything considered.' Unsolicited mss welcome.

Bootleg Theatre Company
Sherborne House, 20 Greyfriars Close, Salisbury, Wiltshire SP1 2LR
☎01722 421476
Contact *Colin Burden*
FOUNDED 1984. Tries to encompass as wide an audience as possible and has a tendency towards plays with socially relevant themes. A good bet for new writing since unsolicited mss are very welcome. 'Our policy is to produce new and/or rarely seen plays and anything received is given the most serious consideration.' Actively seeks to obtain grants to commission new writers for the company. Playwrights whose work has been performed include Tony Marchant, Barrie Keeffe, Sam Snape and Mike Harris. Future productions include Philip Goulding's *Different Animal*, the world première of *Hanging Hanratty* by Michael Burnham (about the A6 murder case), and new work by Michelle Harris, James Morton and Trevor Suthers.

Borderline Theatre Company
Darlington New Church, North Harbour Street, Ayr KA8 8AA
☎01292 281010   Fax 01292 263825
Chief Executive *Eddie Jackson*
FOUNDED 1974. A touring company taking shows to main-house theatres in city centres and small venues in outlying districts, plus the Edinburgh Festival, Mayfest and, occasionally, London. Mainly new and contemporary work, plus revivals: *George's Marvellous Medicine* Roald Dahl (a spectacular children's show); *Misterio Buffo* Dario Fo (one-man show with Robbie Coltrane); *The Odd Couple* Neil Simon; *Trumpets and Raspberries* Dario Fo; *Shanghied* Liz Lochhead; plus pantomime and children's plays. Synopsis with cast size preferred in the first instance. Borderline try to include one new work every season. 'We are looking for writing which is stimulating, relevant and, above all, entertaining, which will lend itself to dynamic physical presentation.'

Bristol Express Theatre Company
16 Frederick Street, Totterdown, Bristol, Avon BS4 3AZ
☎0117 9717279
Director *Andy Jordan*
A non-funded, professional, sometimes middle-scale national touring company which has a continuing commitment to the discovery, development and encouragement of new writing, principally through its research and development

programme *The Play's The Thing!* This consists of public/private staged and rehearsed readings; workshops and full-scale productions. Previous productions: *Child's Play* Jonathan Wolfman; *Winter Darkness* Allan Cubitt; *Prophets in the Black Sky* John Matshikiza; *Lunatic & Lover* Michael Meyer; *Heaven* Sarah Aicher; *Syme* Michael Bourdages; *Gangster Apparel* Richard Vetere. 'We look for plays that are socially/emotionally/theatrically/politically significant, analytical and challenging. The company is keen to produce work which attempts to mix genres (and create new ones!), is eloquent and honest, while remaining accessible and entertaining.'

Bristol Old Vic Company

Theatre Royal, King Street, Bristol, Avon
BS1 4ED
☎0117 9493993   Fax 0117 9493996

Bristol Old Vic is committed to the commissioning and production of new writing in both the Theatre Royal (650 seats) and the New Vic Studio (150 seats). Plays must have the potential to attract an audience of significant size in either auditorium. 'We are eager to discover plays which possess genuine theatricality, are assured in characterisation and dramatic structure, recognise the power of emotion, and display a sense of humour.' The theatre will read and report on unsolicited scripts, and asks for a fee of £10 per script to cover the payments to readers.

Bush Theatre

See **Alternative Theatre Company**

Cambridge Theatre Company

See **Method & Madness**

Carnival (Films & Theatre) Ltd

See **Film, TV and Video Producers**

Cheek By Jowl

Alford House, Aveline Street, London
SE11 5DQ

Produces only one show per year which is almost always classical. Unable to accept scripts. 'We have no mechanism for reading plays and beg writers to save their time and resources by not sending them to us.'

Chester Gateway Theatre Trust Ltd

Hamilton Place, Chester, Cheshire CH1 2BH
☎01244 344238   Fax 01244 317277
Artistic Director *Jeremy Raison*

FOUNDED 1968. Plays to a broad audience across a wide range of work, classical to contemporary, including Shakespeare, John Godber, Ira Levin, Alan Ayckbourn, Arthur Miller, Ibsen, etc. Current season has an emphasis on new writing with five world premières in 1996. 'We are in the process of developing new writing and have a young playwright's group.' Small-cast material, children's and young people, large-scale youth theatre, people with learning difficulties, plays by women and adaptations of novels. Anything with a cast of over eight is unlikely to reach production. The smaller the cast the better. Scripts welcome but reading will take some time. Please send synopsis first.

Churchill Theatre

High Street, Bromley, Kent BR1 1HA
☎0181 464 7131   Fax 0181 290 6968
Artistic Director *Alan Strachan*

Produces a broad variety of popular plays, both new and revivals. Previous productions: *Phantom of the Opera* Ken Hill; *Don't Dress for Dinner* Marc Camoletti (adap. Robin Hawdon); *A Slight Hangover* Ian Ogilvy; *The Heiress* Henry James; *The Father* Strindberg; *The Prime of Miss Jean Brodie; The Hot Mikado.* Most productions go on either to tour or into the West End.

Citizens Theatre

Gorbals, Glasgow G5 9DS
☎0141 429 5561   Fax 0141 429 7374
Artistic Director *Giles Havergal*

No formal new play policy. The theatre has a play reader but opportunities to do new work are limited.

Michael Codron Ltd

Aldwych Theatre Offices, Aldwych, London
WC2B 4DF
☎0171 240 8291   Fax 0171 240 8467
General Manager *Gareth Johnson*

Michael Codron Ltd manages the Aldwych and owns the Vaudeville Theatre in London's West End. The plays it produces don't necessarily go into these theatres, but always tend to be big-time West End fare. Previous productions: *Look Look; Hapgood; Uncle Vanya; The Sneeze; Rise and Fall of Little Voice; Arcadia; Dead Funny.* No particular rule of thumb on subject matter or treatment. The acid test is whether 'something appeals to Michael'. Straight plays rather than musicals.

Colchester Mercury Theatre Limited

Balkerne Gate, Colchester, Essex CO1 1PT
☎01206 577006   Fax 01206 769607

Contact *Pat Trueman, Artistic Director*
Administrator *David Fairclough*

Repertory theatre with a wide-ranging audience. OUTPUT in 1996 included *The Woman in Black; The Last Yankee; Northanger Abbey; Golden Girls; Noises Off*. Expects to commission more new work in the future. Unsolicited scripts not welcome as there is a lack of appropriate staff to process them correctly. The theatre has a Writer in Residence, shared with the University of Essex MA in Theatre Studies Course.

The Coliseum, Oldham

Fairbottom Street, Oldham, Lancashire
OL1 3SW
☎0161 624 1731   Fax 0161 624 5318
Artistic Director *Warren Hooper*

Considered a good bet for new playwrights, the Coliseum is besieged by more scripts than it can read. 'We like to do new writing that's popular and relevant to our audience.' Previous productions: *Girlfriends* Howard Goodall; *The Steamie* Tony Roper; *Clowns on a School Outing* Ken Campbell; *Hotstuff, My Mad Grandad* Mike Scott; *Silver Lining* John Chambers; *Bare* Renny Krupinski. The Coliseum opened up its rehearsal room as a studio theatre (max. capacity audience of 60), and the theatre is therefore looking for new, small-cast plays with simple staging requirements. Plays often come by way of contacts or commissions but good unsolicited scripts still stand a chance. Enclose a large s.a.e.. Response time about eight weeks. Ideas in writing preferred to unsolicited scripts.

Communicado Theatre Company

12A Castle Terrace, Edinburgh EH1 2DP
☎0131 228 5465   Fax 0131 221 9003
Artistic Director *Gerard Mulgrew*

FOUNDED 1982. Scottish touring company which aims to present dynamic and challenging theatre to the widest range of audience in Scotland and internationally. 'We encourage new writing, especially, but not exclusively, of Scots origin. Unfortunately there are no facilities for dealing with unsolicited scripts.' Productions have included: *The House with the Green Shutters* adapt. Gerard Mulgrew; *Carmen 1936* Stephen Jeffreys; *The Hunchback of Notre Dame* adapt. Andrew Dallmeyer; *Mary Queen of Scots Got Her Head Chopped Off* Liz Lochhead; *Blood Wedding* trans. David Johnston; *Cyrano de Bergerac* trans. Edwin Morgan; *Crying Wolf* Gerald Mangan; *Sacred Hearts* Sue Glover; *Tall Tales for Cold Dark Nights; Tales of the Arabian Nights* both by Gerard Mulgrew.

Contact Theatre Company

Oxford Road, Manchester M15 6JA
☎0161 274 3434   Fax 0161 273 6286
Artistic Director *Benjamin Twist*

FOUNDED 1972. Plays predominantly to a young audience (15–30), with an interest in contemporary work, especially from the North-West, and in highly theatrical writing. Limited opportunities for new plays without a specific marketing 'hook' for young people. Recent new productions: *Generations of the Dead in the Abyss of Coney Island Madness* Michael Henry Brown (British première); *Tell Me* Matthew Dunster (world première). Work by black, female and young writers, and work which creates opportunities for black and female performers, is particularly welcome. Commissions up to two plays a year and runs a **Young Playwrights Festival** annually (see under **Festivals**).

Crucible Theatre

55 Norfolk Street, Sheffield S1 1DA
☎0114 2760621   Fax 0114 2701532
Contact *Stephen Wrentmore, Assistant Director*

All unsolicited scripts are seen by a reader and a small number may go on to a rehearsed reading/workshop. Finished scripts are always preferred to synopses or ideas. Scripts sent by a recognised theatre agent, director or actor are given more attention. Scripts only returned if accompanied by s.a.e..

Cwmni Theatr Gwynedd

Deiniol Road, Bangor, Gwynedd LL57 2TL
☎01248 351707   Fax 01248 351915
Artistic Director *Graham Laker*

FOUNDED 1984. A mainstream company, performing in major theatres on the Welsh circuit. Welsh-language work only at present. Classic Welsh plays, translations of European repertoire and new work, including adaptations from novels. New Welsh work always welcome; work in English considered if appropriate for translation (i.e. dealing with issues relevant to Wales). 'We are keen to discuss projects with established writers and offer commissions where possible.' Other activities include the hosting of an annual new writing festival in March.

Derby Playhouse

Eagle Centre, Derby DE1 2NF
☎01332 363271   Fax 01332 294412
Artistic Director *Mark Clements*

FOUNDED 1948. Plays to a mixed audience. Previous productions include *Assassins* Stephen

Sondheim; *Our Boys* Jonathan Lewis; *Ham* Mark Chatterton première; *Comic Cuts* Jack Shepherd première; *Happy Families* John Godber. 'We have a small budget for commissioning and hold several rehearsed readings a season.' Unsolicited mss (excluding Christmas shows) welcome; scripts from the East Midlands area submitted to a separate regional reading pool.

Druid Theatre Company

Chapel Lane, Galway, Republic of Ireland
☎00 353 91 568660   Fax 00 353 91 563109

Literary Manager *Anne Butler*

FOUNDED 1975. Plays to a wide-ranging audience, urban and rural, from young adults to the elderly. National and international theatre with an emphasis on new Irish work, though contemporary European theatre is commonplace in the repertoire. Currently has six writers under commission and is commissioning more. Enclose s.a.e. for return of scripts. Runs workshops.

The Dukes

Moor Lane, Lancaster LA1 1QE
☎01524 67461   Fax 01524 846817

Artistic Director *Han Duijvendak*

FOUNDED 1971. The only producing house in Lancashire. Wide target market. Plays in 322–seater end-on auditorium plus 198–seater in-the-round studio. Promenade performances in the summer months in Williamson Park. No unsolicited mss.

Dundee Repertory Theatre

Tay Square, Dundee DD1 1PB
☎01382 227684   Fax 01382 228609

Artistic Director *Hamish Glen*

FOUNDED 1939. Plays to a varied audience. Translations and adaptations of classics, and new local plays. Most new work is commissioned. Interested in contemporary plays in translation and in new Scottish writing. No scripts except by prior arrangement.

Eastern Angles Theatre Company

Sir John Mills Theatre, Gatacre Road, Ipswich, Suffolk IP1 2LQ
☎01473 218202   Fax 01473 250954

Contact *Ivan Cutting*

FOUNDED 1982. Plays to a rural audience for the most part. New work only: some commissioned, some devised by the company, some researched documentaries. Unsolicited mss welcome. 'We are always keen to develop and produce new writing, especially that which is germane to a

rural area.' Involved in **Eastern Arts**' Write Lines project.

Edinburgh Royal Lyceum Theatre

See **Royal Lyceum Theatre Company**

English Stage Company Ltd

See **Royal Court Theatre**

English Touring Theatre

New Century Building, Hill Street, Crewe CW1 1BX
☎01270 501800   Fax 01270 501888

Artistic Director *Stephen Unwin*

FOUNDED 1993. National touring company visiting middle-scale receiving houses and arts centres throughout England. Mostly mainstream. Largely classical programme, but with increasing interest to tour one modern English play per year. Strong commitment to Education and Community Outreach work.

Everyman Theatre

5–9 Hope Street, Liverpool L1 9BH
☎0151 708 0338   Fax 0151 709 0398

Artistic Director *Peter Rowe*

Currently establishing a script-reading service and will be commissioning new work. There are also plans to establish a short writer's residency for 1996.

Field Day Theatre Company

Foyle Arts Centre, Old Foyle College, Lawrence Hill, Derry BT48 7NJ
☎01504 360196   Fax 01504 365419

ESTABLISHED 1980, Field Day is a touring company which tends to commission plays from Irish writers. Their 1995 production was a version by Frank McGuinness of Chekhov's *Uncle Vanya*.

Robert Fox Ltd

6 Beauchamp Place, London SW3 1NG
☎0171 584 6855   Fax 0171 225 1638

Contact *Robert Fox*

Producers and co-producers of work suitable for West End production. Previous productions: *Another Country; Chess; Lettice and Lovage; Madhouse in Goa; Burn This; When She Danced; The Ride Down Mount Morgan; Me & Mamie O'Rouke; The Importance of Being Earnest; The Seagull; Goosepimples; Vita & Virginia; The Weekend; Three Tall Women*. Scripts, while usually by established playwrights, are always read.

Gate Theatre Company Ltd

11 Pembridge Road, London W11 3HQ
☎0171 229 5387   Fax 0171 221 6055
Literary Manager *Mark Sparrow*

FOUNDED 1979. Plays to a mixed, London-wide audience, depending on production. Aims to produce British premières of plays which originate from abroad and translations of neglected classics. Most work is with translators. Previous productions: *The Boat Plays*; *The Robbers* Schiller; *The Ballad of Wolves and Silver Face* ; *Cat and Mouse (Sheep)* Gregory Motton; *Services, or They All Do It* Elfriede Jelinek(trans. Nick Grindell). Unsolicited scripts welcome. Enclose s.a.e..

Gay Sweatshop

The Holborn Centre, Three Cups Yard,
Sandland Street, London WC1R 4PZ
☎0171 242 1168   Fax 0171 242 3143
Artistic Directors *James Neale-Kennerley,*
 Lois Weaver

FOUNDED 1975. Plays to a wide audience, particularly those interested in lesbian/gay theatre and sexual politics. Previous productions: *Threesome* Claire Dowie, David Greenspan & Phyllis Nagy; *Kitchen Matters* Bryony Lavery; *Raising the Wreck* Sue Frumin; *Compromised Immunity* Andy Kirby; *This Island's Mine* Philip Osment; *Stupid Cupid* Phil Willmott; *Fucking Martin* adapted by Malcolm Sutherland from the novel by Dale Peck. Also experimental performance club *One Night Stands*, annual *Queerschool* for gay and lesbian theatre practitioners; also festivals of new work presented as staged rehearsed readings: *Gay Sweatshop x 10*; *GS x 12*. Committed to encouraging new work by gay, lesbian, black and disabled playwrights. Work submitted generally includes representation of those sections of the community which are under-represented in mainstream theatre. Unsolicited scripts welcome.

Geese Theatre Company

See **MAC – The Centre for Birmingham**

Graeae Theatre Company

Interchange Studios, Dalby Street, London
NW5 3NQ
☎0171 267 1959   Fax 0171 267 2703
Minicom 0171 267 3164
Artistic Director *Ewan Marshall*
Administrative Director *Steve Mannix*
Administrator *Alison Barker*
Associate Director *Colette Conroy*

Europe's premier theatre company of disabled people, the company tours nationally and internationally with innovative theatre productions highlighting both historical and contemporary disabled experience. Graeae also runs T.I.E. and educational programmes available to schools, youth clubs and day centres nationally, provides vocational training in theatre arts (including playwriting) and runs London's only fully accessible Young People's Theatre Programme (called 'The Works') for the disabled community. Unsolicited scripts – particularly from disabled writers – welcome. New work examining disability issues is commissioned.

Greenwich Theatre Ltd

Crooms Hill, London SE10 8ES
☎0181 858 4447   Fax 0181 858 8042
Artistic Director *Matthew Francis*

Policy of encouraging new writing. 'We aim to produce two new plays or adaptations in a year.' Positively encourages writers to send in scripts; 'we are always on the look-out for new writing which is accessible to our mixed audience'. Less keen on initial approach with ideas, preferring to read a finished script, but write in the first instance and do not send scripts until requested.

Hampstead Theatre

Swiss Cottage Centre, Avenue Road, London
NW3 3EX
☎0171 722 9224   Fax 0171 722 3860
Literary Manager *Ben Jancovich*

Produces new plays and the occasional modern classic. Scripts are initially assessed by a team of script readers and their responses are shared with management in monthly script meetings. The literary manager and/or artistic director then read and consider many submissions in more detail. It can therefore take 2–3 months to reach a decision. Writers produced in the past ten years include Marguerite Duras, Terry Eagleton, Brad Fraser, Michael Frayn, Brian Friel, William Gaminara, Beth Henley, Stephen Jeffreys, Terry Johnson, Tom Kempinski, Tony Kushner, Mike Leigh, Doug Lucie, Frank McGuinness, Anthony Minghella, Rona Munro, Jennifer Phillips, Dennis Potter, Philip Ridley, Martin Sherman and Michael Wall.

Harrogate Theatre Company

Oxford Street, Harrogate, North Yorkshire
HG1 1QF
☎01423 502710   Fax 01423 563205
Artistic Director *Andrew Manley*

FOUNDED 1950. Describes its audience as 'eclectic, all ages and looking for innovation'. Previous productions: *The Marriage of Figaro* (commissioned adaptation of Beaumarchais, Mozart, Da Ponte); *Barber of Seville* (commissioned translation and adaptation of Beaumarchais, Rossini and Sterbini); *School for Wives*; *A Man with Connections*; *Don Juan*; *The Baltimore Waltz* Paula Vogel (European première); *Hot 'n' Throbbing* Paula Vogel (European première); *My Children! My Africa!*; *Wings* (Kopit, Lunden & Perlman European première); new adaptations of *The Government Inspector* and *The Turn of the Screw*; European premières of adaptations/translations by David Mamet of *The Cherry Orchard, Uncle Vanya* and *Three Sisters*; *Marisol* Jose Rivera. Always struggling to produce new work.

Haymarket Theatre Company

Haymarket Theatre, Wote Street, Basingstoke, Hampshire RG21 1NW
☎01256 55844   Fax 01256 57130
Theatre Director *Adrian Reynolds*

Main house and studio. Programme in 1996: *Private Lives* Noel Coward; *My Cousin Rachel* adapted from Daphne Du Maurier's novel by Diana Morgan (prior to national tour); *Shadowlands* William Nicholson; *They're Playing Our Song* Neil Simon. In 1995: *Time and Time Again* Alan Ayckbourn; *Sleuth* Anthony Shaffer; *The Frog Prince* Malcolm Sircom (world première). The Haymarket Theatre re-opened in 1993 after a £3.2 million refurbishment funded by Basingstoke and Deane Borough Council.

The Hiss & Boo Company

24 West Grove, Walton on Thames, Surrey KT12 5NX
☎01932 248931   Fax 01932 248946
Contact *Ian Liston*

Particularly interested in new thrillers, comedy thrillers, comedy and melodrama – must be commercial full-length plays. Also interested in plays/plays with music for children. No one-acts. Previous productions: *Sleighrider; Beauty and the Beast; An Ideal Husband; Mr Men's Magical Island; Mr Men and the Space Pirates; Nunsense; Corpse!; Groucho: A Life in Revue; See How They Run; Christmas Cat and the Pudding Pirates; Pinocchio.* No unsolicited scripts; no telephone calls. Send synopsis and introductory letter in the first instance.

Hull Truck Theatre Company

Spring Street, Hull HU2 8RW
☎01482 224800   Fax 01482 581182
General Manager *Simon Stallworthy*

John Godber, of *Teechers, Bouncers, Up 'n'*

Under fame, the artistic director of this high-profile Northern company since 1984, has very much dominated the scene in the past with his own successful plays. The emphasis is still on new writing but Godber's work continues to be toured extensively. Most new plays are commissioned. Previous productions: *Dead Fish* Gordon Steel; *Off Out* Gill Adams; *Fish and Leather* Gill Adams; *Happy Families* John Godber. The company now reads all unsolicited scripts and aims to respond within two months. Bear in mind the artistic policy of Hull Truck, which is 'accessibility and popularity'. In general they are not interested in musicals, or in plays with casts of more than eight.

Humberside Theatre in Education

Humberside Cultural Enterprise Centre, Middleton Street, Springbank, Hull HU3 1NB
☎01482 324256   Fax 01482 326190
Artistic Director *John Hazlett*

FOUNDED 1983. Full-time company playing to Humberside schools, with a strong tradition of devising its own work. Previous productions: *Natural Forces* (for 13–14-year-olds); *The Wrong Side of the River* by Mary Cooper (for 15–18-year-olds); *Whose Voices?* by John Hazlett, Linda Taylor and Carol Bush (for 10–12-year-olds); *Festival* devised by the company for rural schools and communities; Shakespeare's *A Midsummer Night's Dream*; *Bellies* by Linda Taylor, Carol Bush and Janet Gordon. Autumn 1996: a new play about beauty by Linda Taylor. Interested in developments in new writing and in working with new writers.

Richard Jackson

59 Knightsbridge, London SW1X 7RA
☎0171 235 3671   Fax 0171 235 6126

Independent-minded producer who only does 'plays which appeal to me'. Besieged by mss, he tends to go out for what he wants (particularly European material). Works mainly in smaller-scale London fringe theatres taking risks the West End can no longer afford. Credits include bringing *Quentin Crisp* to a theatre audience. Previous productions: *Don't Play with Love* Alfred de Musset; *Pasolini* Michel Azama; *I Ought to Be in Pictures* Neil Simon; *Eden Cinema* and *Suzanna Andler* Marguerite Duras; *Noonbreak* Paul Claudel; *The Eagle Has Two Heads* and *The Human Voice* Jean Cocteau; *Happy Days* Samuel Beckett; *Swimming Pools at War* Yves Navarre.

Pola Jones Associates Ltd

14 Dean Street, London W1V 5AH
☎0171 439 1165   Fax 0171 437 3994

Contact *Andre Ptaszynski, Andrew Fell*

FOUNDED 1982. Comedy and musicals preferred. Previous productions have included: *Neville's Island*; *The Nerd*, with Rowan Atkinson; *Progress* Doug Lucie; *The Gambler*, with Mel Smith. Current productions include: *Crazy for You* and *Tommy*. Also produces comedy for TV: *Tygo Road*; *Joking Apart*; *Chalk*. Unsolicited scripts welcome.

Stephen Joseph Theatre

Westborough, Scarborough, North Yorkshire YO11 1JW
☎01723 370540   Fax 01723 360506

Artistic Director *Alan Ayckbourn*
Director/Literary Manager *Connal Orton*

A two-auditoria complex housing a 165-seat end stage theatre/cinema (the McCarthy) and a 400-seat theatre-in-the-round (the Round). Positive policy on new work. For obvious reasons, Alan Ayckbourn's work features quite strongly but with a new writing programme now in place, plays from other sources are actively encouraged. Previous première productions include: *Neville's Island* Tim Firth; *Woman in Black* (adap. Stephen Mallatratt); *The Ballroom* Peter King; *The End of the Food Chain* Tim Firth; *Penny Blue* Vanessa Brooks; *White Lies* Robert Shearman. Plays should have a strong narrative and be accessible. Submit to Connal Orton enclosing an s.a.e. for return of mss.

Bill Kenwright Ltd

55-59 Shaftesbury Avenue, London W1V 8JA
☎0171 439 4466   Fax 0171 437 8370

Contact *Bill Kenwright*

Presents both revivals and new shows for West End and touring theatres. Although new work tends to be by established playwrights, this does not preclude or prejudice new plays from new playwrights. Scripts should be addressed to Bill Kenwright with a covering letter and s.a.e.. 'We have enormous amounts of scripts sent to us. They are read systematically. Please do not phone; the return of your script or contact with you will take place in time.'

King's Head Theatre

115 Upper Street, London N1 1QN
☎0171 226 8561   Fax 0171 226 8507

The first pub theatre since Shakespearean times and the first venue in the UK for dinner theatre, the King's Head produces some strong work, including previously neglected work by playwrights such as Terence Rattigan and Vivian Ellis. Noël Coward's work also has a strong presence; the company is committed to its contribution to the reappraisal of his work and in 1995 toured *Cavalcade*. Previous productions: *Noël and Gertie*; *The Famous Five*; *Philadelphia, Here I Come!*; *Accapulco*; *Elegies for Angels, Punks and Raging Queens*; *A Day in the Death of Joe Egg*. Unsolicited submissions are not encouraged.

Knightsbridge Theatrical Productions Ltd

21 New Fetter Lane, London EC4A 1JJ
☎0171 583 8687   Fax 0171 583 1040

Contact *Mrs S. H. Gray*

Straight plays and musicals suitable for production in the West End only.

Komedia

14–17 Manchester Street, Brighton, East Sussex BN2 1TF
☎01273 694583   Fax 01273 563515

Contact *David Lavender*

Komedia is a new theatre venue which promotes the innovative and international. It combines theatre and cabaret performance spaces and presents its own productions as well as the work of top small-scale touring companies and performers. Mss of new plays welcome.

Leeds Playhouse

See **West Yorkshire Playhouse**

Leicester Haymarket Theatre

Belgrave Gate, Leicester LE1 3YQ
☎0116 2530021   Fax 0116 2513310

Artistic Director *Paul Kerryson*

'We aim for a balanced programme of original and established works.' Recent productions include: *Edward II* with Eddie Izzard; *The Taming of the Shrew*; *Mack and Mabel*; *Follies*; *Poona* (première). A script-reading panel has been established, and new writing is welcome. An Asian initiative has been set up to promote Asian work and Asian practitioners. Future work includes the European première of a Kroetz play, a full studio season, and a Scandinavian work.

Library Theatre Company

St Peter's Square, Manchester M2 5PD
☎0161 234 1913   Fax 0161 228 6481

Artistic Director *Christopher Honer*

Produces new and contemporary work, as well

as occasional classics. No unsolicited mss. Send outline of the nature of the script first. Encourages new writing through the commissioning of new plays and through a programme of staged readings to help writers' development.

Live Theatre Company

7-8 Trinity Chare, Newcastle upon Tyne NE1 3DF
☎0191 261 2694
Artistic Director *Max Roberts*

FOUNDED 1973. The company has recently won a revenue-funding franchise from Northern Arts to continue to produce work at both its newly refurbished and fully developed 200-seat venue, The Live Theatre, and to tour extensively regionally and nationally. Company policy is to produce high-quality accessible theatrical productions: particularly for those audiences currently alienated from traditional arts and theatre venues. The company is particularly interested in promoting new writing. As well as full-scale productions the company organises workshops, rehearsed readings and other new writing, activities. The company also enjoys a close relationship with Northern Playwrights Society. Recent plays include *Close the Coalhouse Door* Alan Plater; *Only Joking* Steve Chambers; *Blow Your House Down* Sarah Daniels; *The Grass House* Pauline Hadaway; *Your Home in the West* Rod Wooden; *Seafarers* Tom Hadaway; *Up and Running* Phil Woods; *Buffalo Girls* by Karin Young; *Two* Jim Cartwright; *Cabaret*; and an ambitious cycle of plays – the *Tyneside Mysteries* involving 12 writers.

Liverpool Everyman
See **Everyman Theatre**

Liverpool Playhouse

Williamson Square, Liverpool L1 1EL
☎0151 709 8478   Fax 0151 709 7113
Artistic Director (Designate) *Richard Williams*

Regional theatre very active in promoting new writing, with an impressive record of first plays. Previous productions: *Self-Catering: A Short History of the World* Andrew Cullen; *Weldon Rising* Phyllis Nagy; *At Fifty She Discovered the Sea* Denise Chalem; *Boy* Shaun Duggan; *The Dark Side* Liam Lloyd; *Home for the Holidays* Cheryl Martin; *A Message for the Broken Hearted* Gregory Motton; *Somewhere* Judith Johnson. Scripts welcome.

London Bubble Theatre Company

3-5 Elephant Lane, London SE16 4JD
☎0171 237 4434   Fax 0171 231 2366
Artistic Director *Jonathan Petherbridge*

Produces workshops, plays and events for a mixed audience of theatregoers and non-theatregoers, wide-ranging in terms of age, culture and class. Previous productions: *Measure for Measure; The Good Person of Sezuan; Brainpower*. Unsolicited mss welcome but 'our reading service is extremely limited and there can be a considerable wait before we can give a response'. Produces at least one new show a year which is invariably commissioned.

Lyric Theatre Hammersmith

King Street, London W6 0QL
☎0181 741 0824   Fax 0181 741 7694
Chief Executive *Sue Storr*
Artistic Director *Neil Bartlett*
Administrative Producer *Simon Mellor*

Theatre with a long tradition of putting on new work: *State of Affairs* Graham Swannell (trans. Duchess); *Mumbo Jumbo* Robin Glendinning (Mobil prizewinner); *Atonement* Barry Collins; *Asylum* Paul Kember; *Madhouse in Goa* Martin Sherman; *Prin* Andrew Davies (trans. Lyric); *La Bête* David Hirson. Interested in developing projects with writers, translators and adaptors. Treatments, synopses and c.v.s only. No longer able to produce in its 110-seat studio owing to reduced funding but the studio continues to host work, including new, by some of the best touring companies in the country.

MAC - The Centre for Birmingham

Cannon Hill Park, Birmingham B12 9QH
☎0121 440 4221   Fax 0121 446 4372
Programme Director *Dorothy Wilson*

Home of the Geese Theatre Company and a host of other arts/performance-related organisations based in Birmingham. Details on Geese available from the Centre.

Cameron Mackintosh

1 Bedford Square, London WC1B 3RA
☎0171 637 8866   Fax 0171 436 2683

Successful West End producer of musicals. Credits include *Cats; Les Misérables; Phantom of the Opera; Miss Saigon; Oliver!*. Unsolicited scripts are read and considered (there is no literary manager, however) but chances of success are slim.

The Made In Wales Stage Company

Aberdare House, Mount Stuart Square, Cardiff CF1 6DQ
☎01222 484017   Fax 01222 492930
Artistic Director *Jeff Teare*
Administrator *Jan Kreishan*

Varied audience. Works with Welsh and Wales-based writers and actors to create new and exciting plays which reflect the authentic Anglo-Welsh voice, whilst not being parochially Welsh. Formed in 1982, since when it has premièred and toured 27 new plays. Previous productions: *The Search for Odysseus* Charles Way; *Ted's Creatures* Tim Rhys; *Facing Up* Ieuan Watkins; *Wanting* Jane Buckler; *On the Black Hill* Charles Way (adap. from Bruce Chatwin's novel); *Branwen* Tony Conran; *The Scam* Peter Lloyd. In addition, the company mounts a festival of new writing called *Write On*, and runs a programme of development work for playwrights at different levels of experience throughout the year. This includes workshops, rehearsed readings and a free script-reading service.

Major Road Theatre Company

29 Queens Road, Bradford, West Yorkshire BD8 7BS
☎01274 480251   Fax 01274 548528
Artistic Director *Graham Devlin*
General Manager *Sue Cullen*

FOUNDED 1973. Each show has a very specific target audience which varies considerably from show to show. Previous productions include: *The Bottle Imp* Robert Louis Stevenson (middle-scale tour, commissioned by the Warwick Arts Centre); *Final Cargo* Noel Greig (small-scale touring theatre); *Four Note Opera* Tom Johnson (small-scale contemporary opera); *Leaves of Life* Mick Eaton (community show – cast of 100); *Bow Down* Harrison Birtwistle (music-theatre tour); *Wonderland* Mick Martin (young people's touring show). Would prefer a synopsis of unsolicited mss first. Regularly commissions new work, interested in innovative, non-naturalistic work.

Man in the Moon Theatre Ltd

392 Kings Road, Chelsea, London SW3 5UZ
☎0171 351 2876   Fax 0171 351 1873
Artistic Director *Jacqui Somerville*
Administrator *Genene Cooper*

FOUNDED 1982. Fringe theatre, recently awarded the Guinness Ingenuity Award for creativity and innovation. Often tries to fit new plays into seasons such as 'Nationalism' and 'Family Values' and very keen to do rehearsed readings. Unsolicited scripts welcome; 'interested in submissions from first-time writers or writers in the initial stages of their career'. No unfinished scripts or treatments.

Manchester Library Theatre

See **Library Theatre Company**

Method & Madness

25 Short Street, London SE1 8LJ
☎0171 401 9797   Fax 0171 401 9777
Artistic Director *Mike Alfreds*

Formerly known as the Cambridge Theatre Company. Limited script-reading facilities. Unsolicited mss may not be read. Letters and synopses welcome; scripts only returned with s.a.e..

Midland Arts Centre

See **MAC – The Centre for Birmingham**

N.T.C. Touring Theatre Company

The Playhouse, Bondgate Without, Alnwick, Northumberland NE66 1PQ
☎01665 602586
Contact *Gillian Hambleton*

FOUNDED 1978. Formerly Northumberland Theatre Company. Recent winner of one of only two drama production franchises in the Northern region. Predominantly rural, small-scale touring company, playing to village halls and community centres throughout the Northern region, the Scottish Borders and countrywide. Recently expanded into touring middle-scale theatre venues throughout the North. Productions range from established classics to new work and popular comedies, but must be appropriate to their audience. Unsolicited scripts welcome provided they are suitable for touring. The company encourages new writing and commissions when possible. Financial constraints restrict casting to a *maximum* of seven.

New Victoria Theatre

Etruria Road, Newcastle under Lyme, Staffordshire ST5 0JG
☎01782 717954   Fax 01782 712885
Theatre Director *Peter Cheeseman*

FOUNDED 1962. Plays to a fairly broad-based audience which tends to vary from one production to another. A high proportion are not regular theatre-goers and new writing has been one of the main ways of contacting new audiences. Artistic Director Peter Cheeseman reports: 'Recently (last three years) combined effect of recession and local authority grant cuts with Arts Council funding at standstill has seriously affected new play production. Staff, including actors and marketing staff, have been reduced. Contingency funding necessary for risk of presenting new plays has been almost eliminated. Paradoxically, commission money is available but not the funding levels to support new play production. It is hoped this situation is only temporary, as new plays have always been an important element of work.' Recent new plays: *Nice Girls*, documentary; *Come On Stan* Rony Robinson; *The Good Companions* (adaptation from Priestley) Bob Eaton; *The Tinderbox* Peter Whelan. Unsolicited scripts welcome provided they are accompanied by s.a.e. for return.

Newpalm Productions

26 Cavendish Avenue, London N3 3QN
☎0181 349 0802   Fax 0181 346 8257

Contact *Phil Compton*

Rarely produces new plays (*As Is* by William M. Hoffman, which came from Broadway to the Half Moon Theatre, was an exception to this). National tours of productions such as *Noises Off*, *Seven Brides for Seven Brothers* and *Rebecca*, at regional repertory theatres, are more typical examples of Newpalm's work. Unsolicited mss, both plays and musicals, are, however, welcome; scripts are preferable to synopses.

Northampton Royal Theatre

See **Royal Theatre**

Northcott Theatre

Stocker Road, Exeter, Devon EX4 4QB
☎01392 56182   Fax 01392 263108 attn Northcott Theatre

Artistic Director *John Durnin*

FOUNDED 1967. The Northcott is the Southwest's principal subsidised repertory theatre, situated on the University of Exeter campus. Describes its audience as 'geographically diverse, financially comfortable, conservative in taste, with a core audience of AB1s (40–60 age range)'. Currently looking to broaden the base of its audience profile, targeting younger and/or non-mainstream theatregoers in the 16–35 age range. Aims to develop, promote and produce quality new writing which reflects the life of the region and addresses the audience it serves. Previous productions: *Forty Years On* Alan Bennett; *A Midsummer Night's Dream* Shakespeare; *I Have Been Here Before* J. B. Priestley; *The Grapes of Wrath* Steinbeck/Frank Galati; *Neville's Island* Tim Firth. Unsolicited mss welcome but turnaround is necessarily slow and the script-reading service tends to be locally orientated. Not interested in 'pastiche drawing-room comedy, imitation Ayckbourn, farce from the Ray Cooney school of theatre, murder-mysteries or thrillers, or anything that employs TV naturalism'. It is hoped that the company will be able to return to its previous target of a minimum of two new pieces each season, one for the main house, the other for the studio theatre in Emmanuel Hall. The Northcott is a founder-member of the South West Theatre Consortium, which actively supports and participates in a variety of new writing projects, showcases, workshops, rehearsed readings and competitions.

Northern Stage Company

Newcastle Playhouse, Barras Bridge, Newcastle upon Tyne NE1 7RH
☎0191 232 3366   Fax 0191 261 8093

Artistic Director *Alan Lyddiard*

A young company which plans to involve itself in the production of new work, including co-productions with other local companies. Writers' workshops are likely to be arranged. Before submitting unsolicited scripts, please contact Brenda Gray.

Norwich Puppet Theatre

St James, Whitefriars, Norwich, Norfolk NR3 1TN
☎01603 615564   Fax 01603 617578

Artistic Director *Luis Boy*
General Manager *R. W. Skinner*

Plays to a young audience (aged 3–12), with occasional shows for adult audiences interested in puppetry. Christmas/summer season shows, plus school tours. Unsolicited mss welcome if relevant.

Nottingham Playhouse

Nottingham Theatre Trust, Wellington Circus, Nottingham NG1 5AF
☎0115 9474361   Fax 0115 9475759

Artistic Director *Martin Duncan*

Aims to make innovation popular, and present the best of world theatre, working closely with the communities of Nottingham and Nottinghamshire. Unsolicited mss will be read. It normally takes about six months, however, and 'we have never yet produced an unsolicited script. All our plays have to achieve a minimum of sixty per cent audiences in a 732-seat theatre. We have no studio.' Also see **Roundabout** – the

Nottingham Playhouse's theatre-in-education company.

Nuffield Theatre

University Road, Southampton, Hampshire SO172 1TR

☎01703 315500   Fax 01703 315511

Artistic Director *Patrick Sandford*
Script Executive *Penny Gold*

Well-known as a good bet for new playwrights, the Nuffield gets an awful lot of scripts. They do a couple of new plays each season. Previous productions: *Exchange* Yri Trifonov (trans. Michael Frayn) which transferred to the Vaudeville Theatre; *The Floating Light Bulb* Woody Allen (British première); new plays by Claire Luckham: *Dogspot; The Dramatic Attitudes of Miss Fanny Kemble;* and by Claire Tomalin: *The Winter Wife*. Open-minded about subject and style, producing musicals as well as straight plays. Scripts preferred to synopses in the case of writers new to theatre. All will, eventually, be read 'but please be patient. We do not have a large team of paid readers. We read everything ourselves.'

Octagon Theatre Trust Ltd

Howell Croft South, Bolton, Lancashire BL1 1SB

☎01204 529407   Fax 01204 380110

Artistic Director *Lawrence Till*
Administrative Director *Amanda Belcham*

FOUNDED 1967. Audience is made up of a wide age range. Productions include Shakespeare, 'Northern' plays, European plays, new plays, 1960s plays. Unsolicited mss considered, but may take up to six months for reply. Interested in good theatrical pieces that connect with the audience – socially, politically, emotionally and often geographically, with casts of about six. No thin comedies or epic plays with casts over eight.

The Old Vic

Waterloo Road, London SE1 8NB

☎0171 928 2651   Fax 0171 261 9161

General Manager *Andrew Leigh*

The Old Vic produces or co-produces three or four plays a year, normally revivals or classics, preferably with stars. New plays are very rarely done. The season is sold as a package, punctuated by an annual Christmas visit of *The Wind in the Willows*. No unsolicited scripts.

Orange Tree Theatre

1 Clarence Street, Richmond, Surrey TW9 2SA

☎0181 940 0141   Fax 0181 332 0369

Artistic Director *Sam Walters*

One of those theatre venues just out of London which are good for new writing, both full-scale productions and rehearsed readings (although these usually take place in The Room, above the Orange Tree pub). Productions, from August 1995: *Flora, The Red Menace* musical by Kander & Ebb; *The Maitlands* Ronald Mackenzie; *The Simpleton of the Unexpected Isles* G. B. Shaw; *The Good Woman of Setzuan* Brecht; *The Verge* Susan Glaspell; *The Power of the Dog* Ellen Dryden; *The Choice* Claire Luckham. The Room: A season of plays by women, 'Natural Born Writers': *The Jaws of Darkness* Kate O'Riordan; *Temple* Judy Upton; *The Gate* Jane Beeson. Lunchtime shows: *Home Free* Lanford Wilson; *The Dock Brief* John Mortimer; *October Song* Andrew Hinds. Held ten rehearsed readings and one seminar. Unsolicited mss are read, but patience (and s.a.e.) required.

Orchard Theatre

108 Newport Road, Barnstaple, Devon EX32 9BA

☎01271 71475   Fax 01271 71825

Artistic Director *Bill Buffery*

FOUNDED 1969. Plays appealing to a wide age range, which tour some 60 or 70 cities, towns and villages throughout Devon, Cornwall, Dorset, Somerset, Avon and Gloucestershire. Programme includes classics, new adaptations, outstanding modern work and newly commissioned plays. OUTPUT *A Doll's House; East o' the Sun and West o' the Moon; Halfway to Paradise; La Ronde; An Enemy of the People*. Unsolicited mss are usually unsuccessful simply because the theatre is committed to several commissioned new plays at any one time.

Oxford Stage Company

3rd Floor, 15-19 George Street, Oxford OX1 2AU

☎01865 723238   Fax 01865 790625

Artistic Director *John Retallack*

A middle-scale touring company producing established and new plays. At least one new play or new adaptation a year. Special interest in new writing for young people aged 13–18.

Paines Plough – New Writing New Theatre

4th Floor, 43 Aldwych, London WC2B 4DA

☎0171 240 4533   Fax 0171 240 4534

Artistic Director *Penny Ciniewicz*
Literary Development Manager *Mark Ravenhill*

Tours new plays nationally. Works with writers to develop their skill and voices through courses, workshops, free script-reading service and surgeries. Encourages writers to bridge the gap between arthouse and commercial plays with entertaining and provocative work for audiences beyong the London fringe and West End. Welcomes new scripts from writers. For script-reading service send two s.a.e.s for response and return of script.

Palace Theatre, Watford
Clarendon Road, Watford, Hertfordshire WD1 1JZ
☎01923 235455   Fax 01923 819664
Artistic Director *Giles Croft*

An important point of policy is the active commissioning of new plays. Previous productions: *Woman Overboard* Adrian Mitchell; *Diplomatic Wives* Louise Page; *Over A Barrel* Stephen Bill; *The Marriage of Figaro*; *The Barber of Seville* (adap. Ranjit Bolt); Jon Canter's *The Baby*; Lou Stein's musical adaptation of *La Celestina* by Fernando de Rojas, entitled *Salsa Celestina* and *Borders of Paradise* by Sharman Macdonald.

Perth Repertory Theatre Ltd
185 High Street, Perth PH1 5UW
☎01738 638123   Fax 01738 624576
Artistic Director *Michael Winter*
General Manager *Paul McLennan*

FOUNDED 1935. A wide range of productions, including musicals, classics, new plays, comedy, etc. for a loyal audience. Unsolicited mss are read when time permits, but the timetable for return of scripts is lengthy. New plays staged by the company are invariably commissioned under the SAC scheme.

Plymouth Theatre Royal
See **Theatre Royal**

Polka Children's Theatre
240 The Broadway, London SW19 1SB
☎0181 542 4258   Fax 0181 542 7723
Contact *Artistic Director*

This Wimbledon theatre commissions scripts for children, principally 3–5, 5–8 and 9–12. 'Our overall writing policy is to present excellent theatre for children which is both educational and entertaining.' Main-house productions include original plays connected to school project work, Christmas plays, summer musical-plays, adaptations of classic stories, novels and folk tales. Only produces plays that need a cast of no more than five to seven people.

Q20 Theatre Company
Ivy Lea, Fyfe Lane, Baildon, Shipley, West Yorkshire BD17 6DP
☎01274 591417/581316   Fax 01274 591417
Director *John Lambert*

Produces shows mainly for school and community venues. Particularly interested in plays for children. Q20 writes a lot of its own material and rarely has the resources to pay outside professional contributors. Write initially with ideas.

Queen's Theatre, Hornchurch
Billet Lane, Hornchurch, Essex RM11 1QT
☎0078 456118   Fax 01708 452348
Artistic Director *Marina Caldarone*

FOUNDED 1953. Nothing too adventurous for this mainly white, middle-class audience. Modern work, translations or classics are difficult to sell without a household name in the production. Marina Caldarone, however, wishes to broaden the company's repertoire. Committed to producing at least one new work per season (two a year), and keen to set up a complementary studio company which would develop new work. 'We try to offer as broad a repertoire as we can within our economic limitations.' Eight shows a year, including one musical and one Christmas/panto slot. Always interested in 'the well-made play' and now encouraging the submission of more experimental work as well as translations, adaptations, and classics. Has an established tradition of successful comedies and musicals which have transferred to the West End, e.g. *Blood Brothers*. Unsolicited mss welcome; all are assessed but this can take some considerable time.

The Questors Theatre
12 Mattock Lane, Ealing, London W5 5BQ
☎0181 567 0011   Fax 0181 567 8736
Artistic Director *Spencer Butler*
Theatre Manager *Elaine Orchard*
Production Secretary *Christine Greening*

FOUNDED 1929. Attracts an intelligent, discerning, wide age range audience looking for something different, innovative, daring. Recent productions include: *The School for Scandal* Sheridan; *Ghost Train* Ridley; *Amadeus* Shaffer; *Here Comes a Chopper* Ionesco. Unsolicited mss welcome. All new plays are carefully assessed. All scripts received are acknowledged and all writers receive a written response to their work. Some unsolicited plays receive productions, others rehearsed readings. Runs annual **Questors Theatre Student Playwright Competition**.

The Really Useful Group Ltd

20 Tower Street, London WC2H 9NS
☎0171 240 0880   Fax 0171 240 1204
Contact *Tania Slayter*

Commercial/West End theatre producers whose output has included *Sunset Boulevard; Joseph and the Amazing Technicolor Dreamcoat; Cats; Phantom of the Opera; Starlight Express; Daisy Pulls It Off; Lend Me a Tenor; Arturo Ui* and *Aspects of Love.*

Red Ladder Theatre Company

Cobden Avenue, Lower Wortley, Leeds, West Yorkshire LS12 5PB
☎0113 2792228   Fax 0113 2310660
Artistic Director/Literary Manager *Kully Thiarai*
Administrator *Ann Cross*

FOUNDED 1968. Commissioning company touring 2–3 shows a year with a strong commitment to new work and new writers. Aimed at an audience of young people aged between 14–25 years who have little or no access to theatre. Performances held in youth clubs and similar venues (not schools) where young people choose to meet. Recent productions: 1995: *Waking* Lin Coghlan. 1996: *End of Season* Noël Greig, an international collaboration with Theatre Direct of Canada which will tour England and Germany in 1996 and Canada in 1997. 'The company is currently developing its writing policy which will be available to writers interested in working for the company. Whilst unsolicited scripts are not discouraged, the company is particularly keen to enter into a dialogue with writers with regard to creating new work for young people.'

Red Shift Theatre Company

9 The Leathermarket, Weston Street, London SE1 3ER
☎0171 378 9787   Fax 0171 378 9789
Contact *Jonathan Holloway, Artistic Director*
General Manager *Deborah Rees*

FOUNDED 1982. Small-scale touring company which plays to a theatre-literate audience. Unlikely to produce an unsolicited script as most work is commissioned. Welcomes contact with writers – 'we try to see their work ... and welcome receipt of c.v.s and treatments'. Occasionally runs workshops bringing new scripts, writers and actors together. These can develop links with a reservoir of writers who may feed the company. Interested in new plays with subject matter which is accessible to a broad audience and concerns issues of importance; also new translations and adaptations. In 1995, produced a new version of Molière's *George Dandin* written by Ranjit Bolt, *Red Princess*, a new play by Nicholas McInerny, and Mike Dalton's new version of the *Hansel and Gretel* story.

Roundabout Theatre in Education

College Street Centre for Performing Arts, College Street, Nottingham NG1 5AQ
☎0115 9476202   Fax 0115 9539055
Contact *Kitty Parker*

FOUNDED 1973. Theatre-in-Education company of the Nottingham Playhouse. Plays to a young audience aged 5–18 years of age. Some programmes are devised or adapted in-house, some are commissioned. Unable to resource the adequate response required for unsolicited scripts. 'We are committed to the encouragement of new writing as and when resources permit.'

Royal Court Theatre/English Stage Company Ltd

Sloane Square, London SW1W 8AS
☎0171 730 5174   Fax 0171 730 4705
Literary Manager *Graham Whybrow*

The English Stage Company was founded by George Devine in 1956 to put on new plays. John Osborne, John Arden, Arnold Wesker, Edward Bond, Caryl Churchill, Howard Barker and Michael Hastings are all writers this theatre has discovered. Christopher Hampton and David Hare have worked here in the literary department. The aim of the Royal Court is to develop and perform the best in new writing for the theatre, encouraging writers from all sections of society to address the problems and possibilities of our times.

Royal Exchange Theatre Company

St Ann's Square, Manchester M2 7DH
☎0161 833 9333   Fax 0161 832 0881
Literary Manager *Alan Pollock*

FOUNDED 1976. The Royal Exchange has developed a new writing policy, which they find is attracting a younger audience to the theatre. The company produces plays by young dramatists like Iain Heggie, Michael Wall, Alex Finlayson, Rod Wooden, Simon Burke and Randhi McWilliams; also English and foreign classics, modern classics, adaptations and new musicals. The Royal Exchange receives 500–2000 scripts a year. These are read by Alan Pollock and a team of readers. Only a tiny percentage is suitable, but a number of plays are commissioned each year.

Royal Lyceum Theatre Company

Grindlay Street, Edinburgh EH3 9AX
☎0131 229 7404 Fax 0131 228 3955

Artistic Director *Kenny Ireland*
Administrator *Nikki Axford*

FOUNDED 1965. Repertory theatre which plays
to a mixed urban Scottish audience. Produces
classic, contemporary and new plays. Would
like to stage more new plays, especially
Scottish. No full-time literary staff to provide
reports on submitted scripts.

Royal National Theatre

South Bank, London SE1 9PX
☎0171 928 2033 Fax 0171 620 1197

Literary Manager *Jack Bradley*

The majority of the National's new plays come
about as a result of direct commission or from
existing contacts with playwrights. There is no
quota for new work, though so far more than a
third of plays presented have been the work of
living playwrights. Writers new to the theatre
would need to be of exceptional talent to be
successful with a script here, though the Royal
National Theatre Studio acts as a bridge
between the theatre and a limited number of
playwrights, through readings, workshops and
discussion. In some cases a new play is presented
for a shorter-than-usual run in the Cottesloe
Theatre. Scripts considered (send s.a.e).

Royal Shakespeare Company

Barbican Centre, London EC2Y 8BQ
☎0171 628 3351 Fax 0171 374 0818

Literary Manager *Colin Chambers*

The literary department receives around 500
unsolicited mss a year, most of which are
totally unsuitable for the RSC. The RSC is
committed to new plays but the work produced is usually commissioned by the company. Bear in mind that the RSC is not interested in straightforwardly biographical plays or
singlemindedly topical writing, and have no
use for reworkings of Shakespeare or musicals.
RSC actors organise festivals in which new
work is often a prominent feature.

Royal Theatre

15 Guildhall Road, Northampton NN1 1EA
☎01604 38343 Fax 01604 602408

Artistic Director *Michael Napier Brown*

Describes its audience as 'wide-ranging in terms
of taste, with a growing population which is
encouraging a more adventurous and innovative
programme'. Produces at least three new works

each year. The studio theatre, theatre-in-education, community touring and youth theatre tend
to produce the majority of new work, but there
are normally two main-house premières each
year. Previous productions: *Oleanna; An Old
Man's Love; Gasping; Keely and Du; The Winter's
Tale; Top Girls; Shaken not Stirred.* Unsolicited
scripts welcome and always read.

Shared Experience Theatre

Soho Laundry, 9 Dufours Place, London
W1V 1FE
☎0171 434 9248 Fax 0171 287 8763

Artistic Director *Nancy Meckler*

FOUNDED 1975. Varied audience depending on
venue, since this is a touring company. Recent
productions have included: *The Birthday Party*
Harold Pinter; *The Closing Number* (devised by
the company); *Sweet Sessions* Paul Godfrey;
Anna Karenina (adap. Helen Edmundson);
Trilby & Svengali (adap. David Fielder); *Mill on
the Floss* (adap. Helen Edmundson); *The Danube*
Maria Irene Fornes; *Desire Under the Elms*
Eugene O'Neill. No unsolicited mss. Primarily
not a new writing company but 'we are interested in innovative new scripts'.

Sherman Theatre Company

Senghennydd Road, Cardiff CF2 4YE
☎01222 396844 Fax 01222 665581

Artistic Director *Phil Clark*

FOUNDED 1973. Theatre for Young People,
with main house and studio. Encourages new
writing; has produced 50 new plays in the last
five years. Previous productions: *Erogenous Zones,
Drug Faith* Frank Vickery; *Fern Hill, A Long Time
Ago* Mike Kenny; *A Spell of Cold Weather* Charles
Way; *101 Dalmations* adap. Glyn Robbins. In
1995, six half-hour plays by young writers under
25 years were produced. In 1996, the company
will present six new comedies live on stage and
broadcast on BBC Radio Wales, and a new
series of one-act lunchtime plays on stage and
then filmed for HTV Wales. Priority will be
given to Wales-based writers.

Show of Strength

Hebron House, Sion Road, Bedminster,
Bristol, Avon BS3 3BD
☎0117 9637634 ext 239 Fax 0117 9631770

Artistic Directors *Elizabeth Bowden, Alan
Coveney, Sheila Hannon, Bonnie Hurren*
Contact *Sheila Hannon*

FOUNDED 1986. Plays to an informal, younger
than average audience. Aims to stage at least one
new play each season with a preference for work

from Bristol and the South West. Will read unsolicited scripts but a lack of funding means they are unable to provide written reports. Interested in full-length stage plays; 'we are undeterred by large casts'. OUTPUT *A Busy Day* Fanny Burney; *A Man and Some Women* Githa Sowerby; *Blue Murder* Peter Nichols (world première).

Snap People's Theatre Trust

Unit A, Causeway Business Centre, Bishop's Stortford, Hertfordshire CM23 2UB
☎01279 504095/503066   Fax 01279 501472
Contact *Andy Graham, Mike Wood*

FOUNDED 1979. Plays to young people in four age groups (5–7; 7–11; 11–14; 15–21), and to the thirty-something age group. Classic adaptations and new writing. Writers should make an appointment to discuss possibilities rather than submit unsolicited material. New writing encouraged. 'Projects should reflect the writer's own beliefs, be thought-provoking, challenging and accessible.'

Soho Theatre Company

24 Mortimer Street, London W1N 7RD
☎0171 436 8833   Fax 0171 436 8844
Artistic Director *Abigail Morris*
Literary Manager *Paul Sirett*

A new writing theatre company. The company produces around four new shows a year. Previous productions: *Brothers of the Brush* Jimmy Murphy; *Kindertransporte* Diane Samuels; *The Yiddish Trojan Women* Carol Braverman; *Rock Station* Ger FitzGibbon. The system for dealing with unsolicited mss is as follows: scripts go out to a team of readers; those they find interesting are passed on to the artistic director, who invites writers of promise to join the workshop series. Presents the **Verity Bargate Award** annually.

The Sphinx

25 Short Street, London SE1 8LJ
☎0171 713 0991/2
Artistic Director *Sue Parrish*

FOUNDED 1973. Formerly Women's Theatre Group. Tours new plays nationally to studio theatres and arts centres.

Barrie Stacey Productions

9 Denmark Street, London WC2
☎0171 836 4128/6220   Fax 0171 836 2949
Contact *Barrie Stacey*

Touring company, much of the work being Barrie Stacey's own but not exclusively so.

Previous productions: *Adventures of Pinocchio; Snow White and the Seven Dwarfs; West End to Broadway Songbook; Tales From the Jungle Book* Barrie Stacey. Always interested in two/three-handers for production, and in film synopses. Fast, experienced scriptwriters in-house.

The Steam Industry

Finborough Theatre, 118 Finborough Road, London SW10 9ED
☎0171 244 7439   Fax 0171 835 1853
Artistic Director *Phil Willmott*
Contact *The Literary Manager*

Since June 1994, the venue has been a base for The Steam Industry who produce in and out of the building. Their output is diverse and prolific and includes a high percentage of new writing alongside radical adaptations of classics and musicals. The space is also available for a number of hires per year and the hire fee is sometimes waived to encourage innovative work. Unsolicited scripts are welcome but due to minimal resources it can take up to six months to respond. Send s.a.e. with material. The company regularly workshops new scripts at Monday-night play-readings. Previous productions include: *Born Bad; The Oedipus Table; Succulence; Mermaid Sandwich; Illyria*. The venue has presented new works by Anthony Neilson, Jack Bradley, Clare Bayley, Philip Kingston, Mark Ravenhill and Kate Dean.

Stoll Moss Theatres Ltd

Manor House, 21 Soho Square, London W1V 5FD
☎0171 494 5200   Fax 0171 434 1217
Contact *Nica Burns, Peter Cregeen*

Influential theatrical empire, with ten theatres under its umbrella: Apollo; Cambridge; Duchess; Garrick; Gielgud; Her Majesty's; London Palladium; Lyric Shaftesbury Avenue; Queen's and Theatre Royal Drury Lane.

Swan Theatre

The Moors, Worcester WR1 3EF
☎01905 726969   Fax 01905 723738
Artistic Director *Jenny Stephens*

Repertory company producing a wide range of plays to a mixed audience coming largely from the City of Worcester and the county of Hereford & Worcester. A writing group meets at the theatre. Unsolicited scripts are discouraged.

Swansea Little Theatre Ltd
Dylan Thomas Theatre, Maritime Quarter,
Gloucester Place, Swansea, West Glamorgan
SA1 1TY
☎01792 473238

Contact *The Secretary*

A wide variety of plays, from pantomime to
the classics. New writing encouraged. New
plays considered by the Artistic Committee.

Tabard Theatre Company
2 Bath Road, London W4 1LW
☎0181 995 6035   Fax 0181 742 2051

Artistic Director *Kate Bone*

FOUNDED 1985. Interested in new good wri-
ting for a mixed audience. No unsolicited mss.
Previous productions include: Shakespeare
(*Henry V, Richard III*); new writing – *Hungry
Ghosts* P. Kingston; *Theodora* Clare L. Price.

Talawa Theatre Company Ltd
23/25 Great Sutton Street, London EC1V 0DN
☎0171 251 6644   Fax 0171 251 5969

Artistic Director *Yvonne Brewster*
Administrator *Wanjiku Nyachae*

FOUNDED 1985. Plays to an ABC audience of
60% black, 40% white across a wide age range
depending upon the nature of productions and
targeting. Previous productions include all-
black performances of *The Importance of Being
Earnest* and *Antony and Cleopatra*; plus Jamaican
pantomime *Arawak Gold; The Gods Are Not to
Blame; The Road* Wole Soyinka; *O! Babylon*
Derek Walcott. Restricted to new work from
Black writers only. Occasional commissions,
though these tend to go to established writers.
'Interested in the innovative, the modern classic
with special reference to the African diasporic
experience.' No domestic-comedy material.
Runs a Black Women's Writers' project funded
by **London Arts Board** for three years.

Theatr Clwyd
Mold, Clwyd CH7 1YA
☎01352 756331   Fax 01352 758323

Repertory company with a lively programming
policy attracting audiences of all ages. The company has touring commitments within Wales and
tours across Britain. Productions of classics and
revivals have predominated but an international
interest in contemporary drama is being developed. Previous productions: *India Song*
Marguerite Duras; *The Choice* Claire Luckham;
Barnaby and the Old Boys Keith Baxter; *Self
Portrait* Sheila Yeger; *HRH* Snoo Wilson; *Full

Moon by Caradog Prichard, adapt. Helena Kaut-
Howson and John Owen. Unsolicited material is
unlikely to be considered for production, but
special consideration is given to Welsh writers
and scripts with Welsh themes.

Theatre of Comedy Company
210 Shaftesbury Avenue, London WC2H 8DP
☎0171 379 3345   Fax 0171 836 0466

Artistic Director *Alan Strachan*

FOUNDED 1983 to produce new work as well
as classics and revivals. Interested in strong
comedy in the widest sense – Chekhov comes
under the definition as does farce. Also has a
light entertainment division, developing new
scripts for television, namely situation comedy
and series. A good bet for new work.

Theatre Royal, Plymouth
Royal Parade, Plymouth, Devon PL1 2TR
☎01752 668282   Fax 01752 671179

Contact *Liz Turgeon*

Stages small-, middle- and large-scale drama
with an emphasis on musicals and music theatre. Commissions and produces new plays.
Unsolicited scripts are read and reported on.

Theatre Royal Stratford East
Gerry Raffles Square, London E15 1BN
☎0181 534 7374   Fax 0181 534 8381

Literary Manager *Paul Everitt*

Lively East London theatre, catering for a very
mixed audience, both local and London-wide.
Produces plays, musicals, youth theatre and
local community plays/events, all of which is
new work. Special interest in Asian and Black
British work. Unsolicited scripts are welcome.

Theatre Royal Windsor
Windsor, Berkshire SL4 1PS
☎01753 863444   Fax 01753 831673

Artistic Director *Mark Piper*

FOUNDED 1938. Plays to a middle-class, West
End-type audience. Produces thirteen plays a
year and 'would be disappointed to do fewer
than two new plays in a year; always hope to do
half a dozen'. Modern classics, thrillers, comedy
and farce. Only interested in scripts along these
lines.

Theatre Workshop Edinburgh
34 Hamilton Place, Edinburgh EH3 5AX
☎0131 225 7942   Fax 0131 220 0112

Artistic Director *Robert Rae*

Plays to a young, broad-based audience with

much of the work targeted towards particular groups or communities. OUTPUT has included adaptations of Gogol's *The Nose* and Aharon Appelfeld's *Badenheim 1939* – two community performance projects – and *Breaking Free*, a Theatre-in-Education programme touring to secondary schools in Scotland. Particularly interested in new work for children and young people. Frequently engages writers for collaborative/devised projects. Commissions a significant amount of new writing for a wide range of contexts, from large-cast community plays to small-scale professional tours. Favours writers based in Scotland, producing material relevant to a contemporary Scottish audience. Member of Scottish Script Centre to whom it refers senders of unsolicited scripts.

Thorndike Theatre (Leatherhead) Ltd

Church Street, Leatherhead, Surrey
KT22 8DF
☎01372 376211   Fax 01372 362595
Artistic Director *Bill Kenwright*

West End and touring for an audience described as fairly conservative. 70% of the company's work goes out on tour; children's and family plays. Out of a total of ten in-house productions each year, five new plays are sought. Previous productions: *The Master Builder* Ibsen; *Emily Needs Attention* Feydeau; *Private Lives* Coward; *Chapter Two* Neil Simon; *Nicholas Nickleby* Dickens, adapt. David Hare.

Tiebreak Touring Theatre

George White Middle School, Silver Road,
Norwich, Norfolk NR3 4RG
☎01603 426374   Fax 01603 418524
Artistic Director *David Farmer*

FOUNDED 1981. Specialises in high-quality theatre for children and young people, touring schools, youth centres, museums and festivals. Previous productions: *Love Bites; Singing in the Rainforest; Boadicea - The Movie; Dinosaurs on Ice; Touch Wood; The Invisible Boy; My Friend Willy; The Ugly Duckling; Almost Human.* New writing encouraged. Interested in low-budget, small-cast material only. School, educational and socially relevant material of special interest. Scripts welcome.

Torch Theatre

St Peter's Road, Milford Haven,
Pembrokeshire, Dyfed SA73 2BU
☎01646 694192   Fax 01646 690718
Artistic Director *Mike James*

FOUNDED 1976. Plays to a mixed audience hard to attract to new work on the whole. Committed to new work but financing has become somewhat prohibitive. Small-cast pieces with broad appeal welcome. Previous productions: *Frankie and Tommy; School for Wives; Tess of the d'Urbervilles.* The repertoire runs from Ayckbourn to Friel. Scripts sometimes welcome.

Traverse Theatre

Cambridge Street, Edinburgh EH1 2ED
☎0131 228 3223   Fax 0131 229 8443
Literary Manager *Ella Wildridge*

The Traverse is the best-known theatre in Scotland for new writing; indeed it has a policy of putting on nothing but new work by new writers. Also has a strong international programme of work in translation and visiting companies. Previous productions: *Knives in Hens* David Harrower; *The Collection* Mike Cullen; *Europe* David Greig; *Moscow Stations* (adap. Stephen Mulrine). No unsolicited scripts. Writers welcome to make contact by phone or in writing.

Trestle Theatre Company

47-49 Wood Street, Barnet, Hertfordshire
EN5 4BS
☎0181 441 0349   Fax 0181 449 7036
Artistic Directors *Joff Chafer, Toby Wilsher*

FOUNDED 1981. Physical, mask theatre for mostly student-based audiences (18-36 years). All work is devised by the company. Scripts which have the company's special brand of theatre in mind will be considered. No non-physical-based material. New writing welcome.

Tricycle Theatre

269 Kilburn High Road, London NW6 7JR
☎0171 372 6611   Fax 0171 328 0795
Artistic Director *Nicolas Kent*

FOUNDED 1980. Plays to a very mixed audience, in terms of both culture and class. Previous productions: *Two Trains Running* August Wilson; *The Day the Bronx Died* Michael Henry Brown; *Half the Picture* Richard Norton-Taylor and John McGrath; *Nativity* Nigel Williams; *Playboy of the West Indies* Mustapha Matura; *Joe Turner's Come and Gone* and *The Piano Lesson* August Wilson; *Pecong* Steve Carter; *A Love Song for Ulster* Bill Morrison; *Three Hotels* Jon Robin Baitz. New writing welcome from women and ethnic minorities (particularly Black and Irish). Looks for a strong narrative drive with popular appeal, not 'studio' plays. Also runs workshops for writers.

Tron Theatre Company
63 Trongate, Glasgow G1 5HB
☎0141 552 3748   Fax 0141 552 6657

FOUNDED 1981. Plays to a broad cross-section of Glasgow and beyond, including international tours (Toronto 1990; New York 1991; Montreal 1992). Previous productions: *Hosanna* Michel Tremblay (trans. Bowman & Findlay); *Cinzano* Petrushevskaya (trans. Mulrine); *Crow* Hughes & Boyd; *Macbeth* (dir. Michael Boyd); *Dumbstruck* David Kane; *The Trick is to Keep Breathing* Janice Galloway/ Boyd. Interested in premières of ambitious plays by experienced Scottish writers, and in new Irish and international work. No unsolicited mss.

Umoja Theatre Company
The Base, 59 Bethwin Road, London
SE5 0XY
☎0171 701 6396   Fax 0171 703 3796
Artistic Director *To be appointed*

FOUNDED 1983. Plays to a predominantly Black audience with two productions each year. New writers encouraged. The company's own venue, The Base, houses incoming shows, workshops and training.

Unicorn Arts Theatre for Children
Arts Theatre, 6–7 Great Newport Street,
London WC2H 7JB
☎0171 379 3280   Fax 0171 836 5366
Production Director *Kieron Smith*

FOUNDED 1947 as a touring company, and took up residence in the Arts Theatre in 1967. Plays mainly to children between the ages of 4–12. Previous productions: *A Midsummer Night's Dream* and *Stig of the Dump*. Unsolicited scripts welcome. Runs the **Unicorn Arts Theatre National Young Playwrights' Competition** annually (for children between the ages of 6 and 16).

Charles Vance Productions
83 George Street, London W1H 5PL
☎0171 486 1732   Fax 0171 224 2215
Contact *Charles Vance, Jill Streatfeild*

In the market for medium-scale touring productions and summer-season plays. Hardly any new work and no commissions but writing of promise stands a good chance of being passed on to someone who might be interested in it. Occasional try-outs for new work in the Sidmouth repertory theatre. Send s.a.e. for return of mss.

Warehouse Theatre, Croydon
Dingwall Road, Croydon
CR0 2NF
☎0181 681 1257   Fax 0181 688 6699
Artistic Director *Ted Craig*
Writers' Workshop Manager *Sheila Dewey*

South London's new writing theatre, seating 100. Produces six new plays a year and co-produces with companies who share a commitment to new work. Continually building upon a tradition of discovering and nurturing new writers, with activities including a monthly writers workshop and the annual **International Playwriting Festival**. Previous productions: *Fat Souls* James Martin Charlton; *Playing Sinatra* Bernard Kops; *Fighting for the Dunghill* Guy Jenkins; *Eva and the Cabin Boy* Sheila Dewey; *The Astronomers Garden* Kevin Hood; *YoYo* Dino Mahoney; *Dinner with the Borgias* Roy Smiles. Unsolicited scripts welcome but it is more advisable to submit plays through the theatre's International Playwriting Festival. The theatre is committed to productions at least nine months in advance.

Watermill Theatre
Bagnor, Newbury, Berkshire RG20 8AE
☎01635 45834   Fax 01635 523726
Contact *Jill Fraser*

The Watermill tries to put on one new piece of work each year. Previous productions: *Just So* George Stiles & Anthony Drewe; *Hindsight* Richard Everett; *The Great Big Radio Show* Philip Glassboron and David Rhind-Tutt; *The Ugly Duckling* George Stiles & Anthony Drene; *Goodbye Mr Chips* adapt. Norman Coaler; *Laura* (musical) Michael Heath.

Watford Palace Theatre
See **Palace Theatre**

West Yorkshire Playhouse
Playhouse Square, Leeds, West Yorkshire
LS2 7UP
☎0113 2442141   Fax 0113 2448252
Literary Co-ordinator *Claire Malcolm*

Committed to programming new writing as part of its overall policy. Before sending an unsolicited script please phone or write. The Playhouse does readings, workshops and script surgeries on new plays with writers from all over Britain and also has strong links with local writers and Yorkshire Playwrights. The theatre has writers-in-residence. Premières include: *The Gulf Between Us* Trevor Griffiths; *A Passionate Woman* Kay Mellor; *Fathers Day* Maureen Lawrence; *The*

Beatification of Area Bay Wole Soyinka; *The Winter Guest* Sharman Macdonald.

Whirligig Theatre
14 Belvedere Drive, Wimbledon, London SW19 7BY
☎0181 947 1732   Fax 0181 879 7648
Contact *David Wood*

One play a year in major theatre venues, usually a musical for primary school audiences and weekend family groups. Interested in scripts which exploit the theatrical nature of children's tastes. Previous productions: *The See-Saw Tree; The Selfish Shellfish; The Gingerbread Man; The Old Man of Lochnagar; The Ideal Gnome Expedition; Save the Human; Dreams of Anne Frank.*

Michael White Productions Ltd
See **Film, TV and Video Producers**

White Bear Theatre Club
138 Kennington Park Road, London SE11 4DJ
Administration: 3 Dante Road, Kennington, London SE11 4RB ☎0171 793 9193 Fax ☎0171 277 0526
Contact *Michael Kingsbury, Julia Parr*
Administrator *Vanessa Cornford*

FOUNDED 1988. OUTPUT primarily new work for an audience aged 20–35. Unsolicited scripts welcome, particularly new work with a keen eye on contemporary issues, though not agit-prop. Holds readings throughout the year. Recent production: *I Only Have Eyes For You* Barry Keefe. In the process of trying to set up a Lambeth New Play Award.

Windsor Theatre Royal
See **Theatre Royal**

Wolsey Theatre Company
Civic Drive, Ipswich, Suffolk IP1 2AS
☎01473 218911   Fax 01473 212946
Artistic Director *Antony Tuckey*
Contact *Eileen Kidd*

FOUNDED 1979. Tries to do one new play a year in the main house and studio. New writing encouraged. Unsolicited mss welcome. Previous productions: *The Business of Murder; Adam Bede; A Chorus of Disapproval; What Every Woman Knows; Lettice and Lovage.*

Women's Theatre Group
See **The Sphinx**

York Theatre Royal
St Leonard's Place, York YO1 2HD
☎01904 658162   Fax 01904 611534
Artistic Director *John Doyle*

Not a new writing theatre in the main. Previous productions: *The Wars of the Roses; The Madness of George III; The Rivals; Dracula* (adapt. John Doyle). No scripts.

The Young Vic
66 The Cut, London SE1 8LZ
☎0171 633 0133   Fax 0171 928 1585
Artistic Director *Tim Supple*

FOUNDED 1970. The Young Vic produces adventurous and demanding work for an audience with a youthful spirit. The main house is one of London's most exciting spaces and seats up to 500. In addition, a smaller, entirely flexible space, The Young Vic Studio, seats 100 and is used for experiment, performance, rehearsals and installations. 'We are not able to produce many new scripts at the moment; nor are we able to develop or read unsolicited scripts with the care they deserve. However, we are always happy to receive work.'

Riding the Festival Circuit

Never again let it be spread about that the British do not take their culture seriously. This profound thought comes upon me as I and five hundred other fanatics wait in line for a star event at the Hay-on-Wye Festival of Literature. We are in the open and it is raining – hard.

The big attraction, the literary guru we have come to hear is Richard Eyre who has taken time off from the Royal National Theatre to tell us about his controversial production of *Macbeth*. The lecture is billed to start at 2.00pm. It is now 2.30 and the rain is being whipped up by a force nine gale. The doors to the Festival Theatre, otherwise a circus-sized marquee with flapping accessories, remain fastened while engineers check the guy ropes. In the seconds before we are let in, a car revs up to escape the mud and splatters the queue with debris.

'I can't take much more of this,' says a woman in front. But she does. As so do we all.

The experience is not unknown. Arts festivals, of which there are 500 held every year, are notorious for their lack of customer comforts. Yet they attract not far short of £20 million in box office receipts not to mention £7.0 million in business sponsorship and the same again in local authority and arts council funding. They vary wildly in scope and style – from the Edinburgh International Festival and Festival Fringe, which run for several weeks and sell 700,000 tickets between them, to the small town weekend knees-up devoted to folk music and maypole dancing. The expansion of the festival menagerie in recent years is phenomenal. Over half of all festivals were established after 1980. No one has been able to explain the boom, least of all the readiness of otherwise sane people to tolerate hard seats, poor acoustics and the rudeness of volunteer staff who seem to be in training for the prison service. Not all festivals are badly run but a lot are. Responding to an inquiry by the Policy Studies Institute (PSI), the organiser of a prestigious music festival admitted to two big clear outs of stewards within ten years because 'they thought they were more important than the festival'. Such crises appear not to have any long term effect. Public support grows stronger by the year.

If music is the predominant festival activity, literature and drama run it a close second. Between a third and a half of all festivals have a literary element in their programmes. Two of the biggest – Cheltenham and Hay-on-Wye – are devoted almost entirely to the written word. This sounds like a contradiction. Books are ill-suited to public presentation. But it is not the books so much as their authors that attract the customers. Performance skills are more important than writing talent. When both are in the ascendant, as with Sir Dirk Bogarde, you have a star turn and a darling of the festival circuits.

As might be expected of an old pro, Sir Dirk makes it look easy. His technique is to saunter onto the platform (to wild applause) carrying a large holdall of his published books and work in progress. After the preliminaries (when I heard him he referred to a recent mild stroke and his capacity for survival – 'I'm still here' – which brought more applause) he takes questions, breaking off occasionally to give a reading from one of his novels. It works like a dream for the mature generation who recall fondly the weekly visits to the Odeon in the golden days of British cinema. The only disappointment is for the gay activists who expect support from their icon but instead get fobbed off with jokes.

You don't have to be an actor or comedian to achieve top billing at a literary festival but it helps. Organisers will go to the extreme of paying half decent fees to attract John Cleese, Paul Merton or Barry Humphries. On the second rank are names familiar but not famous. George Steiner is the leading exponent of fast talk intellectualism. To hear him on, say, Homeric verse, is to listen to an academic version of a revivalist preacher. Even those who fail to understand a word he utters feel bound to praise what is undeniably a virtuoso rendition of abstruse learning.

The supporting cast – authors in the news who may or may not be able to show themselves off – are packaged by festival organisers to enhance their appeal. A science writer who himself is not much of a draw is thrown together in debate with a dissenting theologian; three women writers conduct a seminar on feminist fiction; a doyen of the best-seller list, with no pretence to platform oratory, is submitted to interview by a well-known press or television practitioner of the art. With rarely any provision for rehearsal, there is a more than evens chance of the fireworks failing to ignite.

Back then to the question, what exactly is the audience appeal? There is, for some, an interest in checking out the famous against their camera images. Are the lines beginning to show on Lady Antonia Fraser? Not at twenty yards in the dusk with the light behind her. Is Jeanette Winterson butch? You had better believe it. Does Peter Mayle come over like the lotus eating ex-pat of his Provençal memoirs? Not at all. He wears a smart blue blazer, grey flannels and shoes with tassels for all the world like the advertising man he used to be. At another level there seems to be a genuine interest in what makes a writer. When I turned up at Cheltenham to do my bit for *The Writer's Handbook* I was aghast to find myself billed in opposition to a lauded one-man show based on Tristan Shandy, described by a *Guardian* critic as one of the best things he'd seen in years. That I captured an audience of over a hundred was less credit to me than to the pulling power of the writer's craft. There was a need to know and my pot pourri of experiences went some way to meeting it.

The 'why' question must also be directed at the speakers. Why do they do it? Money does not come into it, or very rarely. The only material advantage is in selling a few books, assuming of course that the local bookshop is sufficiently well organised to have copies available. At the big festivals there are signing sessions which can shift crate-loads of volumes but few authors would dispute the proposition that there are easier ways of making a living. No, the real reason why writers turn up at festivals – again and again – is that they actually enjoy the experience. Unlike other artists – actors, say, or musicians – writers are short on opportunities of meeting their public. A festival is one of the rare occasions when writers and readers come together. It can be wonderfully encouraging for a study bound novelist to find that someone, somewhere cares enough to want to talk about books. A debate can be stimulating, questions spark off ideas, a lecture concentrates the mind.

'A festival,' said E. M. Forster, 'should be festive. And it should possess something which is distinctive and which could not be so well presented elsewhere.'

Judged by these criteria, the literary festivals can take pride in their achievements. But young people need to be more involved. The PSI says that of the fifty-six per cent of festivals which declare an educational interest, most are linked to general arts or to music. Maybe local authority and arts council grants should be made conditional on a run of educational projects.

The other area for growth is in the commissioning of original work. The leading music festivals are strong here but literature seems bound by what is known and tested. Why? Partly it's a fear of attracting the loony brigade – reams of unpublishable poetry read aloud in a dull monotone. With music, basic demonstrable skills act as a sifter. Anyone can write, or think they can.

But innovative work does not have to be way out; nor, to go to the other extreme, does it have to be tied to the interests of media giants. Aspects of regional or local culture offer more than sufficient opportunities for detecting literary excellence. The Eisteddfods do it best. Among others, the poet R. S. Thomas owes his early recognition to Eisteddfod exposure. And he was nominated for the Nobel Prize.

Festivals

Aldeburgh Poetry Festival
Goldings, Goldings Lane, Leiston, Suffolk
IP16 4EB
☎01728 830631   Fax 01728 832029
Contact *Michael Laskey*

Now in its ninth year, an annual international festival of contemporary poetry held over one weekend each November in Aldeburgh and attracting large audiences. Regular features include a two-week residency leading up to the festival, poetry readings, a children's event, workshops, a public masterclass, a lecture, a performance spot and the festival prize for the year's best first collection (see entry **Prizes**).

Arundel Festival
The Arundel Festival Society Ltd, The Mary Gate, Arundel, West Sussex BN18 9AT
☎01903 883690   Fax 01903 884243
Administrator *Ms Julie Young*

Annual festival held at the end of August/ beginning of September for eleven days. Events include poetry, prose readings and lectures, open-air Shakespeare in Arundel Castle, concerts with internationally known artists, jazz, visual arts and active fringe.

Bath Fringe Festival
The Bell, 103 Walcot Street, Bath BA1 5BW
☎01225 480079   Fax 01225 427441
Chair *David Stevenson*

FOUNDED 1981. Complementing the international music festival, they present theatre, poetry, jazz, blues, comedy, cabaret, storytelling, carnival and more in venues, parks and streets of Bath during late May and early June.

BBC Radio Young Playwrights' Festival
See **FIRST BITE**

Belfast Festival at Queen's
Festival House, 25 College Gardens, Belfast BT9 6BS
☎01232 667687   Fax 01232 663733
Acting Director *Robert Agnew*

FOUNDED 1964. Annual three-week festival held in November. Organised by Queen's University in association with the **Arts Council** of Northern Ireland, the festival covers a wide variety of events, including literature. Programme available in September.

Berkshire Literary Festival
See **Writers Live**

Birmingham Readers and Writers Festival
Festival Office, Central Library, Chamberlain Square, Birmingham B3 3HQ
☎0121 235 4244   Fax 0121 233 9702
Festival Director *Jonathan Davidson*
Festival Organiser *Matthew Gidley*

FOUNDED 1983. Annual nine-day festival held in May. Concerned with all aspects of contemporary reading and writing, with visiting authors, workshops, performances, cabaret, conferences and special programmes for young people.

Black Literature Festival
See **Bradford Festival**

Book Now!
Langholm Lodge, 146 Petersham Road, Richmond, Surrey TW10 6UX
☎0181 332 0534   Fax 0181 940 7568
Director *Nigel Cutting*

FOUNDED 1992. Annual festival which runs throughout the month of November, administered by the Arts Section of Richmond Council. Principal focus is on poetry and serious fiction, but events also cover biography, writing for theatre, children's writing. Programme includes readings, discussions, workshops, debates, exhibitions, schools events. Writers to appear at past festivals include A.S. Byatt, Penelope Lively, Benjamin Zephaniah, Sir Dirk Bogarde, Roger McGough, Rose Tremain, John Mortimer and Sean Hughes.

Bournemouth International Festival
Suite 2, Digby Chambers, Bournemouth, Dorset BH1 1BA
☎01202 297327   Fax 01202 552510
Contact *Julian Robbins, Marketing & Publicity*

FOUNDED 1991. ANNUAL two-week festival held in May. Now under the artistic direction of Gavin Henderson. Features opera, jazz, comedy, literature, theatre, visual arts, concerts (both classical and rock).

Bradford Festival

The Windsor Baths, 11 Great Horton Road, Bradford, West Yorkshire BD7 1AA
☎01274 309199   Fax 01274 724213
Director *Dusty Rhodes*
FOUNDED 1987. June/July; two weeks. The 'largest, award-winning annual community arts festival in the country'. Includes the Mela ('bazaar' or 'fair' in Urdu) which reflects the city's cultural mix. Music, dance, street theatre, spectacle and the annual Black Literature Festival.

Brighton Festival

Festival Office, 21–22 Old Steine, Brighton, East Sussex BN1 1EL
☎01273 713875   Fax 01273 622453
Contact *General Manager*
FOUNDED 1967. For 24 days every May, Brighton hosts England's largest mixed arts festival. Music, dance, theatre, film, opera, literature, comedy and exhibitions. Literary enquiries will be passed to the literature officer. Deadline October for following May.

Bury St Edmunds Festival

Borough Offices, Angel Hill, Bury St Edmunds, Suffolk IP33 1XB
☎01284 757080   Fax 01284 757091
Contact *Kevin Appleby, Festival Manager*
FOUNDED 1986. ANNUAL 17-day spring festival in various venues throughout this historic East Anglian town and outlying areas. Programme features classical music concerts and recitals, lunchtime jazz, theatre, comedy, walks, talks and exhibitions. 1996 highlights included the Royal Philharmonic and BBC Concert Orchestras, Jools Holland, and a Latin and Caribbean Extravaganza.

Buxton Festival

1 Crescent View, Hall Bank, Buxton, Derbyshire SK17 6EN
☎01298 70395   Fax 01298 72289
Contact *General Manager*
FOUNDED 1979. Annual two-and-a-half-week festival held in July. Rarely performed operas are staged in Buxton Opera House and the programme is complemented by a wide variety of other musical events, including recitals, Young Artists series, festival masses, chamber music and cabarets. Also, the Buxton Jazz Festival.

Canterbury Festival

Christ Church Gate, The Precincts, Canterbury, Kent CT1 2EE
☎01227 452853   Fax 01227 781830
Festival Director *Mark Deller*
FOUNDED 1984. Annual two-week festival held in October. A mixed programme of events including talks by visiting authors, readings and storytelling, walks, concerts in the cathedral, jazz, master classes, drama, visual arts, opera, film, cabaret and dance.

Cardiff Literature Festival

The Welsh Academy, 3rd Floor, Mount Stuart House, Mount Stuart Square, Cardiff CF1 6DQ
☎01222 492025   Fax 01222 492930
Director *Kevin Thomas*
FOUNDED 1986. Annual week-long festival held in the spring. Readings, workshops, discussions, children's events, science fiction and fantasy conventions and prize-givings.

The Cheltenham Festival of Literature

Town Hall, Imperial Square, Cheltenham, Gloucestershire GL50 1QA
☎01242 521621   Fax 01242 256457
Festival Organiser *Sarah Smyth*
FOUNDED 1949. Annual festival held in October. The first purely literary festival of its kind, this festival has over the past decade developed from an essentially local event into the largest and most popular in Europe. A wide range of events including talks and lectures, poetry readings, novelists in conversation, exhibitions, discussions, cabaret and a large bookshop.

Chester Literature Festival

8 Abbey Square, Chester CH1 2HU
☎01244 319985   Fax 01244 341200
Chairman *John Elsley*
FOUNDED 1989. Annual festival during October, organised by local bookshops, writers' groups and Chester Arts Association. Major events sponsored by publishers. Authors taking part in the 1995 festival included Lord Jenkins, Michael Parkinson, Brenda Maddox, Juliet Barker, and Booker Prize winner, Pat Barker.

Cleveland Festival
See **Write Around — A Celebration of Cleveland Writing**

Contact Young Playwrights' Festival
Oxford Road, Manchester M15 6JA
☎0161 274 3434

Contact *Lisa Renowden*

FOUNDED 1986. Annual summer festival open to young people aged between 11 and 25 living in the North-west of England. From the entries, which need to be in by the January of the festival year, twenty are selected for workshops and from these, a number are produced by a professional company before a two-week tour to schools in the region. All of the finalists are taken on a residential writing course in the Lake District with professional writers and directors who help them to develop their work. All scripts submitted to the festival receive a critical analysis.

Dartington Literary Festival
See **Ways With Words**

Doncaster Library Festival
Doncaster Central Library, Waterdale, Doncaster, South Yorkshire DN1 3JE
☎01302 734305   Fax 01302 369749

Contact *Festival Organiser*

FOUNDED 1988. Annual festival (4–5 days) in October/November, covering a wide range of events for adults and children. Readings, cabaret, drama, music and creative writing workshops. Visiting authors have included Andrea Newman, Stan Barstow, Michael Hardcastle, Simon Armitage, Carol Ann Duffy, Pete Morgan, Adrian Henri, Matt Simpson, Sarah Harrison, Ian McMillan, Martyn Wiley, Margaret Drabble, Berlie Doherty. Also features the Doncaster Writers' Stakes Race held at the town's racecourse.

The Festival of Dover
Dover District Council, White Cliffs Business Park, Dover, Kent CT16 3PD
☎01304 821199   Fax 01304 827269

Festival Organiser *Sarah Pascoe*

Two-week festival held in May, including a wide variety of arts activities. The programme encompasses exhibitions, concerts, dance, drama, walks and literary talks/workshops. 1996 celebrated the area's maritime history with 'Spirit of the Sea'.

Dublin International Writers' Festival
An Chomhairle Ealaíon (The Arts Council), 70 Merrion Square, Dublin 2
☎00 353 1 6611840   Fax 00 353 1 6761302

Festival Director *Laurence Cassidy*

Biennial festival held in September. Features conference sessions, public interviews, debates, readings and exhibitions, with some of the world's leading authors in attendance.

Durham Literary Festival
Durham City Arts, Byland Lodge, Hawthorn Terrace, Durham City DH1 4TD
☎0191 386 6111 ext. 338 Fax 0191 386 0625

Secretary *Paul Rubinstein*

FOUNDED 1989. Annual 2-3-week event, end of May-beginning of June, held at various locations in the city. Workshops, plus performances, cabaret, and other events.

Edinburgh Book Festival
Scottish Book Centre, 137 Dundee Street, Edinburgh EH11 1BG
☎0131 228 5444   Fax 0131 228 4333

Director *Jan Fairley*

FOUNDED 1983. Biennial book festival held during the first fortnight of the Edinburgh International Festival. Now established as Britain's biggest book event, the programme includes discussions, readings and lectures by writers of national and international reputation.

Exeter Festival
Festival Office, Civic Centre, Exeter, Devon EX1 1JN
☎01392 265200   Fax 01392 265265

Festival Organiser *Lesley Maynard*
Artistic Director *Paul Patterson*

FOUNDED 1980. Annual two-week festival with a variety of events including concerts, theatre, dance and exhibitions.

FIRST BITE – BBC Radio Young Writers' Festival
Room 6067, Broadcasting House, London W1A 1AA

Contact *Jonquil Panting*

FOUNDED 1988 - formerly the Young Playwright's Festival. Takes place every 2/3 years. Open to writers aged 16 - 30 (inclusive) who are new to radio. Plays and stories in five categories. For more details contact the above.

Glasgow Mayfest

See **Mayfest**

Greenwich and Docklands International Festival

6 College Approach, London SE10 9HY
☎0181 305 1818   Fax 0181 305 1188

Director *Bradley Hemmings*

FOUNDED 1970. Annual festival in May/June. Features a wide variety of events, including world music, theatre, dance, classical music, jazz, comedy, art, literature and free open-air events.

Guildford Book Festival

8 Church Path, Cowfold, West Sussex RH13 8DA
☎01403 864917   Fax 01403 864917

Book Festival Organiser *Joan Konig*

FOUNDED 1989. A ten-day celebration of books and writing held annually, during the autumn half-term, throughout the town. The programme includes literary lunches; poetry readings; a writer-in-residence; children's events; the Annual University Poetry Lecture; writing workshops and bookshop events.

Harrogate International Festival

The Festival Office, Royal Baths, Harrogate, North Yorkshire HG1 2RR
☎01423 562303   Fax 01423 521264

Festival Director *William Dodds*
General Administrator *Harriet Jones*

FOUNDED 1966. Annual two-week festival at the end of July and beginning of August. Events include international symphony orchestras, chamber concerts, ballet, celebrity recitals, dance, opera, drama, jazz, comedy, literature plus an international street theatre festival.

The Hay Festival

Festival Office, Hay-on-Wye HR3 5BX
☎01497 821217   Fax 01497 821066

Festival Director *Peter Florence*

FOUNDED 1988. Annual May festival sponsored by *The Sunday Times*. Guests have included Salman Rushdie, Toni Morrison, Stephen Fry, Joseph Heller, Carlos Fuentes, Maya Angelou, Amos Oz, Arthur Miller.

Huddersfield Poetry Festival

c/o The Word Hoard, 46/47 Byram Arcade, Westgate, Huddersfield, West Yorkshire HD1 1ND
☎01484 452070   Fax 01484 455049

Contact *Dianne Darby*

Twice-yearly event consisting of a spring season of around six events over as many weeks, and three weekend writing courses in the autumn, each exploring particular themes. Also occasional one-off events. Though very interested in local writers, the festival has a cosmopolitan outlook and features related performance arts within the curriculum.

Hull Literature Festival

Festival Office, 79 Ferensway, Hull HU2 8LE
☎01759 303454   Fax 01759 303454

Director *David Porter*

FOUNDED 1992. Annual festival running in November.

Ilkley Literature Festival

Festival Office, Manor House Museum, Ilkley, West Yorkshire LS29 9DT
☎01943 601210

Director *David Porter*

FOUNDED 1973. Three festivals a year of 4–5 days' duration. Previous guests have included Tony Harrison, Sarah Dunant, Irina Ratushinskaya, Colin Thubron. Also presents children's events, storytellers, theatre and music, and creative writing workshops. Runs the **Yorkshire Open Poetry Competition**. Telephone to join free mailing list.

International Playwriting Festival

Warehouse Theatre, Dingwall Road, Croydon CR0 2NF
☎0181 681 1257   Fax 0181 688 6699

FOUNDED 1985. Annual autumn competition of full-length unperformed plays, judged by a panel of theatre professionals. Finalists given rehearsed readings during the festival in November. Entries welcomed from all parts of the world. Scripts, plus two stamped addressed envelopes (one script-sized), should reach the **The Warehouse Theatre** by July, accompanied by an entry form (available from the theatre). Previous winners produced at the theatre include: Kevin Hood *Beached;* Anne Aylor *Children of the Dust;* Mark Bunyan *Dinner;* Ellen Fox *Conversations with George Sandburgh After a Solo Flight Across the Atlantic;* Guy Jenkin *Fighting for the Dunghill;* James Martin Charlton *Fat Souls;* Douglas Esson *Nervous Breakdown;* Dino Mahoney *YoYo*.

Kent Literature Festival

The Metropole Arts Centre, The Leas, Folkestone, Kent CT20 2LS
☎01303 255070

Festival Director *David Stone*
Festival Administrator *Ann Fearey*

FOUNDED 1980. Annual week-long festival held at the end of September which aims to bring the best in modern writing to a large audience. Visiting authors and dramatic presentations are a regular feature along with creative writing workshops, seminars, discussions and children's/family events. Also runs the Kent Young Writers of the Year Award and **Short Story Competition**. Brochure for the 1997 festival available from the end of July.

King's Lynn, The Fiction Festival

19 Tuesday Market Place, King's Lynn, Norfolk PE30 1JW
☎01553 691661 (office hours) or 761919
Fax 01553 691779

Contact *Anthony Ellis*

FOUNDED 1989. Annual weekend festival held in March. Over the weekend there are readings and discussions, attended by guest writers of which there are usually eight. Previous guests have included Beryl Bainbridge, Malcolm Bradbury, Marina Warner, William Golding, Hilary Mantel, Elizabeth Jane Howard.

King's Lynn, The Poetry Festival

19 Tuesday Market Place, King's Lynn, Norfolk PE30 1JW
☎01553 691661 (office hours) or 761919
Fax 01553 691779

Contact *Anthony Ellis*

FOUNDED 1985. Annual weekend festival held at the end of September, with guest poets (usually eight). Previous guests have included Carol Ann Duffy, Paul Durcan, Gavin Ewart, Peter Porter, Stephen Spender. Events include readings and discussion panels.

Lancaster LitFest

67 Church Street, Lancaster LA1 1ET
☎01524 62166   Fax 01524 841216

FOUNDED 1978. Regional literature development agency, organising workshops, readings, residencies, publications. Year-round programme of literature-based events; and annual festival in October.

City of London Festival

230 Bishopsgate, London EC2M 4QD
☎0171 377 0540   Fax 0171 377 1972

FOUNDED 1962. Annual three-week festival held in June and July. Features over forty classical and popular music events alongside poetry and prose readings, street theatre and open-air extravaganzas, in some of the most outstanding performance spaces in the world.

London New Play Festival

34 Osnabrook Street, London NW1 3ND
☎0171 209 2326

Artistic Director *Phil Setren*
Literary Manager *Shabnam Shabazi*

FOUNDED 1989. Open to full-length and one-act plays which are assessed for originality, form, etc by a reading committee. Deadline for scripts is the end of January; details can be obtained from **The Writers' Guild**. In 1996, four plays were produced and a number of writers were commissioned for short pieces which were performed at the Young Vic Studio in the autumn.

Ludlow Festival

Castle Square, Ludlow, Shropshire SY8 1AY
☎01584 875070   Fax 01584 877673

Contact *Festival Administrator*

FOUNDED 1959. Annual two-week festival held in the last week of June and first week of July with an open-air Shakespeare production held at Ludlow Castle and a varied programme of events including recitals, opera, dance, popular and classical concerts, literary and historical lectures.

Manchester Festival of Writing

Manchester Central Library, St Peter's Square, Manchester M2 5PD
☎0161 234 1901

Contact *Tang Lin*

FOUNDED 1990. An annual event organised by Manchester Libraries and Commonword community publishers. It consists of a programme of practical writing workshops on specific themes/genres run by well-known writers. Attendance at all workshops is free to Manchester residents.

Mayfest

18 Albion Street, Glasgow G1 1LH
☎0141 552 8000   Fax 0141 552 6612

Director *Paul Bassett*

FOUNDED 1982. Glasgow's annual festival of popular arts and entertainment. 'Mayfest appeals to everyone, presenting both small and large-scale events for thousands of people, many of whom do not regularly attend such events.' Music, dance, theatre, comedy, visual arts, special events and a late night club.

National Student Drama Festival

See **University College, Scarborough** under **Writers' Courses**

Norfolk and Norwich Festival

16 Princes Street, Norwich, Norfolk NR3 1AE
☎01603 614921   Fax 01603 632303
Festival Director *Marcus Davey*

FOUNDED 1972, this performing arts festival is the second oldest in the UK. Held annually in October (10th-20th in 1996), it features performers from all over the world. The 'Book at Lunchtime' series has become a popular feature in recent years and there are also poetry and story-telling events.

Royal Court Young Writers' Festival

Royal Court Young People's Theatre, 309 Portobello Road, London W10 5TD
☎0181 960 4641   Fax 0181 960 1434
Contact *Festival Organiser*

Open to young people up to the age of 23 in targeted regions. Focuses on the process of playwriting: writers and directors from the Royal Court visit a number of selected parts of Britain with five centres in each area, leading a workshop on playwriting. A second visit extends this process to the point at which young people attending are invited to submit work for the festival. Intensive work on the final draft of plays precedes production at the Royal Court Theatre Upstairs, before going on tour in the participating areas.

Salisbury Festival

Festival Office, 75 New Street, Salisbury, Wiltshire SP1 2PH
☎01722 323883   Fax 01722 410552
Director *Helen Marriage*

FOUNDED 1972. Annual festival held in the last two weeks of May. Previous participants have included Max Hastings, Victoria Glendinning, Joanna Trollope, Colin Thubron, Bernice Rubens, Howard Jacobson, Andrew Motion, Jo Shapcott, Leslie Thomas and John Julius Norwich.

Scottish Young Playwrights Festival

Scottish Youth Theatre, Old Athenaeum Theatre, 179 Buchanan Street, Glasgow G1 2JZ
☎0141 332 5127   Fax 0141 333 1021
Aritistic Director *Mary McCluskey*

The Scottish Young Playwrights project operates throughout Scotland. In every region an experienced theatre practitioner runs regular young writers' workshops aimed at developing the best possible scripts from initial ideas. A representative selection of scripts is then selected to form a showcase. The festival is then mounted at the Old Athenaeum in December, in conjunction with the Royal Scottish Academy of Music and Drama. Scripts will be workshopped, revised and developed culminating in an evening presentation. Scripts are welcome throughout the year from young people aged 15-25 who are native Scots and/or resident in Scotland; synopses of unfinished scripts also considered. No restriction on style, content or intended media, but work must be original and unperformed. Further details from above.

South London International Playwriting Festival

See **International Playwriting Festival**

Stratford-upon-Avon Poetry Festival

The Shakespeare Centre, Henley Street, Stratford-upon-Avon, Warwickshire CV37 6QW
☎01789 204016   Fax 01789 296083
Festival Director *Roger Pringle*

FOUNDED 1953. Annual festival held on Sunday evenings during July and August. Readings by poets and professional actors.

Warwick & Leamington Festival

Warwick Arts Society, Northgate, Warwick CV34 4JL
☎01926 410747   Fax 01926 407606
Festival Director *Richard Phillips*

FOUNDED 1980. Annual festival lasting 12 days in the first half of July. Basically a chamber music festival, with some open-air, large-scale concerts in Warwick Castle, the festival also promotes plays by Shakespeare in historical settings. Large-scale education programme. Interested in increasing its literary content, organised in conjunction with Pauline Prior-Pitt.

Ways with Words

Droridge Farm, Dartington, Totnes, Devon
TQ9 6JQ
☎01803 867311 Fax 01803 863688

Festival Director *Kay Dunbar*

Ways with Words runs a major literature festival at Dartington Hall in south Devon at the end of August each year. Features lectures, readings, interviews, discussions, performances, master classes and workshops.

Ways with Words also runs literary weekends in Southwold (Suffolk), Bath, York and Bury St Edmunds, writing courses in the UK and abroad and a literary conference at Dartington.

Write Around, A Celebration of Cleveland Writing

Berwick Hills Library, Ormesby Road, Berwick Hills, Middlesbrough, Cleveland TS3 7RP
☎01642 246947

Contact *Alyson Perry*

FOUNDED 1989. Annual two-week festival with a commitment to local writers. Held during the last two weeks of October, featuring workshops and readings, plus guest writers and opportunities for new writers. Publishes anthologies of poetry and short stories compiled from submissions by Cleveland writers. Contact above for further information. Programmes available in August.

Crossing the Language Barrier

Those who seek to earn a living by translating into English suffer by association with the world's dominant literary language. We have a surfeit of books in English or, more particularly, in American English. Why then, asks the general reader, should we venture beyond our own broad cultural boundaries? A mean spirited view it may be but notwithstanding such recent best selling imports as *Miss Smilla's Feeling for Snow* and *Sophie's World*, that is the reality.

Writing in the *Times Literary Supplement*, Jan Dalley reports that 'In many French publishing houses, the person responsible for acquiring and translating foreign books holds a senior job – sometimes the senior editorial job. Such posts don't even exist on this side of the Channel. And where [abroad] translation provides a substantial part of a company's product, translating as an activity has much higher status – in sharp contrast, again, to Britain.'

There are a few symbols of hope. A number of residential bursaries are offered from time to time by The British Centre for Literary Translation (Department of Modern Languages and European History, The University of East Anglia, Norwich NR4 1TJ). For up-to-date information about similar bursaries abroad, contact the Cultural Attaché of the relevant embassy or bodies such as the French Institute, the Goethe Institut and the Italian Institute. The Arts Council offers bursaries to theatre translators under its Theatre Translation Schemes, and distributes £100,000-plus in translation grants to twenty-four publishers. There is an EU scheme in operation, and the most energetic companies – **Serpent's Tail**, **Harvill Press** and others – can often cover translation costs by these grants, or with money from the cultural organisation of the originating country.

Then again, if a translator does hit the jackpot with a best seller, the rewards can be considerable.

Value in copyright

There is a popular misconception that translating a text from one language into another is a mechanical exercise – a matter of straight conversion or even copying. Yet if two translators are given the same source text, the result may be two quite different but equally valid versions in the target language. In the theatre too, we are used to seeing a succession of new translations of classic plays, proving that each translator creates something original that is specially made to 'speak' to a particular audience. The law recognises this 'original' nature of a translation and affords copyright protection to the translation, separate from the copyright protection to which the original foreign work is entitled and also separate from the protection of someone else's translation of the same work.

Who qualifies?

It is possible to be a translator without holding any formal qualifications. Some translators develop their skills from a bilingual family or having lived for long periods in two countries. However, a formal university education in Modern Languages is helpful, especially if it includes classes in translation. Courses and workshops designed to improve translation techniques may be useful though there is no guarantee of subsequent commissions. The value of language diplomas can be enhanced by specialist qualifications. For example, a publisher who wants a book on genetic engineering translated may be keen to commission a translator with a degree in biology.

The translator needs to have a feeling and fascination for language, an intimate knowledge of the source language of a particular project and of its regional culture and literature as well as a reasonable knowledge of any relevant special subject. But more than this, the translator must be a skilled and creative writer. The aim always should be to convey the meaning of the original work, as opposed to producing a mere accurate rendering of the words. The text must read well, while echoing the style and tone of the original — as if the original author were writing in the target language.

Making a living

Almost without exception, translators of books and plays work on a freelance basis. As in all freelance occupations, it is not easy for the beginner to ensure a constant flow of commissions. Only a few translators can earn a full salary and may well have other sources of income such as language teaching or lecturing. Equally, they may write books themselves as well as translating other authors' work; or be registered with a translation agency and accept shorter (and possibly more lucrative) commercial items between longer stretches of literary translation.

Rate for the job

An established translator may work for as little as £50–£60 per 1000 words but like the original author, the translator should expect remuneration to reflect the amount of use that is made of the translation. If payment is in the form of a fee: i.e. a lump sum, it should not be 'for the translation' but for a specified use of the translator's work, e.g. for the right to print 5,000 copies for sale in the UK. Such an arrangement makes fair allowance for additional fees to be paid, for example if further copies are sold or if the licence is extended to include America. For the translation of a book, the Model Contract issued by the **Translators Association** recommends that there should be an advance payment on account of a royalty on each copy sold and a share of the proceeds from uses such as serialisation. In the case of a play, the translator should receive a percentage of the gross box office receipts. The translator should be able to obtain additional payment if asked to edit a literary work as well as translate it and there should be an additional fee for the preparation of an index for the translated edition. When translations are borrowed from public libraries, the translator receives a 30% share of the full Public Lending Right payment.

Finding work

For the beginner, the usual method of obtaining commissions is to send a letter and a short sample translation to selected publishers.

Only a fraction of all the works published in their original language are published subsequently in translation but a translator who knows the market may spot a likely candidate. The first step is to contact the owner of the translation rights who may be the original author or a foreign publisher. The translator needs to know if rights are available; and, if so, whether the owner is willing to authorise an approach to potential publishers.

Opportunities are likely to arise at trade gatherings such as the Frankfurt Book Fair and the Bologna Children's Book Fair where publishers and literary agents are busily engaged in buying and selling translation rights.

The Translators Association

The Translators Association is a subsidiary group within the Society of Authors. Translators in the making may apply for Associate Membership either when they have received an offer for a full length translation or if they have had occasional translations of shorter material, e.g. articles, short stories and poems, published or performed commercially.

The Association's Model Contract and Guidelines for translators of dramatic works are free to members. The Association's journal, *In Other Words*, keeps members up-to-date with a wide variety of articles, reviews and information.

European Publishers

Austria

Paul Neff, Verlag KG
Hackingerstrasse 52, 1140 Vienna
☎00 43 222 9406115
Fax 00 43 222 947641288

FOUNDED 1829. *Publishes* art, biography, general fiction, music and dance.

Springer-Verlag KG
Jachenplatz 4–6, PO Box 89, 1201 Vienna
☎00 43 222 3302415 Fax 00 43 222 3302426

FOUNDED 1924. *Publishes* environmental studies, engineering (general), nursing, dentistry, medicine and science (general).

Verlag Carl Ueberreuter
Alserstrasse 24, Postfach 306,
A-1090 Vienna
☎00 43 222 404440   Fax 00 43 222 404445

FOUNDED 1548. *Publishes* fiction and general non-fiction: history, government, political science, economics, general science, science fiction, fantasy, music, dance and art.

Paul Zsolnay Verlag GmbH
Prinz-Eugenstrasse 30, Postfach 142,
A-1041 Vienna
☎00 43 222 5057661-0
Fax 00 43 222 5057661-10

FOUNDED 1923. *Publishes* biography, fiction, general non-fiction, history, poetry.

Belgium

Facet NV
Willem Linnigstr 13, 2060 Antwerp
☎00 32 3 2274028   Fax 00 32 3 2273792

FOUNDED 1976. *Publishes* children's books.

Uitgeverij Lannoo NV
Kasteelstr 97, B-8700 Tielt
☎00 32 51 424211   Fax 00 32 51 401152

FOUNDED 1909. *Publishes* art, biography, economics, general non-fiction, gardening, health, history, management, nutrition, photography, poetry, political science, religion, travel.

Standaard Uitgeverij
Belgiëlei 147a, 2018 Antwerp
☎00 32 3 2395900   Fax 00 32 3 2308550

FOUNDED 1919. *Publishes* fiction, humour, education.

Denmark

Forlaget Apostrof ApS
Berggreensgade 24, Postboks 2580,
DK-2100 Copenhagen
☎00 45 31 208420   Fax 00 45 31 208453

FOUNDED 1980. *Publishes* fiction, essays, literature, literary criticism, humour, general non-fiction, psychology, psychiatry.

Aschehoug Fakta
7 Vognmagergade, PO Box 2179,
DK-1017 Copenhagen 0
☎00 45 33 919222   Fax 00 45 33 918218

FOUNDED 1977. *Publishes* cookery, maritime, how-to, health and nutrition.

Borgens Forlag A/S
Valbygardsvej 33, DK-2500 Valby
☎00 45 36 462100   Fax 00 45 36 441488

FOUNDED 1948. *Publishes* fiction, general non-fiction, art, computer science, crafts, education, games, hobbies, health, nutrition, religion, social sciences, sociology.

Forum Publishers
Snaregade 4, DK-1205 Copenhagen K
☎00 45 33 147714   Fax 00 45 33 147791

FOUNDED 1940. *Publishes* fiction and mysteries.

GEC Gads Forlagsaktieselskab
Vimmelskaftet 32, DK-1161 Copenhagen K
☎00 45 33 150558   Fax 00 45 33 123835

FOUNDED 1855. *Publishes* biological sciences, cookery, crafts, games, hobbies, economics, education, English as a second language, environmental studies, gardening, plants, history, law, mathematics, natural history, non-fiction (general), physics, travel.

Gyldendalske Boghandel-Nordisk Forlag A/S

Klareboderne 3, DK-1001 Copenhagen K
☎00 45 33 110775   Fax 00 45 33 110323

FOUNDED 1770. *Publishes* fiction, education, poetry, biography, history, how-to, music, dance, art, philosophy, medicine, nursing, dentistry, psychology, psychiatry, general and social sciences, sociology.

Hekla Forlag

Valbygaardsvej 33, DK-2500 Valby
☎00 45 36 462100   Fax 00 45 36 441488

FOUNDED 1979. *Publishes* general fiction and non-fiction.

Høst & Søns Publishers Ltd

Købmagergade 62, Box 2212,
DK-1018 Copenhagen
☎00 45 33 153031   Fax 00 45 33 155155

FOUNDED 1836. *Publishes* crafts, games, hobbies, linguistics, arts, regional interests, travel, environmental studies.

Lademann A/S

Gerdasgade 37, 2500 Valby
☎00 45 36 441120   Fax 00 45 36 442236

FOUNDED 1954. *Publishes* general non-fiction.

Lindhardt og Ringhof

Kristianiagade 14, DK-2100 Copenhagen
☎00 45 35 434455   Fax 00 45 35 436520

FOUNDED 1971. *Publishes* fiction and general non-fiction.

Nyt Nordisk Forlag Arnold Busck A/S

Købmagergade 49,
DK-1150 Copenhagen K
☎00 45 33 111103   Fax 00 45 33 934490

FOUNDED 1896. *Publishes* fiction, biography, history, how-to, music, dance, art, philosophy, religion, medicine, nursing, dentistry, psychology, psychiatry, general and social sciences, sociology.

Politikens Forlag A/S

Vestergade 26, DK-1456 Copenhagen K
☎00 45 33 112122   Fax 00 45 33 932152

FOUNDED 1946. *Publishes* general non-fiction, art, crafts, dance, history, hobbies, how-to, music, natural history, sports, travel.

Samlerens Forlag A/S

Snaregade 4, DK-1205 Copenhagen K
☎00 45 33 131023   Fax 00 45 33 144314

FOUNDED 1942. *Publishes* biography, history, government, political science, literature, literary criticism, essays, fiction.

Det Schoenbergske Forlag A/S

Landemaerket 5, DK-1119 Copenhagen K
☎00 45 33 113066   Fax 00 45 33 330045

FOUNDED 1857. *Publishes* fiction, art, poetry, humour, biography, history, psychology, psychiatry, philosophy, travel

Spektrum Forlagsaktieselskab

4 Snaregade, DK-1205 Copenhagen K
☎00 45 33 147714   Fax 00 45 33 147791

FOUNDED 1990. *Publishes* general non-fiction.

Tiderne Skifter Forlag A/S

51 Pilestrade, 1001 Copenhagen K
☎00 45 33 325772   Fax 00 45 33 144205

FOUNDED 1979. *Publishes* fiction, literature and literary criticism, essays, photography, behavioural sciences.

Wangels Forlag AS

Gerdasgade 37, 2500 Valby
☎00 45 36 441120   Fax 00 45 36 441162

FOUNDED 1946. *Publishes* fiction.

Finland

Gummerus Publishers

Erottajankatu 5C, PO Box 2,
SF-00130 Helsinki
☎00 358 0 644301   Fax 00 358 0 604998

FOUNDED 1872. *Publishes* fiction and general non-fiction.

Karisto Oy

Paroistentie 2, PO Box 102,
SF-13100 Hämeenlinna
☎00 358 17 6161551   Fax 00 358 17 6161565

FOUNDED 1900. *Publishes* fiction and general non-fiction.

Kirjayhtymä Oy

Eerikinkatu 28, PO Box 207,
SF-00180 Helsinki
☎00 358 0 6937641   Fax 00 358 0 69376366

FOUNDED 1958. *Publishes* fiction and general non-fiction.

Otava Kustannusosakeyhtiö
Uudenmaankatu 8-12, PO Box 134,
00120 Helsinki
☎00 358 0 19961   Fax 00 358 0 643136
FOUNDED 1890. *Publishes* fiction, general non-fiction, biography, history, how-to, art.

Werner Söderström Osakeyhtiö (WSOY)
Bulevardi 12, PO Box 222, 00121 Helsinki
☎00 358 0 61681   Fax 00 358 0 6168405
FOUNDED 1878. *Publishes* fiction, general non-fiction, education.

Tammi Publishers
Eerikinkatu 28, FIN–00180 Helsinki
☎00 358 0 6937621   Fax 00 358 0 69376266
FOUNDED 1943. *Publishes* fiction, general non-fiction.

France
Editions Arthaud SA
20 rue Monsieur-le-Prince, 75006 Paris
☎00 33 1 4329 1220   Fax 00 33 1 4329 2148
FOUNDED 1890. *Publishes* art, history, literature, literary criticism, esays, sport, travel.

Editions Pierre Belfond
216 blvd St-Germain, 75007 Paris
☎00 33 1 4544 3823   Fax 00 33 1 4544 9804
FOUNDED 1963. *Publishes* fiction, literature, literary criticism, essays, art, biography, general non-fiction, history, music, dance, mysteries, poetry, health, nutrition, how-to, romance.

Editions Bordas
17 rue Rémy-Dumoncel, 75661 Paris
Cedex 14
☎00 33 1 4279 6200   Fax 00 33 1 4322 8518
FOUNDED 1946. *Publishes* education and general non-fiction.

Editions Calmann-Lévy SA
3 rue Auber, 75009 Paris
☎00 33 1 4742 3833   Fax 00 33 1 4742 7781
FOUNDED 1836. *Publishes* biography, fiction, history, humour, philosophy, psychology, psychiatry, science fiction, fantasy, social sciences, sociology, sports, economics.

Editions Denoël Sàrl
9 rue du Cherche-Midi, 75006 Paris
☎00 33 1 4439 7373   Fax 00 33 1 4439 7390
Publishes art, economics, fiction, science fiction, fantasy, history, government, philosophy, political science, psychology, psychiatry, sports.

Librairie Arthème Fayard
75 rue des Saints-Pères, 75006 Paris
☎00 33 1 4544 3845   Fax 00 33 1 4222 4017
FOUNDED 1854. *Publishes* biography, fiction, history, social sciences, sociology, general science, dance, music, philosophy, religion, technology.

Librairie Ernest Flammarion
26 rue Racine, 75006 Paris
☎00 33 1 4051 3100   Fax 00 33 1 4329 7644
FOUNDED 1875. *Publishes* general fiction and non-fiction.

Editions Gallimard
5 rue Sébastien-Bottin, 75007 Paris
☎00 33 1 4954 4200   Fax 00 33 1 4544 9919
FOUNDED 1911. *Publishes* fiction, art, poetry, biography, history, music, dance, philosophy.

Société des Editions Grasset et Fasquelle
61 rue des Saints-Pères, 75006 Paris
☎00 33 1 4439 2200   Fax 00 33 1 4222 6418
FOUNDED 1907. *Publishes* fiction and general non-fiction, philosophy, literature, literary criticism, essays.

Hachette Livre
83 ave Marceau, 75116 Paris
☎00 33 1 4069 1600   Fax 00 33 1 4220 3993
FOUNDED 1826. *Publishes* fiction and general non-fiction, history, self-help, architecture and interior design, art, travel, education, general science, engineering, political science, government, economics, social science, sociology, philosophy, sports, language and linguistics.

Editions Robert Laffont
24 ave Marceau, 75381 Paris 08 15
☎00 33 1 5367 1400   Fax 00 33 1 5367 1414
FOUNDED 1941. *Publishes* fiction, history, philosophy, religion, art, music, dance, biography, medicine, nursing, dentistry, general and social sciences, sociology, psychology, psychiatry.

Librairie Larousse
5 Square Max-Hymans, 75741 Paris 15 06
☎00 33 1 4439 4400   Fax 00 33 1 4439 4343
FOUNDED 1852. *Publishes* general and social sciences, sociology, language, linguistics, technology.

Editions Jean-Claude Lattès

17 rue Jacob, 75006 Paris
☎00 33 1 4441 7400   Fax 00 33 1 4325 3047
FOUNDED 1968. *Publishes* fiction and general non-fiction, biography, religion (Catholic and Jewish), music, dance.

Les Editions Magnard Sàrl

6 rue Lacépède, 75005 Paris 06
☎00 33 1 4408 8585   Fax 00 33 1 4331 6613
FOUNDED 1933. *Publishes* education.

Michelin et Cie (Services de Tourisme)

46 ave de Breteuil, 75324 Paris 07
☎00 33 1 4566 1234   Fax 00 33 1 4566 1163
FOUNDED 1900. *Publishes* travel.

Les Editions de Minuit SA

7 rue Bernard-Palissy, 75006 Paris
☎00 33 1 4439 3920   Fax 00 33 1 4544 8236
FOUNDED 1942. *Publishes* fiction, literature, literary criticism, essays, philosophy, social science, sociology.

Fernand Nathan

9 rue Méchain, 75014 Paris
☎00 33 1 4587 5000   Fax 00 33 1 4331 2169
FOUNDED 1881. *Publishes* education, philosophy, psychology, psychiatry, general and social sciences, sociology, history.

Les Presses de la Cité

12 ave d'Italie, 75013 Paris
☎00 33 1 4416 0500   Fax 00 33 1 4416 0505
FOUNDED 1947. *Publishes* literature, literary criticism, essays, history, biography, anthropology, science fiction, fantasy, military science, how-to, travel.

Presses Universitaires de France (PUF)

108 blvd St-Germain, 75006 Paris 06
☎00 33 1 4634 1201   Fax 00 33 1 4634 6541
FOUNDED 1921. *Publishes* biography, history, geography, geology, music, dance, art, philosophy, religion, engineering, psychology, psychiatry, medicine, nursing, dentistry, government, political and social sciences, sociology.

Editions du Seuil

27 rue Jacob, 75006 Paris 06
☎00 33 1 4046 5050   Fax 00 33 1 4329 0829
FOUNDED 1935. *Publishes* fiction, literature, literary criticism, essays, poetry, biography, history, how-to, music, dance, art, philosophy, religion, psychology, psychiatry, general and social sciences, sociology, government, political science, photography.

Les Editions de la Table Ronde

7 rue Corneille, 75006 Paris
☎00 33 1 4326 0395   Fax 00 33 1 4407 0930
FOUNDED 1944. *Publishes* fiction and general non-fiction, biography, history, psychology, psychiatry, religion.

Librairie Vuibert SA

63 blvd St-Germain, 75005 Paris
☎00 33 1 4325 6100   Fax 00 33 1 4325 7586
FOUNDED 1877. *Publishes* economics, law, mathematics, physics, chemistry, chemical engineering, biological and earth sciences.

Germany

Verlag C. H. Beck (OHG)

Wilhelmstr 9, Postfach 400340,
80703 Munich
☎00 49 89 381890   Fax 00 49 89 38189398
FOUNDED 1763. *Publishes* archaeology, history, social sciences, sociology, philosophy, theology, economics, law, art, music, dance, linguistics, general non-fiction, literature, literary criticism, essays, anthropology.

Bertelsmann AG

Carl-Bertelsmann-Str 270, Postfach 111,
33311 Gütersloh
☎00 49 5241 801   Fax 00 49 5241 75166
FOUNDED 1835. *Publishes* fiction and non-fiction, anthropology, art, biography, business, economics, film, history, how-to, law, management, marketing, medicine, dentistry, nursing, radio, television, video, technology, travel.

Carlsen Verlag GmbH

Völckersstr 14-20, Postfach 500380,
22703 Hamburg
☎00 49 40 3910090   Fax 00 49 40 39100962
FOUNDED 1953. *Publishes* humour and general non-fiction.

Deutscher Taschenbuch Verlag GmbH & Co. KG (dtv)

Friedrichstr 1a, Postfach 400422,
80704 Munich
☎00 49 89 3817060   Fax 00 49 89 346428
FOUNDED 1961. *Publishes* fiction, biography, computer science, art, dance, music, poetry, history, how-to, psychiatry, psychology,

philosophy, religion, medicine, dentistry, nursing, social sciences, literature, literary criticism, essays, humour, travel.

Droemersche Verlagsanstalt Th. Knaur Nachfolger
Rauchstr 9–11, 81664 Munich
☎00 49 89 92710   Fax 00 49 89 9271168
FOUNDED 1901. *Publishes* fiction, general non-fiction, cookery, how-to, self-help, travel and general science.

Econ-Verlag GmbH
Kaiserswerthestr 282, Postfach 300321, 40403 Düsseldorf
☎00 49 211 439596 Fax 00 49 211 43959786
Publishes general science, economics and fiction.

Falken-Verlag GmbH
Schöne Aussicht 21, Postfach 1120, 65521 Niederhausen
☎00 49 6127 7020   Fax 00 49 6127 702133
FOUNDED 1923. *Publishes* health, cookery, nutrition, gardening, how-to, humour, history, photography, computer science, crafts, games, hobbies, sports.

S Fischer Verlag GmbH
Hedderichstr 114, Postfach 700355, 60553 Frankfurt am Main
☎00 49 69 60620   Fax 00 49 69 6062319
FOUNDED 1952. *Publishes* fiction, general non-fiction, essays, literature, literary criticism.

Carl Hanser Verlag
Kolbergerstr 22, Postfach 860420, 81631 Munich
☎00 49 89 998300   Fax 00 49 89 984809
FOUNDED 1928. *Publishes* general non-fiction, poetry, economics, computer science, philosophy, mathematics, medicine, nursing, dentistry, electronics, electrical, mechanical and general engineering, physics, management, environmental studies.

Wilhelm Heyne Verlag
Türkenstr 5–7, 80333 Munich
☎00 49 89 2317170   Fax 00 49 89 2800943
FOUNDED 1934. *Publishes* fiction, mystery, romance, humour, science fiction, fantasy, astrology, biography, history, occult, psychology, psychiatry, how-to, film, video, cookery.

Hoffmann und Campe Verlag
Harvestehuder Weg 42, Postfach 13044, 20149 Hamburg
☎00 49 40 441880   Fax 00 49 40 44188-290
FOUNDED 1781. *Publishes* fiction and general

non-fiction, biography, poetry, history, art, philosophy, psychology, psychiatry, music, dance, science, social sciences, sociology.

Ernst Klett Schulbuchverlag
Rotebühlstr 77, Postfach 106016, 70049 Stuttgart
☎00 49 711 66720   Fax 00 49 711 628053
FOUNDED 1977. *Publishes* education.

Gustav Lübbe Verlag GmbH
Scheidtbachstr 29–31, Postfach 200127, 51431 Bergisch Gladbach
☎00 49 2202 1210   Fax 00 49 2202 36727
FOUNDED 1963. *Publishes* fiction and general non-fiction, biography, archaeology, history and how-to.

Mosaik Verlag GmbH
Neumarkter Str 18, Postfach 800360, 81673 Munich 80
☎00 49 89 431890   Fax 00 49 89 4312837
Publishes antiques, child care and development, cookery, gardening, crafts, games, hobbies, health, nutrition, human relations, animals, pets, sports, house and home, architecture and interior design, economics, finance, film, video, self-help, wine and spirits, women's studies.

Pestalozzi-Verlag Graphische Gesellschaft mbH
Am Pestalozziring 14, 91058 Erlangen
☎00 49 9131 60600   Fax 00 49 9131 773090
FOUNDED 1844. *Publishes* crafts, games, hobbies.

Rowohlt Taschenbuch Verlag GmbH
Hamburger Str 17, Postfach 1349, 21465 Reinbeck
☎00 49 40 72720   Fax 00 49 40 7272319
FOUNDED 1953. *Publishes* fiction and general non-fiction, general science, history, archaeology, art, government, political science, psychology, psychiatry, philosophy, education, religion, social sciences, sociology, crafts, games and hobbies.

Springer-Verlag GmbH & Co KG
Heidelberger Platz 3, Postfach, 14197 Berlin 33
☎00 49 30 820710   Fax 00 49 30 8214091
FOUNDED 1842. *Publishes* general science, biology, medicine, nursing, dentistry, chemistry, psychology, psychiatry, physics, mathematics, biological sciences, environmental studies,

computer science, technology, engineering, economics, philosophy, law.

Suhrkamp Verlag
Lindenstr 29-35, Postfach 4229,
60019 Frankfurt am Main
☎00 49 69 756010   Fax 00 49 69 75601522
FOUNDED 1950. *Publishes* fiction, biography, poetry, general science, philosophy, psychology, psychiatry.

K. Thienemanns Verlag
Blumenstr 36, 70182 Stuttgart
☎00 49 711 210550   Fax 00 49 711 2105539
FOUNDED 1849. *Publishes* fiction and general non-fiction.

Verlag Ullstein GmbH
Lindenstr 76, 10969 Berlin
☎00 49 30 25913551 Fax 00 49 30 25913523
FOUNDED 1903. *Publishes* fiction, architecture and interior design, how-to, biography, poetry, dance, music, art, history, ethnology, geography, geology, government, political science, military science, travel, health, nutrition, general science, social sciences, sociology, education.

Italy
Adelphi Edizioni SpA
Via S. Giovanni sul Muro 14, 20121 Milan
☎00 39 2 72000975   Fax 00 39 2 89010337
FOUNDED 1962. *Publishes* fiction, biography, art, philosophy, religion, general science, psychology, psychiatry, music, dance.

Bompiana
Via Mecenate 91, 20138 Milan
☎00 39 2 50951   Fax 00 39 2 5065361
FOUNDED 1929. *Publishes* fiction, general non-fiction, art, drama, theatre and general science.

Bulzoni Editore SRL (Le Edizioni Universitarie d'Italia)
Via Dei Liburni 14, 00185 Rome
☎00 39 6 4455207   Fax 00 39 6 4450355
FOUNDED 1969. *Publishes* fiction, literature, literary criticism, essays, philosophy, art, drama, film, theatre, video, social sciences, sociology, general science, engineering, law, language, linguistics.

Nuova Casa Editrice Licinio Cappelli GEM srl
Via Farini 14, 40124 Bologna
☎00 39 51 239060   Fax 00 39 51 239286
FOUNDED 1851. *Publishes* fiction, government,

political science, poetry, biography, history, art, philosophy, religion, medicine, nursing, dentistry, psychology, psychiatry, general science, social sciences, sociology, film, video, drama, theatre, music and dance.

Gruppo Editoriale Fabbri SpA
Via Mecenate 91, 20138 Milan
☎00 39 2 50951   Fax 00 39 2 5065361
FOUNDED 1945. *Publishes* art, music, dance, medicine, general science, nursing, dentistry, outdoor recreation, environmental studies, history, nature, crafts, games, hobbies, children's.

Garzanti Editore
Via Senato 25, 20121 Milan
☎00 39 2 77871   Fax 00 39 2 76009233
FOUNDED 1861. *Publishes* fiction, literature, literary criticism, essays, biography, poetry, art, history, government, political science.

Giunti Publishing Group
Via Bolognese 165, 50139 Florence
☎00 39 55 66791   Fax 00 39 55 6679298
FOUNDED 1840. *Publishes* fiction, literature, literary criticism, essays, art, history, mathematics, psychology, psychiatry, education, chemistry, chemical engineering, language arts, linguistics, general science, how-to. Italian publishers of National Geographical Society books.

Gremese Editore SRL
Via Agnelli 88, 00151 Rome
☎00 39 6 65740507   Fax 00 39 6 65740509
FOUNDED 1978. *Publishes* music, dance, art, environmental studies, photography, fashion, cookery, travel, literature, literary criticism, sport, crafts, games, hobbies, astrology, occult, drama, theatre, film, video.

Istituto Geografico de Agostini SpA
Via Giovanni da Verrazzano 15,
28100 Novara
☎00 39 321 471830   Fax 00 39 321 471286
FOUNDED 1901. *Publishes* art, literature, literary criticism, essays, history, religion, geology and geography.

Longanesi & C
Corso Italia 13, 20122 Milan
☎00 39 2 8692640   Fax 00 39 2 72000306
FOUNDED 1946. *Publishes* fiction, biography, art, music, dance, history, philosophy, religion, psychology, psychiatry, general and social sciences, sociology, medicine, nursing, dentistry, how-to.

Arnoldo Mondadori Editore SpA
Via Mondadori, 20090 Segrate (Milan)
☎00 39 2 75421   Fax 00 39 2 75422302
FOUNDED 1907. *Publishes* fiction, mystery, romance, biography, art, music, dance, poetry, philosophy, religion, history, how-to, reference, medicine, nursing, dentistry, psychology, psychiatry, general science, education.

Società Editrice Il Mulino
Str Maggiore 37, 40125 Bologna
☎00 39 51 256011   Fax 00 39 51 256034
FOUNDED 1954. *Publishes* language, linguistics, music, dance, drama, theatre, history, philosophy, law, government, political science, economics, social science, sociology, psychology, psychiatry.

Gruppo Ugo Mursia Editore SpA
Via Tadino 29, 20124 Milan
☎00 39 2 29403030   Fax 00 39 2 29525557
FOUNDED 1922. *Publishes* fiction, poetry, sport, art, history, biography, maritime, philosophy, religion, education, general and social sciences, sociology.

RCS Rizzoli Libri SpA
Via Mecenate 91, 20138 Milan
☎00 39 2 50950   Fax 00 39 2 508012131
FOUNDED 1909. *Publishes* fiction, art, biography, crafts, games, hobbies, medicine, nursing, dentistry, music, dance, religion, social sciences, sociology, economics, textbooks and reference.

Societa Editrice Internazionale – SEI
Corso Regina Margherita 176, 10152 Turin
☎00 39 11 52271   Fax 00 39 11 5211320
FOUNDED 1908. *Publishes* literature, literary criticism, essays, geography, geology, mathematics, history, philosophy, physics, religion, psychology, psychiatry, education.

Sonzogno
Via Mecenate 91, 20138 Milan
☎00 39 2 50951   Fax 00 39 2 5065361
FOUNDED 1818. *Publishes* fiction, mysteries, and general non-fiction.

Sperling e Kupfer Editori SpA
Via Borgonuovo 24, 20121 Milan
☎00 39 2 290341   Fax 00 39 2 6590290
FOUNDED 1899. *Publishes* fiction and general non-fiction, general science, biography, health, nutrition, travel, sport, how-to, management, economics.

Sugarco Edizioni SRL
Via Fermi 9, 21040 Carnago (Varese)
☎00 39 331 985511   Fax 00 39 331 985385
FOUNDED 1956. *Publishes* fiction, biography, history, philosophy, how-to.

Todariana Editrice
Via Papi 15, 20135 Milan
☎00 39 2 5460353   Fax 00 39 2 5460353
FOUNDED 1967. *Publishes* fiction, poetry, science fiction, fantasy, literature, literary criticism, essays, social sciences, sociology, psychology, psychiatry, travel, language arts, linguistics.

The Netherlands
De Boekerij BV
Herengracht 540, 1017 CG Amsterdam
☎00 31 20 5353135   Fax 00 31 20 5353130
FOUNDED 1986. *Publishes* fiction and general non-fiction, film, video, mysteries, romance, science fiction and fantasy.

A.W. Bruna Uitgevers
Postbus 8411, 3503 RK Utrecht
☎00 31 30 470411   Fax 00 31 30 410018
FOUNDED 1868. *Publishes* fiction, history, philosophy, psychology, psychiatry, general and social science, sociology, computer science.

Uitgeverij BZZTÔH
Laan van Meerdervoort 10,
2517 AJ The Hague
☎00 31 70 3632934   Fax 00 31 70 3631932
FOUNDED 1970. *Publishes* fiction, mysteries, general non-fiction, travel, cookery, animals, pets, astrology, occult, biography, humour, music, dance, religion (Buddhist), romance.

Elsevier Science BV
Sara Burgerhartstraat 25, 1055 KV Amsterdam
☎00 31 20 5862911   Fax 00 31 20 5862769
FOUNDED 1946. Parent company – Reed Elsevier. *Publishes* sciences (all fields), management and professional, medicine, nursing, dentistry, engineering (computer and general), economics, physics, mathematics, technology, psychology, psychiatry, social sciences, sociology.

Uitgeverij Hollandia BV
Beukenlaan 20, Postbus 70, 3740 AB Baarn
☎00 31 2154 18941   Fax 00 31 2154 21917
FOUNDED 1899. *Publishes* fiction, maritime, travel.

Uitgeversmaatschappij J. H. Kok BV

Gildestraat 5, PO Box 130, 8260 AC Kampen
☎00 31 5202 92555   Fax 00 31 5202 27331
FOUNDED 1894. *Publishes* fiction, poetry, biography, history, art, crafts, games, hobbies, psychology, psychiatry, religion, general and social sciences, sociology, medicine, nursing, dentistry, how-to, education, environmental studies.

M & P Publishing House

Schoutlaan 4, 6002 EA Weert
☎00 31 4950 36880   Fax 00 31 4950 21145
FOUNDED 1974. *Publishes* general non-fiction.

Meulenhoff International

Herengracht 507, PO Box 100,
1000 AC Amsterdam
☎00 31 20 5533500   Fax 00 31 20 6258511
Publishes international co-productions, art and general non-fiction. Specialises in Dutch and translated literature, science fiction, non-fiction and children's.

Uitgeverij Het Spectrum BV

Montalbaendreef 2, Postbus 2073,
3500 GB Utrecht
☎00 31 30 650650   Fax 00 31 30 620850
FOUNDED 1935. *Publishes* science fiction, fantasy, literature, literary criticism, essays, mystery, crime, general non-fiction, computer science, history, travel, astrology, occult, management, environmental studies.

Time-Life Books BV

Ottho Heldringstr 5, 1066 AZ Amsterdam
☎00 31 20 5104911   Fax 00 31 20 6175077
Publishes art, cookery, gardening, how-to, general science, parapsychology, behavioural sciences, biological sciences, history.

Unieboek BV

PO Box 97, 3995 DB Houten
☎00 31 3403 77660   Fax 00 31 3403 77660
FOUNDED 1891. *Publishes* fiction, general nonfiction, architecture and interior design, government, political science, literature, literary criticism, essays, history, cookery, design, archaeology.

Uniepers BV

Postbus 69, 1390 AB Abcoude
☎00 31 294 285111   Fax 00 31 294 283013
FOUNDED 1961. *Publishes* (mostly in co-editions) art, music, dance, antiques, anthropology, architecture and interior design, natural history, culture, nature, gardening, history.

Veen Uitgevers Group

Vinkenburgstr 2a, PO Box 14095,
3508 SC Utrecht
☎00 31 30 349211   Fax 00 31 20 349208
FOUNDED 1887. A member of the Wolters Kluwer Group. *Publishes* general non-fiction, fiction, Dutch and foreign literature, literary criticism, travel, business,

Wolters Kluwer NV

Stadhouderskade 1, PO Box 818,
1000 AV Amsterdam
☎00 31 20 6070400   Fax 00 31 20 6070490
FOUNDED 1889. *Publishes* education, medical, technical encyclopedias, trade books and journals, law and taxation, periodicals.

Norway

H. Aschehoug & Co (W. Nygaard) A/S

Sehestedsgate 3, Postboks 363 Sentrum,
0102 Oslo
☎00 47 22 400400   Fax 00 47 22 206395
FOUNDED 1872. *Publishes* fiction and general non-fiction, general and social science, sociology.

J. W. Cappelens Forlag A/S

Maribosgaten 13, Postboks 350, Sentrum,
0101 Oslo
☎00 47 22 365000   Fax 00 47 22 365040
FOUNDED 1829. *Publishes* fiction, general nonfiction, religion.

N. W. Damm & Søn A/S

Kristian Augustsgt 3, Postboks 1755, Vika,
0122 Oslo
☎00 47 22 941500   Fax 00 47 22 360874
FOUNDED 1845. *Publishes* fiction and general non-fiction.

Ex Libris Forlag A/S

Nordregt 22, PO Box 2130 Grünerløkka,
0505 Oslo 5
☎00 47 22 384450   Fax 00 47 22 385160
FOUNDED 1982. *Publishes* fiction, general nonfiction, art, biography and philosophy.

Gyldendal Norsk Forlag A/S

Sehestedsgt 4, Postboks 6860, St Olaf,
0130 Oslo
☎00 47 22 034100   Fax 00 47 22 034105

FOUNDED 1925. *Publishes* fiction, science fiction, fantasy, social sciences, sociology, poetry, art, music, dance, biography, history, how-to, government, political science, philosophy, psychology, psychiatry, religion.

Hjemmets Bokforlag AS
Tordenskioldsgate 6B, N–0055 Oslo
☎00 47 22 471000   Fax 00 47 22 471097
FOUNDED 1969. *Publishes* fiction and general non-fiction.

NKS–Forlaget
Postboks 5853 Majorstua, Industrigata 41, 0308 Oslo
☎00 47 22 568500   Fax 00 47 22 566820
FOUNDED 1971. *Publishes* health, nutrition and mathematics.

Tiden Norsk Forlag
PO Box 8813, Youngstorget, 0028 Oslo
☎00 47 22 429520   Fax 00 47 22 426458
FOUNDED 1933. *Publishes* fiction, general non-fiction.

Portugal
Bertrand Editora Lda
Rua Anchieta 29 – 1, 1200 Lisbon
☎00 351 1 3420084   Fax 00 351 1 3479728
FOUNDED 1727. *Publishes* literature (Portuguese and foreign), literary criticism, art, essays, social sciences, sociology.

Editorial Caminho SARL
Al Santo Antonio dos Capuchos 6B, 1100 Lisbon
☎00 351 1 3152683   Fax 00 351 1 534346
FOUNDED 1977. *Publishes* fiction, government, political science.

Livraria Civilizacão (Américo Fraga Lamares & Ca Lda)
Rua Alberto Aires de Gouveia 27, 4000 Porto
☎00 351 2 2002286   Fax 00 351 2 2012382
FOUNDED 1921. *Publishes* fiction, history, social and political science, government, sociology, economics and art.

Publicações Dom Quixote Lda
Rua Luciano Cordeiro 116-2, 1098 Lisbon
☎00 351 1 3158079   Fax 00 351 1 574595
FOUNDED 1965. *Publishes* fiction, poetry, philosophy, general and social sciences, sociology, history, education.

Publicações Europa-America Lda
Apdo 8, Estrada Lisbon-Sintra Km 14, 2726 Mem Martins
☎00 351 1 9211461   Fax 00 351 1 9217940
FOUNDED 1945. *Publishes* fiction, poetry, biography, art, music, dance, history, philosophy, general and social sciences, sociology, how-to, medicine, nursing, dentistry, psychology, psychiatry, education, technology, engineering.

Gradiva – Publicações Lda
Rua Almeida e Sousa 21 r/c Esq, 1350 Lisbon
☎00 351 1 3974067   Fax 00 351 1 3953471
FOUNDED 1981. *Publishes* general science, philosophy, history, education, fiction, science fiction, fantasy, human relations.

Livros Horizonte Lda
Rua das Chagas 17 – 1 Dto, 1121 Lisbon
☎00 351 1 3466917   Fax 00 351 1 3426921
FOUNDED 1953. *Publishes* education, social sciences, sociology, psychology, psychiatry, history, art.

Editorial Verbo SA
Rua Carlos Testa 1, 1000 Lisbon
☎00 351 1 3562131   Fax 00 351 1 3562139
FOUNDED 1959. *Publishes* education, general science, history.

Spain
Editorial Alhambra SA
Fernandez de la Hoz 9, 28010 Madrid
☎00 34 1 5940020   Fax 00 34 1 5921220
FOUNDED 1942. *Publishes* medicine and nursing, dentistry, general science, psychology, psychiatry, philosophy, education, art, history, language arts, linguistics.

Alianza Editorial SA
Juan Ignacio Luca de Tena 15, 28027 Madrid
☎00 34 1 7416600   Fax 00 34 1 7414343
FOUNDED 1965. *Publishes* fiction, poetry, art, dance, music, philosophy, government, political and social sciences, sociology, history, mathematics and general science.

Ediciones Anaya SA
Aragó 237, 08007 Barcelona
☎00 34 3 2160480   Fax 00 34 3 2160480
FOUNDED 1959. *Publishes* education.

Editorial Don Quijote
Compás del Porvenir 6, 41013 Seville
☎00 34 58 4235080

FOUNDED 1981. *Publishes* fiction, literature, literary criticism, poetry, essays, drama, theatre, history.

EDHASA (Editora y Distribuidora Hispano - Americana SA)
Av Diagonal 519, 08029 Barcelona
☎00 34 3 4395104   Fax 00 34 3 4194584

FOUNDED 1946. *Publishes* history, fiction, literature, literary criticism, essays.

Editorial Espasa–Calpe SA
Apdo 547, Carretera de Irún Km 12, 200, 28049 Madrid
☎00 34 1 358 9689   Fax 00 34 1 358 9505

FOUNDED 1925. *Publishes* fiction, science fiction, fantasy, social sciences, sociology, English as a second language, general non-fiction, biography, history, self-help.

Ediciones Grijalbo SA
Aragò 385, 08013 Barcelona
☎00 34 3 4587000   Fax 00 34 3 4580495

FOUNDED 1942. *Publishes* fiction, general non-fiction, biography, history, government, political science, philosophy, religion, psychology, psychiatry, social sciences, sociology, technology, art.

Grupo Editorial CEAC SA
C/Peru 164, 08020 Barcelona
☎00 34 3 3073004   Fax 00 34 3 2660067

Formerly Editorial Timun Mas SA. *Publishes* education, technology, science fiction, fantasy.

Ediciones Hiperión SL
Salustiano Olózaga 14, 28001 Madrid
☎00 34 1 4010234

FOUNDED 1976. *Publishes* fiction, poetry, literature, literary criticism, essays, religions (Islamic and Jewish).

Editorial Laia SA
Guitard 43, 08014 Barcelona
☎00 34 3 3215562   Fax 00 34 3 3217975

FOUNDED 1972. *Publishes* general non-fiction, literature, literary criticism, essays, education, social sciences, sociology, psychology, psychiatry.

LaSal (Edicions de les Dones)
Riereta 13, 08001 Barcelona
☎00 34 3 3298450

FOUNDED 1978. *Publishes* women's studies only.

Editorial Molino
Calabria 166 baixos, 08015 Barcelona
☎00 34 3 2260625   Fax 00 34 3 2266998

FOUNDED 1933. *Publishes* education, fiction, cookery.

Mondadori España SA
Aragó 385, 08013 Barcelona
☎00 34 1 4587000   Fax 00 34 1 4159033

FOUNDED 1987. *Publishes* fiction, biography, history, general science, general non-fiction.

Editorial Planeta SA
Córcega 273, 08008 Barcelona
☎00 34 3 4154100   Fax 00 34 3 2177140

FOUNDED 1952. *Publishes* fiction and general non-fiction.

Plaza y Janés SA
Enrique Granados 86–88, 08008 Barcelona
☎00 34 3 4151100   Fax 00 34 3 4156976

FOUNDED 1959. *Publishes* fiction and general non-fiction.

Santillana SA
Elfo 32, 28027 Madrid
☎00 34 1 3224500   Fax 00 34 1 3224475

FOUNDED 1964. *Publishes* fiction, literature, literary criticism, essays, travel.

Editorial Seix Barral SA
Córcega 270, 4, 08008 Barcelona
☎00 34 3 2186400   Fax 00 34 3 2184773

FOUNDED 1945. *Publishes* fiction, poetry, drama, theatre.

Tusquets Editores
Iradier 24 bajos, 08017 Barcelona
☎00 34 3 4174170   Fax 00 34 3 4176703

FOUNDED 1969. *Publishes* fiction, biography, art, literature, literary criticism, essays, eroticism, history, social sciences, sociology.

Ediciones Versal SA
Calabria 108, 08015 Barcelona
☎00 34 3 3257404   Fax 00 34 3 4236898

FOUNDED 1984. *Publishes* literature, literary criticism, essays, general non-fiction, biography.

Editorial Luis Vives (Edelvives)
Ctra de Madrid, km 315700, Apdo 387, 50012 Zaragoza
☎00 34 76 344100   Fax 00 34 76 345979

FOUNDED 1890. *Publishes* education.

Sweden

Bokförlaget Bonnier Alba AB
Box 3159, S-103 63 Stockholm
☎00 46 8 6968620   Fax 00 46 8 6968359
FOUNDED 1981. *Publishes* general non-fiction, fiction, art, cookery.

Albert Bonniers Förlag AB
Box 3159, Sveavägen 56, S-103 63 Stockholm
☎00 46 8 6968620   Fax 00 46 8 6968359
FOUNDED 1837. *Publishes* fiction and general non-fiction.

Bokförlaget Bra Böcker AB
Södra Vägen, S-26380 Höganäs
☎00 46 42 339000   Fax 00 46 42 330504
FOUNDED 1965. *Publishes* fiction, history, geography and geology.

Brombergs Bokförlag AB
Industrigaton 4A, Box 12886,
11298 Stockholm
☎00 46 8 6503390   Fax 00 46 8 6500160
FOUNDED 1973. *Publishes* fiction, general non-fiction, general science, government, political science.

Bokförlaget Forum AB
Box 14115, S-104 41 Stockholm
☎00 46 8 6968440   Fax 00 46 8 6968367
FOUNDED 1944. *Publishes* fiction and general non-fiction.

Bokförlaget Natur och Kultur
Karlavägen 31, Box 27323,
S-102 54 Stockholm
☎00 46 8 4538600   Fax 00 46 8 4538790
FOUNDED 1922. *Publishes* fiction and general non-fiction, general science, biography, history, psychology, psychiatry.

Norstedts Förlag AB
Box 2052, S-103 12 Stockholm
☎00 46 8 7893000   Fax 00 46 8 214006
FOUNDED 1823. *Publishes* fiction and general non-fiction.

AB Rabén och Sjögren Bokförlag
PO Box 45022, S-104 30 Stockholm
☎00 46 8 4570300   Fax 00 46 8 4570331
FOUNDED 1942. *Publishes* fiction and general non-fiction.

Richters Förlag AB
Ostra Förstadsgatan 46, 205 75 Malmö
☎00 46 40 380600   Fax 00 46 40 930820
FOUNDED 1942. *Publishes* fiction.

Tiden
Box 45022, S-104 30 Stockholm
☎00 46 8 4570300
FOUNDED 1912. *Publishes* fiction, general non-fiction, history, poetry, government, political science, social sciences, sociology, psychology, psychiatry.

B Wählströms Bokförlag AB
Box 30022, S-104 25 Stockholm
☎00 46 8 6198600   Fax 00 46 8 6189761
FOUNDED 1911. *Publishes* fiction and general non-fiction.

Switzerland

Arche Verlag AG, Raabe und Vitali
Hoelderlinstr 14, CH-8032 Zurich
☎00 41 1 2522410   Fax 00 41 1 2611115
FOUNDED 1944. *Publishes* literature and literary criticism, essays, biography, fiction, poetry, travel.

Artemis Verlags AG
Munstergasse 9, CH-8024 Zurich
☎00 41 1 2521100   Fax 00 41 1 2624792
FOUNDED 1943. *Publishes* art, architecture and interior design, travel, philosophy, history, biography, political science, government.

Diogenes Verlag AG
Sprecherstr 8, CH-8032 Zurich
☎00 41 1 2548511   Fax 00 41 1 2528407
FOUNDED 1952. *Publishes* fiction, mysteries, essays, drama, theatre, literature, literary criticism, essays, philosophy and art.

Langenscheidt AG Zürich-Zug
Gubelstr 11, CH-6301 Zug
☎00 41 42 232300   Fax 00 41 42 232325
Publishes art, linguistics and languages.

Larousse (Suisse) SA
3 Route du Grand-Mont,
CH-1052 Le Mont-sur-Lausanne
☎00 41 22 369140
Publishes dictionaries, reference and textbooks.

Neptun-Verlag
Fidlerstr 6, Postfach 171,
CH-8272 Ermatingen
☎00 41 72 642020   Fax 00 41 72 642023
FOUNDED 1946. *Publishes* history and travel.

Orell Füssli Verlag
Dietzingerstr 3, CH-8036 Zurich
☎00 41 1 4667711   Fax 00 41 1 4667412

FOUNDED 1519. *Publishes* educational, art, how-to, history, geography, geology, economics, biography.

Editions Payot Lausanne

33 ave de la Gare, CH-1001 Lausanne
☎00 41 21 3495015   Fax 00 41 21 3495029

FOUNDED 1875. *Publishes* art, music, dance, literature, literary criticism, essays, history, general science, law, business, psychology, psychiatry, philosophy, agriculture, sport, environmental studies.

Verlag Rot-Weiss AG

Frutigenstr 6, Postfach 1308, CH-3601 Thun
☎00 41 33 229803   Fax 00 41 33 229810

FOUNDED 1988. *Publishes* travel, cookery, dictionaries, encyclopedias.

Sauerländer AG

Laurenzenvorstadt 89, CH-5001 Aarau
☎00 41 64 268626   Fax 00 41 64 245780

FOUNDED 1807. *Publishes* education, poetry, biography, social sciences, sociology, medicine, nursing, dentistry, general science, history.

Scherz Verlag AG

Theaterplatz 4-6, CH-3000 Berne 7
☎00 41 31 3117337   Fax 00 41 31 3120375

FOUNDED 1939. *Publishes* fiction, biography, history, psychology, psychiatry, philosophy, parapsychology; general non-fiction.

European Television Companies

ARD - Das Erste
Arnulfstrasse 42, 80335 Munich, Germany
☎00 49 89 59 0001   Fax 00 49 89 59 003249
Director *Dr Günter Struve*

BRTN
August Reyerslaan 52, B-1043 Brussels, Belgium
☎00 32 2 741 3111   Fax 00 32 2 734 9351
Director General *Jan Ceuleers*

Danmarks Radio-TV
TV Centre - Morkhojvej 170,
DK-2860 Soborg, Denmark
☎00 45 35 20 3040   Fax 00 45 35 20 2644
Director of Programmes *Finn Rowold*

DRS
Fernsehen DRS/SRG Fernsehenstrasse 1-4,
CH-8052 Zurich, Switzerland
☎00 41 1 305 66 11   Fax 00 41 1 305 63 69
President *Peter Schellenberg*

Finnish Broadcasting Company
PO Box 10, SF-0241 Helsinki 24, Finland
☎00 358 0 14801

France 2
22 ave Montaigne, 75008 Paris, France
☎00 33 1 44 21 42 42Fax 00 33 1 44 21 51 45
Director of Programmes *Bibiane Godfroid*

France 3
116 ave du Président Kennedy, 75790 Paris,
France
☎00 33 1 42 30 22 22Fax 00 33 1 46 47 94 13
Director of Programmes *Marie-Claire Grunau*

Nederlandse Omroep Stichting
Postbus 26444, 1202 JJ Hilversum, Netherlands
☎00 31 35 77 92 22   Fax 00 31 35 77 35 86

NRK (Norwegian Broadcasting Corporation)
Bjornstein Bjornsons Place 1, N-0340 Oslo 3,
Norway
☎00 47 22 45 9050
Director *Andéas Skarpveit*

ORF
30 Würzburggasse, A-1136 Vienna, Austria
☎00 43 1 50 2770
Director *Gerd Bascher*

Radio Telefis Eireann (RTE-RTE 1)
Donnybrook, Dublin 4, Ireland
☎00 353 1 208 3111   Fax 00 353 1 208 3080
Director General *Joe Barry*

Radio-Télévision Belge de la Communauté Française (RTBF)
52 Boulevard Auguste Reyers, 1044 Brussels,
Belgium
☎00 32 2 737 2111   Fax 00 32 2 737 2556
Director General *Jean-Louis Stalport*

RAI (Radiotelevisione Italiana)
Viale Mazzini 14, 00195 Rome, Italy
☎00 39 6 361 3608   Fax 00 39 6 323 1010
President *Letizia Moratti*

Radiotelevisão Portuguesa (RTP)
Av 5 de Outubro 197, 1094 Lisbon, Portugal
☎00 35 11 793 1774   Fax 00 35 11 793 1758
Director of Programmes *Louise Andrade*

RTVE (Radiotelevision Española)
Edificio Prado del Rey - 3a planta,
22224 Madrid, Spain
☎00 34 1 581 7000   Fax 00 34 1 581 7757

SVT (Sveriges Television)
Oxenstiernsgatan 26-34, S-10510 Stockholm,
Sweden
☎00 46 8 784 0000   Fax 00 46 8 784 1500
Director General *Sam Nilsson*

TSR (Télévision Suisse Romande)
20 Quai Ernest Ansermet, Case Postale 234,
1211 Geneva 8, Switzerland
☎00 41 22 708 9911
Director of Programmes *Raymond Vouillamoz*

TV2/Denmark
Rugaardsvej 25, DK-4100 Odense, Denmark
☎00 45 65 91 12 44   Fax 00 45 65 91 33 22

ZDF (Zweites Deutsches Fernsehen)
ZDF-Strasse, PO Box 4040, 55100 Mainz,
Germany
☎00 49 61 31 70 2060
Fax 00 49 61 31 70 2052
President *Dieter Stolte*

US Publishers

International Reply Coupons

For return postage, send International Reply Coupons (IRSs), available from the Post Office. Letters 60 pence; mss according to weight.

ABC–Clio, Inc.

Suite 350, 501 South Cherry Street, Denver CO 80222
☎001 303 333 3003   Fax 001 303 333 4037
President *Heather Cameron*
Editorial Director *Jeff Serena*

FOUNDED 1955. *Publishes* non-fiction: reference, including mythology, native American studies, government and politics, history, military and war, women's studies/issues, current world issues. About 35–40 titles a year. No unsolicited mss; synopses and ideas welcome.

Royalties paid annually. *UK subsidiary* **ABC-Clio Ltd**, Oxford.

Abingdon Press

201 Eighth Avenue South, Box 801, Nashville TN 37202-0801
☎001 615 749 6404   Fax 001 615 749 6512
Editorial Director *Neil M. Alexander*

Publishes non-fiction: religious (lay and professional), children's religious and academic texts. About 100 titles a year. Approach in writing only with synopsis and samples. IRCs essential.

William Abrahams

See **Penguin USA**

Harry N. Abrams, Inc.

100 Fifth Avenue, New York NY 10011
☎001 212 206 7715   Fax 001 212 645 8437
Publisher/Editor-in-chief *Paul Gottlieb*

Subsidiary of Times Mirror Co. *Publishes* illustrated books: art, architecture, design, nature, entertainment. No fiction. Submit completed mss (no dot matrix), together with sample illustrations.

Academy Chicago Publishers

363 W. Erie Street, Chicago IL 60610
☎001 312 751 7300   Fax 001 312 751 7306
Editorial Director *Anita Miller*

FOUNDED 1975. *Publishes* fiction: mystery and mainstream; and non-fiction: art, history, women's studies, true crime and historical. No romance, children's, young adult, religious, sexist or avant-garde. About 22 titles a year.

IMPRINT **Cassandra Editions** ('Lost' Women Writers) TITLES *Murder on the Thirteenth* A. E. Eddenden; *Memoirs of an Ex-Prom Queen* Alix Kates Shulman; *A Mirror for Witches* Esther Forbes. Send first three chapters only, accompanied by IRCs; no synopses or ideas.

Royalties paid twice-yearly. *Distributed* in the UK and Europe by Gazelle, Lancaster.

Ace Science Fiction

See **Berkley Publishing Group**

Adams Media Corporation

260 Center Street, Holbrook MA 02343
☎001 617 767 8100   Fax 001 617 767 0994
President *Robert L. Adams*

FOUNDED 1980. *Publishes* general non-fiction: careers, business, personal finance, relationships, parenting and maternity, self-improvement, reference, cooking, sports, games and humour. TITLES *101 Reasons Why a Cat is Better Than a Man; I Fall To Pieces: The Biography of Patsy Cline; Wake Me When it's Funny, The Biography of Garry Marshall; Adams Streetwise Small Business Startup; 100 Best Mutual Funds You Can Buy.* Ideas welcome.

Addison–Wesley Longman Publishing Co., Inc.

General Publishing Group, One Jacob Way, Reading MA 01867
☎001 617 944 3700   Fax 001 617 944 8243
Publisher *David Goehring*

Publishes general non-fiction, business, science, health, parenting/childcare, psychology, current affairs, biography/memoir, social science/history/politics, narrative non-fiction, children's multimedia. No fiction. About 125 titles a year. Approach in writing or by phone in first instance, then submit synopsis and one sample chapter.

Royalties paid.

University of Alabama Press
Box 870380, Tuscaloosa AL 35487
☎001 205 348 5180   Fax 001 205 348 9201
Director *Nicole Mitchell*

Publishes academic books in the fields of American history, American and British literature, history of science and technology, linguistics, archaeology, rhetoric and speech communication. About 40 titles a year.

Aladdin Books
See **Simon & Schuster Children's Publishing Division**

University of Alaska Press
1st Floor, Gruening Building,
PO Box 756240, University of Alaska,
Fairbanks AK 99775-6240
☎001 907 474 6389   Fax 001 907 474 5502
Manager *Debbie Van Stone*
Managing Editor *Carla Helfferich*
Acquisitions *Pam Odom*

Traces its origins back to 1927 but was relatively dormant until the early 1980s. *Publishes* scholarly works about Alaska and the North Pacific rim, with a special emphasis on circumpolar regions. 5–10 titles a year. No fiction or poetry.

DIVISIONS
Ramuson Library Historical Translation Series *Marvin Falk* TITLES *The Great Russian Navigator, A. I. Chirikov; Journals of the Priest Ioann Veniaminov in Alaska, 1923 to 1836.* **Oral Biography Series** *William Schneider* TITLES *The Life I've Been Living; Kusiq: An Eskimo Life History from the Arctic Coast of Alaska.* **Monograph Series** *Carla Helfferich* TITLES *Intertidal Bivalves: A Guide to the Common Marine Bivalves of Alaska.* **Classic Reprint Series** *Terrence Cole* TITLES *Fifty Years Below Zero, A Lifetime of Adventure in the Far North; The Thousand-Mile War, World War II in Alaska and the Aleutians.* **Lanternlight Library** informal non-fiction covering Northern interest. TITLES *Aleutian Echoes.* Unsolicited mss, synopses and ideas welcome.

AMACOM
1601 Broadway, New York
NY 10019-7406
☎001 212 903 8081   Fax 001 212 903 8083
Director/Submissions *Weldon P. Rackley*

Owned by American Management Association. *Publishes* business books only, including general management, business communications, sales and marketing, small business, finance, computers and information systems, human resource management and training, career/personal growth skills, research development, project management and manufacturing, quality/customer service titles. 65–70 titles a year. TITLES *Corporate Executions; The Great Transition; Knock Your Socks Off Answers; Straight Talk About Gays in the Workplace; Diary of a Small Business Owner.* Proposals welcome.
Royalties paid twice-yearly.

University Press of America, Inc.
4720 Boston Way, Lanham MD 20706
☎001 301 459 3366   Fax 001 301 459 2118
Publisher *James E. Lyons*

FOUNDED 1975. *Publishes* scholarly monographs, college and graduate level textbooks. No children's, elementary or high school. About 450 titles a year. Submit outline or request proposal questionnaire.
Royalties paid annually. *Distributed* by Eurospan Ltd, London.

Anchor
See **Bantam Doubleday Dell Publishing Group, Inc.**

Anvil
See **Krieger Publishing Co., Inc.**

Ann Arbor Paperbacks
See **University of Michigan Press**

Archway
See **Pocket Books**

University of Arizona Press
1230 North Park Avenue, Suite 102,
Tucson AZ 85719-4140
☎001 520 621 1441   Fax 001 520 621 8899
Director *Stephen Cox*
Senior Editor *Joanne O'Hare*

FOUNDED 1959. *Publishes* academic non-fiction, particularly with a regional/cultural link, plus Native-American and Hispanic literature. About 50 titles a year.

Arkana
See **Penguin USA**

University of Arkansas Press
McIlroy House, 201 Ozark Avenue,
Fayetteville AR 72701
☎001 501 575 3246   Fax 001 501 575 6044
Director *Miller Williams*

FOUNDED 1980. *Publishes* scholarly monographs, poetry and general trade including essays, biography, etc. Particularly interested at present in scholarly works in history, politics, sociology and literary criticism. About 30 titles a year. TITLES *Meter in English: A Critical Engagement* ed. David Baker; *It's About Time: The Dave Brubeck Story* Fred Hall; *Savannah, 1788-1864* Whittington Johnson.

Royalties paid annually.

Aspect
See **Warner Books Inc.**

Atheneum Books for Young Readers
See **Simon & Schuster Children's Publishing Division**

Atheneum Publishers
See **Simon & Schuster Trade Division**

Atlantic Disk Publishers, Inc.
1465 Shiloh Road, Kennesaw
GA 30144
☎001 404 425 9624   Fax 001 404 424 0445
Exec. Editor/Publisher *Dorothy Deering*
Editor-in-Chief/Publisher *Charles Deering*

Publishes mass-market fiction as well as non-fiction on DOS, IBM compatible/readable disks and CD-ROM. Send query/synopsis/mss disk. Reports in 4–6 weeks. 170 titles in 1995.
Royalties Pays 35%. No advances.

Atlantic Monthly Press
See **Grove/Atlantic Inc**

AUP (Associated University Presses)
AUP New Jersey titles are handled in the UK by **Golden Cockerel Press** (see **UK Publishers**).

Avery Publishing Group, Inc.
120 Old Broadway, Garden City Park, New York NY 11040
☎001 516 741 2155   Fax 001 516 742 1892
Managing Editor *Rudy Shur*

FOUNDED 1976. *Publishes* adult trade non-fiction, specialising in childbirth, childcare, alternative health, self-help, New Age and natural cooking. About 30 titles a year. TITLES *Smart Medicine for a Healthier Child* Janet Zand, Rachel Walton and Robert Rountree; *Secrets of Fat-Free Cooking* Sandra Woodruff; *How to Teach Your Baby to Read* Glenn Doman. No unsolicited mss; synopses and ideas welcome if accompanied by s.a.e..
Royalties paid twice-yearly.

Avon Books
1350 Avenue of the Americas, New York NY 10019
☎001 212 261 6800   Fax 001 212 261 6895
Vice President/Publisher *Elizabeth Perle-McKenna*

FOUNDED 1941. A division of the Hearst Corporation. *Publishes* mass-market and trade paperbacks, adult, young adult and children's. Fiction: contemporary and historical romance, science fiction and fantasy, action and adventure, suspense and thrillers, mystery and westerns. Non-fiction (all types): how-to, popular psychology, self-help, health, history, war, sports, business and economics, biography and politics. No textbooks. 388 titles in 1995.

DIVISIONS **Avon Books** Adult mass-market paperbacks and trade paperbacks **Avon Camelot Books** Children's books **Avon Flare** Young adult readers. Submit query letter only in the first instance.

Back Bay Books
See **Little, Brown & Co. Inc.**

Baker Book House
PO Box 6287, Grand Rapids MI 49516-6287
☎001 616 676 9185   Fax 001 616 676 9573
President *Richard Baker*
Director of Publications *Allan Fisher*

FOUNDED 1939. Began life as a used-book store and began publishing in earnest in the 1950s, primarily serving the evangelical Christian market. *Publishes* religious non-fiction and fiction; children's books; college/seminary textbooks and academic; Bible reference and professional (pastors and church leaders) books. About 190 titles a year.

DIVISIONS/IMPRINTS
Trade *Allan Fisher* TITLES *The Hope at Hand* David Bryant; *Real Presence* Leanne Payne. **Children's** *Betty De Vries.* **Academic & Reference** *Jim Weaver* TITLES *God in Three Persons* Millard Erickson; *20th Century Dictionary of Christian Biography.* **Professional Books** *Paul Engle* TITLES *Marketplace Preaching* Calvin Miller. No unsolicited mss. Send for proposal outlines specifying whether you will be proposing a trade, professional or academic book. **Chosen Books** *Jane Campbell* FOUNDED 1971. *Publishes* charismatic adult non-fiction for a Christian market. TITLES *Healing Evangelism* Don Dunkerley; *Angels All Around* Sarah Hornsby. About 10 titles a year. Synopses or ideas welcome. **Fleming H. Revell; Spire Books**

William J. Petersen Adult fiction and non-fiction for evangelical Christians. A family-owned business until 1978, Fleming H. Revell was one of the first Christian publishers to take the step into secular publishing. TITLES *The Dual-Earner Marriage* Jack and Judy Balswick; *The Search for Lost Fathering* James Schaller. About 40 titles a year. Synopses or ideas welcome.

Royalties paid twice-yearly.

Balch Institute Press
See **Golden Cockerel Press** under **UK Publishers**

Ballantine/Del Rey/Fawcett/Ivy Books
201 East 50th Street, New York NY 10022
☎001 212 572 2110   Fax 001 212 572 4912
President *Linda Grey*
Publisher *Clare Ferraro*

FOUNDED 1952. Division of **Random House, Inc.** *Publishes* fiction and non-fiction, science fiction. 462 titles in 1995.

IMPRINTS **Ballantine Books; Del Rey; Fawcett Columbine; Fawcett Crest; Fawcett Gold Medal; Fawcett Juniper; House of Collectibles; Moorings; One World.**

Banner Books
See **University Press of Mississippi**

Bantam Doubleday Dell Publishing Group, Inc.
1540 Broadway, New York NY 10036
☎001 212 354 6500   Fax 001 212 302 7985
Chairman/CEO/President *Jack Hoeft*
President/Publisher, Bantam Books *Irwyn Applebaum*
President/Publisher, Doubleday *Arlene Friedman*
President/Publisher, Dell Publishing *Carole Baron*
President/Publisher *William T. Shinker*
Vice President/Publisher, Books for Young Readers *Craig Virden*

Publishes general commercial fiction: mysteries, westerns, romance, war, science fiction and fantasy, crime and thrillers, adventure; non-fiction, including New Age, crime and adventure, African-American/Latino, feminist, gay/lesbian studies; young readers and children's.

DIVISIONS/IMPRINTS **Bantam Books; Dell Publishing Broadway Books; Doubleday; Books for Young Readers); International Division; Anchor; Island; Spectra; Currency;**

Main Street; Loveswept; New Age Books. Most work comes through agents. No unsolicited mss.

Barron's Educational Series
250 Wireless Boulevard, Hauppauge NY 11788
☎001 516 434 3311   Fax 001 516 434 3723
Chairman/President *Manuel H. Barron*
Managing Editor *Grace Freedson*

FOUNDED 1942. *Publishes* adult non-fiction, children's fiction and non-fiction, test preparation materials and language materials/tapes, cookbooks, gardening, pets, business, art and painting. No adult fiction. 200 titles a year. Unsolicited mss, synopses and ideas for books welcome.

Royalties paid twice-yearly.

Basic Books
See **HarperCollins Publishers, Inc.**

Beacon Press
25 Beacon Street, Boston MA 02108
☎001 617 742 2110   Fax 001 617 723 3097
Director *Helene Atwan*

Publishes general non-fiction. About 50 titles a year. Approach in writing, or submit synopsis and sample chapters (with IRCs) to the editorial department.

Bedford Books
See **St Martin's Press, Inc.**

Beech Tree Books
See **William Morrow & Co., Inc.**

Berkley Publishing Group
200 Madison Avenue, New York NY 10016
☎001 212 951 8800   Fax 001 212 213 6706
Senior VP/Editorial Director *Leslie Gelbman*

FOUNDED 1954. Subsidiary of **The Putnam Berkley Group.** *Publishes* paperbacks: general interest fiction and non-fiction. About 700 titles a year. IMPRINTS **Ace Science Fiction & Fantasy** Submit synopsis and first three chapters; **Berkley Books; Berkley Trade Paperbacks; Boulevard; Jove.**

Royalties paid twice-yearly.

H. & R. Block
See **Simon & Schuster Trade Division**

Boulevard
See **Berkley Publishing Group**

Bowling Green State University Popular Press

Bowling Green OH 43403
☎001 419 372 7867   Fax 001 419 372 8095

Managing Director *Pat Browne*

FOUNDED 1970. *Publishes* non-fiction for libraries as reference or textbooks. 25 titles a year. Unsolicited mss, synopses and ideas welcome. No fiction.
Royalties paid twice-yearly.

Boyds Mills Press

815 Church Street, Honesdale PA 18431
☎001 717 253 1164   Fax 001 717 253 0179

Publisher *Kent Brown Jr*
Editorial Director *Larry Rosier*

A subsidiary of Highlights for Children, Inc. FOUNDED 1990 as a publisher of children's trade books. *Publishes* children's fiction, non-fiction and poetry. About 50 titles a year. TITLES *Been to Yesterdays* Lee Bennett Hopkins; *Bingleman's Midway* Barry Moser; *The Always Prayer Shawl* Sheldon Oberman; *I Don't Want to go to Camp* Eve Bunting. Unsolicited mss, synopses and ideas for books welcome. No romance.
Royalties paid twice-yearly.

Bradford Books

See **The MIT Press**

Brassey's, Inc.

1313 Dolley Madison Boulevard, Suite 401, McLean VA 22101
☎001 703 442 4535   Fax 001 703 442 9848

President and Publisher *Franklin D. Margiotta, Ph.D.*

FOUNDED 1983. Associated with **Brassey's** of London. *Publishes* primarily non-fiction titles on defence and military affairs, national and international, current affairs, foreign policy, history, biography, intelligence and sports. About 30 titles a year. TITLES *Mexico: From Montezuma to NAFTA, Chiapas and Beyond* Jaime Suchlicki; *No Surprises: Two Decades of Clinton-Watching* Paul Greenberg; *Fifty Years at the Front: The Life of War Correspondent Frederick Palmer* Nathan A. Haverstock; *The World Factbook: 1996-97* The Central Intelligence Agency. No unsolicited mss; synopses and ideas welcome.
Royalties paid twice-yearly.

Browndeer Press

See **Harcourt Brace Children's Books Division**

Bulfinch Press

See **Little, Brown & Co., Inc.**

University of California Press

2120 Berkeley Way, Berkeley CA 94720
☎001 510 642 4247   Fax 001 510 643 7127

Director *James H. Clark*

Publishes academic non-fiction and some fiction and poetry in translation. About 180 titles a year. Preliminary letter with outline preferred.

Carol Publishing Group

600 Madison Avenue, New York NY 10022
☎001 212 486 2200   Fax 001 212 486 2231

Publisher *Steven Schragis*

FOUNDED 1989. *Publishes* some fiction but mostly non-fiction: biography and autobiography, history, science, humour, how-to, illustrated and self-help. About 150 titles a year.

Carolrhoda Books, Inc.

241 First Avenue North, Minneapolis MN 55401
☎001 612 332 3344   Fax 001 612 332 7615

Editorial Director *Emily Kelley*
Submissions Editor *Rebecca Poole*

Publishes children's: nature, biography, history, beginners' readers, world cultures, photo essays and historical fiction. Please send s.a.e. for author guidelines.

Cassandra Editions

See **Academy Chicago Publishers**

Charlesbridge Publishing

85 Main Street, Watertown MA 02172-4411
☎001 617 926 0329   Fax 001 617 926 5720

Chairman *Brent Farmer*
Managing Editor *Elena Wright*

FOUNDED 1980 as an educational publisher focusing on teaching thinking processes. *Publishes* children's educational programmes (pre-kindergarten through to grade 8), non-fiction picture books and multicultural fiction for 3- to 12-year-olds. 30 titles in 1995. TITLES include *In My Own Backyard* Judi Kurjian; *A Walk in the Wild* Lorraine Ward; *Albertina anda arriba/Albertina Goes Up*, an alphabet book in Spanish and English by Nancy Maria Grande Tabor. Complete mss or proposal welcome with self-addressed envelope and IRCs. Mss should be paged, with suggested illustrations described for each page. No talking animals.
Royalties paid yearly.

University of Chicago Press

5801 South Ellis Avenue, Chicago
IL 60637-1496
☎001 312 702 7700   Fax 001 312 702 9756

FOUNDED 1891. *Publishes* academic non-fiction
only. 264 titles in 1995.

Children's Press

See **Grolier, Inc.**

Chosen Books

See **Baker Book House**

Chronicle Books

275 Fifth Street, San Francisco CA 94103
☎001 415 777 7240   Fax 001 415 777 2289

From end of November 1996: 85 Second
Street, San Francisco CA 94105

Publisher *Jack Jensen*
Executive Editor *Christine Carswell*

FOUNDED 1966. Division of Chronicle
Publishing. *Publishes* art and design, food and
cookery, gardening, nature, photography,
leisure and travel, adult fiction and short stories,
children's, and stationery/gift items. About 200
titles a year.

DIVISIONS
Art *Annie Barrows* **Children's** *Victoria Rock*
Cooking *Bill LeBond* **Gardening** *Leslie Jonath*
Regional *Karen Silver* **Fiction** *Jay Schaefer*
Giftworks *Debra Lande* **Multimedia** *Nion
McEvoy* **Nature/Humour** *Charlotte Stone*
Nature/Novelty *Leslie Bruynesteyn*. Query or
submit outline/synopsis and sample chapters
and artwork.
Royalties paid twice-yearly.

Clarion Books

215 Park Avenue South, New York NY 10003
☎001 212 420 5800   Fax 001 212 420 5855

VP/Editor-in-Chief *Dorothy Briley*
Executive Editor *Dinah Stevenson*

Clarion Books began in 1965 as an imprint of
Seabury Press. The Clarion name was inaugu-
rated in 1974 and acquired by **Houghton
Mifflin Co.** in 1979. *Publishes* children's and
young adult books. TITLES *Tuesday* David
Wiesner; *Red Fox Running* Eve Bunting; *It Goes
Eeeeeeeeeeee!* Jamie Gilson; *Across America on an
Emigrant Train* Jim Murphy. About 60 titles a
year. No novelty, series or genre fiction. Unsolicited mss, synopses and ideas welcome. Synopses should be accompanied by sample chap-
ter(s).
Royalties paid twice-yearly.

Clarkson Potter

See **Crown Publishing Group**

Classic Reprint

See **University of Alaska Press**

Cobblehill Books

See **Penguin USA**

Contemporary Books, Inc.

Two Prudential Plaza, Suite 1200, Chicago
IL 60601
☎001 312 540 4500   Fax 001 312 540 4657

Publisher *Christine Albritton*
Editorial Director *Nancy Crossman*

FOUNDED 1947. *Publishes* general adult non-
fiction and adult education books. 60 titles in
1994. Submissions require s.a.e. for response.

Crown Publishing Group

201 East 50th Street, New York
NY 10022
☎001 212 572 6117   Fax 001 212 572 6161

President/Publisher *Michelle Sidrane*

FOUNDED 1933. Division of **Random House,
Inc.** *Publishes* popular trade fiction and non-
fiction. 259 titles in 1994. IMPRINTS **Clarkson
Potter** *Lauren Shakely*; **Harmony** *Leslie
Meredith*; **Living Language**; *Kathy Mintz*
Crown Trade Paperbacks *Adrienne Ingrum*.

Currency

See **Bantam Doubleday Dell Publishing
Group, Inc.**

DAW Books, Inc.

375 Hudson Street, 3rd Floor, New York
NY 10014-3658
☎001 212 366 2096/Submissions 366 2095
Fax 001 212 366 2090

Publishers *Elizabeth R. Wollheim, Sheila E.
Gilbert*
Submissions Editor *Peter Stampfel*

FOUNDED 1971 by Donald and Elsie Wollheim
as the first mass-market publisher devoted to science fiction and fantasy. *Publishes* science fic-
tion/fantasy, and some horror. No short stories,
anthology ideas or non-fiction. Unsolicited mss,
synopses and ideas for books welcome. About
36 titles a year. TITLES *Emperors of the Twilight* S.
Andrew Swann; *Stronghold* Melanie Rawn;
Celebrity Vampires ed. Martin H. Greenberg.
Royalties paid twice-yearly.

Dearborn Financial Publishing, Inc.

155 N. Wacker Drive, Chicago IL 60606-1719
☎001 312 836 4400   Fax 001 312 836 1021
President *Dennis Blitz*
Chairman *Robert C. Kyle*
Senior Vice Presidents *Anita A. Constant,
Tim Honaker*

A niche publisher serving the financial services
industries. Formerly part of Longman. *Publishes*
real estate, insurance, financial planning, secu-
rities, commodities, investments, banking, professional education, motivation and reference
titles, investment reference and how-to books
for the consumer (individual investor) and
small business owner. About 150 titles a year.

DIVISIONS/IMPRINTS
Trade/Professional *Anita A. Constant* TITLES
*The Century 21 Guide to Buying a Home; 365
Ways to Simplify Your Work Life.* **Textbook:
Real Estate Education Company** *Carol
Luitjens* TITLES *Modern Real Estate Practice* (13th
ed.); *Realty Blue Book* (30th ed.). **Course:
Dearborn/R&R Newkirk** *Marjorie Sher*
Insurance titles. TITLES *Solutions Handbook;
Variable Contracts.* **Training-Securities** *Kim
Walker-Daniels* TITLES *PassTrak Series 6
Principles & Practices; One Track Professional Sales
Assistant.* **Upstart Publishing Co., Inc.** *Jere
Calmes* TITLES *Anatomy of a Business Plan,* 4th
ed.; Small Steps, Smart Choices. **Commodity
Trend Service** *Dennis Blitz* TITLES *Futures
Charts.* **Vernon Publishing, Inc.** *Tim
Honaker* TITLES *Personal Financial Plan; Financial
Need Analysis II.* **Enterprise** *Kevin Shanley*
TITLES *The Complete Book of Corporate Forms;
The Executive's Business Letter Book.* Unsolicited
mss, synopses and ideas welcome.
Royalties paid twice-yearly.

Del Rey
See **Ballantine/Del Rey/Fawcett/Ivy
Books**

Dell Publishing
See **Bantam Doubleday Dell Publishing
Group, Inc.**

Michael di Capua Books
See **HarperCollins Publishers**

Dial Books for Young Readers
375 Hudson Street, New York NY 10014-3657
☎001 212 366 2800   Fax 001 212 366 2020
Queries *Manuscript Reader*
FOUNDED 1961. Part of **Penguin USA**.
Publishes children's books, including picture
books, beginners' readers, fiction and non-fiction
for junior and young adults. 70 titles a year.
   IMPRINTS **Dial Easy-to-Read** Hardback and
softcover editions; **Puffin Pied Piper/Puffin
Pied Piper Giant** Softcover only. No unsolicited mss; queries only.
   Royalties paid twice-yearly.

Dimensions for Living
201 Eighth Avenue South, Box 801, Nashville
TN 37203-3957
☎001 615 749 6400   Fax 001 615 749 6512
Acquisitions Editor *Sally Sharpe*

Publishes non-fiction books for laity (inspirational, Christian living and self-help). 14 titles
in 1995.

Doubleday
See **Bantam Doubleday Dell Publishing
Group, Inc.**

Lisa Drew
See **Simon & Schuster Trade Division**

Thomas Dunne Books
See **St Martin's Press, Inc.**

Sanford J. Durst Publications
11 Clinton Avenue, Rockville Centre,
New York NY 11570
☎001 516 766 4444   Fax 001 516 766 4520
Owner *Sanford J. Durst*

FOUNDED 1975. *Publishes* non-fiction: numis-
matic and related, philatelic, legal and art. Also
children's books. About 12 titles a year.
   Royalties paid twice-yearly.

Dutton/Dutton Children's Books
See **Penguin USA**

Dutton/Signet
See **Penguin USA**

William B. Eerdmans Publishing Co.
255 Jefferson Avenue SE, Grand Rapids
MI 49503
☎001 616 459 4591   Fax 001 616 459 6540
President *William B. Eerdmans Jr*
Vice President/Editor-in-Chief *Jon Pott*

FOUNDED 1911 as a theological and reference
publisher. Gradually began publishing in other
genres with authors like C. S. Lewis, Dorothy
Sayers and Malcolm Muggeridge on its lists.
Publishes religious: theology, biblical studies,

ethical and social concern, social criticism and children's.

DIVISIONS **Children's** *Amy Eerdmans* **Other** *Jon Pott* TITLES *Dictionary of Biblical Tradition in English Literature; Embodying Forgiveness: A Theological Analysis.* Unsolicited mss, synopses and ideas welcome.

Royalties paid twice-yearly.

Enterprise
See **Dearborn Financial Publishing, Inc.**

M. Evans & Co., Inc.
216 East 49th Street, New York NY 10017
☎001 212 688 2810   Fax 001 212 486 4544
Chairman *George C. de Kay*

FOUNDED 1954 as a packager. Began publishing in 1962. Best known for its popular psychology and medicine books, with titles like *Body Language, Open Marriage, Pain Erasure* and *Aerobics. Publishes* general non-fiction and western fiction. TITLES *The Arthritis Breakthrough* Henry Scammell; *Total Concentration* Harold Levinson; *Born in Blood* and *Dungeon, Fire and Sword* John J. Robinson; *Dr Atkins' Diet Revolution* Robert Atkins. About 40 titles a year. No unsolicited mss; query first. Synopses and ideas welcome.

Royalties paid twice-yearly.

Everyman's Library
See **Alfred A. Knopf, Inc.**

Faber & Faber, Inc.
53 Shore Road, Winchester MA 08190
☎001 617 721 1427   Fax 001 617 729 2783
Chairman *Tom Kelleher*
Approx. Annual Turnover $4.5 million

Part of the UK-based company. *Publishes* fiction and non-fiction for adults. About 100 titles a year. No unsolicited mss. Send brief synopsis, chapter outlines, etc, together with IRCs for response or return.

Royalties paid twice-yearly.

Facts On File, Inc.
460 Park Avenue South, New York
NY 10016
☎001 212 683 2244   Fax 001 212 683 3633
President *Thomas C. Conoscenti*
Publisher *Remmel Nunn*

Started life in the early 1940s with News Digest subscription series to libraries. Began publishing on specific subjects with the Checkmark Books series and developed its current reference and trade book programme in the 1970s. *Publishes* general trade and academic reference only. *Specialises* in single subject encyclopedias. About 135 titles a year. No fiction, cookery or popular non-fiction.

DIVISIONS
General Reference *Susan Schwartz* TITLES *Shakespeare A-Z; Eyewitness History Series.* **Academic Reference** *Eleanora Von Dehsen* TITLES *Maps on File; Encyclopedia of the Third World.* **Young Adult** *James Warren* TITLES *Discovering Science Series; Fashions of the Decade Series.* **Electronic Publishing** *Thomas Hitchings* TITLES *Facts On File News Digest CD-ROM; The American Indian Multimedia CD-ROM.* Unsolicited synopses and ideas welcome; no mss. Send query letter in the first instance.

Royalties paid twice-yearly.

Farrar, Straus & Giroux, Inc.
19 Union Square West, New York
NY 10003
☎001 212 741 6900   Fax 001 212 633 9385
President/Chief Executive *Roger W. Straus III*
Snr Vice-President/Editor-in-Chief *Jonathan Galassi*

FOUNDED 1946. *Publishes* general fiction, non-fiction, juveniles. About 190 titles a year.

DIVISIONS
Children's Books *Margaret Ferguson.* Publishes fiction and non-fiction, books and novels for children and young adults. Approximately 100 titles a year. Submit synopsis and sample chapters (copies of artwork/ photographs as part of package). **Hill & Wang** *Elisabeth Sifton*
IMPRINTS **MIRASOL Libros Juveniles**; **Noonday Press** *Elisabeth Dyssegaard*; **North Point Press**; **Sunburst Books**.

Fawcett
See **Ballantine/Del Rey/Fawcett/Ivy Books**

Fireside
See **Simon & Schuster Trade Division**

Fodor's Travel Publications
See **Random House, Inc.**

Forge
See **St Martin's Press, Inc.**

The Free Press
See **Simon & Schuster Trade Division**

Samuel French, Inc.

45 West 25th Street, New York NY 10010
☎001 212 206 8990   Fax 001 212 206 1429

Editors *Lawrence Harbison, William Talbot*

FOUNDED 1830. *Publishes* plays in paperback: Broadway and off-Broadway hits, light comedies, mysteries, one-act plays and plays for young audiences. Unsolicited mss welcome. No synopses. About 80 titles a year.

Royalties paid annually (books); twice-yearly (amateur productions); monthly (professional productions). *Overseas associates* in London, Toronto and Sydney.

The Globe Pequot Press

PO Box 833, 6 Business Park Road,
Old Saybrook CT 06475
☎001 860 395 0440   Fax 001 860 395 0312

President *Linda Kennedy*
Associate Publisher *Michael K. Urban*

Publishes regional and international travel, cooking, how-to, personal finance, and outdoor recreation. About 100 titles a year.

IMPRINTS **Voyager Books**. TITLES include the *Off The Beaten Path* series, of which there are currently 40 titles, e.g. *Ohio: Off the Beaten Path*. Also publishes the *Recommended Country Inns* guides. Unsolicited mss, synopses and ideas welcome, particularly for travel and outdoor recreation books.

Royalties paid.

Greenwillow Books

See **William Morrow and Co., Inc.**

Griffin Trade Paperbacks

See **St Martin's Press**

Grolier, Inc.

Sherman Turnpike, Danbury CT 06816
☎001 203 797 3500   Fax 001 203 797 3197

Chief Executive Officer *Arnaud Lagardere*

FOUNDED 1895. *Publishes* juvenile non-fiction, encyclopedias, speciality reference sets, children's fiction and picture books, professional and scholarly. 650 titles in 1995.

DIVISIONS **Children's Press; Grolier Educational Corp.; Grolier Reference; Orchard Books; Scarecrow Press, Inc.** (see entry); **Franklin Watts** (see entry).

Grosset & Dunlap

See **Putnam & Grosset Group**

Grove/Atlantic Inc.

841 Broadway, New York NY 10003–4793
☎001 212 614 7850   Fax 001 212 614 7886

President/Publisher *Morgan Entrekin*
Senior Editor *Anton Mueller*

FOUNDED 1952. *Publishes* general fiction and non-fiction. 70 titles in 1995. IMPRINTS **Atlantic Monthly Press; Grove Press.**

Gulliver Books

See **Harcourt Brace Children's Books Division**

Harcourt Brace Children's Books Division

525 B Street, Suite 1900, San Diego
CA 92101–4495
☎001 619 699 6810   Fax 001 619 699 6777

Vice President/Publisher *Louise Howton*

A division of Harcourt Brace & Company. *Publishes* fiction, poetry and non-fiction covering a wide range of subjects: biography, environment and ecology, history, travel, science and current affairs for children and young adults. About 200 titles a year.

IMPRINTS **Browndeer Press; Gulliver Books; Gulliver Green® Books** Ecology and environment; **Harcourt Brace Children's Books; Harcourt Brace Paperbacks; Odyssey Paperbacks** Novels; **Red Wagon Books** For ages 6 months to 3 years; **Voyager Paperbacks** Picture books; **Jane Yolen Books**. No unsolicited mss.

Harlequin Historicals

See **Silhouette Books**

Harmony

See **Crown Publishing Group**

HarperCollins Publishers, Inc.

10 East 53rd Street, New York
NY 10022
☎001 212 207 7000   Fax 001 212 207 7797

President/Chief Executive *Anthea Disney*

FOUNDED 1817. Owned by News Corporation. *Publishes* general fiction, non-fiction and college textbooks in hardcover, trade paperback and mass-market formats.

DIVISIONS/IMPRINTS
Adult Trade *Jack McKeown* President/Publisher; **Harper Business** *Virginia Smith* Executive Editor; **Harper Reference** *Linda Cunningham* Vice President/Associate Publisher/Editorial Director; **HarperCollins Children's**

Books *Marilyn Kriney* Senior Vice President/ Publisher; **Harper Paperbacks & Audio** *Geoff Hannell* Senior Vice President/ Publisher; **Basic Books** *Mike Mueller* Managing Editor; **Michael di Capua Books** *Michael di Capua* Vice President/ Publisher.

SUBSIDIARIES **Scott, Foresman & Co** (see entry); **Zondervan Publishing House** (see entry).

Harvard University Press
79 Garden Street, Cambridge
MA 02138
☎001 617 495 2611   Fax 001 617 496 4677
Editor-in-Chief *Aida D. Donald*

Publishes scholarly non-fiction only: general interest, science and behaviour, social science, history, humanities, psychology, political science, sociology, economics, business, classics, religion. 120 new titles a year and 80–90 paperbacks. Free book catalogue available.

Harvest House Publishers
1075 Arrowsmith, Eugene OR 97402
☎001 541 343 0123   Fax 001 541 342 6410
President *R. C. Hawkins Jr*
Editorial Director *Carolyn McCready*

Publishes Christian living, fiction, children's and contemporary issues. TITLE *Beloved* Kay Arthur. Unsolicited mss, synopses and ideas for books welcome, with IRCs; no children's books or juvenile fiction at present.
Royalties paid annually.

Hearst Books/Hearst Marine Books
See **William Morrow & Co., Inc.**

Hill & Wang
See **Farrar, Straus & Giroux, Inc**

Hippocrene Books, Inc.
171 Madison Avenue, New York
NY 10016
☎001 212 685 4371   Fax 001 212 779 9338
President/Editorial Director *George Blagowidow*

FOUNDED 1971. *Publishes* general non-fiction and reference books. Particularly strong on foreign language dictionaries, language studies and military history. No fiction. Send brief summary, table of contents and one chapter for appraisal. S.a.e. essential for response. For manuscript return include sufficient postage cover (IRCs).

Holiday House, Inc.
425 Madison Avenue, New York NY 10017
☎001 212 688 0085   Fax 001 212 421 6134
Vice President/Editor-in-Chief *Regina Griffin*

Publishes children's general fiction and non-fiction (pre-school to secondary). About 50 titles a year. TITLES *Wicked Jack* Connie Wooldridge, illus. Will Hillenbrand; *The Life and Death of Crazy Horse* Russell Freedman. Submit synopsis and three sample chapters for novels and chapter books; complete mss (without artwork) for picture books.

Henry Holt and Company, Inc.
115 West 18th Street, New York NY 10011
☎001 212 886 9200   Fax 001 212 633 0748
President/CEO *Michael Naumann*

FOUNDED 1866. Henry Holt is one of the oldest publishers in the United States. *Publishes* fiction, by both American and international authors, biographies, and books on history and politics, ecology and psychology. AUTHORS include: Sue Grafton, Norman Mailer, Toni Morrison, Thomas Pynchon and Kurt Vonnegut.

Houghton Mifflin Co.
222 Berkeley Street, Boston MA 02116
☎001 617 351 5000
Contact *Submissions Editor*

FOUNDED 1832. *Publishes* literary fiction and general non-fiction, including autobiography, biography and history. Also school and college textbooks; children's fiction and non-fiction. Average 100 titles a year. Queries only for adult material; synopses, outline and sample chapters for children's non-fiction; complete mss for children's fiction. IRCs required with all submissions/queries.

DIVISIONS **Riverside Publishing Co.**; **Clarion Books** (see entry).

House of Collectibles
See **Ballantine/Del Rey/Fawcett/Ivy Books**

Hudson River Editions
See **Simon & Schuster Trade Division**

University of Illinois Press
1325 South Oak Street, Champaign IL
61820-6903
☎001 217 333 0950   Fax 001 217 244 8082
Editorial Director *Richard L. Wentworth*

Publishes non-fiction, scholarly and general,

with special interest in Americana, women's studies and African-American studies. Poetry - three volumes a year. Short fiction programme, sporadic; please enquire. About 110-120 titles a year.

Indiana University Press
601 North Morton Street, Bloomington
IN 42404-3797
☎001 812 855 4203   Fax 001 812 855 7931
Director *John Gallman*
Publishes scholarly non-fiction in the following subject areas: African studies, anthropology, Asian studies, Black studies, criminal justice, environment and ecology, film, folklore, history, Jewish studies, literary criticism, medical ethics, Middle East studies, military, music, philanthropy, philosophy, politics, religion, semiotics, Russian and East European studies, Victorian studies, women's studies. Query in writing in first instance.

University of Iowa Press
Kuhl House, 119 West Park Road, Iowa City
IA 52242
☎001 319 335 2000   Fax 001 319 335 2055
Director *Paul Zimmer*
FOUNDED 1969 as a small scholarly press publishing about five books a year. Now publishing about 35 a year in a variety of scholarly fields, plus local interest, short stories, autobiography and poetry. No unsolicited mss; query first. Unsolicited ideas and synopses welcome.
Royalties paid annually.

Iowa State University Press
2121 South State Avenue, Ames IA 50010
☎001 515 292 0140   Fax 001 515 292 3348
Director *Linda Speth*
FOUNDED 1934 as an offshoot of the university's journalism department. *Publishes* agriculture, aviation, economics, regional history, consumer science, journalism, and veterinary medicine.
Royalties paid annually; sometimes twice yearly.

Island
See **Bantam Doubleday Dell Publishing Group, Inc.**

Ivy Books
See **Ballantine/Del Rey/Fawcett/Ivy Books**

Jove
See **Berkley Publishing Group**

University Press of Kansas
2501 West 15th Street, Lawrence
KS 66049-3904
☎001 913 864 4154   Fax 001 913 864 4586
Director *Fred M. Woodward*
FOUNDED 1946. Became the publishing arm for all six state universities in Kansas in 1976. *Publishes* scholarly books in American history, women's studies, presidential studies, social and political philosophy, political science, military history, environmental and rural studies. About 45 titles a year. Proposals welcome.
Royalties paid annually.

Jean Karl Books
See **Simon & Schuster Children's Publishing Division**

Kent State University Press
Kent OH 44242-0001
☎001 216 672 7913   Fax 001 216 672 3104
Director *John T. Hubbell*
Editor *Julia Morton*
FOUNDED 1965. *Publishes* scholarly works in history and biography, literary studies and general non-fiction. 20-25 titles a year. Queries welcome; no mss.
Royalties paid annually.

Martin Kessler Books
See **Simon & Schuster Trade Division**

Alfred A. Knopf Inc.
201 East 50th Street, New York NY 10022
☎001 212 751 2600   Fax 001 212 572 2593
President/Editor-in-Chief *Sonny Mehta*
FOUNDED 1915. Division of **Random House, Inc.** *Publishes* fiction and non-fiction, poetry, juvenile. 167 titles in 1995.
IMPRINT **Everyman's Library**

Krieger Publishing Co., Inc.
PO Box 9542, Melbourne FL 32902-9542
☎001 407 724 9542   Fax 001 407 951 3671
Chairman *Robert E. Krieger*
President *Donald E. Krieger*
Editorial Head *Mary Roberts*
FOUNDED 1970. *Publishes* business science and economics, education and communication, history, mathematics and computer science, medical science, psychology, chemistry, physical and natural sciences, reference, technology and engineering.
IMPRINTS **Anvil; Exploring Community History Series; Open Forum; Orbit;**

Professional Practices in Adult Education and Human Resource Development; **Public History**. Unsolicited mss welcome. Not interested in synopses/ideas.

Royalties paid yearly.

Lanternlight Library
See **University of Alaska Press**

Lehigh University Press
See **Golden Cockerel Press** under **UK Publishers**

Lerner Publications Co.
241 First Avenue North, Minneapolis MN 55401
☎001 612 332 3344   Fax 001 612 332 7615
Editorial Director *Nancy Campbell*

Publishes children's and young adults: art, nature, biography, history, world cultures, world and US geography, aviation, sports, fiction, mysteries, physical science. 60 titles in 1995. Please send IRCs for author guidelines.

Little Simon
See **Simon & Schuster Children's Publishing Division**

Little, Brown and Co., Inc.
1271 Avenue of the Americas, New York NY 10020
☎001 212 522 8700

Children's & Bulfinch editorial at: 34 Beacon Street, Boston, MA 02108
☎001 617 227 0730
President *Charles E. Hayward*

Division of Time Warner, Inc. FOUNDED 1837. *Publishes* contemporary popular fiction and literary fiction. Also non-fiction: distinctive cookbooks, biographies, history, poetry, art, photography, science, sport, and children's. About 100 titles a year.

IMPRINTS **Back Bay Books; Bulfinch Press**. No unsolicited mss. Query letter in the first instance.

Living Language
See **Crown Publishing Group**

Llewellyn Publications
PO Box 64383, St Paul MN 55164-0383
☎001 612 291 1970   Fax 001 612 291 1908
President/Publisher *Carl L. Weschcke*
Acquisitions Manager *Nancy J. Mostad*

Division of Llewellyn Worldwide Ltd. FOUNDED 1901. *Publishes* self-help and how-to: astrology, alternative health, tantra, Fortean studies, tarot, yoga, Santeria, dream studies, metaphysics, magic, witchcraft, herbalism, shamanism, organic gardening, women's spirituality, graphology, palmistry, parapsychology. Also fiction with an authentic magical or metaphysical theme. About 72 titles a year. Unsolicited mss welcome; proposals preferred. IRCs essential in all cases. Books are distributed in the UK by Airlift Book Co.

Lodestar Books
See **Penguin USA**

Lothrop, Lee & Shepard
See **William Morrow and Co., Inc.**

Louisiana State University Press
Baton Rouge LA 70893
☎001 504 388 6294   Fax 001 504 388 6461
Director *L. E. Phillabaum*

Publishes non-fiction: Southern history, American history, Southern literary criticism, American literary criticism, biography, political science, music (jazz) and Latin American studies. About 70 titles a year. Send IRCs for mss guidelines.

Loveswept
See **Bantam Doubleday Dell Publishing Group, Inc.**

Lyons & Burford, Publishers
31 West 21st Street, New York NY 10010
☎001 212 620 9580   Fax 001 212 929 1836
Chairman *Nick Lyons*
Managing Director *Peter Burford*

Publishes outdoor, nature, sports, gardening and angling titles, plus cookery and art. About 75 titles a year. No unsolicited mss; synopses and ideas welcome.

Royalties paid twice-yearly.

Macmillan/McGraw-Hill School Publishing Group
See **McGraw-Hill, Inc.**

Main Street
See **Bantam Doubleday Dell Publishing Group, Inc.**

University of Massachusetts Press
PO Box 429, Amherst MA 01004-0429
☎001 413 545 2217   Fax 001 413 545 1226
Managing Director *Bruce Wilcox*

FOUNDED 1964. *Publishes* scholarly, general

interest, Black, ethnic, women's studies, cultural criticism, architecture and environmental design, literary criticism, poetry, philosophy, political science, sociology. Unsolicited mss considered but query letter preferred in the first instance. Synopses and ideas welcome. About 40 titles a year.

Royalties paid annually.

Margaret K. McElderry Books
See **Simon & Schuster Children's Publishing Division**

McFarland & Company, Inc., Publishers
PO Box 611, Jefferson NC 28640
☎001 910 246 4460   Fax 001 910 246 5018
President/Editor-in-Chief *Robert Franklin*
Vice President *Rhonda Herman*
Editors *Lisa Camp, Steve Wilson, Barry Greene*
FOUNDED 1979. A library-orientated press, publishing reference books and scholarly monographs in many fields: international studies, performing arts, popular culture, sports, women's studies, music and fine arts, business, history, war memoirs and librarianship. *Specialises* in general reference. No fiction, poetry, children's, New Age or inspirational works. About 130 titles a year. TITLES *Heads of States and Governments*; *International Holidays*; *African Placenames*; *Opera Companies and Houses*; *Christopher Lee and Peter Cushing*; *The Sexual Harassment of Women*; *The Recreation Handbook*. No unsolicited mss; send query letter first. Synopses and ideas welcome.

Royalties paid annually.

McGraw-Hill, Inc.
1221 Avenue of the Americas, New York NY 10020
☎001 212 512 2000
Contact *Submissions Editor*
FOUNDED 1873. US parent of the UK-based **McGraw-Hill Book Co. Europe**. *Publishes* a wide range of business and computing books.

DIVISIONS **Legal Information Group**; **Macmillan/ McGraw-Hill School Publishing Group**; **Osborne/McGraw-Hill**; **Professional Publishing Group**.

Mentor
See **Penguin USA**

Meridian
See **Penguin USA**

The University of Michigan Press
839 Greene Street, PO Box 1104, Ann Arbor MI 48106
☎001 313 764 4394   Fax 001 313 936 0456
Managing Director *Colin Day*
FOUNDED 1930. *Publishes* non-fiction, textbooks, literary criticism, theatre, economics, political science, history, classics, anthropology, law studies, women's studies, and English as a second language textbooks. 140 titles in 1995.

IMPRINTS
University of Michigan Press *LeAnn Fields* Specialises in monographs in anthropology, economics, classics, women's studies, theatre, political science. **Ann Arbor Paperbacks** TITLES *The Legacy of Tiananmen - China in Disarray* James A. R. Miles; *James Joyce and the Art of Mediation* David Weir; *Discovering American Culture* Cheryl L. Delk. No unsolicited mss. Synopses and ideas welcome.

Royalties paid twice-yearly.

The Millbrook Press, Inc.
2 Old New Milford Road, PO Box 335, Brookfield CT 06804
☎001 203 740 2220   Fax 001 203 740 2526
President *Jean Reynolds*
Editorial Director *Jean Reynolds*
Managing Editor *Marilyn Smith*
FOUNDED 1989. *Publishes* mainly non-fiction, children's and young adult, for trade, school and public library. About 120 titles a year.

Royalties paid twice-yearly.

Minstrel Books
See **Pocket Books**

MIRASOL Libros Juveniles
See **Farrar, Straus & Giroux, Inc**

University Press of Mississippi
3825 Ridgewood Road, Jackson MS 39211-6492
☎001 601 982 6205   Fax 001 601 982 6217
Chairman *Dr O. Finley Graves*
Managing Director *Dr Richard Abel*
Associate Director/Editor-in-Chief *Seetha A-Srinivasan*
Approx. Annual Turnover $1.5 million
FOUNDED 1970. The non-profit book publisher partially supported by the eight State universities. *Publishes* scholarly and trade titles in literature, history, American culture, Southern culture, African-American, women's studies, popular culture, folklife, ethnic, performance,

art and photography, and other liberal arts. About 50 titles a year. TITLES *Anabasis* Ellen Gilchrist; *Country Music Culture; Punk and Neo-Tribal Body Art*.

IMPRINTS
Muscadine Books *JoAnne Prichard* Regional trade titles. TITLES *The New Orleans Garden; The Crawfish Book; The Catfish Book*. **Banner Books** Paperback reprints of significant fiction and non-fiction. TITLES *Savage Holiday* Richard Wright; *Dark Princess* W. E. B. DuBois. Send letter of enquiry, prospectus, table of contents and sample chapter prior to submission of full mss.

Royalties paid annually. *Represented* world-wide. UK representatives: **Roundhouse Publishing Ltd**, PO Box 140, Oxford OX2 7FF; tel: 01865 512682/fax: 01865 59594.

University of Missouri Press
2910 LeMone Boulevard, Columbia
MO 65201-8227
☎001 573 882 7641   Fax 001 573 884 4498

Director/Editor-in-Chief *Beverly Jarrett*

Publishes academic: history, literary criticism, intellectual history and related humanities disciplines and short stories – usually four volumes a year. Best approach is by letter. Send one short story for consideration, and synopses for academic work. About 50 titles a year.

The MIT Press
55 Hayward Street, Cambridge MA 02142
☎001 617 253 5646   Fax 001 617 258 6779

Managing Editor *Michael Sims*

Publishes non-fiction: technologically sophisticated books, including computer science and artificial intelligence, economics, architecture, cognitive science, neuroscience, environmental studies, linguistics and philosophy. 229 titles in 1995. IMPRINT **Bradford Books**.

Monograph Series
See **University of Alaska Press**

Moorings
See **Ballantine/Del Rey/Fawcett/Ivy Books**

William Morrow & Co., Inc.
1350 Avenue of the Americas, New York
NY 10019
☎001 212 261 6500   Fax 001 212 261 6595

Editor-in-Chief *William Schwalbe*

FOUNDED 1926. *Publishes* fiction, poetry and general non-fiction. Approach in writing only.

No unsolicited mss or proposals for adult books. Proposals read only if submitted through a literary agent. About 600 titles a year.

IMPRINTS
Hearst Books/Hearst Marine Books *Ann Bramson*; **Quill Trade Paperbacks** *Toni Sciarra*; **Morrow Junior Books** *David Reuther*; **Lothrop, Lee & Shepard** *Susan Pearson*; **Greenwillow Books** *Susan Hirschman*; **Tambourine Books** *Paulette Kaufmann*; **Mulberry Books/Beech Tree Books** (trade paperbacks) *Paulette Kaufmann*; **Rob Weisbach Books** *Rob Weisbach*.

Mulberry Books
See **William Morrow and Co., Inc.**

Muscadine Books
See **University Press of Mississippi**

Mysterious Press
See **Warner Books Inc.**

University of Nevada Press
MS 166, Reno NV 89557-0076
☎001 702 784 6573   Fax 001 702 784 6200

Director *Thomas Radko*
Editor-in-Chief *Margaret Dalrymple*

FOUNDED 1960. *Publishes* serious fiction, Native American studies, natural history, Western Americana, Basque studies and regional studies. About 40 titles a year including reprints. Unsolicited material welcome if it fits in with areas published, or offers a 'new and exciting' direction.

Royalties paid twice-yearly.

New Age Books
See **Bantam Doubleday Dell Publishing Group, Inc.**

University Press of New England
23 South Main Street, Hanover
NH 03755-2048
☎001 603 643 7100   Fax 001 603 643 1540

Chair/Director *Thomas L. McFarland*
Editorial Director *Philip Pochoda*

FOUNDED 1970. A scholarly book publisher sponsored by ten institutions of higher education in the region: Brandeis, Brown, Dartmouth, Middlebury, Tufts, Wesleyan and the universities of New Hampshire, Rhode Island, Vermont and the Salzburg Seminar. *Publishes* general and scholarly non-fiction; plus poetry, essays and short stories through the

Wesleyan Poetry Series, Bread Loaf Writers Conference and Hardscrabble Books, contemporary and classic fiction from New England. About 65 titles a year.

IMPRINTS **Wesleyan University Press** Interdisciplinary studies, history, literature, women's studies, government and public issues, biography, poetry, social and natural sciences. Unsolicited material welcome.

Royalties paid annually. *Overseas associates:* UK – University Presses Marketing; Europe – Trevor Brown Associates.

University of New Mexico Press

1720 Lomas NE, Albuquerque
NM 87131-1591
☎001 505 277 2346   Fax 001 505 277 9270

Editor *Larry Durwood Ball*

Publishes scholarly non-fiction across a wide range of fields, plus illustrated and biography. No fiction, how-to, children's, humour, self-help, technical or textbooks. About 70 titles a year.

Noonday Press

See **Farrar, Straus & Giroux, Inc**

North Point Press

See **Farrar, Straus & Giroux, Inc**

University of North Texas Press

PO Box 13856, Denton TX 76203
☎001 817 565 2142   Fax 001 817 565 4590

Director *Frances B. Vick*
Editor *Charlotte M. Wright*

FOUNDED 1987. *Publishes* folklore, ecology, regional interest, contemporary, social issues, history, military, women's issues, writing and publishing reference, and Western literature. About 14 titles a year. No unsolicited mss. Approach by letter in the first instance. Synopses and ideas welcome.

Royalties paid annually.

W. W. Norton & Company

500 Fifth Avenue, New York NY 10110
☎001 212 354 5500   Fax 001 212 869 0856

Editor *Liz Malcolm*

FOUNDED 1923. *Publishes* quality fiction and non-fiction, college textbooks, professional and medical books. No occult, paranormal, religious, arts and crafts, genre fiction (formula romances, science fiction or westerns), children's books or young adult. About 300 titles a year. Query letters should include brief description of submission, writing credentials and experience relevant

to submissions. Submissions should consist of 2 or 3 sample chapters including the first; non-fiction submissions should also include a detailed outline of content. Return postage essential for response.

Odyssey Paperbacks

See **Harcourt Brace Children's Books Division**

University of Oklahoma Press

1005 Asp Avenue, Norman OK 73019-0445
☎001 405 325 5111   Fax 001 405 325 4000

Editor-in-Chief *John N. Drayton*

FOUNDED 1928. *Publishes* general scholarly non-fiction only: American Indian studies, history of American West, classical studies, literary theory and criticism, anthropology, archaeology, natural history, political science and women's studies. About 100 titles a year.

One World

See **Ballantine/Del Rey/Fawcett/Ivy Books**

Onyx

See **Penguin USA**

Open Forum

See **Krieger Publishing Co., Inc.**

Orbit

See **Krieger Publishing Co., Inc.**

Orchard Books

See **Grolier, Inc.**

Osborne/McGraw Hill

2600 Tenth Street, Berkeley CA 94710
☎001 510 549 6600   Fax 001 510 549 6603

Publisher *Larry Levitsky*

FOUNDED 1970. Osborne has been publishing computer books for almost twenty years and has grown to become a leader in its field. *Publishes* computer software and microcomputer titles. About 85 titles a year. TITLES *Windows 95 series; Busy People series.* Co-publisher of Oracle Press, Corel Press.

Royalties paid twice-yearly.

Pantheon Books/Schocken Books

201 East 50th Street, New York NY 10022
☎001 212 751 2600   Fax 001 212 572 6030

Senior Editor (Pantheon) *Shelley Wanger*
Editor Director (Shocken) *Arthur Samuelson*

FOUNDED 1942. Division of **Random House,**

Inc. *Publishes* Fiction and non-fiction, Jewish interest (Shocken Books). 88 titles in 1995.

Paragon House

370 Lexington Avenue, New York
NY 10017
☎001 212 953 5950   Fax 001 212 953 5940
Director/Vice-President *Mike Giampaoli*
FOUNDED 1982. *Publishes* non-fiction: reference and academic. Subjects include history, religion, philosophy, New Age, Jewish interest. 24 titles in 1995.
Royalties paid twice-yearly.

Pelican Publishing Company

1101 Monroe Street, Box 3110, Gretna
LA 70053
☎001 504 368 1175
Editor-in-Chief *Nina Kooij*
Publishes general non-fiction: popular history, cookbooks, travel, art, business, children's, editorial cartoon, architecture and motivational. About 70 titles a year. Initial enquiries required for all submissions.

Pelion Press

See **Rosen Publishing Group, Inc.**

Penguin USA

375 Hudson Street, New York
NY 10014
☎001 212 366 2000   Fax 001 212 366 2666
Chairman *Peter Mayer*
Owned by Pearson. *Publishes* fiction and non-fiction in paperback; adult and children's. About 1000 titles a year. IMPRINTS: **Arkana; Mentor; Meridian; Onyx; Penguin Classics** *K. Court*; **Plume** *Arnold Dolin*; **Puffin** *Tracy Tang*; **ROC Books** *Amy Stout*; **Signet; Signet Classics; Topaz** *Michaela Hamilton*; **Viking** *Barbara Grossman*; **Viking Studio** *Michael Fragnito*; **Frederick Warne.**

DIVISIONS
Dutton/Signet *Elaine Koster* FOUNDED 1852. IMPRINTS **William Abrahams; Dutton; Truman M. Talley. Dial Books for Young Readers** *Phyllis J. Fogelman* (see entry); **Dutton Children's Books** *Christopher Franceschelli/Lucia Monfried* FOUNDED 1852. *Publishes* picture books, fiction and non-fiction, board and novelty books. IMPRINTS **Cobblehill Books** *Rosanne Lauer*, **Lodestar Books** *Rosemary Brosnan*; **Viking Children's Books** *Regina Hayes.*
Royalties paid twice-yearly.

University of Pennsylvania Press

418 Service Drive, Philadelphia PA 19104
☎001 215 898 1671   Fax 001 215 898 0404
Managing Director *Eric Halpern*
FOUNDED 1896. *Publishes* serious non-fiction: scholarly, reference, professional, textbooks and trade. No fiction or poetry. TITLES *Ceramic Technology for Potters and Sculptors; The Steelband Movement; Television Culture and Women's Lives.* About 70 titles a year. No unsolicited mss but synopses and ideas for books welcome.
Royalties paid annually.

Perigree Books

See **Putnam Berkley Publishing Group**

Philomel Books

See **Putnam & Grosset Group**

Picador USA

See **St Martin's Press, Inc.**

Players Press

PO Box 1132, Studio City CA 91614–0132
☎001 818 789 4980
Chairman *William-Alan Landes*
Managing Director *Sharon Gorrell*
Editorial Head *Robert W. Gordon*
FOUNDED 1965 as a publisher of plays; now publishes across the entire range of performing arts: plays, musicals, theatre, film, cinema, television, costume, puppetry, plus technical theatre and cinema material. 55–65 titles a year. TITLES *Principles of Stage Combat Handbook; Stage Crafts Handbook; Scenes for Acting & Directing, vol 2; Performance One - Monologues for Women; Period Costume for Stage and Screen - Medieval to 1500; Three Sisters.* No unsolicited mss; synopses/ideas welcome. Send query letter.
Royalties paid twice-yearly. *Overseas subsidiaries* in Canada, Australia and the UK.

Plenum Publishing

233 Spring Street, New York NY 10013
☎001 212 620 8000   Fax 001 212 463 0742
Executive Editor, Trade Books *Linda Greenspan Regan*
FOUNDED 1946. *Publishes* quality non-fiction for the intelligent layman and the professional: trade science, social sciences, health, psychology, anthropology and criminology. Over 300 titles a year. Queries only. DIVISION **Plenum Trade** About 12–15 titles a year.

Plume

See **Penguin USA**

Pocket Books
1230 Avenue of the Americas, New York
NY 10020
☎001 212 698 7000   Fax 001 212 698 7007
President *Jack Romanos*

FOUNDED 1939. A division of Simon & Schuster
Consumer Group. *Publishes* trade paperbacks
and hardcovers; mass-market, reprints and origi-
nals. IMPRINTS **Archway**; **Minstrel Books**;
Pocket Star Books; **Washington Square
Press**.

Clarkson Potter
See **Crown Publishing Group**

Price, Stern, Sloan
See **Putnam & Grosset Group**

Princeton University Press
41 William Street, Princeton NJ 08540
☎001 609 258 4900   Fax 001 609 258 6305
Editor-in-Chief *Ann Himmelberger Wald*

Publishes scholarly non-fiction: art and architecture, anthropology, history, philosophy,
religion, political science, music, biological and
physical sciences, biography, computer science,
language and literature. About 180 titles a year.
Queries only.

Public History
See **Krieger Publishing Co., Inc.**

Puffin
See **Penguin USA**

Puffin Pied Piper
See **Dial Books for Young Readers**

Putnam & Grosset Group
200 Madison Avenue, New York NY 10016
☎001 212 951 8700   Fax 001 212 532 3693
Chairman *Margaret Frith*
President *Douglas Whiteman*
**President & Publisher, G. P. Putnam's
  Sons** *Nancy Paulsen*
President & Publisher, Grosset & Dunlap
  Jane O'Connor

The children's book division of the **Putnam
Berkley Publishing Group** (see entry).
  IMPRINTS **G. P. Putnam's Sons** *Refna
Wilkin* Executive Editor; **Philomel Books**
Patricia Lee Gauch Editorial Director; **Grosset &
Dunlap** *Judy Donnelly* Editor-in-Chief; **Price,
Stern, Sloan** 11150 Olympic Boulevard, Los
Angeles, CA 90064, *Tanni Tytel* Publisher. All

imprints *publish* picture books, activity books,
fiction and non-fiction for children.

Putnam Berkley Publishing Group
200 Madison Avenue, New York NY 10016
☎001 212 951 8400   Fax 001 212 213 6706
President *David Shanks*

FOUNDED 1838. *Publishes* general fiction and
non-fiction, including children's. Also business, how-to, nutrition and general fiction
under the **Berkley** imprints. **Putnam &
Grosset Group** is the children's book division
(see entry).
  DIVISIONS **Berkley** Mass-market paperback
division (see entry). **Perigree Books** *John
Duff/Steve Ross* Trade paperback division.
Non-fiction: cookbooks, crafts, humour,
music & dance, health, nutrition, psychology,
self-help, social sciences and sociology, biography, child care and development, behavioural
sciences, business, human relations, education.
  Royalties paid twice-yearly.

Questar
See **Warner Books Inc.**

Quill Trade Paperbacks
See **William Morrow and Co., Inc.**

Rabbit Ears
See **Simon & Schuster Children's
Publishing Division**

Rand McNally & Co.
8255 North Central Park Avenue, Skokie
IL 60076
☎001 847 329 6772   Fax 001 847 329 1985
Editor *Jon Leverenz*

Publishes world atlases and maps, road atlases of
North America and Europe, city and state maps
of the United States and Canada, educational
wall maps, atlases and globes, plus children's
products. Includes electronic publications.

Random House, Inc.
201 East 50th Street, New York NY 10022
☎001 212 751 2600   Fax 001 212 572 8700
Chairman/President & CEO *Alberto Vitale*

FOUNDED 1925. *Publishes* trade fiction: adventure, confessional, experimental, fantasy, historical, horror, humour, mainstream, mystery
and suspense; and non-fiction: biography, history, economics, politics, health, business,
sports, humour, food and cookery, self-help,
Americana, nature and environment, psychol-

ogy, religion, sociology. Plus children's fiction: adventure, confessional (young adult), fantasy, historical, horror, humour, mystery, picture books, science fiction, suspense, young adult; and children's non-fiction: biography, humour, illustrated, nature and the environment, leisure, science and sport. 3107 titles in 1995. Submissions via agents preferred.

DIVISIONS

Juvenile & Merchandise Group (Tel: 940 7682. Fax: 940 7640) IMPRINTS **Random House Juvenile** *Alice Alfonsi* Editor; **Knopf Juvenile** *Arthur Levine* Editor-in-Chief; **Crown Juvenile** *Tracy Gates* Senior Editor; **Bullseye Books** *Lisa Banim* Executive Editor. **Crown Publishing Group** (see entry). **Ballantine/Del Rey/Fawcett/Ivy Books** (see entry). **Alfred A. Knopf, Inc.** (see entry). **Pantheon Books/Shocken Books** (see entry). **Random House Adult Trade Books** (Tel: 572 2120. Fax: 572 4949) *Harold Evans* President/Publisher. **Times Books** (see entry); **Villard Books** Fiction and non-fiction; **Vintage Books** Trade paperbacks. Other divisions: **Random House Reference and Electronic Publishing; Fodor's Travel Publications, Inc.**

Royalties paid twice-yearly.

Rawson Associates
See **Simon & Schuster Trade Division**

Red Wagon Books
See **Harcourt Brace Children's Books Division**

Fleming H. Revell
See **Baker Book House**

Riverside Publishing Co.
See **Houghton Mifflin Co.**

ROC Books
See **Penguin USA**

The Rosen Publishing Group, Inc.
29 East 21st Street, New York NY 10010
☎001 212 777 3017   Fax 001 212 777 0277

President *Roger Rosen*
Editorial Director *Patra McSharry Sevastiades*
Managing Editor *Jane Kelly Kosek*
Editors *Gina Strazzabosco-Hayn, Jennifer Croft*

Publishes non-fiction books (supplementary to the curriculum, reference and self-help) for a young adult audience on careers and personal guidance. Reading levels are 7-9 and 4-6 (high-low books for reluctant readers). Areas of interest include health, careers, self-esteem,

drug abuse prevention, African studies, personal safety, other multicultural titles. About 100 titles a year.

IMPRINT **Pelion Press** Music titles. Write with outline and sample chapters.

Rutgers University Press
Bldg 4161, PO Box 5062, Livingston Campus, New Brunswick NJ 08903-5062
☎001 908 445 7762   Fax 001 908 445 7039

Editor-in-Chief *Leslie Mitchner*

FOUNDED 1936. *Publishes* scholarly books, regional and social sciences. Unsolicited mss, synopses and ideas for books welcome. No original fiction or poetry. About 70 titles a year.

Royalties paid annually.

Scarecrow Press, Inc.
4720 Boston Way, Lanham Maryland 20706
☎001 301 459 3366   Fax 001 301 459 2118

Editorial Director *Shirley Lambert*

FOUNDED 1950 as a short-run publisher of library reference books. Acquired by **University Press of America, Inc.** in 1995. *Publishes* reference, scholarly and monographs (all levels) for libraries. Reference books in all areas except sciences, specialising in the performing arts, music, cinema and library science. About 165 titles a year. Publisher for the Medical Library Association, Society of American Archivists, Children's Literature Association, Institute of Jazz Studies of Rutgers – the State University of New Jersey, the American Theological Library Association. Also publisher of *VOYA* (Voice of Youth Advocates); 6 issues a year. Unsolicited mss welcome but material will not be returned unless requested and accompanied by return postage. Unsolicited synopses/ideas for books welcome.

Royalties paid annually.

Schocken Books
See **Pantheon Books**

Scholastic, Inc.
555 Broadway, New York NY 10012
☎001 212 343 6100   Fax 001 212 343 6390

Editorial Director *Kevin Lewis*
Executive Editor (picture books) *Dianne Hess*
Executive Editor (middle grade, young adult, non-fiction) *Ann Reit*
Executive Editor (middle grade, young adult, fiction) *Regina Griffin*

FOUNDED 1920. *Publishes* picture books and fiction for middle grade (8-12-year-olds) and young adults: family stories, friendship, humour, fantasy, mysteries and school. Also non-fiction: biography and multicultural subjects. 500+ titles in 1995. Mss with outlines and three sample chapters welcome.

IMPRINT **The Blue Sky Press**.

Anne Schwartz Books
See **Simon & Schuster Children's Publishing Division**

Scott, Foresman/Addison Wesley
1900 E Lake Avenue, Glenview IL 60025
☎001 708 729 3000   Fax 001 708 486 3999

President, School Publishing Group *Pat Donaghy*

FOUNDED 1896. Merged with **Addison-Wesley Longman Co.** in 1996. *Publishes* elementary and secondary education books. 1300 titles in 1995.

Scribner
See **Simon & Schuster Trade Division**

Signet/Signet Classics
See **Penguin USA**

Silhouette Books
300 East 42nd Street, New York NY 10017
☎001 212 682 6080   Fax 001 212 682 4539

Editorial Director *Isabel Swift*

FOUNDED 1979 as an imprint of **Simon & Schuster** and was acquired by a wholly owned subsidiary of Toronto-based Harlequin Enterprises Ltd in 1984. *Publishes* category, contemporary romance fiction and historical romance fiction only. Over 360 titles a year across a number of imprints.

IMPRINTS **Silhouette Romance** *Melissa Senate*; **Silhouette Desire** *Lucia Macro*; **Silhouette Special Edition** *Tara Gavin*; **Silhouette Intimate Moments** *Leslie Wainger*; **Silhouette Yours Truly** *Leslie Wainger*; **Harlequin Historicals** *Tracy Farrell*. No unsolicited mss. Submit query letter in the first instance or write for detailed submission guidelines/tip sheets.

Royalties paid twice-yearly. *Overseas associates* worldwide.

Simon & Schuster Children's Publishing Division
1230 Avenue of the Americas, New York NY 10020
☎001 212 698 7200   Fax 001 212 605 3068

President and Publisher *Willa Perlman*

A division of the Simon & Schuster Consumer Group. *Publishes* pre-school to young adult, picture books, hardcover and paperback fiction, non-fiction, trade, library and mass-market titles.

IMPRINTS
Aladdin Books *Ellen Krieger* Picture books, paperback fiction and non-fiction reprints and originals, and limited series for ages pre-school to young adult; **Atheneum Books for Young Readers** *Jonathan Lanman* Picture books, hardcover fiction and non-fiction books across all genres for ages 3 to young adult. Two lines within this imprint are **Jean Karl Books** quality fantasy-fiction; and **Anne Schwartz Books** distinct picture books and high-quality fiction; **Little Simon** *Robin Corey* Mass-market novelty books (pop-ups, board books, colouring & activity) and merchandise (book and audiocassette) for ages birth through 8; **Margaret K. McElderry Books** *Margaret K. McElderry* Picture books, hardcover fiction and non-fiction trade books for children ages 3 to young adult; **Rabbit Ears** *Robin Corey* Children's audiocassettes of tales narrated by celebrities, featuring soundtracks by popular musicians and illustrations by acclaimed artists, packaged with companion books in hardcover, paperback, and mini-book formats. Entire programme derived from the videos produced by the entertainment company, Rabbit Ears; **Simon & Schuster Books for Young Readers** *Stephanie Owens Lurie* Picture books, hardcover fiction and non-fiction for children ages 3 to young adult.

For submissions to all imprints: send envelope (US size 10) for guidelines, attention: *Manuscript Submissions Guidelines*.

Simon & Schuster Trade Division
1230 Avenue of the Americas, New York NY 10020
☎001 212 698 7000   Fax 001 212 698 7007

President/Publisher *Carolyn K. Reidy*
Snr Vice President/Editor-in-Chief *Michael V. Korda*

A division of the Simon & Schuster Consumer Group. *Publishes* fiction and non-fiction.

DIVISIONS
The Free Press *Michael Jacobs* VP & Publisher, *Adam Bellow*; **Fireside/Touchstone** *Mark Gompertz* VP & Publisher, *Trish Todd*; **Scribner** *Susan Moldow* VP & Publisher, *Nan Graham*; **Simon and Schuster** *Michele Martin* VP & Associate Publisher, *Michael V. Korda, Alice Mayhew*.

IMPRINTS **H. & R. Block**; **Lisa Drew Books**; **Fireside**; **The Free Press**; **Hudson**

River Editions; Martin Kessler Books; Rawson Associates; Scribner, Scribner Paperback Fiction ; Atheneum Publishers; S&S Aguilar-Libros eñ Espanol; Simon & Schuster; Touchstone. No unsolicited mss.
Royalties paid twice-yearly.

Southern Illinois University Press

PO Box 3697, Carbondale IL 62902
☎001 618 453 2281   Fax 001 618 453 1221
Editorial Director *James Simmons*
FOUNDED 1953. *Publishes* scholarly non-fiction books and educational materials. 50 titles a year.
Royalties paid annually.

Spectra

See **Bantam Doubleday Dell Publishing Group, Inc.**

Spire Books

See **Baker Book House**

St Martin's Press, Inc.

175 Fifth Avenue, New York NY 10010
☎001 212 674 5151   Fax 001 212 420 9314
Chairman/Chief Executive *Thomas J. McCormack*
President/Publisher (Trade Division) *Sally Richardson*
FOUNDED 1952. A subsidiary of **Macmillan Publishers** (UK), St Martin's Press made its name and fortune by importing raw talent from the UK to the States and has continued to buy heavily in the UK. *Publishes* general fiction, especially mysteries and crime; and adult non-fiction: history, self-help, political science, travel, biography, scholarly, popular reference, college textbooks. 1500 titles in 1995.
IMPRINTS **Picador USA; Griffin Trade Paperbacks; St Martin's Paperbacks (Mass); Thomas Dunne Books; Wyatt Books; Tor; Forge; Bedford Books**; .

Stackpole Books

5067 Ritter Road, Mechanicsburg PA 17055
☎001 717 796 0411   Fax 001 717 796 0412
President *M. David Detweiler*
Vice President/Editorial Director *Judith Schnell*
FOUNDED 1933. *Publishes* outdoors, nature, gardening, crafts and hobbies, adventure, military reference, history, fishing, hunting, woodworking and carving. 70 titles in 1995.
Royalties paid twice-yearly.

Stanford University Press

Stanford CA 94305-2235
☎001 415 723 9598   Fax 001 415 725 3457
Director *Norris Pope*
Publishes non-fiction: scholarly works in all areas of the humanities, social sciences and natural sciences, plus a few general interest titles. About 100 titles a year. No unsolicited mss; query in writing first.

Sterling Publishing Co. Inc.

387 Park Avenue South, 5th Floor, New York NY 10016-8810
☎001 212 532 7160   Fax 001 212 213 2495
President/Editor *Burton Hobson*
Contact *Sheila Barry*
FOUNDED 1949. *Publishes* non-fiction: reference and information books, science, nature, arts and crafts, architecture, home improvement, history, photography, humour, careers, health, wine and food, social sciences, sports, music, psychology, occult, woodworking, pets, hobbies, business, military science, gardening, puzzles. Also juvenile and young adult fiction. 441 titles in 1994.

Stonehenge Press

See **Time-Life Inc.**

Sunburst Books

See **Farrar, Straus & Giroux, Inc**

Susquehanna University Press

See **Golden Cockerel Press** under **UK Publishers**

Syracuse University Press

1600 Jamesville Avenue, Syracuse NY 13244-5160
☎001 315 443 5541   Fax 001 315 443 5545
Director *Robert Mandel*
FOUNDED 1943. *Publishes* scholarly books in the following areas: contemporary Middle East studies, international affairs, Irish studies, Iroquois studies, women and religion, Jewish studies, peace studies. About 30 titles a year. TITLES *Intellectual Life in Arab East* M. Buheiry; *Middle Eastern Lives* M. Kramer. SERIES TITLES *Irish Studies; New York Classics; Syracuse Studies on Peace and Conflict Resolution; Utopianism and Communitarianism*. Also co-publishes with a number of organisations such as the American University of Beirut. No unsolicited mss. Send query letter with IRCs.
Royalties paid annually.

Truman M. Talley
See **Penguin USA**

Tambourine Books
See **William Morrow and Co., Inc.**

Temple University Press
Broad and Oxford Streets, Philadelphia
PA 19122
☎001 215 204 8787   Fax 001 215 204 4719

Editor-in-Chief *Michael Ames*

Publishes scholarly non-fiction: American history, Latin American studies, gay and lesbian studies, ethnic studies, psychology, Asian American studies, anthropology, law, cultural studies, sociology, women's studies, health care, philosophy, public policy, labour studies, urban and environmental studies, photography and Black studies. About 70 titles a year. Authors generally academics. Write in first instance.

University of Tennessee Press
293 Communications Building, Knoxville
TN 37996-0325
☎001 615 974 3321   Fax 001 615 974 3724

FOUNDED in 1940. *Publishes* non-fiction: anthropology, folklore, literature, American history, Southern studies, feminist literary criticism, women's studies, American religious history and African-American studies. Unsolicited material/outlines welcome in these areas. About 28-32 titles a year.

Royalties paid twice-yearly.

University of Texas Press
PO Box 7819, Austin TX 78713-7819
☎001 512 471 7233/Editorial: 471 4278
Fax 001 512 320 0668

Director *Joanna Hitchcock*
Assistant Director/Executive Editor
Theresa J. May

Publishes scholarly non-fiction: anthropology, archaeology, cultural geography, Latin/Mexican/native American studies, politics, biology and earth sciences, environmental, American/Texan urban studies, Texana, women's, film, cultural, media, literary studies, Middle Eastern studies, regional cookbooks, natural history, Latin American/Middle Eastern literature in translation, art and architecture, classics. Unsolicited material welcome in above subject areas only. About 85 titles a year and 14 journals. TITLES *Endangered and Threatened Animals of Texas* Linda Campbell; *Texan Jazz* Dave Oliphant; *The Story of Big Bend National Park* John Jameson.

Royalties paid annually.

Time-Life Inc.
777 Duke Street, Alexandria VA 22314
☎001 703 838 7000   Fax 001 703 838 7474

President/Chief Executive *George Artandi*

FOUNDED 1961. *Publishes* non-fiction: art, cooking, crafts, food, gardening, health, history, home maintenance, nature, photography, science. No unsolicited mss. 300 titles in 1995.

DIVISIONS/IMPRINTS **Time-Life Books**; **Time-Life Education**; **Time-Life Music**; **Time-Life International**; **Time-Life Video & Television**; **Stonehenge Press**.

Times Books
201 East 50th Street, New York
NY 10022
☎001 212 572 2120   Fax 001 212 940 7464

Editorial Director *Steve Wasserman*

FOUNDED 1959. A division of **Random House**. *Publishes* general non-fiction only. 98 titles in 1995. Unsolicited mss not considered. Letter essential.

Topaz
See **Penguin USA**

Tor
See **St Martin's Press, Inc.**

Touchstone
See **Simon & Schuster Trade Division**

Tyndale House Publishers, Inc.
351 Executive Drive, PO Box 80, Wheaton
IL 60189
☎001 630 668 8300   Fax 001 630 668 6885

Chairman *Kenneth N. Taylor*
President *Mark D. Taylor*

FOUNDED 1962 by Kenneth Taylor. Non-denominational religious publisher of around 100-150 titles a year for the evangelical Christian market. Books cover a wide range of categories from home and family to inspirational, theology, doctrine, Bibles and general reference. Also produces video material, calendars and audio books for the same market. No poetry. No unsolicited mss; they will be returned unread. Synopses and ideas considered. Send query letter summarising contents of books and length. Include a brief biography, detailed outline and sample chapters. IRCs essential for response or return of material. No audio cassettes, disks or video tapes in lieu of mss. Response time around 6-12 weeks. No phone calls. Send s.a.e. for free catalogue and full submission guidelines.

Royalties paid annually, sometimes twice-yearly.

Upstart Publishing Co., Inc.
See **Dearborn Financial Publishing, Inc.**

Van Nostrand Reinhold
115 Fifth Avenue, New York NY 10003
☎001 212 254 3232   Fax 001 212 475 2548
President/CEO *Marianne J. Russell*

FOUNDED 1848. A division of International Thomson Publishing, Inc. *Publishes* professional and reference information products in the following fields: culinary arts/hospitality, architecture/design, environmental sciences and business technology. Approximately 150 titles a year.

Vernon Publishing Inc.
See **Dearborn Financial Publishing, Inc.**

Viking/Viking Studio/Viking Children's Books
See **Penguin USA**

Villard Books
See **Random House, Inc.**

Vintage Books
See **Random House, Inc.**

Voyager Books
See **The Globe Pequot Press**

Voyager Paperbacks
See **Harcourt Brace Children's Books Division**

Walker & Co.
435 Hudson Street, New York NY 10014
☎001 212 727 8300   Fax 001 212 727 0984
Contact *Submissions Editor*

FOUNDED 1959. *Publishes* fiction: mystery and suspense, westerns and children's; and non-fiction. Unsolicited submissions are welcome as follows:
Mystery/suspense *Michael Seidman* 60-70,000 words. Send first three chapters and 3-5 page synopsis. **Westerns** *Jacqueline Johnson* 65,000 words, strong plot and character development. 50-75 pages plus short synopsis, or complete mss. **Trade non-fiction** Permissions and documentation must be available with mss. Submit prospectus first, with sample chapters and marketing analysis. **Books for Young Readers** *Emily Easton* Fiction and non-fiction. Query before sending non-fiction proposals. Especially interested in young science, photoessays, historical fiction for middle grades, biographies, current affairs, and YA non-fiction.

Frederick Warne
See **Penguin USA**

Warner Books Inc.
1271 Avenue of the Americas, New York NY 10020
☎001 212 522 7200   Fax 001 212 522 7991
Executive Editor *Joann Davis*

FOUNDED 1961. *Publishes* fiction and non-fiction, audio books, gift books, electronic and multimedia products. 330 titles in 1995.
IMPRINTS **Aspect** *Betsy Mitchell*; **Mysterious Press** *William Malloy*; **Questar**. Query or submit outline with sample chapters and letter.

Washington Square Press
See **Pocket Books**

Washington State University Press
Cooper Publications Building, Pullman WA 99164-5910
☎001 509 335 3518   Fax 001 509 335 8568
Director *Thomas H. Sanders*

FOUNDED 1928. Revitalised in 1984 to publish hardcover originals, trade paperbacks and reprints. *Publishes* mainly on the history, prehistory and culture of the Northwest United States (Washington, Idaho, Oregon, Montana, Alaska) and British Columbia, but works that focus on national topics or other regions may also be considered. 8-10 titles a year. TITLES *Iron in Her Soul: Elizabeth Gurley Flynn and the American Left*; *Grand Coulee: Harnessing a Dream*; *Confederate Raider in the North Pacific*; *Raise Hell and Sell Newspapers: Alden J. Blethen and 'The Seattle Times'*; *Fighting the Odds: The Life of Senator Frank Church*; *Fields of Toil: A Migrant Family's Journey*. Unsolicited mss welcome. No synopses or ideas.
Royalties paid annually.

Franklin Watts
(A Division of Grolier Publishing), Sherman Turnpike, Danbury CT 06813
☎001 203 797 3500   Fax 001 203 797 6986
Vice President/Publisher *John W. Selfridge*

FOUNDED 1942 and acquired by **Grolier** in 1975. *Publishes* non-fiction: curriculum-based material for ages 5-18 across a wide range of subjects, including history, social sciences, natural and physical sciences, health and medicine, biography. Over 100 titles a year. No unsolicited mss. Synopses and ideas considered.

Address samples to 'Submissions' and include IRCs if response required. Be prepared for a three-month turnaround.

Royalties paid twice-yearly.

Rob Weisbach Books
See **William Morrow & Co., Inc.**

Wesleyan University Press
See **University Press of New England**

J. Weston Walch, Publisher
321 Valley Street, PO Box 658, Portland ME 04104-0658
☎001 207 772 2846   Fax 001 207 772 3105
President *Suzanne Austin*
Editor-in-Chief *Joan Whitney*

FOUNDED 1927. *Publishes* supplementary educational materials for secondary schools across a wide range of subjects, including art, business, technology, languages, careers, health and fitness, home economics, literacy, mathematics, science, music, social studies, special needs, etc.

Always interested in ideas from secondary school teachers who develop materials in the classroom. About 70 titles a year. Unsolicited mss, synopses and ideas welcome.

Royalties paid twice-yearly.

Wyatt Books
See **St Martin's Press, Inc.**

Jane Yolen Books
See **Harcourt Brace Children's Books Division**

Zondervan Publishing House
5300 Patterson Avenue SE, Grand Rapids MI 49530
☎001 616 698 6900   Fax 001 616 698 3439
President/Chief Executive *Bruce E. Ryskamp*

FOUNDED 1931. Subsidiary of **HarperCollins Publishers, Inc.** *Publishes* Protestant religion, Bibles, mini-books, audio & video, computer software, calendars and speciality items.

US Agents

International Reply Coupons

For return postage, send International Reply Coupons (IRSs), available from the Post Office. Letters 60 pence; mss according to weight.

Adler & Robin Books, Inc.

3409 29th Street NW, Washington DC 20008

☎001 202 363 7410   Fax 001 202 686 1804

President/Agent *Bill Adler Jr*
Agent *Lisa Swayne*

FOUNDED 1988. *Handles* popular adult fiction and non-fiction, specialising in how-to. Represents illustrators. Occasionally represents children's books. Unsolicited mss, synopses and queries welcome. Send letter with outline or proposal and sample chapters if possible. Electronic submissions accepted. No reading fee or any other charges. CLIENTS Laura Bergheim, Michael Leccese, Peggy Robin, Jennifer Toth. *Commission* Home 15%; UK 20%.

The Ahearn Agency, Inc.

2021 Pine Street, New Orleans LA 70118

☎001 504 861 8395   Fax 001 504 866 6434

President *Pamela G. Ahearn*

FOUNDED 1992. *Handles* general and genre fiction, and non-fiction. Particularly interested in women's fiction, suspense fiction and historical romance. No children's books, poetry, autobiography, plays, screenplays or short fiction. Reading fee charged to unpublished authors. Send brief query letter with s.a.e. for reply in the first instance. CLIENTS include John Ames, Meagan McKinney, Marc Vargo. *Commission* Home 15%; Translation and UK 20%. *Overseas associates* in Europe and Latin America.

Marcia Amsterdam Agency

Suite 9A, 41 West 82nd Street, New York NY 10024

☎001 212 873 4945

Contact *Marcia Amsterdam*

FOUNDED 1969. *Specialises* in mainstream fiction, horror, suspense, humour, young adult, TV and film scripts. No poetry, books for the 8-10 age group or how-to. No unsolicited mss. First approach by letter only and enclose IRCs. No reading fee for outlines and synopses. CLIENTS include Kristopher Franklin, Ruby Jean Jensen, Robert Leininger, William H. Lovejoy, Patricia

Rowe, Joyce Sweeney. *Commission* Home 15%; Dramatic 10%; Foreign 20%.

Bart Andrews & Associates

7510 Sunset Boulevard 100, Los Angeles CA 90046

☎001 213 271 9916

Contact *Bart Andrews*

FOUNDED 1982. General non-fiction: show business, biography and autobiography, film books, trivia, TV and nostalgia. No scripts. No fiction, poetry, children's or science. No books of less than major commercial potential. *Specialises* in working with celebrities on autobiographies. No unsolicited mss. 'Send a brilliant letter (with IRCs for response) extolling your manuscript's virtues. Sell me!' CLIENTS J. Randy Taraborrelli, Wayne Newton, Bart Andrews. No reading fee. *Commission* Home & Translation 15%. *Overseas associates* **Abner Stein**, London.

Joseph Anthony Agency

15 Locust Court Road, 20 Mays Landing, New Jersey NJ 08330

☎001 609 625 7608

Contact *Joseph Anthony*

FOUNDED 1964. *Handles* all types of novel and scripts for TV: 2-hour mini-series, screenplays and ½-hour sitcoms. No poetry, short stories or pornography. *Specialises* in action, romance and detective novels. Unsolicited mss welcome. Return postage essential. Reading fee charged to new writers: novels $85; screenplays $100. CLIENTS include Ed Adair, Robert Long, Joseph McCullough, Sandi Wether. Signatory of the Writer's Guild of America. *Commission* Home 15%; Dramatic & Translation 20%.

The Artists Group

10100 Santa Monica Boulevard, Suite 2490, Los Angeles CA 90067

☎001 310 552 1100   Fax 001 213 277 9513

Contact *Robert Malcolm, Hal Stalmaster*

FOUNDED 1978. Screenplays and plays for film and TV. No unsolicited mss. Write with list of credits, if any. No reading fee. *Commission* 10%.

Author Aid Associates

340 East 52nd Street, New York NY 10022
☎001 212 758 4213/980 9179

Editorial Director *Arthur Ormont*

FOUNDED 1967. *Handles* fiction and non-fiction, both children's and adult, scripts for film, TV and theatre. No cookbooks, computing. No unsolicited mss. Advance query essential. Reading fee charged to new/unpublished authors. Short queries answered by return mail. CLIENTS include Eddie Ensley, Maurice Rowdon, John S. Snydet. *Commission* Home 15%; Dramatic & Translation 20%.

Julian Bach Literary Agency
See **IMG**

Malaga Baldi Literary Agency

PO Box 591, Radio City Station, New York NY 10101
☎001 212 222 1221

Contact *Malaga Baldi*

FOUNDED 1986. *Handles* quality fiction and non-fiction. No scripts. No westerns, men's adventure, science fiction/fantasy, romance, how-to, young adult or children's. Writers of fiction should send mss with covering letter, including IRCs for return of mss and stamped addressed postcard for notification of receipt. Allow ten weeks minimum for response. For non-fiction, approach in writing with a proposal, table of contents and two sample chapters. No reading fee. CLIENTS include Margaret Erhart, Heather Lewis, Felice Picano, David J. Skal. *Commission* 15%. *Overseas associates* **Abner Stein**, **Marsh & Sheil Ltd**, London; Japan Uni.

The Balkin Agency, Inc.

PO Box 222, Amherst MA 01004
☎001 413 548 9835   Fax 001 413 548 9836

Contact *Richard Balkin*

FOUNDED 1973. *Handles* adult non-fiction only. No reading fee for outlines and synopses. *Commission* Home 15%; Foreign 20%.

Maximilian Becker Agency
See **Aleta M. Daley**

Meredith Bernstein Literary Agency, Inc.

2112 Broadway, Suite 503A, New York NY 10023
☎001 212 799 1007   Fax 001 212 799 1145

Contact *Meredith Bernstein, Elizabeth Cavanaugh*

FOUNDED 1981. Fiction and non-fiction of all types. Send query letter first; unpublished authors welcome. IRCs essential for response. CLIENTS include Marilyn Campbell, Georgina Gentry, Patricia Ireland, David Jacobs, Nancy Pickard. *Commission* Home & Dramatic 15%; Translation 20%. *Overseas associates* **Abner Stein**, London; Lennart Sane, Holland; Scandinavia and Spanish language; Thomas Schluck, Germany; Bardon Chinese Media Agency; William Miller, Japan; Frederique Porretta, France; Agenzia Letteraria, Italy.

Reid Boates Literary Agency

PO Box 328, 274 Cooks Crossroad, Pittstown NJ 08867-0328
☎001 908 730 8523   Fax 001 908 730 8931

Contact *Reid Boates*

FOUNDED 1985. *Handles* general fiction and non-fiction. *Specialises* in journalism and media, serious self-help, biography and autobiography, true crime and adventure, popular science, current affairs, trade reference and quality fiction. No scripts. No science fiction, fantasy, romance, western, gothic, children's or young adult. Enquire by letter with IRCs in first instance. No reading fee. CLIENTS include Dr James Rippe, Stephen Singular, Jon Winokur and the estate of Ava Gardner. *Commission* Home & Dramatic 15%; Translation 20%. *Overseas associates* **David Grossman Literary Agency Ltd**, **The Marsh Agency** (Paul Marsh), London; Japan Uni.

Georges Borchardt, Inc.

136 East 57th Street, New York NY 10022
☎001 212 753 5785   Fax 001 212 838 6518

FOUNDED 1967. Works mostly with established/published authors. *Specialises* in fiction, biography, and general non-fiction of unusual interest. Unsolicited mss not read. *Commission* Home, UK, Dramatic 15%; Translation 20%. *UK associates* **Sheil Land Associates Ltd** (Richard Scott Simon), London.

Brandt & Brandt Literary Agents, Inc.

1501 Broadway, New York NY 10036
☎001 212 840 5760   Fax 001 212 840 5776

Contact *Carl D. Brandt, Gail Hochman, Charles Schlessiger*

FOUNDED 1914. *Handles* non-fiction and fiction. No poetry or children's books. No unsolicited mss. Approach by letter describing background and ambitions. No reading fee. *Commission* Home & Dramatic 15%; Foreign 20%. *UK associates* **A. M. Heath & Co. Ltd**.

Pema Browne Ltd

Pine Road, HCR Box 104B, Neversink
NY 12765
☎001 914 985 2936   Fax 001 914 985 7635

Contact *Pema Browne, Perry Browne*

FOUNDED 1966. *Handles* mass-market mainstream and hardcover fiction: romance, men's adventure, horror, humour, westerns, children's picture books and young adult; non-fiction: how-to, politics, religion and reference; also scripts for film. No unsolicited mss; send query letter with IRCs. Selected reading fee charged according to length of mss. Also handles illustrators' work. CLIENTS include Joanne Goodman, Eilene Hehl, Valerie Mangrum, Catherine Toothman. *Commission* Home & Translation 15%; Dramatic 10%; Overseas authors 20%.

Sheree Bykofsky Associates, Inc.

11 East 47th Street, New York
NY 10017
☎001 212 308 1253

Contact *Sheree Bykofsky*

FOUNDED 1985. *Handles* adult fiction and non-fiction. No scripts. No children's, young adult, horror, science fiction, romance, westerns, occult or supernatural. *Specialises* in popular reference, self-help, psychology, biography and highly commercial or highly literary fiction. No unsolicited mss. Send query letter first with brief synopsis or outline and writing sample (1-3 pp) for fiction. IRCs essential for reply or return of material. No phone calls. No reading fee. CLIENTS include Ken & Lois Anderson, Richard Coulson & Benjamin Shield, Glenn Ellenbogen, Merrill Furman, Don Gabor, Ed Morrow. *Commission* Home 15%; UK (including sub-agent's fee) 25%. Member A.A.R.

Maria Carvainis Agency, Inc.

235 West End Avenue, New York NY 10023
☎001 212 580 1559   Fax 001 212 877 3486

Contact *Maria Carvainis*

FOUNDED 1977. *Handles* fiction: literary and mainstream, contemporary women's, mystery, suspense, fantasy, historical, children's and young adult novels; non-fiction: business, finance, women's issues, political and film biography, medicine, psychology and popular science. No film scripts unless from writers with established credits. No science fiction. No unsolicited mss; they will be returned unread. Queries only, with IRCs for response. No reading fee. *Commission* Home & Dramatic 15%; Translation 20%.

Martha Casselman, Literary Agent

PO Box 342, Calistoga CA 94515-0342
☎001 707 942 4341

Contact *Martha Casselman, Judith Armenta*

FOUNDED 1979. *Handles* all types of non-fiction. No fiction at present. Main interests: food/cookery, biography, current affairs, popular sociology. No scripts, textbooks, poetry, coming-of-age fiction or science fiction. Especially interested in cookery with an appeal to the American market for possible co-publication in UK. Send queries and brief summary, with return postage. No mss. If you do not wish return of material, please state so. Also include, where applicable, any material on previous publications, reviews, brief biography. No proposals via fax. No reading fee. *Commission* Home 15%.

The Catalog Literary Agency

PO Box 2964, Vancouver WA 98668
☎001 206 694 8531

Contact *Douglas Storey*

FOUNDED 1986. *Handles* popular, professional and textbook material in all subjects, especially business, health, money, science, technology, computers, electronics and women's interests; also how-to, self-help, mainstream fiction and children's non-fiction. No genre fiction. No scripts, articles, screenplays, plays, poetry or short stories. No reading fee. No unsolicited mss. Query with an outline and sample chapters and include IRCs. CLIENTS include Malcolm S. Foster, Isaac O. Olaleye, Deborah Wallace. *Commission* 15%.

The Linda Chester Literary Agency

666 Fifth Avenue, 37th Floor, New York
NY 10103
☎001 219 439 0881   Fax 001 212 439 9858

Contact *Billie Fitzpatrick*

FOUNDED 1978. *Handles* literary and commercial fiction and non-fiction in all subjects. No scripts, children's or textbooks. No unsolicited mss; send query letter with IRCs for reply. No reading fee for solicited material. *Commission* Home & Dramatic 15%; Translation 25%.

Connie Clausen Associates

250 East 87th Street, Suite 16H, New York
NY 10128
☎001 212 427 6135   Fax 001 212 996 7111

Contact *Connie Clausen, Lisa Kaiser*

Handles non-fiction work such as self-help, psychology, spirituality, health, fashion and beauty, women's issues, entertainment, humour, cookbooks etc. Books include Quentin Crisp's *How to Go to the Movies*, the Pulitzer Prize-winning Jackson Pollack biography, Robert Haas' *Eat to Win*, Sonya Hamlin's *How to Talk So People Listen*. Send query letter and/or proposal, outline and sample chapter. Include IRCs. Do not send complete mss. *Commission* 15%. *UK associates* **David Grossman Literary Agency Ltd**.

Hy Cohen Literary Agency Ltd
111 West 57th Street, New York NY 10019
☎001 212 757 5237   Fax 001 212 397 1580
President *Hy Cohen*
FOUNDED 1975. Fiction and non-fiction. No scripts. Unsolicited mss welcome, but synopsis with sample 100 pp preferred. IRCs essential. No reading fee. *Commission* Home & Dramatic 10%; Foreign 20%. *Overseas associates* **Abner Stein**, London.

Ruth Cohen, Inc.
Box 7626, Menlo Park CA 94025
☎001 415 854 2054
President *Ruth Cohen*
FOUNDED 1982. Works mostly with established/published authors but will consider new writers. *Specialises* in high-quality children's, young adult and women's fiction, plus genre fiction: mystery and historical romance. No poetry, short stories or film scripts. No unsolicited mss. Send opening 10 pp with synopsis. Include enough IRCs for return postage or materials will not be returned. No reading fee. *Commission* Home & Dramatic 15%; Foreign 20%.

Frances Collin Literary Agent
PO Box 33, Wayne PA 19087-0033
☎001 610 254 0555   Fax 001 610 254 5029
Contact *Frances Collin*
FOUNDED 1948. Successor to Marie Rodell. *Handles* general fiction and non-fiction. No scripts. No unsolicited mss. Send query letter only, with IRCs for reply. No reading fee. Rarely accepts non-professional writers or writers not represented in the UK. *Overseas associates* worldwide.

Don Congdon Associates, Inc.
156 Fifth Avenue, Suite 625, New York NY 10010-7002
☎001 212 645 1229   Fax 001 212 727 2688
Contact *Don Congdon, Michael Congdon, Susan Ramer*
FOUNDED 1983. *Handles* fiction and non-fiction. No academic, technical, romantic fiction, or scripts. No unsolicited mss. Approach by letter in the first instance. No reading fee. *Commission* Home 10%; UK & Translation 19%. *Overseas associates* **The Marsh Agency** (Europe), **Abner Stein** (UK), Michelle Lapautre (France), Tuttle Mori Agency (Japan).

The Connor Literary Agency
7333 Gallagher Drive, Edina MN 55435
☎001 612 835 7251
Also at: 640 West 153rd Street, D2, New York, NY 10031
☎001 212 491 5233
Contact *Marlene Connor, John Lynch*
FOUNDED 1985. *Handles* general non-fiction, contemporary women's fiction, popular fiction, Black fiction and non-fiction, how-to, mysteries and crafts. Particularly interested in illustrated books. No unsolicited mss; send query letter in the first instance. Previously published authors preferred. CLIENTS include Simplicity Pattern Company, *Essence Magazine*, Bonnie Allen, Ron Elmore, Nadezda Obradovic. *Commission* Home 15%; UK & Translation 25%. *Overseas associates* in England, Spain, Japan, France and Germany.

The Content Company
See **Richard Curtis Associates, Inc.**

Richard Curtis Associates, Inc./ The Content Company
171 East 74th Street, Second Floor, New York NY 10021
☎001 212 772 7363   Fax 001 212 772 7393
Contact *Richard Curtis*
FOUNDED 1969. *Handles* genre and mainstream fiction, plus commercial non-fiction. Scripts rarely. *Specialises* in electronic rights and multimedia.

Curtis Brown Ltd
10 Astor Place, New York NY 10003
☎001 212 473 5400
Book Rights *Laura Blake, Emilie Jacobson, Ginger Knowlton, Marilyn E. Marlow, Maureen Walters*
Film, TV, Audio Rights *Timothy Knowlton, Jess Taylor*
Translation *Dave Barbor*
FOUNDED 1914. *Handles* general fiction and non-fiction. Also scripts for film, TV, theatre and radio. No unsolicited mss; queries only, with IRCs for reply. No reading fee. *Overseas*

associates representatives in all major foreign countries.

Aleta M. Daley/ Maximilian Becker Agency

444 East 82nd Street, New York NY 10028
☎001 212 744 1453

Contact *Aleta M. Daley*

FOUNDED 1950. *Handles* non-fiction and fiction; also scripts for film and TV. No unsolicited mss. Send query letter in the first instance with sample chapters or a proposal. No reading fee, but handling fee is charged to cover postage, telephone, etc. *Commission* Home 15%; UK 20%.

Joan Daves Agency

21 West 26th Street, New York
NY 10010-1003
☎001 212 685 2663   Fax 001 212 685 1781

Director *Jennifer Lyons*
Assistant *Edward Lee*

FOUNDED 1952. Trade fiction and non-fiction. No romance or textbooks. No scripts. Send query letter in the first instance. 'A detailed synopsis seems valuable only for non-fiction work. Material submitted should specify the author's background, publishing credits and similar pertinent information.' No reading fee. CLIENTS include Frederick Franck, Frank Browning, Suzy McKee Charnas, Mike Maples, Elizabeth Holtzman, Melvin Jules Bukret, Jeff Weinstein and the estates of Isaac Babel, Heinrich Böll and Martin Luther King Jr. *Commission* Home 15%; Dramatic 10-25%; Foreign 20%.

Elaine Davie Literary Agency

620 Park Avenue, Rochester NY 14607
☎001 716 442 0830

President *Elaine Davie*

FOUNDED 1986. *Handles* all types of adult fiction and non-fiction, specialising in books by and for women. Particularly interested in commercial genre fiction. No scripts. No short stories, anthologies, poetry or children's. Submit synopsis and sample chapters or complete mss together with IRCs. No reading fee. CLIENTS include Marcia Evanick, Jane Kidder, Merline Lovelace, Maggie Shayne, Christina Skye. *Commission* Home 15%; Dramatic & Translation 20%.

The Deering Literary Agency

106 N. Main Street, Nicholasville GA 40356
☎001 606 887 5862   Fax 001 606 885 0254

Director *Dorothy Deering*

Manager *Charles F. Deering*

FOUNDED 1989. *Handles* non-fiction (all subjects) and fiction: historical, mystery, romance, literary, religious, horror, science fiction and fantasy. Unsolicited mss welcome. *Specialises* in new authors. Reading fee of $125 (under 100,000 words); $150 (over 100,000). CLIENTS include Dr Paul Damien, Christine Drake, Dr Norma Goodrich, Daniel Marder, Theodore J. Nottingham. *Commission* Home 12%; Dramatic 18%; Foreign & Translation 15%.

Anita Diamant Literary Agency

Suite 1105, 310 Madison Avenue, New York NY 10017
☎001 212 687 1122

Contact *Anita Diamant, Robin Rue*

FOUNDED 1917. *Handles* fiction and non-fiction. No academic, children's, science fiction and fantasy, poetry, articles, short stories, screenplays or teleplays. Works in association with Hollywood film agent. No unsolicited mss. Write with description of work, short synopsis and details of publishing background. No reading fee. CLIENTS include V. C. Andrews, Elliott Baker, Carol Brennan, James Elward, Oscar Fraley, Pat Hagan, Linda Howard, Richard Lederer, Mark McGarrity, Andrew Neiderman, Penny Thornton. *Commission* Home & Dramatic 15%; Translation 20%. *Overseas associates* **A. M. Heath & Co. Ltd**, London.

Sandra Dijkstra Literary Agency

1155 Camino del Mar, Suite 515, Del Mar CA 92014
☎001 619 755 3115

Contact *Debra Ginsberg*

FOUNDED 1981. *Handles* quality and commercial non-fiction and fiction, including some genre fiction. No scripts. No westerns, contemporary romance or poetry. Willing to look at children's projects. *Specialises* in quality fiction, mystery/ thrillers, psychology, self-help, science, health, business, memoirs, biography. Dedicated to promoting new and original voices and ideas. For fiction: send brief synopsis (1 page) and first 50 pages; for non-fiction: send proposal with overview, chapter outline, author biog. and two sample chapters. All submissions should be accompanied by IRCs. No reading fee. CLIENTS include Amy Tan, Anchee Min, Maxine Hong Kingston, Susan Faludi, Abigail Padgett, Max De Pree, Deb Waterhouse. *Commission* Home 15%; Translation 20%. *Overseas associates* **Abner Stein**, London; Ursula Bender, Agence Hoffman,

Germany; Monica Heyum, Scandinavia; Luigi Bernabo, Italy; M. Casanovas, Spain; Caroline Van Gelderen, Netherlands; M. Kling (La Nouvelle Agence), France; William Miller, The English Agency, Japan.

Robert Ducas Literary Agency
See **Caroline Davidson & Robert Ducas Literary Agency** under **UK Agents**

Dykeman Associates, Inc.
4115 Rawlins, Dallas TX 75219-3661
☎001 214 528 2991   Fax 001 214 528 0241
Contact *Alice Dykeman*

FOUNDED 1974. *Handles* non-fiction, namely celebrity profiles and biographies, fiction and movie scripts. No unsolicited mss; send outline or synopsis. Reading fee of $250 charged for manuscripts (not movie scripts). *Commission* 15%.

Jane Dystel Literary Management
One Union Square West, Suite 904, New York NY 10003
☎001 212 627 9100   Fax 001 212 627 9313
Contact *Jane Dystel, Miriam Goderich*

FOUNDED 1975. *Handles* non-fiction and fiction. *Specialises* in politics, history, biography, cookbooks, current affairs, celebrities, commercial and literary fiction. No reading fee. CLIENTS include Lorene Cary, Thomas French, Dan Gearino, Lynne Rossetto Kasper, Gus Lee, Alice Medrich, Barack Obama, Elaine St James, Michael Tucker.

Educational Design Services, Inc.
PO Box 253, Wantagh NY 11793
☎001 718 539 4107/516 221 0995
President *Bertram Linder*
Vice President *Edwin Selzer*

FOUNDED 1979. *Specialises* in educational material and textbooks for sale to school markets. IRCs must accompany submissions. *Commission* Home 15%; Foreign 25%.

Elek International Rights Agents
457 Broome Street, New York NY 10013
☎001 212 431 9368   Fax 001 212 966 5768
Contact *Debbie Miketta*

FOUNDED 1979. *Handles* adult non-fiction and children's picture books. No scripts, novels, psychology, New Age, poetry, short stories or autobiography. No unsolicited mss; send letter of enquiry with IRCs for reply; include résumé, credentials, brief synopsis. No reading fee.

CLIENTS Tedd Arnold, Dr Robert Ballard, Patrick Brogan, Robert Bateman, Laura Cornell, Chris Dodd, Sally Placksin. *Commission* Home 15%; Dramatic & Foreign 20%. Through wholly-owned subsidiary The Content Company Inc., licenses and manages clients' intellectual property for development into electronic formats – CD-ROM/CD-I/CD-Plus, etc.

Ann Elmo Agency, Inc.
60 East 42nd Street, New York NY 10165
☎001 212 661 2880/1   Fax 001 212 661 2883
Contact *Lettie Lee, Mari Cronin, Andree Abecassis*

FOUNDED in the 1940s. *Handles* literary and romantic fiction, mysteries and mainstream; also non-fiction in all subjects, including biography and self-help. Some children's (8–12-year-olds) and young adult. Query letter with outline of project in the first instance. No reading fee. *Commission* Home 15–20%. *Overseas associates* John Johnson Ltd, London.

Florence Feiler Literary Agency
1524 Sunset Plaza Drive, Los Angeles CA 90069
☎001 310 652 6920   Fax 001 310 659 0945
Contact *Florence Feiler*

FOUNDED 1967. *Specialises* in fiction, non-fiction, how-to textbooks, translations, TV and film scripts/tapes. No short stories or pornography. No unsolicited mss. First approach by letter. No reading fee. CLIENTS include literary estates of Isak Dinesen (*Out of Africa* and *Babette's Feast*) and Bess Streeter Aldrich. Submission procedure: letter of enquiry, samples of previously published work, if recommended by an editor or another client, or if you have heard Ms Feiler lecture. No multiple submissions accepted. Will consider negotiating contracts and sales but, 'First I must read the material. Nothing leaves this office unless I have read it first and approve mailing under my name. I suggest the craft be taken seriously and severe editing be accomplished before submission. I do not wish to hear from writers who think they have good ideas and are Sunday writers'.

Commission 10% text domestic; 20% foreign. No other fees unless another agent is used, then 15%.

Frieda Fishbein Ltd
2556 Hubbard Street, Brooklyn NY 11235
☎001 212 247 4398
President *Janice Fishbein*
Associates *Heidi Carlson, Douglas Michael*

FOUNDED 1925. Eager to work with new/ unpublished writers. *Specialises* in historical romance, historical adventure, male adventure, mysteries, thrillers, family sagas, 'non-reporting' and how-to. Also non-fiction, plays and screenplays. No poetry, magazine articles, short stories or young children's. First approach with query letter. No reading fee for outlines at our request or for published authors working in the same genre. CLIENTS include Gary Bohlke, Alan Brandt, Herbert Fisher, David Gilman, Jeanne Mackin, Robert Simpson, Alicen White. *Commission* Home & Dramatic 10%; Foreign 20%.

Flannery, White & Stone
1675 Larimer Street, Suite 410, Denver CO 80202
☎001 303 571 4001   Fax 001 303 534 0577
Contact *Robin Ann Barrett, Connie Solowiej*
FOUNDED 1987. *Handles* literary and mainstream fiction, children's, general non-fiction and business. No poetry, theatre or radio. No pornography. Call or write with query in first instance. No unsolicited mss. CLIENTS include Reginald McKnight, Maxine Schur, David Seals, Don Wulffson. *Commission* Home 15%; Dramatic & Translation 20%.

ForthWrite Literary Agency
3579 E. Foothill Boulevard, Suite 327, Pasadena CA 91107
☎001 818 798 0793   Fax 001 818 798 5653
Contact *Wendy L. Zhorne*
FOUNDED 1988. *Specialises* in non-fiction, especially business (marketing, management and sales), alternative health, popular psychology, history (English and Scottish), self-help, home and health, crafts, computer, how-to, illustrated, animal care. Handles electronic, foreign (translation and distribution) and resale rights for previously published books. Send query letter with IRCs. *Commission* Home & Dramatic 15%; Translation 20%.

Robert A. Freedman Dramatic Agency, Inc.
Suite 2310, 1501 Broadway, New York NY 10036
☎001 212 840 5760
President *Robert A. Freedman*
Vice President *Selma Luttinger*
FOUNDED 1928 as Brandt & Brandt Dramatic Department, Inc.. Took its present name in 1984. Works mostly with established authors. *Specialises* in plays, film and TV scripts. Unsolicited mss not read. *Commission* Dramatic 10%.

Jay Garon-Brooke Associates, Inc.
101 West 55th Street, Suite 5K, New York NY 10019
☎001 212 581 8300   Fax 001 212 581 8397
Executive Agents *Dick Duane, Robert Thixton*
Vice President *Jean Free*
Agent *Nancy Coffey*
FOUNDED 1951. Fiction and non-fiction: history and historical romance, suspense/thrillers, political intrigue, horror/occult, self-help. No category romance, westerns or mysteries. No unsolicited mss. First approach by query letter. No reading fee. CLIENTS include Virginia Coffman, Elizabeth Gage, Curtis Gathje, John Grisham, Eric Harry, Patricia Matthews. *Commission* Home 15%; Dramatic 10-15%; Foreign 30%. *Overseas associates* **Abner Stein**, London; Translation: Bernard Kurman.

Max Gartenberg, Literary Agent
521 Fifth Avenue, Suite 1700, New York NY 10175
☎001 212 860 8451   Fax 001 201 535 5033
Contact *Max Gartenberg*
FOUNDED 1954. Works mostly with established/published authors. *Specialises* in non-fiction and trade fiction. Query first. CLIENTS include William Ashworth, Linda Davis, Ralph Hickok, Charles Little, Howard Owen, David Roberts. *Commission* Home & Dramatic 10%; 15% on initial sale, 10% thereafter; Foreign 15-20%.

Gelfman Schneider Literary Agents, Inc.
250 West 57th Street, Suite 2515, New York NY 10107
☎001 212 245 1993   Fax 001 212 245 8678
Contact *Deborah Schneider, Jane Gelfman*
FOUNDED 1919 (London), 1980 (New York). Formerly John Farquharson Ltd. Works mostly with established/published authors. *Specialises* in general trade fiction and non-fiction. No poetry, short stories or screenplays. No reading fee for outlines. Submissions must be accompanied by IRCs. *Commission* Home 15%; Dramatic 10%; Foreign 20%. *Overseas associates* **Curtis Brown Group Ltd**, London.

Lucianne Goldberg Literary Agents, Inc.

255 West 84th Street, New York NY 10024
☎001 212 799 1260

Editorial Director *Kathrine Butler*

FOUNDED 1974. *Handles* fiction and non-fiction. No unsolicited mss. Send query letter describing work in the first instance. No reading fee. *Commission* Home 10%; UK 20%. *Overseas associate* Peter Knight, London.

Sanford J. Greenburger Associates

15th Floor, 55 Fifth Avenue, New York NY 10003
☎001 212 206 5600   Fax 001 212 463 8718

Contact *Heide Lange, Faith Hamlin, Beth Vesel, Theresa Park, Elyse Cheney*

Handles fiction and non-fiction. No unsolicited mss. First approach with query letter, sample chapter and synopsis. No reading fee.

The Charlotte Gusay Literary Agency

10532 Blythe Avenue, Los Angeles CA 90064
☎001 310 559 0831   Fax 001 310 559 2639

Contact *Charlotte Gusay*

FOUNDED 1988. *Handles* fiction, both literary and commercial, plus non-fiction: children's and adult humour, parenting, gardening, women's and men's issues, feminism, psychology, memoirs, biography, travel. No science fiction, horror, short pieces or collections of stories. No unsolicited mss; send query letter first, then if your material is requested, send succinct outline and first three sample chapters for fiction, or proposal for non-fiction. No response without IRCs. No reading fee. *Commission* Home 15%; Dramatic 10%; Translation & Foreign 25%.

Joy Harris Literary Agency
See **Robert Lantz**

John Hawkins & Associates, Inc.

71 West 23rd Street, Suite 1600, New York NY 10010
☎001 212 807 7040   Fax 001 212 807 9555

Contact *John Hawkins, William Reiss*

FOUNDED 1893. *Handles* film and TV rights and software. No unsolicited mss; send queries with 1–3 page outline and 1 page c.v.. IRCs necessary for response. No reading fee. *Commission* Apply for rates. *UK associates* **Murray Pollinger** London.

Heacock Literary Agency, Inc.

1523 Sixth Street, Suite 14, Santa Monica CA 90401
☎001 310 393 6227/451 8523
Fax 001 310 451 8524

President *Rosalie G. Heacock*

FOUNDED 1978. Works with a small number of new/unpublished authors. *Specialises* in non-fiction on a wide variety of subjects: new ideas, new ways of solving problems, futurism, art criticism and techniques, health, nutrition, beauty, women's studies, popular psychology, crafts, business expertise, alternative health concepts, contemporary celebrity biographies. Also novels by established authors and film/TV scripts by full-time professionals and members of the Writer's Guild. No unsolicited mss. Queries with IRCs only. No reading fee. CLIENTS include Dr Joseph Bark, Larry D. Brimner, Dr Allan Chinen, Dr Arnold Fox & Barry Fox, John Goldhammer, Paul Horn, Don & Audrey Wood. *Commission* Home 15% on first $50,000 each year, 10% thereafter; Foreign 15% if sold direct, 25% if agent used.

The Jeff Herman Agency, Inc.

500 Greenwich Street, Suite 501C, New York NY 10013
☎001 212 941 0540   Fax 001 212 941 0614

Contact *Jeffrey H. Herman*

Handles non-fiction, textbooks and reference and commercial fiction. No scripts. No unsolicited mss. Query letter with IRCs in the first instance. No reading fee. Jeff Herman publishes a useful reference guide to the book trade called *The Insider's Guide to Book Editors, Publishers & Literary Agents* (Prima). *Commission* Home 15%; Translation 10%.

Susan Herner Rights Agency, Inc.

PO Box 303, Scarsdale NY 10583
☎001 914 725 8967   Fax 001 914 725 8969

Contact *Susan N. Herner, Sue P. Yuen*

FOUNDED 1987. Adult fiction and non-fiction in all areas. No children's books. *Handles* film and TV rights and software. Send query letter with outline and sample chapters. No reading fee. *Commission* Home 15%; Dramatic & Translation 20%. *Overseas associates* **David Grossman Literary Agency Ltd**, London.

Frederick Hill Associates

1842 Union Street, San Francisco CA 94123
☎001 415 921 2910   Fax 001 415 921 2802

Contact *Fred Hill, Bonnie Nadell*

FOUNDED 1979. General fiction and non-fiction. No scripts. Send query letter detailing past publishing history if any. IRCs required. CLIENTS include Katherine Neville, Richard North Patterson, Randy Shilts. *Commission* Home & Dramatic 15%; Foreign 20%. *Overseas associates* **Mary Clemmey Literary Agency**, London.

Hull House Literary Agency
240 East 82nd Street, New York NY 10028
☎001 212 988 0725   Fax 001 212 794 8758
President *David Stewart Hull*
Associate *Lydia Mortimer*

FOUNDED 1987. *Handles* commercial fiction, mystery, biography, military history and true crime. No scripts, poetry, short stories, romance, science fiction and fantasy, children's or young adult. No unsolicited mss; send single-page letter describing project briefly, together with short biographical note and list of previous publications if any. IRCs essential. No reading fee. *Commission* Home 15%; Translation 20%.

IMG-Julian Bach Literary Agency
22 East 71st Street, New York NY 10021
☎001 212 772 8900   Fax 001 212 772 2617
Contact *Julian Bach, Carolyn Krupp*

FOUNDED 1959. *Handles* non-fiction and fiction. No science fiction, fantasy, poetry or photography. No scripts. Query first. Submissions should include brief synopsis (typed), sample chapters (50 pp maximum), publishing history, etc. Send IRCs for return. CLIENTS include Jerry Baker, Pat Conroy, Jan Morris, Liz Nickles, Hedrick Smith, Adam Ulam, Robin Winks. *Commission* Home & Dramatic 15%; Foreign 25%. *Overseas associates* worldwide.

Kidde, Hoyt & Picard Literary Agency
333 East 51st Street, New York NY 10022
☎001 212 755 9461/9465
Fax 001 212 593 4688
Chief Associate *Katharine Kidde*
Associate *Laura Langlie*

FOUNDED 1981. *Specialises* in mainstream and literary fiction, romantic fiction (historical and contemporary), and quality non-fiction in humanities and social sciences (biography, history, current affairs, the arts). No reading fee. Query first, include s.a.e.. CLIENTS include Michael Cadnum, Bethany Campbell, Jim Oliver, Patricia Robinson. *Commission* 15%.

Daniel P. King
5125 North Cumberland Boulevard, Whitefish Bay WI 53217
☎001 414 964 2903   Fax 001 414 964 6860
President *Daniel P. King*

FOUNDED 1974. *Specialises* in mystery and non-fiction books on crime and espionage. Also handles mainstream fiction including crime/mystery and science fiction. Scripts handled by representative office in Beverly Hills, California. No unsolicited mss. Send synopsis or sample chapter first or (and preferably) a concise letter (1-2 pages) describing the book. No reading fee unless an author wants a critique on his material. CLIENTS include John Bonnet, Ella Griffiths, Cyril Joyce. *Commission* Home & Dramatic 10%; Foreign 20%.

Kirchoff/Wohlberg, Inc.
866 United Nations Plaza, 525, New York NY 10017
☎001 212 644 2020   Fax 001 212 223 4387
Authors' Representative *Elizabeth Pulitzer-Voges*

FOUNDED 1930. *Handles* books for children and young adults, specialising in children's picture books. No adult material. No scripts for TV, radio, film or theatre. Send letter of enquiry with synopsis or outline and IRCs for reply or return. No reading fee. CLIENTS Lizi Boyd, Lois Ehlert, Suçie Stevenson, Gloria Whelan.

Paul Kohner, Inc.
9300 Wilshire Boulevard, Suite 555, Beverly Hills CA 90212
☎001 310 550 1060   Fax 001 310 276 1083
Contact *Gary Salt*

FOUNDED 1938. *Handles* a broad range of books for subsidiary rights sales to film and TV. Few direct placements with publishers as film and TV scripts are the major part of the business. No short stories, poetry, science fiction or gothic. Unsolicited material will be returned unread, if accompanied by s.a.e.. Approach via a third-party reference or send query letter with professional résumé. No reading fee. *Commission* Home & Dramatic 10%; Book Subsidiary Rights 15%.

Barbara S. Kouts, Literary Agent
PO Box 560, Bellport NY 11713
☎001 516 286 1278   Fax 001 516 286 1538
Contact *Barbara S. Kouts*

FOUNDED 1980. *Handles* fiction, non-fiction and children's. No romance, science fiction or scripts. No unsolicited mss. Query letter in the first instance. No reading fee. CLIENTS include Hal Gieseking, Nancy Mairs, Robert San Souci. *Commission* Home 10%; Foreign 20%. *Overseas associates* **Murray Pollinger**, London.

Lucy Kroll Agency

390 West End Avenue, New York NY 10024
☎001 212 877 0627   Fax 001 212 769 2832

Contact *Lucy Kroll, Barbara Hogenson*

FOUNDED in 1949. *Handles* non-fiction: science, travel, art, humanities and psychiatry. Handles film and TV rights. No unsolicited mss. Recommendations from clients are preferred but unsolicited queries welcome and should be accompanied by IRCs. No reading fee. *Commission* Home & Dramatic 10%; Translation 20%.

Peter Lampack Agency, Inc.

551 Fifth Avenue, Suite 1613, New York NY 10176
☎001 212 687 9106   Fax 001 212 687 9109

Contact *Peter Lampack, Sandra Blanton, Deborah T. Brown*

FOUNDED in 1977. *Handles* commercial fiction: male action and adventure, contemporary relationships, historical, mysteries and suspense, literary fiction; also non-fiction from recognised experts in a given field, plus biographies, autobiographies. Also handles theatrical, motion picture, and TV rights from book properties. No original scripts or screenplays, series or episodic material or category novels, particularly science fiction, horror and romance. Best approach by letter in first instance. Include s.a.e.. 'We will respond within three weeks and invite the submission of manuscripts which we would like to examine.' No reading fee. CLIENTS include J. M. Coetzee, Clive Cussler, Martha Grimes, Judith Kelman, Johanna Kingsley, Jessica March, Doris Mortman, Fred Mustard Stewart, David Osborn, Gerry Spence, Derek Van Arman. *Commission* Home & Dramatic 15%; Translation & UK 20%.

Robert Lantz/Joy Harris Literary Agency, Inc.

156 Fifth Avenue, Suite 617, New York NY 10010-617
☎001 212 924 6269   Fax 001 212 924 6609

Contact *Joy Harris*

Handles adult non-fiction and fiction. No unsolicited mss. Query letter in the first instance. No reading fee. *Commission* Home & Dramatic 15%; Foreign 20%. *Overseas associates* Michael Meller,

Germany; **Abner Stein**, London; Tuttle Mori, Japan/China; Eliane Benisti, France.

The Lazear Agency, Inc.

430 First Avenue North, Suite 416, Minneapolis MN 55401
☎001 612 332 8640   Fax 001 612 332 4648

Contact *Jonathon Lazear, Wendy Lazear, Eric Vrooman, Susanne Moncur, Dennis Cass, Sarah Nelson Hunter*

FOUNDED 1984. *Handles* fiction: mysteries, suspense, young adult and literary; also true crime, addiction recovery, biography, travel, business, and scripts for film and TV, CD-ROM and CD-I, broad band interactive television. Children's books from previously published writers. No poetry or stage plays. Approach by letter, with description of mss, short autobiography and IRCs. No reading fee. CLIENTS include Noah Adams, Andrei Codrescu, Al Franken, Merrill Lynch, Harvey Mackay, Gary Paulsen, The Pillsbury Co., Will Weaver, Bailey White. *Commission* Home & Dramatic 15%; Translation 20%.

L. Harry Lee Literary Agency

PO Box 203, Rocky Point NY 11778
☎001 516 744 1188

Contacts *Charles Rothery* (science fiction), *Sue Hollister Barr* (adventure/humour/westerns), *Patti Roenbeck* (romance/mainstream/ mystery/suspense), *Diane Clerke* (historical/fantasy), *Cami Callirgos* (horror/erotica), *Colin James* (mainstream/military/war), *Katie Polk* (mystery/detective), *Mary Lee Gaylor* (mainstream/contemporary), *James Kingston* (motion pictures), *Stacy Parker/Anastassia Evereaux* (TV, episodic), *Vitor Brenna* (plays)

FOUNDED 1979. *Handles* adventure, westerns, horror, romance, mainstream/contemporary, science fiction, humour, detective, military, war, historical, erotica, fantasy, occult, suspense, plays, literature. Also scripts for film, TV and theatre: handles a lot of material which goes into motion pictures/TV. No gay, lesbian, feminist, confessional, religious, poetry, how-to, children's, biographies, cookery, picture or textbooks. Strictly fiction. Keen on comedy and currently looking for comedy screenplays. No unsolicited mss; query letter first with IRCs, details (a page or two), on project and one-page autobiography. Response time two weeks. Critique fee charged depending on appraisal ($250 screenplays; $115 novels, first 70-75 pp; $1.10 per page plays). CLIENTS include Luis Anguilar, James Colaneri, Steve Blower, Anastassia Evereaux, Dennis Glover, James G. Kingston, John Lubas, Charlie Purpura, Bill Tyman, Fay Van. *Commission* Novels 15%; Film & Drama 10%.

Lee Allan Agency

PO Box 18617, Milwaukee WI 53218
☎001 414 357 7708   Fax 001 414 357 7708
Contact *Lee A. Matthias, Andrea Knickerbocker*

FOUNDED 1983. *Handles* fiction: science fiction, fantasy, mystery, horror, thrillers, men's adventure, historical, westerns and mainstream. No poetry or textbooks. Also handles feature film screenplays properly formatted to the Writer's Guild of America guidelines. No unsolicited mss. Send query letters first, with IRCs, giving length/word count. Novels - minimum 50,000 words; scripts - minimum 90 pp, maximum 140 pp. No reading fee. *Commission* Home 15%; Dramatic 10%; Foreign up to 20%.

Levant & Wales, Literary Agency, Inc.

108 Hayes Street, Seattle WA 98109
☎001 206 284 7114   Fax 001 206 284 0190
Contact *Dan Levant, Elizabeth Wales, Valerie Griffith, Adrienne Reed*

FOUNDED 1988. *Handles* quality fiction and non-fiction. No scripts except via sub-agents. No genre fiction, westerns, romance, science fiction or horror. Special interest in local (Pacific Northwest) clients. No unsolicited mss; send query letter with publication list and writing sample. No reading fee. *Commission* Home 15%; Dramatic & Translation 25%.

Ellen Levine, Literary Agency, Inc.

Suite 1801, 15 East 26th Street, New York NY 10010–1505
☎001 212 899 0620   Fax 001 212 725 4501
Contact *Diane Finch, Ellen Levine*

FOUNDED 1980. *Handles* all types of books. No scripts. No unsolicited mss, nor any other material unless requested. No telephone calls. First approach by letter; send US postage or IRCs for reply. Material not returned. No reading fee. *Commission* Home 15%; Foreign 20%. *Overseas associates* **A. M. Heath & Co. Ltd**, London.

Ray Lincoln Literary Agency

Elkins Park House, Suite 107-B,
7900 Old York Road, Elkins Park PA 19027
☎001 215 635 0827
Contact *Mrs Ray Lincoln*

FOUNDED 1974. *Handles* adult and children's fiction and non-fiction: biography, science, nature, popular medicine, psychology and psychiatry, history. Scripts as spin-offs from book mss only. No poetry or plays unless adaptations from published book. Keenly interested in adult biography, in all types of children's books (age five and upwards, not illustrated), in fine adult fiction, science and nature. No unsolicited mss; send query letter first, including IRCs for response. If interested, material will then be requested. No reading fee. Postage fee for projects handled by the agency. *Commission* Home & Dramatic 15%; Translation 20%.

Literary & Creative Artists Agency

3543 Albemarle Street NW, Washington DC 20008
☎001 202 362 4688   Fax 001 202 362 8875
Contact *Muriel G. Nellis, Jane F. Roberts, Karen S. Gerwin-Stoopack*

FOUNDED 1981. *Specialises* in a broad range of non-fiction. No poetry, pornography, academic or educational textbooks. No unsolicited mss; query letter in the first instance. Include IRCs for response. No reading fee. *Commission* Home 15%; Dramatic 20%; Translation 20–25%.

The Literary Group International

270 Lafayette Street, Suite 1505, New York NY 10012
☎001 212 274 1616   Fax 001 212 274 9876
President *Frank Weimann*
Associates *James Hornfischer, Jessica Wainwright*

FOUNDED 1987. *Handles* true crime, biography, self-help and fiction. *Specialises* in organised crime and exposés. No scripts or textbooks. Unsolicited mss, synopses and ideas welcome. Submit first three chapters only. No reading fee. CLIENTS include Sam Giancana, Reggie Miller, Nicholas Rescher, Clint Richmond, Joseph Starita. *Commission* Home 15%; UK 20% (including sub-agent's fee).

Sterling Lord Literistic, Inc.

65 Bleecker Street, New York NY 10012
☎001 212 780 6050
Contact *Peter Matson, Sterling Lord*

FOUNDED 1979. *Handles* all genres, fiction and non-fiction, plus scripts for TV, radio, film and theatre. Unsolicited mss will be considered. Prefer letter outlining all non-fiction. No reading fee. *Commission* Home 15%; UK & Translation 20%. *Overseas associates* **Peters Fraser & Dunlop Group Ltd**, London.

Denise Marcil Literary Agency, Inc.

685 West End Avenue, Suite 9C, New York NY 10025

☎001 212 932 3110

President Denise Marcil

FOUNDED 1977. Specialises in non-fiction: money, business, health, popular reference, childcare, parenting, self-help and how-to; and commercial fiction, especially women's, and psychological suspense. Query letters only, with IRCs. CLIENTS include Rosanne Bittner, Arnette Lamb, Carla Neggers, Dr William Sears. Commission Home & Dramatic 15%; Foreign 20%.

Betty Marks

176 East 77th Street, Apt. 9F, New York NY 10021

☎001 212 535 8388

Contact Betty Marks

FOUNDED 1969. Works mostly with established/published authors. Specialises in journalists' non-fiction and novels. No unsolicited mss. Query letter and outline in the first instance. No reading fee for outlines. Commission Home 15%; Foreign 20%. Overseas associates **Abner Stein**, London; Mohrbooks, Germany; International Editors, Spain & Portugal; Rosemary Buchman, Europe; Tuttle Mori, Japan.

The Evan Marshall Agency

6 Tristam Place, Pine Brook NJ 07058-9445

☎001 201 882 1122   Fax 001 201 882 3099

Contact Evan Marshall

FOUNDED 1987. Handles general adult fiction and non-fiction, and scripts for film and television. No unsolicited mss; send query letter first. Handling fee charged to unpublished authors. Commission Home 15%; UK & Translation 20%.

Richard P. McDonough, Literary Agent

551 Franklin Street, Cambridge MA 02139

☎001 617 354 6440   Fax 001 617 354 6607

Contact Richard P. McDonough

FOUNDED 1986. General non-fiction and literary fiction. No scripts. No genre fiction. No unsolicited mss; query first with three sample chapters and include IRCs. No reading fee. CLIENTS John Dufresne, Peter Guralnick, Jane Holtz Kay, M. R. Montgomery. Commission 15%.

McIntosh & Otis, Inc.

310 Madison Avenue, New York NY 10017

☎001 212 687 7400   Fax 001 212 687 6894

President Eugene H. Winick

Adult Books Julie Fallowfield

Children's Dorothy Markinko, Renée Cho

FOUNDED 1928. Adult and juvenile literary fiction and non-fiction. No textbooks or scripts. No unsolicited mss. Query letter indicating nature of the work plus details of background. IRCs for response. No reading fee. CLIENTS include Mary Higgins Clark, Shirley Hazzard, Victoria Holt, Harper Lee. Commission Home & Dramatic 15%; Foreign 20%. Overseas associates **A. M. Heath & Co. Ltd**, London.

Mews Books Ltd

c/o Sidney B. Kramer, 20 Bluewater Hill, Westport CT 06880

☎001 203 227 1836   Fax 001 203 227 1144

Contact Sidney B. Kramer, Fran Pollak

FOUNDED 1970. Handles adult fiction and non-fiction, children's, pre-school and young adult. No scripts, short stories or novellas (unless by established authors). Specialises in cookery, medical, health and nutrition, scientific non-fiction, children's and young adult. Also handles electronic rights to published books and represents publisher purchasing electronic rights. Unsolicited material welcome. Presentation must be professional. Partial submissions should include summary of plot/characters, one or two sample chapters, personal credentials and brief on target market. No reading fee. If material is accepted, agency asks $350 circulation fee (4–5 publishers), which will be applied against commissions (waived for published authors). Charges for photocopying, postage expenses, telephone calls and other direct costs. Principal agent is an attorney and former publisher. Offers consultation service through which writers can get advice on a contract or on publishing problems.

Commission Home 15%; Film & Translation 20%. Overseas associates **Abner Stein**, London.

Robert P. Mills

See **Richard Curtis Associates, Inc./The Content Company**

Maureen Moran Agency

PO Box 20191, New York NY 10017

☎001 212 222 3838

Contact Maureen Moran

Formerly Donald MacCampbell, Inc.. Handles novels only. No scripts, non-fiction, science fiction, westerns or suspense. Specialises in romance. No unsolicited mss; approach by letter. No reading fee. *Commission* US Book Sales 10%; First Novels US 15%.

Howard Morhaim Literary Agency
175 Fifth Avenue, Suite 709, New York
NY 10010
☎001 212 529 4433   Fax 001 212 995 1112
Contact *Howard Morhaim, Allison Mullen*

FOUNDED 1979. *Handles* general adult fiction and non-fiction. No scripts. No children's or young adult material, poetry or religious. No unsolicited mss. Send query letter with synopsis and sample chapters for fiction; query letter with outline or proposal for non-fiction. No reading fee. *Commission* Home 15%; UK & Translation 20%. *Overseas associates* worldwide.

Henry Morrison, Inc.
PO Box 235, Bedford Hills NY 10507
☎001 914 666 3500   Fax 001 914 241 7846
Also at: 105 So. Bedford Road, Ste 306A, Mt. Kisco, NY 10549
Contact *Henry Morrison, Joan Gurgold*

FOUNDED 1965. *Handles* general fiction, crime and science fiction, and non-fiction. No scripts unless by established writers. Unsolicited material welcome; send query letter with outline of proposal (1-5 pp). No reading fee. CLIENTS Beverly Byrne, Joe Gores, Robert Ludlum. *Commission* Home 15%; UK & Translation 20%.

Ruth Nathan Agency
80 Fifth Avenue, Suite 706, New York
NY 10011
☎001 212 675 6063   Fax 001 212 675 6063

FOUNDED 1984. *Specialises* in illustrated books, fine art & decorative arts, historical fiction with emphasis on Middle Ages, true crime, showbiz. Query first. No unsolicited mss. No reading fee. *Commission* 15%.

B. K. Nelson Literary Agency
84 Woodland Road, Pleasantville
NY 10570-1322
☎001 914 741 1322   Fax 001 914 741 1324
President *Bonita K. Nelson*

FOUNDED 1979. *Specialises* in business, self-help, how-to, political, autobiography, celebrity biography. Major motion picture and TV documentary success. No unsolicited mss. Letter of inquiry. Reading fee charged. *Commission* 20%. Lecture Bureau for Authors founded 1994; Foreign Rights Catalogue established 1995; BK

Nelson Infomercial Marketing Co. 1996, primarily for authors and endorsements.

New Age World Services & Books
62091 Valley View Circle, Joshua Tree
CA 92252
☎001 619 366 2833
Contact *Victoria E. Vandertuin*

FOUNDED 1957. New Age fiction and non-fiction, young adult fiction and non-fiction, and poetry. No scripts, drama, missionary, biography, sports, erotica, humour, travel or cookbooks. *Specialises* in New Age, self-help, health and beauty, meditation, yoga, channelling, how-to, metaphysical, occult, psychology, religion, lost continents, time travel. Unsolicited mss and queries welcome. Reading fee charged. *Commission* Home 15%; Foreign 20%.

New England Publishing Associates, Inc.
Box 5, Chester CT 06412
☎001 203 345 7323   Fax 001 203 345 3660
Contact *Elizabeth Frost Knappman, Edward W. Knappman*

FOUNDED 1983. *Handles* non-fiction and (clients only) fiction. *Specialises* in current affairs, history, science, women's studies, reference, psychology, biography, true crime. No textbooks or anthologies. No scripts. Unsolicited mss considered but query letter or phone call preferred first. No reading fee. CLIENTS include Lary Bloom, Kathryn Cullen-Du Pont, Sharon Edwards, Elizabeth Lewin, Philip Ginsburg, Dandi MacKall, Mike Nevins, William Packard, John Philpin, Art Plotnik, Carl Rollyson, Robert Sherrill, Orion Magazine, Claude Summers, Ann Waldron. *Commission* Home 15%. *Overseas associates* throughout Europe and Japan; Scott-Ferris, UK. Dramatic rights: Renaissance Agency, Los Angeles.

The Betsy Nolan Literary Agency
224 West 29th Street, 15th Floor, New York
NY 10001
☎001 212 967 8200   Fax 001 212 967 7292
Contact *Betsy Nolan, Carla Glasser, Donald Lehr*

FOUNDED 1980. *Specialises* in non-fiction: popular culture, music, gardening, childcare, cooking, how-to. Some fiction, film & TV rights. No unsolicited mss. Send query letter with synopsis first. No reading fee. *Commission* Home 15%; Foreign 20%.

The Otte Co

9 Goden Street, Belmont MA 02178-3002
☎001 617 484 8505

Contact *Jane H. Otte*

FOUNDED 1973. *Handles* adult fiction and non-fiction. No scripts. No unsolicited mss. Approach by letter. No reading fee. *Commission* Home 15%; Dramatic 7½%; Foreign 20%.

Richard Parks Agency

138 East 16th Street, Suite 5B, New York NY 10003
☎001 212 254 9067

Contact *Richard Parks*

FOUNDED 1989. *Handles* general trade fiction and non-fiction: literary novels, mysteries and thrillers, commercial fiction, science fiction, biography, pop culture, psychology, self-help, parenting, medical, cooking, gardening, etc. No scripts. No technical or academic. No unsolicited mss. Fiction read by referral only. No reading fee. CLIENTS include Scott Campbell, Jo Coudert, Jonathan Lethem, Abraham Rodriguez Jr, Audrey Schulman. *Commission* Home 15%; UK & Translation 20%. *Overseas associates* **Marsh & Sheil Ltd, Barbara Levy Literary Agency**.

Pegasus International

PO Box 5470, Winter Park FL 32793-5470
☎001 407 699 1299

Director *Gene Lovitz*

FOUNDED 1987. 'We work with unpublished authors. Once an author comes aboard we work together to accomplish a marketable work, and never abandon the author once she or he is accepted as a client. Accordingly, we are rather selective in whom we represent.' *Handles* non-fiction and fiction: regency and historical romances, horror, New Age, fantasy and magic, gothic, science fiction, war, mystery, plus film/TV scripts. *Specialises* in science fiction, the 'intellectual novel', and translations into English. No hard-core pornography or verse. 'We will accept erotica done on the level of Anaïs Nin, making a distinction between pornography and erotica.' Approach in writing with proposal. Reading fee charged but reimbursed upon publication. *Commission* 15%.

Penmarin Books

PO Box 286, Woodacre CA 94973
☎001 415 488 1628   Fax 001 415 488 1123

Contact *Hal Lockwood*

FOUNDED 1987. *Handles* projects for popular trade publication, both fiction and non-fiction. No poetry or children's; no school, scholarly or academic books. Unsolicited mss welcome; initial approach in writing preferred: send professional/personal background details, project outline or synopsis (2-3 pp), sample of past or current writing (5-8 pp) and pre-paid return postage. No reading fee for initial reading. *Commission* 15%.

James Peter Associates, Inc.

PO Box 772, Tenafly NJ 07670
☎001 201 568 0760   Fax 001 201 568 2959

Contact *Bert Holtje*

FOUNDED 1971. Non-fiction only. 'Many of our authors are historians, psychologists, physicians - all are writing trade books for general readers.' No scripts. No fiction or children's books. *Specialises* in history, popular culture, business, health, biography and politics. No unsolicited mss. Send query letter first, with brief project outline, samples and biographical information. No reading fee. CLIENTS include Jim Wright, Alan Axelrod, Charles Phillips, David Stutz, Carol Turkington. A member of the Association of Author's Representatives. *Commission* 15%.

Stephen Pevner, Inc.

248 West 73rd Street, 2nd Floor, New York NY 10023
☎001 212 496 0474   Fax 001 212 496 0796

Contact *Stephen Pevner*

FOUNDED 1991. *Handles* pop culture, novels and film-related books. Also handles TV, film, theatre and radio scripts. Approach in writing with synopsis (include first chapters for a novel). No reading fee. CLIENTS Greg Araki, Tom DiCillo, Richard Linkletter, Todd Solanz, Rose Troche. *Commission* Home 15%.

Alison J. Picard Literary Agent

PO Box 2000, Cotuit MA 02635
☎001 508 477 7192   Fax 001 508 420 0762

Contact *Alison Picard*

FOUNDED 1985. *Handles* mainstream and literary fiction, contemporary and historical romance, children's and young adult, mysteries and thrillers; plus non-fiction. No short stories unless suitable for major national publications, and no poetry. Rarely any science fiction and fantasy. Particularly interested in expanding non-fiction titles. Approach with written query. No reading fee. *Commission* 15%. *Overseas associates* **A. M. Heath & Co. Ltd**, London.

Arthur Pine Associates, Inc.
250 West 57th Street, New York NY 10107
☎001 212 265 7330   Fax 001 212 265 4650

Contact *Richard S. Pine, Lori Andiman, Sarah Piel*

FOUNDED 1970. *Handles* fiction and non-fiction (adult books only). No scripts, children's, autobiographical (unless celebrity), textbooks or scientific. No unsolicited mss. Send query letter with synopsis, including IRCs in first instance. All material must be submitted to the agency on an exclusive basis with s.a.e.. *Commission* 15%.

PMA Literary & Film Management, Inc.
132 West 22nd Street, 12th Floor, New York NY 10011
☎001 212 929 1222   Fax 001 212 206 0238
President *Peter Miller*
Vice President *Jennifer Robinson*
Associates *Harrison McGuigan, Eric Wilinski, Yuri Skujins, John Stryder, Giselle Dean Miller*

FOUNDED 1976. Commercial fiction, non-fiction and screenplays. *Specialises* in books with motion picture and television potential, and in true crime. No poetry, pornography, non-commercial or academic. No unsolicited mss. Approach by letter with one-page synopsis. Editing service available for unpublished authors (non-obligatory). Fee recoupable out of first monies earned. CLIENTS include Vincent T. Bugliosi, Jay R. Bonansinga, Martin Caidin, Michael Eberhardt, Christopher Cook Gilmore, Sarah Lovett, Michael Peak, Nancy Taylor Rosenberg, Ted Sennett, Gene Walden, Steven Yount. *Commission* Home 15%; Dramatic 10-15%; Foreign 20-25%.

Susan Ann Protter Literary Agent
Suite 1408, 110 West 40th Street, New York NY 10018-3616
☎001 212 840 0480
Contact *Susan Protter*

FOUNDED 1971. *Handles* general fiction, mysteries, thrillers, science fiction and fantasy; non-fiction: history, general reference, biography, science, health and parenting. No romantic fiction, poetry, religious, children's or sport manuals. No scripts. First approach with letter, including IRCs. No reading fee. CLIENTS include Lydia Adamson, Terry Bisson, David G. Hartwell, John G. Cramer, Kathleen McCoy PhD, Lynn Armistead McKee, Rudy Rucker, Barbara C. Unell. *Commission* Home & Dramatic 15%;

Foreign 25%. *Overseas associates* **Abner Stein**, London; agents in all major markets.

Puddingstone Literary/ SBC Enterprises, Inc.
11 Mabro Drive, Denville NJ 07834-9607
☎001 201 366 3622
Contact *Alec Bernard, Eugenia Cohen*

FOUNDED 1972. Works with new/unpublished writers as well as with established ones. *Handles* trade fiction, non-fiction, film and telemovies. No unsolicited mss. Send query letter with IRCs. No reading fee. *Commission* varies.

Quicksilver Books, Literary Agents
50 Wilson Street, Hartsdale NY 10530
☎001 914 946 8748
President *Bob Silverstein*

FOUNDED 1973. *Handles* literary fiction and mainstream commercial fiction: blockbuster, suspense, thriller, contemporary, mystery and historical; and general non-fiction, including self-help, psychology, holistic healing, ecology, environmental, biography, fact crime, New Age, health, nutrition, enlightened wisdom and spirituality. No scripts, science fiction and fantasy, pornographic, children's or romance. UK material being submitted must have universal appeal for the US market. Unsolicited material welcome but must be accompanied by IRCs for response, together with biographical details, covering letter, etc. No reading fee. CLIENTS include John Harricharan, Susan S. Lang, Brad Steiger, Grace Speare, Melvin van Peebles. *Commission* Home & Dramatic 15%; Translation 20%.

Helen Rees Literary Agency
308 Commonwealth Avenue, Boston MA 02115
☎001 617 262 2401   Fax 001 617 236 0133
Contact *Joan Mazmanian*

FOUNDED 1982. *Specialises* in books on health and business; also handles biography, autobiography and history; quality fiction. No scholarly, academic or technical books. No scripts, science fiction, children's, poetry, photography, cooking. No unsolicited mss. Send query letter with IRCs. No reading fee. CLIENTS include Donna Carpenter, Alan Dershowitz, Alexander Dubcek, Harry Figgie Jr, Senator Barry Goldwater, Sandra Mackey, Price Waterhouse, Chet Raymo. *Commission* Home 15%; Foreign 20%.

Rights Unlimited, Inc.

101 West 55th Street, Suite 2D, New York
NY 10019
☎001 212 246 0900   Fax 001 212 246 2114
Contact *Bernard Kurman*

FOUNDED 1985. *Handles* adult fiction, non-fiction. No scripts, poetry, short stories, educational or literary works. Unsolicited mss welcome; query letter with synopsis preferred in the first instance. Reading fee $50. CLIENTS Charles Berlitz, Gyo Fujikawa, Norman Lang. *Commission* Home 15%; Translation 20%.

Rosenstone/Wender

3 East 48th Street, 4th Floor, New York
NY 10017
☎001 212 832 8330   Fax 001 212 759 4524
Contact *Phyllis Wender, Susan Perlman Cohen*

FOUNDED 1981. *Handles* fiction, non-fiction, children's and scripts for film, TV and theatre. No material for radio. No unsolicited mss. Send letter outlining the project, credits, etc. No reading fee. *Commission* Home 15%; Dramatic 10%; Foreign 20%. *Overseas associates* La Nouvelle Agence, France; Andrew Nurnberg, Netherlands; The English Agency, Japan; Mohrbooks, Germany; Ole Licht, Scandinavia.

Shyama Ross 'The Write Therapist'

2000 North Ivar Avenue, Suite 3, Hollywood
CA 90068
☎001 213 465 2630
Contact *Shyama Ross*

FOUNDED 1979. *Handles* non-fiction trade books: New Age, health and fitness, philosophy, psychology, trends, humour, business, mysticism; also fiction: thrillers, romance, suspense, mystery, contemporary. No scripts. No Christian evangelical, travel, sleazy sex or children's. *Specialises* in health, how-to, mainstream fiction, healing and women's issues. New writers welcome. Query by letter with brief outline of contents and background (plus IRCs). Fee charged ($120 for up to 50,000 words) for detailed analysis of mss. Professional editing also available (rates per page or hour). *Commission* Home & Film rights 15%; Translation 20%.

Jane Rotrosen Agency

318 East 51st Street, New York NY 10022
☎001 212 593 4330   Fax 001 212 935 6985

Branch office: PO Box 1331, Taos, NM 87571
☎001 505 758 5991   Fax: 001 505 758 7108

Contact *Meg Ruley, Andrea Cirillo, Ruth Kagle (New York); Stephanie Tade (Taos)*

Handles commercial fiction: romance, horror, mysteries, thrillers and fantasy and popular non-fiction. No scripts, educational, professional or belles lettres. No unsolicited mss; send query letter in the first instance. No reading fee. CLIENTS include Barbara Bickmore, Julie Garwood, Tami Hoag, Judith Michael, Michael Palmer, John Saul. *Commission* Home 15%; UK & Translation 20%. *Overseas associates* worldwide and film agents on the West Coast.

Victoria Sanders Literary Agency

241 Avenue of the Americas, New York
NY 10014
☎001 212 633 8811   Fax 001 212 633 0525
Contact *Victoria Sanders, Diane Dickensheid*

FOUNDED 1993. *Handles* general trade fiction and non-fiction, plus ancillary film and television rights. CLIENTS Connie Briscoe, Yolanda Joe, Alexander Smalls, Colin Kersey, J. M. Redmann. *Commission* Home & Dramatic 15%; Translation 20%.

Sandum & Associates

144 East 84th Street, New York
NY 10028
☎001 212 737 2011
Contact *Howard E. Sandum*

FOUNDED 1987. *Handles* all categories of general adult non-fiction, plus commercial and literary fiction. No scripts. No children's, poetry or short stories. No unsolicited mss. Third-party referral preferred but direct approach by letter, with synopsis, brief biography and IRCs, is accepted. No reading fee. CLIENTS include James Cowan, Charles Kutcher, Ward Morehouse III, Silvia Sanza. *Commission* Home & Dramatic 15%; Translation & Foreign 20%. *Overseas associates* Scott Ferris Associates.

SBC Enterprises, Inc.

See **Puddingstone Literary**

Jack Scagnetti Literary Agency

5118 Vineland Avenue, Suite 102, North Hollywood CA 91601
☎001 818 762 3871
Contact *Jack Scagnetti*

FOUNDED 1974. Works mostly with established/published authors. *Handles* non-fiction, fiction, film and TV scripts. No reading fee for outlines. *Commission* Home & Dramatic 10%; Foreign 15%.

Susan Schulman, A Literary Agency

454 West 44th Street, New York NY 10036
☎001 212 713 1633/4/5
Fax 001 212 581 8830

FOUNDED 1979. *Specialises* in non-fiction of all types but particularly in psychology-based self-help for men, women and families. Other interests include business, the social sciences, biography, language and linguistics. Fiction interests include contemporary fiction, including women's, mysteries, historical and thrillers 'with a cutting edge'. Always looking for 'something original and fresh'. No unsolicited mss. Query first including outline and three sample chapters with IRCs. No reading fee. Represents properties for film and television, and works with agents in appropriate territories for translation rights. *Commission* Home & Dramatic 15%; Translation 20%. *Overseas associates* Plays: **Rosica Colin Ltd** and **The Agency**, London; Film: **Michelle Kass Associates**, London; Children's books: Marilyn Malin, London, Commercial fiction: **MBA Literary Agents** London.

Shapiro–Lichtman Talent Agency

8827 Beverly Boulevard, Los Angeles CA 90048
☎001 310 859 8877   Fax 001 310 859 7153

FOUNDED 1969. Works mostly with established/published authors. *Handles* film and TV scripts. Unsolicited mss will not be read. *Commission* Home & Dramatic 10%; Foreign 20%.

The Shepard Agency

Pawling Savings Bank Building, Suite 3, Southeast Plaza, Brewster NY 10509
☎001 914 279 2900/3236
Fax 001 914 279 3239

Contact *Jean Shepard, Lance Shepard*

FOUNDED 1987. *Handles* non-fiction: business, food, self-help and travel; some fiction: adult, children's and young adult and the occasional script. No pornography. *Specialises* in business. Send query letter, table of contents, sample chapters and IRCs for response. No reading fee. *Commission* Home & Dramatic 15%; Translation 20%.

Lee Shore Agency

440 Friday Road, Pittsburgh PA 15209
☎001 412 821 0440   Fax 001 412 821 6099

Contact *Cynthia Sterling, Tricia Smith, Mark Maier, Jennifer Blose*

FOUNDED 1988. *Handles* non-fiction, including textbooks, and mass-market fiction: horror, romance, mystery, westerns, science fiction. Also some young adult and, more recently, screenplays. *Specialises* in New Age, self-help, how-to and quality fiction. No children's. No unsolicited mss. Send IRCs for guidelines before submitting work. Reading fee charged. CLIENTS include Mel Blount, Francisco Cruz, Dr Laura Essen, Dr Lynn Hawker, Susan Sheppard. *Commission* Home 15%; Dramatic 20%.

Bobbe Siegel Literary Agency

41 West 83rd Street, New York NY 10024
☎001 212 877 4985   Fax 001 212 877 4985

Contact *Bobbe Siegel*

FOUNDED 1975. Works mostly with established/published authors. *Specialises* in literary fiction, detective, suspense, historical, fantasy, biography, how-to, women's interest, fitness, health, beauty, sports, pop psychology. No scripts. No cookbooks, crafts, children's, short stories or humour. First approach with letter including IRCs for response. No reading fee. Critiques given if the writer is taken on for representation. CLIENTS include Michael Buller, Eileen Curtis, Margaret Mitchell Dukore, Primo Levi, John Nordahl, Curt Smith, Bonnie Tucker. *Commission* Home 15%; Dramatic & Foreign 20%. (Foreign/Dramatic split 50/50 with sub-agent.) *Overseas associates* **John Pawsey**, London; others in other countries.

The Evelyn Singer Literary Agency, Inc.

PO Box 594, White Plains NY 10602
☎001 914 949 1147/914 631 5160

Contact *Evelyn Singer*

FOUNDED 1951. Works mostly with established/published authors. *Handles* fiction and non-fiction, both adult and children's. Adult: health, medicine, how-to, diet, biography, celebrity, conservation, political, serious novels, suspense and mystery. Children's: educational non-fiction for all ages and fiction for the middle/teen levels. No picture books unless the author is or has an experienced book illustrator. No formula romance, poetry, sex, occult, textbooks or specialised material unsuitable for trade market. No scripts. No unsolicited mss. First approach with letter giving writing background, credits, publications, including date of publication and publisher. IRCs essential. No phone calls. No reading fee. CLIENTS include John Armistead, Mary Elting, Franklin Folsom, William F. Hallstead, Rose Wyler. *Commission* Home 15%; Dramatic 20%; Foreign 25%.

Overseas associates **Laurence Pollinger Ltd**, London.

Singer Media Corporation
Seaview Business Park, 1030 Calle Cordillera, Unit 106, San Clemente CA 92673
☎001 714 498 7227   Fax 001 714 498 2162
Contact *Kristy Lee, Acquisitions Dept.*

FOUNDED 1940. Places foreign language rights of previously published books throughout the world. Subjects include business, health, fitness, self-help, biographies of world-renowned figures/celebrities etc. Also a newspaper/magazine syndicate. Looking for syndication rights to previously published or unpublished features on above subjects. Will consider unpublished mss of action thrillers, contemporary romances and biographies of celebrities. No unsolicited mss. Send query letter with synopsis and s.a.e. for reply. Reading fee of $350 for complete comprehensive critique and suggestions applies to unpublished authors. Retains 15% of all domestic book rights sales; 20% of foreign language translation rights sales; 50% on all syndication sales.

Michael Snell Literary Agency
PO Box 1206, Truro MA 02666-1206
☎001 508 349 3718
President *Michael Snell*
Vice President *Patricia Smith*

FOUNDED 1980. Eager to work with new/unpublished writers. *Specialises* in business and computer books (professional and reference to popular trade how-to); general how-to and self-help on all topics, from diet and exercise to sex, psychology and personal finance, plus literary and suspense fiction. No unsolicited mss. Send outline and sample chapter with return postage for reply. No reading fee for outlines. Brochure available on how to write a book proposal. Rewriting, developmental editing, collaborating and ghostwriting services available on a fee basis. Send IRCs. *Commission* Home 15%.

Southern Writers
5120 Prytania Street, New Orleans LA 70115
☎001 504 899 5889
President *William Griffin*

FOUNDED 1979. *Handles* fiction and non-fiction of general interest. No scripts, short stories, poetry, autobiography or articles. No unsolicited mss. Approach in writing with query. Reading fee charged to authors unpub-lished in the field. *Commission* Home 15%; Dramatic & Translation 20%.

Spieler Literary Agency
154 West 57th Street, Room 135, New York NY 10019
☎001 212 757 4439   Fax 001 212 333 2019
The Spieler Agency/West, 1328 Sixth Street, #3, Berkeley, CA 94710
☎001 510 528 2616   Fax 001 510 528 8117
Contact *Joseph Spieler, Lisa M. Ross, John Thornton (NY); Victoria Shoemaker (Berkeley)*

FOUNDED 1980. *Handles* literary fiction and non-fiction. No how-to or genre romance. *Specialises* in history, science, ecology, social issues and business. No scripts. Approach in writing with IRCs. No reading fee. CLIENTS James Chace, Amy Ehrlich, Paul Hawken, Joe Kane, Walter Laqueur, Catherine MacCoun, Akio Morita, Marc Reisner. *Commission* Home & Dramatic 15%; Translation 20%. *Overseas associates* **Abner Stein, The Marsh Agency**, London.

Philip G. Spitzer Literary Agency
50 Talmage Farm Lane, East Hampton NY 11937
☎001 516 329 3650   Fax 001 516 329 3651
Contact *Philip Spitzer*

FOUNDED 1969. Works mostly with established/published authors. *Specialises* in general non-fiction and fiction - thrillers. No reading fee for outlines. *Commission* Home & Dramatic 15%; Foreign 20%.

Lyle Steele & Co. Ltd Literary Agents
511 East 73rd Street, Suite 6, New York NY 10021
☎001 212 288 2981
President *Lyle Steele*

FOUNDED 1985. *Handles* general non-fiction and category fiction, including mysteries (anxious to see good British mysteries), thrillers, horror and occult. Also North American rights to titles published by major English publishers. No scripts unless derived from books already being handled. No romance. No unsolicited mss: query with IRCs in first instance. No reading fee. *Commission* 10%. *Overseas associates* worldwide.

Gloria Stern Agency
2929 Buffalo Speedway, Suite 2111, Houston TX 77098
☎001 713 963 8360   Fax 001 713 963 8460
Contact *Gloria Stern*

FOUNDED 1976. *Specialises* in non-fiction, including biography, history, politics, women's issues, self-help, health, science and education; also adult fiction. No scripts, how-to, poetry, short stories or first fiction from unpublished authors. First approach by letter stating content of book, including one chapter, list of competing books, qualifications as author and IRCs. No reading fee. *Commission* Home 10-15%; Dramatic 10%; Foreign 20% shared; Translation 20% shared. *Overseas associates* **A. M. Heath & Co. Ltd**, London, and worldwide.

Gloria Stern Agency (Hollywood)
12535 Chandler Boulevard, Suite 3, North Hollywood CA 91607
☎001 818 508 6296   Fax 001 818 508 6296
Contact *Gloria Stern*
FOUNDED 1984. *Handles* film scripts, genre (romance, detective, thriller and sci-fi) and mainstream fiction; electronic media. 'No books containing gratuitous violence.' Approach with letter, biography and synopsis. Reading fee charged by the hour. *Commission* Home 15%; Offshore 20%.

Jo Stewart Agency
201 East 66th Street, Suite 18G, New York NY 10021
☎001 212 879 1301
Contact *Jo Stewart*
FOUNDED 1978. *Handles* fiction and non-fiction. No scripts. No unsolicited mss; send query letter first. No reading fee. *Commission* Home 10%; Foreign 20%; Unpublished 15%. *Overseas associates* **Murray Pollinger**, London.

Gunther Stuhlmann Author's Representative
PO Box 276, Becket MA 01223
☎001 413 623 5170
Contact *Gunther Stuhlmann, Barbara Ward*
FOUNDED 1954. *Handles* literary fiction, biography and serious non-fiction. No film/TV scripts unless from established clients. No short stories, detective, romance, adventure, poetry, technical or computers. *Specialises* in 20th-century literature, translations of Japanese and Spanish literature, and modern American writers. Query first with IRCs, including sample chapters and synopsis of project. 'We take on few new clients.' No reading fee. CLIENTS include Joe Bernardini, Julieta Campos, B. H. Friedman, Anaïs Nin, Richard Powers, Otto Rank. *Commission* Home 10%; Foreign 15%; Translation 20%.

H. N. Swanson, Inc.
8523 Sunset Boulevard, Los Angeles CA 90069
☎001 310 289 3636   Fax 001 310 289 3637
President *Joel Gotler*
Literary Associates *Steven Fisher, Alan Nevins, Irv Schwartz*
FOUNDED 1934. Fiction and non-fiction; film and TV rights. No unsolicited mss. Send query letter with IRCs in the first instance. No reading fee. *Commission* Home 10-15%.

The Tantleff Office
375 Greenwich Street, Suite 700, New York NY 10013
☎001 212 941 3939   Fax 001 212 941 3948
Contact *Jack Tantleff, John B. Santoianni, Jill Bock, Anthony Gardner, Charmaine Ferenczi*
FOUNDED 1986. *Handles* primarily scripts for TV, film and theatre. Also fiction and non-fiction books. No unsolicited mss; queries only. No reading fee. CLIENTS include Brian Friel, Howard Korder, Marsha Norman, Mark O'Donnell. *Commission* Scripts 10%; Books 15%.

2M Communications Ltd
121 West 27th Street, Suite 601, New York NY 10001
☎001 212 741 1509   Fax 001 212 691 4460
Contact *Madeleine Morel*
FOUNDED 1982. *Handles* non-fiction only: everything from pop psychology and health to cookery books, biographies and pop culture. No scripts. No fiction, children's, computers or science. No unsolicited mss; send letter with sample pages and IRCs. No reading fee. CLIENTS include David Steinman, Janet Wolfe, Donald Woods. *Commission* Home & Dramatic 15%; Translation 20%. *Overseas associates* **Gregory & Radice Authors' Agents**, London; Thomas Schluck Agency, Germany; Asano Agency, Japan; Bengt Nordin Agency, Scandinavia; EAIS, France; Living Literary Agency, Italy; Nueva Agencia Literaria Internacional, Spain.

Susan P. Urstadt, Inc.
PO Box 1676, New Canaan CT 06840
☎001 203 972 8226   Fax 001 203 966 2249
President *Susan P. Urstadt*
FOUNDED 1975. *Specialises* in decorative arts, health, antiques, architecture, gardening, cookery, biography, history, performing arts, sports, women's issues, current affairs, natural history and environment, lifestyle, current living trends and popular reference. No unsolicited fiction or

children's. Query with outline, sample chapter, author biography and IRCs to cover return postage. CLIENTS include Elliott Dacher MD, Emyl Jenkins, Thomas Powers, Evelyn Rose. *Commission* Home 15%; Dramatic & Foreign 20%.

Van der Leun & Associates
22 Division Street, Easton CT 06612
☎001 203 259 4897

Contact *Patricia Van der Leun*

FOUNDED 1984. *Handles* fiction and non-fiction. No scripts. No science fiction or fantasy romance. *Specialises* in art and architecture, science, biography and fiction. No unsolicited mss; query first, with proposal and short biography. No reading fee. CLIENTS include David Darling, Robert Fulghum, Marion Winik. *Commission* 15%. *Overseas associates* **Abner Stein**, UK; Michelle Lapautre, France; English Agency, Japan; Carmen Balcells, Spain; Lijnkamp Associates, The Netherlands; Karin Schindler, South America; Susanna Zevi, Italy.

Bess Wallace Associates Literary Agency
PO Box 972, Duchesne UT 84021
☎001 801 738 2317

Contact *Bess Wallace*

FOUNDED 1977. *Handles* non-fiction only. No eroticism or poetry. No scripts. Unsolicited mss welcome but query first. No reading fee. *Commission* Home 15%; Dramatic & Translation 10%.

Wallace Literary Agency, Inc.
177 East 70th Street, New York NY 10021
☎001 212 570 9090   Fax 001 212 772 8979

Contact *Lois Wallace, Thomas C. Wallace*

FOUNDED 1988. No unsolicited mss. No faxed queries. *Commission* Rates upon application. *UK representative* **A. M. Heath & Co. Ltd**; *European representative* **Andrew Nurnberg Associates**.

Gerry B. Wallerstein Agency
2315 Powell Avenue, Suite 12, Erie PA 16506
☎001 814 833 5511   Fax 001 814 833 6260

Contact *Gerry B. Wallerstein*

FOUNDED 1984. Adult fiction and non-fiction. No scripts unless by established clients. No children's, textbooks, esoteric or autobiographical (unless celebrity). Broad range of clients, main interest being marketability of material. No unsolicited mss. Send IRCs for information regarding submissions. Reading fee charged for non-established authors. CLIENTS include Carl Caiati, Jack D. Coombe, Nan DeVincentis-Hayes, Gregory Janicki, Mark Pickvet. *Commission* Home & Dramatic 15%; Translation 20%.

John A. Ware Literary Agency
392 Central Park West, New York NY 10025
☎001 212 866 4733   Fax 001 212 866 4734

Contact *John Ware*

FOUNDED 1978. *Specialises* in non-fiction: biography, history, current affairs, investigative journalism, science, inside looks at phenomena, medicine and psychology (academic credentials required). Also handles literary fiction, mysteries/thrillers; sport, oral history, Americana and folklore. Unsolicited mss not read. Send query letter first with IRCs to cover return postage. No reading fee. CLIENTS include Caroline Fraser, Jon Krakauer, Jack Womack. *Commission* Home & Dramatic 15%; Foreign 20%.

Waterside Productions, Inc.
2191 San Elijo Avenue, Cardiff by the Sea CA 92007-1839
☎001 619 632 9190   Fax 001 619 632 9295

Contact *William Gladstone*

FOUNDED 1982. *Handles* mainstream and category fiction, and general non-fiction: computers and technology, psychology, science, women's issues, business, sports. All types of multimedia. No science fiction or horror. No unsolicited mss; send query letter. No reading fee. *Commission* Home 15%; Dramatic 20%; Translation 25%. *Overseas associates* **Serafina Clarke**, England; Asano Agency, Japan; Ulla Lohren, Sweden; Ruth Liepman, Germany; Vera Le Marie, EAIS, France; Bardon Chinese Media Agency, China; Grandi & Vitali, Italy; DRT, Korea; Mercedes Casanovas, Spain.

Watkins Loomis Agency, Inc.
133 East 35th Street, Suite 1, New York NY 10016
☎001 212 532 0080   Fax 001 212 889 0506

Contact *Lily Oei*

FOUNDED 1904. *Handles* fiction and non-fiction, political and cultural. No scripts for film, radio, TV or theatre. No science fiction, fantasy or horror. No reading fee. No unsolicited mss. Approach in writing with enquiry or proposal and s.a.e.. CLIENTS include Maureen Howard, Walter Mosley. *Commission* Home 15%; UK & Translation 20%. *Overseas associates* **Abner Stein**; **The Marsh Agency**, London.

Wecksler-Incomco

170 West End Avenue, New York NY 10023
☎001 212 787 2239   Fax 001 212 496 7035

Contact *Sally Wecksler, Joann Amparan*

FOUNDED 1971. *Handles* fiction and non-fiction (biographies, performing arts), heavily illustrated books, business and reference. Film and TV rights. No unsolicited mss; queries only. No reading fee. *Commission* Home 15%; Translation 20% and British rights 20%.

Cherry Weiner Literary Agency

28 Kipling Way, Manalapan NJ 07726
☎001 908 446 2096 Fax 001 908 446 2096 3★

Contact *Cherry Weiner*

FOUNDED 1977. *Handles* more or less all types of genre fiction: science fiction and fantasy, romance, mystery, westerns. No scripts. No non-fiction. No unsolicited mss. No submissions except through referral. No reading fee. *Commission* 15%. *Overseas associates* **Abner Stein**, London; Thomas Schluck, Germany; International Editors Inc., Spain.

Wieser & Wieser, Inc.

118 East 25th Street, New York NY 10010
☎001 212 260 0860   Fax 001 212 505 7186

Contact *Olga B. Wieser, George J. Wieser, Jake Elwell*

FOUNDED 1976. Works mostly with established/published authors. *Specialises* in literary and mainstream fiction, serious and popular historical fiction, and general non-fiction: business, finance, aviation, sports, photography, cookbooks, travel and popular medicine. No poetry, children's, science fiction or religious. No unsolicited mss. First approach by letter with IRCs. No reading fee for outlines. *Commission* Home & Dramatic 15%; Foreign 20%.

Ruth Wreschner, Authors' Representative

10 West 74th Street, New York NY 10023
☎001 212 877 2605   Fax 001 212 595 5843

Contact *Ruth Wreschner*

FOUNDED 1981. Works mostly with established/published authors but 'will consider very good first novels, both mainstream and genre, particularly British mystery writers'. *Specialises* in popular medicine, psychology, health, self-help, business. No screenplays or dramatic plays. First approach with query letter and IRCs. For fiction, send a synopsis and first 100 pp; for non-fiction, an outline and two sample chapters. No reading fee. *Commission* Home 15%; Foreign 20%.

Ann Wright Representatives

165 West 46th Street, Suite 1105, New York NY 10036-2501
☎001 212 764 6770   Fax 001 212 764 5125

Contact *Dan Wright*

FOUNDED 1961. *Specialises* in screenplays for film and TV. Also handles novels, drama and fiction. No academic, scientific or scholarly. Approach by letter; no reply without IRCs. Include outline and credits only. New film and TV writers encouraged. No reading fee. CLIENTS include Theodore Bonnet, Liam Burke, Joy Chambers, Tom Dempsey, Owen McKevit, John Peer Nugent, James O'Hare, Brian Reich, William H. Selzer, Joseph H. Sheehy. Signatory to the Writers Guild of America Agreement. *Commission* Home varies according to current trend (10-20%); Dramatic 10% of gross.

Writers House, Inc.

21 West 26th Street, New York NY 10010
☎001 212 685 2400   Fax 001 212 685 1781

Contact *Albert Zuckerman, Amy Berkower, Merrilee Heifetz, Susan Cohen, Susan Ginsburg, Liza Landsman, Fran Lebowitz, Karen Solem, Michelle Rubin*

FOUNDED 1974. *Handles* all types of fiction, including children's and young adult, plus narrative non-fiction: history, biography, popular science, pop and rock culture. Also represents designers and developers of CD-ROM computer games. *Specialises* in popular fiction, women's novels, thrillers and children's. Represents novelisation rights for film producers such as New Line Cinema. No scripts. No professional or scholarly. For consideration of unsolicited mss, send letter of enquiry, 'explaining why your book is wonderful, briefly what it's about and outlining your writing background'. No reading fee. CLIENTS include Barbara Delinsky, Ken Follett, Eileen Goudge, Stephen Hawking, Michael Lewis, Robin McKinley, Ann Martin, Francine Pascal, Ridley Pearson, Nora Roberts, Craig Thomas, Cynthia Voigt, F. Paul Wilson. *Commission* Home & Dramatic 15%; Foreign 20%. *Overseas associates* **Blake Friedmann Literary Agency Ltd**, London. Albert Zuckerman is author of *Writing the Blockbuster Novel*, published by **Little, Brown & Co.**

Susan Zeckendorf Associates, Inc.

171 West 57th Street, Suite 11B, New York NY 10019

☎001 212 245 2928   Fax 001 212 977 2643

President *Susan Zeckendorf*

FOUNDED 1979. Works with new/unpublished writers. *Specialises* in literary fiction, commercial women's fiction, international espionage, thrillers and mysteries. Non-fiction interests: science, parenting, music and self-help. No category romance, science fiction or scripts. No unsolicited mss. Send query letter describing mss. No reading fee. CLIENTS include Linda Dahl, James N. Frey, Una-Mary Parker, Jerry E. Patterson, Boyce Rensberger, Kathleen Wallace King. *Commission* Home & Dramatic 15%; Foreign 20%. *Overseas associates* **Abner Stein**, London; V. K. Rosemarie Buckman, Europe, South America; Tom Mori, Japan, Taiwan.

US Press, Journals and Broadcasting

ABC News Intercontinental Inc.
8 Carburton Street, London W1P 7DT
☎0171 637 9222   Fax 0171 631 5084
Chief of Bureau & Director, News Coverage, Europe, Middle East & Africa *Rex Granum*

Alaska Journal of Commerce
58 Jubilee Place, London SW3 3TQ
☎0171 376 7316   Fax 0171 376 7316
Bureau Chief *Robert Gould*

The Associated Press
12 Norwich Street, London EC4A 1BP
☎0171 353 1515   Fax 0171 353 8118
Chief of Bureau/Managing Director *Myron L. Belkind*

The Baltimore Sun
11 Kensington Court Place, London W8 5BJ
☎0171 353 3531   Fax 0171 353 5331
Bureau Chief *Bill Glauber*

Bloomberg Business News
City Gate House, 39–45 Finsbury Square, London EC2A 1PX
☎0171 256 7500   Fax 0171 374 6138
European Bureau Chief *Guy Collins*

Business Week
34 Dover Street, London W1X 4BR
☎0171 491 8985   Fax 0171 409 7152
Bureau Manager *Paula Dwyer*

Cable News Network Inc.
CNN House, 19–22 Rathbone Place, London W1P 1DF
☎0171 637 6800   Fax 0171 637 6868
Bureau Chief *Charles Hoff*

CBC Television and Radio
43/51 Great Titchfield Street, London W1P 8DD
☎0171 412 9200   Fax 0171 631 3095
Bureau Chief *John Owen*

CBS News
68 Knightsbridge, London SW1X 7LL
☎0171 581 4801   Fax 0171 581 4431
Bureau Chief *Marcy McGinnis*

Chicago Tribune Press Service
169 Piccadilly, London W1V 9DD
☎0171 499 8769   Fax 0171 499 8781
Chief European Correspondent *Ray Moseley*

The Christian Science Monitor
49 Chartfield Avenue, London SW15 6HW
☎0181 543 9393   Fax 0181 545 0392
British Isles Correspondent *Alexander Macleod*

CNBC
8 Bedford Avenue, London WC1B 3NQ
☎0171 927 6759   Fax 0171 636 2628
Correspondent *Sissel McCarthy*

Cox Newspapers
The Atlanta Journal Constitution, 29 Ferry Street, Isle of Dogs, London E14 3DT
☎0171 537 0765   Fax 0171 537 0766
European Correspondent *Lou Salome*

Dow Jones Telerate–Commodities & Finance
10 Fleet Place, Limeburner Lane, London EC4M 7RB
☎0171 832 9522   Fax 0171 832 9894
Managing Editor *James Dyson*

Fairchild Publications of New York
121 Kingsway, London WC2B 6PA
☎0171 831 3607   Fax 0171 831 6485
Bureau Chief *James Fallon*

Forbes Magazine
51 Charles Street, London W1X 7PA
☎0171 495 0120   Fax 0171 495 0170
European Bureau Manager *Peter Fuhrman*

Fortune Magazine
Brettenham House, Lancaster Place, London WC2E 7TL
☎0171 499 4080
European Editor *Rick Kirkland*

Futures World News
2 Royal Mint Court, Dexter House,
London EC3N 4QN
☎0171 867 8867   Fax 0171 867 1368
Editor-in-Chief & European Editor *Terry Wooten*

The Globe and Mail
26a Aberdeen Road, London
N5 2UH
☎0171 359 4536   Fax 0171 359 4586
European Correspondent *Madelaine Drohan*

International Herald Tribune
63 Long Acre, London WC2E 9JH
☎0171 836 4802   Fax 0171 240 2254
London Correspondent *Erik Ipsen*

Journal of Commerce
Totara Park House, 3rd Floor, 34/36 Gray's
Inn Road, London WC1X 8HR
☎0171 430 2495   Fax 0171 837 2168
Chief European Correspondent *Janet Porter*

Knight-Ridder Financial News
K. R. House, 78 Fleet Street, London
EC4Y 1HY
☎0171 842 4000   Fax 0171 583 5032
Editor for Europe, Middle East & Africa
Barry Schneider

Life Magazine
Brettenham House, Lancaster Place, London
WC2E 7TL
☎0171 499 4080   Fax 0171 322 1021
Contact *Gail Ridgwell*

Los Angeles Times
150 Brompton Road, London
SW3 1HX
☎0171 823 7315   Fax 0171 823 7308
Bureau Chief *William D. Montalbano*

Maclean's Magazine
60/62 Great Titchfield Street, London
W1P 7FL
☎0171 637 7410   Fax 0171 637 7195
London Bureau Chief *Bruce Wallace*

Market News Service Inc.
Wheatsheaf House, 4 Carmelite Street,
London EC4Y 0BN
☎0171 353 4462   Fax 0171 353 9122
Bureau Chief *Jon Hurdle*

McGraw-Hill International
34 Dover Street, London W1X 4BR
☎0171 493 0538   Fax 0171 493 9896
Bureau Chief *David Brezovec*

Monitor Radio
69 Cholmley Gardens, Fortune Green Road,
London NW6 1AJ
☎0171 433 1552   Fax 0171 433 1552
European Affairs Correspondent *Megan Cox Gurdon*

National Public Radio
Room G-10 East Wing, Bush House, Strand,
London WC2B 4PH
☎0171 257 8086   Fax 0171 379 6486
London Bureau Chief *Andrew Bowers*

NBC News Worldwide Inc.
8 Bedford Avenue, London WC1B 2NQ
☎0171 637 8655   Fax 0171 636 2628
Bureau Chief *Karen Curry*

The New York Times
66 Buckingham Gate, London SW1E 6AU
☎0171 799 5050   Fax 0171 799 2962
Chief Correspondent *John Darnton*

Newsweek
18 Park Street, London W1Y 4HH
☎0171 629 8361   Fax 0171 408 1403
Bureau Chief *Daniel Pedersen*

People Magazine
Brettenham House, Lancaster Place, London
WC2E 7TL
☎0171 499 4080   Fax 0171 322 1125
Special Correspondent *Jerene Jones*

Philadelphia Inquirer
36 Agate Road, London W6 0AH
☎0181 932 8856   Fax 0181 932 8854
Correspondent *Fawn Vrazo*

Reader's Digest Association
Berkeley Square House, Berkeley Square,
London W1X 6AB
☎0171 629 8144   Fax 0171 408 0748
Editor-in-Chief, British Edition *Russell Twisk*

Time Magazine
Brettenham House, Lancaster Place, London
WC2E 7TL
☎0171 499 4080   Fax 0171 322 1230
Bureau Chief *Barry Hillenbrand*

United Press International
408 Strand, London WC2R 0NE
☎0171 333 0999   Fax 0171 333 1690
Regional Editor *David Alexander*

US News and World Report
3 Chiswick Wharf, London W4 2SZ
☎0181 995 3300   Fax 0181 995 1277
Senior European Editor *Robin Knight*

Voice of America
IPC, 76 Shoe Lane, London EC4A 3JB
☎0171 410 0960   Fax 0171 410 0966
Senior Editor *Mark Hopkins*

Wall Street Journal
10 Fleet Place, London EC4M 7RB
☎0171 832 9200   Fax 0171 832 9201
London Bureau Chief *Lawrence Ingrassia*

Washington Post
18 Park Street, London W1Y 4HH
☎0171 629 8958   Fax 0171 629 0050
Bureau Chief *Fred Barbash*

Who Weekly
Brettenham House, Lancaster Place, London
WC2E 7TL
☎0171 322 1118   Fax 0171 322 1199
Special Correspondent *Moira Bailey*

Worldwide Television News (WTN)
The Interchange, Oval Road, Camden Lock,
London NW1 7EP
☎0171 410 5200   Fax 0171 410 8302
Chairman *Kenneth A. Coyte*

Professional Associations

Alliance of Literary Societies
71 Stepping Stones Road, Coventry CV5 8JT
☎01203 592231
President *Gabriel Woolf*
Chairman *J. Hunt*
Honorary Secretary *Bill Adams*

FOUNDED 1974. Acts as a liaison body between member societies and, when necessary, as a pressure group. Deals with enquiries and assists in preserving buildings and places with literary connections. 30–40 societies hold membership. It maintains a directory of literary societies. Also produces an annual fanzine, *Chapter One*, which is distributed to affiliated societies, carrying news of personalities, activities and events. Details of this from Kenneth Oultram, Editor, Chapter One, Clatterwick Hall, Little Leigh, Northwich, Cheshire CW8 4RJ (Tel: 01606 891303).

Arvon Foundation
Totleigh Barton, Sheepwash, Beaworthy, Devon EX21 5NS
☎01409 231338   Fax 01409 231338
Lumb Bank, Heptonstall, Hebden Bridge, West Yorkshire HX7 6DF
☎01422 843714   Fax 01422 843714
Moniack Mhor, Teavarran, Kiltarlity, Beauly, Inverness-shire IV4 7HT
☎01463 741675
President *Terry Hands*
Chairman *Professor Brian Cox, CBE*
National Director *David Pease*

FOUNDED 1968. Offers people of any age (over 16) and any background the opportunity to live and work with professional writers. Five-day residential courses are held throughout the year at Arvon's three centres, covering poetry, narrative, drama, writing for children, songwriting and the performing arts. A number of bursaries towards the cost of course fees are available for those on low incomes, the unemployed, students and pensioners. Runs a biennial poetry competition (see under **Prizes**).

Association for Business Sponsorship of the Arts (ABSA)
Nutmeg House, 60 Gainsford Street, Butlers Wharf, London SE1 2NY
☎0171 378 8143   Fax 0171 407 7527

ABSA is the independent national association that exists to promote and encourage partnerships between the private sector and the arts to their mutual benefit and to that of the community at large. ABSA represents the interests of the business sponsor, in particular those of its business members, and also advises and trains the arts community both individually and corporately on the development of private sector support. A major initiative of ABSA is *Business in the Arts* which encourages business men and women to share their management skills with the arts to their mutual benefit. The *Business Sponsorship Incentive Scheme*, relaunched in 1995 as the *National Heritage Arts Sponsorship Scheme* (commonly known as the 'Pairing Scheme'), is designed to increase the level of sponsorship of the arts. Also runs *ABSA Consulting*.

Association of American Correspondents in London
12 Norwich Street, London EC4A 1BP
☎0171 353 1515   Fax 0171 936 2229
Contact *Sandra Marshall*
Subscription £90 (Organisations)

FOUNDED 1919 to serve the professional interests of its member organisations, promote social cooperation among them, and maintain the ethical standards of the profession. (An extra £30 is charged for each department of an organisation which requires separate listing in the Association's handbook.)

Association of Authors' Agents
c/o Greene & Heaton Ltd, 37 Goldhawk Road, London W12 8QQ
☎0181 749 0315   Fax 0181 749 0318
Secretary *Carol Heaton*
Membership £50 p.a.

FOUNDED 1974. Membership voluntary. The AAA maintains a code of practice, provides a forum for discussion, and represents its members in issues affecting the profession.

Association of British Editors
Broadvision, 49 Frederick Road, Edgbaston, Birmingham B15 1HN
☎0121 455 7949   Fax 0121 454 6187
Executive Director/Honorary Secretary
Jock Gallagher

Subscription £50 p.a.

FOUNDED 1985. Independent organisation for the study and enhancement of journalism world-wide. Established to protect and promote the freedom of the Press. Members are expected to 'maintain the dignity and rights of the profession; consider and sustain standards of professional conduct; exchange ideas for the advancement of professional ideals; work for the solution of common problems'. Membership is limited, but open to persons who have immediate charge of editorial or news policies in all media.

Association of British Science Writers (ABSW)

c/o British Association for the Advancement of Science, Fortress House, 23 Savile Row, London W1X 2NB
☎0171 439 1205   Fax 0171 973 3051
Administrator *Barbara Drillsma*
Membership £20 p.a.; £15 (Associate)

ABSW has played a central role in improving the standards of science journalism in the UK over the last 40 years. The Association seeks to improve standards by means of networking, lectures and organised visits to institutional laboratories and industrial research centres. Puts members in touch with major projects in the field and with experts worldwide. A member of the European Union of Science Journalists' Associations, ABSW is able to offer heavily subsidised places on visits to research centres in most other European countries, and hosts reciprocal visits to Britain by European journalists. Membership open to those who are considered to be *bona fide* science writers/editors, or their film/TV/radio equivalents, who earn a substantial part of their income by promoting public interest in and understanding of science. Runs the administration and judging of the **Glaxo Science Writers' Awards**, for outstanding science journalism in newspapers, journals and broadcasting.

Association of Freelance Journalists

5 Beacon Flats, Kings Haye Road, Wellington, Telford, Shropshire TF1 1RG
Founding President *Martin Scholes*
Subscription £30 p.a.

Offers membership to local correspondents, those making a modest sum writing for the specialist press and those writing for a hobby, with or without an income. Members receive newsletters, information networking, discounts on services, etc.

Association of Golf Writers

c/o Sports Desk, Daily Express, Blackfriars Road, London SE1 9UX
☎0171 922 7118   Fax 0171 922 7974
Contact *Frances Jennings*

FOUNDED 1938. Aims to cooperate with golfing bodies to ensure best possible working conditions.

Association of Illustrators

First Floor, 32–38 Saffron Hill, London EC1N 8FH
☎0171 831 7377   Fax 0171 831 6277
Contact *Stephanie Smith*

FOUNDED 1973 to promote illustration and illustrators' rights, and encourage professional standards. The AOI is a non-profit-making trade association dedicated to its members, to protecting their interests and promoting their work. Talks, seminars, a newsletter, regional groups, legal and portfolio advice as well as a number of related publications such as *Rights, The Illustrator's Guide to Professional Practice*, and *Survive, The Illustrator's Guide to a Professional Career*.

Association of Independent Libraries

Birmingham and Midland Institute, Margaret Street, Birmingham B3 3BS
☎0121 236 3591
Secretary *Philip Fisher*

Established to 'further the advancement, conservation and restoration of a little-known but important living portion of our cultural heritage'. Members include the **London Library, Devon & Exeter Institution, Linen Hall Library** and **Plymouth Proprietary Library**.

Association of Independent Radio Companies

Radio House, 46 Westbourne Grove, London W2 5SH
☎0171 727 2646   Fax 0171 229 0352
Chief Executive *Paul Brown*
Research Communications Manager
  Rachell Fox

The AIRC is the trade body for the independent radio stations. It represents members' interests to Government, the Radio Authority, trade unions, copyright organisations and other bodies.

Association of Learned and Professional Society Publishers
48 Kelsey Lane, Beckenham, Kent BR3 3NE
☎0181 658 0459   Fax 0181 663 3583
Secretary-General *Bernard Donovan*

FOUNDED 1972 to foster the publishing activities of learned societies and academic and professional bodies. Membership is limited to such organisations, those publishing on behalf of member organisations and those closely associated with the work of academic publishers.

Association of Little Presses
86 Lytton Road, Oxford OX4 3NZ
☎01865 718266
Co-ordinator *Stan Trevor*
Subscription £12.50 p.a.

FOUNDED 1966 as a loosely knit association of individuals running little presses, who grouped together for mutual self-help and encouragement. First acted as a pressure group to extend the availability of grant aid to small presses and later became more of an information exchange, advice centre and general promoter of small press publishing. Currently represents over 300 publishers and associates throughout Britain. Membership is open to presses and magazines as well as to individuals and institutions.

ALP publishes a twice-yearly magazine, *Poetry and Little Press Information* (PALPI); a *Catalogue of Little Press Books in Print*; information booklets such as *Getting Your Poetry Published* (over 35,000 copies sold since 1973) and *Publishing Yourself: Not Too Difficult After All* which advises those who are thinking of self-publishing; and a regular newsletter. A full list of little presses (some of which, like **Bloodaxe Books**, are now sufficiently established and successful to be considered in the mainstream of the business) is available from ALP.

ALP organises frequent bookfairs. Its main focus, that of supporting members' presses, brings it into contact with organisations worldwide. Over 80% of all new poetry in Britain is published by small presses and magazines but the Association is by no means solely devoted to publishers of poetry; its members produce everything from comics to cookery, novels and naval history.

Association of Scottish Motoring Writers
c/o 85 East King Street, Helensburgh, Dunbartonshire G84 7RG
☎01436 672187   Fax 01436 674118
Contact *Ross Finlay*

Subscription £35 (Full); £20 (Associate)

FOUNDED 1961. Aims to co-ordinate the activities of, and provide shared facilities for, motoring writers resident in Scotland, as well as creating opportunities for them to keep in touch when working outside of Scotland. Membership is by invitation only.

Author–Publisher Enterprise
12 Mercers, Hawkhurst, Kent TN18 4LH
☎01580 753346
Chairman *John Dawes*
Secretary *Trevor Lockwood*
Subscription £12 (p.a.)

FOUNDED 1993. The association aims to provide an active forum for writers publishing their own work. An information network of ideas and opportunities for self-publishers. Explores the business and technology of writing and publishing. Regular newsletter, seminars and workshops, etc.

Authors North
c/o The Society of Authors, 84 Drayton Gardens, London SW10 9SB
☎0171 373 6642
Secretary *Ray Dunbobbin*

A group within **The Society of Authors** which organises meetings for members living in the North of England.

The Authors' Club
40 Dover Street, London W1X 3RB
☎0171 499 8581   Fax 0171 409 0913
Secretary *Mrs Ann Carter*

FOUNDED in 1891 by Sir Walter Besant, the Authors' Club welcomes as members writers, publishers, critics, journalists, academics and anyone involved with literature. Administers the **Authors' Club Best First Novel Award; Sir Banister Fletcher Award; Marsh Biography Award** and the **Marsh Award for Children's Literature in Translation**. Membership fee: apply to secretary.

Authors' Licensing and Collecting Society
74 New Oxford Street, London WC1A 1EF
☎0171 255 2034   Fax 0171 323 0486
Secretary General *Malcolm Derbyshire*
Subscription £5.88 incl. VAT (free to members of **The Society of Authors** and **The Writers' Guild**); £5 (Residents of EC countries); £7 (Overseas)

A non-profit-making society collecting and distributing payment to writers in areas where they are unable to administer the rights themselves, such as reprography, certain lending rights, private and off-air recording and simultaneous cabling. Open to writers and their heirs.

The Bibliographical Society

c/o The National Art Library, Victoria & Albert Museum, London SW7 2RL
☎0171 938 8312   Fax 0171 938 8461
President *P. Isaac*
Honorary Secretary *D. Pearson*
Subscription £28 p.a.

Aims to promote and encourage the study and research of historical, analytical, descriptive and textual bibliography, and the history of printing, publishing, bookselling, bookbinding and collecting; to hold meetings at which papers are read and discussed; to print and publish works concerned with bibliography; to form a bibliographical library. Awards grants and bursaries for bibliographical research. *Publishes* a quarterly magazine called *The Library*.

Book Packagers Association

93A Blenheim Crescent, London W11 2EQ
☎0171 221 9089
Secretary *Rosemary Pettit*
Subscription £150 p.a.; Associate
  membership £75 p.a.

Aims to provide members with a forum for the exchange of information, to improve the image of packaging and to represent the interests of members. Activities include meetings, seminars, the provision of standard contracts and a joint stand at London Book Fair.

Book Trust

Book House, 45 East Hill, London
SW18 2QZ
☎0181 870 9055   Fax 0181 874 4790
Chief Executive *Brian Perman*
Subscription £25 p.a.; £28 (Overseas)

FOUNDED 1925. Book Trust, the independent educational charity promoting books and reading, includes Young Book Trust (formerly Children's Book Foundation). The Trust offers a book information service (free to the public and on subscription to the trade); administers many literary prizes (including the **Booker**); carries out surveys, *publishes* useful reference books and resource materials; houses a children's book reference library; and promotes children's books through activities like Children's Book Week.

Book Trust Scotland

The Scottish Book Centre, 137 Dundee Street, Edinburgh EH11 1BG
☎0131 229 3663   Fax 0131 228 4293
Contact *Lindsey Fraser*

FOUNDED 1956. Book Trust Scotland works with schools, libraries, writers, artists, publishers, bookshops and individuals to promote the pleasures of reading to people of all ages. It provides a book information service which draws on the children's reference library (a copy of every children's book published in the previous twelve months), the Scottish children's book collection, a range of press cuttings on Scottish literary themes and a number of smaller collections of Scottish books. Book Trust Scotland administers the **Kathleen Fidler Award** and the **McVitie's Prize for the Scottish Writer of the Year**; and *publishes* guides to Scottish books and writers, both adult and children's. Book Trust Scotland also produces a range of children's reading posters and Scottish poetry posters.

Booksellers Association of Great Britain & Ireland

Minster House, 272 Vauxhall Bridge Road, London SW1V 1BA
☎0171 834 5477   Fax 0171 834 8812
Chief Executive *Tim Godfray*

FOUNDED 1895. The BA helps 3,300 independent, chain and multiple members to sell more books and reduce costs. It represents members' interests to publishers, Government, authors and others in the trade as well as offering marketing assistance, running training courses, conferences, seminars and exhibitions. *Publishes* directories, catalogues, surveys and various other publications connected with the book trade and administers the **Whitbread Book of the Year and Literary Awards**.

BAFTA (British Academy of Film and Television Arts)

195 Piccadilly, London W1V 0LN
☎0171 734 0022   Fax 0171 734 1792
Chief Executive *Harry Manley*
Subscription £140 p.a.; £72.50 (Country)

FOUNDED 1947. Membership limited to 'those who have contributed to the industry' over a minimum period of three years. Provides facilities for screening and discussions; encourages research and experimentation; lobbies Parliament; and makes annual awards.

BASCA (British Academy of Songwriters, Composers and Authors)

34 Hanway Street, London W1P 9DE
☎0171 436 2261   Fax 0171 436 1913
Contact *Amanda Harcourt*
Subscription from £35 + VAT p.a.

FOUNDED 1947. The Academy offers advice and support for songwriters and composers and represents members' interests to the music industry. It also issues a standard contract between publishers and writers and a collaborators' agreement. Members receive the Academy's quarterly magazine, and can attend fortnightly legal and financial seminars and creative workshops. The Academy administers Britain's annual awards for composers, the Ivor Novello Awards, now in their 41st year. BASCA is a member of the Alliance of Composer Organisations, ACO.

British Amateur Press Association (BAPA)

Flat 36, Priory Park, Botanical Way, St Osyth, Essex CO16 8TE
Secretary/Treasurer *L. E. Linford*

A non-profit-making, non-sectarian hobby organisation (founded in 1890) to 'promote the fellowship of amateur writers, artists, editors, printers, publishers and other craftsmen/women. To encourage them to edit, print and publish, *as a hobby*, magazines and newsletters, etc' by letterpress and other processes, including photo-copiers and computer DTP/word-processors. Not an outlet for placing work commercially, only with other members in their private publications circulated within the association and amongst friends. A fraternity providing contacts between amateur writers, poets, editors, artists, etc. Postal enquiries only, please enclose first-class stamp to the Secretary at the above address.

British American Arts Association

116 Commercial Street, London E1 6NF
☎0171 247 5385   Fax 0171 247 5256
Director *Jennifer Williams*

A non-profit organisation working in the field of arts and education. BAAA conducts research, organises conferences, produces a quarterly newsletter and is part of an international network of arts and education organisations. As well as a specialised arts and education library, BAAA has a more general library holding information on opportunities for artists and performers both in the UK and abroad. BAAA is not a grant-giving organisation.

British Association of Communicators in Business

3 Locks Yard, High Street, Sevenoaks, Kent TN13 1LT
☎01732 459331   Fax 01732 461757

FOUNDED 1949. The Association aims to be the 'market leader for those involved in corporate media management and practice by providing professional, authoritative, dynamic, supportive and innovative services'.

British Association of Journalists

88 Fleet Street, London EC4Y 1PJ
☎0171 353 3003   Fax 0171 353 2310
General Secretary *Steve Turner*
Subscription National newspaper staff, national broadcasting staff, national news agency staff: £12.50 a month. Other seniors, including magazine journalists, PRs and freelancers who earn the majority of their income from journalism: £7.50 a month. Journalists under 24: £5 a month. Student journalists: Free.

FOUNDED 1992. Aims to protect and promote the industrial and professional interests of journalists.

BAPLA (British Association of Picture Libraries and Agencies)

18 Vine Hill, London EC1R 5DX
☎0171 713 1780   Fax 0171 713 1211
Administrator *Jane L. North*

Represents 95 per cent of the British picture library and agency industry offering more than 300 million pictures. The Association offers advice on costs, an annual membership directory, a picture-sourcing database, and produces an internationally admired journal.

British Copyright Council

Copyright House, 29-33 Berners Street, London W1P 4AA
Contact *The Secretary*

Works for the national and international acceptance of copyright and acts as a lobby/watchdog organisation on behalf of creators, publishers and performers on copyright and associated matters. Publications include *Guide to the Law of Copyright and Rights in Performances in the UK*; *Photocopying from Books and Journals*. An umbrella organisation which does not deal with individual enquiries.

The British Council

10 Spring Gardens, London SW1A 2BN
☎0171 930 8466/Press Office: 389 4878
Fax 0171 389 4971

Head of Literature *Neil Gilroy-Scott*

The British Council promotes Britain abroad. It provides access to British ideas, talents, expertise and experience in education and training, books and periodicals, the English language, literature and the arts, sciences and technology. An independent, non-political organisation, the British Council works in over 100 countries running a mix of offices, libraries, resource centres and English teaching operations.

British Equestrian Writers' Association

Priory House, Station Road, Swavesey, Cambridge CB4 5QJ
☎01954 232084   Fax 01954 231362

Contact *Gillian Newsum*
Subscription £10

FOUNDED 1973. Aims to further the interests of equestrian sport and improve, wherever possible, the working conditions of the equestrian press. Membership is by invitation of the committee. Candidates for membership must be nominated and seconded by full members and receive a majority vote of the committee.

British Film Commission

70 Baker Street, London W1M 1DJ
☎0171 224 5000   Fax 0171 224 1013

Chief Executive *Andrew Patrick*

FOUNDED 1991 the BFC is funded through the Department of National Heritage. Its remit is to promote the United Kingdom as an international production centre, to encourage the use of British personnel, technical services, facilities and locations, and to provide wide-ranging support to those filming and contemplating filming in the UK.

British Film Institute

21 Stephen Street, London W1P 2LN
☎0171 255 1444   Fax 0171 436 7950

Membership from £11.95-£56.60 p.a.
  (concessions available)

FOUNDED 1933. Exists to encourage the development of film, television and video in the UK. Its divisions include: National Film and Television Archive; BFI on the South Bank (National Film Theatre, London Film Festival and Museum of the Moving Image); **BFI Production**; **BFI Library and Information**

Services; and BFI Research & Education (including Publishing, *Sight and Sound*). It also provides programming support to a regional network of 46 film theatres.

British Guild of Beer Writers

PO Box 900, Hemel Hempstead, Herts HP3 0RJ
☎01442 834900   Fax 01442 834901

Contact *Peter Coulson*
Subscription £25 p.a.

FOUNDED 1988. Aims to improve standards in beer writing and at the same time extend public knowledge of beers and brewing. Publishes a directory of members with details of their publications and their particular areas of interest; this is then circulated to newspapers, magazines, trade press and broadcasting organisations. As part of the plan to improve writing standards and to achieve a higher profile for beer, the Guild offers annual awards, The Gold and Silver Tankard Awards, to writers and broadcasters judged to have made the most valuable contribution towards this end in their work. Meetings are held regularly.

British Guild of Travel Writers

90 Corringway, London W5 3HA
☎0181 998 2223

Chairman *John Bell*
Honorary Secretary *John Harrison*
Subscription £50 p.a.

The professional association of travel writers, broadcasters, photographers and editors which aims to serve its members' professional interests by acting as a forum for debate, discussion and 'networking'. It holds monthly meetings and has a monthly newsletter. Members are required to earn the majority of their income from travel reporting. The Guild represents its members to the BTA.

British Science Fiction Association

52 Woodhill Drive, Grove, Wantage, Oxon OX12 0DF

Membership Secretary *Ms Alison Cook*
Subscription £18 p.a.; £9 p.a. (Unwaged, with proof)

FOUNDED originally in 1958 by a group of authors, readers, publishers and booksellers interested in science fiction. With a worldwide membership, the Association aims to promote the reading, writing and publishing of science fiction and to encourage SF fans to maintain contact with each other. Also offers postal writers workshop, a magazine chain and an information service. *Publishes Matrix* bi-monthly newsletter with comment and opinions, news of conventions, etc. Contributions from members welcomed; *Vector* bi-monthly critical journal – reviews of books and magazines. Edited by Catie Cary; *Focus* bi-annual magazine with articles, original fiction and letters column. Edited by Carol Ann Green.

British Screen Finance
14–17 Wells Mews, London W1P 3FL
☎0171 323 9080   Fax 0171 323 0092
Contact *Simon Perry, Stephen Cleary*

A private company aided by government grant; shareholders are Rank, **Channel 4**, **Granada** and Pathé. Exists to invest in British films specifically intended for cinema release in the UK and worldwide. Divided into two functions: project development (contact *Stephen Cleary*), and production investment (contact *Simon Perry*). British Screen also manages the European Co-production Fund which exists to support feature films co-produced by the UK with other European countries. British Screen develops around 40 projects per year, and has invested in 115 British feature film productions in the last nine years.

British Society of Magazine Editors (BSME)
137 Hale Lane, Edgware, Middlesex HA8 9QP
☎0181 906 4664   Fax 0181 959 2137
Contact *Gill Branston*

FOUNDED 1960, aims to represent interests and needs of magazine editors in the UK from both business and consumer sectors.

Broadcasting Press Guild
Tiverton, The Ridge, Woking, Surrey GU22 7EQ
☎01483 764895   Fax 01483 764895
Membership Secretary *Richard Last*
Subscription £15 p.a.

FOUNDED 1973 to promote the professional interests of journalists specialising in writing or broadcasting about the media. Organises monthly lunches addressed by top broadcasting executives, and annual TV and radio awards.

Campaign for Press and Broadcasting Freedom
8 Cynthia Street, London N1 9JF
☎0171 278 4430   Fax 0171 837 8868
Subscription £12 p.a. (concessions

available); £25 p.a. (Institutions); £20 p.a. (Organisations)

Broadly based pressure group working for more accountable and accessible media in Britain. Advises on right of reply and takes up the issue of the portrayal of minorities. Members receive *Free Press* (bi-monthly), discounts on publications and news of campaign progress.

The Caravan Writers' Guild
Hillside House, Beach Road, Benllech, Anglesey, Gwynedd LL74 8SW
☎01248 852248   Fax 01248 852107
Contact *The Secretary*
Subscription £5 joining fee plus £10 p.a.

Guild for writers active in the specialist fields of caravan and camping journalism.

Careers Writers' Association
Manor Farm Lodge, Upper Wield, Alresford, Hampshire SO24 9RU
☎01420 562046
Membership Secretary *Katherine Lea*

FOUNDED 1979. The association aims to promote high standards of careers writing, improve access to sources of information, provide a network for members to exchange information and experience, hold meetings on topics of relevance and interest to members. Also produces an occasional newsletter and maintains a membership list. Forges links with organisations sharing related interests, and maintains regular contact with national education and training bodies, government agencies and publishers.

Chartered Institute of Journalists
2 Dock Offices, Surrey Quays Road, London SE16 2XU
☎0171 252 1187   Fax 0171 232 2302
General Secretary *Christopher Underwood*
Subscription £105–£170 (by assessment)

FOUNDED 1884. The Chartered Institute is concerned with professional journalistic standards and with safeguarding the freedom of the media. It is open to writers, broadcasters and journalists (including self-employed) in all media. Affiliation is available to part-time or occasional practitioners and to overseas journalists who can join the Institute's International Division. Members also belong to the IOJ (Institute of Journalists), an independent trade union which protects, advises and represents them in their employment or freelance work; negotiates on their behalf and provides legal assistance and support. The IOJ (TU) is a certificated trade union which represents members' interests in the workplace.

Children's Book Circle
c/o Orchard Books, 96 Leonard Street,
London EC2A 4RH
☎0171 739 2929   Fax 0171 739 2318
Contact *Nicola Noble*

The Children's Book Circle provides a discussion forum for anybody involved with children's books. Monthly meetings are addressed by a panel of invited speakers and topics focus on current and controversial issues. Administers the **Children's Book Circle Eleanor Farjeon Award**.

Children's Book Foundation
See **Book Trust**

Circle of Wine Writers
44 Oaklands Avenue, Droitwich,
Worcestershire WR9 7BT
☎01905 773707   Fax 01905 773707
Vice Chairman *Philippe Boucheron*
Membership £25 p.a.

FOUNDED 1962. Open to all *bona fide* authors, broadcasters, journalists, lecturers and tutors who are engaged in, or earn a significant part of their income from, communicating about wine and spirits. Aims to improve the standard of writing, broadcasting and lecturing about wine; to contribute to the growth of knowledge and interest in wine; to promote wine of quality in the UK and to comment adversely on faulty products or dubious practices which could lead to a fall in consumption; to establish and maintain good relations between the Circle and the wine trade in the best interests of the consumer.

Clé, The Irish Book Publishers Association
The Writers' Centre, 19 Parnell Square,
Dublin 1, Republic of Ireland
☎00 353 1 8729090   Fax 00 353 1 8722035
President *John Spillane*
Administrator *Hilary Kennedy*

FOUNDED 1970 to promote Irish publishing, protect members' interests and train the industry.

Comedy Writers' Association of Great Britain
61 Parry Road, Ashmore Park,
Wolverhampton, West Midlands WV11 2PS
☎01902 722729   Fax 01902 722729
Contact *Ken Rock*

FOUNDED 1981 to assist and promote the work of comedy writers. The Association is a self-help group designed to encourage and advise its members to sell their work. It is an international organisation with representatives in Britain, Germany, Cyprus, Sweden, Belgium, Luxembourg, Czechoslovakia, Denmark, Finland and Canada. International seminar with videos of foreign TV comedy programmes, bookshop and business club where members can discuss opportunities. Members often come together to work jointly on a variety of comedy projects for British and overseas productions. *Publishes* regular magazines and monthly market information.

The Copyright Licensing Agency Ltd
90 Tottenham Court Road, London
W1P 0LP
☎0171 436 5931   Fax 0171 436 3986
Chief Executive/Secretary *Colin P. Hadley*
Office Manager *Kate Gardner*

FOUNDED 1982 by the **Authors' Licensing and Collecting Society (ALCS)** and the **Publishers Licensing Society Ltd (PLS)**, the CLA administers collectively photocopying and other copying rights that it is uneconomic for writers and publishers to administer for themselves. The Agency issues collective and transactional licences, and the fees it collects, after the deduction of its operating costs, are distributed at regular intervals to authors and publishers via their respective societies (i.e. PLS or ALCS). Since 1987 CLA has distributed almost £40 million.

Council for British Archaeology
Bowes Morrell House, 111 Walmgate, York
YO1 2UA
☎01904 671417   Fax 01904 671384
Information Officer *Mike Heyworth*

FOUNDED 1944 to represent and promote archaeology at all levels. Its aims are to improve the public's awareness in and understanding of Britain's past; to carry out research; to survey, guide and promote the teaching of archaeology at all levels of education; to publish a wide range of academic, educational, general and bibliographical works (see **CBA Publishing**).

Council of Academic and Professional Publishers
See **The Publishers Association**

Crime Writers' Association (CWA)

PO Box 10772, London N6 4RY
Secretary *Richard Grayson*
Membership £40 (Town); £35 (Country)

Full membership is limited to professional crime writers, but publishers, literary agents, booksellers, etc., who specialise in crime are eligible for Associate membership. Meetings are held monthly in Soho, with informative talks frequently given by police, scenes of crime officers, lawyers, etc., and a weekend conference is held annually in different parts of the country. Produces a monthly newsletter for members called *Red Herrings* and presents various annual awards.

The Critics' Circle

c/o The Stage (incorporating Television Today), 47 Bermondsey Street, London SE1 3XT
☎0171 403 1818   Fax 0171 357 9287
President *Stephen Pettitt*
Honorary General Secretary *Peter Hepple*
Subscription £12 p.a.

Membership by invitation only. Aims to uphold and promote the art of criticism (and the commercial rates of pay thereof) and preserve the interests of its members: professionals involved in criticism of film, drama, music and dance.

Department of National Heritage

2-4 Cockspur Street, London SW1Y 5DH
☎0171 211 6000   Fax 0171 211 6270
Senior Press Officer, Arts *Toby Sargent*

The Department of National Heritage has responsibilities for Government policies relating to the arts, museums and galleries, public libraries, sport, broadcasting, Press standards, film, the built heritage, tourism and the National Lottery. It funds **The Arts Council**, national museums and galleries, **The British Library** (including the new library building at St Pancras), the Public Lending Right and the Royal Commission on Historical Manuscripts. It is responsible within Government for the public library service in England, and for library and information matters generally, where they are not the responsibility of other departments.

Directory Publishers Association

93A Blenheim Crescent, London W11 2EQ
☎0171 221 9089
Contact *Rosemary Pettit*

Subscription £100–£1000 p.a.

FOUNDED 1970 to promote the interests of *bona fide* directory publishers and protect the public from disreputable and fraudulent practices. The objectives of the Association are to maintain a code of professional practice to safeguard public interest; to raise the standard and status of directory publishing throughout the UK; to promote business directories as a medium for advertising; to protect the legal and statutory interests of directory publishers; to foster bonds of common interest among responsible directory publishers and provide for the exchange of technical, commercial and management information between members. Meetings, seminars, conference, newsletter and representation at book fairs.

Drama Association of Wales

The Library, Singleton Road, Splott, Cardiff CF2 2ET
☎01222 452200   Fax 01222 452277
Contact *Aled Rhys-Jones*

Runs a large playscript lending library; holds an annual playwriting competition (see under **Prizes**); offers a script-reading service (£10 per script) which usually takes three months from receipt of play to issue of reports. From plays submitted to the reading service, selected scripts are considered for publication of a short run (250-750 copies). Writers receive a percentage of the cover price on sales and a percentage of the performance fees.

East Anglian Writers

47 Christchurch Road, Norwich, Norfolk NR2 3NE
☎01603 455503   Fax 01603 455503
Chairman *Michael Pollard*

A group of over 80 professional writers living in Norfolk and Suffolk. Business and social meetings and informal contacts with regional publishers and other organisations interested in professional writing.

Edinburgh Bibliographical Society

Dept of Special Collections, Edinburgh University Library, George Square, Edinburgh EH8 9LJ
☎0131 650 3412   Fax 0131 650 6863
Honorary Secretary *Dr M. Simpson*
Subscription £7; £5 (Students)

FOUNDED 1890. Organises lectures on bibliographical topics and visits to libraries. *Publishes* a biennial journal called *Transactions*, which is free to members, and other occasional publications.

Educational Publishers Council
See **The Publishers Association**

Educational Television Association
37 Monkgate, York YO3 7PB
☎01904 639212   Fax 01904 639212
Administrator *Josie Key*

An umbrella organisation for individuals and organisations using television and other media for education and training. Annual awards scheme (video competition), and annual conferences. New members always welcome.

Electronic Publishers' Forum
See **The Publishers Association**

The English Association
University of Leicester, University Road, Leicester LE1 7RH
☎0116 252 3982   Fax 0116 252 2301
Secretary *Helen Lucas*

FOUNDED 1906 to promote understanding and appreciation of the English language and its literatures. Activities include sponsoring a number of publications and organising lectures and conferences for teachers, plus annual sixth-form conferences. Publications include *Year's Work in Critical and Cultural Theory, English, Use of English, Primary English, Year's Work in English Studies, Essays and Studies* and *Year's Work in English Studies.*

European Association for the Promotion of Poetry
See **Organisations of Interest to Poets**

Federation of Entertainment Unions
1 Highfield, Twyford, Nr Winchester, Hampshire SO21 1QR
☎01962 713134
Secretary *Steve Harris*

Plenary meetings six times annually and meetings of The Film and Electronic Media Committee six times annually on alternate months. Additionally, there are Training & European Committees. Represents the following unions: British Actors' Equity Association; Broadcasting Entertainment Cinematograph and Theatre Union; Musicians' Union; **National Union of Journalists; The Writers' Guild of Great Britain.**

The Federation of Worker Writers and Community Publishers (FWWCP)
PO Box 540, Burslem, Stoke on Trent ST6 6DR
☎01782 822327   Fax 01782 822327
Administrator/Coordinator *Tim Diggles*

The FWWCP is a federation of writing groups who are committed to writing and publishing based on working-class experience and creativity. The FWWCP is the membership's collective national voice and has for some time been given funding by **The Arts Council**. It was founded in 1976 and comprises around 50 member groups, each one with its own identity, reflecting its community and membership, offering a wealth of experience and support. The membership includes groups involved with community history, poetry, adult learners, local publishing, Black publishing, lesbian and gay writing, women's writing as well as open writers' groups. The main activities include training days and weekends to learn and share skills, a twice-yearly magazine, a major annual festival of writing, networking between member organisations and a regular newsletter. The FWWCP has published a number of anthologies and is willing to work with other organisations on publishing projects. Membership is only open to groups but individuals will be put in touch with groups which can help them, and become friends of the Federation. Send to the above address for an information leaflet.

Foreign Press Association in London
11 Carlton House Terrace, London SW1Y 5AJ
☎0171 930 0445   Fax 0171 925 0469
Contact *Davina Crole, Catherine Flury*
Membership (not incl. VAT) £91.50 p.a. (Full); £84 (Associate Journalists); £102 (Associate Non-Journalists)

FOUNDED 1888. Non-profit-making service association for foreign correspondents based in London, providing a variety of press-related services.

The Gaelic Books Council (Comhairle nan Leabhraichean)
22 Mansfield Street, Partick, Glasgow G12
Chairman *Professor Donald MacAulay*
Chief Executive *Ian MacDonald*

FOUNDED 1968. Encourages and promotes Gaelic publishing by offering grants to publishers and writers; providing editorial services; retailing and cataloguing Gaelic books; and answering enquiries related to them.

The Garden Writers' Guild

c/o Institute of Horticulture, 14/15 Belgrave Square, London SW1X 8PS
☎0171 245 6943

Contact *Angela Clarke*
Subscription £15; (£10 to Institute of Horticulture members)

FOUNDED 1990. Aims to revise the status and standing of gardening communicators. Administers an annual awards scheme. Operates a mailing service and organises press briefing days.

General Practitioner Writers' Association

Jasmine Cottage, Hampton Lucy, Warwick CV35 8BE
☎01789 840509

Contact *Dr F. M. Hull*
Subscription £30 p.a.; £40 (Joint)

FOUNDED 1986 to promote and improve writing activities within and for general practices. Open to general practitioners, practice managers, nurses, etc. and professional journalists writing on anything pertaining to general practice. Very keen to develop input from interested parties who work mainly outside the profession. Regular workshops, discussions and a twice-yearly newsletter.

Guild of Agricultural Journalists

The Farmers Club, 3 Whitehall Court, London SW1A 2EL
☎0171 930 3557   Fax 0171 839 7864

Honorary General Secretary *Don Gomery*
Subscription £25 p.a.

FOUNDED 1944 to promote a high professional standard among journalists who specialise in agriculture, horticulture and allied subjects. Represents members' interests with representative bodies in the industry; provides a forum through meetings and social activities for members to meet eminent people in the industry; maintains contact with associations of agricultural journalists overseas; promotes schemes for the education of members and for the provision of suitable entrants into agricultural journalism.

Guild of British Newspaper Editors

See **The Newspaper Society**

The Guild of Erotic Writers

PO Box 381, Selsdon Way, London E14 9GL
☎0171 987 5090   Fax 0171 538 3690

Contact *Elizabeth Coldwell, Zak Jane Keir*
Subscription £10 p.a.

FOUNDED 1995. Aims to provide a network for all authors of erotic fiction, both published and unpublished and to promote erotica as a valid form of writing. Members receive quarterly newsletters and a tip sheet on getting work accepted, together with discounts on quarterly conferences and a manuscript-reading service (also available to non-members).

Guild of Motoring Writers

30 The Cravens, Smallfield, Surrey RH6 9QS
☎01342 843294   Fax 01342 844093

General Secretary *Sharon Scott-Fairweather*

FOUNDED 1944. Represents members' interests and provides a forum for members to exchange information.

The Guild of Regional Film Writers

22 Gray Court, Gray Road, Sunderland, Tyne & Wear SR2 8DU
☎0191 565 0395

Secretary *Bernice Saltzer*

Subscription £40 p.a.

FOUNDED 1986. Aims to strengthen the voice of the regional film writers and broadcasters within the industry. Works with the publicists and attends screenings and press conferences with major stars. Members are invited to 'cinema days' and weekends. Would-be members have to supply cuttings/tapes to prove they work in the industry.

Humberside Writers' Association (HWA)

'Fairoaks', West Promenade, Driffield, East Yorkshire YO25 7TZ
☎01377 255542

Chairman *Glynn S. Russell*
Annual membership fee £2

FOUNDED 1987 by local writers, would-be writers and people interested in new writing who gathered together with the backing of their regional arts association to create a platform for local scribblers, published or otherwise. Organises and promotes writing-related events and workshops within the Humberside area. *Publishes* information about events, competitions, workshops, publications and any other news, local or national, about opportunities of interest to members. Regular meetings (last Wednesday of the month) to which writers, publishers and agents are invited; plus day schools, readings, newsletter and library/ resource unit.

Independent Publishers Guild

25 Cambridge Road, Hampton, Middlesex
TW12 2JL
☎0181 979 0250   Fax 0181 979 6393
Secretary *Yvonne Messenger*
Subscription approx. £75 p.a.

FOUNDED 1962. Membership open to independent publishers, packagers and suppliers, i.e. professionals in allied fields. Regular meetings, conferences, seminars, a bulletin and regional groups.

Independent Television Association
See **ITV Network Centre**

Independent Theatre Council

12 The Leathermarket, Weston Street,
London SE1 3ER
☎0171 403 1727/6698 (general/training)
Fax 0171 403 1745

Contact *Charlotte Jones*

The management association and representative body for small/middle-scale theatres (up to around 350 seats) and touring theatre companies. Negotiates contracts and has established standard agreements with Equity on behalf of all professionals working in the theatre. Negotiations with the **Theatre Writers' Union** and **The Writers' Guild** for a contractual agreement covering rights and fee structure for playwrights were concluded in 1991. Copies of the minimum terms agreement can be obtained from The Writers' Guild. *Publishes* a booklet giving guidance to writers on how to submit scripts to theatres and guidance to theatres on how to deal with them, called *A Practical Guide for Writers and Companies* (£3.50 plus p&p).

Institute of Translation and Interpreting

377 City Road, London EC1V 1NA
☎0171 713 7600   Fax 0171 713 7650

Membership is open to those who satisfy stringent admission criteria and can provide evidence of adequate professional translation or interpreting experience. Offers affiliation and student membership. Benefits include listing in an index which specifies the skills and languages of each member. *Publishes* a bi-monthly bulletin and a

Directory of Translators & Interpreters, listing qualified members of the ITI.

International Association of Puzzle Writers

11 Ratcliffe Avenue, Ryde, Isle of Wight
PO33 3DN
☎01983 565805

Contact *Dr Jeremy Sims*

FOUNDED 1996 for writers of brainteasing puzzles, crosswords and word games, and for designers of word games in general. Aims to provide support and information and to promote the art of puzzle writing and games design to publishers, games manufacturers and the general public. *Publishes* bi-monthly newsletter – contributions welcome. Membership is free but stamps or IRCs are necessary to cover the costs of postage of the newsletter. For further information, send s.a.e. to the above address.

International Cultural Desk

6 Belmont Crescent, Glasgow G12 8ES
☎0141 339 0090   Fax 0141 337 2271
Development Manager *Hilde Bollen*
Information Assistant *Anne Robb*

FOUNDED 1994. Aims to assist the Scottish cultural community to operate more effectively in an international context by providing timely and targeted information and advice. The Desk provides and disseminates information on funding sources, international opportunities and cultural policy development in Europe, and also assists with establishing contacts internationally. The Desk is not a funding agency. *Publishes Communication*, a bi-monthly information update about forthcoming international opportunities across the whole range of cultural and artistic activity.

Irish Book Publishers Association
See **Clé**

Irish Copyright Licensing Agency Ltd

19 Parnell Square, Dublin 1
Republic of Ireland
☎00 353 1 872 9090   Fax 00 353 1 872 2035

FOUNDED 1992 by writers and publishers in Ireland to provide a scheme through which rights holders can give permission, and users of copyright material can obtain permission, to copy. Established with the support of and advice from **The Copyright Licensing Agency Ltd** of the UK, and has a reciprocal agreement with CLA for an exchange of repertoires.

Irish Writers' Union
19 Parnell Square, Dublin 1
Republic of Ireland
☎00 353 1 872 1302   Fax 00 353 1 872 6282
Secretary *Sam McAughtry*
Subscription £20 p.a.

FOUNDED 1986 to promote the interests and protect the rights of writers in Ireland.

Isle of Man Authors
24 Laurys Avenue, Ramsey, Isle of Man
IM8 2HE
☎01624 815634
Secretary *Mrs Beryl Sandwell*
Subscription £7 p.a. (Free to members of The Society of Authors)

An association of writers living on the Isle of Man, which has links with **The Society of Authors**.

ITV Network Centre
200 Gray's Inn Road, London W1X 8HF
☎0171 843 8000   Fax 0171 843 8158

The ITV Network Centre, wholly owned by the ITV companies, independently commissions and schedules the television programmes which are shown across the ITV network. As a successor to the Independent Television Association, it also provides a range of services to the ITV companies where a common approach is required.

IVCA (International Visual Communication Association)
Bolsover House, 5–6 Clipstone Street, London
W1P 8LD
☎0171 580 0962   Fax 0171 436 2606
Chief Executive *Martin Walter*

The only European organisation which represents the interests of the users and suppliers of the corporate video, film, multimedia and live events industry.

The Kitley Trust
Toadstone Cottage, Edge New, Litton
SK17 8QU
☎01298 871564
Contact *Rosie Ford*

FOUNDED 1991 to promote creative writing. Aims to pay for a writer to go into one school per year for one day. 'Other activities are more ad hoc.'

The Library Association
7 Ridgmount Street, London WC1E 7AE
☎0171 636 7543   Fax 0171 436 7218

Chief Executive *Ross Shimmon*

The professional body for librarians and information managers, with 25,000 individual and institutional members. **Library Association Publishing** produces 25 new titles each year and has over 200 in print. The *LA Record* is the monthly magazine for members. Further information from Information Services, The Library Association.

The Media Society
PO Box 120, East Rudham, Norfolk
PE31 8TT
☎01485 528664   Fax 01485 528155
Contact *Rodney Bennett-England*
Subscription £25 p.a.; £10 entry fee

FOUNDED 1973. A registered charity which aims to provide a forum for the exchange of knowledge and opinion between those in public and political life, the professions, industry and education. Meetings (about six a year) usually take the form of luncheons and dinners in London with invited speakers. Also acts as a 'think tank' and submits evidence and observations to royal commissions, select committees and review bodies.

Medical Journalists' Association
Barley Mow, 185 High Street, Stony
Stratford, Milton Keynes MK11 1AP
☎01908 564623
Chairman *Michael Jeffries*
Honorary Secretary *Gwen Yates*
Subscription £20 p.a.

FOUNDED 1966/7. Aims to improve the quality and practice of medical and health journalism and to improve relationships and understanding between medical and health journalists and the health and medical professions. Regular meetings with senior figures in medicine and medico politics; teach-ins on particular subjects to help journalists with background information; weekend symposium for an invited audience of members and people with newsworthy stories in the field; awards for medical journalists offered by various commercial sponsors, plus MJA's own award financed by members. *Publishes* a detailed directory of members and freelances and two-monthly newsletter.

Medical Writers' Group
The Society of Authors, 84 Drayton Gardens,
London SW10 9SB
☎0171 373 6642   Fax 0171 373 5768
Contact *Jacqueline Granger-Taylor*

FOUNDED 1980. A specialist group within **The**

Society of Authors offering advice and help to authors of medical books. Administers the **Royal Society of Medicine Prizes**.

National Association of Writers Groups (NAWG)

The Arts Centre, Biddick Lane, Washington, Tyne & Wear NE38 2AB

Contact *The Secretary*

FOUNDED 1995 with the object of furthering the interests of writers' groups throughout the UK. Produces a bi-monthly newsletter, distributed to member groups, and a directory containing more than 900 writers' groups. Details available from the secretary at the above address.

National Association of Writers in Education

PO Box 1, Sheriff Hutton, York YO6 7YU
☎01653 618429   Fax 01653 618429

Contact *Paul Munden*
Subscription £12 p.a.

FOUNDED 1991. Aims to promote the contribution of living writers to education and to encourage both the practice and the critical appreciation of creative writing. Has over 400 members. Organises national conferences and training courses. *Publishes* a directory of writers who work in schools, colleges and the community and a magazine, *Writing in Education*, issued free to members three times per year.

National Campaign for the Arts

Francis House, Francis Street, London SW1P 1DE
☎0171 828 4448   Fax 0171 931 9959

Director *Jennifer Edwards*

FOUNDED 1984 to represent the cultural sector in Britain and to make sure that the problems facing the arts are properly put to Government, at local and national level. The NCA is an independent body relying on finance from its members. Involved in all issues which affect the arts: public finance, education, broadcasting and media affairs, the fight against censorship, the rights of artists, the place of the arts on the public agenda and structures for supporting culture. Membership open to all arts organisations (except government agencies) and to individuals. Overseas Associate Membership available.

National Poetry Foundation

See **Organisations of Interest to Poets**

The National Small Press Centre

c/o Middlesex University, White Hart Lane, London N17 8HR

The National Small Press Centre is committed to small presses in Britain, providing a focal point while actively raising the profile of small presses. Formerly known as the Small Press Group of Britain, it continues to raise public awareness of small presses and provides a programme of events which not only takes place at Middlesex University but also travels around Britain and abroad. Promotes small presses as a whole with exhibitions, talks, courses, workshops, conferences, regional small press fairs, small press-athons, small press studies, etc. *Publishes NSPC Handbook 1997; Small Press Listings* and *News From the Centre*.

National Union of Journalists

Acorn House, 314 Gray's Inn Road, London WC1X 8DP
☎0171 278 7916   Fax 0171 837 8143

General Secretary *John Foster*

Subscription £135 p.a. (Freelance) or 1% of annual income if lower

Represents journalists in all sectors of publishing, print and broadcast. Responsible for wages and conditions agreements which apply across the industry. Provides advice and representation for its members, as well as administering unemployment and other benefits. *Publishes* various guides and magazines: *Freelance Directory, Fees Guide, The Journalist* and *The Freelance* (see **Magazines**).

New Playwrights Trust

Interchange Studios, 15 Dalby Street, London NW5 3NQ
☎0171 284 2818   Fax 0171 482 5292

Contact *John Deeney, Research Director*
Subscription (information on rates available by post)

New Playwrights Trust is the national research and development organisation for writing for all forms of live and recorded performance. *Publishes* a range of information pertinent to writers on all aspects of development and production in the form of pamphlets, and a six-weekly journal which also includes articles and interviews on aesthetic and practical issues. NPT also runs a script-reading service and a link service between writers and producers, organises seminars and conducts research projects. The latter includes research into the use of bilingual techniques in playwriting (*Two Tongues*), documentation of training programmes for writers

(*Black Theatre Co-operative*) and an investigation of the relationship between live art and writing *Writing Live*.

New Producers Alliance (NPA)
9 Bourlet Close, London W1P 7PJ
☎0171 580 2480   Fax 0171 580 2484
Contact *Harriet Bass*
FOUNDED 1992. Aims to encourage the production of commercial feature films for an international audience and to educate and inform feature film producers in the UK. The NPA does not produce films so please do not send scripts or treatments.

The New SF Alliance (NSFA)
c/o BBR Magazine, PO Box 625, Sheffield, South Yorkshire S1 3GY
Contact *Chris Reed*
FOUNDED 1989. Committed to supporting the work of new writers and artists by promoting independent and small press publications worldwide. 'Help with finding the right market for your material by providing a mail-order service which allows you to sample magazines, and various publications including *BBR* magazine and *Scavenger's Newsletter*, which features the latest market news and tips.'

Newspaper Conference
See **The Newspaper Society**

The Newspaper Society
Bloomsbury House, 74–77 Great Russell Street, London WC1B 3DA
☎0171 636 7014   Fax 0171 631 5119
Director *Dugal Nisbet-Smith*
Young Newspaper Executives'
    Association *David Brown*
The association of publishers of the regional and local Press, representing 1,400 regional daily and weekly, paid and free, newspaper titles in the UK. The Newspaper Conference is an organisation within the Society for London editors and representatives of regional newspapers. Bloomsbury House is also home to the Guild of British Newspaper Editors and to the Young Newspaper Executives' Association.

Outdoor Writers Guild
PO Box 520, Bamber Bridge, Preston, Lancashire PR5 8LF
☎01772 696732   Fax 01772 696732
Honorary Secretary *Terry Marsh*
Subscription £35 p.a.
FOUNDED 1980 to promote a high professional standard among writers who specialise in outdoor activities; to represent members' interests; to circulate members with news of writing opportunities; to provide advice to members. Presents awards for excellence to members.

PACT (Producers Alliance for Cinema and Television)
Gordon House, Greencoat Place, London SW1P 1PH
☎0171 233 6000   Fax 0171 233 8935
Chief Executive *John Woodward*
Membership Officer *David Alan Mills*
FOUNDED 1992. PACT is the trade association of the UK independent television and feature film production sector and is a key contact point for foreign producers seeking British co-production, co-finance partners and distributors. Works for producers in the industry at every level and operates a members' regional network throughout the UK with a divisional office in Scotland. Membership services include: a dedicated industrial relations unit; discounted legal advice; a varied calendar of events; business advice; representation at international film and television markets; a comprehensive research programme; various publications: a monthly magazine, an annual members' directory; affiliation with European and international producers' organisations; extensive information and production advice. Lobbies actively with broadcasters, financiers and governments to ensure that the producer's voice is heard and understood in Britain and Europe on all matters affecting the film and television industry.

PEN
7 Dilke Street, London SW3 4JE
☎0171 352 6303   Fax 0171 351 0220
General Secretary *Gillian Vincent*
Membership £40 (London/Overseas);
£35 (members resident 50 miles from London)
English PEN is part of International PEN, a worldwide association of writers which fights for freedom of expression and speaks out for writers who are imprisoned or harassed for having criticised their governments, or for publishing other unpopular views. FOUNDED in London in 1921, International PEN now consists of 126 centres in 92 countries. PEN originally stood for poets, essayists and novelists, but membership is now also open to published playwrights, editors, translators and journalists. A programme of talks and discussions is supplemented by the publication of a twice-yearly magazine.

The Penman Club

185 Daws Heath Road, Benfleet, Essex
SS7 2TF
☎01702 557431

Subscription £15 in the first year; £8.25
thereafter

FOUNDED 1950. Writers' society offering criticism of members' work and general advice.
Send s.a.e. for prospectus to the General
Secretary.

Performing Right Society

29-33 Berners Street, London W1P 4AA
☎0171 580 5544   Fax 0171 631 4138

Collects and distributes royalties arising from
the performance and broadcast of copyright
music on behalf of its composer, lyricist and
music publisher members and members of affiliated societies worldwide.

Periodical Publishers Association (PPA)

Queens House, 28 Kingsway, London
WC2B 6JR
☎0171 379 6268   Fax 0171 379 5661

Contact *Nicholas Mazur*

FOUNDED 1913 to promote and protect the
interests of magazine publishers in the UK.

The Personal Managers' Association Ltd

1 Summer Road, East Molesey, Surrey
KT8 9LX
☎0181 398 9796   Fax 0181 398 9796

Co-chairs *Jane Annakin, Marc Berlin, David
Wilkinson*
Secretary *Angela Adler*
Subscription £200 p.a.

An association of artists' and dramatists' agents
(membership not open to individuals).
Monthly meetings for exchange of information
and discussion. Maintains a code of conduct
and acts as a lobby when necessary. Applicants
screened. A high proportion of play agents are
members of the PMA.

Player-Playwrights

9 Hillfield Park, London N10 3QT
☎0181 883 0371

President *Jack Rosenthal*
Contact *Peter Thompson (at the above address)*
Subscription £5 p.a., plus £1 per attendance

FOUNDED 1948. A society giving opportunity
for writers new to stage, radio and television, as
well as others finding difficulty in achieving
results, to work with writers established in
those media. At weekly meetings (7.45-10.00
p.m., Mondays, St Augustine's Hall, Queen's
Gate, London SW7), members' scripts are read
or performed by actor members and afterwards
assessed and dissected in general discussion.
Newcomers and new acting members are
always welcome.

Poetry Association of Scotland

See **Organisations of Interest to Poets**

Poetry Book Society

See **Organisations of Interest to Poets**

Poetry Ireland

See **Organisations of Interest to Poets**

The Poetry Society

See **Organisations of Interest to Poets**

Private Libraries Association

16 Brampton Grove, Kenton, Harrow,
Middlesex HA3 8LG
☎0181 907 6802   Fax 0181 907 6802

Honorary Secretary *Frank Broomhead*
Membership £25 p.a.

FOUNDED 1956. An international society of
book collectors. The Association's objectives
are to promote and encourage the awareness of
the benefits of book ownership, and the study
of books, their production, and ownership; to
publish works concerned with this, particularly
those which are not commercially profitable,
to hold meetings at which papers on cognate
subjects can be read and discussed. Lectures and
exhibitions are open to non-members.

The Publishers Association

19 Bedford Square, London WC1B 3HJ
☎0171 580 6321-5/580 7761/323 1548
Fax 0171 636 5375

Chief Executive *Clive Bradley*

The national UK trade association for books,
learned journals, and electronic publications,
with around 300 member companies in the
industry. Very much a trade body representing
the industry to Government and the European
Commission, and providing services to publishers. *Publishes* the *Directory of Publishing* in association with **Cassell**. Also home of the General
Books Council (trade books), the Educational
Publishers Council (school books), PA's
International Division (BDC), the Council of
Academic and Professional Publishers, and the
Electronic Publishers' Forum.

Publishers Licensing Society Ltd

90 Tottenham Court Road, London
W1P 9HE
☎0171 436 5931   Fax 0171 436 3986
Manager *Caroline Elmslie*

FOUNDED 1981 to exercise and enforce on behalf of publishers the rights of copyright and other rights of a similar nature; to authorise the granting of licences for the making of reprographic copies; and to receive and distribute to the relevant publisher and copyright proprietors the sums accruing from such licensed use.

Publishers Publicity Circle

48 Crabtree Lane, London SW6 6LW
☎0171 385 3708   Fax 0171 385 3708
Contact *Christina Thomas*

Enables book publicists from both publishing houses and freelance PR agencies to meet and share information regularly. Meetings are held monthly in central London which provide a forum for press journalists, television and radio researchers and producers to meet publicists collectively. A directory of the PPC membership is published each year and distributed to over 2000 media contacts.

Queer Scribes

c/o MASG, PO Box 11, Liverpool L69 1SN
☎0151 260 8990
Contact *Joe Lavelle*

FOUNDED 1994 to provide a forum for lesbian, gay and bisexual writers (new or experienced) living or working in the Merseyside area. Holds monthly meetings, workshops and readings. A sample copy of *Outlines*, the group's bimonthly newsletter, is available by sending £1 to Queer Scribes; send s.a.e. for details of meetings. Eager to network with other organisations and share information.

The Romantic Novelists' Association

Queens Farm, 17 Queens Street, Tintinhull, Somerset BA22 8PG
☎01935 822808
Contact *Margaret Graham*
Subscription £20 p.a.

Membership is open to published writers of romantic novels, or two or more full-length serials. Associate membership is open to publishers, editors, literary agents, booksellers, librarians and others having a close connection with novel writing and publishing. Meetings are held in London and guest speakers are often invited.

RNA News is published quarterly and issued free to members. The Association makes two annual awards. **The Major Award** for the Romantic Novel of the Year, and **The New Writers Award**

Royal Festival Hall Literature Office

Performing Arts Department, Royal Festival Hall, South Bank Centre, London SE1 8XX
☎0171 921 0907   Fax 0171 928 2049
Head of Literature *Antonia Byatt*

The Royal Festival Hall presents a year-round literature programme covering all aspects of writing. Regular series range from New Voices to Fiction International and there is a biennial Poetry International Festival. Literature events are now programmed in the Voice Box, Purcell Room and Queen Elizabeth Hall. Mike Phillips is the Writer in Residence. To join the free mailing list, phone 0171 921 0906.

Royal Society of Literature

1 Hyde Park Gardens, London W2 2LT
☎0171 723 5104   Fax 0171 402 0199
President *Lord Jenkins of Hillhead*
Subscription £25 p.a.

FOUNDED 1823. Membership by application to the Secretary. Fellowships are conferred by the Society on the proposal of two Fellows. Membership benefits include journal *Letters*, lectures, discussion meetings and poetry readings in the Society's rooms. Lecturers have included Patrick Leigh Fermor, Germaine Greer, Seamus Heaney, John Mortimer and Tom Stoppard. Presents the **W. H. Heinemann Prize** and the **Winifred Holtby Memorial Prize**.

Royal Television Society

Holborn Hall, 100 Gray's Inn Road, London WC1X 8AL
☎0171 430 1000   Fax 0171 430 0924
Subscription £52

FOUNDED 1927. Covers all disciplines involved in the television industry. Provides a forum for debate and conferences on technical, social and cultural aspects of the medium. Presents various awards including journalism, programmes, technology, design and commercials. *Publishes Television Magazine* eight times a year for members and subscribers.

Science Fiction Foundation

c/o Liverpool University Library, PO Box 123, Liverpool L69 3DA
☎0151 794 2696/2733   Fax 0151 794 2681

The SFF is a national academic body for the furtherance of science fiction studies. *Publishes* a thrice-yearly magazine, *Foundation* (see under **Magazines**), which features academic articles and reviews of new fiction. It also has a reference library (see under **Library Services**), now housed at Liverpool University.

Scottish Library Association
Motherwell Business Centre, Coursington Road, Motherwell, Strathclyde ML1 1PW
☎01698 252526   Fax 01698 252057
Director *Robert Craig*

FOUNDED 1908 to bring together everyone engaged in or interested in library work in Scotland. The Association has over 2300 members, covering all aspects of library and information work. Its main aims are the promotion of library services and the qualifications and status of librarians.

Scottish Newspaper Publishers Association
48 Palmerston Place, Edinburgh EH12 5DE
☎0131 220 4353   Fax 0131 220 4344
Director *Mr J. B. Raeburn*

FOUNDED around 1905. The representative body for the publishers of paid-for weekly and associated free newspapers in Scotland. Represents the interests of the industry to Government, public and other bodies and provides a range of services including industrial relations, education and training, and advertising. It is an active supporter of the Press Complaints Commission.

Scottish Print Employers Federation
48 Palmerston Place, Edinburgh EH12 5DE
☎0131 220 4353   Fax 0131 220 4344
Director *Mr J. B. Raeburn*

FOUNDED 1910. Employers' organisation and trade association for the Scottish printing industry. Represents the interests of the industry to Government, public and other bodies and provides a range of services including industrial relations. Negotiates a national wages and conditions agreement with the Graphical, Paper and Media Union, as well as education, training and commercial activities. The Federation is a member of Intergraf, the international confederation for employers' associations in the printing industry. In this capacity its views are channelled on the increasing number of matters affecting print businesses emanating from the European Union.

The Scottish Publishers Association
Scottish Book Centre, 137 Dundee Street, Edinburgh EH11 1BG
☎0131 228 6866   Fax 0131 228 3220
Director *Lorraine Fannin*
Administrator *Neil Gowans*

The Association represents nearly 70 Scottish publishers, from multinationals to very small presses, in a number of capacities, but primarily in the cooperative promotion and marketing of their books. The SPA also acts as an information and advice centre for both the trade and general public. *Publishes* seasonal catalogues, membership lists, a directory of publishing in Scotland and regular newsletters. Represents members at international book fairs; provides opportunities for publishers' training; carries out market research; and encourages export initiatives.

'Sean Dorman' Manuscript Society
See **Writers' Courses, Circles and Workshops**

Small Press Group of Great Britain
See **National Small Press Centre**

The Society of Authors in Scotland
24 March Hall Crescent, Edinburgh EH16 5HL
☎0131 667 5230
Secretary *Alanna Knight*

The Scottish branch of **The Society of Authors**, which organises business meetings and social events in Scotland.

The Society of Authors
84 Drayton Gardens, London SW10 9SB
☎0171 373 6642   Fax 0171 373 5768
General Secretary *Mark Le Fanu*
Subscription £65/70 p.a.

FOUNDED 1884. The Society of Authors is an independent trade union with some 5800 members. It advises on negotiations with publishers, broadcasting organisations, theatre managers and film companies; takes up complaints and pursues legal action for breach of contract, copyright infringement, etc. Together with **The Writers' Guild**, the Society has played a major role in advancing the Minimum Terms Agreement for authors. Among the Society's publications are *The Author* (a quarterly journal), *The Electronic Author* (twice yearly) and the *Quick Guides* series to various aspects of writing (all free of charge to members). Other services include emergency funds for writers and various special discounts. There are groups within the Society for scriptwriters, children's writers and illustrators, educational writers, medical writers and translators. Authors under 35, who are not yet earning a significant income from their writing, may apply for membership at a lower subscription of £52. Contact the Society for a free booklet giving further information.

Society of Civil Service Authors

4 Top Street, Wing, Nr Oakham, Rutland LE15 8SE

Membership Secretary *Mrs Joan Hykin*
Subscription £12 p.a.

FOUNDED 1935. Aims to encourage authorship by present and past members of the Civil Service and to provide opportunities for social and cultural relationships between civil servants who are authors or who aspire to be authors. Annual competitions, open to members only, are held for short stories, poetry, sonnets, travel articles, humour, etc. Members receive *The Civil Service Author*, a bi-monthly magazine. Occasional meetings in London, one or two weekends outside London.

Society of Freelance Editors and Proofreaders (SFEP)

c/o SFEP Office, 38 Rochester Road, London NW1 9JJ
☎0171 813 3113

Chair *Michèle Clarke*
Vice-chair *Mary Fox*
Secretary *Valerie Elliston*
Subscription £35.25 p.a. (Individuals); £23.50 (Joint); £70 – £176 (Corporate, depending on size of company); plus £11.75 registration fee for new members

FOUNDED 1988 in response to the growing number of freelance editors and their increasing importance to the publishing industry. Aims to promote high editorial standards by disseminating information and through advice and training, and to achieve recognition of the professional status of its members. The Society also supports moves towards recognised standards of training and qualifications, and is currently putting in place accredited and registered membership of SFEP.

Society of Indexers

38 Rochester Road, London NW1 9JJ
☎0171 916 7809

Secretary *Claire Troughton*

Subscription £25 p.a.; £38 (Institutions)

FOUNDED 1957. Publishes *The Indexer* (bi-annual, April and October) and a quarterly newsletter. Issues an annual list of members and the *(IA) Indexers Available*, which lists members and their subject expertise. In addition the Society runs an open-learning course entitled *Training in Indexing* and recommends rates of pay (currently £11 per hour).

Society of Picture Researchers & Editors (SPREd)

455 Finchley Road, London NW3 6HN
☎0171 431 9886   Fax 0171 431 9887

Subscription Members: Intermediate £30; Full £40. Magazine only: £25 per year quarterly

FOUNDED 1977 as a professional body for picture researchers and picture editors. Not a trade union but a society for those who wish to share problems and exchange information on all aspects dealing with illustration. The Society's main aims are to promote the recognition of picture research as a profession; to promote and maintain professional standards; to bring together those involved in the research and publication of visual material and provide a forum for the exchange of information; to encourage the use of trained researchers throughout publishing and other media; and to provide guidance to its members. Regular meetings and a quarterly magazine.

Society of Sussex Authors

Bookends, Lewes Road, Horsted Keynes, Haywards Heath, West Sussex RH17 7DP
☎01825 790755   Fax 01825 790755

Contact *Michael Legat*
Subscription £8 p.a.

FOUNDED 1968 to promote the interests of its members and of literature, particularly within the Sussex area. Regular meetings and exchange of information; plus social events. Membership restricted to writers who live in Sussex and who have had at least one book commercially published. Meetings held six times a year in Lewes.

Society of Women Writers and Journalists

110 Whitehall Road, London E4 6DW
☎0181 529 0886

Honorary Secretary *Jean Hawkes*
Subscription £25 (Town); £21 (Country); £15 (Overseas). £10 joining fee

FOUNDED 1894. The first of its kind to be run as

an association of women engaged in journalism. Aims to encourage literary achievement, uphold professional standards, and establish social contacts with other writers. Lectures given at monthly lunchtime meetings. Offers advice to members and has regular seminars, etc. *Publishes* a quarterly society journal, *The Woman Journalist*.

Society of Young Publishers
12 Dyott Street, London WC1A 1DF
Subscription £20 p.a.; £15 (Student/ unwaged)

Provides facilities whereby members can increase their knowledge and widen their experience of all aspects of publishing. Open to those in related occupations, with associate membership available for over-35s. *Publishes* a monthly newsletter called *Inprint* and holds meetings on the last Wednesday of each month at **The Publishers Association**.

The South and Mid-Wales Association of Writers (S.A.M.W.A.W)
c/o I.M.C. Consulting Group, Denham House, Lambourne Crescent, Cardiff CF4 5ZW
☎01222 761170   Fax 01222 761304
Contact *Julian Rosser*
Subscription £7 (Single); £12 (Joint)

FOUNDED 1971 to foster the art and craft of writing in all its forms. Provides a common meeting ground for writers, critics, editors, adjudicators from all over the UK and abroad. Organises an annual residential weekend conference and a day seminar in May and October respectively. Holds competitions - two for members only and two which are open to the public - **The Mathew Pritchard Award for Short Story Writing** (£1500 prize) and The HMSO Poetry Competition.

South Eastern Writers' Association
47 Sunningdale Avenue, Leigh-on-Sea, Essex SS9 1JY
☎01702 77083   Fax 01702 77083
President *Marion Hough*

FOUNDED 1989 to bring together writers, both experienced and novice, in an informative but informal atmosphere. A non-profit-making organisation, the Association holds a weekend residential conference in March each year at the Smoke House, Mildenhall, Suffolk. Recent guest speakers: Simon Brett, Jonathan Gash, George Layton, Maureen Lipman, Terry Pratchett, Jack Rosenthal.

Sports Writers' Association of Great Britain
c/o Sports Council Press Office, 16 Upper Woburn Place, London WC1H 0QP
☎0171 387 9415   Fax 0171 383 0273
Secretary *Trevor Bond*
Subscription £15 p.a.

FOUNDED 1948 to promote and maintain a high professional standard among journalists who specialise in sport in all its branches and to serve members' interests.

SPREd
See **Society of Picture Researchers & Editors**

Sussex Playwrights' Club
2 Princes Avenue, Hove, East Sussex BN3 4GD
☎01273 734985
Secretary *Mrs Constance Cox*
Subscription £5 p.a.

FOUNDED 1935. Aims to encourage the writing of plays for stage, radio and TV by giving monthly dramatic readings of members' work by experienced actors, mainly from local drama groups. Gives constructively criticised suggestions as to how work might be improved, and suggests possible marketing. Membership is not confined to writers but to all who are interested in theatre in all its forms, and all members are invited to take part in such discussions. Guests are always welcome at a nominal 50p. Meetings held at New Venture Theatre, Bedford Place, Brighton, East Sussex.

Theatre Writers' Union
c/o The Actors' Centre, 1A Tower Street, London WC2H 9ND
☎0181 673 6636
Chair *David Edgar*
Administrator *Suzy Gilmour*

Formed in the mid 1970s. Specialises in the concerns of all who write for theatre, of whatever kind. Has national branch network. Actively seeks a membership which represents the diversity of playwriting today. Many members are also active in other media: radio, TV, film and video. Responsible for the very first standard agreements on minimum pay and conditions for playwrights working in British theatre. Any playwright who has written a play is eligible to join. Annual subscription is related to income from playwriting. Members may receive legal and professional advice, copies of standard contracts and regular newsletters. As affiliates to the

General Federation of Trade Unions, TWU has access to their legal and education services.

The Translators Association
84 Drayton Gardens, London SW10 9SB
☎0171 373 6642   Fax 0171 373 5768
Contact *Gordon Fielden*

FOUNDED 1958 as a subsidiary group within **The Society of Authors** to deal exclusively with the special problems of literary translators into the English language. Members are entitled to all the benefits and services of the parent Society without extra charge. The Association offers them free legal and general advice and assistance on all matters relating to translators' work, including the vetting of contracts and information about improvements in fees. Membership is normally confined to translators who have had their work published in volume or serial form or produced in this country for stage, television or radio. Translators of technical work for industrial firms or government departments are in certain cases admitted to membership if their work, though not on general sale, is published by the organisation commissioning the work.

Ver Poets
Haycroft, 61–63 Chiswell Green Lane, St Albans, Hertfordshire AL2 3AL
☎01727 867005
Chairman *Ray Badman*
Editor/Organiser *May Badman*
Membership £10 p.a.; £12.50 or US$25 (Overseas)

FOUNDED 1966 to promote poetry and to help poets. With postal and local members, holds meetings in St Albans; runs a poetry bookstall for members' books and publications from other groups; publishes members' work in magazines; and organises poetry competitions, including the annual **Ver Poets Open** competition. Gives help and advice whenever they are sought; and makes information available to members about other poetry groups, events and opportunities for publication.

Voice of the Listener and Viewer
101 Kings Drive, Gravesend, Kent DA12 5BQ
☎01474 352835

An independent, non-profit-making society working to ensure independence and high standards in broadcasting. The only consumer body speaking for listeners and viewers on the whole range of broadcasting issues. VLV is funded by its members and is free from sectarian, commercial and political affiliations. Holds public lectures, seminars and conferences, and has frequent contact with MPs, civil servants, the BBC and independent broadcasters, regulators, academics and other consumer groups. VLV has responded to all parliamentary and public enquiries on broadcasting since 1984 and to all consultation documents issued by the ITC and Radio Authority since 1990.

W.A.T.C.H.
See **Writers and their Copyright Holders**

Welsh Academy
3rd Floor, Mount Stuart House, Mount Stuart Square, Cardiff CF1 6DQ
☎01222 492025   Fax 01222 492930
Director *Kevin Thomas*

FOUNDED 1968. The Welsh Academy is the English Language section of **Yr Academi Gymreig**, the national society of Welsh writers. The Academy exists to promote English literature in Wales. Organises readings, an annual conference (usually held in May) and literary events such as the **Cardiff Literature Festival**. There are three tiers of membership: Fellow (max. 12, an honorary position offered to those who have made an outstanding contribution to the literature of Wales over a number of years); Member (open to all who are deemed to have made a contribution to the literature of Wales whether writers, editors or critics); Associate Member (open to all who are interested in the Academy's work). Publications include: *BWA*, the Academy's newsletter; *The Oxford Companion to the Literature of Wales*; *Writing in Wales*; *The Literature of Wales in Secondary Schools*; *How the Earth Was Formed Quiz And Other Poems and Stories by Children*; *The New Welsh Review*; *A Bibliography of Anglo-Welsh Literature*; *Interweave*.

Welsh Books Council (Cyngor Llyfrau Cymru)
Castell Brychan, Aberystwyth, Dyfed SY23 2JB
☎01970 624151   Fax 01970 625385
Director *Gwerfyl Pierce Jones*
Head of Editorial Department *Dewi Morris Jones*

FOUNDED 1961 to stimulate interest in Welsh literature and to support authors. The Council distributes the government grant for Welsh language publications and promotes and fosters all aspects of both Welsh and Welsh interest book production. Its Editorial, Design, Marketing and

Children's Books departments and wholesale distribution centre offer central services to publishers in Wales. Writers in Welsh and English are welcome to approach the Editorial Department for advice on how to get their manuscripts published. *Books in Wales/Llais Llyfrau* is a quarterly publication which includes book lists, reviews and articles on various aspects of Welsh writing and publishing (see under **Magazines**).

Welsh Union of Writers
13 Richmond Road, Roath, Cardiff
CF2 3AQ
☎01222 490303
Secretary *John Harrison*
Subscription £10 p.a.; £5 joining fee

FOUNDED 1982. Independent union. Full membership by application to persons born or working in Wales with at least one publication in a quality journal or other outlet. Associate membership now available for other interested supporters. Lobbies for writing in Wales, represents members in disputes; annual conference and occasional events and publications.

West Country Writers' Association
Malvern View, Garway Hill, Hereford,
Hereford & Worcester HR2 8EZ
☎01981 580495
President *Christopher Fry*
Honorary Secretary *Mrs Anne Double*
Subscription £10 p.a.

FOUNDED 1951 in the interest of published authors with an interest in the West Country. Meets to discuss news and views and to listen to talks. Conference and newsletters.

Women in Publishing
c/o The Bookseller, 12 Dyott Street, London
WC1A 1DF
Contact *Information Officer*
Membership £20 p.a. (Individuals); £15
   (Unwaged); £25 (if paid for by company)

Aims to promote the status of women working within the publishing industry and related trades, to encourage networking, and to provide training for career and personal development. Meetings held on the second Wednesday of the month at **The Publishers Association** (see entry for address) at 6.30 pm. Monthly newsletter.

Women Writers Network (WWN)
23 Prospect Road, London NW2 2JU
☎0171 794 5861
Membership Secretary *Cathy Smith*

Subscription £25 p.a.; £30 p.a. (Overseas)

FOUNDED 1985. Provides a forum for the exchange of information, support, career and networking opportunities for working women writers. Meetings, seminars, excursions, newsletter and directory. Branches in the north-east and north-west of England; details from the Membership Secretary at the above address.

Writers and their Copyright Holders (W.A.T.C.H.)
The Library, The University of Reading,
PO Box 223, Whiteknights, Reading,
Berkshire RG6 6AE
☎0118 9318783   Fax 0118 9316636
Contact *Dr David Sutton*

FOUNDED 1994. Provides an on-line database of information about the copyright holders of literary authors. The database is available free of charge on the Internet and the world wide web. W.A.T.C.H. is the successor project to the Location Register of English Literary Manuscripts and Letters, and continues to deal with location register enquiries.

Writers in Oxford
7 London Place, Oxford OX4 1BD
☎01865 251250
Contact *Sara Banerji*
Subscription £15 p.a.

FOUNDED 1992. Open to published authors, playwrights, poets and journalists. Linked to **The Society of Authors** but organised locally. Arranges a programme of meetings, seminars and functions. *Publishes* quarterly newsletter, *The Oxford Writer*.

The Writers' Guild of Great Britain
430 Edgware Road, London W2 1EH
☎0171 723 8074   Fax 0171 706 2413
General Secretary *Alison V. Gray*

Annual subscription 1% of that part of the author's income earned in the areas in which the Guild operates, with a basic subscription of £70 and a maximum of £920

FOUNDED 1959. The Writers' Guild is the writers' trade union, affiliated to the TUC. It represents writers in film, radio, television, theatre and publishing. The Guild has negotiated agreements on which writers' contracts are based with the BBC, Independent Television companies, and **PACT** (the Producers' Alliance for Cinema and Television). Those agreements are regularly renegotiated, both in terms of finance and conditions.

In 1979, together with the **Theatre Writers' Union**, the Guild negotiated the first ever industrial agreement for theatre writers, the TNC Agreement, which covers the Royal National Theatre, the RSC, and the English Stage Company. Further agreements have been negotiated with the Theatre Management Association which covers regional theatre and the **Independent Theatre Council**, the organisation which covers small theatres and the Fringe.

The Guild initiated a campaign over ten years ago which achieved the first ever publishing agreement for writers with the publisher W. H. Allen. Jointly with **The Society of Authors**, that campaign has continued and each year sees new agreements with more publishers. Perhaps the most important breakthrough came with **Penguin** on 20 July 1990. The Guild now also has agreements covering **HarperCollins**, **Random House Group** and **Transworld**.

The Guild regularly provides individual help and advice to members on contracts, conditions of work, and matters which affect a member's life as a professional writer. Members are given the opportunity of meeting at craft meetings, which are held on a regular basis throughout the year. Membership is by a points system. One major piece of work (a full-length book, an hour-long television or radio play, a feature film, etc.) entitles the author to full membership; writers who do not qualify for Full Membership may qualify for Associate Membership; they currently pay the basic subscription only of £70.

Yachting Journalists' Association

3 Friars Lane, Maldon, Essex CM9 6AG
☎01621 855943   Fax 01621 855943
Honorary Secretary *Peter Cook*
Subscription £30 p.a.

To further the interest of yachting, sail and power, and to provide support and assistance to journalists in the field. A handbook listing members' details available free of charge.

Young Newspaper Executives' Association
See **The Newspaper Society**

Yr Academi Gymreig

3rd Floor, Mount Stuart House, Mount Stuart Square, Cardiff CF1 6DQ
☎01222 492064   Fax 01222 492930
Director *Dafydd Rogers*

FOUNDED 1959. National society of Welsh writers. Aims to encourage writing in Welsh. *Publishes Taliesin*, plus books on Welsh literature and an English/Welsh dictionary. Organises readings, conferences and general literary events. Various tiers of membership available.

Publish And Be Sued

An update on changes to the Libel Laws

The softly, softly reform of the libel laws surfaced briefly last year when the judge in the David Ashby case set guidelines for damages the jury might see fit to award. Anything less than £50,000 would be niggardly, he said, while a run in excess of £120,000 would be extravagant. In the event Mr Ashby lost his action against *The Sunday Times* so instead of collecting a cheque, however moderate, he was handed a legal bill estimated to be around £350,000. At this point the Conservative MP might have wished that the judge had exercised a wider discretion by advising lawyers to put the lid on their fees.

No such luck, Mr Ashby. Not now; not ever. The libel litigant, says Tom Crone, author of *Law and the Media*, must possess two prime qualities. One is a deep pocket. The other, a strong nerve.

The standard definition of libel is the publication of a statement which tends to lower a person's reputation in the estimation of 'right thinking members of society'. Twenty years ago the Faulkes Committee on Defamation suggested minimising the value judgement implied by 'right thinking' by relying instead on the estimation of 'reasonable people'. But the arcane form of words survives, presumably, on the assumption that in our muddled world and despite all contrary evidence, 'right thinking' is still an identifiable attribute.

The obvious defence to libel – that a statement, however defamatory – is true in substance and in fact, is usually hard to prove. That Maxwell managed to get away with his crimes for so long was largely because of his skilful deployment of the libel laws. A second line of defence turns on the assertion that the words complained of are fair comment on a matter of public interest. The trick here is for the defendant to show that he was not activated by malice. But if the facts on which he based his comment are untrue, he is in trouble anyway.

Where libel has been committed unintentionally or 'innocently' it is possible to avoid dire consequences by 'an offer to make amends'. Under new rules, this may take the form of a public apology. Previously an apology depended on its being agreed between the parties. If damages cannot be agreed, a judge, sitting without a jury, will assess them. In doing so, credit will be given for having made the offer of amends. For an author who has strayed, a public apology by way of a statement in open court or an advertisement in a book trade publication might be deemed appropriate.

If the offer of amends procedure is not available, a writer may be able to rely on the fast track procedure that will soon be introduced to deal with the less complicated type of libel action. David Hooper, author of *Public Scandal, Odium and Contempt*, tells us that 'at an early stage in each libel action, a judge will review the case. If satisfied that the claim has no reasonable prospect of success, the action can be dismissed without the need for a full trial. If, on the other hand, the judge thinks there is no real defence to the claim and the libel is not particularly serious, the case can be dealt with summarily – without a jury. The judge may award up to £10,000 damages and can order the publication of a suitable apology or correction. The innovation is that in libel litigation a plaintiff can now, as in other types of litigation, seek summary judgement where there is no viable defence without having to go to a full trial.' The substantial saving of legal costs, however, must be balanced against the possibility of more libel claims now that they look like being cheaper.

Another change to the law is the reduction of the limitation period for bringing libel claims from three years to one year. This may not be as helpful as it first appears since each sale, even out of long-remaindered stock, is a fresh act of publication. Claims many years after first publication will probably be dealt with summarily though the draft Bill builds in a number of safeguards for the plaintiff who is unable to bring an action within the limitation period. Potentially a libel claim can be brought years after the event based on a single sale or a trip to a databank. In 1849 the Duke of Brunswick successfully sued a Mr Harmer after sending out his servant to buy a back number of a newspaper published seventeen years previously. This remains the law.

In libel there is no obligation to prove that any actual damage as opposed to hurt to reputation has been suffered. It may be that the defendant in a libel case did not intend harm. No matter. All that the plaintiff need show is that the offending statement would be understood by right thinking people to refer to him. There is a clear warning here for fiction writers not to venture too close to real life. It may seem a neat idea to introduce friends and neighbours into a story – it is so much easier to describe people you know – but if one of them is cast in an unsavoury light and recognises himself, albeit in an unlikely role, then a solicitor's letter will surely follow.

Names, too, can be a trap for the unwary. If a novel features a corrupt member of parliament, a financier who fiddles his tax or a vicar with an obsessive interest in choirboys, it is as well to check that the names given to these characters do not correspond to flesh and blood people.

Paul Watkins' novel *Stand Up Before Your God*, based on his days at Eton, featured an undesirable called Wilbraham. It was a name he had picked at random from a New York telephone directory. Unfortunately, it happened also to be the name of a school contemporary. Neither the author nor the real Wilbraham could remember ever having met. It was an unfortunate misunderstanding which nonetheless ended with author and publisher paying damages in the region of £15,000. Since one cannot libel the dead, a valuable and safe source of names is *Who Was Who?*

If this seems unfair on the dear departed, Dr Johnson, as ever, has some wise words for you:

It is of so much more consequence that truth should be told, than that individuals should not be made uneasy, that it is much better that the law does not restrain writing freely concerning the characters of the dead. Damages will be given to a man who is calumniated in his lifetime, because he may be hurt in his worldly interest, or at least hurt in his mind: but the law does not regard that uneasiness which a man feels on having his ancestor calumniated. That is too nice. Let him deny what is said, and let the matter have a fair chance by discussion. But, if a man could say nothing against a character but what he can prove, history could not be written; for a great deal is known of men of which proof cannot be brought.

Every writer is responsible for his own work. But this should not mean that when he makes mistakes he alone carries the can.

Journalists are usually covered by their employers who take on the whole cost of a libel action. Authors, on the other hand, are more exposed to the rigours of legal censorship. A typical publishing contract includes a warranty clause which entitles the publisher to be indemnified by the author against damages and costs if any part of the work turns out to be libellous.

Publishers excuse their weakness of backbone by arguing that only the author is in a position to know whether or not a work is libellous and that the onus should be on the author to check facts before they are published. In fairness, it must be said that the indemnity is rarely invoked unless a publisher feels he has been deceived or misled. But, at the very least, the author should insist that his publisher has the manuscript read for libel and that his contract does not specify unlimited liability.

There are many cases where a cost-conscious publisher has played safe by amending a text to a point where it loses its cutting edge and thus its sales appeal. It is not unknown for an entire book to be jettisoned to save on lawyers' bills.

Another limitation on libel insurance is that few policies extend to the US market, where claims and awards can take off like Concorde. There, a thriving libel industry has been made yet more prosperous by enterprising lawyers who assess fees as a percentage of whatever they can persuade juries to award. The consolation for defendants is that while the law of libel in the States is similar to the law here, in practical terms it is more favourable to authors, in that the reputations of public figures are thought to be in less need of protection. A politician, say, who sues for libel is ridiculed as a bad sport. Whoever puts his head above the parapet, goes the argument, should expect to be shot at. Judges are more understanding of ordinary citizens particularly when there is an invasion-of-privacy claim but as a general rule, for libel damages to be awarded in an American court, someone must publish untruths knowing them to be untrue.

Libel insurance offers some sort of safeguard and a publisher who is insured is clearly preferable to one who is not. But most insurance policies carry severe limitations, not least a ceiling on the payout of damages. Peter Marsh, a barrister specialising in defamation, offers these tips for writers about to embark on a controversial project:

> If the subject or subjects of critical comment are still alive, beware; if you are writing a book about real life incidents but have changed names to avoid identification, take extreme care in the choice of names for your characters; remember that damage to a person's reputation can be caused by innuendo. For example, to write of someone that most people thought he was taking advantage of the Inland Revenue may suggest some improper and unethical practice. If a living person is going to be the subject of comment which is expressly or implicitly derogatory, make absolutely sure your facts are correct and can be substantiated. Otherwise, your publisher is going to be propelled into the courtroom naked of a defence.

In one important respect, authors and publishers suffer more than anyone from the application of the libel laws. At the root of the problem is the ease with which determined plaintiffs can get a book withdrawn from circulation. The process, successfully used by Sir James Goldsmith in his litigation against *Private Eye*, was given a shot in the arm by Maxwell in his tussles with Tom Bower over a biography of which Maxwell did not approve.

Is there anything to be said for those who bring libel actions? No better summary of the risks and tribulations for all but the excessively rich appears in Adam Raphael's absorbing indictment, *Grotesque Libels*:

> The problems of a libel action can be stated quite simply. The law is highly technical and the pleadings so complex that even its skilled practitioners often differ on the most basic questions. The costs of the lawyers involved are so high that they make the fees charged by any other profession appear to be a mere bagatelle. The opportunities for obstruction and delay are such that it can take as long as five years to bring a libel action to court. When it eventually does reach the court, the damages left to the whim of a jury are so uncertain that the result is often no sounder than a dodgy fruit machine. A libel action has in fact more in common with a roulette wheel than justice. The net result for both plaintiffs and defendants is that such actions are a nightmare with only the lawyers able to sleep soundly.

No wonder Bernard Levin asserts 'If I were libelled (I have frequently been) and were given the choice of suing or having all my toenails pulled out with red-hot pincers while listening to *Pelléas et Mélisande*, I think it would be a close run thing.'

Literary Societies

Most literary societies exist on a shoestring budget; it is a good idea to enclose an A5 s.a.e. with all correspondence needing a reply.

The Abbey Chronicle
32 Tadfield Road, Romsey, Hampshire
SO51 5AJ
Contact *Ms Ruth Allen*
Subscription £6 p.a.

FOUNDED 1989 to promote the works of Elsie J. Oxenham. Publishes three newsletters a year.

Margery Allingham Society
3 Corringham Road, Wembley, Middlesex
HA9 9PX
☎0181 904 5994　　　Fax 0181 904 5994
Contact *Mrs Pat Wat*
Subscription £7 p.a.

FOUNDED 1988 to promote interest in and study of the works of Margery Allingham. The London Society *publishes* two newsletters yearly, *The Bottle Street Gazette*. Contributions welcome. Two social events a year. Open membership.

Jane Austen Society
Carton House, Redwood Lane, Medstead, Alton, Hampshire GU34 5PE
☎01705 475855　　　Fax 01705 788842
Honorary Secretary *Susan McCartan*
Subscription UK: £10 (Annual);
　£15 (Joint); £30 (Corporate); £150 (Life);
　Overseas: £12 (Annual); £18 (Joint);
　£33 (Corporate); £180 (Life)

FOUNDED 1940 to promote interest in and enjoyment of Jane Austen's novels and letters. The society has branches in Bath & Bristol, Midlands, London, Oxford, Kent and Hampshire. Also overseas branches in North America and Australia.

William Barnes Society
51 Binghams Road, Crossways, Dorchester, Dorset DT2 8BW
☎01305 853338　　　Fax 01305 854212
Contact *Mrs J. R. Bryant*
Subscription £6 p.a.

FOUNDED 1983 to provide a forum in which admirers of the Dorset poet could share fellowship and pleasure in his work. William Barnes (1801–86) is best known as the writer of Dorset dialect poetry. His interest in dialect prompted him to become a learned philologist and he published many papers in defence of native English against the incursions of French and Latin. Quarterly meetings and newsletter.

The Baskerville Hounds
6 Bramham Moor, Hill Head, Fareham, Hampshire PO14 3RU
☎01329 667325
Chairman *Philip Weller*
Subscription £7.00 p.a.

FOUNDED 1989. An international Sherlock Holmes society specialising solely in studies of *The Hound of the Baskervilles* and its Dartmoor associations. *Publishes* a quarterly newsletter, an annual journal, and specialist monographs. It also organises many social functions, usually on Dartmoor. Open membership.

Arnold Bennett Society
106 Scotia Road, Burslem, Stoke on Trent, Staffordshire ST6 4ET
☎01782 816311
Secretary *Mrs Jean Potter*
Subscription £5 (Single); £6 (Family); £4
　(Unwaged)

Re-formed in 1954 to promote interest in the life and works of 'Five Towns' author Arnold Bennett and other North Staffordshire writers. Annual dinner and other events. Quarterly newsletter. Open membership.

E. F. Benson Society
88 Tollington Park, London N4 3RA
☎0171 272 3375　　　Fax 0171 580 0763
Secretary *Allan Downend*
Subscription £7.50 (UK/Europe);
　£12.50 (Overseas)

FOUNDED 1985 to promote the life and work of E. F. Benson and the Benson family. Organises social and literary events, exhibitions and talks. *Publishes* a quarterly newsletter and annual journal, *The Dodo*, postcards and reprints of E. F. Benson articles and short stories. Holds an archive which includes the Seckersen Collection (transcriptions of the Benson collection at the Bodleian Library in Oxford).

E. F. Benson/The Tilling Society

Martello Bookshop, 26 High Street, Rye, East
Sussex TN31 7JJ
☎01797 222242   Fax 01797 227335

Contact *Cynthia Reavell*
Subscription Full starting membership
(members receive all back newsletters) £20
(UK); £24 (Overseas); or Annual
Membership (members receive only current
year's newsletters) £8 (UK); £10
(Overseas).

FOUNDED 1982 for the exchange of news,
information and speculation about E. F. Benson
and his *Mapp & Lucia* novels. Readings, discussions and twice-yearly newsletter. Acts as a
clearing house for every sort of news and activity concerning E. F. Benson.

The Betjeman Society

35 Eaton Court, Boxgrove Avenue,
Guildford, Surrey GU1 1XH
☎01483 560882

Honorary Secretary *John Heald*
Subscription £7 (Individual); £9 (Family);
£3 (Student); £2 extra each category for
overseas members

Aims to promote the study and appreciation of
the work and life of Sir John Betjeman. Annual
programme includes poetry reading, lectures,
discussions, visits to places associated with
Betjeman, and various social events. Meetings
are held in London and other centres. Regular
newsletter and annual journal, *The Betjemanian*.

The Bewick Society

c/o The Dean's Office, Faculty of Arts and
Design, University of Northumbria, Squires
Building, Sandyford Road, Newcastle upon
Tyne NE1 8ST
☎0191 227 3138   Fax 0191 227 4077

Chairman *Kenneth McConkey*
Subscription £7 p.a.

FOUNDED 1988 to promote an interest in the
life and work of Thomas Bewick, wood-
engraver and naturalist (1753–1828). Organises
related events and meetings, and is associated
with the Bewick birthplace museum.

Biggles & Co

See **The W. E. Johns Society**

Birmingham Central Literary Association

c/o Birmingham & Midland Institute,
Margaret Street, Birmingham B3 3DS
Contact *The Honorary Secretary*

Holds fortnightly meetings at the Birmingham
Midland Institute to discuss the lives and work
of authors and poets. Holds an annual dinner to
celebrate Shakespeare's birthday.

The George Borrow Society

The Gables, 112 Irchester Road, Rushden,
Northants NN10 9XQ
☎01933 312965   Fax 01933 312965

President *Sir Angus Fraser, KCB TD*
Honorary Secretary *Dr James H. Reading*
Honorary Treasurer *Mrs Ena R. J. Reading*
Subscription £7 p.a.

FOUNDED 1991 to promote knowledge of the
life and works of George Borrow (1803–81),
traveller, linguist and writer. The Society holds
biennial conferences (with published proceedings) and informal intermediate gatherings, all at
places associated with Borrow. *Publishes* the
George Borrow Bulletin twice yearly, a newsletter
containing scholarly articles, publications relating to Borrow, reports of past events and news
of forthcoming events. Member of the
Alliance of Literary Societies and corporate
associate member of the Centre of East Anglian
Studies (CEAS) at the University of East Anglia,
Norwich (Borrow's home city for many years).

Elinor Brent-Dyer

See **Friends of the Chalet School**

British Fantasy Society

2 Harwood Street, Heaton Norris, Stockport,
Cheshire SK4 1JJ
☎0161 476 5368

President *Ramsey Campbell*
Vice-President *Jan Edwards*
Secretary *Robert Parkinson*
Subscription from £17 p.a. (Apply to
secretary)

FOUNDED 1971 for devotees of fantasy, horror
and related fields in literature, art and the cinema. *Publishes* a regular newsletter with information and reviews of new books and films, plus
related fiction and non-fiction magazines.
Annual conference at which the **British
Fantasy Awards** are presented.

The Brontë Society

Brontë Parsonage Museum, Haworth,
Keighley, West Yorkshire BD22 8DR
☎01535 642323   Fax 01535 647131

Contact *Membership Secretary*
Subscription £14 p.a. (UK/Europe);
£7.50 (Student); £5 (Junior – up to age 14);

£20 (Overseas); joint subscriptions and life membership also available

FOUNDED 1893. Aims and activities include the preservation of manuscripts and other objects related to or connected with the Brontë family, and the maintenance and development of the museum and library at Haworth. The society holds regular meetings, lectures and exhibitions; and *publishes* information relating to the family, a bi-annual society journal *Transactions* and a bi-annual *Gazette*. Freelance contributions for either publication should be sent to the Publications Secretary at the address above.

The Browning Society

Cherry Tree Cottage, Fyning Lane, Rogate, Petersfield, Hampshire GU31 5DQ
☎01730 821666
Honorary Secretary *Dr Mairi Calcraft-Rennie*
Subscription £10 p.a.
FOUNDED 1969 to promote an interest in the lives and poetry of Robert and Elizabeth Barrett Browning. Meetings are arranged in the London area. On 12th September 1996, the 150th anniversary of the Brownings' marriage, the society plans to hold a special ceremony in St Marylebone Church in London plus other events.

The John Buchan Society

Limpsfield, 16 Ranfurly Road, Bridge of Weir PA11 3EL
☎01505 613116
Secretary *Russell Paterson*
Subscription £10 (Full/Overseas); £4 (Associate); £6 (Junior); £20 (Corporate); £90 (Life)

To perpetuate the memory of John Buchan and to promote a wider understanding of his life and works. Holds regular meetings and social gatherings, *publishes* a journal, and liaises with the John Buchan Centre at Broughton in the Scottish borders.

The Burns Federation

The Dick Institute, Elmbank Avenue, Kilmarnock, Strathclyde KA1 3BU
☎01563 526401   Fax 01563 529661
Honorary Secretary *John Inglis*
Subscription £12 p.a.
FOUNDED 1885 to encourage interest in the life and work of Robert Burns and keep alive the old Scottish Tongue. The Society's interests go beyond Burns himself in its commitment to the development of Scottish literature, music and

arts in general. *Publishes* the quarterly *Burns Chronicle/Burnsian*.

The Byron Society/International Byron Society

The Byron Society, Byron House, 6 Gertrude Street, London SW10 0JN
☎0171 352 5112
Honorary Director, Byron Society *Mrs Elma Dangerfield OBE*
Joint International Secretary *Mrs Maureen Crisp*
Subscription £18 p.a.
Also at: International Byron Society, Newstead Abbey, Newstead Abbey Park, Nottingham NG15 8GE.
☎01623 797392

FOUNDED 1876; revived in 1971. Aims to promote knowledge and discussion of Lord Byron's life and works, and those of his contemporaries, through lectures, readings, concerts, performances and international conferences. *Publishes* annually in April *The Byron Journal*, a scholarly journal – £5 plus 60p p&p.

Randolph Caldecott Society

Clatterwick Hall, Little Leigh, Northwich, Cheshire CW8 4RJ
☎01606 891303
Honorary Secretary *Kenneth N. Oultram*
Subscription £7-£10 p.a.
FOUNDED 1983 to promote the life and work of artist/book illustrator Randolph Caldecott. Meetings held in the spring and autumn in Caldecott's birthplace, Chester. Guest speakers, outings, newsletter, exchanges with the society's American counterpart. (Caldecott died and was buried in St Augustine, Florida.) A medal in his memory is awarded annually in the US for children's book illustration.

The Carlyle Society, Edinburgh

Dept of English Literature, The University of Edinburgh, David Hume Tower, George Square, Edinburgh EH8 9JX
Fax 0131 650 6989
Contact *The President*
Subscription £2 p.a.; £10 (Life); $20 (US)
FOUNDED 1929 to examine the lives of Thomas Carlyle and his wife Jane, his writings, contemporaries, and influences. Meetings are held about six times a year, and an annual members' journal is published. Enquiries should be addressed to the President of the Society at the above address or to the Secretary at 15 Lennox Street, Edinburgh EH4 1QB.

Lewis Carroll Society

Little Folly, 105 The Street, Willesborough,
Ashford, Kent TN24 0NB
☎01233 623919

Secretary *Sarah Stanfield*
Subscription £10 (Individual);
£12 (Institutions); £6 (Concessions)

FOUNDED 1969 to bring together people with an
interest in Charles Dodgson and promote
research into his life and works. *Publishes* quarterly journal *Jabberwocky*, featuring scholarly articles and reviews; plus a newsletter (*Bandersnatch*)
which reports on Carrollian events and the
Society's activities. Regular meetings held in
London with lectures, talks, outings, etc.

Lewis Carroll Society (Daresbury)

Clatterwick Hall, Little Leigh, Northwich,
Cheshire CW8 4RJ
☎01606 891303

Honorary Secretary *Kenneth N. Oultram*
Subscription £5 p.a.

FOUNDED 1970. To promote the life and work
of Charles Dodgson, author of the world-famous
Alice's Adventures. Holds regular meetings in the
spring and autumn in Carroll's birthplace,
Daresbury, in Cheshire. Guest speakers, theatre
visits and a newsletter.

Friends of the Chalet School

4 Rock Terrace, Coleford, Bath, Avon
BA3 5NF
☎01373 812705   Fax 01373 813517

Contact *Ann Mackie-Hunter, Clarissa Cridland*
Subscription £6 p.a.; £5 (Under-18);
   Outside Europe: details on application

FOUNDED 1989 to promote the works of
Elinor Brent-Dyer. The society has members
worldwide; *publishes* four newsletters a year and
runs a lending library.

The Chesterton Society

11 Lawrence Leys, Bloxham, Near Banbury,
Oxfordshire OX15 4NU
☎01295 720869

Honorary Secretary *Robert Hughes*
Subscription £20 p.a.

FOUNDED 1964 to promote the ideas and writings of G. K. Chesterton.

The Children's Books History Society

25 Field Way, Hoddesdon, Hertfordshire
EN11 0QN
☎01992 464885

Membership Secretary *Mrs Pat Garrett*
Subscription £7.50 p.a.

ESTABLISHED 1969. Aims to promote an appreciation of children's books and to study their history, bibliography and literary content. The
Society holds approximately six meetings per
year in London and a Summer meeting to a collection, or to a location with a children's book
connection. Two to three newsletters issued
annually. The Society constitutes the British
branch of the Friends of the Osborne and Lillian
H. Smith Collections in Toronto, Canada, and
also liaises with the **Library Association**. In
1990 the Society established its biennial Harvey
Darton Award for a book, published in English,
which extends our knowledge of some aspect of
British children's literature of the past. 1996 winner: Marina Warner *From the Beast to the Blonde*.

The John Clare Society

The Stables, 1A West Street, Helpston,
Peterborough PE6 7DU
☎01733 252678

Honorary Secretary *Mrs J. Mary Moyse*
Subscription £9.50 (Individual);
   £12.50 (Joint); £7.50 (Fully Retired);
   £9 (Joint Retired); £10 (Group/Library);
   £3 (Student, Full-time); £12.50 sterling
   draft/$25 (Overseas)

FOUNDED 1981 to promote a wider appreciation of the life and works of the poet John Clare
(1793–1864). Organises an annual festival in
Helpston in July; arranges exhibitions, poetry
readings and conferences; and *publishes* an
annual society journal and quarterly newsletter.

Wilkie Collins Society

10A Tibberton Square, Islington, London
N1 8SF

Chairman *Andrew Gasson*
Membership Secretary *Louise Marchant (at*
   above address)
Subscription £7.50 (UK); $10 (US)

FOUNDED 1980 to provide information on and
promote interest in the life and works of Wilkie
Collins, one of the first English novelists to deal
with the detection of crime. *The Woman in
White* appeared in 1860 and *The Moonstone* in
1868. *Publishes* newsletters, a journal and occasional reprints of Collins' work.

The Arthur Conan Doyle Society

Ashcroft, 2 Abbottsford Drive, Penyffordd,
Chester CH4 0JG
☎01244 545210

Contact *Christopher Roden, Barbara Roden*

Subscription £15 (UK); £16 (Overseas); Family rates available

FOUNDED 1989 to promote the study and discussion of the life and works of Sir Arthur Conan Doyle. Occasional meetings, functions and visits. *Publishes* an annual journal and twice-yearly news magazine, together with reprints of Conan Doyle's writings.

The Dickens Fellowship

48 Doughty Street, London
WC1N 2LF
☎0171 405 2127   Fax 0171 831 5175

Honorary General Secretary *Edward G. Preston*

FOUNDED 1902. The society's particular aims and objectives are: to bring together lovers of Charles Dickens; to spread the message of Dickens, his love of humanity ('the keynote of all his work'); to remedy social injustice for the poor and oppressed; to assist in the preservation of material and buildings associated with Dickens. Annual conference. *Publishes* journal called *The Dickensian* and organises a full programme of lectures, discussions, visits and conducted walks throughout the year. Branches worldwide.

Early English Text Society

Christ Church, Oxford OX1 1DP
Fax 01865 794199

Executive Secretary *R. F. S. Hamer* (at above address)
Editorial Secretary *Dr H. L. Spencer* (at Exeter College, Oxford OX1 3DP)
Subscription £15 p.a.; $30 (US); $35 (Canada)

FOUNDED 1864. Concerned with the publication of early English texts. Members receive annual publications (one or two a year) or may select titles from the backlist in lieu.

The Eighteen Nineties Society

97D Brixton Road, London SW9 6EE
☎0171 582 4690

Honorary Secretary *G. Krishnamurti*
Subscription £10 p.a. (UK); $25 (US)

FOUNDED 1963 to bring together admirers of the work of Francis Thompson, the Society widened its scope in 1972 to embrace the artistic and literary scene of the entire decade (Impressionism, Realism, Naturalism, Symbolism). Assists members' research into the literature and art of the period; mounts exhibitions; and *publishes* an annual journal and quarterly newsletter.

The George Eliot Fellowship

71 Stepping Stones Road, Coventry,
Warwickshire CV5 8JT
☎01203 592231

Contact *Mrs Kathleen Adams*
Subscription £8 p.a.; £80 (Life); concessions for pensioners

FOUNDED 1930. Exists to honour George Eliot and promote interest in her life and works. Readings, memorial lecture, birthday luncheon and functions. Issues a quarterly newsletter and an annual journal.

Folly (Fans of Light Literature for the Young)

21 Warwick Road, Pokesdown,
Bournemouth, Dorset BH7 6JW
Contact *Mrs Sue Sims*
Subscription £6 p.a. (UK); £7 (Europe); £8.50 (Worldwide)

FOUNDED 1990 to promote interest in a wide variety of children's authors – with a bias towards writers of girls' books and school stories. *Publishes* three magazines a year.

The Franco-Midland Hardware Company

6 Bramham Moor, Hill Head, Fareham,
Hampshire PO14 3RU
☎01329 667325

Chairman *Philip Weller*
Subscription £14 p.a.

FOUNDED 1989. 'The world's leading Sherlock Holmes correspondence study group and the most active Holmesian society in Britain.' The Society *publishes* a quarterly journal and at least six specialist monographs a year. It provides certificated self-study courses and organises functions at Holmes-associated locations. Open membership.

The Gaskell Society

Far Yew Tree House, Over Tabley,
Knutsford, Cheshire WA16 0HN
☎01565 634668

Honorary Secretary *Joan Leach*
Subscription £7 p.a.; £10 (Overseas)

FOUNDED 1985 to promote and encourage the study and appreciation of the life and works of Elizabeth Cleghorn Gaskell. Meetings held in Knutsford, Manchester and London; residential study weekends and visits; annual journal and bi-annual newsletter.

The Ghost Story Society

Ashcroft, 2 Abbottsford Drive, Penyffordd,
Chester CH4 0JG
☎01244 545210

Contacts *Barbara Roden, Christopher Roden*
Subscription £13 (UK); £14.50 (Overseas)
currency options available

FOUNDED 1988. Devoted mainly to supernatural fiction in the literary tradition of M. R. James, Walter de la Mare, Algernon Blackwood, E. F. Benson, A. N. L. Murphy, R. H. Malden, etc. *Publishes* a thrice-yearly journal, *All Hallows*, which includes new fiction in the genre and non-fiction of relevance to the genre.

The Gothic Society

Chatham House, Gosshill Road, Chislehurst,
Kent BR7 5NS
☎0181 467 8475   Fax 0181 295 1967

Contact *Jennie Gray*
Subscription £20 p.a.; £23 (Overseas)

FOUNDED 1990 for the amusement of 'those who delight in morbid, macabre and black-hued themes, both ancient and modern Gothick!' *Publishes* high-quality paperbacks on related subjects, and four large-format illustrated magazines yearly. Some scope for original and imaginative fiction, but preference is for history, biography and intelligent but amusing essays on the arts. Members have a definite advantage over writers outside the Society. (Also see **Small Presses**).

Rider Haggard Appreciation Society

27 Deneholm, Whitley Bay, Tyne & Wear
NE25 9AU
☎0191 252 4516

Contact *Roger Allen*
Subscription £8 p.a. (UK); £10 (Overseas)

FOUNDED 1985 to promote appreciation of the life and works of Sir Henry Rider Haggard, English novelist, 1856-1925. News/books exchange, and meetings every two years.

The Thomas Hardy Society

PO Box 1438, Dorchester, Dorset DT1 1YH
☎01305 251501

Honorary Secretary *Mrs Margaret Johnson*
Subscription £12 (Individual);
£16 (Corporate); £15 (Individual
Overseas); £20 (Corporate Overseas)

FOUNDED 1967 to promote the reading and study of the works and life of Thomas Hardy. Thrice-yearly journal, events and a biennial conference.

The Henty Society

Fox Hall, Kelshall, Royston, Hertfordshire
SG8 9SE
☎01763 287208

Honorary Secretary *Mrs Ann J. King*
Subscription £12 p.a. (UK); £15 (Overseas)

FOUNDED 1977 to study the life and work of George Alfred Henty, and to publish research, bibliographical data and lesser-known works, namely short stories. Organises conferences and social gatherings in the UK and Canada, and *publishes* quarterly bulletins to members.

Sherlock Holmes Society (Northern Musgraves)

Overdale, 69 Greenhead Road, Huddersfield,
West Yorkshire HD1 4ER
☎01484 426957   Fax 01484 426957

Contact *David Stuart Davies, Kathryn White*
Subscription £15 p.a. (UK)

FOUNDED 1987 to promote enjoyment and study of Sir Arthur Conan Doyle's Sherlock Holmes through publications and meetings. One of the largest Sherlock Holmes societies in Great Britain. Honorary members include Dame Jean Conan Doyle, Richard Lancelyn Green, Edward Hardwicke and Douglas Wilmer. Past honorary members: Peter Cushing and Jeremy Brett. Open membership. Lectures, presentations and consultation on matters relating to Holmes and Conan Doyle available.

The Sherlock Holmes Society of London

13 Crofton Avenue, Orpington, Kent
BR6 8DU
☎01689 811314

Membership Secretary *R. J. Ellis*
Subscription £9.50 p.a. (Associate);
£14 (Full)

FOUNDED 1951 to promote the study of the life and work of Sherlock Holmes and Dr Watson, and their creator, Sir Arthur Conan Doyle. Offers correspondence and liaison with international societies, plus a bi-annual society journal.

Sherlock Holmes

See **The Franco-Midland Hardware Company**

Hopkins Society

Daniel Owen Centre, Earl Road, Mold,
Clwyd CH7 1AP
☎01352 758403   Fax 01352 700236

Contact *Sandra Wynne*

Subscription £5 p.a.

FOUNDED 1990 to celebrate the life and work of Gerard Manley Hopkins; to inform members of any publications, courses or events about the poet. Holds an annual lecture on Hopkins in the spring; produces two newsletters a year; sponsors and organises educational projects based on Hopkins' life and works.

W. W. Jacobs Appreciation Society

3 Roman Road, Southwick, West Sussex BN42 4TP

☎01273 871017　　　　Fax 01273 871017

Contact A. R. James

FOUNDED 1988 to encourage and promote the enjoyment of the works of W. W. Jacobs, and stimulate research into his life and works. *Publishes* a quarterly newsletter free to those who send s.a.e. (9in x 4in). Contributions welcome but no payment made. Preferred lengths 600–1200 words. No subscription charge. Biography, bibliography, directories of plays and films are available for purchase.

Richard Jefferies Society

Eidsvoll, Bedwells Heath, Boars Hill, Oxford OX1 5JE

☎01865 735678

Honorary Secretary Mrs Phyllis Treitel
Membership Secretary Sheila Povey
Subscription £5 p.a. (Individual); £6 (Joint); life membership for those over 50

FOUNDED 1950 to promote understanding of the work of Richard Jefferies, nature/country writer, novelist and mystic (1848–87). Produces newsletters, reports and an annual journal; organises talks, discussions and readings. Library and archives. Assists in maintaining museum in Jefferies' birthplace at Coate near Swindon. Membership applications should be sent to *Sheila Povey*, 20 Farleigh Crescent, Swindon, Wiltshire SN3 1JY.

Jerome K. Jerome Society

The Birthplace Museum, Belsize House, Bradford Street, Walsall, West Midlands WS1 1PN

☎01922 27686　　　　Fax 01922 721065

Honorary Secretary Tony Gray
Subscription £5 p.a. (Ordinary); £25 (Corporate); £6 (Joint); £2.50 (Under 21/Over 65)

FOUNDED 1984 to stimulate interest in Jerome K. Jerome's life and works (1859–1927). One of the Society's principal activities is the support of a small museum in the author's birthplace, Walsall. Meetings, lectures, events and a twice-yearly newsletter *Idle Thoughts*. Annual dinner in Walsall near Jerome's birth date (2nd May).

The W. E. Johns Society

4 Ashendene Road, Bayford, Hertfordshire SG13 8PX

☎01992 511588　　　　Fax 01992 511382

Contact John Trendler
Subscription £12 p.a.

Publishes four newsletters, *Biggles & Co* per year and holds an annual meeting.

Johnson Society

Johnson Birthplace Museum, Breadmarket Street, Lichfield, Staffordshire WS13 6LG

☎01543 264972

Secretary Mr W. J. Wilson
Subscription £5 p.a.; £7 (Joint)

FOUNDED 1910 to encourage the study of the life, works and times of Samuel Johnson (1709–1784) and his contemporaries. The Society is committed to the preservation of the Johnson Birthplace Museum and Johnson memorials.

Johnson Society of London

255 Baring Road, Grove Park, London SE12 0BQ

☎0181 851 0173

Honorary Secretary Mrs Z. E. O'Donnell
Subscription £6 p.a.; £7 (Joint)

FOUNDED 1928 to promote the knowledge and appreciation of Dr Samuel Johnson (1709–1784) and his works. Regular meetings from October to May in London on the third Saturday of each month, and a commemoration ceremony around the anniversary of Johnson's death, held in Westminster Abbey.

The Just William Society

15 St James' Avenue, Bexhill-on-Sea, East Sussex TN40 2DN

☎01424 216065

Secretary Michael Vigar
Treasurer Phil Woolley
Subscription £7 p.a. (UK); £10 (Overseas); £5 (Juvenile/Student); £15 (Family)

FOUNDED 1994 to further knowledge of Richmal Crompton's *William* and *Jimmy* books. An annual 'William' meeting is held in April, although this is not currently organised by the Society. The Honorary President of the Society is Richmal Crompton's niece, Richmal Ashbee.

The Keats–Shelley Memorial Association

1 Lewis Road, Radford Semele, Warwickshire
CV31 1UB
Contact *Honorary Treasurer* (at 10 Lansdowne
Rd, Tunbridge Wells, Kent TN1 2NJ.
☎01892 533452 Fax 01892 519142)
Subscription £10 p.a.; £100 (Life)

FOUNDED 1909 to promote appreciation of the
works of Keats and Shelley, and their contemporaries. One of the Society's main tasks is the
preservation of 26 Piazza di Spagna in Rome as
a memorial to the British Romantic poets in
Italy, particularly Keats and Shelley. *Publishes*
an annual review of Romantic Studies called
the *Keats-Shelley Review* and arranges events
and lectures for Friends. The review is edited
by *Angus Graham-Campbell*, c/o Eton College,
Windsor, Berkshire SL4 6DL.

Kent & Sussex Poetry Society

Costens, Carpenters Lane, Hadlow, Kent
TN11 0EY
☎01732 851404
Honorary Secretary *Mrs Doriel Hulse*
Subscription £5 p.a.; £3 (Country)

FOUNDED 1946 to promote the enjoyment of
poetry. Monthly meetings, including readings
by major poets, and a monthly workshop.
Produces an annual folio of members' work,
adjudicated and commented upon by a major
poet; and runs an open poetry competition (see
Prizes) annually.

The Kilvert Society

The Old Forge, Kinnersley, Hereford
HR3 6QB
Secretary *Mr M. Sharp*
Subscription £5 p.a.; £50 (Life)

FOUNDED 1948 to foster an interest in the
Diary, the diarist and the countryside he loved.
Publishes three newsletters each year; during
the summer holds three weekends of walks,
commemoration services and talks.

The Kipling Society

P.O. Box 68, Haslemere, Surrey GU27 2YR
☎01428 652709
Secretary *Norman Entract*
Subscription £20 p.a.

FOUNDED 1927. The Society's main activities
are: maintaining a specialised library; answering
enquiries from the public (schools, publishers,
writers and the media); arranging a regular programme of lectures and an annual luncheon

with guest speaker; and issuing a quarterly
journal. Open to anyone interested in the prose
and verse, life and times of Rudyard Kipling
(1865-1936). Approach in writing; no visits.

The Kitley Trust

Toadstone Cottage, Edge View, Litton,
Derbyshire SK17 8QU
☎01298 871564
Contact *Rosie Ford*

FOUNDED 1990 by a teacher in Sheffield to
promote the art of creative writing, in memory
of her mother, Jessie Kitley. Activities include:
bi-annual poetry competitions; a 'Get Poetry'
Day (distribution of children's poems in shopping malls); annual sponsorship of a writer for a
school; campaigns; organising conferences for
writers and teachers of writing. Funds are provided by donations and profits (if any) from
competitions.

Charles Lamb Society

1A Royston Road, Richmond, Surrey
TW10 6LT
☎0181 940 3837
General Secretary *Mrs M. R. Huxstep*
Membership Secretary *Mrs Audrey Moore*
Subscription £12 p.a. (Single); £18 (Joint &
Corporate); £28 (Overseas personal);
£42 (Overseas corporate)

FOUNDED 1935 to promote the study of the life,
works and times of English essayist Charles Lamb
(1775-1834). Holds regular monthly meetings
and lectures in London and organises society
events over the summer. *Publishes* a quarterly
bulletin, *The Charles Lamb Bulletin*. Contributions of Elian interest are welcomed by the editor
Dr Duncan Wu at Dept of English Literature,
University of Glasgow, Glasgow G12 8QH. Tel:
0141 332 3742. Membership applications should
be sent to the Membership Secretary at Shelley
Cottage, 108 West Street, Marlow, Buckinghamshire SL7 2BP. The Society's library is
housed in the **Guildhall Library**, Aldermanbury, London EC2P 2EJ (Tel: 0171 606 3030).
Member of the **Alliance of Literary Societies**.
Registered Charity No: 803222.

Lancashire Authors' Association

Heatherslade, 5 Quakerfields, Westhoughton,
Bolton, Lancashire BL5 2BJ
☎01942 791390
General Secretary *Eric Holt*
Subscription £9 p.a.; £12 (Joint);
£1 (Junior)

FOUNDED 1909 for writers and lovers of

Lancashire literature and history. Aims to foster and stimulate interest in Lancashire history and literature as well as in the preservation of the Lancashire dialect. Meets four times a year on Saturday at various locations. *Publishes* a quarterly journal called *The Record* which is issued free to members and holds eight annual competitions (open to members only) for both verse and prose. Comprehensive library with access for research to members.

The Philip Larkin Society
Dept of American Studies, The University of Hull, Hull HU6 7RX
Contact *Dr John Osborne*
Subscription £12; £9 (unwaged)

A new society, launched at the Hull Literary Festival in 1995 during which a number of events were associated with the society and its aims. Promotes awareness of the life and work of Philip Larkin and organises occasional seminars, conferences and exhibitions. *Publishes* a bi-annual newsletter and *Philip Larkin's Hull and East Yorkshire*.

The D. H. Lawrence Society
Dept of French, University of Hull, Cottingham Road, Hull HU6 7RX
Contact *Dr Catherine Greensmith*
Subscription £10; £9 (Concession); £11 (Joint); £12 (European); £15 (RoW)

FOUNDED 1974 to increase knowledge and the appreciation of the life and works of D. H. Lawrence. Monthly meetings, addressed by guest speakers, are held in the library at Eastwood (birthplace of DHL). Organises visits to places of interest in the surrounding countryside, supports the activities of the D. H. Lawrence Centre at Nottingham University, has close links with DHL Societies worldwide. *Publishes* two newsletters and a journal each year, free to members.

The T. E. Lawrence Society
PO Box 728, Oxford OX2 6YP
Secretary & Librarian *Mrs A. Horsfield*
Subscription £14 p.a. (UK); £18 (Overseas)

FOUNDED 1985 to advance the education of the public in the life and works of T. E. Lawrence, and to promote and publish research into both areas.

The Leamington Literary Society
15 Church Hill, Leamington Spa, Warwickshire CV32 5AZ
☎01926 425733
Honorary Secretary *Mrs Margaret Watkins*

Subscription £5 p.a.

FOUNDED 1912 to promote the study and appreciation of literature and the arts. Holds regular meetings every second Tuesday of the month (except August) at the Regent Hotel, Leamington Spa, and lectures. The Society has published various books of local interest.

Wyndham Lewis Society
8 Montgomery Road, Chiswick, London W4 5LZ
☎0181 995 4457
Contact *Anthony Wilcock*
Subscription £6 p.a. (UK/Europe); £7.30 p.a. (Institutions); $16-21 (Elsewhere) (Dollar subs to be sent to Prof. Reed Way Dasenbrock, English Dept. Box 3E/NMSU, Las Cruces, New Mexico 88013, USA)

FOUNDED 1974 to promote recognition of the value of Lewis's works and encourage scholarly research on the man, his painting and his writing. *Publishes* inaccessible Lewis writings; the annual society journal *The Wyndham Lewis Annual* plus two newsletters; and reproduces Lewis's paintings. The journal is chiefly edited by *Paul Edwards*, 53A Moorland Road, Bath, Avon BA2 3PJ.

Arthur Machen Literary Society
19 Cross Street, Caerleon, Gwent NP6 1AF
☎01633 422520   Fax 01633 421055
President *Barry Humphries*
Patron *Julian Lloyd Webber*
Contact *Rita Tait*
Subscription £15 (UK); £18 (Overseas)

Exists to honour the life and work of writer Arthur Machen (1863-1947). *Publishes* a newsletter *The Silurist* and a journal *Avallaunius*, both twice yearly; also hardback books by and about Machen and his circle, under its own Green Round Press imprint. Gives assistance to researchers on the 1890s mystery and imagination genre of which Machen was part.

William Morris Society
Kelmscott House, 26 Upper Mall, Hammersmith, London W6 9TA
☎0181 741 3735
Contact *David Rodgers*
Subscription £13.50 p.a.

FOUNDED 1953 to promote interest in the life, work and ideas of William Morris (1834-1923), English poet and craftsman.

Violet Needham Society

c/o 19 Ashburnham Place, London SE10 8TZ
☎0181 692 4562

Honorary Secretary *R. H. A. Cheffins*
Subscription £6 p.a. (UK & Europe); £9
(outside Europe)

FOUNDED 1985 to celebrate the work of children's author Violet Needham and stimulate critical awareness of her work. *Publishes* thrice-yearly *Souvenir*, the Society journal with an accompanying newsletter; organises meetings and excursions to places associated with the author and her books. The journal includes articles about other children's writers of the 1940s and 50s. Contributions welcome.

The Wilfred Owen Association

17 Belmont, Shrewsbury, Shropshire SY1 1TE
☎01743 235904

Chairman *Helen McPhail*
Subscription Adults £4 (£6 Overseas);
£2 (Senior Citizens/Students/
Unemployed); £10 (Groups/Institutions)

FOUNDED 1989 to commemorate the life and works of Wilfred Owen by promoting readings, talks and performances relating to Owen and his work. Membership is international with 650 members in 16 countries. *Publishes* a newsletter two or three times a year. Contact the Association for information on their activities or on Owen. Speakers are available for schools or clubs etc. In 1993 (the centenary of Owen's birth and the 75th anniversary of his death) the Association established permanent memorials to Owen in Shropshire.

Thomas Paine Society U.K.

43 Wellington Gardens, Selsey, West Sussex
PO20 0RF
☎01243 605730

President *The Rt. Hon. Michael Foot*
Honorary Secretary/Treasurer *Eric Paine*
Subscription (Minimum) £10 p.a. (UK);
£20 (Overseas)

FOUNDED 1963 to promote the life and work of Thomas Paine, and continues to expound his ideals. Meetings, newsletters, lectures and research assistance. Membership badge. The Society has members worldwide and keeps in touch with American and French Thomas Paine associations. *Publishes* annual magazine *Bulletin*.

The Polidori Society

Ebenezer House, 31 Ebenezer Street, Langley
Mill, Nottinghamshire NG16 4DA
☎0181 994 5902   Fax 0181 995 3275

Founder & President *Franklin Charles Bishop*
Honorary Patron/Secretary (London)
Kathleen McGrath
Subscription £15 p.a. (Individual or Joint
Husband/Wife); £8 (Students)

FOUNDED 1990 to promote and encourage appreciation of the life and works of John William Polidori MD (1795-1821) – novelist, poet, tragedian, philosopher, diarist, essayist, traveller and one of the youngest students to obtain a medical degree (at the age of 19). He was one-time intimate of the leading figures in the Romantic movement and travelling companion and private physician to Lord Byron. He was a pivotal figure in the infamous Villa Diodati ghost story sessions in which he assisted Mary Shelley in her creation of the Frankenstein tale. Polidori introduced into literature the enduring icon of the vampire portrayed as a handsome seducer with his seminal work *The Vampyre - A Tale*, published in 1819. Members receive exclusive newsletters, unique publications and invitations to special period events (Regency style). International membership.

The Beatrix Potter Society

32 Etchingham Park Road, Finchley, London
N3 2DT
☎0181 346 8031

Secretary *Mrs Marian Werner*
Subscription UK: £7 p.a. (Individual);
£10 (Institutions); Overseas: £14 (Or
US$25/Can.$27.50/Aust.$30) (Individual);
£20 (US$35/Can.$40/Aust.$45) (Institutions)

FOUNDED 1980 to promote the study and appreciation of the life and works of Beatrix Potter (1866-1943). Potter was not only the author of *The Tale of Peter Rabbit* and other classics of children's literature; she was also a landscape and natural history artist, diarist, farmer and conservationist, and was responsible for the preservation of large areas of the Lake District through her gifts to the National Trust. The Society upholds and protects the integrity of her inimitable and unique work, her aims and bequests. Holds regular talks and meetings in London with visits to places connected with Beatrix Potter. Biennial International Study Conferences are held in the UK and occasionally in the USA. The Society has an active publishing programme.

The Powys Society

Keeper's Cottage, Montacute, Somerset
TA15 6XN
☎01935 824077

Hon. Secretary *John Batten*

Subscription £13.50 (UK); £16 (Overseas)

The Society aims to promote public education and recognition of the writings, thought and contribution to the arts of the Powys family; particularly of John Cowper, Theodore and Llewelyn, but also of the other members of the family and their close associates. The Society holds two major collections of Powys published works, letters, manuscripts and memorabilia. *Publishes* the *Powys Society Newsletter* in April, June and November and *The Powys Journal* in August. Organises an annual conference as well as lectures and meetings in Powys places.

The Arthur Ransome Society

Abbot Hall Art Gallery, Kirkland, Kendal, Cumbria LA9 5AL
☎01539 722464   Fax 01539 722494
Chairman *M. Temple*
Secretary *Dr K. Cochrane*
Contact *Gillian Riding*
Subscription £5 (Junior); £10 (Student); £15 (Adult); £20 (Family/Overseas); £40 (Corporate); Concessions for retired persons

FOUNDED 1990 to celebrate the life and promote the works and ideas of Arthur Ransome, author of the world-famous *Swallows and Amazons* titles for children and biographer of Oscar Wilde. TARS seeks to encourage children and adults to engage in adventurous pursuits, to educate the public about Ransome and his works, and to sponsor research into his literary works and life.

The Followers of Rupert

31 Whiteley, Windsor, Berkshire SL4 5PJ
☎01753 865562
Membership Secretary *Mrs Shirley Reeves*
Subscription UK: £8; £10 (Joint); Europe: £9 (Airmail); £11 (Joint); Worldwide: £11 (Airmail); £13 (Joint)

FOUNDED in 1983. The Society caters for the growing interest in the Rupert Bear stories, past, present and future. *Publishes* the *Nutwood Newsletter* quarterly which gives up-to-date news of Rupert and information on Society activities. A national get-together of members – the Followers Annual – is held during the autumn in venues around the country.

The Ruskin Society of London

351 Woodstock Road, Oxford OX2 7NX
☎01865 310987/515962
Honorary Secretary *Miss O. E. Forbes-Madden*

Subscription £10 p.a.

FOUNDED 1986 to promote interest in John Ruskin (1819–1900) and various aspects of Ruskiana. Functions are held in London. *Publishes* the annual *Ruskin Gazette*, a learned journal concerned with Ruskin's influence in England and abroad.

The Dorothy L. Sayers Society

Rose Cottage, Malthouse Lane, Hurstpierpoint, West Sussex BN6 9JY
☎01273 833444
Contact *Christopher Dean*
Subscription £9 p.a.

FOUNDED 1976 to promote the study of the life, works and thoughts of Dorothy Sayers; to encourage the performance of her plays and publication of her books and books about her; to preserve original material and provide assistance to researchers. Acts as a forum and information centre, providing material for study purposes which would otherwise be unavailable. Annual seminars and other meetings. Co-founder of the Dorothy L. Sayers Centre in Witham. *Publishes* bi-monthly bulletin.

The Robert Southey Society

16 Rhydhir, Longford, Neath Abbey, Neath, West Glamorgan SA10 7HP
☎01792 814783
Contact *Robert King*
Subscription £10 p.a.

FOUNDED 1990 to promote the work of Robert Southey. *Publishes* an annual newsletter and arranges talks on his life and work. Open membership.

The Friends of Shandy Hall (The Laurence Sterne Trust)

Shandy Hall, Coxwold, York YO6 4AD
☎01347 868465
Honorary Secretary *Mrs J. Monkman*
Subscription £6 (Annual); £60 (Life)

Promotes interest in the works of Laurence Sterne and aims to preserve the house in which they were created (open to the public). *Publishes* annual journal *The Shandean*. An Annual Memorial Lecture is delivered at Shandy Hall each summer.

Robert Louis Stevenson Club

5 Albyn Place, Edinburgh EH2 4NJ
☎0131 225 6665   Fax 0131 220 1015
Contact *Alistair J. R. Ferguson*

Subscription £10 p.a. (Individual);
£80 (Life)

FOUNDED 1920 to promote the memory of Robert Louis Stevenson and interest in his works.

The R. S. Surtees Society

Manor Farm House, Nunney, Near Frome, Somerset BA11 4NJ
☎01373 836937   Fax 01373 836574

Contact *Lady Helen Picthorn*
Subscription £10

FOUNDED 1979 to republish the works of R. S. Surtees and others.

The Tennyson Society

Central Library, Free School Lane, Lincoln LN2 1EZ
☎01522 552866   Fax 01522 552858

Honorary Secretary *Miss K. Jefferson*
Subscription £8 p.a. (Individual); £10 (Family); £15 (Corporate); £125 (Life)

FOUNDED 1960. An international society with membership worldwide. Exists to promote the study and understanding of the life and work of Alfred, Lord Tennyson. The Society is concerned with the work of the Tennyson Research Centre, 'probably the most significant collection of mss, family papers and books in the world'. *Publishes* annually the *Tennyson Research Bulletin*, which contains articles and critical reviews; and organises lectures, visits and seminars. Annual memorial service at Somersby in Lincolnshire.

The Edward Thomas Fellowship

Butlers Cottage, Halswell House, Goathurst, Bridgwater, Somerset TA5 2DH
☎01278 662856

Secretary *Richard Emeny*
Subscription £5 p.a. (Single); £7 p.a. (Joint)

FOUNDED 1980 to perpetuate and promote the memory of Edward Thomas and to encourage an appreciation of his life and work. The Fellowship holds a commemorative birthday walk on the Sunday nearest the poet's birthday, 3 March; issues newsletters and holds various events.

The Trollope Society

9A North Street, Clapham, London SW4 9HY
☎0171 720 6789   Fax 0171 978 1815

Contacts *John Letts, Phyllis Eden*

FOUNDED 1987 to study and promote Anthony Trollope's works. Linked with the publication of the first complete edition of his novels.

Edgar Wallace Society

Am Felshan 18, D-52223 Stolberg Germany
☎00 49 2402 91720   Fax 00 49 2402 909104

Organiser *K-J. Hinz*
Subscription £10 p.a.; £15 (Overseas); £5 (Senior Citizens)

FOUNDED 1969 by Edgar's daughter, Penelope, to bring together all who have an interest in Edgar Wallace. Members receive a brief biography of her father by Penelope Wallace, with a complete list of all published book titles. A 24-page quarterly newsletter, *Crimson Circle*, is issued in February, May, August and November.

The Walmsley Society

April Cottage, No 1 Brand Road, Hampden Park, Eastbourne, East Sussex BN22 9PX
☎01323 506447

Honorary Secretary *Fred Lane*
Subscription £8 p.a.; £9 (Family); £7 (Students/Senior Citizens)

FOUNDED 1985 to promote interest in the art and writings of Ulric and Leo Walmsley. Two annual meetings, one held in Robin Hood's Bay on the East Yorkshire coast, spiritual home of the author Leo Walmsley. The Society also seeks to foster appreciation of the work of his father Ulric Walmsley. *Publishes* a journal twice-yearly and newsletters, and is involved in other publications which benefit the aims of the Society.

Mary Webb Society

Tansy Cottage, Clunbury, Craven Arms, Shropshire SY7 0HF

Secretary *Margaret Austin*
Subscription £7.50 p.a.

FOUNDED 1972. Attracts members from the UK and overseas who are devotees of the literature of Mary Webb and of the beautiful Shropshire countryside of her novels. *Publishes* annual journal in September, organises summer schools in various locations related to the authoress's life and works. Archives; lectures; tours arranged for individuals and groups.

H. G. Wells Society

75 Wellmeadow Road, Blackheath, London SE13 6TA
☎0181 461 4583

Honorary Membership Secretary *Mary Mayer*
Subscription £12 (UK/EU); £18 (Overseas); £20 (Corporate); £6 (Concessions)

FOUNDED 1960 to promote an interest in and

appreciation of the life, work and thought of Herbert George Wells.

The Charles Williams Society
26 Village Road, London N3 1TL
Contact *Honorary Secretary*

FOUNDED 1975 to promote interest in, and provide a means for, the exchange of views and information on the life and work of Charles Williams.

The Henry Williamson Society
16 Doran Drive, Redhill, Surrey RH1 6AX
☎01737 763228
Membership Secretary *Mrs Margaret Murphy*
Subscription £8 p.a.; £10 (Family); £4 (Students)

FOUNDED 1980 to encourage, by all appropriate means, a wider readership and deeper understanding of the literary heritage left by the 20th-century English writer Henry Williamson (1895-1977). *Publishes* annual journal.

The Wodehouse Society
Box 133, Northampton NN2 6QY
☎01604 710500

Contact *Richard Morris*
Subscription £8 (Student or under 18); £12 (Adult trial membership, 1 year); £60 (Life); £85 (Patronage); £18 (Overseas)

'The most exclusive society in Britain' (according to *The Times*). FOUNDED in 1994 to promote the prose and lyricism of the Master. Will deal with all enquiries on PGW through an eminent network of contacts in the UK and abroad. *Publishes* quarterly newsletter *The Journal* for which unsolicited mss are invited, not necessarily to do with Wodehouse but peripheral figures also, such as Guy Bolton. Trying to interest Royal Mail into supporting a Wodehousean set of stamps for the year 2001. Society patrons include Rt. Hon. Tony Blair MP, Richard Briers, Stephen Fry, Tom Sharpe and Richard Usborne. Planning and social meetings are approx. three times a year plus annual celebratory cricket match and Christmas bash.

WW2 HMSO PPBKS Society
3 Roman Road, Southwick, West Sussex
BN42 4TP
☎01273 871017   Fax 01273 871017
Contact *A. R. James*
Subscription £2 p.a.

FOUNDED 1994 to encourage collectors of, and promote research into HM Stationery Office's World War II series of paperbacks, most of which were written by well-known authors, although, in many cases, anonymously. *Publishes* quarterly newsletter for those who send s.a.e. (9in x 4in). Contributors welcome; preferred length 600 - 1200 words but no payment made. Bibliography available for purchase (£3); Collectors' Guide (£5).

Yorkshire Dialect Society
Farfields, Weeton Lane, Weeton, Near Leeds, West Yorkshire LS17 0AN
☎01423 734377
Secretary *Stanley Ellis*
Subscription £6 p.a.

FOUNDED 1897 to promote interest in and preserve a record of the Yorkshire dialect. *Publishes* dialect verse and prose writing. Two journals to members annually. Details of publications are available from the Librarian, YDS, School of English, University of Leeds, LS2 9JT.

Francis Brett Young Society
52 Park Road, Hagley, Near Stourbridge, West Midlands DY9 0QF
☎01562 882973
Honorary Secretary *Mrs Jean Pritchard*
Subscription £5 p.a. (Individuals); £7 (Married couples sharing a journal); £3 (Students); £5 (Organisations/Overseas); £45 (Life)

FOUNDED 1979. Aims to provide a forum for those interested in the life and works of English novelist Francis Brett Young and to collate research on him. Promotes lectures, exhibitions and readings; *publishes* a regular newsletter; and seeks to support writers born in Young's birthplace, Halesowen.

Arts Councils and Regional Arts Boards

The Arts Council of England
14 Great Peter Street, London SW1P 3NQ
☎0171 333 0100 Fax 0171 973 6590
Chairman *Lord Gowrie*
Secretary General *Mary Allen*

The 1996/97 government grant dispensed by the Arts Council stands at approximately £186.1 million. From this fund the Arts Council supports arts organisations, artists, performers and others: grants can also be made for particular productions, exhibitions and projects. Grants available to individuals are detailed in the free Arts Council folder: *Development Funds 1996/97*. The total amount set aside for literature in 1996/97 is £1,723,000.

Drama Director *Nick Jones* New writing is supported through *Theatre Writing Allocations* (contact the Drama Department for more details).

Literature Director *Alastair Niven* The Literature Department has defined support for writers, education, access to literature including the touring of authors and literary exhibitions, cultural diversity, and an international view of writing including more translation into English among its top priorities. Lord Gowrie is chairman of the Literature Advisory Panel. This year the Arts Council will be giving at least 15 grants of £7,000 each to individual writers. Applicants must have at least one published book. Details available from the Literature Department from July 1996.

The Arts Council, Ireland
An Chomhairle Ealaíon, 70 Merrion Square, Dublin 2
☎00 353 1 6611840 Fax 00 353 1 6761302
Literature Officer *Laurence Cassidy*

The Irish Arts Council has programmes under six headings to assist in the area of literature and the book world: a) Writers; b) Literary Organisations; c) Publishers; d) Literary Magazines; e) Participation Programmes; f) Foreign Representation. It also gives a number of annual bursaries (see **Arts Council Literature Bursaries, Ireland**) and organises the **Dublin International Writers' Festival**.

The Arts Council of Northern Ireland
185 Stranmillis Road, Belfast BT9 5DU
☎01232 381591 Fax 01232 661715
Literature Officer *Ciaran Carson*

Funds book production by established publishers, programmes of readings, literary festivals, writers-in-residence schemes and literary magazines and periodicals. Occasional schools programmes and anthologies of children's writing are produced. Annual awards and bursaries for writers are available. Holds information also on various groups associated with local arts, workshops and courses.

Scottish Arts Council
12 Manor Place, Edinburgh EH3 7DD
☎0131 226 6051 Fax 0131 225 9833
Literature Director *Jenny Brown*
Literature Officer *Shonagh Irvine*
Literature Secretary *Catherine Allan*

The Council's work for Scottish-based writers who have a track record of publication includes: bursaries (considered twice yearly); travel and research grants (considered three times yearly); writing fellowships (posts usually advertised) and an international writing fellowship (organised reciprocally with the Canada Council); and two schemes: *Writers in Schools* and *Writers in Public* (the Writer's Register is a list of writers willing to participate in the schemes). Also publishes lists of Scottish writers' groups, workshops, circles, awards and literary agents.

The Arts Council of Wales
Museum Place, Cardiff CF1 3NX
☎01222 394711 Fax 01222 221447
Literature Director *Tony Bianchi*
Drama Director *Michael Baker*

Funds literary magazines and book production; *Writers on Tour* and bursary schemes; **Welsh Academy, Welsh Books Council, Hay-on-Wye Literature Festival, Cardiff Literature Festival**, and **Tŷ Newydd Writers' Centre** at Cricieth; also children's literature, annual awards. The Council's Drama Board aims to develop theatrical experience among Wales-based writers through a variety of schemes – in particular, by funding writers on year-long attachments.

Arts Council of Wales – North Wales Office

10 Wellfield House, Bangor, Gwynedd LL57 1ER
☎01248 353248   Fax 01248 351077
Regional Director *Sandra Wynne*
Arts Officer (Literature) *J. Clifford Jones*

The region includes Gwynedd, Clwyd and the Montgomeryshire district of Powys. The Regional Board's role in the field of literature is fourfold: to highlight all aspects of the literary heritage in both English and Welsh; to foster an understanding and appreciation of this tradition; to stimulate others to develop these traditions; to encourage promising new initiatives. Priorities include the *Authors in Residence, Authors on Video* and *Writers on Tour* schemes, and the support of literary circles, Eisteddfodau and community newspapers. Can supply list of names and addresses of regional groups and circles in the region. Contact the Literature Officer.

Arts Council of Wales – South East Wales Office

Victoria Street, Cwmbran, Gwent NP44 3YT
☎01633 875075   Fax 01633 875389
Literature Officer *Bob Mole*

Can supply names and addresses of local groups, workshops and writing courses, and information on local writing schemes, and writers.

Arts Council of Wales – West Wales Office

6 Gardd Llydaw, Jacksons Lane, Carmarthen, Dyfed SA31 1QD
☎01267 234248   Fax 01267 233084
Regional Executive Officer *Marion Morris*

ACW West Wales covers Dyfed and West Glamorgan. It supports a network of writers' groups through the **Arts Council of Wales** *Writers on Tour* scheme and organises an ongoing series of community writing projects. Writers receive additional support through their participation in residencies and other activities in the education and healthcare sectors. In conjunction with the Welsh Language Board, the ACW also supports a network of

Welsh language community newspapers. Publishing ventures are referred to other agencies. Supplies a list of names and addresses of over 20 groups in Dyfed and West Glamorgan, including groups like Carmarthen Writers' Circle.

English Regional Arts Boards

5 City Road, Winchester, Hampshire SO23 8SD
☎01962 851063   Fax 01962 842033
Chief Executive *Christopher Gordon*
Assistant *Carolyn Nixson*

English Regional Arts Boards is the representative body for the 10 Regional Arts Boards (RABs) in England. Its Winchester secretariat provides project management, services and information for the members, and acts on their behalf in appropriate circumstances. Scotland, Northern Ireland and Wales have their own Arts Councils. The three Welsh Regional Arts Associations are now absorbed into the Welsh Arts Council. RABs are support and development agencies for the arts in the regions. Policies are developed in response to regional demand, and to assist new initiatives in areas of perceived need; they may vary from region to region.

DIRECT GRANTS FOR WRITERS
While most of the RABs designate part of their budget for allocation direct to writers, this is often a minor proportion, which new or aspiring playwrights stand little chance of receiving. Money is more readily available for the professional, though, because of the emphasis on community access to the arts in many of the Boards, this is often allocated to writers' appearances in schools and community settings, theatre workshops, etc, rather than to support the writer at the typewriter. New writing is also encouraged through the funding of small presses and grants to theatre companies for play commissions. Details of schemes available from individual Boards.

Cleveland Arts

7-9 Eastbourne Road, Linthorpe, Middlesbrough, Cleveland TS5 6QS
☎01642 812288   Fax 01642 813388
Contact *Literature Development Officer*

Cleveland Arts is an independent arts development agency working in the county of Cleveland. The company works in partnership with local authorities, public agencies, the business sector, schools, colleges, individuals and organisations to coordinate, promote and develop the arts – crafts, film, video, photography, music, drama, dance, literature, public arts, disability, Black arts, community arts. The Literature Development Officer promotes writing classes, poetry readings and cabarets, issues a free newsletter and assists publishers and writers.

East Midlands Arts

Mountfields House, Epinal Way,
Loughborough, Leicestershire LE11 0QE
☎01509 218292   Fax 01509 262214
Literature Officer *Debbie Hicks*
Drama Officer *Helen Flach*

Covers Leicestershire, Nottinghamshire, Derbyshire (excluding the High Peak district) and Northamptonshire. A comprehensive information service for regional writers includes an extensive *Writers' Information Pack*, with details of local groups, workshops, residential writing retreats, publishers and publishing information, regional magazines which offer a market for work, advice on approaching the media, on unions, courses and grants. Also available is a directory of writers, primarily to aid people using the *Artists At Your Service* scheme and to establish *Writers' Attachments*. Writers' bursaries are granted for work on a specific project – all forms of writing are eligible except for local history and biography. Writing for the theatre can come under the aegis of both Literature and Drama. A list of writers' groups is available, plus *Foreword*, the literature newsletter.

Eastern Arts Board

Cherry Hinton Hall, Cambridge
CB1 4DW
☎01223 215355   Fax 01223 248075
Literature Officer *Emma Drew*
Drama Officer *Alan Orme*

Covers Bedfordshire, Cambridgeshire, Essex, Hertfordshire, Norfolk, Suffolk and Lincolnshire. Policy emphasises quality and access. As a self-styled arts development agency, great stress is placed upon work with publishers within the region and on literature in performance. In literature, support is given to projects which develop an audience for literature, festivals and performances, and publishing. The Board organises a critical reading service which runs on a first-come, first-served basis while funds last, and it also offers a range of bursaries annually for individual published writers. Supplies a list of literary groups, workshops and local writing courses.

London Arts Board

Elme House, 3rd Floor, 133 Long Acre,
London WC2E 9AF
☎0171 240 1313/Help Line: 0171 240 4578
Fax 0171 240 4580
Principal Literature Officer *John Hampson*
Principal Drama Officer *Sue Timothy*

The London Arts Board is the Regional Arts Board for the Capital, covering the 32 boroughs and the City of London. Potential applicants for support for literature and other arts projects should contact the Board for information.

North West Arts Board

Manchester House, 22 Bridge Street,
Manchester M3 3AB
☎0161 834 6644   Fax 0161 834 6969
Literature Officer *Marc Collett*
Drama Officer *Jane Dawson*

NWAB covers Cheshire, Greater Manchester, Merseyside, Lancashire and the High Peak district of Derbyshire. Offers financial assistance to a great variety of organisations and individuals through a number of schemes, including Writers' Bursaries, Residencies and Placements and the Live Writing scheme. NWAB publishes a directory of local writers groups, a directory of writers and a range of information sheets covering topics such as performance and publishing. For further details please contact the Literature Department.

Northern Arts Board

9-10 Osborne Terrace, Jesmond, Newcastle upon Tyne NE2 1NZ
☎0191 281 6334   Fax 0191 281 3276
Head of Published and Broadcast Arts
 Margaret O'Connor

Covers Cleveland, Cumbria, Durham, Northumberland and Tyne and Wear, and was the first regional arts association in the country to be set up by local authorities. It supports both organisations and writers and aims to stimulate public interest in artistic events. Offers Writers Awards for published writers to release them from work or other commitments for short periods of time to enable them to concentrate on specific literary projects. It also has a film/TV script development fund operated through the Northern Production Fund. A separate scheme for playwrights is operated by the Northern Playwrights Society. Northern Arts makes drama awards to producers only. Also funds writers' residencies, and has a fund for publications. Contact list of regional groups and workshops available.

South East Arts

10 Mount Ephraim, Tunbridge Wells, Kent
TN4 8AS
☎01892 515210   Fax 01892 549383
Literature Officer *Anne Downes*
Drama Officer *Linda Lewis*

Covers Kent, Surrey, East and West Sussex
(excluding the London boroughs). The literature programme aims to raise the profile of contemporary literature across the region and to
support new and established writers. Priorities
include writers' residencies, *Writers-in-Education*
and *Live Literature* schemes; also the continued
support of literature festivals in the region. New
writers are also supported by the *Bursary Scheme*.
A regular newsletter is available (£3 p.a./£5 to
those outside the region).

South West Arts

Bradninch Place, Gandy Street, Exeter, Devon
EX4 3LS
☎01392 218188   Fax 01392 413554
Director of Media & Published Arts
  David Drake
Director of Performing Arts *Nick Capaldi*
Media & Published Arts Administrator
  Sara Fasey

Covers Avon, Cornwall, Devon, much of
Dorset, Gloucestershire and Somerset. 'The
central theme running through the Board's
aims are access, awareness and quality.' The literature policy aims to promote a healthy environment for writers of all kinds and to encourage a high standard of new writing. There is
direct investment in small presses, publishers
and community groups. Literary festivals, societies and arts centres are encouraged. The theatre department aims to support the development of theatre writing by funding the
development of literary management programmes of dramaturgy and seasons of new
plays. List of regional groups and workshops
available from the Information Service.

Southern Arts

13 St Clement Street, Winchester, Hampshire
SO23 9DQ
☎01962 855099   Fax 01962 861186
Literature Officer *Keiren Phelan*
Film, Video & Broadcasting Officer *Jane
  Gerson*
Theatre Officer *Sheena Wrigley*

Covers Berkshire, Buckinghamshire, Hampshire,
the Isle of Wight, Oxfordshire, Wiltshire and
South East Dorset. The Literature Department
funds fiction and poetry readings, festivals, magazines, bursaries, a literature prize, publications,
residencies and a scheme which subsidises writers
working in education and the community.

West Midlands Arts

82 Granville Street, Birmingham B1 2LH
☎0121 631 3121   Fax 0121 643 7239
Literature Officer *David Hart*

There are special criteria across the art forms,
so contact the Information Office for details of
New Work & Production and other schemes as
well as for the *Reading (Correspondence Mss
Advice) Service*. There are contact lists of writers,
storytellers, writing groups etc. WMA supports
the regional magazine, *Raw Edge Magazine*:
contact PO Box 4867, Birmingham B3 3HD.

Yorkshire & Humberside Arts

21 Bond Street, Dewsbury, West Yorkshire
WF13 1AY
☎01924 455555   Fax 01924 466522
Literature Officer *Steve Dearden*
Drama Officer *Shea Connolly*
Administrator *Jill Leahy*

'Libraries, publishing houses, local authorities
and the education service all make major contributions to the support of literature. Recognising the resources these agencies command,
Yorkshire & Humberside Arts actively seeks
ways of acting in partnership with them, whilst
at the same time retaining its particular responsibility for the living writer and the promotion
of activities currently outside the scope of these
agencies.' Funding goes to the Black Literature
Project; **Yorkshire Art Circus** (community
publishing); *Live Writing*, which subsidises projects involving professional writers and young
people at all levels as well as writing and community groups; and to awards for local independent publishers. Also offers support for literature in performance and for the **Ilkley
Literature Festival**, The Word Hoard and
Bête Noire magazine. New Beginnings is a bursary scheme for writers. Holds a list of workshops and writers' groups throughout the
region, and publishes a writers' directory and a
newsletter, *Write Angles*, bi-monthly. Contact
the Literature Officer.

Writers' Courses, Circles and Workshops

Courses
Courses are listed under country and county

England

Avon

Bath College of Higher Education
Newton Park, Bath, Avon BA2 9BN
☎01225 425264

Postgraduate Diploma/MA in Creative Writing. Includes poetry, fiction, playwriting and scriptwriting. Visiting writers have included Roy Fisher, Marion Lomax, William Stafford and Fay Weldon.

University of Bristol
Department for Continuing Education,
8–10 Berkeley Square, Bristol, Avon BS8 1HH
☎0117 9287172   Fax 0117 9254975

Courses in Bristol and the surrounding counties (Avon, Dorset, Gloucestershire, Somerset and Wiltshire). *Women and Writing*, for women who write or would like to begin to write (poetry, fiction, non-fiction, journals); *Certificate in Creative Writing*. Detailed brochure available.

Bucks, Berks & Oxon

Missenden Abbey
Missenden Abbey, Great Missenden, Buckinghamshire HP16 0BD
☎01494 890296   Fax 01494 866737

Residential courses, weekend workshops and a regular writers circle available. The 1996 programme included *Writing Magazine Articles and Getting Them Published; Writing Comedy for Television and Radio; The Art of Travel Writing; Making Crime Pay.*

National Film & Television School
Beaconsfield Studios, Station Road, Beaconsfield, Buckinghamshire HP9 1LG
☎01494 671234   Fax 01494 674042

Writers' course designed for students who already have experience of writing in other fields. The course is divided into two parts: a self-contained intensive five-week course, concentrating on the fundamentals of screenwriting, and an 18-month course for 8–10 students selected from the one-month course: intensive programme of writing and analysis combined with an understanding of the practical stages involved in the making of film and television drama.

University of Reading
Department of Extended Education, London Road, Reading, Berkshire RG1 5AQ
☎0118 9318347

Creative writing courses have included *Life into Fiction; Poetry Workshop; Getting Started; Writers Helping Writers* (with **Southern Arts'** help, the course includes visits from well-known writers); *Writing Popular Fiction*. There is also a support group for teachers of creative writing, a public lecture by a writer and a reading by students of their work. Fees vary depending on the length of course. Concessions available.

Cambridgeshire

National Extension College
18 Brooklands Avenue, Cambridge CB2 2HN
☎01223 316644

Runs a number of home-study courses on writing. Courses include: *Essential Editing; Creative Writing; Writing for Money; Copywriting; Essential Desktop Publishing; Essential Design.* Contact the NEC for copy of the guide to courses which includes details of fees.

PMA Training
The Old Anchor, Church Street, Hemmingford Grey, Cambridgeshire PE18 9DF
☎01480 300653   Fax 01480 496022

One-/two-/three-day editorial, PR, design and publishing courses held in central London. High-powered, intensive courses run by Fleet Street journalists and magazine editors. Courses include: *News Writing, Journalistic Style, Feature Writing, Investigative Reporting, Basic Writing Skills.* Fees range from £150 to £495 plus VAT. Special rates for freelancers.

Cheshire

**The College of Technical Authorship –
Distance Learning Course**
The College of Technical Authorship,
PO Box 7, Cheadle, Cheshire SK8 3BT
☎0161 437 4235

Distance learning courses for City & Guilds
Tech 536, Part 1, Technical Communication
Techniques, and Part 2, Technical Authorship.
Individual tuition by correspondence and fax
includes some practical work done at home.
Contact: John Crossley, DipDistEd, DipM,
MCIM, MISTC, LCGI.

Cleveland

University of Leeds
Adult Education Centre, 37 Harrow Road,
Middlesbrough, Cleveland TS5 5NT
☎01642 814987

Creative writing courses held in the autumn,
spring and summer terms. Contact Rebecca
O'Rourke for details.

Cumbria

Higham Hall College
Bassenthwaite Lake, Cockermouth, Cumbria
CA13 9SH
☎017687 76276   Fax 017687 76013

Residential courses. Summer 1994 programme
included *Creative Writing* and *Memoir Writing*.
Detailed brochure available.

Devon

Dartington College of Arts
Totnes, Devon TW9 6EJ
☎01803 862224

BA(Hons) course in *Performance Writing*:
exploratory approach to writing as it relates to
performance. Can be taken as a single honours
subject or in combination with *Music, Theatre,
Visual Performance* or *Arts Management*. Contact
John Hall, Vice-Principal.

Exeter & Devon Arts Centre
Bradninch Place, Gandy Street, Exeter, Devon
EX4 3LS
☎01392 219741   Fax 01392 499929

Holds weekly courses: *Poetry Project; Advanced
Poetry; Poetry Masterclass; Writing for Television;
TV and Creative Writing* as well as a range of other
workshops. There is also a regular programme of
poetry and literature events, plus the annual
Exeter Poetry Prize. Copies of the Courses &
Classes or Events brochures can be obtained free
from the Centre.

University of Exeter
Exeter, Devon EX4 4QW
☎01392 263263

BA(Hons) in Drama with a third-year option
in *Playwriting*. Contact Professor Peter
Thomson.

Dorset

Bournemouth University
Talbot Circus, Fern Barrow, Poole, Dorset
BH12 5BB
☎01202 524111

Three-year, full-time BA(Hons) course in
Scriptwriting for Film and Television. Contact
Frank Matthews-Finn.

Essex

**National Council for the
Training of Journalists**
Latton Bush Centre, Southern Way, Harlow,
Essex CM18 7BL
☎01279 430009   Fax 01279 438008

For details of journalism courses, both full-time
and via distance learning, please write to the
NCTJ enclosing a large s.a.e..

Hampshire

Highbury College of Technology
Dovercourt Road, Cosham, Portsmouth,
Hampshire PO6 2SA
☎01705 383131   Fax 01705 383131

Courses include: one-year *Pre-entry Magazine
Journalism* course (mainly post-graduate intake).
Run under the auspices of the Periodicals
Training Council. One-year *Pre-entry Newspaper
Journalism* course, under the auspices of the
National Council for Training of Journalists.
One-year course in *Broadcasting Journalism*.
Contact Mrs Paulette Miller, Faculty Secretary,
Tel: 01705 283287.

King Alfred's College of Higher Education
Winchester, Hampshire SO22 4NR
☎01962 841515   Fax 01962 842280

Three-year course on *Drama, Theatre and
Television Studies*, including *Writing for Devised
Community Theatre* and *Writing for Television
Documentary*. Contact Tim Prentki.

MA course in *Writing for Children* (subject to
validation) available on either a one- or two-year
basis. Admissions enquiries: Linda Richards
(01962 827235); Programme enquiries: Jo
Roffey (01962 827375).

School of Creative Writing

Clarendon Court, Over Wallop, Stockbridge,
Hampshire SO20 8HU
☎01264 782298

A correspondence course for beginners, covering all the basics of writing articles, features, short stories, novels, non-fiction, marketing and writing for publication. Assignments are assessed and advice is given by experienced writing tutors. Contact: Paul King.

University of Southampton

Department of Adult Continuing Education,
Southampton SO17 1BJ
☎01703 592833

Creative writing courses and writers' workshops. Courses are held in local/regional centres.

Hertfordshire

West Herts College

Faculty of Visual Communication,
Hempstead Road, Watford, Hertfordshire
WD1 3EZ
☎01923 257654 (Admissions)

The one-year BTEC postgraduate course in *Writing and Production for the Media* covers two options: *Creative, Business and Technical Writing* and *Radio Writing and Production*. The college also offers a postgraduate diploma in *Publishing* with an option in *Multimedia Publishing*. Contact the Admissions Secretary on the number above.

The Writers' Workshop

23 Upper Ashlyns Road, Berkhamsted,
Hertfordshire HP4 3BW
☎01442 871004

The Writers' Workshop at Frieth, near High Wycombe, offers classes in creative writing, plus workshop opportunities. Professional assessments optional. Now publishes a twice-yearly literary magazine, *Rivet*, and holds an annual poetry competition. Contact Maggie Prince at the above address.

Humberside

Hull College of Further Education

Queen's Gardens, Hull, North Humberside
HU1 3DG
☎01482 329943   Fax 01482 219079

Offers part-time day/evening writing courses, including *Novel Writing* and *Short Story Writing*, at various centres within the city. Most courses begin each academic term and last for a period of ten weeks. Publishes an anthology of students' work each year entitled, *Embryo*. Contact Ed Strauss.

Kent

International Forum

The Oast House, Plaxtol, Sevenoaks, Kent
TN15 0QG
☎01732 810925

Wide range of courses (one-/two-/three-day) on screenwriting and other key creative roles in film and television. Courses run throughout the year and concessions are available for members of certain trade organisations. Contact: Joan Harrison.

University of Kent at Canterbury

School of Continuing Education,
Rutherford College, Canterbury,
Kent CT2 7NX
☎01227 823662

Creative writing courses. Contact: Vicki Inge.

Lancashire

Edge Hill College of Higher Education

St Helen's Road, Ormskirk, Lancashire
L39 4QP
☎01695 575171

Offers a two-year, part-time MA in *Writing Studies*. Combines advanced-level writers' workshops with closely related courses in critical theory and contemporary writing in English.

Lancaster University

Department of Creative Writing, Lonsdale
College, Bailrigg, Lancaster LA1 4YN
☎01524 594169

Offers practical graduate and undergraduate courses in writing fiction, poetry and scripts. All based on group workshops – students' work-in-progress is circulated and discussed. Visiting writers have included: Carol Ann Duffy, Kazuo Ishiguro, Bernard MacLaverty, David Pownall. Contact Linda Anderson for details.

London

The Central School of Speech and Drama

Embassy Theatre, Eton Avenue, London
NW3 3HY
☎0171 722 8183   Fax 0171 722 4132

Post-Graduate Diploma in *Advanced Theatre Practice*. One-year, full-time course aimed at providing a grounding in principal areas of professional theatre practice - *Writing, Directing, Performance, Puppetry* and *Design*, with an emphasis on collaboration between the various strands. Entrants to the *Writing* strand are required to submit two pieces of writing together with completed application form. Prospectus available.

The City Literary Institute
Humanities Dept, Stukeley Street, London
WC2B 5LJ
☎0171 430 0542

The Writing School offers a wide range of courses from *Radio Drama Writing* and *Writing for Children* to *Autobiographical Writing* and *Writing Short Stories*. The Department offers information and advice during term time on the above telephone number.

City University
Northampton Square, London EC1V 0HB
☎0171 477 8268

Creative writing classes include: *Writer's Workshop; Wordshop* (poetry); *Writer's Craft; Writing Fiction; Writing Comedy; Playwright's Workshop; Writing Freelance Articles for Newspapers; Women Writer's Workshop; Creative Writing*. Contact: Courses for Adults.

London College of Printing & Distributive Trades
Elephant & Castle, London SE1 6SB
☎0171 514 6500

Courses in journalism. Short courses run by DALI (Developments at the London Institute) at the Elephant & Castle address above: *Writing for Magazines; English for Journalists; Sub-editing and Layout*. Full-time courses (held at the School of Media Studies, Back Hill, London EC1R 5EN): *BAHons. in Journalism; HND in Journalism; Periodical Journalism for Graduates*. Prospectus and information leaflets available.

London School of Journalism
22 Upbrook Mews, London W2 3HG
☎0171 706 3536/01225 444774 (Admin)
Fax 0171 706 3780/01225 313986 (Admin)

Correspondence courses with an individual and personal approach. Students remain with the same tutor throughout their course. Options include: *Short Story Writing; Writing for Children; Poetry; Freelance Journalism; Improve Your English; English for Business; Journalism and Newswriting*. Fees vary but range from £145 for *Poetry* to £360 for *Journalism and Newswriting*. Contact Antoinette Winckworth at the Administration Office, PO Box 1745, Bath, Avon BA2 6YE.

Middlesex University
School of English Cultural and
Communication Studies, White Hart Lane,
London N17 8HR
☎0181 362 5000   Fax 0181 362 6299
Undergraduate courses (full-time, part-time, associate) for those interested in writing, publish-

ing and the media. Writing & Publishing Studies Set includes: *Editing* and *Marketing* (contact Juliet Gardiner); BA(Hons) Writing programme includes: *Journalism, Scriptwriting and Narrative* and *Poetry Workshops* (contact Susanna Gladwin).

Roehampton Institute
Senate House, Roehampton Lane, London
SW15 5PU
☎0181 392 3000

Three-year BA(Hons) course in *Drama and Theatre Studies* which includes writing for the theatre and associated media. Contact Jeremy Ridgman.

Scriptwriters Tutorials
65 Lancaster Road, London N4 4PL
☎0171 272 2335/720 7047

Offers professional *one-to-one* scriptwriting tuition by working writers in film, television, radio or stage. Beginners, intermediate and advanced courses. Script evaluation service and correspondence courses. Also holds an annual writers retreat in Gascony.

Thames University
St Mary's Road, London W5 5RF
☎0181 231 2271

Offers a course in *Scriptwriting for Television, Stage and Radio*. Aims to provide the fundamental principles of the craft of script writing. Contact Tony Dinner.

University of Westminster
Short Courses Unit, 35 Marylebone Road,
London NW1 5LS
☎0171 911 5000

Short courses in writing, including *Basic News and Feature Writing*.

The Write Space, The London Academy of Playwriting
75 Hillfield Park, London N10 3QU
☎0181 444 5228

Two-year, part-time, post-graduate course in playwriting. Director: Tony Dinner. Contact Sonja Lyndon, Registrar.

Manchester
University of Manchester
Department of American Studies, Arts
Building, Oxford Road, Manchester M13 9PL
☎0161 275 3054   Fax 0161 2753054
Offers a one-year MA in *Novel Writing*. Contact Richard Francis.

Password Training

23 New Mount Street, Manchester M4 4DE
☎0161 953 4009   Fax 0161 953 4090

Publishing training for both individuals and organisations. *Foundation in Publishing* for those new to the industry or needing to understand it further; *Marketing in Publishing*; *Design & Production*. Full grants are available. Contact Claire Turner, Training Manager for further information.

The Writers Bureau

Sevendale House, 7 Dale Street, Manchester M1 1JB
☎0161 228 2362   Fax 0161 228 3533

Comprehensive home-study writing course with personal tuition service from professional writers (fee approx. £219); Professional Business Writing Course which covers the writing of letters, memos, reports, minutes etc. (fee £199); and a Poetry Course which covers all aspects of writing poetry (fee £119).

Merseyside

University of Liverpool

Centre for Continuing Education,
19 Abercromby Square, Liverpool L69 3BX
☎0151 794 6900 (24 hours)

General creative writing courses for beginners. *Poetry, Writing and Performance; The Short Story and the Novel; Scripting for Television, Radio, Comedy, Including Stand Up; Women's Writing; Asian Voices, Asian Lives; Writing for Children; Chinese and South East Asia Writing; An Introduction to Journalism; Feature Writing for Magazines and Newspapers; The Art and Craft of Songwriting.* Most courses are run in the evening over 10 or 20 weeks. Weekend and residential courses in the summer. No pre-entry qualifications required. Fees vary; some courses may be free. For further information and copy of current prospectus, phone or write to Keith Birch, Academic Organiser, Creative Arts (address as above).

Writing in Merseyside

c/o Writing Liaison Office, Toxteth Library, Windsor Street, Liverpool L8 1XF
☎0151 708 0143

A mini-directory which lists facilities, resources and opportunities in the Merseyside area. Excellent publication for putting writers in touch with what's available in their area. Everything from workshops and courses to competitions, research and library facilities, plus tips. Comprehensive course information on all areas of writing is provided.

Norfolk

University of East Anglia

School of English & American Studies, Norwich, Norfolk NR4 7TJ
☎01603 593262

UEA has a history of concern with contemporary literary culture. Among its MA programmes is one in *Creative Writing*, Stream 1: Prose Fiction; Stream 2: Script and Screenwriting.

Northamptonshire

Swanwick Writers' Summer School

The New Vicarage, Parson's Street, Woodford Halse, Daventry, Northants NN11 3RE
☎01327 261477

A week-long summer school held at The Hayes, Swanwick, Derbyshire. Lectures, informal talks and discussion groups, forums, panels, quizzes and competitions, and 'a lot of fun'. Open to everyone, from absolute beginners to published authors. Held in August from late Saturday to Friday morning. Cost (1996) £185+, all inclusive. Contact the Secretary, Brenda Courtie at the above address.

Staffordshire

Keele University

Adult and Continuing Education, Keele University, (Freepost ST1666), Newcastle under Lyme, Staffordshire ST5 5BR
☎01782 625116

Weekend courses on literature and creative writing. The 1996 programme included a fiction-writing weekend and a poetry weekend. Also runs study days where major novelists or poets read and discuss their work.

Suffolk

Suffolk College

Rope Walk, Ipswich, Suffolk IP4 1LT
☎01473 296646   Fax 01473 216416

Summer School courses; the 1996 programme included *Writing for Radio*. Contact Audrey Semple, Summer School Co-ordinator for details.

Write on Course

1 Waterloo Road, Ipswich, Suffolk IP1 2NY
☎01473 210199

A variety of one-day and weekend residential courses on topics such as *Ways to Make Money from Spare-time Writing, Self-Publishing, Erotic Writing, Writing Short Stories,* and *Getting into*

Technical Writing. Courses are held in East Anglia and other parts of the country.

Surrey
Royal Holloway and Bedford New College
University of London, Egham Hill, Egham, Surrey TW20 0EX
☎01784 443922   Fax 01784 431018

Three-year BA course in *Theatre Studies* during which playwriting can be studied as an option in the second and third years. Contact Dan Rebellato or David Wiles.

University of Surrey
Department of Educational Studies, Guildford, Surrey GU2 5XH
☎01483 259754

The programme 'Courses For All' includes a *Creative Writing* course, held at the University, the Guildford Institute and throughout the county. Contact Karen Fisher for details.

Writing School
Nationwide House, Hyland Business Centre, 78–86 Garlands Road, Redhill, Surrey RH1 6NT
☎01737 779065

Correspondence course covering writing for articles, short stories, books, plays and scripts, with a strong emphasis on writing to sell. Fee £299 (1996). Contact the Director of Studies for enrolment details.

Sussex
Chichester Institute of Higher Education
Bishop Otter College, College Lane, Chichester, West Sussex PO19 4PE
☎01243 787911   Fax 01243 536011

Postgraduate Certificate/Diploma MA in *Creative Writing*. Contact Dr Paul Foster, Head of English Studies for details.

The Earnley Concourse
Earnley, Chichester, West Sussex PO20 7JL
☎01243 670392   Fax 01243 670832

Offers a range of residential and non-residential courses throughout the year. The 1996 programme included *Writing Fiction; You Can Sell What You Write*. Brochure available.

University of Sussex
Centre for Continuing Education Centre, Education Development Building, Falmer, Brighton, East Sussex BN1 9RG
☎01273 678040   Fax 01273 678848

Courses in creative writing, autobiographical writing, and dramatic writing. Day and evening courses. Concessions available.

Tyne & Wear
University of Newcastle upon Tyne
Centre for Continuing Education, Newcastle upon Tyne NE1 7RU
☎0191 222 6542

Writing-related courses include: *Writing From the Inside Out; Dramatic Writing for Film, TV and Radio*. Contact the Secretary, Adult Education Programme.

Warwickshire
University of Warwick
Open Studies, Continuing Education Dept, Coventry, Warwickshire CV4 7AL
☎01203 523831

Creative writing courses held at the university or in regional centres. Subjects have included: *Starting to Write; Creative Writing; Express Yourself in Writing*. A two-year certificate in *Creative Writing* is available.

West Midlands
University of Birmingham
School of Continuing Studies, Edgbaston, Birmingham B15 2TT
☎0121 414 5607   Fax 0121 414 5619

Day and weekend classes, including creative writing, writing for radio and television. Courses are held at locations throughout Birmingham, the West Midlands, Hereford & Worcester and Shropshire. Detailed course brochures are available from the above address. Please specify which course you are interested in.

The University also offers an MA course in *Playwriting Studies* established by David Edgar in 1970. Contact Brian Crow at the Department of Drama and Theatre Arts (Tel 0121 414 5993).

Sandwell College
Smethwick Campus, Crocketts Lane, Smethwick B66 3BU
☎0121 556 6000

Creative writing courses held afternoons/evenings, from September to July. General courses covering short stories, poetry, autobiography, etc. Also women's writing courses (accreditation pending). Contact Roz Goddard.

Worcestershire
Loch Ryan Writers
Loch Ryan Hotel, 119 Sidbury, Worcester
WR5 2DH
☎01905 351143   Fax 01905 764407

Weekend residential writing workshops throughout the year. Emphasis on poetry, but also prose and drama. Contact Gwynneth Royce for details and all-inclusive prices.

Yorkshire
ARTTS International
Highfield Grange, Bubwith, North Yorkshire
YO8 7DP
☎01757 288088

Theatre, television, film and radio courses. Two-week introductory courses, including *Scriptwriting for Stage and Screen.*

The Northern School of Film and Television
Leeds Metropolitan University, 2–8 Merrion Way, Leeds, West Yorkshire LS2 8BT
☎0113 2833193   Fax 0113 2833194

A relatively new film school, the NSFT offers a Postgraduate Diploma/MA course in *Fiction Screenwriting.* One to two years, full-/part-time. Contact Ian Macdonald.

Open College of the Arts
Houndhill, Worsbrough, Barnsley, South Yorkshire S70 6TU
☎01226 730495   Fax 01226 730838

The OCA correspondence course, *Starting to Write,* offers help and stimulus, without an emphasis on commercial success, from experienced writers/tutors. Subsequent levels available include specialist poetry, fiction and biographical writing courses. Audio-cassette versions of these courses are available.

Sheffield Hallam University
School of Cultural Studies, Sheffield Hallam University, Psalter Lane, Sheffield S11 8UZ
☎0114 2532662   Fax 0114 2532603

Offers MA in *Creative Writing* (one-year, full-time/two-year, part-time course).

University College Bretton Hall
School of English, Faculty of Art, Design and Humanities, University College Bretton Hall, West Bretton, Wakefield, West Yorkshire WF4 4LG
☎01924 830261   Fax 01924 830521

Offers one-year full-time/two-years part-time MA course in *Creative Writing* designed for competent though not necessarily published writers. Contact Dr L. Peach for details.

University College, Scarborough
North Riding College, Filey Road, Scarborough, North Yorkshire YO11 3AZ
☎01723 362392   Fax 01723 362392

BA Combined Arts Degree in which *Theatre Studies* contains modules in *Writing for Theatre* and *English Studies* contains the module *Writing and the Writer.* Contact Dr Eric Prince. University College Scarborough hosts the annual National Student Drama Festival which includes the International Student Playscript Competition (details from Clive Wolfe on 0181 883 4586).

University of Sheffield
Division of Adult Continuing Education, 196–198 Wear Street, Sheffield S1 4ET
☎0115 2825400

Creative writing courses and workshops. Day/evening classes, residential courses.

Northern Ireland
The Poets' House
80 Portmuck Road, Portmuck, Islandmagee, Co. Antrim BT40 3TP
☎01960 382646

Affiliated to Lancaster University, The Poets' House offers a one-year, full-time MA course in *Creative Writing: Poetry.*

Queen's University of Belfast
Institute of Continuing Education, Belfast
BT7 1NN
☎01232 245133 ext. 3326

Courses have included *Creative Writing* and *Journal Writing.*

University of Ulster
Short Course Unit, Belfast BT37 0QB
☎01232 365131

Creative writing course/workshop, usually held in the autumn and spring terms. Concessions available. Contact the Administrative Officer.

Scotland
University of Aberdeen
Centre for Continuing Education, Regent Building, Regent Walk, Aberdeen AB9 1FX
☎01224 272448   Fax 01224 272478

Creative writing evening class held weekly, taught by published author.

Creative Space Summer School
Lunga Mill, Ardfern, Argyll PA31 8QR
☎01852 500526

For two weeks in July the Creative Space Summer School offers residential courses on art and writing. In 1996, poet and playwright Liz Lochhead was one of the visiting tutors. Courses are designed for beginner writers as well as more experienced poets and short prose writers. Contact Bella Green for details.

University of Dundee
Centre for Continuing Education, Perth Road, Dundee DD1 4HN
☎01382 344128

Various creative writing courses held at the University and elsewhere in Dundee, Perthshire and Angus. Detailed course brochure available.

Edinburgh University
Centre for Continuing Education,
11 Buccleuch Place, Edinburgh EH8 9LW
☎0131 650 4400   Fax 0131 667 6097

Several writing-orientated courses and summer schools. Beginners welcome. Publishes a series of occasional papers - eg: *No. 4 - Creative Writing: Towards a Framework for Evaluation* by Graham Hartill, available from the above address (£2). In 1996, offered *Film Studies* in association with the Edinburgh Filmhouse. Course brochure available.

University of Glasgow
Department of Adult and Continuing Education, 59 Oakfield Avenue, Glasgow G12 8LW
☎0141 330 4032/4394 (Brochure/Enquiries)

In 1995/6 ran several writers' workshops and courses at all levels; all friendly and informal. Both daytime and evening meetings. Tutors are all experienced and published writers in all fields.

University of St Andrews
School of English, The University,
St Andrews, Fife KY16 9AL
☎01334 462666   Fax 01334 462655

Offers postgraduate study in *Creative Writing*. Candidates choose two topics from: *Fiction: The Novel; Craft and Technique in Poetry; The Short Story*, and also write their own poetry and/or prose for assessment.

Wales

University of Glamorgan
Treforest, Pontypridd CF37 1DL
☎01443 482551

MA in Writing – a two-year part-time Master of Arts degree for writers of fiction and poets. ESTABLISHED 1993. Contact Professor Tony Curtis at the School of Humanities and Social Sciences. Also, BA in Theatre and Media Drama. Modules include *Scriptwriting: Theatre, Radio, TV and Video*. Contact Steven Blandford

Taliesin Trust
Tŷ Newydd, Llanystumdwy, Cricieth,
Gwynedd LL52 0LW
☎01766 522811   Fax 01766 523095

Residential writers' centre set up by the Taliesin Trust with the support of the **Arts Council of Wales** to encourage and promote writing in both English and Welsh. Most courses run from Monday evening to Saturday morning. Each course has two tutors and takes a maximum of 16 participants. The centre offers a wide range of specific courses. 1996 course tutors included Gillian Clarke, Liz Lochhead, Clare Boylan and Kevin Crossley-Holland. Early booking essential. Fee £255 inclusive. People on low incomes may be eligible for a grant or bursary. Course leaflet available.

Tre Fechan
Tre Fechan Arts Centre, Pennant Melangell,
Nr Llangynog, Powys SY10 0EU
☎01691 860346

Occasional residential courses on fiction held in north Wales run by Shelley Weiner and Alice Thomas Ellis.

Circles and Workshops

Directory of Writers' Circles
Oldacre, Horderns Park road, Chapel en le Frith, Derbyshire SK12 6SY
☎01298 812305

Comprehensive directory of writers' circles, containing contacts and addresses of hundreds of groups and circles including postal circles, meeting throughout the country. Some overseas entries too. Available from Jill Dick at the above address. £4 post free.

Alston Hall
Alston Lane, Longridge, Preston, Lancashire PR3 3BP
☎01772 784661   Fax 01772 785835

Holds regular day-long creative writing workshops. Brochure available.

Black Coral Productions Ltd
See under **Film, TV and Video Producers**

Chiltern Writers' Group
31 Cressex Road, High Wycombe HP12 4PG
☎01494 520375

Invites writers, publishers, editors and agents to speak at its monthly meetings at Wendover Public Library. Regular newsletter and competitions. Annual subscription: £10; concessions: £6. Trial meeting: £2. Contact Karen Hemmingham at the above address.

The Cotswold Writers' Circle
Dar-es-Salaam, Beeches Park, Hampton Fields, Minchinhampton, Gloucestershire GL6 9BA

Contact *Charles Hooker*, Honorary Treasurer, for details of the Circle's activities.

Croftspun
Drakemyre Croft, Cairnorrie, Methlick, Ellon, Aberdeenshire AB41 0JN
☎01651 806252

Publishes a small booklet entitled *The Cottage Guide to Writers' Postal Workshops*, a directory giving the contact names and addresses of postal folios for writers (£2 post free).

'Sean Dorman' Manuscript Society
Cherry Tree, Crosemere Road, Cockshutt, Ellesmere, Shropshire SY12 0JP
☎01939 270293

FOUNDED 1957. The Society provides mutual help among writers and aspiring writers in England, Wales and Scotland. By means of circulating manuscript parcels, members receive constructive criticism of their own work and read and comment on the work of others. Each 'Circulator' has up to nine participants and members' contributions may be in any medium: short stories, chapters of a novel, poetry, magazine articles etc. Members may join two such circulators if they wish. Each circulator has a technical section and a letters section in which friendly communication between members is encouraged, and all are of a general nature apart from one, specialising in mss for the Christian market. Full details and application forms available on receipt of s.a.e.. Director: Mary Driver. Subscription £6.50 p.a..

Equinoxe Screenwriting Workshops (in association with the Sundance Institute)
Association Equinoxe, 85–89 Quai André Citroën, 75711 Paris, France
☎00 33 1 4425 7146   Fax 00 33 1 4425 7142

FOUNDED 1993, with Jeanne Moreau as president, to promote screenwriting and to establish a link between European and American film production. In adapting the Sundance Institute's concept (founded by Robert Redford), Equinoxe supports young writers of all nationalities by creating a screenwriting community capable of appealing to an international audience. For selected professional screenwriters able to speak either English or French fluently. Contact Claire Dubert.

Gay Authors Workshop
BM Box 5700, London WC1N 3XX
☎0181 520 5223

Established 1978 to encourage and support lesbian/gay writers. Regular meetings and a newsletter. Contact Kathryn Byrd. Membership £5; £2 unwaged.

Historical Novel Folio
17 Purbeck Heights, Mount Road, Parkstone, Poole, Dorset BH14 0QP
☎01202 741897

An independent postal workshop – single folio dealing with any period before World War II. Send s.a.e. for details. Contact: Doris Myall-Harris.

London Screenwriters' Workshop
84 Wardour Street, London W1V 3LF
☎0171 434 0942

Established by writers in 1983 as a forum for contact, information and tuition. LSW helps new and developing writers in the film, TV and video industries. Organises a continuous programme of workshops, events with industry figures, seminars and courses. Free monthly events and magazine newsletter every two months. Contact Paul Gallagher or Anji Loman Field. Membership £25 p.a.

London Writer Circle
110 Whitehall Road, London E4 6DW
☎0181 529 0886
FOUNDED 1924. Aims to help and encourage writers of all grades. Monthly evening meetings with well-known speakers on aspects of literature and journalism, and workshops for short story writing, poetry and feature writing. Occasional social events and quarterly magazine. Subscription: £16 (Town); £9 (Country); £6 (Overseas). Contact Jean Hawkes, Membership Secretary.

NWP (North West Playwrights)
Contact Theatre, Oxford Road, Manchester M15 6JA
☎0161 274 4418   Fax 0161 274 4418
FOUNDED 1982. Award-winning organisation whose aim is to encourage, develop and promote new theatre writing. Operates a script-reading service, Commission and Residency Award Scheme, The Lowdown newsletter and the Summer Workshops – an annual showing of six workshopped plays by local writers. Previous participants include Charlotte Keatley, Kevin Fegan, Lavinia Murray and James Stock. Services available only to North West writers.

Nottingham Writers Contact
W.E.A. Centre, 16 Shakespeare Street, Nottingham NG1 4GF
☎01159 288913
A group of professional and amateur writers which meets every third Saturday in the month at the U. A. E. C. Centre, 10.00am – 12.30pm. 'If you are visiting the city contact Keith Taylor at the above telephone number.'

Playwrights' Workshop
22 Brown Street, Altrincham, Cheshire WA14 2EU
☎0161 928 3095
Monthly meetings, readings, guest speakers, etc.

Peer Poetry Postal Workshops
26(w) Arlington House, Bath Street, Bath BA1 1QN
Each 'workshop' contains a group of five poets chosen to complement one another. A folder (folio) containing work by each member is circulated within the group, giving the authors

valuable feed-back. A charge of £1 is made each time the folio passes through a member's hands. Joining fee: £3; send s.a.e. and cheque or postal order made payable to Peer Poetry Workshops.

Repwriters
See **Birmingham Repertory Theatre** under **Theatre Producers**

Scribo
Flat 1, 31 Hamilton Road, Boscombe, Bournemouth, Dorset BH1 4EQ
☎01202 302533
FOUNDED in the early 70s, Scribo circulates folios (published and unpublished work) to its members, who currently number about 40 and rising. The only criteria for joining is that you must be actively engaged in writing novels. Forum folios discuss anything of interest to novelists; problems are shared and information exchanged. Manuscript folios offer friendly criticism and advice. Besides 'general' mss folios there are three specialist folios: crime; aga-saga/saga/ romance; fantasy/science-fiction. A new folio has been launched for the more literary novelist. Members – mostly graduates, published and unpublished – would welcome a few similarly dedicated serious novelists. 'No pornography.' Contact: K. Sylvester, P. A. Sylvester.

Southport Writers' Circle
53 Richmond Road, Birkdale, Southport, Merseyside PR8 4SB
Runs a poetry competition (see **Prizes**). Contact Alison Chisholm.

Speakeasy
14 Langcliffe Drive, Heelands, Milton Keynes MK13 7AL
☎01908 318722
Invites poets and writers to Milton Keynes most months. Also runs workshops according to demand. Monthly meetings are held where people can read their own work. Contact Anita Packwood.

University of Southampton Annual Writers' Conference
Dept of Adult Continuing Education, University of Southampton, Southampton, Hampshire SO17 1BJ
☎01703 593469
Having grown over the past 16 years from a creative writing workshop, this event is now the largest writers' conference in the country attracting international authors, playwrights, poets, agents and editors who give workshops, lectures and seminars to help writers harness

their creativity and develop technical skills. The conference is held in April (11th–13th in 1997) and offers a variety of writing competitions. For programme, booking forms and further information, please write to Barbara Large, Conference Organiser.

University of Stirling
Continuing Education, Airthrey Castle, Stirling FK9 4LA
☎01786 473171

Holds writers' workshop at Airthrey Castle one evening per week for eight weeks. Covers writing short stories, poetry, novels, letters, diaries, drama, newspaper articles, biography and autobiography, etc.

Ways With Words
See under **Festivals**

Workers' Educational Association
National Office: Temple House, 17 Victoria Park Square, London E2 9PB
☎0181 983 1515   Fax 0181 983 4840

FOUNDED in 1903, the WEA is a voluntary body with members drawn from all walks of life. It runs writing courses and workshops throughout the country and all courses are open to everyone. Branches in most towns and many villages, with 13 district offices in England and 1 in Scotland. Contact your district WEA office for courses in your region. All correspondence should be addressed to the District Secretary.

Cheshire, Merseyside & West Lancashire: 7/8 Bluecoat Chambers, School Lane, Liverpool L1 3BX (☎0151 709 8023)

Eastern: Botolph House, 17 Botolph Lane, Cambridge CB2 3RE (☎01223 350978).

East Midlands: 16 Shakespeare Street, Nottingham NG1 4GF (☎01159 475162).

London: 44 Crowndale Road, London NW1 1TR (☎0171 388 7261).

Northern: 51 Grainger Street, Newcastle upon Tyne NE1 5JE (☎0191 232 3957)

North Western: 4th Floor, Crawford House, University Precinct Centre, Oxford Road, Manchester M13 9GH (☎0161 273 7652).

South Eastern: 4 Castle Hill, Rochester, Kent ME1 1QQ (Tel: 01634 842140).

South Western: Martin's Gate Annexe, Bretonside, Plymouth, Devon PL4 0AT (☎01752 664989).

Thames & Solent: 6 Brewer Street Oxford OX1 1QN (☎01865 246270).

Western: 40 Morse Road, Redfield, Bristol, Avon BS5 9LB (☎01179 351764).

West Mercia: 78–80 Sherlock Street, Birmingham B5 6LT (Tel: 0121 666 6101).

Yorkshire North: 6 Woodhouse Square, Leeds, W. Yorkshire LS3 1AD (☎01132 453304).

Yorkshire South: Chantry Buildings, 6–20 Corporation Street, Rotherham S60 1NG (☎01709 837001).

Scottish Association: Riddle's Court, 322 Lawnmarket, Edinburgh EH1 3PG (☎0131 226 3456).

Yorkshire Playwrights
3 Trinity Road, Scarborough, North Yorkshire YO11 2TD

FOUNDED 1989 out of an initiative by Jude Kelly and William Weston of the **West Yorkshire Playhouse**. A group of professional writers of plays for stage, TV and radio whose aims are to encourage the writing and performance of new plays in Yorkshire. Open to any writers living in Yorkshire who are members of the **Theatre Writers Union, The Writers' Guild** or **The Society of Authors**. Contact the administrator, *Ian Watson*, for an information sheet.

Editorial, Research and Other Services

Lesley & Roy Adkins
Longstone Lodge, Aller, Langport, Somerset
TA10 0QT
☎01458 250075   Fax 01458 250858
Contact *Lesley Adkins, Roy Adkins*

Offers indexing, research, copy-editing, manuscript criticism/advice, contract writing for publishers, rewriting, book reviews and feature writing. *Special interests* archaeology (worldwide), history and heritage. See also **Lesley & Roy Adkins Picture Library**.

Anagram Editorial Service
26 Wherwell Road, Guildford, Surrey
GU2 5JR
☎01483 33497   Fax 01483 306848
Contact *Martyn Bramwell*

Full range of editorial services available from project development through commissioning, editing and proof-reading to production of finished books. Specialises in earth sciences, natural history, environment, general science and technology. Also author of over 30 non-fiction titles for young readers. Clients include UK, German, American and Middle East publishers, United Nations agencies (UNEP, FAO) and international conservation organisations.

Arioma Editorial Services
Gloucester House, High Street, Borth, Dyfed
SY24 5HZ
☎01970 871296   Fax 01970 871296
Contact *Moira Smith*

FOUNDED 1987. Staffed by ex-London journalists, who work mainly with authors wanting to self-publish. Editing, indexing, ghost writing, cover design, plus initial help with marketing and publicity. Sample chapter and synopsis required. All types of book welcome, but work must be of a 'sufficiently high standard'. No reading fee. Rates on application. Please send s.a.e. with all submissions.

Ascribe
112 Mildred Avenue, Watford, Hertfordshire
WD1 7DX
☎01923 238899
Contact *Mary Baginsky*

Complete book production services for chari-ties, small societies and individuals, as well as editorial, writing, rewriting, research and any emergency projects. Specialist areas include education, law, criminology and other social sciences.

Astron Appointments Ltd
77 New Bond Street, London W1Y 9DB
☎0171 495 2230   Fax 0171 495 4472
Managing Director *Colin Ancliffe*

In addition to a long-standing register of permanent job-seekers within publishing, Astron has a freelance register with details of a large number of experienced people available to undertake all types of freelance assignments within the publishing field.

Authors' Research Services
32 Oak Village, London NW5 4QN
☎0171 284 4316
Contact *Richard Wright*

Research and document supply service, particularly to authors, academics and others without easy access to London libraries and sources of information. Also indexing of books and journals. Rates negotiable.

Joanna Billing
1 Holly Farm Mews, Green Lane, Great
Sutton, South Wirral L66 4XX
☎0151 339 9740   Fax 0151 339 9740
Contact *Joanna Billing*

Specialises in writing, copy-editing, proof-reading, researching, desk-top publishing (with laser printer), word-processing and print production for technical books, company newsletters and journals, corporate literature, brochures, training documents, confidential reports, publicity materials and public relations. With expertise in technical and scientific, travel, commercial and education fields.

Brooks Krikler Research
455 Finchley Road, London NW3 6HN
☎0171 431 9886   Fax 0171 431 9887
Contact *Emma Krikler*

Provides a full picture-research service to all those involved in publishing and the media. Educational and non-educational books, magazines, advertising, CD-ROM & Multimedia, brochures, video and computer games manufacturers and designers. The service includes finding, editing and providing images, negotiating all reproduction charges inclusive of full copyright clearance. Has special arrangements with photographic libraries worldwide and a variety of photographers can undertake commissioned work. An on-line service is available with all requests.

D. Buckmaster

Wayfarer House, 51 Chatsworth Road, Torquay, Devon TQ1 3BJ
☎01803 294663

Contact *Mrs D. Buckmaster*

General editing of mss, specialising in traditional themes in religious, metaphysical and esoteric subjects. Also success and inspirational books or articles.

Graham Burn Productions

9–13 Soulbury Road, Linslade, Leighton Buzzard, Bedfordshire LU7 7RL
☎01525 377963/376390   Fax 01525 382498

Offers complete production services to writers wishing to publish their own material, and pre-press services to other publishers.

CIRCA Research and Reference Information Ltd

13–17 Sturton Street, Cambridge CB1 2SN
☎01223 568017   Fax 01223 354643

An editorial co-operative
Approx. turnover £500,000

ESTABLISHED 1989. Specialises in researching, writing and editing of reference works on international politics and economics, including *Cassell Dictionary of Modern Britain; Dorling Kindersley World Reference Atlas; Keesing's Record of World Events; Keesing's UK Record; People in Power*. All work is fee-based.

Creative Communications

11 Belhaven Terrace, Glasgow G12 0TG
☎0141 334 9577   Fax 0141 334 9577

Contact *Ronnie Scott*

Creative Comunications delivers professional corporate communication services to leading Scottish organisations. It also provides effective writing (including copywriting and script writing), editing and newspaper design, and consults on all aspects of communications.

E. Glyn Davies

Cartref, 21 Claremont Avenue, Bishopston, Bristol, Avon BS7 8JD
☎0117 9756793   Fax 0117 9246248

Contact *E. Glyn Davies*

Editorial services for writers whose first language is not English: rewriting, revision, proof-reading, translation into English. Quotations on request.

Deeson Editorial Services

Ewell House, Faversham, Kent ME13 8UP
☎01795 535468   Fax 01795 535469

Also at: 100 Grove Vale, London SE22 8DR
☎0181 693 3383   Fax 0181 299 0862

Contact *Dr Tony Deeson, Dominic Deeson*

ESTABLISHED 1959. A comprehensive research/writing/editing service for books, magazines, newspapers, articles, annual reports, submissions, presentations. Design and production facilities. Specialists in scientific, technical, industrial and business-to-business subjects including company histories.

Flair for Words

5 Delavall Walk, Eastbourne, East Sussex BN23 6ER
☎01323 640646

Directors *Cass and Janie Jackson*

ESTABLISHED 1988. Offers wide range of services to writers, whether beginners or professional, through the Flair Network. Offers assessment, editing and advisory service. Publishes bi-monthly newsletter, handbooks on all aspects of writing, and audio tapes.

F. G. & K. M. Gill

11 Cranmore Close, Aldershot, Hampshire GU11 3BH
☎01252 25881/24067   Fax 01252 25881

Contacts *Fred and Kathie Gill*

ESTABLISHED over 16 years. Proof-reading, copy-editing and indexing services. Fiction and non-fiction (all subjects). Clients include UK, North American and continental publishers. Rates on application.

Valerie Grosvenor Myer

34 West End, Haddenham, Cambridge CB6 3TE
☎01353 740738   Fax 01353 740738

Contact *Valerie Grosvenor Myer*

Copy-editing of manuscripts and typescripts for publication. Research in English literature, post-15th century. Learned periodical articles and bibliographies a speciality. Experienced indexer. Hourly fees by agreement.

Indexing Specialists
202 Church Road, Hove, East Sussex
BN3 2DJ
☎01273 323309   Fax 01273 323309
Contact *Richard Raper*

ESTABLISHED over 30 years. Indexing for a wide range of subjects for all manner of books, journals and other publications. Also offers copy-editing and proof-reading services. Quotations available on request.

Ink Inc. Ltd
1 Anglesea Road, Kingston on Thames,
Surrey KT1 2EW
☎0181 549 3174   Fax 0181 546 2415
Managing Director *Richard Parkes*
Editorial Head *Barbara Leedham*

Publishing consultants. Clients range from very small dtp operations through to large plcs. Advise on every aspect of publishing, including production, design, editorial, marketing, distribution and finance. Also take on editorial, design, production and project management work.

J G Editorial
54 Mount Street, Lincoln LN1 3JG
☎01522 530758   Fax 01522 575679
Contact *Jenni Goss*

ESTABLISHED 1988. Freelance editors with 20 years' experience offering full editorial service to authors and typesetters. Independent critique service for fiction, general non-fiction and academic/business (no poetry) – includes structure and presentation; rewriting/ghosting; word processing/presentation/keying; project management; editorial reports; copy and disk editing (IBM/AppleMac); proofreading. Quotations on request.

J. P. Lethbridge
245 St Margaret's Road, Ward End,
Birmingham B8 2DY
☎0121 783 0548
Contact *J. P. Lethbridge*

Experienced historical researcher. Searching through old newspapers and checking birth, marriage and death certificates a speciality. Special interest in crime. Rates negotiable.

The Literary Consultancy
26 Crouch Hill, London N4 4AU
☎0181 372 3922   Fax 0181 372 3922
Contact *Rebecca Swift, Hannah Griffiths*

Founded by former publishers to offer an editorial service for aspiring writers. Will provide an appraisal of fiction, poetry and most categories of non-fiction. Charges range from £30 for three poems (maximum 25 lines each) to £300 for a full mss of 300–500 pages.

LJC Permission Services
11 Monkswell Lane, Chipstead, Coulsdon,
Surrey CR5 3SX
☎01737 833536   Fax 01737 833004
Contacts *Louisa Clements, Robert Young*

A copyright clearing agency used widely by publishers and authors who wish to reproduce copyright material. The agency undertakes to obtain permission for articles, photographs, artwork and music to be reproduced in another publication or on cassettes. Part of the service includes preparing acknowledgement copy if requested and negotiating the reproduction fee with the copyright holder. Full breakdown of costs on larger projects. Large database of copyright sources. Multimedia permissions also undertaken. Fixed fee per permission.

Deborah Manley
57 Plantation Road, Oxford OX2 6JE
☎01865 310284   Fax 01865 59671
Contact *Deborah Manley*

Offers (to publishers) editorial reports, copy-editing, writing, rewriting, research, anthologising, indexing, proof-reading and caption copy. Specialises mainly in educational, children's, reference and travel. NUJ rates.

Duncan McAra
30 Craighall Crescent, Edinburgh EH6 4RZ
☎0131 552 1558   Fax 0131 552 1558
Contact *Duncan McAra*

Consultancy on all aspects of general trade publishing: editing, rewriting, copy-editing, proof-reading. *Specialises* in art, architecture, archaeology, biography, film, military and travel. Also runs a literary agency (see **UK Agents**).

Minett Media
6 Middle Watch, Swavesey, Cambridge
CB4 5RN
☎01954 230250   Fax 01954 232019
Contact *Dr Steve Minett, Gunnel Minett*

Minett Media specialises in the production of press releases and feature articles for multinational business-to-business companies, offering a comprehensive editorial service (including site visits anywhere in Europe, writing draft text, securing approval and best effort at publication in the international trade press). Also offers management of press relations with the international business-to-business trade press, complete-package production of business-to-business, multi-language customer magazines (including translation, design, artwork, repro, printing and distribution) and enquiry database management. Clients include ITT Flygt, Anglian Water International, IMO, Celleco-Hedemora (part of Alfa Laval).

Murder Files

Marienau, Brimley Road, Bovey Tracey, Devon TQ13 9DH
☎01626 833487   Fax 01626 835797
Contact *Paul Williams*

Crime writer and researcher specialising in UK murders. Can provide information on thousands of well-known and less well-known cases dating from 1400. Copies of press cuttings relating to murder available for cases from 1920 onwards. Research also undertaken for general enquirers, writers, TV, radio, video, etc. Rates on application.

Northern Writers Advisory Services (NWAS)

77 Marford Crescent, Sale, Cheshire M33 4DN
☎0161 969 1573
Contact *Jill Groves*

Offers publishing services such as copy-editing, proof-reading, word-processing and desktop publishing (with laser printing). Does much of its work with societies (mainly local history), and small presses. NWAS's specialist subject is history of all types, but especially local and family history. Also handles biographies and leisure books. No computer software material. Rates on application, but very reasonable.

Ormrod Research Services

Weeping Birch, Burwash, East Sussex TN19 7HG
☎01435 882541   Fax 01435 882541
Contact *Richard Ormrod*

ESTABLISHED 1982. Comprehensive research service: literary, historical, academic, biographical, commercial. Critical reading with report,

editing, indexing, proof-reading, ghosting. Verbal quotations available.

Out of Print Book Service

13 Pantbach Road, Birchgrove, Cardiff CF4 1TU
☎01222 627703
Contact *L. A. Foulkes*

FOUNDED 1971. Covers all subjects including fiction and non-fiction. No charge for search. Send s.a.e for details.

Pages Editorial & Publishing Services

Ballencrieff Cottage, Ballencrieff Toll, Bathgate, West Lothian EH48 4LD
☎01506 632728   Fax 01506 632728
Contact *Susan Coon*

Contract-publishing service for magazines and newsletters, including journalism, editing, advertising, production and mailing. Also editorial advice, word processing and short-run publishing service for authors and publishers.

Roger Palmer Limited, Media Contracts and Copyright

18 Maddox Street, Mayfair, London W1R 9PL
☎0171 499 8875   Fax 0171 499 9580
Contact *Roger Palmer, Stephen Aucutt*

ESTABLISHED 1993. Drafts, advises on and negotiates all media contracts (on a regular or *ad hoc* basis) for publishers, literary and merchandising agents, packagers, charities and others. Manages and operates clients' complete contracts functions, undertakes contractual audits, devises contracts systems, advises on copyright and related issues and provides training and seminars. Growing private client list, with special rates for members of **The Society of Authors**. Roger Palmer (Managing Director) was for many years Contracts and Intellectual Property Director of the Hodder & Stoughton Group; Stephen Aucutt (Senior Consultant) was previously Contracts Manager for Reed Children's Books.

Penman Literary Service

185 Daws Heath Road, Benfleet, Essex SS7 2TF
☎01702 557431
Contact *Mark Sorrell*

ESTABLISHED 1950. Advisory, editorial and typing service for authors. Rewriting, ghosting, proof-reading; critical assessment of manuscripts.

Perfect English
11 Hill Square, Upper Cam, Dursley,
Gloucestershire GL11 5NJ
☎01453 547320   Fax 01453 521525
Contact *James Alexander*

'Meticulous reading and editing to remove errors of spelling, grammar, punctuation, word choice and meaning. Mss returned fully checked and as perfect as possible within the structure and style of the original material.' Rates on application.

Plain Words (Business Writers)
96 Wellmeadow Road, London SE6 1HW
☎0181 698 5269/697 3227
Fax 0181 461 5705
Contact *Henry Galgut, Judy Byrne*

Provides industrial and commercial businesses with a copywriting and editing service. Sectors served include oil, petrochemicals, banking, public transport, travel, retail, publishing and catering. Henry Galgut and Judy Byrne have backgrounds in human resource management consulting, journalism, psychology and psychotherapy.

Reading & Righting (Robert Lambolle Services)
618B Finchley Road, London NW11 7RR
☎0181 455 4564   Fax 0181 455 4564
Contact *Robert Lambolle*

Reader/literary editor, with agency, publishing and theatre experience. Offers detailed manuscript evaluation, analysis of prospects and next-step guidelines. Fiction, non-fiction, drama and screenplays. Special interests include cinema, the performing arts, popular culture, psychotherapy and current affairs. Also editorial services, creative writing workshops and lectures. Services do not include representing writers in an agent's capacity. Leaflet available on request.

Science and Technology Reference Publishing
2 Pell Hill Cottages, Wadhurst, East Sussex
TN5 6DS
☎01892 783652   Fax 01892 784287
Contact *Peter Lafferty*

Specialises in researching, writing and editing of reference works such as dictionaries and encyclopedias in science and technology, including *Hutchinson Dictionary of Science* and *Hutchinson Encyclopedia of Science*. Works for children and general family audiences a particular interest.

Scriptmate
See **Book-in-Hand Ltd** under **Small Presses**

Strand Editorial Services
16 Mitchley View, South Croydon, Surrey
CR2 9HQ
☎0181 657 1247   Fax 0181 657 1247
Contact *Derek Bradley*

All stages of editorial production of house journals, magazines, newsletters, publicity material, etc. Short-term, long-term and emergency projects. Sub-editing, proof-reading, and book reviews (education, training and business). Reasonable rates (negotiable).

Teral Research Services
45 Forest View Road, Moordown,
Bournemouth, Dorset BH9 3BH
☎01202 516834   Fax 01202 516834
Contact *Terry C. Treadwell*

All aspects of research undertaken but specialises in all military, aviation, naval and defence subjects, both past and present. Extensive book and photographic library, including one of the best collections of World War One aviation photographs. Terms by arrangement.

WORDSmith
2 The Island, Thames Ditton, Surrey KT7 0SH
☎0181 339 0945   Fax 0181 339 0945
Contact *Michael Russell*

Copy-editing, both on paper and on-screen. Specialises in rewriting and abridging, particularly new writer fiction. Also magazine articles and stories, company literature, user guides, copywriting, film-script editing. Everything from 2000 to 200,000 words. Please phone for details.

The Writers Advice Centre for Children's Books
Palace Wharf, Rainville Road, London
W6 9HN
☎0181 874 7347   Fax 0181 874 7347
Contact *Louise Jordan*

Offers editorial and marketing advice to children's writers – both published and unpublished – by Readers who are all currently connected with children's publishing. Plus personal introductions to publishers/agents where appropriate. Also runs courses and small agenting service.

The Writers' Exchange

14 Yewdale, Clifton Green, Swinton
M27 8GN
☎0161 281 0544

Contact *Peter Collins, The Secretary*

FOUNDED 1978. Full range of copywriting, ghostwriting and editorial services, including appraisal service for amateur writers preparing to submit material to or having had material rejected by, literary agents and/or publishers. Novels, short stories, film, TV, radio, and stage plays. Appraisal fee £5 per 1000 words. Send s.a.e. for details.

Press Cuttings Agencies

The Broadcast Monitoring Company

89½ Worship Street, London EC2A 2BE
☎0171 377 1742   Fax 0171 377 6103

Television, radio, national and European press monitoring agency. Cuttings from national and all major European press available seven days a week, with early morning delivery. Also monitoring of all news and current affairs programmes – national, international and satellite. Retrospective research service and free telephone notification. Sponsorship evaluation from all media sources.

Durrants Press Cuttings Ltd

103 Whitecross Street, London EC1Y 8QT
☎0171 588 3671   Fax 0171 374 8171

Wide coverage of all print media sectors; foreign press in association with agencies abroad; current affairs and news programmes from UK broadcast media. High speed, early morning press cuttings from the national press. Overnight delivery via courier to most areas or first-class mail. Well presented, laser printed, A4 cuttings. Monthly reading fee of £40 per instruction plus 80p per cutting.

International Press-Cutting Bureau

224–236 Walworth Road, London SE17 1JE
☎0171 708 2113   Fax 0171 701 4489

Contact *Robert Podro*

Covers national, provincial, trade, technical and magazine press. Cuttings are normally sent twice weekly by first-class post and there are no additional service charges or reading fees. Subscriptions for 100 and 250 cuttings are valid for six months. Larger subscriptions expire after one year even if the total number of cuttings subscribed for has not been reached. 100 cuttings (£146, plus VAT); 250 (£330, plus VAT).

Premium Press Monitoring

Bear Wharf, 27 Bankside, London
SE1 9DP
☎0171 203 3500   Fax 0171 203 0101

Contact *Lesley Jackson*

Offers an overnight national press monitoring service with same day, early morning delivery. Also coverage of regional papers and weekly/monthly business/trade magazines. Rates on application.

PressCheck

9-10 Great Sutton Street, London
EC1V 0BX
☎0171 490 5591   Fax 0171 251 4940

Contact *Charles Stuart Hunt*

A fast, easy, economical way to check press and publicity coverage. A service specialising in organisations that deal with public schools, theatres, museums, art galleries, clubs etc.

Romeike & Curtice

Hale House, 290-296 Green Lanes, London
N13 5TP
☎0800 289543   Fax 0181 882 6716

Contact *Richard Silver*

Covers national and international dailies and Sundays, provincial papers, consumer magazines, trade and technical journals, national radio/TV logs and teletext services. Back research and advertising checking services are also available.

We Find It (Press Clippings)

103 South Parade, Belfast BT7 2GN
☎01232 646008

Contact *Avril Forsythe*

Specialises in Northern Ireland press and magazines, both national and provincial. Rates on application.

Bursaries, Fellowships and Grants

Aosdána Scheme

An Chomhairle Ealaíon (The Arts Council),
70 Merrion Square, Dublin 2, Republic of
Ireland
☎00 353 1 6611840   Fax 00 353 1 6761302

Literature Officer *Laurence Cassidy*

Aosdána is an affiliation of creative artists
engaged in literature, music and the visual arts,
and consists of not more than 200 artists who
have gained a reputation for achievement and
distinction. Membership is by competitive
sponsored selection and is open to Irish citizens
or residents only. Members are eligible to
receive an annuity for a five-year term to assist
them in pursuing their art full-time.

Award IR£8000 (annuity).

Arts Council Literature Bursaries, Ireland

An Chomhairle Ealaíon, 70 Merrion Square,
Dublin 2, Republic of Ireland
☎00 353 1 6611840   Fax 00 353 1 6761302

Literature Officer *Laurence Cassidy*

Bursaries in literature awarded to creative writers of fiction, poetry and drama in Irish and
English to enable concentration on, or completion of, specific projects. A limited number of
bursaries may be given to non-fiction projects.
Open to Irish citizens or residents only. Final
entry date 8 April.

Award IR£2000–£8000.

Arts Council Theatre Writing Bursaries

Arts Council of England, 14 Great Peter
Street, London SW1P 3NQ
☎0171 333 0100 ext 431   Fax 0171 973 6590

Contact *Drama Director*

Intended to provide experienced playwrights
with an opportunity to research and develop a
play for the theatre independently of financial
pressures and free from the need to write for a
particular market. Bursaries are also available
for theatre translation projects. Writers must be
resident in England. Writers resident in Wales,
Scotland or Northern Ireland should approach
their own Arts Council. Final entry date 8
January 1997.

Award £3000.

Arts Council Writers' Awards

14 Great Peter Street, London
SW1P 3NQ
☎0171 973 6234   Fax 0171 973 6590

Literature Assistant *Valerie Olteanu*

ESTABLISHED 1965. The Arts Council offers 15
bursaries a year. Applications should be accompanied by a c.v., description and sample of work
in progress, statement of annual income and
three copies of a previously published creative
work. Judges will make their choices principally
on the grounds of artistic quality, basing that
judgment on their reading of work in progress
and evidence before them of the writer's past
achievement. Past winners include: Donald
Atkinson, Olivia Fane, Jonathan Treitel, Subniv
Babuta, Jon Silkin, Margaret Wilkinson, Robert
Edric, Sue Thomas, Sally Cline, Jocelyn M.
Ferguson, Lavinia Greenlaw, Charlotte Cory,
David Gale, Nicola Barker, Ruth Padell,
Duncan Sprott. Final entry date 30 September.

Award 15 awards of £7000.

The Authors' Contingency Fund

The Society of Authors, 84 Drayton Gardens,
London SW10 9SB
☎0171 373 6642   Fax 0171 373 5768

This fund makes modest grants to published
authors who find themselves in sudden financial difficulties.

The Authors' Foundation

The Society of Authors, 84 Drayton Gardens,
London SW10 9SB
☎0171 373 6642   Fax 0171 373 5768

Annual grants to writers whose publisher's
advance is insufficient to cover the costs of
research involved. Application by letter to The
Authors' Foundation giving details, in confidence, of the advance and royalties, together
with the reasons for needing additional funding. Grants are sometimes given even if there is
no commitment by a publisher, so long as the
work will almost certainly be published.
£75,000 was distributed in 1995. Contact the
Society of Authors for an information sheet.
Final entry date 30 April.

The K. Blundell Trust

The Society of Authors, 84 Drayton Gardens, London SW10 9SB
☎0171 373 6642   Fax 0171 373 5768

Annual grants to writers whose publisher's advance is insufficient to cover the costs of research. Author must be under 40, has to submit copy of his/her previous book and the work must 'contribute to the greater understanding of existing social and economic organisation'. Application by letter. Contact the Society of Authors for an information sheet. Final entry date 30 April. Total of £15,000 available.

Alfred Bradley Bursary Award

c/o Network Radio Drama, BBC North, New Broadcasting House, Oxford Road, Manchester M60 1SJ
☎0161 200 2020

Contact *Melanie Harris*

ESTABLISHED 1992. Biennial award in commemoration of the life and work of the distinguished radio producer Alfred Bradley. Aims to encourage and develop new writing talent in the **BBC North** region. There is a change of focus for each award; details of the theme for the next award (1997) were not available at the time of going to press. Entrants must live or work in the North region. The award is given to help authors to pursue a career in writing for radio. Support and guidance is given from regional BBC radio producers. Previous winners: Lee Hall, Julie Clark.

Award not less than £3000 a year for 2 years

British Academy Publication Subventions

20-21 Cornwall Terrace, London NW1 4QP
☎0171 487 5966   Fax 0171 224 3807

Contact *Assistant Secretary, Research Grants*

Thrice-yearly award to help defray production costs of scholarly publications which might otherwise not succeed in finding a publisher. Work to be published must be a serious contribution to scholarship and the manuscript must have been completed and accepted by a publisher prior to application. Subventions do not normally exceed 25% (up to a maximum of £2000) of the direct costs of production, excluding any element of publisher's overheads.

British Academy Small Personal Research Grants

20-21 Cornwall Terrace, London NW1 4QP
☎0171 487 5966   Fax 0171 224 3807

Contact *Assistant Secretary, Research Grants*

Quarterly award to further original creative research at postdoctoral level in the humanities and social sciences. Entrants must no longer be registered for postgraduate study, and must be resident in the UK. Final entry dates end of September, November, February and April.

Award maximum £5000.

Cholmondeley Awards

The Society of Authors, 84 Drayton Gardens, London SW10 9SB
☎0171 373 6642   Fax 0171 373 5768

FOUNDED 1965 by the late Dowager Marchioness of Cholmondeley. Annual non-competitive awards for the benefit and encouragement of poets of any age, sex or nationality, for which submissions are not required. Presentation date June. 1996 winners: Elizabeth Bartlett, Dorothy Nimmo, Peter Scupham, Iain Crichton Smith.

Award (total) £8000, usually shared.

The Economist/Richard Casement Internship

The Economist, 25 St James's Street, London SW1A 1HG
☎0171 839 7000

Contact *Business Affairs Editor (re. Casement Internship)*

For a journalist under 24 to spend three months in the summer writing for *The Economist* about science and technology. Applicants should write a letter of introduction along with an article of approximately 600 words suitable for inclusion in the Science and Technology Section. Competition details normally announced in the magazine late January and 4-5 weeks allowed for application.

Fulbright T. E. B. Clarke Fellowship in Screenwriting

The Fulbright Commission, Fulbright House, 62 Doughty Street, London WC1N 2LS
☎0171 404 6880   Fax 0171 404 6834

Contact *Programme Director*

Award offered to a young (normally, under 35) British film screenwriter to spend nine months in the US developing his/her expertise and experience. The successful candidate will follow postgraduate courses in screenwriting at a US institution, attend real-life story conferences and write a screenplay and some treatments during the award period. Final entry date end February.

Award air travel and grant of £18,000 plus approved tuition fees.

Fulton Fellowship

David Fulton (Publishers) Ltd, 2 Barbon Close, Great Ormond Street, London WC1N 3JX
☎0171 405 5606　　　　Fax 0171 831 4840
Contact *David Fulton*

ESTABLISHED 1995. Annual award to support research in special educational needs. Recipients will have the opportunity to publish their work in a form accessible to teachers with the help of the publisher, David Fulton and the Centre of the Study of Special Education at Westminster College, Oxford. 1995 Fellow: Erica Brown.

The Tony Godwin Memorial Award

The Tony Godwin Memorial Trust,
c/o Laurence Pollinger Ltd, 18 Maddox Street, London W1R 0EU
☎0171 629 9761　　　　Fax 0171 629 9765
Contact *Lesley Hadcroft (at above address)*
Chairman *Iain Brown* (0171 627 4244)

Biennial award established to commemorate the life of Tony Godwin, a prominent publisher in the 1960s/70s. Open to all young people (under 35 years old) who are UK nationals and working, or intending to work, in publishing. The award provides the recipient with the means to spend at least one month as the guest of a publishing house in the US in order to learn about American publishing. The recipient is expected to submit a report upon return to the UK. Final entry date for next award: 31 December, 1997. Previous winners: George Lucas (Hodder), Richard Scrivener (Penguin).

Prize a bursary of approx. $5000.

Eric Gregory Trust Fund

The Society of Authors, 84 Drayton Gardens, London SW10 9SB
☎0171 373 6642　　　　Fax 0171 373 5768

Annual competitive awards of varying amounts are made each year for the encouragement of young poets under the age of 30 who can show that they are likely to benefit from an opportunity to give more time to writing. Open only to British-born subjects resident in the UK. Final entry date, 31 October. Presentation date June.

Contact The Society of Authors for further information. 1996 winners: Sue Butler, Cathy Cullis, Jane Griffiths, Jane Holland, Chris Jones, Sinead Morrissey, Kate Thomas.

Award (total) £21,000.

The Guardian Research Fellowship

Nuffield College, Oxford OX1 1NF
☎01865 278520　　　　Fax 01865 278676
Contact *Warden's Secretary*

One-year fellowship endowed by the Scott Trust, owner of *The Guardian*, to give someone working in the media the chance to put their experience into a new perspective, publish the outcome and give a *Guardian* lecture. Applications welcomed from journalists and management members, in newspapers, periodicals or broadcasting. Research or study proposals should be directly related to experience of working in the media. Accommodation and meals in college will be provided, and a 'modest' supplementary stipend might be arranged to ensure the Fellow does not lose out from the stay. Advertised annually in November.

Hawthornden Castle Fellowship

Hawthornden Castle, The International Retreat for Writers, Lasswade, Midlothian EH18 1EG
☎0131 440 2180

Administrator *Emma Lovegrove*

ESTABLISHED 1982 to provide a peaceful setting where published writers can work without disturbance. The Retreat houses five writers at a time, who are known as Hawthornden Fellows. Writers from any part of the world may apply for the fellowships. No monetary assistance is given, nor any contribution to travelling expenses, but once arrived at Hawthornden, the writer is the guest of the Retreat. Application must be made one year in advance; application forms available from March with the deadline in mid-September. Previous winners include: Daisy Waugh, Julian Smith, Wendy Richmond, J. G. Nichols, Marilyn Duckworth.

Francis Head Bequest

The Society of Authors, 84 Drayton Gardens, London SW10 9SB
☎0171 373 6642　　　　Fax 0171 373 5768

Provides grants to published British authors over the age of 35 who need financial help during a period of illness, disablement or temporary financial crisis.

Ralph Lewis Award

University of Sussex Library, Brighton, East
Sussex BN1 9QL
☎01273 678158   Fax 01273 678441

ESTABLISHED 1985. Triennial award set up by
Ralph Lewis, a Brighton author and art collector
who left money to fund awards for promising
manuscripts which would not otherwise be published. The award is given in the form of a grant
to a UK-based publisher in respect of an agreed
three-year programme of publication of literary
works by new authors or by established authors
using new styles or forms. No direct applications
from writers. Previous winners: **Peterloo Poets**
(1989–91); **Serpent's Tail** (1992–94).

London Arts Board Publishing New Writing Fund

Elme House, 133 Long Acre, London
WC2E 9AF
☎0171 240 1313   Fax 0171 240 4580

Aims to support and develop small presses and
literary magazines in the publishing of new or
under-represented fiction and poetry. This fund
is only open to groups for whom publishing is a
central activity. Contact the Principal Literature
Officer for further details and deadline.

Macaulay Fellowship

An Chomhairle Ealaíon (The Arts Council),
70 Merrion Square, Dublin 2, Republic of
Ireland
☎00 353 1 6611840   Fax 00 353 1 6761302
Literature Officer *Laurence Cassidy*

To further the liberal education of a young
creative artist. Candidates for this triennial
award must be under 30 on 30 June, or 35 in
exceptional circumstances, and must be Irish
citizens or residents. Last awarded 1993.

Award IR£4000.

The John Masefield Memorial Trust

The Society of Authors, 84 Drayton Gardens,
London SW10 9SB
☎0171 373 6642   Fax 0171 373 5768

This trust makes occasional grants to professional poets (or their immediate dependants)
who are faced with sudden financial problems.

Somerset Maugham Trust Fund

The Society of Authors, 84 Drayton Gardens,
London SW10 9SB
☎0171 373 6642   Fax 0171 373 5768

The annual awards arising from this Fund are

designed to encourage young writers to travel
and to acquaint themselves with the manners
and customs of other countries. Candidates
must be under 35 and their publishers must
submit a published literary work in volume
form in English. They must be British subjects
by birth. Final entry date 31 December.
Presentation in June. 1996 winners: Katherine
Pierpoint *Truffle Beds*; Alan Warner *Morvern
Caller*.

Award £5000 each.

National Poetry Foundation Grants

27 Mill Road, Fareham, Hampshire
PO16 0TH
☎01329 822218
Contact *Johnathon Clifford*

The **National Poetry Foundation** considers
applications for grant aid of up to £1000
where other funding is not available and the
product will benefit poetry in general. Send
details together with s.a.e. to NPF (Grants) at
the above address.

The Airey Neave Trust

40 Charles Street, London
WC1X 7PB
☎0171 495 0554   Fax 0171 491 1118
Contact *Hannah Scott*

INITIATED 1989. Annual research fellowships
for up to three years – towards a book or paper
– for serious research connected with national
and international law, and human freedom.
Must be attached to a particular university in
Britain. Interested applicants should come forward with ideas, preferably before March in
any year.

New London Writers' Awards

London Arts Board, Elme House,
133 Long Acre, London WC2E 9AF
☎0171 240 1313   Fax 0171 240 4580
Contact *John Hampson*

ESTABLISHED 1993/94. Four bursaries awarded
annually to London writers who have published a first book of fiction (novel, short stories, etc) or poetry and who need to 'buy time'
to complete a second work. Application form
available from the above address. Final entry
date: mid-January 1997. Previous winners:
Pauline Melville, Leena Dhingra, M. Dooley,
Kirsty Gunn, Mick Imlah, Bridget O'Connor.

Awards £3500 each.

Newspaper Press Fund

Dickens House, 35 Wathen Road, Dorking, Surrey RH4 1JY
☎01306 887511   Fax 01306 876104

Director/Secretary *Peter Evans*

Aims to relieve distress among journalists and their dependants. Limited help available to non-member journalists. Continuous and/or occasional financial grants; also retirement homes for eligible beneficiaries. Information and subscription details available from The Secretary.

Northern Arts Literary Fellowship

Northern Arts, 10 Osborne Terrace, Jesmond, Newcastle upon Tyne NE2 1NZ
☎0191 281 6334   Fax 0191 281 3276

Contact *Published & Broadcast Arts Department*

A competitive fellowship tenable at and co-sponsored by the universities of Durham and Newcastle upon Tyne for a period of two academic years.
Award £15,000 p.a.

Northern Arts Writers Awards

Northern Arts, 10 Osborne Terrace, Jesmond, Newcastle upon Tyne NE2 1NZ
☎0191 281 6334   Fax 0191 281 3276

Contact *Published & Broadcast Arts Department*

Awards are offered to established authors resident in the **Northern Arts** area on the basis of literary merit. Application spring/summer. Also available, one-month residencies at Tyrone Guthrie Centre, Ireland.
Award variable.

The PAWS (Public Awareness of Science) Drama Script Fund

The PAWS Office, OMNI Communications, Osborne House, 111 Bartholomew Road, London NW5 2BJ
☎0171 267 2555   Fax 0171 482 2394

Contacts *Barrie Whatley, Andrew Millington*

ESTABLISHED 1994. Annual award aimed at encouraging television scriptwriters to include science and engineering scenarios in their work. Grants (currently £2000) are given to selected writers to develop their script ideas into full treatments; Prizes are awarded for the best of these treatments (Grand Prix currently £5000). The PAWS Fund holds meetings enabling writers to meet scientists and engineers and also offers a contacts service to put writers in 'one-to-one' contact with specialists who can help them develop their ideas.

Pearson Television Theatre Writers' Scheme

Teddington Lock, Teddington, Middlesex TW11 9NT
☎0181 948 1154

Contact *Jack Andrews*

Awards bursaries to playwrights. Applicants must be sponsored by a theatre which then submits the play for consideration by a panel. Each award allows the playwright a twelve-month attachment. Applications invited via theatres at the end of 1996 and the end of 1997. For up-to-date information, contact Jack Andrews.

The Margaret Rhondda Award

The Society of Authors, 84 Drayton Gardens, London SW10 9SB
☎0171 373 6642   Fax 0171 373 5768

Competitive award given to a woman writer as a grant-in-aid towards the expenses of a research project in journalism. Triennial. 1996 winner: Laura Spinney. Next award, final entry date 31 December 1998; presentation date May 1999.
Award (total) approx. £1000.

The Royal Literary Fund

144 Temple Chambers, Temple Avenue, London EC4Y 0DA
☎0171 353 7150

Secretary *Mrs Fiona Clark*

Grants and pensions are awarded to published authors in financial need, or to their dependants. Examples of author's works are needed for assessment by Committee. Write for further details and application form.

Southern Arts Literature Award

13 St Clement Street, Winchester, Hampshire SO23 9DQ
☎01962 855099   Fax 01962 861186

Contact *Literature Officer*

Offers an annual award of £3,500 to a published writer living in the region to assist a specific project. Awards can be used to cover a period of unpaid leave while writing from home, to finance necessary research and travel, or to purchase equipment. Final entry date: 16 August.

Laurence Stern Fellowship

Graduate Centre for Journalism, City University, Northampton Square, London EC1V 0HB
☎0171 477 8224   Fax 0171 477 8574

Contact *Robert Jones*

Awarded to a young journalist experienced enough to work on national stories. It gives them the chance to work on the national desk of the *Washington Post*. Benjamin Bradlee, the *Post*'s Vice-President, selects from a shortlist drawn up in March/April. 1995 winner: Sarah Neville of the *Yorkshire Post*. Full details available on the web: http://www.city.ac.uk/journalism/index.htm

Thames Television Theatre Writers' Scheme

See **Pearson Television Theatre Writers' Scheme**

David Thomas Prize

The Financial Times (L), 1 Southwark Bridge, London SE1 9HL

☎0171 873 3000   Fax 0171 873 3924

Managing Editor *Robin Pauley*

FOUNDED 1991. Annual award in memory of David Thomas, *FT* journalist killed on assignment in Kuwait in April 1991, whose 'life was characterised by original and radical thinking coupled with a search for new subjects and orthodoxies to challenge'. The award will provide an annual study/travel grant to enable the recipient to take a career break to explore a theme in the fields of industrial policy, Third World development or the environment. Entrants may be of any nationality; age limits vary. A given theme which changes from year to year is announced in the early autumn. The 1995 theme was: Does free trade threaten the environment? Entrants should submit up to 1000 words on the theme, together with a brief c.v. and proposal outlining how the award could be used to explore the theme further. Award winners will be required to write an essay of 1500–2000 words at the end of the study period which will be considered for publication in the newspaper. Final entry date end December/early January.

Prize £3000 travel grant.

Tom-Gallon Trust

The Society of Authors, 84 Drayton Gardens, London SW10 9SB

☎0171 373 6642   Fax 0171 373 5768

A biennial award is made from the Trust Fund to fiction writers of limited means who have had at least one short story accepted. Authors wishing to enter should send a list of their already published fiction, giving the name of the publisher or periodical in each case and the approximate date of publication; one published short story; a brief statement of their financial position; an undertaking that they intend to devote a substantial amount of time to the writing of fiction as soon as they are financially able to do so; and an s.a.e. for the return of work submitted. Final entry date 20 September 1998. Presentation date June.

Award £1000.

The Betty Trask Awards

The Society of Authors, 84 Drayton Gardens, London SW10 9SB

☎0171 373 6642   Fax 0171 373 5768

These annual awards are for authors who are under 35 and Commonwealth citizens, awarded on the strength of a first novel (published or unpublished) of a traditional or romantic (rather than experimental) nature. The awards must be used for a period or periods of foreign travel. Final entry date 31 January. Presentation June. Contact The Society of Authors for an information sheet. 1996 winners: John Lanchester *The Debt to Pleasure*, Meera Syal *Anita and Me*; Rhidian Brook *The Testimony of Taliesin Jones*; Louis Caron Buss *The Luxury of Exile*

Award (total) £25,000.

The Travelling Scholarships

The Society of Authors, 84 Drayton Gardens, London SW10 9SB

☎0171 373 6642   Fax 0171 373 5768

Annual, non-competitive awards for the benefit of British authors, to enable them to travel abroad. 1996 winners: Stewart Conn, Annette Kobak and Theo Richmond.

Award (total) £6000.

UEA Writing Fellowship

University of East Anglia, University Plain, Norwich NR4 7TJ

☎01603 592734   Fax 01603 593522

Director of Personnel & Registry Services *J. R. L. Beck*

ESTABLISHED 1971. Awarded to a writer of established reputation in any field for a period of six months, January to end June. The duties of the Fellowship are discussed at an interview. It is assumed that one activity will be the pursuit of the Fellow's own writing. In addition the Fellow will be expected to (a) offer an undergraduate creative writing course in the School of English and American Studies during the Spring semester, and to read and grade work received; (b) offer 15 less formal sessions of one hour or more made up of readings, workshops, tutorials, and/or visits to seminars;

(c) arrange, with help from UEA and **Eastern Arts**, additional visits and readings by other writers from outside the university; (d) make contact with groups around the county, and participate with Eastern Arts in organising off-campus visits for writers from the performance programme. A handbook including guidelines for this scheme and all the necessary form letters will be provided by EAB; (e) take part in a project on the future of undergraduate creative writing teaching in the School of English and American Studies, and, after discussion with relevant faculty, write a brief report. It is hoped that (b), (c) and (d) above will involve students from the University as a whole, as well as participants from the city and the region. An office and some limited secretarial assistance will be provided, and some additional funds will be available to help the Fellow with the activities described above. Applications for the fellowship should be lodged with the Director of Personnel & Registry Services in the autumn; candidates should submit at least two examples of recent work. Previous winner: Janette Turner Hospital.

Award £5000 plus free flat on campus.

Prizes

ABSW/Glaxo Science Writers' Awards

Association of British Science Writers, c/o British Association for the Advancement of Science, 23 Savile Row, London W1X 2NB
☎0171 439 1205   Fax 0171 973 3051
ABSW Administrator *Barbara Drillsma*

A series of annual awards for outstanding science journalism in newspapers, journals and broadcasting.

J. R. Ackerley Prize

English Centre of International PEN,
7 Dilke Street, London SW3 4JE
☎0171 352 6303   Fax 0171 351 0220

Commemorating the novelist/autobiographer J. R. Ackerley, this prize is awarded for a literary autobiography, written in English and published in the year preceding the award. Entry restricted to nominations from the Ackerley Trustees only. Previous winners include: Eric Lomax *The Railway Man*; Paul Binding *St Martin's Ride*; Germaine Greer *Daddy, We Hardly Knew You*; John Osborne *Almost a Gentleman*; Barry Humphries *More Please*; Blake Morrison *And When Did You Last See Your Father?*; Paul Vaughan *Something in Linoleum*.

The Acorn Award

See **Nottinghamshire Children's Book Award**

Age Concern Book of the Year

See **The Seebohm Trophy**

Aldeburgh Poetry Festival Prize

Goldings, Goldings Lane, Leiston, Suffolk IP16 4EB
☎01728 830631   Fax 01728 832029
Festival Coordinator *Michael Laskey*

ESTABLISHED 1989 by the Aldeburgh Poetry Trust. Sponsored jointly by Waterstone's and the Aldeburgh Bookshop for the best first collection published in Britain or the Republic of Ireland in the preceding twelve months. Open to any first collection of poetry of at least 40 pp. Final entry date 1 October. Previous winners: Donald Atkinson, Mark Roper, Susan Wicks, Sue Stewart, Gwyneth Lewis.

Prize £500, plus an invitation to read at the following year's festival.

Alexander Prize

Royal Historical Society, University College London, Gower Street, London WC1E 6BT
☎0171 387 7532   Fax 0171 387 7532
Contact *Literary Director*

Awarded for a historical essay of not more than 8000 words. Competitors may choose their own subject for the essay, but must submit their choice for approval in the first instance to the Literary Director of the Royal Historical Society.
Prize £250.

Allied Domecq Playwright Award

c/o Scope Communications, Tower House, 8-14 Southampton Street, London WC2E 7HA
☎0171 379 3234   Fax 0171 240 7729
Contact *Lucy McCrickard, Lucy Cohn*

ESTABLISHED 1995. Biennial award, founded by Allied Domecq and the **Bush Theatre** in London, to encourage new writing talent. Open to writers (over the age of 18) who have not yet had a play produced professionally. Entrants must submit a 1000-word outline plus examples of previously completed work. First winner: Jacinta Stringer.
Prize £5000 to help with development of the outline; if appropriate, the play will be staged at the Bush Theatre.

An Duais don bhFilíocht i nGaeilge

An Chomhairle Ealaíon (The Arts Council), 70 Merrion Square, Dublin 2, Republic of Ireland
☎00 353 1 6611840   Fax 00 353 1 6761302
Literature Officer *Laurence Cassidy*

Triennial award for the best book of Irish poetry. Works must have been published in the Irish language in the preceding three years. Last award 1995.
Prize £1500.

Hans Christian Andersen Awards

IBBY, Nonnenweg 12, Postfach CH-4003, Basle, Switzerland
☎00 41 61 272 2917   Fax 00 41 61 272 2757
Executive Director *Leena Maissen*

The highest international prizes for children's literature: The Hans Christian Andersen Award for Writing ESTABLISHED 1956; The Hans Christian Andersen Award for Illustration ESTABLISHED 1966. Candidates are nominated by National Sections of IBBY (The International Board on Books for Young People). Biennial prizes are awarded, in even-numbered years, to an author and an illustrator whose body of work has made a lasting contribution to children's literature. Next award 1996. Previous winners: Award for Writing: Michio Mado (Japan), Virginia Hamilton (USA); Award for Illustration: Jörg Müller (Switzerland), Květa Pacovská (Czech Republic).

Award Gold medals.

Eileen Anderson Central Television Drama Award

Central Broadcasting, Central House, Broad Street, Birmingham B1 2JP
☎0121 643 9898   Fax 0121 634 4137
Manager, Corporate PR & Promotions
Kevin Johnson

ESTABLISHED 1987 with money left by the late Dr Eileen Anderson and contributed to by **Central Television**, this is an annual award to encourage new theatre writing in the Midlands. Open to all new plays or an adaptation commissioned or premièred by a building-based theatre company in the Central region. Previous winners include: David Edgar *Pentecost* (premièred at the **Royal Shakespeare Company**'s The Other Place); Sean Street *Honest John* (premièred on Community Tour by the **Royal Theatre Northampton**); Vilma Hollingbery & Michael Napier Brown *Is This the Day?* (premièred at the Royal Theatre Northampton); Timberlake Wertenbaker *The Love of the Nightingale* (commissioned by the Royal Shakespeare Company's The Other Place in Stratford); Lucy Gannon *Wicked Old Nellie* (**Derby Playhouse**); Pam Gem's *The Blue Angel* (premièred at the Royal Shakespeare Company's The Other Place) and Rod Dungate for *Playing By The Rules* (premièred at the **Birmingham Repertory Theatre**).

Prize £1500, plus trophy worth an additional £500 designed each year by a local college of education. A plaque is awarded to the theatre which commissioned the work.

The Aristeion Prize

Commission of the European Communities, Culture Unit, Rue de la Loi 200, B-1049 Brussels, Belgium
☎00 32 22 99 92 40   Fax 00 32 22 99 92 83

Contact *The Culture Unit*

ESTABLISHED 1990 to bring knowledge and appreciation of European literature to a wider public and to celebrate the strength and diversity of the European literary tradition. Member countries of the EC nominate their best works of literature and translation from the last three years. Sponsored by the Commission. 1995 winners: Herta Müller *Hertztier* (Literary Prize); Dieter Hornig *Ein Barbar in Asien* (Translation Prize).

Prize 20,000 ecus (about £14,000) for each category.

Rosemary Arthur Award

National Poetry Foundation, 27 Mill Road, Fareham, Hampshire PO16 0TH
Contact *Johnathon Clifford*

ESTABLISHED 1989. Annual award to get poets of merit published in book form. Anyone resident in the UK who has not previously had a book published may submit 40 poems together with s.a.e. and £5 reading fee at any time during the year. Winners are announced in February.

Award Complete funding for a book of the poet's work, plus £100 and an engraved carriage clock.

Arvon Foundation International Poetry Competition

Kilnhurst, Kilnhurst Road, Todmorden, Lancashire OL14 6AX
☎01706 816582   Fax 01706 816359
Contact *David Pease*

ESTABLISHED 1980. Biennial competition (odd years) for poems written in English and not previously broadcast or published. There are no restrictions on the number of lines, themes, age of entrants or nationality. No limit to the number of entries. Entry fee: £3.50 per poem. Previous winners: Paul Farley *Laws of Gravity*; Don Paterson *A Private Bottling*.

Prize (1st) £5000 and £5000 worth of other prizes sponsored by *The Observer* and Duncan Lawrie Limited.

Authors' Club First Novel Award

The Authors' Club, 40 Dover Street, London W1X 3RB
☎0171 499 8581   Fax 0171 409 0913
Contact *Mrs Ann Carter*

ESTABLISHED 1954. This award is made for the most promising work published in Britain by a British author, and is presented at a dinner held at the Authors' Club. Entries for the award are accepted from publishers and must be full-length – short stories are not eligible. Previous winners: T. J. Armstrong *Walter and the Resurrection of G*; Nadeem Aslam *Season of the Rainbirds*; David Park *The Healing*; Andrew Cowan *Pig*.

Award £750.

BAAL Book Prize

BAAL Publications Secretary, School of Education, Open University, Milton Keynes MK7 6AA

☎01908 653383   Fax 01908 654111

Contact *David Graddol*

Annual award made by the British Association for Applied Linguistics to an outstanding book in the field of applied linguistics. Final entry at the end of February. Nominations from publishers only. Previous winners: Ruth Lesser and Lesley Milroy *Linguistics and Aphasia*; *Dictionary of British Sign Language*; Susan Berk-Seligson *The Bilingual Courtroom*; Joshua A. Fishman *Reversing Language Shift*.

The Barclays Bank Prize

See **Lakeland Book of the Year Awards**

Verity Bargate Award

The Soho Theatre Company, 24 Mortimer Street, London W1N 7RD

☎0171 436 8833   Fax 0171 436 8844

Contact *Paul Syrett*

To commemorate the late Verity Bargate, founder and director of the **Soho Theatre Company**. This award is presented bi-annually for a new and unperformed full-length play. Send s.a.e. for details; if submitting scripts, enclose one s.a.e. script-size and one standard-size. The Soho Theatre Company also runs many courses for new writers. Previous winners: Mick Mahoney, Gillian Plowman, Lyndon Morgans, Diane Samuels, Judy Upton, Angela Meredith.

Award £1500, plus production by the Soho Theatre Company.

H. E. Bates Short Story Competition

Events Team, Directorate of Environment Services, Northampton Borough Council, Cliftonville House, Bedford Road, Northampton NN4 7NR

☎01604 233500   Fax 01604 29571

Contact *Liz Carroll*

Named after the late H. E. Bates, one of the masters of the short story form. Entries should

preferably be typed, 2000 words maximum on any subject. Any writer resident in Great Britain is eligible and there are categories for children under 11 and under 16.

Prize (1st) £200.

BBC Wildlife Magazine Awards for Nature Writing

BBC Wildlife Magazine, Broadcasting House, Whiteladies Road, Bristol, Avon BS8 2LR

☎0117 9738402   Fax 0117 9467075

Editor *Rosamund Kidman Cox*

Annual competition for professional and amateur writers. Entries should be a single essay, either on personal observations of or thoughts about nature – general or specific – or about reflections on human relationships with nature. Entry forms published usually in the late spring and early summer issues of the magazine.

Prizes £1000 for best essay by a professional or amateur writer; £400 for best essay by an amateur writer (only if a professional writer wins the top award); £200 for best essay by a young writer aged between 13 and 17; £100 for best essay by a young writer aged 12 or under.

Samuel Beckett Award

c/o Faber & Faber, 3 Queen Square, London WC1N 3AU

☎0171 465 0045   Fax 0171 465 0034

Contact *Editorial Department*

This award aims to give support and encouragement to new playwrights at a crucial stage of their careers. Rules of eligibility currently under review.

David Berry Prize

Royal Historical Society, University College London, Gower Street, London WC1E 6BT

☎0171 387 7532   Fax 0171 387 7532

Triennial award (next in 1997) for an essay of not more than 10,000 words on Scottish history within the period of James I to James VI. Candidates may select any subject from the relevant period, providing it has been submitted to, and approved by, the Council of the Royal Historical Society.

Prize £250.

Besterman Medal

See **The Library Association Besterman Medal**

James Tait Black Memorial Prizes

University of Edinburgh, David Hume Tower, George Square, Edinburgh EH8 9JX
☎0131 650 3619   Fax 0131 650 6898

Contact *Department of English Literature*

ESTABLISHED 1918 in memory of a partner of the publishing firm of **A. & C. Black Ltd** and supported since 1979 by the **Scottish Arts Council**. Two prizes, one for biography and one for fiction. Closing date for submissions: 30 September. Each prize is awarded for a book published in Britain in the previous twelve months. Prize winners are announced in November each year. Previous winners include: Christopher Priest *The Prestige*; Gitta Sereny *Albert Speer: His Battle with Truth*; Alan Hollinghurst *The Folding Star*, Doris Lessing *Under My Skin*; Caryl Phillips *Crossing the River;* Richard Holmes *Dr Johnson and Mr Savage*.

Prizes £3000 each.

Boardman Tasker Award

14 Pine Lodge, Dairyground Road, Bramhall, Stockport, Cheshire SK7 2HS
☎0161 439 4624

Contact *Dorothy Boardman*

ESTABLISHED 1983, this award is given for a work of fiction, non-fiction or poetry, whose central theme is concerned with the mountain environment and which can be said to have made an outstanding contribution to mountain literature. Authors of any nationality are eligible, but the book must have been published or distributed in the UK for the first time between 1 November 1996 and 31 October 1997. Entries from publishers only. 1995 winner: Alan Hankinson *Geoffrey Winthrop Young*.

Prize £2000 (at Trustees' discretion).

Booker Prize for Fiction

Book Trust, Book House, 45 East Hill, London SW18 2QZ
☎0181 870 9055   Fax 0181 874 4790

Contact *Sandra Vince*

The leading British literary prize, set up in 1968 by Booker McConnell Ltd, with the intention of rewarding merit, raising the stature of the author in the eyes of the public and increasing the sale of the books. The announcement of the winner has been televised live since 1981, and all books on the shortlist experience a substantial increase in sales. Eligible novels must be written in English by a citizen of Britain, the Commonwealth, the Republic of Ireland or South Africa, and must be published in the UK for the first time between 1

October and 30 September of the year of the prize. Self-published books are no longer accepted. Entries are accepted from UK publishers who may each submit not more than two novels within the appropriate scheduled publication dates. The judges may also ask for certain other eligible novels to be submitted to them. Annual award. Previous winners include: James Kelman *How Late It Was, How Late*; Ben Okri *The Famished Road*; Michael Ondaatje *The English Patient*; Barry Unsworth *Sacred Hunger*; Roddy Doyle *Paddy Clarke Ha, Ha, Ha*. 1995 winner: Pat Barker *The Ghost Road*.

Prize £20,000.

Author of the Year Award

Booksellers Association of Great Britain and Ireland

272 Vauxhall Bridge Road, London SW1V 1BA
☎0171 834 5477   Fax 0171 834 8812

Contact *Administrator*

Founded as part of BA Annual Conference to involve authors more closely in the event. Authors must be British or Irish. Not an award open to entry but voted on by the membership. Previous winner: Alan Bennett.

Award £1000 plus trophy.

Border Television Prize

See **Lakeland Book of the Year Awards**

Bournemouth International Festival Open Poetry Competition

2 Digby Chambers, Post Office Road, Bournemouth, Dorset BH1 1BA
☎01202 297327   Fax 01202 552510

Contact *Julian Robbins*

A feature of the **Bournemouth International Festival**, held during the last two weeks of May, the annual open poetry competition attracts hundreds of entries from all over the world. 1995 winners: Sam Gardiner, Paul Groves, Elsa Corbluth. Write enclosing s.a.e. for more information and entry form.

Prizes 1st prize £200; 2nd prize £100; 3rd prize £50; plus poetry books for runners-up. All award-winning poets are invited to read their poems at the Festival.

The BP Conservation Book Prize

Book Trust, Book House, 45 East Hill, London SW18 2QZ
☎0181 870 9055   Fax 0181 874 4790

Contact *Sandra Vince*

ESTABLISHED by BP Exploration for a book on creative conservation of the environment. Entries from UK publishers only. Previous winners: Oliver Rackham *The Illustrated History of the Countryside*; Edward O. Wilson *The Diversity of Life*; Jo Readman *Muck and Magic*; Philip Wayne *Operation Otter*; Jonathan Kingdon *Island Africa*; George Monbiot *Amazon Watershed*; Iain & Oria Douglas-Hamilton *Battle for the Elephants*.

Prizes (1st) £5000; £2000 prize for book on conservation for 5-12-year-olds.

The Micháel Breathnach Literary Memorial Award
Cló Iar-Chonnachta Teo, Indreabhán, Conamara, Co. Galway Republic of Ireland
☎00 353 91 593307   Fax 00 353 91 593362
Literature & Music Editor *Nóirín Ní Ghrádaigh*

As part of their 10-year celebration, Cló Iar-Chonnachta have established an annual award for the best Irish-language work in any literary form; novel, drama, poetry collection or short story collection. Open to writers under 30 years of age. Closing date for entries on 1 December annually.

Prize IR£1000.

Bridport Arts Centre
The Bridport Prize
Arts Centre, South Street, Bridport, Dorset DT6 3NR
☎01308 427183   Fax 01308 427183
Contact *Bridport Prize Administrator*

Annual competition for poetry and short story writing. Unpublished work only, written in English. Winning stories are read by leading London literary agent and an anthology of prize-winning entries is published. Also runs a young writers competition with variable prizes. Final entry date 30 June (early April for young writers award). Send s.a.e. for entry forms.

Prizes £2,500, £1000 & £500 in each category, plus supplementary runners-up prizes.

Katharine Briggs Folklore Award
The Folklore Society, University College London, Gower Street, London WC1E 6BT
☎0171 387 5894
Contact *The Convenor*

ESTABLISHED 1982. An annual award in November for the book, published in Britain between 1 June and 30 May in the previous calendar year, which has made the most distinguished non-fiction contribution to folklore studies. Intended to encourage serious research in the field which Katharine Briggs did so much to establish. The term folklore studies is interpreted broadly to include all aspects of traditional and popular culture, narrative, belief, custom and folk arts. Previous winners include: Claudia Kinmouth *Irish Country Furniture 1700-1950*.

Prize £50, plus engraved goblet.

British Book Awards
Publishing News, 43 Museum Street, London WC1A 1LY
☎0171 404 0304   Fax 0171 242 0762

ESTABLISHED 1988. Viewed by the book trade as the one to win, 'The Nibbies' are presented annually in February. The 1995 Awards were in the following categories: Children's Book; Distributor; Editor; Publisher Marketing; Bookshop Marketing; Illustrated Book; Author; Book; Innovation in Publishing; Independent Bookseller; Chain Bookseller; Services to Bookselling; Publisher. Each winner receives the prestigious Nibbie and the awards are presented to those who have made the most impact in the book trade during the previous year. Previous winners have included: Alan Bennett, Sebastian Faulks, Jung Chang, Anne Fine, Books etc., and the publisher **Little, Brown**. For further information contact: Merric Davidson, Oakwood, Ashley Park, Tunbridge Wells, Kent TN4 8UA (Tel/Fax 01892 514282).

British Comparative Literature Association/British Centre for Literary Translation Competition
Dept of English Literature, University of Glasgow, Glasgow G12 8QQ
Competition Secretary *Dr Stuart Gillespie*

ESTABLISHED 1983. Annual competition open to unpublished literary translations from all languages. Maximum submission 25 pages. Special prizes for translations from Swedish (biennial). Final entry date 28 February.

Prizes (1st) £350; (2nd) £150; plus publication of all winning entries in the Association's annual journal *Comparative Criticism* (**Cambridge University Press**). Other entries may receive commendations.

British Fantasy Awards
2 Harwood Street, Heaton Norris, Stockport, Cheshire SK4 1JJ
☎0161 476 5368 (after 6 p.m.)
Secretary *Robert Parkinson*

Awarded by the **British Fantasy Society** at its annual conference for Best Novel and Best Short Story categories, among others. Previous winners include: Piers Anthony, Clive Barker, Ken Bulmer, Ramsey Campbell.

British Literature Prize
See **David Cohen British Literature Prize**

British Science Fiction (Association) Award
60 Bournemouth Road, Folkestone, Kent CT19 5AZ
☎01303 252939

Award Administrator *Maureen Speller*

ESTABLISHED 1966. The BSFA awards a trophy each year in three categories – novel, short fiction and artwork – published in the preceding year. Previous winners: Iain Banks *Feersum Endjinn*; Paul di Filippo *The Double Felix*.

James Cameron Award
City University, Department of Journalism, Northampton Square, London EC1V 0HB
☎0171 477 8221   Fax 0171 477 8594

Contact *The Administrator*

Annual award for journalism to a reporter of any nationality, working for the British media, whose work is judged to have contributed most during the year to the continuance of the Cameron tradition. Administered by City University Department of Journalism. 1995 winner: George Alagiah, BBC South Africa correspondent.

The City of Cardiff International Poetry Competition
The Welsh Academy, 3rd Floor, Mount Stuart House, Mount Stuart Square, Cardiff CF1 6DQ
☎01222 492025   Fax 01222 492930

Contact *Kevin Thomas*

ESTABLISHED 1986. An annual competition for unpublished poems in English of up to 50 lines. Launched in the spring with a summer closing date.

Prize (total) £5000.

Carey Award
Society of Indexers, 38 Rochester Road, London NW1 9JJ
☎0171 916 7809

Secretary *Claire Troughton*

A private award made by the Society to a member who has given outstanding services to indexing. The recipient is selected by Council

with no recommendations considered from elsewhere.

Carmarthen Writers' Circle Short Story Competition
79 Bronwydd Road, Carmarthen, Dyfed SA31 2AP
☎01267 230900

Contact *Madeline Mayne*

ESTABLISHED 1990. Annual. All stories must be unpublished and not yet accepted for publication. Entries *must* be anonymous and an A4 cover page giving story title, name, address and telephone number must be attached to submissions. Any number may be submitted; entry fee £4 per story. Stories must be typed in double-spacing on one side of A4 paper. Send s.a.e. for details.

Prizes (1st) £120; (2nd) £80; (3rd) £60. All prize winners will be put on tape for the Talking Newspaper and considered by Radio 4 for broadcasting.

Carnegie Medal
See **The Library Association Carnegie Medal**

Children's Book Award
The Federation of Children's Book Groups, 30 Senneleys Park Road, Birmingham B31 1AL
☎0121 427 4860   Fax 0121 643 3152

Contact *Jenny Blanch*

ESTABLISHED 1980. Awarded annually for best book of fiction suitable for children. Unique in that it is judged by the children themselves. Previous winners include: Ian Strachan *The Boy in the Bubble*; Mick Inkpen *Threadbear*; Robert Swindells *Room 13*; Elizabeth Laird *Kiss the Dust*; and Jaqueline Wilson *The Suitcase Kid*.

Award A splendid silver and oak sculpture made by Graham Stewart and Tim Stead, plus portfolio of letters, drawings and comments from the children who took part in the judging; category winners receive silver bowls designed by the same artists and portfolios.

Children's Book Circle Eleanor Farjeon Award
c/o Macmillan Publishers Ltd, 25 Eccleston Place, London SW1W 9ND
☎0171 881 8000   Fax 0171 881 8001

Contact *Susie Gibbs*

This award, named in memory of the much-loved children's writer, is for distinguished services to children's books either in this country or overseas, and may be given to a librarian, teacher, publisher, bookseller, author, artist, reviewer, television producer, etc. Nominations from members of the **Children's Book Circle**. 1996 winner: Books for Keeps.

Award £500.

Arthur C. Clarke Award for Science Fiction

60 Bournemouth Road, Folkestone, Kent CT19 5AZ

☎01303 252939   Fax 01303 252939

Administrator *Paul Kincaid*

ESTABLISHED 1986. The Arthur C. Clarke Award is given yearly to the best science fiction novel with first UK publication in the previous calendar year. Both hardcover and paperback books qualify. Made possible by a generous donation from Arthur C. Clarke, this award is selected by a rotating panel of six judges nominated by the **British Science Fiction Association**, the International Science Policy Foundation and the **Science Fiction Foundation**. Previous winners include: Paul J. McAuley *Fairyland*; Pat Cadigan *Fools*; Jeff Noon *Vurt*; Marge Piercy *Body of Glass*; Pat Cadigan *Synners*; Colin Greenland Take Back Plenty.

Award £1000 plus trophy.

The Cló Iar-Chonnachta Literary Award

Cló Iar-Chonnachta Teo, Indreabhán, Conamara, Co. Galway Republic of Ireland

☎00 353 91 593307   Fax 00 353 91 593362

Literature & Music Editor *Nóirín Ní Ghrádaigh*

As part of their 10-year celebration, **Cló Iar-Chonnachta** have established an annual prize for a newly written and unpublished work in the Irish language. Awarded in 1996 for the best novel, 1997 for the best poetry collection, and 1998 for the best short story collection or drama. Last date of entry for 1997 Poetry Award: 1 December 1996.

Prize IR£5000.

David Cohen British Literature Prize in the English Language

Arts Council of Great Britain, 14 Great Peter Street, London SW1P 3NQ

☎0171 333 0100   Fax 0171 973 6590

Literature Director *Dr Alastair Niven*
Literature Assistant *Susan White*

ESTABLISHED 1993. By far the most valuable literature prize in Britain, the British Literature Prize, launched by the **Arts Council**, is awarded biennially. Anyone is eligible to suggest candidates and the award recognises writers who use the English language and who are British citizens, encompassing dramatists as well as novelists, poets and essayists. The prize is for a lifetime's achievement rather than a single play or book and is donated by the David Cohen Family Charitable Trust in association with Coutts Bank.

The David Cohen Trust was set up in 1980 by David Cohen, general practitioner son of a property developer. The Trust has helped composers, choreographers, dancers, poets, playwrights and actors.

The Council is providing a further £10,000 to enable the winner to commission new work, with the dual aim of encouraging young writers and readers. Next award 1997. Previous winners: Harold Pinter, V. S. Naipaul.

Award £30,000, plus £10,000 towards new work.

Collins Biennial Religious Book Award

HarperCollins Publishers, 77–85 Fulham Palace Road, London W6 8JB

☎0181 741 7070   Fax 0181 307 4064

Contact *Lesley Walmsley*

Biennial award given for the book which has made the most distinguis.hed contribution to the relevance of Christianity in the modern world, written by a living citizen of the Commonwealth, the Republic of Ireland or South Africa. Previous winners include: John MacQuarrie *Jesus Christ in Modern Thought*.

Award £5000.

The Commonwealth Writers Prize

The Commonwealth Foundation, Marlborough House, Pall Mall, London SW1Y 5HY

☎0171 930 3783

Contact *Ms Diana Bailey* (enquiries only)

ESTABLISHED 1987. An annual award to reward and encourage the upsurge of new Commonwealth fiction. Any work of prose or fiction is eligible, i.e. a novel or collection of short stories. No drama or poetry. The work must be written in English by a citizen of the Commonwealth and be first published in the year before its entry for the prize. Entries must be submitted by the publisher to the region of the writer's Commonwealth citizenship. Final entry date: 31 March. Previous winners: Louis de Bernières *Captain Corelli's Mandolin* (Best

Book); Adib Khan *Seasonal Adjustments* (Best First Book).

Prizes £10,000 for Best Book; £3000 for Best First Book.

The Thomas Cook/Daily Telegraph Travel Book Award

The Thomas Cook Group, 45 Berkeley Street, London W1A 1EB

☎0171 408 4218   Fax 0171 408 4551

Contact *Alexis Coles, Corporate Affairs*

Annual award given to the author of the book, published (in the English language) in the previous year, which most inspires the reader to want to travel. Previous winners: Gavin Bell *In Search of Tusitala: Travels in the South Pacific after Robert Louis Stevenson*; William Dalrymple *City of Djinns*; Nik Cohn *The Heart of the World*.

Award £7500.

Catherine Cookson Fiction Prize

Transworld Publishers Ltd, 61-63 Uxbridge Road, London W5 5SA

☎0181 579 2652   Fax 0181 579 5479

Contact *Catherine Cookson Fiction Prize Administrator*

ESTABLISHED 1992 by **Transworld Publishers Ltd**, in celebration of the achievement of Catherine Cookson. Annual award for a novel, of at least 70,000 words, which possesses strong characterisation, authentic background and storytelling quality, which are the mark of Cookson's work. The work may be contemporary or historical. Submissions must be in English and original (no translations), and must not have been previously published in any form. Final entry date 31 May; winner announced in Autumn. Previous winner: Susanna Kearsley *Mariana*.

Award £10,000, plus publication by Transworld. Runners-up may be offered publication on terms to be negotiated.

The Duff Cooper Prize

54 St Maur Road, London SW6 4DP

☎0171 736 3729   Fax 0171 731 7638

Contact *Artemis Cooper*

An annual award for a literary work of biography, history, politics or poetry, published by a recognised publisher (member of **The Publishers Association**) during the previous 12 months. The book must be submitted by the publisher, not the author. Financed by the interest from a trust fund commemorating Duff Cooper, first Viscount Norwich (1890-1954).

1995 winner: David Gilmour *Curzon*.

Prize £2000.

Rose Mary Crawshay Prize

The British Academy, 20-21 Cornwall Terrace, London NW1 4QP

☎0171 487 5966   Fax 0171 224 3807

Contact *British Academy Secretary*

ESTABLISHED 1888 by Rose Mary Crawshay, this prize is given for a historical or critical work by a woman of any nationality on English literature, with particular preference for a work on Keats, Byron or Shelley. The work must have been published in the preceding three years.

Prize normally two prizes of approximately £500 each.

Crime Writers' Association (Gold Dagger Award for Non-Fiction)

Crime Writers' Association, PO Box 10772, London N6 4RY

Contact *The Secretary*

Annual award for the best non-fiction crime book published during the year. Previous winners include: Martin Beales *Dead Not Buried*; David Canter *Criminal Shadows*; Alexandra Artley *Murder in the Heart*; Charles Nicholl *The Reckoning*; John Bossy *Giordano Bruno and the Embassy Affair*.

Award Dagger, plus cheque (sum varies).

Crime Writers' Association (Gold, Silver & Diamond Dagger Awards for Fiction)

Crime Writers' Association, PO Box 10772, London N6 4RY

Contact *The Secretary*

Three annual awards: Gold and Silver for the best crime fiction published during the year; Diamond for outstanding contribution to the genre. Nominations for Gold Dagger from publishers only. Previous winners include: Reginald Hill; Michael Gilbert, Ellis Peters (Diamond); Val McDermid *The Mermaids Singing*; Minette Walters *The Scold's Bridle*; Patricia Cornwell *Cruel and Unusual* (Gold); Peter Lovesey *The Summons*; Peter Høeg *Miss Smilla's Feeling for Snow*; Sarah Dunant *Fatlands* (Silver).

Award Dagger, plus cheque (sum varies).

Crime Writers' Association (John Creasey Memorial Dagger)

Crime Writers' Association, PO Box 10772, London N6 4RY

Contact *The Secretary*

ESTABLISHED 1973 following the death of crime writer John Creasey, founder of the **Crime Writers' Association**. This award is given annually for the best crime novel by an author who has not previously published a full-length work of fiction. Nominations from publishers only. Previous winners include: Janet Evanovich *One For the Money*; Doug J. Swanson *Big Town*.
Award Cheque, plus dagger.

Crime Writers' Association (Last Laugh Dagger)
Crime Writers' Association, PO Box 10772, London N6 4RY
Contact *The Secretary*

Annual award for the funniest crime novel published during the year. Nominations from publishers only. Previous winners include: Laurence Shames *Sunburn*; Simon Shaw *The Villain of the Earth*; Michael Pearce *The Mamur Zapt and the Spoils of Egypt*.
Award Cheque plus dagger.

Crime Writers' Association (The Macallan Short Story Award)
6 Ainscow Avenue, Lostock, Bolton, Lancashire BL6 4LR
Contact *Val McDermid*

ESTABLISHED 1993. An award for a published crime story. Publishers should submit three copies of the story to the address above by 30 September 1996. 1995 winner: Larry Beinhart *Funny Story*.
Prize £200 and a silver-plated brooch/tie-pin of crossed daggers.

Crime Writers' Association Dagger in the Library
Crime Writers' Association, PO Box 10772, London N6 4RY
Contact *The Secretary*

ESTABLISHED 1995. Annual award sponsored by N. B. Magazine for librarians. The winner – an author popular with library borrowers – is selected by librarians liaising with the committee of the CWA. 1995 winner: Lindsey Davis.
Prize Gold-plated dagger and cheque.

The Daily Telegraph National Power Young Science Writer Awards
Electric Echo, 334A Goswell Road, London EC1V 7LQ
☎0171 713 5525

Contact *Gerry Fallon*

ESTABLISHED 1988. The awards are open to anyone aged between 16-28 for a short article (maximum 700 words) on any scientific or science-related subject suitable for publication in *The Daily Telegraph*. Two age groups: 16-19 and 20-28. Substantial prizes include a trip to the US for the annual meeting of the American Association for the Advancement of Science. Entry details from the above address.

Harvey Darton Award
See **The Children's Books History Society** under **Literary Societies**

The Hunter Davies Prize
See **Lakeland Book of the Year Awards**

Isaac & Tamara Deutscher Memorial Prize
157 Fortis Green Road, London N10 3AX
☎0181 883 7063
Secretary *Ann Jungmann*

An annual award in recognition of, and as encouragement to, outstanding research in the Marxist tradition of Isaac Deutscher. Made to the author of an essay or full-scale work published or in manuscript. Final entry date 1 May.
Award £500.

George Devine Award
17A South Villas, London NW1 9BS
☎0171 267 9793 (evenings)
Contact *Christine Smith*

Annual award for a promising new playwright writing for the stage in memory of George Devine, artistic director of the **Royal Court Theatre**, who died in 1965. The play does not need to have been produced. Send two copies of the script to Christine Smith by March. Information leaflet available.
Prize £5000.

Denis Devlin Memorial Award for Poetry
An Chomhairle Ealaíon (The Arts Council), 70 Merrion Square, Dublin 2, Republic of Ireland
☎00 353 1 6611840   Fax 00 353 1 6761302
Literature Officer *Laurence Cassidy*

Triennial award for the best book of poetry in English by an Irish poet, published in the preceding three years. Next award 1997.
Award £1500.

Dillons First Fiction Award

Dillons UK Ltd., Publicity Dept., Royal
House, Prince's Gate, Homer Road, Solihull,
West Midlands B91 3QQ
☎0121 703 8000

Contact *Allan Stenhouse, Ruth Killick*

ESTABLISHED 1994. Annual award to 'acknowledge and encourage new novel-writing talent'.
Open to full-length first novels written in
English by a UK or Irish resident. Books must
be published in the UK during the calendar
year of the award. Previous winner: William
Corlett *Now and Then*.

Prize £5000 plus extensive promotion in all
Dillons branches.

Dog Watch Open Poetry Competition

267 Hillbury Road, Warlingham, Surrey
CR6 9TL
☎01883 622121

Contact *Michaela Edridge*

ESTABLISHED 1993. Dog Watch is a charity that
rescues and finds new homes for badly abused
dogs. The annual prize is awarded only to
authors of unpublished works. Final entry date
is 1 January each year and entrants should send
s.a.e. for details.

Prize (1st) £25 (to be increased as entries
increase).

Drama Association of Wales Playwriting Competition

The Library, Singleton Road, Splott, Cardiff
CF2 2ET
☎01222 452200   Fax 01222 452277

Contact *Gary Thomas*

Annual competition held to promote the writing of one act plays in English and Welsh of
between 20 and 45 minutes playing time. The
theme of the competition is changed each year
– the 1996 title was *Germination*. Application
forms from the above address.

Prizes £100; £50; £25, plus a special prize
for the most outstanding author under 25 years
of age; performance at 'dramaffest', the
National Drama Festival; and publication by
DAW Publications.

Eccles Prize

Columbia Business School, 810 Uris Hall,
New York NY 10027, USA
☎001 212 854 2747   Fax 001 212 854 3050

Contact *Office of Public Affairs*

ESTABLISHED 1986 by Spencer F. Eccles in commemoration of his uncle, George S. Eccles, a
1922 graduate of the Business School. Annual
award for excellence in economic writing. One
of the US's most prestigious book prizes. Books
must have a business theme and be written for a
general audience. Previous winners: *The Warbugs*
Ron Chernow; *The New Palgrave Dictionary of
Money and Finance* ed. Peter Newman, Murray
Milgate and John Eatwell; *The Prize* Daniel
Yergin.

The T.S. Eliot Prize

The Poetry Book Society, Book House,
45 East Hill, London SW18 2QZ
☎0181 870 8403/877 1615 (24-hr answerphone/fax)

Contact *Betty Redpath*

ESTABLISHED 1993. Annual award named after
T. S. Eliot, one of the founders of the Poetry
Book Society. Open to books of new poetry
published in the UK and Republic of Ireland
during the year and over 32 pages in length. At
least 75 per cent of the collection must be previously unpublished in book form. Final entry date
is in September/October. Previous winners: *First
Language* Ciaran Carson; *The Annals of Chile* Paul
Muldoon; *My Alexandria* Mark Doty.

The Encore Award

The Society of Authors, 84 Drayton Gardens,
London SW10 9SB
☎0171 373 6642   Fax 0171 373 5768

ESTABLISHED 1990. Awarded to an author who
has had one (and only one) novel previously published. Details from **The Society of Authors**.
1995 winner: Dermot Healy; *A Goat's Song*.

Prize (total) £7500.

Envoi Poetry Competition

Envoi, 44 Rudyard Road, Biddulph Moor,
Stoke on Trent, Staffordshire ST8 7JN
☎01782 517892

Contact *Roger Elkin*

Run by *Envoi* poetry magazine. Competitions
are featured regularly, with prizes of £200, plus
three annual subscriptions to *Envoi*. Winning
poems along with full adjudication report are
published. Send s.a.e. to Competition Secretary,
17 Millcroft, Bishops Stortford, Hertfordshire
CM23 2BP.

Esquire/Apple/Waterstone's Non-Fiction Award

National Magazine Co Ltd, 72 Broadwick
Street, London W1V 2BP
☎0171 439 5000   Fax 0171 439 5067

Editor *Rosie Boycott*

ESTABLISHED 1993 by *Esquire* as a major annual literary award. The award 'seeks to reflect an exciting new spirit in non-fiction writing', and is open to any work published by a British publisher between November of one year and October of the following. The final entry date is end of July. 1995 winner: Eric Lomax *The Railway Man*.

Prizes (1st) £10,000 plus £5000 of Apple Computer equipment; (5 finalists) £1000 each plus £1000 of Apple Computer equipment.

European Literary Prize/European Translation Prize

See **The Aristeion Prize**

Geoffrey Faber Memorial Prize

Faber & Faber Ltd, 3 Queen Square, London WC1N 3AU

☎0171 465 0045   Fax 0171 465 0034

ESTABLISHED 1963 as a memorial to the founder and first chairman of **Faber & Faber**, this prize is awarded in alternate years for the volume of verse and the volume of prose fiction published in the UK in the preceding two years, which is judged to be of greatest literary merit. Authors must be under 40 at the time of publication and citizens of the UK, Commonwealth, Republic of Ireland or South Africa. 1995 winner: Livi Michael *Their Angel Reach*.

Prize £1000.

Eleanor Farjeon Award

See **Children's Book Circle**

Prudence Farmer Award

New Statesman and Society, Foundation House, Perseverance Works, 38 Kingsland Road, London E2 8DQ

☎0171 739 3211   Fax 0171 739 9307

Contact *Adrian Mitchell, Poetry Editor*

For the best poem to have been published in the *New Statesman and Society* during the previous year.

Award £100.

Fawcett Society Book Prize

New Light on Women's Lives, 46 Harleyford Road, London SE11 5AY

☎0171 587 1287   Fax 0171 793 0451

Contact *Charlotte Burt*

Awarded annually to the author of the book which gives us a greater understanding of women's lives, whether it be a book of fiction, non-fiction, biography, etc. All works submitted

for the prize are placed in the **Fawcett Library** at London Guildhall University. Previous winners: Jung Chang *Wild Swans*; Margaret Forster *Daphne du Maurier*.

Prize £2000.

The Kathleen Fidler Award

c/o Book Trust Scotland, The Scottish Book Centre, 137 Dundee Street, Edinburgh EH11 1BG

☎0131 229 3663   Fax 0131 228 4293

For an unpublished novel for children aged 8–12, to encourage authors new to writing for this age group. Authors should not previously have had a novel published for this age group. The award is administered by **Book Trust Scotland**. Final entry date end October. Previous winners: Theresa Breslin *Simon's Challenge*; Catherine McPhail *Run Zan Run*.

Award £1000, plus publication.

Sir Banister Fletcher Award

The Authors' Club, 40 Dover Street, London W1X 3RB

☎0171 499 8581   Fax 0171 409 0913

Contact *Mrs Ann Carter*

This award was created by Sir Bannister Fletcher, who was president of **The Authors' Club** for many years. The prize is donated by Nelson Hurst & Marsh, insurance brokers, and is presented annually for the best book on architecture or the fine arts published in the preceding year. Submissions: Fletcher Award Committee, RIBA, 66 Portland Place, London W1N 4AD. Previous winners: Dr Megan Aldrich *Gothic Revival*; Professor Thomas Markus *Building and Power*; John Onians *Bearers of Meaning: Classical Orders in Antiquity*; Sir Michael Levey *Giambattista Tiepolo: His Life and Art*; John Allan *Berthold Lubetkin - Architecture and The Tradition of Progress*.

Award £750.

The John Florio Prize

The Translators Association, 84 Drayton Gardens, London SW10 9SB

☎0171 373 6642   Fax 0171 373 5768

Contact *Kate Pool*

ESTABLISHED 1963 under the auspices of the Italian Institute and the British-Italian Society, this prize is awarded biennially for the best translation into English of a twentieth-century Italian work of literary merit and general interest, published by a British publisher in the preceding two years. Previous winners include: Tim Parks for *The Road to San Giovanni* by Italo Calvino.

Prize £1000.

The Forward Prizes for Poetry

Colman Getty PR, Carrington House,
126–130 Regent Street, London W1R 5FE
☎0171 439 1783   Fax 0171 439 1784

Contact *Liz Sich, Margot Weale*

ESTABLISHED 1992. Three awards, sponsored by Forward Publishing, for the best collection of poetry, the best first collection of poetry, and the best single poem which is not already part of an anthology or collection. All entries must be published in the UK or Eire and submitted by poetry publishers (collections) or newspaper and magazine editors (single poems). Previous winners: Thom Gunn, Simon Armitage, Jackie Kay, Carol Ann Duffy, Don Paterson, Vicki Feaver, Alan Jenkins, Kwame Dawes, Iain Crichton Smith, Sean O'Brien, Jane Duran, Jenny Joseph.

Prizes £10,000 for best collection; £5000 for best first collection; £1000 for best single poem.

Anne Frankel Prize

c/o Critics' Circle, 47 Bermondsey Street,
London SE1 3XT
☎0171 403 1818   Fax 0171 357 9287

Contact *Peter Hepple, Catherine Cooper*

ESTABLISHED 1991. Annual prize for young film critics in memory of the late Anne Frankel, who wrote on film. Set up by her father William Frankel, former editor and now chairman of the *Jewish Chronicle*. Age limit for entrants is 25. Entries should be self-submitted and have been published in a local/national/student newspaper or periodical. Submit three examples of work, sending four copies of each to the above address. Final entry date usually end August.

Prize £500.

The Frogmore Poetry Prize

The Frogmore Press, 42 Morehall Avenue,
Folkestone, Kent CT19 4EF

Contact *Jeremy Page*

ESTABLISHED 1987. Awarded annually and sponsored by the Frogmore Foundation. The winning poem, runners-up and short-listed entries are all published in the magazine. Previous winners have been: David Satherley, Caroline Price, Bill Headdon, John Latham, Diane Brown, Tobias Hill.

Prize The winner receives 100 guineas and a life subscription to the biannual literary magazine *The Frogmore Papers*.

David Gemmell Cup

Hastings Writers Group, 39 Emmanuel Road,
Hastings, East Sussex TN34 3LB
☎01424 442471

Contact *Mrs R. Bartholomew* (for entry form)

ESTABLISHED 1988. Annual award to encourage writers of short fiction (1500 words) resident in East and West Sussex, Kent, Surrey and London. Final entry date end August. The competition is organised by Hastings Writers' Group and is presented by its sponsor David Gemmell. Previous winners: Barbara Couvela, Stella Radford, Carol Bostock, Sarah Mills.

Prizes 1st £200 plus David Gemmell Cup; 2nd £150; 3rd £100; 4th £50; 5th £30; 6th £20. Additionally, certificates of commendation issued at the discretion of the judge, David Gemmell.

Glaxo Science Writers' Awards

See **ABSW/Glaxo Science Writers' Awards**

Glenfiddich Awards

27 Fitzroy Square, London W1P 5HH
☎0171 383 3024   Fax 0171 383 4593

A series of awards to writers and broadcasters who have contributed most to the civilised appreciation of food and drink through articles, books, illustration and photography published in the UK. Also covers TV and radio programmes, as well as a Special Award for outstanding work or event. 1996 winners: Food Book of the Year: *The River Cafe Cook Book* Rose Gray and Ruth Rogers; Drink Book of the Year: *Rhône Renaissance* Remington Norman; Food Writer of the Year: A. A. Gill for work in *Tatler*; Drink Writer of the Year: Jancis Robinson for work in the *Financial Times*; Cookery Writer of the Year: Philippa Davenport for work in the *Financial Times* and *Country Living*; Restaurant Writer of the Year: A. A. Gill for work in *The Sunday Times*; Whisky Writer of the Year: Jim Murray for work in the *The Scotsman* and *The Connoisseur Scotland*; Regional Writer of the Year: Caroline Stacey for work in *Time Out*; Magazine of the Year: *Wine*; Television Programme of the Year: *Rick Stein's A Taste of the Sea* presented by Rick Stein, directed by David Pritchard and produced by Chris Denham of Denham Productions for BBC Bristol; Radio Programme of the Year: *Lashings of Ginger Beer!*, presented by Michael Rosen, produced by Jill Burridge and edited by Sally Feldman for BBC Radio 4; Visual Award: *Country Living*; 1996 Special Awards: Derek Cooper, 'for his perception, professionalism and integrity in reporting important food and drink issues and news over the past two decades'; Margaret Costa 'for her inspiration and professionalism over the past 25 years in bringing the pleasure of good food to a wider audience'; 1996 Glenfiddich Trophy Winner: Jancis Robinson.

Award Overall winner (chosen from the category winners) £3000, plus the Glenfiddich Trophy (which is held for one year); category winners £800 each, plus a case of Glenfiddich Single Malt Scotch Whisky and an engraved commemorative quaich.

Edgar Graham Book Prize
c/o Centre for Development Studies, School of Oriental and African Studies, Thornhaugh Street, Russell Square, London WC1H 0XG
☎0171 436 7295   Fax 0171 323 6605
Contact *The Secretary*
ESTABLISHED 1984. Biennial award in memory of Edgar Graham. Aims to encourage research work in Third World agricultural and industrial development. Open to published works of original scholarship on agricultural and/or industrial development in Asia and/or Africa. No edited volumes. Next award 1998; final entry date 30 September 1997.
Prize £1500.

Kate Greenaway Medal
See **The Library Association Kate Greenaway Medal**

The Guardian Children's Fiction Award
The Guardian, 119 Farringdon Road, London EC1R 3ER
☎0171 278 2332   Fax 0171 837 2114
Children's Book Editor *Joanna Carey*
ESTABLISHED 1967. Annual award for an outstanding work of fiction for children by a British or Commonwealth author, first published in the UK in the preceding year, excluding picture books and previous winners. Final entry date end December. Previous winners: Lesley Howarth *MapHead*; Rachel Anderson *Paper Faces*; Hilary McKay *The Exiles*; William Mayne *Low Tide*; Sylvia Waugh *The Mennyms*. 1996 joint winners: Philip Pullman *Dark Materials I: Northern Lights* and Alison Prince *The Sherwood Hero*.
Award £1000.

The Guardian Fiction Prize
The Guardian, 119 Farringdon Road, London EC1R 3ER
☎0171 278 2332   Fax 0171 837 2114

Contact *Literary Editor*
ESTABLISHED 1965. An annual award for a novel published by a British, Irish or Commonwealth writer, which is chosen by the literary editor in conjunction with the paper's regular reviewers of fiction. Previous winners: James Buchan *Heart's Journey into Winter*, Candia McWilliam *Debatable Land*; Alasdair Gray *Poor Things*; Alan Judd *The Devil's Own Work*; Pat Barker *The Eye in the Door*.
Prize £2000.

W. H. Heinemann Prize
Royal Society of Literature, 1 Hyde Park Gardens, London W2 2LT
☎0171 723 5104   Fax 0171 402 0199
ESTABLISHED 1945. Works of any kind of literature may be submitted by publishers under this award, which aims to encourage genuine contributions to literature. Books must be written in the English language and have been published in the previous year; translations are not eligible for consideration. Preference tends to be given to publications which are unlikely to command large sales: poetry, biography, criticism, philosophy, history. Final entry date 31 October. Up to three awards may be given. Previous winners: Patrick French *Young Husband*; Paul Durcan *Give Me Your Hand*; Vicky Feaver *The Handless Maiden*; John Hale *The Civilisation of Europe In the Renaissance*.

Felicia Hemans Prize for Lyrical Poetry
University of Liverpool, PO Box 147, Liverpool, Merseyside L69 3BX
☎0151 794 2458   Fax 0151 794 2454
Contact *The Registrar*
ESTABLISHED 1899. Annual award for published or unpublished verse. Open to past or present members and students of the University of Liverpool. One poem per entrant only. Closing date 1 May.
Prize £30.

Heywood Hill Literary Prize
10 Curzon Street, London W1Y 7FJ
☎0171 629 0647
Contact *John Saumarez Smith*
ESTABLISHED 1995 by the Duke of Devonshire to reward a lifetime's contribution to the enjoyment of books. Three judges chosen annually. No applications are necessary for this award. 1995 winner: Patrick O'Brian.
Prize £10,000.

David Higham Prize for Fiction

c/o Book Trust, Book House, 45 East Hill, London SW18 2QZ

☎0181 870 9055   Fax 0181 874 4790

Contact *Sandra Vince*

ESTABLISHED 1975. An annual award for a first novel or book of short stories published in the UK in the year of the award by an author who is a citizen of Britain, the Commonwealth, the Republic of Ireland or South Africa. Previous winners: Vikram Chandra *Red Earth and Pouring Rain*; Fred D'Aguiar *The Longest Memory*; Nicola Barker *Love Your Enemies*; John Loveday *Halo*; Elspeth Barker *O Caledonia*.
Award £1000.

William Hill Sports Book of the Year

GCI Group, 1 Chelsea Manor Gardens, London SW3 5PN

☎0181 365 7211 (Graham Sharpe)/
0171 349 5075 (Tim Shaw)
Fax 0171 352 624

Contact *Graham Sharpe, Tim Shaw*

ESTABLISHED 1989. Annual award introduced by Graham Sharpe of bookmakers William Hill. Sponsored by William Hill and thus dubbed the 'bookie' prize, it is the first, and only, Sports Book of the Year award. Final entry date September. Previous winners: John Feinstein *A Good Walk Spoiled*; Simon Kuper *Football Against the Enemy*; Stephen Jones *Endless Winter*; Nick Hornby *Fever Pitch: A Fan's Life*.
Prize (reviewed annually) £7500 package including £5000 cash, hand-bound copy, free bet and a day at the races.

Calvin & Rose G. Hoffman Prize

King's School, Canterbury, Kent CT1 2ES

☎01227 595501

Contact *The Headmaster*

Annual award for distinguished publication on Christopher Marlowe, established by the late Calvin Hoffman, author of *The Man Who was Shakespeare* (1955) as a memorial to himself and his wife. For unpublished works of at least 5000 words written in English for their scholarly contribution to the study of Christopher Marlowe and his relationship to William Shakespeare. Final entry date 1 September. Previous winners: Prof. Dr Kurt Tetzeli von Rosador, Dr R. Dutton, Prof. R. Danson, Prof. T. Cartelli, Dr. David Pascoe, Dr Lisa Hopkins, Prof. J. Shapiro, Prof. J. Bate.
Prize in the region of £6,500.

Winifred Holtby Memorial Prize

Royal Society of Literature, 1 Hyde Park Gardens, London W2 2LT

☎0171 723 5104   Fax 0171 402 0199

ESTABLISHED 1966 by Vera Brittain who gave a sum of money to the RSL to provide an annual prize in honour of Winifred Holtby who died at the age of 37. Administered by the **Royal Society of Literature**. The prize is for the best regional novel of the year written in the English language. The writer must be of British or Irish nationality, or a citizen of the Commonwealth. Translations, unless made by the author himself of his own work, are not eligible for consideration. If in any year it is considered that no regional novel is of sufficient merit the prize money may be awarded to an author, qualified as aforesaid, of a literary work of non-fiction or poetry, concerning a regional subject. Publishers are invited to submit works (three copies of each) published during the current year to the Secretary, labelled 'Winifred Holtby Prize'. Final entry date 31 October. Previous winners: Carl MacDougall *The Lights Below*; Adam Thorpe *Ulverton*; Elspeth Barker *O Caledonia*.
Prize £800.

Ilkley Literature Festival Poetry Competition

Manor House Museum, Ilkley, West Yorkshire LS29 9DT

☎01943 601210

Contact *David Porter*

Annual open poetry competition run by the **Ilkley Literature Festival**. Final entry date August each year. entry fee: £2.50 per poem. Previous winners: Anthony Dunn, John Sewell.
Prize (total) £600.

The Richard Imison Memorial Award

The Society of Authors, 84 Drayton Gardens, London SW10 9SB

☎0171 373 6642   Fax 0171 373 5768

Contact *The Secretary, The Broadcasting Committee*

Annual award established 'to perpetuate the memory of Richard Imison, to acknowledge the encouragement he gave to writers working in the medium of radio, and in memory of the support and friendship he invariably offered writers in general, and radio writers in particular'. Administered by the Society of Authors, the purpose is 'to encourage new talent and high standards in writing for radio by selecting the

radio drama by a writer new to radio which, in the opinion of the judges, is the best of those submitted. An adaptation for radio of a piece originally written for the stage, television or film will not be eligible. Any radio drama first transmitted in the UK between 1 January and 31 December by a writer or writers new to radio, is eligible, provided the work is an original piece for radio and it is the first dramatic work by the writer(s) that has been broadcast. Submission may be made by any party to the production in the form of two copies of an audio cassette (not-returnable) accompanied by a nomination form. 1996 winner: Lee Hall *I Love U Jimmy Spud.*
Prize £1000.

The Independent/Scholastic Story of the Year

Postal box address changes each year (see below)
ESTABLISHED 1993. Open competition for the best short story for children aged 6–9. One story per entrant (between 1500–2500 words). Details of the competition, including the postal box address are published in *The Independent* in April of each year.
Prize £2000; two runners-up of £500 each. The winning story will be published in the newspaper and in an anthology published by **Scholastic Children's Books**, along with a selection of the best entries.

The International IMPAC Dublin Literary Award

Dublin City Public Libraries, Administrative Headquarters, Cumberland House, Fenian Street, Dublin 2 Republic of Ireland
☎00 353 1 6619000   Fax 00 353 1 6761628
Chairman *Freddie Cooke*
ESTABLISHED 1995. Sponsored by a US-based management consultancy firm, IMPAC, this major prize for literature is awarded for a work of fiction written and published in the English language or written in a language other than English and published in English translation. Initial nominations are made through municipal public libraries in world capital cities, each library putting forward 3 books to the panel of judges in Dublin. 1996 wnner: David Malouf *Remembering Babylon*.
Prize IR£100,000.

International Reading Association Literacy Award

International Reading Association, 800 Barksdale Road, PO Box 8139, Newark Delaware 19714-8139, USA
☎001 302 731 1600   Fax 001 302 731 1057

Marketing Manager *Steven C. LaMarine*
The International Reading Association is a non-profit education organisation devoted to improving reading instruction and promoting literacy worldwide. In addition to the US $10,000 award presented each year on International Literacy Day (September 8), the organisation gives more than 25 awards in recognition of achievement in reading research, writing for children, media coverage of literacy, and literacy instruction.

Irish Times International Fiction Prize

The Irish Times Ltd, 10–16 D'Olier Street, Dublin 2, Republic of Ireland
☎00 353 1 679 2022   Fax 00 353 1 670 9383
Administrator, Book Prizes *Gerard Cavanagh*
FOUNDED 1989. Biennial award to the author of a work of fiction written in the English language and published in Ireland, the UK or the US in the two years of the award. Next award to be announced in October 1997, the short list having been announced in September. Books are nominated by literary critics and editors only. Previous winners: J. M. Coetzee *The Master of Petersburg*; Annie Proulx *The Shipping News*; Norman Rush *Mating*; Louis Begley *Wartime Lies*.
Prize IR£7500.

Irish Times Irish Literature Prizes

The Irish Times Ltd, 10–16 D'Olier Street, Dublin 2, Republic of Ireland
☎00 353 1 679 2022   Fax 00 353 1 670 9383
Administrator, Book Prizes *Gerard Cavanagh*
FOUNDED 1989. Biennial prizes awarded in three different categories: fiction (a novel, novella or collection of short stories), non-fiction prose (history, biography, autobiography, criticism, politics, sociological interest, travel, current affairs and belles-lettres), and poetry (collection or a long poem or a sequence of poems, or a revised/updated edition of a previously published selection/collection). The author must have been born in Ireland or be an Irish citizen, but may live in any part of the world. Books are nominated by literary editors and critics, and are then called in from publishers. Previous winners: Paddy Devlin *Straight Left* (non-fiction); Kathleen Ferguson *A Maid's Tale* (fiction); Robert Greacen *Collected Poems* (poetry); Brian Keenan *An Evil Cradling*; John MacKenna *The Fallen and Other Stories*.
Prizes IR£5,000 each category.

Jewish Quarterly Literary Prizes

PO Box 2078, London W1A 1JR
☎0171 485 4062   Fax 0171 629 5110

Contact *Gerald Don*

Formerly the H. H. Wingate Prize. Annual awards (one for fiction, one for non-fiction and one for poetry) for works which best stimulate an interest in and awareness of themes of Jewish interest. Books must have been published in the UK in the year of the award and be written in English by an author resident in Britain, Commonwealth, Israel, Republic of Ireland or South Africa. Previous winners: Amos Oz *Black Box*; Anton Gill *The Journey Back from Hell*; Bernice Rubens *Kingdom Come*; Leo Abse *Wotan My Enemy*; Ronald Harwood *Home*; The Prince of West End Avenue Alan Isler; *Konin: A Quest* Theo Richmond.

Prizes Fiction: £4000; Non-fiction: £3000; Poetry: £1000.

Mary Vaughan Jones Award

Cyngor Llyfrau Cymru (Welsh Books Council), Castell Brychan, Aberystwyth, Dyfed SY23 2JB
☎01970 624151   Fax 01970 625385

Contact *The Administrator*

Triennial award for distinguished services in the field of children's literature in Wales over a considerable period of time.

Award Silver trophy to the value of £750.

Kent & Sussex Poetry Society Open Competition

8 Edward Street, Southborough, Tunbridge Wells, Kent TN4 0HP
☎01892 543862

Chairman *Clive R. Eastwood*

After 1996 this open poetry competition will become biennial and, therefore, will not run in 1997. No details available for 1998 at the time of going to press. Queries to the Chairman.

The Sir Peter Kent Conservation Book Prize

See **The BP Conservation Book Prize**

Kent Short Story Competition

Kent Literature Festival, The Metropole Arts Centre, The Leas, Folkestone, Kent CT20 2LS
☎01303 255070

Contact *Ann Fearey*

ESTABLISHED 1992. For a short story of up to 3000 words by anyone over the age of 16. Supported by **South East Arts**, Kent County Council Arts & Libraries and Shepway District Council. Send s.a.e. for entry forms, available from March.

Prizes (1st) £250; (2nd) £125; (3rd) £75.

Kraszna-Krausz Book Awards

122 Fawnbrake Avenue, London SE24 0BZ
☎0171 738 6701

Administrator *Andrea Livingstone*

ESTABLISHED 1985. Annual award to encourage and recognise oustanding achievements in the publishing and writing of books on the art, practice, history and technology of photography and the moving image (film, television, video and related screen media). Books in any language, published worldwide, are eligible. Entries must be submitted by publishers only. Prizes for books on stills photography alternate with those for books on the moving image (1996: stills photography). Previous winners: Mark Litwak *Dealmaking in the Film and Television Industry: From Negotiations to Final Contracts*; Nicholas Negroponte *Being Digital*; Robert Skiar *Film: An International History of the Medium*.

Prizes £10,000 in each of the main categories; £1000 special commendations.

Lakeland Book of the Year Awards

Cumbria Tourist Board, Ashleigh, Holly Road, Windermere, Cumbria LA23 2AQ
☎015394 44444   Fax 015394 44041

Contact *Regional Publicity Officer*

Four annual awards set up by Cumbrian author Hunter Davies and the Cumbria Tourist Board.

The **Hunter Davies Prize** was established in 1984 and is awarded for the book which best helps visitors or residents enjoy a greater love or understanding of any aspect of life in Cumbria and the Lake District.

Three further awards were set up in 1993 with funding from the private sector: **The Tullie House Prize** is for the book which best helps develop a greater appreciation of the built and/or natural environment of Cumbria; **The Barclays Bank Prize** is for the best small book on any aspect of Cumbrian life, its people or culture; and **The Border Television Prize** is for the book which best illustrates the beauty and character of Cumbria. Final entry date mid-March.

1995 winners: Hunter Davies Prize: John Heelis *The Tale of Mrs William Heelis*; Border Television Prize: John Marsh and John Garbutt

The Lake Counties of One Hundred Years Ago;
Barclays Bank Prize: Robert Gambles *Borders of
Lakeland*; Tullie House Prize: *Keswick - The
Story of a Lake District Town.*
Prize £100 and certificate.

Lancashire County Library/NWB Children's Book of the Year Award

Lancashire County Library Headquarters,
143 Corporation Street, Preston, Lancashire
PR1 2UQ
☎01772 264010   Fax 01772 555919

**Assistant County Librarian, Operations
and Development** *D. G. Lightfoot*

ESTABLISHED 1986. Annual award sponsored by
the National Westminster Bank for a work of
original fiction suitable for 11–14-year-olds. The
winner is chosen by 13–14-year-old secondary
school pupils in Lancashire. Books must have
been published between 1 September and 31
August in the year of the award and authors must
be UK residents. Final entry date 1 September
each year. Previous winners: Robert Westall
Gulf; Brian Jacques *Salamandastron*; Robin Jarvis
The Whitby Witches; Ian Strachan *The Boy in the
Bubble*; Garry Kilworth *The Electric Kid.*
Prize £500 plus engraved glass decanter.

D.H. Lawrence/GPT Short Story Competition

Broxtowe Borough Council, Technical &
Leisure Services, Council Offices, Foster
Avenue, Beeston, Nottingham NG9 1AB
☎0115 9254891 ext. 4654

Contacts *Mrs Joan Wildgust, Miss Kaye
Needham*

Annual short story awards. ESTABLISHED in 1980,
the year of the 50th anniversary of the death of
D.H. Lawrence. The competition aims to
encourage young writers between the ages of 13
and 19 years of age. Stories must be no more
than 5000 words in length and on any topic of
local relevance. Entrants must live in Nottinghamshire or a district adjacent to Broxtowe
Borough. Final entry date is the last day of June.
Prizes a trophy in the form of a Phoenix,
made by Plessey apprentices for the school
with the best level of entries; book tokens for
individuals.

The Library Association Besterman Medal

7 Ridgmount Street, London WC1E 7AE
☎0171 636 7543   Fax 0171 436 7218

ESTABLISHED 1970. Sponsored by Whitaker

Bibliographic Services. Awarded annually for an
outstanding bibliography or guide to literature
first published in the UK during the preceding
year. Recommendations for the award are
invited from members of **The Library Association**. Among criteria taken into consideration
in making the award are: authority of the work
and quality of articles or entries; accessibility and
arrangement of the information; scope and coverage; quality of indexing; adequacy of references; accuracy of information; physical presentation; and the originality of the work. Previous
winners include: Heather Creaton *Bibliography of
Printed Works on London History to 1939*; John
McIlwaine *Africa: A Guide to Reference Material*;
Katherine Pantzer *A Short-title Catalogue of Books
Printed in England, Scotland, Ireland and English
Books Printed Abroad 1475-1640 Vol 3.*
Award Medal.

The Library Association Carnegie Medal

7 Ridgmount Street, London WC1E 7AE
☎0171 636 7543   Fax 0171 436 7218

ESTABLISHED 1936. Sponsored by Peters Library
Service. Presented for an outstanding book for
children written in English and first published
in the UK during the preceding year. This
award is not necessarily restricted to books of an
imaginative nature. Previous winners include:
Anne Fine *Flour Babies*; Theresa Breslin
Whispers in the Graveyard.
Award Medal.

The Library Association Kate Greenaway Medal

7 Ridgmount Street, London WC1E 7AE
☎0171 636 7543   Fax 0171 436 7218

ESTABLISHED 1955. Sponsored by Peters Library
Service. Presented annually for the most distin-
guished work in the illustration of children's
books first published in the UK during the pre-
ceding year. Previous winners include: Alan
Lee *Black Ships Before Troy*; Gregory Rogers
Way Home.
Award Medal.

The Library Association McColvin Medal

7 Ridgmount Street, London WC1E 7AE
☎0171 636 7543   Fax 0171 436 7218

ESTABLISHED 1970. Sponsored by Whitaker
Bibliographic Services. Annual award for an out-
standing reference book first published in the
UK during the preceding year. Books eligible for

consideration include: encyclopedias, general and special; dictionaries, general and special; biographical dictionaries; annuals, yearbooks and directories; handbooks and compendia of data; atlases. Recommendations invited from members of **The Library Association**. Previous winners include: Colin Matthew *The Gladstone Diaries*; Ray Desmond *Dictionary of British and Irish Botanists*; Edward Peget-Tomlinson *The Illustrated History of Canal and River Navigation*.
Award Medal.

The Library Association Walford Award
7 Ridgemount Street, London WC1E 7AE
☎0171 636 7543   Fax 0171 436 7218

Awarded to an individual who has made a sustained and continual contribution to British bibliography over a period of years. The nominee need not be resident in the UK. The award is named after Dr A. J. Walford, a bibliograper of international repute. Previous winners include: Prof. Stanley Wells, Prof. J. D. Pearson and Prof. R. C. Alston.
Award Cash prize and certificate.

The Library Association Wheatley Medal
7 Ridgmount Street, London WC1E 7AE
☎0171 636 7543   Fax 0171 436 7218

ESTABLISHED 1962. Sponsored by Whitaker Bibliographic Services. Annual award for an outstanding index first published in the UK during the preceding three years. Whole work must have originated in the UK and recommendations for the award are invited from members of **The Library Association**, the **Society of Indexers**, publishers and others. Previous winners include: Elizabeth Moys *British Tax Encyclopedia*; Paul Nash *The World of Environment 1972-1992*; Richard Raper *The Works of Charles Darwin*.
Award Medal.

Lichfield Prize
c/o Tourist Information Centre, Donegal House, Bore Street, Lichfield, Staffordshire WS13 6NE
☎01543 252109   Fax 01543 417308
Contact *Mrs Alison Bessey* at Lichfield District Council on 01543 414000 ext. 2047

ESTABLISHED 1988. Biennial award initiated by Lichfield District Council to coincide with the Lichfield Festival. Run in conjunction with James Redshaw Booksellers of Lichfield and 1997 Prize co-sponsors, **Hodder & Stoughton**

publishers. Awarded for a previously unpublished novel based upon the geographical area of Lichfield district, contemporary or historical, but not futuristic. Previous winners: Valerie Kershaw *Rockabye*; Gary Coyne *The Short Caution*. Next award 1997. Final entry date in April of that year.
Prize £5000, plus possible publication.

Literary Review Grand Poetry Competition
See *Literary Review* under **Magazines**

Lloyds Private Banking Playwright of the Year Award
Tony Ball Associates Plc, 174–178 North Gower Street, London NW1 2NB
☎0171 380 0953   Fax 0171 387 9004
Contact *Stephen Harrison*

LAUNCHED in February 1994. The Award aims to provide support and encouragement for writing talent to flourish and gain greater recognition, as well as to help widen interest in regional and London theatres. Playwrights must be of British or Irish nationality and have written a new play which was first performed in the previous year. Nominations are made by theatre critics from which a shortlist of ten is selected. Winner is announced in Feb/March. 1996 winner: Sebastian Barry *The Steward of Christendom*.
Prize £25,000.

London Writers Competition
See **Wandsworth London Writers Competition**

Lost Poet
PO Box 136, Norwich, Norfolk NR3 3LJ
☎01603 440944   Fax 01603 440940
Contact *Tricia Frances*

Lost Poet runs six literary competitons per year. All profits go to the work of the International Light Foundation whose aim is to 'help the population become more aware of personal, planetary and evolutionary issues'. For more details, send s.a.e. to the above address.
Prizes reflect the amount of entries received.

LWT Plays on Stage
LWT, The London Television Centre, Upper Ground, London SE1 9LT
☎0171 620 1620
Contact *Suzy Stoyel, Regional Affairs Manager*

ESTABLISHED 1987. Annual award to encourage contemporary writing talent and to enable the winner to stage a new theatre production.

Open to all professional drama companies, repertory companies, producing managements and producing theatres within the LWT transmission area. The winner is announced during the *Evening Standard* Drama Awards in November and LWT retain an exclusive option to acquire the television and film rights. 1995 winner: **Paines Plough** for *Resurrection* by Maureen Lawrence.

Prize £20,000.

Sir William Lyons Award

The Guild of Motoring Writers, 30 The Cravens, Smallfield, Surrey RH6 9QS
☎01342 843294   Fax 01342 844093
Contact *Sharon Scott-Fairweather*

An annual competitive award to encourage young people in automotive journalism and to foster interests in motoring and the motor industry. Entrance by two essays and interview with Awards Committee. Applicants must be British, aged 17–23 and resident in UK. Final entry date 1 August. Presentation date December.

Award £1000 plus trophy.

Agnes Mure Mackenzie Award

The Saltire Society, 9 Fountain Close, 22 High Street, Edinburgh EH1 1TF
☎0131 556 1836   Fax 0131 557 1675
Administrator *Kathleen Munro*

ESTABLISHED 1965. Biennial award in memory of the late Dr Agnes Mure Mackenzie for a published work of distinguished Scottish historical research of scholarly importance (including intellectual history and the history of science). Editions of texts are not eligible. The 1996 award is open to books published between 1st January 1995 and 31st December 1996. Nominations are invited and should be sent to the Administrator.

Prize Bound and inscribed copy of the winning publication.

W. J. M. Mackenzie Book Prize

Political Studies Association, Dept of Politics, Queen's University, Belfast BT7 1NN
☎01232 245133 ext. 3224 Fax 01232 235373
PSA Administrative Secretary *Lynn Corken*

ESTABLISHED 1987. Annual award to best work of political science published in the UK during the previous year. Submissions from publishers only. Final entry date in March. Previous winners: James Mayall *Nationalism and International Society*; Brian Barry *Theories of Justice;* Avi Shlaim *Collusion Across the Jordan*; Colin Crouch *Industrial Relations and European State Tradition*; Iain Hampsher-Monk *A History of Modern*

Political Thought; Patrick Dunleavy *Democracy, Bureaucracy and Public Choice*.

Prize £100, plus travel/attendance at three-day annual conference.

Macmillan Prize for a Children's Picture Book

Macmillan Children's Books, 25 Eccleston Place, London SW1W 9NF
☎0171 881 8000   Fax 0171 881 8001
Contact *Marketing Dept., Macmillan Children's Books*

Set up in order to stimulate new work from young illustrators in art schools, and to help them start their professional lives. Fiction or non-fiction. **Macmillan** have the option to publish any of the prize winners.

Prizes (1st) £1000; (2nd) £500; (3rd) £250.

Macmillan Silver PEN Award

The English Centre of International PEN, 7 Dilke Street, London SW3 4JE
☎0171 352 6303   Fax 0171 351 0220
Sponsored by **Macmillan Publishers**. An annual award for a volume of short stories written in English by a British author and published in the UK in the year preceding the prize. Nominations by the PEN Executive Committee only. Previous winners: Jane Gardham *Going into a Dark House*; Nicola Barker *Love Your Enemies*; Clive Collins *Misunderstandings*; John Arden *Cogs Tyrannic*; Pauline Melville *Shape-Shifter*. 1996 winner: Fay Weldon *Wicked Women*.

Prize £500, plus silver pen.

The Mail on Sunday Novel Competition

The Mail on Sunday, PO Box 2, Central Way, Feltham, Middlesex TW14 0TG
☎0171 938 6000

Annual award ESTABLISHED 1983. Judges look for a story/character that springs to life in the 'tantalising opening 50–150 words of a novel'. Previous winners: Jill Roe, Judy Astley, Simon Levack, Sarah Cooper, Terry Eccles, Jillian Hart. *Awards* (1st) £400 book tokens and a weekend writing course at the **Arvon Foundation**; (2nd) £300 tokens; (3rd) £200 tokens; three runners-up receive £150 tokens each.

The Mail on Sunday/ John Llewellyn Rhys Prize

Book Trust, Book House, 45 East Hill, London SW18 2QZ
☎0181 870 9055   Fax 0181 874 4790
Contact *Sandra Vince*

ESTABLISHED 1942. An annual young writer's award for a memorable work of any kind. Entrants must be under the age of 35 at the time of publication; books must have been published in the UK in the year of the award. The author must be a citizen of Britain or the Commonwealth, writing in English. Previous winners: Matthew Kneale *Sweet Thames*; Jason Goodwin *On Foot to the Golden Horn*. 1995 winner: Jonathan Coe *What a Carve Up!*.

Prize £5000 (1st); £500 for shortlisted entries.

Marsh Award for Children's Literature in Translation

The Authors' Club, 40 Dover Street, London W1X 3RB
☎0171 499 8581   Fax 0171 409 0913
Contact *Mrs Ann Carter*

ESTABLISHED 1995 and sponsored by the Marsh Christian Trust, the award aims to encourage translation of foreign children's books into English. It is a biennial award (first year: 1996), open to British translators of books for 4–16-year-olds, published in the UK by a British publisher. Final entry date was March 1996. Any category will be considered with the exception of encyclopedias and reference. No electronic books.

Prize £750.

Marsh Biography Award

The Authors' Club, 40 Dover Street, London W1X 3RB
☎0171 499 8581   Fax 0171 409 0913
Contact *Mrs Ann Carter*

A biennial award for the most significant biography published over a two-year period by a British publisher. Previous winners: Hugh & Mirabel Cecil *Clever Hearts*; Patrick Marnham *The Man Who Wasn't Maigret*; Lady Selina Hastings *Evelyn Waugh*. Next award October 1997.

Award £3500, plus silver trophy presented at a dinner.

Kurt Maschler Award

Book Trust, Book House, 45 East Hill, London SW18 2QZ
☎0181 870 9055   Fax 0181 874 4790
Contact *Sandra Vince*

ESTABLISHED 1982. Annual award for 'a work of imagination in the children's field in which text and illustration are of excellence and so presented that each enhances, yet balances the other'. Books published in the current year in the UK by a British author and/or artist, or by someone resident for ten years, are eligible.

Previous winners: Kathy Henderson and Patrick Benson *The Little Boat*; Trish Cooke, illus. Helen Oxenbury *So Much*; Karen Wallace, illus. Mike Bostock *Think of an Eel*; Raymond Briggs *The Man*; Colin McNaughton *Have You Seen Who's Just Moved in Next Door to Us?* .

Award £1000 plus bronze Emil trophy.

MCA Book Prize

122 Fawnbrake Avenue, London SE24 0BZ
☎0171 738 6701
Administrator *Andrea Livingstone*

ESTABLISHED 1993. Annual award sponsored by the Management Consultancies Association to recognise and reward books that contribute stimulating, original and progressive ideas on management. Entries should have been published first in the UK during the calendar year of the Award and written by British subjects living in the UK. Submissions by publishers only. Previous winners: Clive Morton *Becoming World Class*; Richard Whittington *What is Strategy and Does it Matter?*.

Prizes £5000 for best management book. In addition, a prize of £2000 for best management book by a writer under 35 may be given.

McColvin Medal

See **The Library Association McColvin Medal**

McKitterick Prize

Society of Authors, 84 Drayton Gardens, London SW10 9SB
☎0171 373 6642   Fax 0171 373 5768
Contact *Awards Secretary*

Annual award for a full-length work in the English language, first published in the UK or unpublished. Open to writers over 40 who have not had any adult novel published other than the one submitted. Closing date 16 December. 1996 winner: Stephen Blanchard *Gagarin and I*.

Prize £4–5000.

Enid McLeod Prize

Franco-British Society, Room 623, Linen Hall, 162–168 Regent Street, London W1R 5TB
☎0171 734 0815   Fax 0171 734 0815
Executive Secretary *Mrs Marian Clarke*

ESTABLISHED 1982. Annual award to the author of the work of literature published in the UK which, in the opinion of the judges, has contributed most to Franco-British understanding. Any full-length work written in English by a citizen of the UK, Commonwealth, Republic of Ireland, Pakistan, Bangladesh and South

Africa. No English translation of a book written originally in any other language will be considered. Nominations from publishers for books published between 1 January and 31 December of the year of the prize. Previous winners: Jonathan Keates *Stendhal*; Sebastian Faulks *Birdsong*; Margaret Crosland *Simone de Beauvoir - The Woman and Her Work*; Frank Giles *The Locust Years*.

Prize Cheque.

The McVitie's Prize for the Scottish Writer of the Year

c/o Book Trust Scotland, The Scottish Book Centre, 137 Dundee Street, Edinburgh EH11 1BG
☎0131 229 3663   Fax 0131 228 4293

Contact *Kathryn Ross*

ESTABLISHED 1987. Sponsored by United Biscuits (Holdings) plc for the best substantial work of an imaginative nature, including TV and radio scripts and writing for children, first published, performed, filmed or transmitted between 1st August and 31st July. Writers born in Scotland, or who have Scottish parents, or who have been resident in Scotland for a considerable period, or who take Scotland as their inspiration are all eligible. Submissions accepted in English, Scots or Gaelic. Recent winners: Janice Galloway, William Boyd and Frank Kuppner.

Prize £10,000, plus £1,000 to each of the other four shortlisted writers.

Meyer-Whitworth Award

Arts Council of England, 14 Great Peter Street, London SW1P 3NQ
☎0171 333 0100 ext 431   Fax 0171 973 6590

Contact *The Drama Director*

In 1908 the movement for a National Theatre joined forces with that to create a memorial to William Shakespeare. The result was the Shakespeare Memorial National Theatre Committee, the embodiment of the campaign for a National Theatre. This award, bearing the name of but two protagonists in the movement, has been established to commemorate all those who worked for the SMNT. Endowed by residual funds of the SMNT, the award is intended to help further the careers of UK playwrights who are not yet established, and to draw contemporary theatre writers to the public's attention. The award is given to the writer whose play most nearly satisfies the following criteria: a play which embodies Geoffrey Whitworth's dictum that 'drama is important in so far as it reveals the truth about the relationships of human beings with each other and the world at large'; a play which shows promise of a developing new talent; a play in which the writing is of individual quality. Nominations from professional theatre companies. Plays must have been written in the English language and produced professionally in the UK in the 12 months preceding the award.

Award £8000.

MIND Book of the Year/ Allen Lane Award

Granta House, 15-19 Broadway, London E15 4BQ
☎0181 519 2122 ext. 225   Fax 0181 522 1725

ESTABLISHED 1981. Annual award, in memory of Sir Allen Lane, for the author of a book published in the current year (fiction or non-fiction), which furthers public understanding of mental health problems. Previous winner: Lois Keith (ed.) *Musn't Grumble*.

Award £1000.

The Mitchell Prize for Art History/The Eric Mitchell Prize

c/o The Burlington Magazine, 14-16 Duke's Road, London WC1H 9AD
☎0171 388 8157   Fax 0171 388 1230

Executive Director *Caroline Elam*

ESTABLISHED 1977 by art collector, philanthropist and businessman, Jan Mitchell, to draw attention to exceptional achievements in the history of art. Consists of two prizes: The Mitchell Prize, given for an outstanding and original contribution to the study and understanding of visual arts, and The Eric Mitchell Prize, given for the most outstanding first book in this field. The prizes are awarded to authors of books in English that have been published in the previous 12 months (i.e. 1 January–31 December 1995 for the 1996 award). Books are submitted by publishers before the end of February. Previous winners: The Mitchell Prize: *Colour and Culture* John Gage; The Eric Mitchell Prize: *Fra Angelico at San Marco* William Hood.

Prizes $15,000 (Mitchell Prize); $5000 (Eric Mitchell Prize)

Scott Moncrieff Prize

The Translators Association, 84 Drayton Gardens, London SW10 9SB
☎0171 373 6642

Contact *Kate Pool*

An annual award for the best translation published by a British publisher during the previous

year of a French work, which must have been published within the last 150 years, of literary merit and general interest. Previous winners include: Gilbert Adair *A Void* by Georges Perec.
Prize £1000.

The Montagu of Beaulieu Trophy
Guild of Motoring Writers, 30 The Cravens, Smallfield, Surrey RH6 9QS
☎01342 843294   Fax 01342 844093
Contact *Sharon Scott-Fairweather*

First presented by Lord Montagu on the occasion of the opening of the National Motor Museum at Beaulieu in 1972. Awarded annually to a member of the **Guild of Motoring Writers** who, in the opinion of the nominated jury, has made the greatest contribution to recording in the English language the history of motoring or motor cycling in a published book or article, film, television or radio script, or research manuscript available to the public.
Prize Trophy.

The Mother Goose Award
Books for Children, 4 Furzeground Way, Stockley Park, Uxbridge, Middlesex UB11 1DP
☎0181 606 3061   Fax 0181 606 3099
Contact *Sian Hardy, Editorial Manager*

ESTABLISHED 1979. Annual award for the most exciting newcomer to British children's book illustration. 1995 winner: Flora McDonnell *I Love Animals*.
Prize £1000, plus Golden Egg trophy.

NASEN Special Educational Needs Award
The Educational Publishers Council, The Publishers Association, 19 Bedford Square, London WC1B 3HJ
☎0171 580 6321   Fax 0171 636 5375
ESTABLISHED 1992. Organised by tthe National Association for Special Educational Needs (NASEN) and the **Educational Publishers Council**. Two awards: the *Academic Book Award*, for a book which enhances the knowledge and understanding of those engaged in the education of children with special needs; the *Children's Book Award*, for a book written for children under the age of 16 which does most to put forward a positive image of children with special education needs. Books must have been published in the UK within the two years preceding the award. Previous winners: Paul Greenhalgh *Emotional Growth and Learning* (Academic); David Hill *See ya, Simon* (Children's).
Prize £500.

National Student Playscript Competition
See **University College, Scarborough** under **Writers' Courses, Circles and Workshops**

Natural World Book of the Year Award
Natural World Magazine, 20 Upper Ground, London SE1 9PF
☎0171 805 5555   Fax 0171 805 5911
Contact *Linda Bennett*

ESTABLISHED 1987. Annual award to encourage the publication of high-quality natural history books. Open to books published between 1 October and 30 September about British and European wildlife or countryside. Final entry date end of August. Previous winners: David Macdonald *European Mammals*; Oliver Rackham *The Illustrated History of the Countryside*; Sir Peter Scott *Images from a Lifetime*; Jeremy Thomas *The Butterflies of Britain & Ireland*. Administered by *Natural World* magazine.
Prize £500, plus magazine promotion feature of book.

NCR Book Award for Non-Fiction
NCR, 206 Marylebone Road, London NW1 6LY
☎0171 723 7070   Fax 0171 724 6519
Contact *The Administrator*

ESTABLISHED 1987 (first award made 1988), the NCR Book Award for Non-Fiction is for a book written in English by a living writer from Britain, the Commonwealth or Republic of Ireland, and published in the UK. One of the UK's single most valuable annual book prizes, with a total prize money of £31,000, and the only major prize specifically for non-fiction. Only publishers may submit titles, limited to three per imprint. The award covers all areas of adult non-fiction except academic, guidebooks and practical listings (such as cookery books). Titles must be published in the 12 months between 1 April and 31 March. A shortlist of four books is announced in mid-April and the winning book in early/mid-May. The aim of the award is to stimulate interest in non-fiction writing, reading and publishing in the UK. 1996 winner: Erica Lomax *The Railway Man*.
Prizes (1st) £25,000 and computer equipment; three runners-up shortlisted £1500 and computer equipment.

Nobel Prize

The Nobel Foundation, Box 5232/Sturegatan 14, Stockholm, Sweden S-10245

☎00 46 8 663 0920   Fax 00 46 8 660 3847

Contact *Information Section*

Awarded yearly for outstanding achievement in physics, chemistry, physiology or medicine, literature and peace. FOUNDED by Alfred Nobel, a chemist who proved his creative ability by inventing dynamite. In general, individuals cannot nominate someone for a Nobel Prize. The rules vary from prize to prize but the following are eligible to do so for Literature: members of the Swedish Academy and of other academies, institutions and societies similar to it in membership and aims; professors of history of literature or of languages at universities or colleges; Nobel Laureates in Literature; presidents of authors' organisations which are representative of the literary activities of their respective countries. British winners of the literature prize, first granted in 1901, include Rudyard Kipling, John Galsworthy and Winston Churchill. Recent winners: Seamus Heaney; Camilio Jose Cela (Spain); Octavio Paz (Mexico); Nadine Gordimer (South Africa); Derek Walcott (St Lucia); Toni Morrison (USA); Kenzaburo Oe (Japan).

Prize 1995: SEK7,200,000 (about £700,000), increasing each year to cover inflation.

Northern Short Stories Competition

ARC Publications, Nanholme Mill, Shaw Wood Road, Todmorden, Lancashire OL14 6DA

☎01706 812338   Fax 01706 818948

Contact *Rosemary Jones*

ESTABLISHED 1988. Annual award set up to stimulate the writing and reading of quality short fiction. Open to all living in the area covered by the three Northern regional arts boards (**North West Arts**, **Northern Arts**, **Yorkshire & Humberside Arts**). Final entry date 30 June. Please send s.a.e. for entry form.

Prize Guaranteed same-year publication in anthology, plus small cash prize.

Nottinghamshire Children's Book Award

Nottinghamshire County Council, Education Library Service, Glaisdale Parkway, Nottingham NG8 4GP

☎0115 9854200   Fax 0115 9286400

Contact *Ann Fairbairn* (Library)

ESTABLISHED 1989. Annual award jointly organised and promoted by Nottingham Libraries and Dillons Bookstore, who sponsor the award. The aim is to encourage reading and draw attention to the exciting range of children's books available. The award is given in two categories: **The Acorn Award**, for an outstanding book written and illustrated for the 0–7 age group; and **The Oak Tree Award**, for an outstanding book written and illustrated for the 8–12 age group. Books must have been published for the first time in the UK in the preceding year. Shortlist drawn up by librarians and bookshop staff. Authors and publishers are not required to nominate books. Previous winners: Anne Fine *Diary of a Killer Cat*; Colin McNaughton *Suddenly*.

Award £250 (each category).

The Oak Tree Award

See **Nottinghamshire Children's Book Award**

C. B. Oldman Prize

Aberdeen University Library, Queen Mother Library, Meston Walk, Aberdeen AB9 2UE

☎01224 272592   Fax 01224 487048

Contact *Richard Turbet*

ESTABLISHED 1989 by the International Association of Music Libraries, UK Branch. Annual award for best book of music bibliography, librarianship or reference published the year before last (i.e. books published in 1996 considered for the 1998 prize). Previous winners: Andrew Ashbee, Michael Talbot, Donald Clarke, John Parkinson, John Wagstaff, Stanley Sadie, William Waterhouse.

Prize £150.

One Voice Monologue Competition

c/o Pro Forma, Box 29, Neath, West Glamorgan SA11 1WL

Contact *Nicola Davies*

ESTABLISHED 1992. An international competition run by playwright Nicola Davies with the support of a team of writers/actors. The competition has been supported by Catrin Collier, Sir Anthony Hopkins, Simon Callow and Miriam Margolyes. Finalists' work is performed at the Finals and published in a glossy illustrated book. A selection is later performed at London's Theatre Museum. The Catrin Collier Random House award enables the winner to spend a day in London with novelist Catrin Collier and an editor from **Random House**. There are three categories: Monologue/ Duologue, Story,

Letter. Please send s.a.e. for entry form. Final entry date October 1997.

Prizes in 1997 are anticipated as being a total of £5000.

Orange Prize for Fiction

The Book Trust, 45 East Hill, London SW18 2QZ

☎0181 870 9055　　　Fax 0181 874 4790

Contact *Sandra Vince*

ESTABLISHED 1996. Annual award founded by a group of senior women in publishing to 'create the opportunity for more women to be rewarded for their work and to be better known by the reading public'. Awarded for a full-length novel written in English by a woman of any nationality, and published in the UK between 1 April and 31 March of the following year. 1996 winner: Helen Dunmore *A Spell of Winter*.

Prize £30,000 and a work of art (a limited edition bronze figurine to be known as 'The Bessie' in acknowledgement of anonymous prize endowment).

Outposts Poetry Competition

Outposts, 22 Whitewell Road, Frome, Somerset BA11 4EL

☎01373 466653

Contact *Roland John*

Annual competition for an unpublished poem of not more than 40 lines run by **Hippopotamus Press**.

Prize £1000.

OWG/COLA Awards for Excellence

Outdoor Writers' Guild, PO Box 520, Bamber Bridge, Preston, Lancashire PR5 8LF

☎01772 696732　　　Fax 01772 696732

Contact *Terry Marsh*

ESTABLISHED 1980. Annual award by the **Outdoor Writers' Guild** and the Camping & Outdoor Leisure Association to raise the standard of outdoor writing, journalism and broadcasting. Winning categories include best book, best guidebook, best feature, best technical report. Open to OWG members only. Final entry date March. Previous winners include: Leigh Hatts, Steve Venables, Hazel Constance, Catherine Moore, John and Anne Nuttall, Roland Smith, Terry Marsh, Peter and Leni Gillman, Alastair Macdonald, Richard Gilbert.

Prize (total) £1250.

Catherine Pakenham Award

The Sunday Telegraph, 1 Canada Square, Canary Wharf, London E14 5DT

☎0171 538 6259　　　Fax 0171 513 2512

Contact *Joanne Henwood*

ESTABLISHED 1970, this is an annual award in memory of Lady Catherine Pakenham, and is given for a non-fiction article (750-2000 words) by a woman aged between 18 and 25, resident in Britain and involved in or intending to take up a career in journalism. Previous winners: Elizabeth Brooks; Esther Oxford.

Award £1000 and a writing commission with one of the Telegraph publications; three runner-up prizes of £200 each.

Peer Poetry Competition

26(c) Arlington House, Bath Street, Bath BA1 1QN

Contact *Competition Editor*

Bi-annual open competition for one or more poems of any type or style, up to 200 lines in total. All qualifying poems will be printed in *Peer Poetry Magazine*. Free entry to subscribers, others £2.50 inclusive. Send two copies of each poem, double-spaced on A4, plus two A4 s.a.e.s. Closing dates: end April and October. Judging is by the votes of all successful entrants and subscribers.

Prizes £120 (1st); £60 (2nd); £30 (3rd).

PEN Awards

See **Macmillan Silver PEN Award; Silver PEN Non-Fiction Award**

Peterloo Poets Open Poetry Competition

2 Kelly Gardens, Calstock, Cornwall PL18 9SA

☎01822 833473

Contact *Lynn Chambers*

ESTABLISHED 1986. Annual competition sponsored by Marks & Spencer for unpublished English language poems of not more than 40 lines. Final entry date 1 March. Previous winners: John Watts, David Craig, Rodney Pybus, Debjani Chatterjee, Donald Atkinson, Romesh Gunesekera, Shafi Ahmed, Anna Crowe, Carol Ann Duffy, Mimi Khalvati, John Lyons, M. R. Peacocke, Carol Shergold, David Simon, Maureen Wilkinson, Chris Woods.

Prize £3000 (1st).

Poetry Business Competition

The Studio, Byram Arcade, Westgate, Huddersfield, West Yorkshire HD1 1ND

☎01484 434840　　　Fax 01484 426566

Contact *The Competition Administrator*

ESTABLISHED 1986. Annual award which aims to discover and publish new writers. Entrants should submit 24 pp of poems. Entry fee £15. Winners will have their work published by the **Poetry Business** under the Smith/Doorstop imprint. Final entry date end of October. Previous winners: Pauline Stainer, Michael Laskey, Mimi Khalvati, David Morley, Julia Casterton, Liz Cashdan, Moniza Alvi, Selima Hill. Send s.a.e. for full details.

Prize publication of full collection; runners-up have pamphlets; 20 complimentary copies.

Poetry Life Poetry Competition

Poetry Life, 14 Pennington Oval, Lymington, Hampshire SO41 8BQ
Contact *Adrian Bishop*

ESTABLISHED 1993. Open competition for original poems in any style which have not been published in a book. Maximum length of 80 lines. Entry fee of £2 per poem (£10 for seven poems). Send s.a.e. for details.

Prize £500 (1st); £100 (2nd); £50 each (3rd & 4th).

The Poetry Society's National Poetry Competition

The Poetry Society, 22 Betterton Street, London WC2H 9BU
☎0171 240 4810   Fax 0171 240 4818
Contact *Competition Organiser*

One of Britian's major open poetry competitions. Closing date 31 October. Poems on any theme, up to 100 lines; special category for poems of 40-100 lines. For rules and entry form send s.a.e. to the Competition Organiser at the above address.

Prize (1st) £4000; (2nd) £1000; (3rd) £500; (Special category) £1000.

Peter Pook Humorous Novel Competition

See **Emissary Publishing** under **UK Publishers**

The Portico Prize

The Portico Library, 57 Mosley Street, Manchester M2 3HY
☎0161 236 6785
Contact *Mrs Jo Francis*

ESTABLISHED 1985. Administered by the Portico Library in Manchester. Biennial award (odd-numbered years) for a published work of fiction or non-fiction set wholly or mainly in the North-West/Cumbria. Previous winners include: Richard Francis *Taking Apart the Poco Poco*; Alan Hankinson *Coleridge Walks the Fells*; Jenny Uglow *Elizabeth Gaskell: A Habit of Stories*.

Prize £2500.

The Dennis Potter Television Play of the Year Award

Room D333, BBC, Centre House, 56 Wood Lane, London, W12 7SB
☎0181 576 8536

ESTABLISHED 1994 in memory of the late television playwright to 'bring out courageous and imaginative voices'. Annual award for writers who have not had single plays produced on television. Nominees are put forward by independent and BBC producers. 1996 winner: John Milarky *Lah a Note to Follow Soh*.

Prize commission worth £10,000.

Michael Powell Book Award

British Film Institute, 21 Stephen Street, London W1P 1PL
☎0171 255 1444   Fax 0171 436 7950
Contact *BFI Press Office*

ESTABLISHED 1984. Annual award given by the **British Film Institute**. At the time of going to press the award was under review.

Premio Langhe Ceretto – Sei Per La Cultura Del Cibo

Biblioteca Civica 'G. Ferrero', Via Paruzza 1, 12051 Alba Italy
☎00 39 173 290092
Contact *Gianfranco Maggi*

ESTABLISHED 1991. Annual award, founded by the wine company Filli Ceretto, for published works dealing with historical, scientific, dietological, gastronomical or sociological aspects of food and wine. Previous winners: E. Gowes, A. Kanafahi-Zahar.

The Mathew Prichard Award for Short Story Writing

95 Celyn Avenue, Lakeside, Cardiff CF2 6EL
Competition Secretary *Mrs Betty Persen*
Organiser *Philip Beynon*

ESTABLISHED 1996 to provide sponsorship and promote Wales and its writers. Competition open to all writers in English; the final entry date is 1 March each year.

Prizes (1st) £1000; (2 runners-up) £250 each.

Pulitzer Prizes

The Pulitzer Prize Board, 702 Journalism,
Columbia University, New York NY 10027,
USA
☎001 212 854 3841/2

Awards for journalism in US newspapers, and for
published literature, drama and music by
American nationals. Deadline 1 February (jour-
nalism); 1 March (music); 1 March (drama);
1 July for books published between 1 Jan–30
June, and 1 Nov for books published between 1
July–31 Dec (literature). 1995 winners included:
Carol Shields *The Stone Diaries*. Previous
winners: E. Annie Proulx *The Shipping News*;
David Levering Lewis *W. E. B. DuBois*; David
Remnick *Lenin's Tomb: The Last Days of the
Soviet Empire*.

The Questors Theatre National Student Playwright Competition

12 Mattock Lane, Ealing, London W5 5BQ
☎0181 567 0011   Fax 0181 567 8736
Theatre Manager *Elaine Orchard*

ESTABLISHED 1985. Annual award. The winning play, and sometimes the runner–up, is/are
performed at Questors Theatre. Deadline for
entries 31st March.
    Prize £1000.

Trevor Reese Memorial Prize

Institute of Commonwealth Studies,
University of London, 28 Russell Square,
London WC1B 5DS
☎0171 580 5876   Fax 0171 255 2160
Contact *Seminar Secretary*

ESTABLISHED 1979 with the proceeds of contributions to a memorial fund to Dr Trevor Reese,
Reader in Commonwealth Studies at the
Institute and a distinguished scholar of imperial
history (d.1976). Biennial award (next award
1998) for a scholarly work, usually by a single
author, in the field of Imperial and Commonwealth History published in the preceding two
years. All correspondence relating to the prize
should be marked *Trevor Reese Memorial Prize*.
Previous winners: Professor Bruce Berman and
Dr John Lonsdale *Unhappy Valley: Conflict in
Kenya and Africa, Books One & Two*.
    Prize £1000.

Regional Press Awards

Press Gazette, EMAP Business
Communications, 33-39 Bowling Green Lane,
London EC1R 0DA
☎0171 505 8000   Fax 0171 505 8220

Comprehensive range of journalist and newspaper awards for the regional press. Five newspapers of the year, by circulation and frequency,
and a full list of journalism categories. Open to all
regional journalists, whether freelance or staff.
Final entry date 3 May. Run by the *Press Gazette*.

Renault UK Journalist of the Year Award

Guild of Motoring Writers, 30 The Cravens,
Smallfield, Surrey RH6 9QS
☎01342 843294   Fax 01342 844093
Contact *Sharon Scott-Fairweather*

Originally the Pierre Dreyfus Award and
ESTABLISHED 1977. Awarded annually by
Renault UK Ltd in honour of Pierre Dreyfus,
president director general of Renault 1955–75,
to the member of the **Guild of Motoring
Writers** who is judged to have made the most
outstanding journalistic effort during the year.
    Prizes 1st £1000, plus trophy; 2nd £500;
3rd £250.

The Rhône–Poulenc Prizes for Science Books

COPUS, c/o The Royal Society, 6 Carlton
House Terrace, London SW1Y 5AG
☎0171 839 5561 ext. 2580 Fax 0171 451 2693
Contact *Imelda Topping*

ESTABLISHED 1987 by COPUS (Committee on
the Public Understanding of Science) with the
Science Museum. Sponsored by Rhône-
Poulenc. Annual awards for popular non-fiction
science and technology books judged to contribute most to the public understanding of
science. Books must be published during the
previous calendar year in their first English edition in the UK. The prizes, totalling £20,000,
are divided between two categories: the Rhône-
Poulenc Prize awarded for a book for general
readership; and the Junior Prize for books written primarily for young people. Final entry date
January. 1996 winners: Arno Karlen *Plague's
Progress*; Chris Maynard *The World of Weather*
(Junior Prize).
    Prizes Rhône-Poulenc Prize £10,000;
Junior Prize £10,000.

Rhyme International Prize

c/o Orbis Magazine, 199 The Long Shoot,
Nuneaton, Warwickshire CV11 6JQ
☎01203 327440   Fax 01203 327440
Contact *Mike Shields*

ESTABLISHED 1982. Annual competition aimed
at promoting rhyming poetry. Minimum entry

fee £5 (£2.50 per poem). Entries may fall into two categories: rhymed poems of less than 50 lines; or formal: sonnet, villanelle, etc. Final entry date end September.

Prize (1995 total) £1200.

John Llewellyn Rhys Prize
See **The Mail on Sunday/John Llewellyn Rhys Prize**

Rogers Prize
Academic Trust Funds, Room 21A, University of London, Senate House, London WC1E 7HU
☎0171 636 8000 ext. 3147
Contact *Mrs M. Praulins*

Annual award for an essay or dissertation on alternately a medical or surgical subject, which is named and appointed by the University of London – in 1996 for 'An Advance in Medicine'. Essays and dissertations must be in English and shall be typewritten or printed and submitted by 30 June.

Prize £250.

Romantic Novelists' Association Major Award
3 Arnesby Lane, Peatling Magna, Leicester LE8 5UN
☎0116 2478330   Fax 0116 2478330
Organiser *Jean Chapman*
ESTABLISHED 1960. Annual award for the best romantic novel of the year, open to non-members as well as members of the **Romantic Novelists' Association**. Novels must be published between specified dates which vary year to year. Authors must be based in the UK. Previous winners include: Rosamunde Pilcher *Coming Home*; Susan Kay *Phantom*; Reay Tannahill *Passing Glory*; Elizabeth Buchan *Consider the Lily*; Charlotte Bingham *A Change of Heart*. Contact the Organiser for entry form.

Award £5000.

Romantic Novelists' Association New Writers Award
RNA, Cobble Cottage, 129 New Street, Baddesley Ensor, Nr Atherstone, Warwickshire CV9 2DL
☎01827 714776
Secretary *Joyce Bell*
ESTABLISHED 1962, the award is for unpublished writers in the field of the romantic novel. Entrants are required to join the Association as probationary members. Mss entered for this award must be specifically written for it.

Rooney Prize for Irish Literature
Rooney Prize, Strathin, Templecarrig, Delgany, Co. Wicklow, Republic of Ireland
☎00 353 1 287 4769   Fax 00 353 1 287 2595
Contact *Jim Sherwin, Barbara Norman*
ESTABLISHED 1976. Annual award to encourage young Irish writing to develop and continue. Authors must be Irish, under 40 and published. A non-competitive award with no application procedure.

Prize IR£5000.

Rover Group Award
Guild of Motoring Writers, 30 The Cravens, Smallfield, Surrey RH6 9QS
☎01342 843294   Fax 01342 844093
Contact *Sharon Scott-Fairweather*
Awarded annually to the Guild member judged to have done most towards improving reader understanding of the issues affecting the vehicle industry.

Prize £1000.

Royal Economic Society Prize
c/o University of York, York YO1 5DD
☎01904 433575   Fax 01904 433575
Contact *Prof. Mike Wickens*
Biennial award for the best article published in *The Economic Journal*. Open to members of the Royal Economic Society only. Next award 1998. Final entry date December 1997. Previous winners: Drs O. P. Attanasio & Guglielmo Weber; Prof. M. H. Pesaran; Prof. J. Pemberton.

Prize £1000.

Royal Society of Literature Awards
See **Winifred Holtby Memorial Prize** and **W. H. Heinemann Prize**

The Royal Society of Medicine Prizes
The Society of Authors, 84 Drayton Gardens, London SW10 9SB
☎0171 373 6642   Fax 0171 373 5768
Contact *Jacqueline Granger-Taylor*
Annual award in five categories: textbook, illustrated textbook, atlas, electronic format and first textbook, published in the UK in the year preceding the awards. Previous winners: Peter G. Isaacson and Andrew J. Norton *Extranodal Lymphomas*; John A. Kanis *Osteoporosis*; Bruce Benjamin, Brian Bingham, Michael Hawke and

Heinz Stammberger *A Colour Atlas of Otorhino-laryngology*; Alain C. Masquelet, Alain Gilbert and Leon Dorn *An Atlas of Flaps in Limb Reconstruction*; R. M. Winter and M. Baraitser *London Dysmorphology Database, London Neuro-genetics Database, Dysmorphology Photo Library on CD-ROM*; Roger A. Fisken *House Physician's Survival Guide*.

Prizes £1000 (each category).

The RTZ David Watt Memorial Prize

RTZ Corporation UK, 6 St James's Square, London SW1Y 4LD
☎0171 930 2399   Fax 0171 930 3249

INITIATED in 1987 to commemorate the life and work of David Watt. Annual award, open to writers currently engaged in writing for newspapers and journals, in the English language, on international and political affairs. The winners are judged as having made 'outstanding contributions towards the greater understanding and promotion of national and international political issues'. Entries must have been published during the year preceding the award. Final entry date 31 March. The 1995 winner was Martin Wolf for his article 'If you go down to the woods today', published in the *Financial Times*. Previous winners include: David Rose for 'Silent Revolution', published in the *Observer*; Martin Woollacott of *The Guardian* for 'Grail or bitter cup?'; Dr Avi Shlaim for an article on Israel and the Gulf published in the *London Review of Books*.

Prize £5000.

Runciman Award

Anglo-Hellenic League, Flat 4, 68 Elm Park Gardens, London SW10 9PB
☎0171 352 2676   Fax 0171 351 5657
Contact *Mrs N. White-Gaze*

ESTABLISHED 1985. Annual award, founded by the Anglo-Hellenic League and funded by the Onassis Foundation, to promote Anglo-Greek understanding and friendship. Named after Sir Steven Runciman, former chairman of the Anglo-Hellenic League. Awarded to a work wholly or mainly about Greece or the Hellenic scene: fiction, poetry, translation, drama or non-fiction (guidebook), concerned (academically or non-academically) with history of any period, biography or autobiography, the arts, archaeology, the country, etc. Books must have been published in their first English edi-

tion in the UK during the previous calendar year. Final entry date in February; awards presented in May. Previous winners include: *The Empire of Manuel I Komnenos 1143-1180* Paul Magdalino; *Greece and the Inter-War Economic Crisis* Dr Mark Mazower; *Crete: the Battle and the Resistance* Antony Beevor; *A Concise History of Greece* Richard Clogg; *An Introduction to Modern Greek Literature* Roderick Beaton.

Award (total) £1800.

The SAGA Prize

Book Trust, Book House, 45 East Hill, London SW18 2QZ
☎0181 870 9055   Fax 0181 874 4790
Contact *Sandra Vince*

ESTABLISHED 1995. Annual award for the best unpublished novel by a black writer born in Great Britain or the Republic of Ireland and having a black African ancestor. Established by Marsha Hunt and sponsored by The SAGA Group. Mss must be unpublished and of no more than 80,000 words. Entry fee of £15 per mss. Final entry date is in July. 1995 winner: Diran Adebayo *Some Kind of Black*.

Prize £3000 plus publication by **Virago Press**.

Sagittarius Prize

Society of Authors, 84 Drayton Gardens, London SW10 9SB
☎0171 373 6642   Fax 0171 373 5768

ESTABLISHED 1990. For first published novel by an author over the age of 60. Final entry date mid December. 1996 winner: Samuel Lock *As Luck Would Have It*.

Prize £2000.

The Salaman Prize for Non-Fiction

42 Irwin Avenue, Heworth Green, York YO3 7TU
☎01904 422464
Contact *A. Mitchell*

ESTABLISHED 1994. Annual award for the best published work of non-fiction by writers living in, born in, or writing about the North of England. Named after Redcliffe Salaman, author of *The History & Social Influence of the Potato*, the prize is awarded in association with the York and District Writers Circle. £4 administration fee for each entry; further details and entry forms from the above address. Final entry date is in April. Previous winner: *Charlotte Brontë and Her 'Dearest Nell'* E. Whitehead.

Prize £150, trophy and certificate.

The Saltire Literary Awards

Saltire Society, 9 Fountain Close, 22 High
Street, Edinburgh EH1 1TF
☎0131 556 1836   Fax 0131 557 1675
Administrator *Kathleen Munro*

ESTABLISHED 1982. Annual awards, one for
Book of the Year, the other for Best First Book
by an author publishing for the first time.
Open to any author of Scottish descent or living in Scotland, or to anyone who has written
a book which deals with either the work and
life of a Scot or with a Scottish problem, event
or situation. Nominations are invited from editors of leading newspapers, magazines and periodicals. Previous winners: Scottish Book of the
Year: *The Black Sea* Neal Ascherson; *So I Am
Glad* A. L. Kennedy (joint winners); Best First
Book: *Free Love* Ali Smith.
   Cash prize.

Schlegel–Tieck Prize

The Translators Association, 84 Drayton
Gardens, London SW10 9SB
☎0171 373 6642   Fax 0171 373 5768
Contact *Kate Pool*

An annual award for the best translation of a
German 20th-century work of literary merit
and interest published by a British publisher
during the preceding year. Previous winners
include: Ronald Spiers for *The Political Writings
of Max Weber* and William Yuill for *The Making
of Europe: The Enlightenment* by Ulrich Im Hof.
   Prize £2200.

Scottish Arts Council Book Awards

Scottish Arts Council, 12 Manor Place,
Edinburgh EH3 7DD
☎0131 226 6051   Fax 0131 225 9833
Literature Officer *Shonagh Irvine*

A number of awards given biannually to authors
of published books in recognition of high standards in new writing from new and established
writers. Authors should be Scottish, resident in
Scotland or have published books of Scottish
interest. Applications from publishers only.
   Award £1000 each.

Scottish Book of the Year

See **The Saltire Literary Awards**

SCSE Book Prizes

Department of Education Studies, University
of Reading, Bulmershe Court, Reading,
Berkshire RG6 1HY
☎0118 9318861   Fax 0118 9352080
Contact *Professor P. Croll*

Annual awards given by the Standing Conference on Studies in Education for the best
book on education published during the preceding year and for the best book by a new
author. Nomination by members of the Standing
Conference and publishers.
   Prizes £1000 and £500.

The Seebohm Trophy – Age Concern Book of the Year

1268 London Road, London SW16 4ER
☎0181 679 8000
Contact *Michael Addison, Jane Marsh*

ESTABLISHED 1995. Annual award in memory
of the late Lord Seebohm, former President of
Age Concern England. Awarded to the author
and publisher of a non-fiction title published in
the previous calendar year which, in the opinion of the judges, is most successful in promoting the well-being and understanding of older
people. Final entry by the end of March for
presentation in October. 1995 winner: Ken
Blakemore and Margaret Boneham *Age, Race
and Ethnicity: A Comparative Approach.*
   Prize £1000 (author); Trophy (publisher),
for one year.

Bernard Shaw Translation Prize

The Translators Association, 84 Drayton
Gardens, London SW10 9SB
☎0171 373 6642
Contact *Kate Pool*

ESTABLISHED 1990. Triennial award funded by
the Anglo-Swedish Literary Foundation for the
best translation of a Swedish work published in
the UK in the three years preceding the closing
date. Final entry date 31 December 1996 for
1997 award. Winners include: David McDuff for
A Valley in the Midst of Violence by Gösta Ågren.
   Prize £1000.

Signal Poetry for Children Award

Thimble Press, Lockwood, Station Road,
South Woodchester, Stroud, Gloucestershire
GL5 5EQ
☎01453 873716/872208   Fax 01453 878599
Contact *Nancy Chambers*

This award is given annually for particular
excellence in one of the following areas: single-poet collections published for children; poetry
anthologies published for children; the body of
work of a contemporary poet; critical or educational activity promoting poetry for children.
All books for children published in Britain are
eligible regardless of the original country of
publication. Unpublished work is not eligible.

Previous winners include: Philip Gross *The All-Nite Café*; Helen Dunmore *Secrets*.

Award £100 plus certificate designed by Michael Harvey.

Silver PEN Non-Fiction Award

English Centre of International PEN, 7 Dilke Street, London SW3 4JE
☎0171 352 6303   Fax 0171 351 0220

ESTABLISHED 1986. An annual award, the winner being nominated by the PEN Executive Committee, for an outstanding work of non-fiction written in English and published in England in the year preceding the prize. Previous winners: Alan Bullock *Hitler and Stalin*; Brian Keenan *An Evil Cradling*; John Hale *The Civilization of Europe in the Renaissance*; Eric Hobsbawm *Age of Extremes*. 1996 winner: Neal Ascherson *Black Sea*.

Prize £1000, plus silver pen.

André Simon Memorial Fund Book Awards

5 Sion Hill Place, Bath, Avon BA1 5SJ
☎01225 336305   Fax 01225 421862
Contact *Tessa Hayward*

ESTABLISHED 1978. Three awards given annually for the best book on drink, best on food and special commendation in either. Previous winners: Rick Stein *Taste of the Sea* (food); Anthony Hanson *Burgundy* and Remington Norman *Rhone Renaissance* (drink book joint winners); Robert Neil *The French, the English and the Oyster* (special award).

Awards £2000 (best books); £1000 (special commendation); £200 to shortlisted books.

Smarties Book Prize

Book Trust, Book House, 45 East Hill, London SW18 2QZ
☎0181 870 9055   Fax 0181 874 4790
Contact *Sandra Vince*

ESTABLISHED 1985 to encourage high standards and stimulate interest in books for children, this prize is given for a children's book (fiction), written in English by a citizen of the UK or an author resident in the UK, and published in the UK in the year ending 31 October. There are three age-group categories: 0–5, 6–8 and 9–11. An overall winner from these categories is chosen for the Smarties Book Prize. Previous winners include: Jill Murphy *The Last Noo Noo* (0–5); Jill Paton Walsh (illus. Alan Marks) *Thomas and the Tinners* (6–8); Lesley Howarth *Weather Eye* (9–11 joint category winner);

Jacqueline Wilson *Double Act* (9–11 joint category and overall winner).

Prizes £8000 (overall winner); £2000 (other categories).

W. H. Smith Literary Award

W. H. Smith plc, Strand House, 7 Holbein Place, London SW1W 8NR
☎0171 824 5458   Fax 0171 824 5445
Contact *Lois Beeson*

FOUNDED 1959. Annual prize awarded to a UK, Republic of Ireland or Commonwealth citizen for the most oustanding contribution to English literature, published in English in the UK in the preceding year. Writers cannot submit work themselves. Previous winners include: Alice Munro *Open Secrets*; Vikram Seth *A Suitable Boy*; Michèle Robert *Daughters of the House*; Thomas Pakenham *The Scramble for Africa*; Derek Walcott *Omeros*; 1996 winner: Simon Schama *Landscape and Memory*. Four previous winners have gone on to win the Nobel Prize for Literature – Derek Walcott, Nadine Gordimer, Patrick White and Seamus Heaney.

Prize £10,000.

W. H. Smith's Mind Boggling Books Award

Scope Communications, Tower House, 8–14 Southampton Street, London WC2E 7HA
☎0171 379 3234   Fax 0171 240 7729
Contact *Serena De Morgan*

ESTABLISHED 1993. Annual award. The six shortlisted books are chosen by a panel of ten children aged between nine and twelve. Authors must be British and have had their book published in paperback during the previous year. Like Smith's Thumping Good Read Award for adult fiction, this award focuses on 'the type of book which will really appeal to the majority of our customers'. 1996 winner: Andrew Klavan *True Crime*.

Award £5000.

W. H. Smith's Thumping Good Read Award

Scope Communications, Tower House, 8–14 Southampton Street, London WC2E 7HA
☎0171 379 3234   Fax 0171 240 7729
Contact *Serena De Morgan*

ESTABLISHED 1992 to promote new writers of popular fiction. Books must have appeared on W. H. Smith's bestseller list for the first time and must have been published in the 12 months preceding the award. Submissions by publishers are judged by a panel of customers and the winner is the most un-put-downable from a shortlist of six. Final entry date February each year. 1996 winner: Andrew Klaven *The Crime*.

Award £5000.

W. H. Smith's Young Writers' Competition

W. H. Smith plc, Strand House, 7 Holbein Place, London SW1W 8NR
☎0171 824 5456   Fax 0171 824 5445

Contact *Lois Beeson*

Annual awards for poems or prose by anyone in the UK aged 16 or under. There are three age groups. Over 60 individual winners have their work included in a paperback every year.

Prize (total) over £7000.

Smith Corona Prize

3A High Street, Rickmansworth, Hertfordshire WD3 1HP
☎01923 777111   Fax 01923 896370

Contact *Debra Simpson*

Quarterly competition sponsored by Smith Corona (UK) Ltd (manufacturers of electronic typewriters, personal word processors and other office equipment) for a short story or piece of writing on a selected topic. Featured in *Writers Monthly* magazine.

Prize Personal word processor or electronic typewriter.

Sony Radio Awards

Zazer, 47-48 Chagford Street, London NW1 6EB
☎0171 723 0106

Contact *Francesca Watt, Suzy Langford*

ESTABLISHED 1981 by the **Society of Authors** and sponsored by Sony, these annual awards recognise excellence in radio broadcasting. Entries must have been broadcast in the UK between 1 January and 31 December in the year preceding the award. Categories are reviewed each year – in 1996 there was The Society of Authors' Award for Best Radio Writer.

Southern Arts Literature Prize

Southern Arts, 13 St Clement Street, Winchester, Hampshire SO23 9DQ
☎01962 855099   Fax 01962 861186

Contact *Literature Officer*

ESTABLISHED 1991, this prize is awarded annually to an author living in the **Southern Arts** region for the most promising work of prose or poetry published during the year. The 1996

prize will be awarded for fiction. Previous winner: Jon Stallworthy *Louis MacNeice* (biography). Final entry date 4 October.

Prize £1000, plus a craft commission to the value of £600.

Southport Writers' Circle Poetry Competition

53 Richmond Road, Birkdale, Southport, Merseyside PR8 4SB

Contact *Mrs Alison Chisholm*

For previously unpublished work which has not been entered in any other current competition. Entry fee £1.50 first poem, plus £1 for each subsequent entry. Maximum 40 lines on any subject and in any form. Closing date end April. Poems must be entered under a pseudonym, accompanied by a sealed envelope marked with the pseudonym and title of poem, containing s.a.e.. Entries must be typed on A4 paper and be accompanied by the appropriate fee payable to Southport Writers' Circle. No application form is required. Envelopes should be marked 'Poetry Competition'. Postal enquiries only. No calls.

Prizes (1st) £100; (2nd) £50; (3rd) £25.

Ian St James Awards

c/o The New Writers' Club, PO Box 101, Tunbridge Wells, Kent TN4 8YD
☎01892 511322   Fax 01892 514282

ESTABLISHED 1989. Administered by the New Writers' Club. Presented annually to approximately 20 writers of short stories. These awards are 'an opportunity for talented and as yet unpublished writers to achieve recognition'. Ian St James is a successful novelist who hopes to attract both literary and commercial fiction from aspiring writers. Winning entries are published in a paperback anthology. The Awards are open to international writers who have not had a novel or novella previously published. Final entry date 30 April each year. Previous top prize winners: Joshua Davidson *The Saviour*, Anna McGrail *The Welfare of the Patient*. Entry forms available from around October from above address.

Award Top prize: £2000 plus runners-up cash prizes. Shortlisted stories are published throughout the year in *Acclaim* magazine.

Stand Magazine Poetry Competition

Stand Magazine, 179 Wingrove Road, Newcastle upon Tyne NE4 9DA
☎0191 273 3280

Contact *The Administrator*

Biennial award for poems written in English and not yet published, broadcast or under consideration elsewhere. Next award 1997. Send s.a.e. for entry form.

Prize (total) £2500.

Stand Magazine Short Story Competition

Stand Magazine, 179 Wingrove Road, Newcastle upon Tyne NE4 9DA
☎0191 273 3280

Contact *The Administrator*

Biennial award for short stories written in English and not yet published, broadcast or under consideration elsewhere. Next award 1997. Send s.a.e. for entry form.

Prize (total) £2500.

Staple First Editions Project 1997–98

Tor Cottage, 81 Cavendish Road, Matlock, Derbyshire DE4 3HD
☎01629 582764

Contact *Donald Measham*

Biennial open competition for collections (poetry, prose) run by *Staple* magazine. Final entry date March 1998. Publication of winning monograph, July 1998; of shared collection, July 1999.

Prize share of £400, complimentary copies, publication and distribution.

Steinbeck Award

William Heinemann Ltd, Michelin House, 81 Fulham Road, London SW3 6RB
☎0171 581 9393   Fax 0171 225 9095

Contact *The Awards Secretary*

ESTABLISHED 1994. Annual award, sponsored by **William Heinemann** to support a young writer (under 40) for a new full-length work of fiction, first published in the UK, and written in the spirit of the works of John Steinbeck. Final closing date end of October 1996. Entries are submitted by publishers and not authors. Information sheet available. Previous winner: Pinckney Benedict *The Dogs of God*.

Prizes £10,000, of which £5000 is donated to a charity chosen by the winner.

Sunday Times Award for Small Publishers

Independent Publishers Guild, 25 Cambridge Road, Hampton, Middlesex TW12 2JL
☎0181 979 0250   Fax 0181 979 6393

Contact *Yvonne Messenger*

ESTABLISHED 1988, the first winner was **Fourth**

Estate. Open to any publisher producing between five and forty titles a year, which must primarily be original titles, not reprints. Entrants are invited to submit their catalogues for the last twelve months, together with two representative titles. Previous winners: **Polygon**; **Nick Hern Books**. 1995 winner: **Tarquin Publications**.

Sunday Times Special Award for Excellence in Writing

The Sunday Times, 1 Pennington Street, London E1 9XW
☎0171 782 5774   Fax 0171 782 5798

Contact *The Literary Editor*

ESTABLISHED 1987. Annual award to fiction and non-fiction writers. The panel consists of *Sunday Times* journalists, publishers and other figures from the book world. Previous winners: Anthony Burgess, Seamus Heaney, Stephen Hawking, Ruth Rendell, Muriel Spark, William Trevor and Martin Amis.

Award Silver trophy in the shape of a book, inscribed with the winner's name.

Sunday Times Young Writer of the Year Award

The Society of Authors, 84 Drayton Gardens, London SW10 9SB
☎0171 373 6642   Fax 0171 373 5768

Contact *Awards Secretary*

ESTABLISHED 1991. Annual award given on the strength of the promise shown by a full-length published work of fiction, non-fiction, poetry or drama. Entrants must be British citizens, resident in Britain and under the age of 35 at the closing date of 31 December. The work must be by one author, in the English language and published in Britain in the 12 months prior to the closing date. Full details available from the above address. Previous winners: Katherine Pierpont *Truffle Beds*; Andrew Cowan *Pig*; William Dalrymple *City of Djinns*; Simon Armitage *Xanadu and Kid*; Caryl Phillips *Cambridge*.

Prize £5000.

Reginald Taylor and Lord Fletcher Essay Prize

Journal of the British Archaeological Association, Institute of Archaelogy, 36 Beaumont Street, Oxford OX1 2PG

Contact *Dr Martin Henig*

A biennial prize, in memory of the late E. Reginald Taylor and of Lord Fletcher, for the best unpublished essay, not exceeding 7500 words, on a subject of archaeological, art history or antiquarian interest within the period from the Roman era to AD 1830. The essay should show *original* research on its chosen subject, and the author will be invited to read the essay before the Association. The essay may be published in the journal of the Association if approved by the Editorial Committee. Closing date for entries in 1998 will be announced in the next edition of *The Writer's Handbook*. All enquiries by post please. No phone calls. Send s.a.e. for details.

Prize £300.

The Teixeira Gomes Prize

The Translators Association, 84 Drayton Gardens, London SW10 9SB
☎0171 373 6642   Fax 0171 373 5768
Contact *Kate Pool*

ESTABLISHED 1989. Triennial award funded by the Calouste Gulbenkian Foundation and the Portuguese Book Institute for the best translation of a work by a Portuguese national published in the UK in the three years preceding the closing date, or unpublished. Previous winners: Giovanni Pontiero *The Gospel According to Jesus Christ* by Jose Saramago. Final entry date is 31 December 1997 for 1998 award.

Anne Tibble Poetry Competition

Events Team, Directorate of Environment Services, Northampton Borough Council, Cliftonville House, Bedford Road, Northampton NN4 7NR
☎01604 233500   Fax 01604 29571

Entries should preferably be typed, 20 lines maximum, any subject. Writers must be resident in the UK; categories for children under 11 and under 16.

Prize £200 (1st).

The Times Educational Supplement Books and Resources Awards

Times Educational Supplement, Admiral House, 66–68 East Smithfield, London E1 9XY
☎0171 782 3000   Fax 0171 782 3200
Contact *Literary Editor*

ESTABLISHED 1973. Annual awards for the best books used in schools, and for innovative mixed media resources (first awarded 1996). The books must have been published in Britain. Previous winners: Junior Information Book Award: *Think of an Eel* Karen Wallace, illus. Mike Bostock; Senior Information Book Award: *Getting Physical* Dr Aric Sigman; Primary Schoolbook Award: *Bathtime* Gill Tanner and Tim Wood; Secondary Schoolbook Award: *Discovering Medieval Realms* Colin Shephard and Alan Large.

The Tir Na N–Og Award

Welsh Books Council, Castell Brychan, Aberystwyth, Dyfed SY23 2JB
☎01970 624151   Fax 01970 625385

An annual award given to the best original book published for children in the year prior to the announcement. There are three categories: Best Welsh Fiction; Best Welsh Non-fiction; Best English Book with an authentic Welsh background.

Award £1000 (each category).

Marten Toonder Award

An Chomhairle Ealaíon (The Arts Council), 70 Merrion Square, Dublin 2, Republic of Ireland
☎00 353 1 6611840   Fax 00 353 1 6761302
Literature Officer *Laurence Cassidy*

A triennial award for creative writing. Awarded in 1995. Given to an established writer in recognition of achievement. Open to Irish citizens or residents only.

Award IR£3500.

John Tripp Award

The Welsh Academy, 3rd Floor, Mount Stuart House, Mount Stuart Square, Cardiff CF1 6DQ
☎01222 492025   Fax 01222 492930
Contact *Kevin Thomas*

ESTABLISHED 1990. Open to Welsh nationals or residents only. Usually launched in the spring with closing date in summer. Themes and rules vary from year to year. Send s.a.e. for details.

The Tullie House Prize

See **Lakeland Book of the Year Awards**

Dorothy Tutin Award

National Poetry Foundation, 27 Mill Road, Fareham, Hampshire PO16 0TH
Contact *Johnathon Clifford*

ESTABLISHED 1979. An occasional award to the person whom it is felt has done the most to encourage the writing of poetry throughout the UK. By recommendation only.

Award Engraved carriage clock.

UNESCO/PEN Short Story Competition

English Centre of International PEN, 7 Dilke Street, London SW3 4JE
☎0171 352 6303

ESTABLISHED 1993. Biennial award, funded by UNESCO and administered by the English Centre of PEN. It is intended to reward the efforts of those who write in English despite the fact that it is not their mother tongue (the Irish, Scots and Welsh are not eligible). Entries in the form of short stories not exceeding 1500 words should be submitted to the writer's home country PEN centre. The top three entries are then forwarded to the English PEN centre for final judging. Final entry date end December of year preceding award. First awarded March 1993. 1995 winner: Kiruvin Boon *The Dream*.

Prizes (1st) $3000; (2nd) $2000; (3rd) $500.

Unicorn Arts Theatre National Young Playwrights' Competition

Unicorn Theatre for Children, Arts Theatre, Great Newport Street, London WC2H 7JB
☎0171 379 3280   Fax 0171 836 5366

Contact *Kieron Smith*

Annual awards to young playwrights aged 6–16 for plays on a theme decided by the theatre. Three age groups: 6–8; 9–12; 13–16. The plays are judged by a committee of writers. Winners take part in workshops on the plays with members of the Unicorn Theatre for Children Club in preparation for rehearsed readings on stage the following spring. Final entry date end December.

T. E. Utley Memorial Award

111 Sugden Road, London SW11 5ED
☎0171 228 3900

Contact *The Secretary*

ESTABLISHED 1988 in memory of the political journalist T. E. Utley. In 1995, two awards were given for unpublished essays by aspiring journalists who were still at school or university.

Prizes £2500 (under 25); £1500 (under 18).

Vauxhall Trophy

Guild of Motoring Writers, 30 The Cravens, Smallfield, Surrey RH6 9QS
☎01342 843294   Fax 01342 844093

Contact *Sharon Scott-Fairweather*

Awarded annually to the Guild member judged to have written the best article(s) explaining any aspect of automotive design or technology.

Prize Trophy, plus £750.

Ver Poets Open Competition

Haycroft, 61–63 Chiswell Green Lane, St Albans, Hertfordshire AL2 3AL
☎01727 867005

Contact *May Badman*

Various competitions are organised by **Ver Poets**, the main one being the annual Open for unpublished poems of no more than 30 lines

written in English. Entry fee £2 per poem. Entries must be made under a pseudonym, with name and address on form or separate sheet. *Vision On,* the anthology of winning and selected poems, and the adjudicators' report are normally available from mid-June. Final entry date 30 April. Back numbers of the anthology are available for £2, post-free.

Prizes (1st) £500; (2nd) £300; two runners-up £100.

Vogue Talent Contest

Vogue, Vogue House, Hanover Square, London W1R 0AD
☎0171 499 9080   Fax 0171 408 0559

Contact *Frances Bentley*

ESTABLISHED 1951. Annual award for young writers and journalists (under 25 on 1 January in the year of the contest). Final entry date end of April. Entrants must write three pieces of journalism on given subjects.

Prizes £1000, plus a month's work experience with *Vogue*; (2nd) £500.

The Vondel Translation Prize

The Translators Association, 84 Drayton Gardens, London SW10 9SB
☎0171 373 6642   Fax 0171 373 5768

Contact *Kate Pool*

ESTABLISHED 1995. Award funded by the Foundation for the Production and Translation of Dutch Literature and the Ministry of the Flemish Community for the best translation of a Dutch or Flemish work published in the UK or the USA. Inaugural award 1996 for translations published in 1990–1995.

Prize £1000.

Wadsworth Prize for Business History

Business Archives Council, The Clove Building, 4 Maguire Street, London SE1 2NQ
☎0171 407 6110

Contact *Wadsworth Prize Coordinator*

Annual award for the best book published on British business history. Previous winners: Sir Peter Thompson *Sharing the Success: The Story of NFC* and T. R. Gourvish and R. Wilson *The British Brewing Industry: A History*.

Prize £200.

Arts Council of Wales Book of the Year Awards

Arts Council of Wales, Museum Place, Cardiff CF1 3NX
☎01222 394711   Fax 01222 221447

Contact *Tony Bianchi*

Annual non-competitive prizes awarded for works of exceptional literary merit written by Welsh authors (by birth or residence), published in Welsh or English during the previous calendar year. There is one major prize in English, the Book of the Year Award, and one major prize in Welsh, Gwobr Llyfr y Flwyddyn. Shortlists of three titles in each language are announced in April; winners announced in May.

Prizes £3000 (each); £1000 to each of four runners-up.

Walford Award
See **The Library Association Walford Award**

Wandsworth London Writers Competition
Room 224, Town Hall, Wandsworth High Street, London SW18 2PU
☎0181 871 7037   Fax 0181 871 7560
Contact *Arts Office*

An annual competition, open to all writers of 16 and over who live, work or study in the Greater London Area. There are two categories, all for previously unpublished work, in poetry and short story.

Prizes £1000 for each class, divided between the top three in each category; plus two runners-up in each class.

Wheatley Medal
See **The Library Association Wheatley Medal**

Whitbread Book of the Year and Literary Awards
Minster House, 272 Vauxhall Bridge Road, London SW1V 1BA
☎0171 834 5477   Fax 0171 834 8812
Contact *Gillian Cronin*

ESTABLISHED 1971. Publishers are invited to submit books for this annual competition designed for writers who have been resident in Great Britain or the Republic of Ireland for three years or more. The awards are made in two stages. First, nominations are selected in five categories: novel, first novel, biography, children's novel and poetry. One of these is then voted by the panel of judges as Whitbread Book of the Year. 1995 winners: Kate Atkinson *Behind the Scenes at the Museum* (first novel and Book of the Year); Salman Rushdie *The Moor's Last Sigh* (novel); Michael Morpurgo *The Wreck*

of the Zanzibar (Beefeater Children's Novel Award); Roy Jenkins *Gladstone* (biography); Bernard O'Donoghue *Gunpowder* (poetry).

Awards £21,000 (Book of the Year); £2000 (all nominees).

Whitfield Prize
Royal Historical Society, University College London, Gower Street, London WC1E 6BT
☎0171 387 7532   Fax 0171 387 7532
Contact *Literary Director*

ESTABLISHED 1977. An annual award for the best new work within a field of British history, published in the UK in the preceding calendar year. The book must be the author's first (solely written) history book and be an original and scholarly work of historical research. Final entry date end December.

Prize £1000.

John Whiting Award
Arts Council of England, 14 Great Peter Street, London SW1P 3NQ
☎0171 333 0100 ext 431   Fax 0171 973 6590
Contact *The Drama Director*

FOUNDED 1965. Annual award to commemorate the life and work of the playwright John Whiting (*The Devils, A Penny for a Song*). Any writer who has received during the previous two calendar years an award through the **Arts Council's Theatre Writing Schemes** or who has had a première production by a theatre company in receipt of annual subsidy is eligible to apply. Awarded to the writer whose play most nearly satisfies the following criteria: a play in which the writing is of special quality; a play of relevance and importance to contemporary life; a play of potential value to the British theatre. Previous joint winners: Kate Dean and Joe Penhall.

Prize £6000.

Alfred and Mary Wilkins Memorial Poetry Competition
Birmingham & Midland Institute, 9 Margaret Street, Birmingham B3 3BS
☎0121 236 3591
Administrator *Mr P. A. Fisher*

An annual competition for an unpublished poem not exceeding 40 lines, written in English by an author over the age of 15 and living, working or studying in the UK. The poem should not have been entered for any other poetry competition. Six prizes awarded in all.

Prize (total) £400.

Griffith John Williams Memorial Prize

3rd Floor, Mount Stuart House, Mount Stuart Square, Cardiff CF1 6DQ
☎01222 492064   Fax 01222 492930
Contact *Dafydd Rogers*

FOUNDED 1965. Biennial award in honour of the first president of the **Welsh Academy** which aims to promote writing in Welsh. Entries must be the first published work of authors or poets writing in Welsh and have been published in the two-year period preceding the award.
Award £400.

Raymond Williams Community Publishing Prize

Literature Dept, Arts Council of England, 14 Great Peter Street, London SW1P 3NQ
☎0171 973 6442   Fax 0171 973 6590
Contact *Susan White*

ESTABLISHED 1990. Award for published work which exemplifies the values of ordinary people and their lives – as often embodied in Raymond Williams' own work. Submissions may be in the form of poetry, fiction, biography, autobiography, drama or even local history, providing they are literary in quality and intent. They are likely to be produced by small community or cooperative presses, but other forms of publication will be considered. Final entry date end April. Winner announced in July. 1995 winner: *Luminous and Forlorn* published by **Honno**.
Prizes (1st) £3000; runner-up £2000. Prizes are divided between publisher and author.

H. H. Wingate Prize

See **Jewish Quarterly Literary Prize**

Wolfson History Awards

Wolfson Foundation, 18–22 Haymarket, London SW1Y 4DQ
☎0171 930 1057   Fax 0171 930 1036
Contact *The Director*

ESTABLISHED 1972. An award made annually to authors of published historical works, with the object of encouraging historians to communicate with general readers as well as with their professional colleagues. Previous winners include: Fiona MacCarthy *William Morris*; John G. C. Rohl *The Kaiser and His Court: Wilhelm II and the Government of Germany*; Lord Skidelsky *John Maynard Keynes: The Economist as Saviour 1920-1937*; Professor Linda Colley *Britons: Forging the Nation 1707-1837*.
Award (total) £20,000.

Woolwich Young Radio Playwrights' Competition

Independent Radio Drama Productions Ltd, PO Box 518, Manningtree, Essex CO11 1XD
Contact *Marja Giejgo*

ESTABLISHED 1990 and sponsored by the Woolwich Building Society, with writer and broadcaster Melvyn Bragg as patron. This is a national scheme which aims to discover and professionally produce radio drama writing talent among young people aged 25 and under. The competition involves national and regional script writing competitions with various workshop programmes at independent and BBC local radio stations. Send s.a.e. for further details. Writers selected for production receive a **Writers' Guild** approved contract.

The Writers Bureau Poetry and Short Story Competition

The Writers Bureau, Sevendale House, 7 Dale Street, Manchester M1 1JB
☎0161 228 2362
Competition Secretary *Angela Cox*

ESTABLISHED 1994. Annual award. Poems should be no longer than 40 lines and short stories no more than 2000 words. £3.50 entry fee. Previous winners: Jean Simister (Poetry); Adrienne Howell (Short Story).
Prizes in each category: £275 (1st); £175 (2nd); £100 (3rd).

The Writers' Guild Awards

430 Edgware Road, London W2 1EH
☎0171 723 8074   Fax 0171 706 2413

Originally ESTABLISHED 1961 and relaunched in 1991. Five categories of awards: radio (original drama, comedy/light entertainment, dramatisations, children's); theatre (West End, fringe, regional, children's); books (non-fiction, fiction, children's); film (best screenplay); television (original play/film, original drama series, original drama serial, dramatisation/ adaptation, situation comedy, light entertainment, children's). There are also awards for: Non-English Language, New Writer of the Year (won by Jez Butterworth in 1995) and Lifetime Achievement (won by Jimmy Perry in 1995). The various short-lists are prepared by a different jury in each category and presented to the full Guild membership for its final vote.

Xenos Short Story Competition

See **Xenos** under **Magazines**

Yorkshire Open Poetry Competition

See **Ilkley Literature Festival Poetry Competition**

Yorkshire Post Art and Music Awards

Yorkshire Post, PO Box 168, Wellington Street, Leeds, West Yorkshire LS1 1RF
☎0113 2432701

Contact *Margaret Brown*

Two annual awards made to the authors whose work has contributed most to the understanding and appreciation of art and music. Books should have been published in the preceding year in the UK. Previous winners: Charles Hemming *British Landscape Painters: A History and Gazetteer;* David Cairns *Berlioz: The Making of An Artist.*
Award £1000 each.

Yorkshire Post Best First Work Awards

Yorkshire Post, PO Box 168, Wellington Street, Leeds, West Yorkshire LS1 1RF
☎0113 2432701

Contact *Margaret Brown*

An annual award for a work by a new author published during the preceding year. Previous winners include: Harriet O'Brien *Forgotten Land.*
Prize £1000.

Yorkshire Post Book of the Year Award

Yorkshire Post, PO Box 168, Wellington Street, Leeds, West Yorkshire LS1 1RF
☎0113 2432701

Contact *Margaret Brown*

An annual award for the book (either fiction or non-fiction) which, in the opinion of the judges, is the best work published in the preceding year. Previous winner: Nicholas Timmins *The Five Giants: A Biography of the Welfare State.*
Prize £1200.

Yorkshire Post Yorkshire Author of the Year Award

Yorkshire Post, PO Box 168, Wellington Street, Leeds, West Yorkshire LS1 1RF
☎0113 2432701

Contact *Margaret Brown*

Award sponsored by Marriott Hotel, Leeds. Author must have been born in Yorkshire. Fiction and non-fiction accepted. Previous winner: Leslie Glaister *Limestone and Clay.*
Prize £1000.

Young Science Writer Awards

See **The Daily Telegraph National Power Young Science Writer Awards**

Where we are with PLR

Those of us who find true happiness surrounded by shelves of books are bound to feel a pang of regret as libraries head for the electronic ages. But we might as well get used to it. Before long we will have the biggest and best library ever conceived by man right there in our own front rooms, available at the press of a button.

At which point writers might well begin to wonder how that estimable institution, the Public Lending Right (PLR) will rise to the challenge. The powers are giving it their serious consideration, you will be pleased to hear. The question was raised at last year's international conference of PLR experts. Predictably, no conclusions were reached, but the ACLS is moving ahead with ideas for protecting authors' rights against the new technology (see When in Rom, p. 101). One possibility is the introduction of the right to 'dip into' online material on condition that it is recorded for PLR. This has the benefit of rewarding compilers of reference books (like the editor of *The Writer's Handbook*) who at present are excluded from the scheme because their books are rarely taken out on loan.

Meanwhile, words between covers still have an appeal. Libraries process some 550 million books a year at a cost of around £740 million or 12 pence a head for every man, woman and child in the United Kingdom. Not all that much comes back to authors since royalty payments on books purchased represent an infinitesimal proportion of the libraries' total expenditure. But we can rely on PLR to top up the kitty - not by much, it is true but every little is welcome. The first payments under PLR were made in 1984 when £1.5 million was divided between 6000 authors. The latest funding (for 1996-97) is just over £5 million but now 25,000 authors are registered which allows for a rate per loan of just 2 pence. Around three quarters of registered authors qualify for payment. Most are down at the lower levels with 14,000 getting under £100. The maximum handout - £6000 - goes to just over a hundred top authors. One apparent silliness is that 2000 authors receive minimum payments of between £1 and £5. There has been a suggestion from the PLR administration that the downward limit should not fall below £5. This would release some £8000 for distribution among the survivors but, as the writers' organisations point out, it does seem a bit rough that the lowest earners should be sacrificed to the better off. The £1 minimum is also a powerful propaganda weapon, not to be carelessly discarded. It shows how miserably the scheme is funded. No wonder the Heritage Secretary would like to get rid of it.

To qualify, an author must be resident in the United Kingdom or Germany (the latter as part of a reciprocal deal). For a book to be eligible it must be printed, bound and put on sale. It must not be mistaken for a newspaper or periodical, or be a musical score. Crown copyright, where it relates to authors in government service, is excluded, also books where authorship is attributed to a company or association. But – and this is where mistakes often occur – the author does not have to own copyright to be eligible for PLR. Anyone who has disclaimed copyright as part of a flat fee commission, for instance, will still have a claim if his name is on the title page.

Under PLR, the sole writer of a book may not be its sole author. Others named on the title page, such as illustrators, translators, compilers, editors and revisers, may have a claim to authorship. Where there are joint authors – two writers, say, or a writer and illustrator – they can strike their own bargain on how their entitlement is to be split. But translators may apply, without reference to other authors, for a 30 per cent fixed share (to be divided equally between joint translators). Similarly, an editor or compiler may register a 20 per cent share provided he has written 10 per cent of the book or at least ten pages of text. Joint editors or compilers must divide the 20 per cent share equally.

Authors and books can be registered for PLR only when application is made during the author's lifetime. However, once an author is registered, the PLR on his books continues for the period of copyright. If he wishes, an author can assign PLR to other people and bequeath it by will. If a co-author is dead or untraceable, the remaining co-author can still register for a share of PLR so long as he provides supporting evidence as to why he alone is making application.

Where an author's name is not given on the title page, or where a book lacks a conventional title page it is now possible for a writer to register if he is named elsewhere in the book and where he can show that his contribution would normally merit a title page credit. Alternatively, proof of a royalty payment is acceptable. Where there are several writers, one of whom cannot prove eligibility, the co-authors can provide a signed statement testifying to their colleague's right to a share of the PLR payment. There is now no maximum limit on the number of authors who can apply for part-shares. But authors cannot register books that do not have an ISBN. Tracing them is too expensive.

A note on German PLR: some authors are wondering why their payments are so small. The answer is that under the German system after the 10 per cent deduction for administrative costs, a further 10 per cent is paid into a 'social fund', which is set aside for making *ex gratia* payments to authors who are in need, and yet another 45 per cent is paid into a 'social security' fund. Foreign authors, however, are not entitled to benefit from either fund. After the 65 per cent deductions, the remaining amount is divided between the authors (who take 70 per cent) and the publishers (who take 30 per cent). Furthermore, under German law, the translator is entitled to 50 per cent of the author's share, and if there are editors involved, they are also entitled to a percentage of the fee.

There are various ideas for extending PLR. Reference book authors may not have to wait for an internet deal to see some money back. An earlier possibility is for payments to be based on the number of copies held in the sample libraries. The 'value' of each copy would then be equated with the average number of loans of books in the lending stock. There are also good legal, moral and tactical arguments for extending PLR to all authors living in the European Union. This might persuade other European countries to follow Germany's example with reciprocal payments to UK authors.

Next in line for a claim on PLR are the authors and presenters of talking books. The Spoken Word Publishers Association reckons that last year some 4.5 million audio books were borrowed from public libraries. The only reason why the spoken word is currently excluded from PLR is that the producers of talking books are also the exclusive copyright holders. But a directive from the European Community suggests that copyright in audio and visual productions can be reclaimed by those responsible for creative input. Expect a settlement for the spoken word before long. Doubtless, this will start a debate on PLR for computer books. The queue of potential supplicants is never-ending.

Trouble is, unless funding is increased, which seems unlikely in the short run, more claimants means less money per author. One possible corrective is to raise the minimum payment level from £1 to £10 or possibly £20. But redistribution which favours the better off is not likely to go down well with the writers' associations. For now, they will not go above £5 as a minimum payment. Another possible saving is to cut the retention time for unclaimed PLR payments from six to two years. But we are talking peanuts here.

Maybe the solution rests with the libraries themselves. Once they have got their own economic house in order by winning concessions from publishers, say, or saving on administration, there might be a little left over from their £740 million budget to support hard-pressed writers.

PLR application forms and details can be obtained from: The Registrar, PLR Office, Bayheath House, Prince Regent Street, Stockton on Tees, Cleveland TS18 1DF (Tel: 01642 604699)

Libraries

Aberdeen City Council Arts & Recreation Division, Libraries Department

Central Library, Rosemount Viaduct, Aberdeen AB9 1GU
☎01224 634622   Fax 01224 641985

Open 9.00 am to 8.00 pm Monday to Friday (Reference & Local Studies 9.00 am to 9.00 pm); 9.00 am to 5.00 pm Saturday. Branch library opening times vary.

Open Access
General reference and loans. Books, pamphlets, periodicals and newspapers; videos, CDs, records and cassettes; arts equipment lending service; recording studio; DTP and WP for public access; photographs of the Aberdeen area; census records, maps; on-line database, patents and standards. The library is supported by a mobile library and offers special services to housebound readers. In the belief that extension activities now form a prominent part of the library's role in modern-day society, a publishing and recording dimension is also available, thereby heightening the profile of arts in the community.

Armitt Library

Ambleside, Cumbria LA22 9BL
☎015394 33949

Open 10.00 am to 12.30 pm & 1.30 pm to 4.00 pm Monday, Tuesday, Wednesday, Friday.

Access By arrangement (phone or write)
A small but unique reference library of rare books, manuscripts, pictures, antiquarian prints and museum items, mainly about the Lake District. It includes early guidebooks and topographical works, books and papers relating to Wordsworth, Ruskin, H. Martineau and others; fine art including work by W. Green, J. B. Pyne, John Harden, K. Schwitters, and Victorian photographs by Herbert Bell; also a major collection of Beatrix Potter's scientific watercolour drawings and microscope studies.

Art & Design Department, Westminster Reference Library

2nd Floor, Westminster Reference Library, St Martin's Street, London WC2H 7HP
☎0171 798 2038   Fax 0171 798 2040

Open 10.00 am to 7.00 pm Monday to Friday; 10.00 am to 5.00 pm Saturday

Access For reference only (stacks are closed to the public)
Located on the second floor of the City of Westminster's main reference library. An excellent reference source for fine and applied arts, including antiques, architecture, ceramics, coins, costume, crafts, design, furniture, garden history, interior decoration, painting, sculpture, textiles. Complete runs of major English Language periodicals such as *Studio*; exhibition catalogues; guidebooks to historic houses, castles, gardens and churches. Some older books and most periodicals earlier than 1980 are in storage and at least one day's notice is required before they can be obtained.

The Athenaeum, Liverpool

Church Alley, Liverpool L1 3DD
☎0151 709 7770   Fax 0151 709 0418

Open 9.00 am to 5.00 pm Monday to Friday

Access To club members; researchers by application only
General collection, with books dating from the 15th century, now concentrated mainly on local history with a long run of Liverpool directories and guides. *Special collections* Liverpool playbills; William Roscoe; Blanco White; Robert Gladstone; 18th-century plays; 19th-century economic pamphlets; the Norris books; Bibles; Yorkshire and other genealogy. Some original drawings, portraits, topographical material and local maps.

Avon Library & Information Service

P.O Box 1037, Avon House North, St James, Barton, Bristol, Avon BS99 1VR
☎0117 9875160   Fax 0117 9875168

There is a total of 59 libraries under the aegis of the Avon Library & Information Service. Lending, reference, art, music, commerce and local studies are particularly strong.

Bristol Central Library College Green, Bristol, Avon BS1 5TL
☎0117 9276121 Fax 0117 9226775

Open 10.00 am to 7.30 pm Monday to Thursday; 9.30 am to 7.30 pm Friday; 9.30 am to 5.00 pm Saturday

Open Access

Bank of England Library and Information Services

Threadneedle Street, London EC2R 8AH

☎0171 601 4715   Fax 0171 601 4356

Open 9.30 am to 5.30 pm Monday to Friday

Access For research workers by prior arrangement only, when material is not readily available elsewhere

50,000 volumes of books and periodicals. 3000 periodicals taken. UK and overseas coverage of banking, finance and economics. *Special collections* Central bank reports; UK 17th–19th–century economic tracts; Government reports in the field of banking.

Barbican Library

Barbican Centre, London EC2Y 8DS

☎0171 638 0569

Open 9.30 am to 5.30 pm Monday, Wednesday, Thursday, Friday; 9.30 am to 7.30 pm Tuesday; 9.30 am to 12.30 pm Saturday

Open Access

Situated on Level 7 of the Barbican Centre, this is the Corporation of London's largest lending library. Limited study facilities are available. In addition to a large general lending library, the library seeks to reflect the Centre's emphasis on the arts and includes strong collections, including videos, on painting, sculpture, theatre, cinema and ballet, as well as a large music library with books, scores, cassettes and CDs (sound recording loans available at a small charge). Also houses the City's main children's library and has special collections on finance, natural resources, conservation, socialism and the history of London. Service available for housebound readers.

Barnsley Public Library

Central Library, Shambles Street, Barnsley, South Yorkshire S70 2JF

☎01226 773930   Fax 01226 773955

Open 9.30 am to 8.00 pm Monday and Wednesday; 9.30 am to 6.00 pm Tuesday, Thursday, Friday; 9.30 am to 5.00 pm Saturday; Archive Collection: 9.30 am to 1.00 pm and 2.00 pm to 6.00 pm (closed all day Thursday and Saturday afternoon)

Open Access

General library, lending and reference. Archive collection of family history and local firms; local studies: coalmining, local authors, Yorkshire and Barnsley; European Business Information Unit; music library (books, CDs, records, tapes); large junior library. (Specialist departments are closed on certain weekday evenings and Saturday afternoons.)

BBC Written Archives Centre

Peppard Road, Caversham Park, Reading, Berkshire RG4 8TZ

☎0118 9472742 ext. 280/1/2/3

Fax 0118 9461145

Contact *Jacqueline Kavanagh*

Open 9.45 am to 5.15 pm Wednesday to Friday

Access For reference, by appointment only

Holds the written records of the BBC, including internal papers from 1922–69 and published material to date. Charges for certain services.

Bedford Central Library

Harpur Street, Bedford MK40 1PG

☎01234 350931   Fax 01234 342163

Open 9.30 am to 7.00 pm Monday to Friday; 9.30 am to 4.00 pm Saturday

Open Access

Reference and lending library with a wide range of stock, including books, music (CD-ROMs and cassettes), audio books and videos, information services, children's library, local history library, Internet facilities, gallery and coffee bar.

Belfast Public Libraries: Central Library

Royal Avenue, Belfast BT1 1EA

☎01232 243233   Fax 01232 332819

Open 9.30 am to 8.00 pm Monday and Thursday; 9.30 am to 5.30 pm Tuesday, Wednesday, Friday; 9.30 am to 1.00 pm Saturday

Open Access To lending libraries; reference libraries by application only

Over 2 million volumes for lending and reference. *Special collections* United Nations/Unesco depository; complete British Patent Collection; Northern Ireland Newspaper Library; British and Irish government publications. The Central Library offers the following reference departments: Humanities and General Reference; Irish and Local Studies; Business and Law; Science and Technology; Fine Arts, Language and Literature; Music and Recorded Sound. The lending library, supported by twenty branch libraries and two mobile libraries, offers special services to hospitals, prisons and housebound readers.

BFI Library and Information Services

21 Stephen Street, London W1P 2LN
☎0171 255 1444   Fax 0171 436 7950

Open 10.30 am to 5.30 pm Monday and Friday; 10.30 am to 8.00 pm Tuesday and Thursday; 1.00 pm to 8.00 pm Wednesday; Telephone Enquiry Service operates from 10.00 am to 5.00 pm

Access For reference only; annual and limited day membership available

The world's largest collection of information on film and television including periodicals, cuttings, scripts, related documentation, personal papers. Information available through SIFT (Summary of Information on Film and Television).

Birmingham and Midland Institute

Margaret Street, Birmingham B3 3BS
☎0121 236 3591   Fax 0121 233 4946

Administrator *Philip Fisher*

Access For research, to students (loans restricted to members)

ESTABLISHED 1855. Later merged with the Birmingham Library (now renamed the Priestley Library), which was founded in 1779. The Priestley Library specialises in the humanities, with approx. 100,000 volumes in stock. Headquarters and founder member of the **Association of Independent Libraries** and headquarters of the **Alliance of Literary Societies**. Meeting-place of many affiliated societies including many devoted to poetry and literature.

Birmingham Library Services

Central Library, Chamberlain Square, Birmingham B3 3HQ
☎0121 235 2615   Fax 0121 233 4458

Open 9.00 am to 8.00 pm Monday to Friday; 9.00 am to 5.00 pm Saturday

Over a million volumes. *Special collections* include the Shakespeare Library; War Poetry Collection; Parker Collection of Children's Books and Games; Johnson Collection; Milton Collection; Cervantes Collections; Early and Fine Printing Collection (including the William Ridler Collection of Fine Printing); Joseph Priestley Collection; Loudon Collection; Railway Collection; Wingate Bett Transport Ticket Collection; Labour, Trade Union and Co-operative Collections. Photographic Archives: Sir John Benjamin Stone; Francis Bedford; Francis Frith; Warwickshire Photographic Survey; Boulton and Watt Archive; Charles

Parker Archive; Birmingham Repertory Theatre Archive and Sir Barry Jackson Library; Local Studies (Birmingham); Patents Collection; Song Sheets Collection; Oberammergau Festival Collection.

Bradford Central Library

Princes Way, Bradford, West Yorkshire BD1 1NN
☎01274 753600   Fax 01274 395108

Open 9.00 am to 7.30 pm Monday to Friday; 9.00 am to 5.00 pm Saturday

Open Access

Wide range of books and media loan services. Comprehensive reference and information services, including major local history collections and specialised business information service. Bradford Libraries runs its own publishing programme, and has a number of creative writing projects – *In Your Own Write* (for local writers), *The Writeplace* (DTP facility for writers), *Poet of the Month*, and an annual programme of performance events.

Brighton Central Library

Church Street, Brighton, East Sussex BN1 1UE
☎01273 691195   Fax 01273 695882

Open 10.00 am to 7.00 pm Monday to Friday (closed Wednesday); 10.00 am to 4.00 pm Saturday

Reference Library ☎01273 601197
Fax 01273 625234

Access Limited stock on open access; all material for reference use only

FOUNDED 1869, the library has a large stock covering most subjects. Specialisations include art and antiques, history of Brighton and Sussex, family history, local illustrations, HMSO, business and large bequests of antiquarian books and ecclesiastical history.

Bristol Central Library

See **Avon Library & Information Service**

British Architectural Library

Royal Institute of British Architects, 66 Portland Place, London W1N 4AD
☎0171 580 5533   Fax 0171 631 1802
Members' Information Line: 0891 234 444;
Public Information Line: 0891 234 400

Open 1.30 pm to 5.00 pm Monday; 10.00 am to 8.00 pm Tuesday; 10.00 am to 5.00 pm Wednesday, Thursday, Friday; 10.00 am to 1.30 pm Saturday

Access Free to RIBA members; non-members

must buy a day ticket (£10/£5 concessions but on Tuesday between 5–8.00 pm and Saturday £5/£2.50); annual membership (£96/£48 concessions); loans available to RIBA and library members only

Collection of books, drawings, manuscripts, photographs and periodicals, 400 of which are indexed. All aspects of architecture, current and historical. Material both technical and aesthetic, covering related fields including: interior design, landscape architecture, topography, the construction industry and applied arts. Brochure available; queries by telephone, letter or in person. Charge for research £40 per hour (min. charge £10).

The British Library Business Information Service (BIS)

25 Southampton Buildings, London WC2A 1AW
☎0171 412 7454/7977 (Free)/0171 412 7457 Priced Enquiry Service)   Fax 0171 412 745

Open 9.30 am to 9.00 pm Monday to Friday; 10.00 am to 1.00 pm Saturday; Free Enquiry Service 9.30 am to 5.00 pm Monday to Friday; Priced Enquiry Service 9.30 am to 5.00 pm Monday to Friday

Open Access

BIS holds the most comprehensive collection of business information literature in the UK. This includes market research reports and journals, directories, company annual reports, trade and business journals, house journals, trade literature and CD-ROM services.

British Library Department of Manuscripts

Great Russell Street, London WC1B 3DG
☎0171 412 7513   Fax 0171 412 7745

Open 10.00 am to 4.45 pm Monday to Saturday; enquiries and applications up to 4.30 pm (closed one week in November)

Access Reading facilities only, by British Library reader's pass and supplementary mss pass, for which a written letter of recommendation is required

Two useful publications, *Index of Manuscripts in the British Library*, Cambridge 1984–6, 10 vols, and *The British Library: Guide to the Catalogues and Indexes of the Department of Manuscripts* by M. A. E. Nickson, help to guide the researcher through this vast collection of manuscripts dating from Ancient Greece to the present day. Approximately 300,000 mss, charters, papyri and seals are housed here.

British Library Information Sciences Service

7 Ridgmount Street, London WC1E 7AE
☎0171 412 7688   Fax 0171 412 7691

Open 9.00 am to 6.00 pm Monday and Wednesday; 9.00 am to 8.00 pm Tuesday and Thursday; 9.00 am to 5.00 pm Friday. July–September: 9.00 am to 6.00 pm Monday to Thursday; 9.00 am to 5.00 pm Friday

Access For reference only (loans restricted to members of the Library Association, Book Trust, Society of Indexers, or by British Library form)

Provides British and foreign material on librarianship, information science and related subjects. *Special collections* theses on librarianship.

British Library Map Library

Great Russell Street, London WC1B 3DG
☎0171 412 7700   Fax 0171 412 7780

Open 10.00 am to 4.30 pm Monday to Saturday

Access By British Library reader's pass or Map Library day pass

A collection of two million maps, charts and globes with particular reference to the history of British cartography. Maps for all parts of the world in wide range of scales and dates, including the most comprehensive collection of Ordnance Survey maps and plans. *Special collections* King George III Topographical Collection and Maritime Collection, and the Crace Collection of maps and plans of London.

British Library Music Library

Great Russell Street, London WC1B 3DG
☎0171 412 7752   Fax 0171 412 7751

Open 9.30 am to 4.45 pm Monday to Friday; on Saturday material is made available 10.00 am to 4.45 pm in the Manuscripts students' room

Access By British Library reader's pass

Special collections The Royal Music Library (containing almost all Handel's surviving autograph scores) and the Paul Hirsch Music Library. Also a large collection (about one and a quarter million items) of printed music, both British and foreign.

British Library National Sound Archive

29 Exhibition Road, London SW7 2AS
☎0171 412 7440   Fax 0171 412 7416

Open 10.00 am to 5.00 pm Monday to Friday (Thursday till 9.00 pm)

Listening service (by appointment) 10.00 am to 5.00 pm Monday to Friday (Thursday till 9.00 pm)

Northern Listening Service
British Library Document Supply Centre, Boston Spa, West Yorkshire: 9.15 am to 4.30 pm Monday to Friday

Open Access
An archive of over 900,000 discs and more than 125,000 tape recordings, including all types of music, oral history, drama, wildlife, selected BBC broadcasts and BBC Sound Archive material. Produces a thrice-yearly newsletter, *Playback*.

British Library Newspaper Library
Colindale Avenue, London NW9 5HE
☎0171 412 7353   Fax 0171 412 7379

Open 10.00 am to 4.45 pm Monday to Saturday (last newspaper issue 4.15 pm)

Access By British Library reader's pass or Newspaper Library day pass (available from and valid only for Colindale Avenue)
English provincial, Scottish, Welsh, Irish, Commonwealth and foreign newspapers from *c*.1700 are housed here. London newspapers from 1801 and many weekly periodicals are also in stock as well as selected newspapers from overseas. (London newspapers pre-dating 1801 are housed in Great Russell Street.) Readers are advised to check availability of material in advance.

British Library Oriental and India Office Collections
Orbit House, 197 Blackfriars Road, London SE1 8NG
☎0171 412 7873   Fax 0171 412 7641

Open 9.30 am to 5.45 pm Monday to Friday; 9.30 am to 12.45 pm Saturday

Open Access By British Library reader's pass or day pass (identification required)
A comprehensive collection of printed volumes and manuscripts in the languages of North Africa, the Near and Middle East and all of Asia, plus official records of the East India Company and British government in India until 1947. Also prints, drawings and paintings by British artists of India.

British Library Reading Room
Great Russell Street, London WC1B 3DG
☎0171 412 7676 (Reading Room/ Bibliographical holdings enquiries)
Fax 0171 412 755

☎0171 412 7677 (Admissions)

Open 9.00 am to 5.00 pm Monday, Friday, Saturday; 9.00 am to 9.00 pm Tuesday, Wednesday, Thursday (closed week following the last complete week in October). The Admissions Office is open 9.00 am to 4.30 pm Monday, Friday, Saturday; 10.00 am to 6.00 pm Tuesday, Wednesday, Thursday.

Access By British Library reader's pass
Large and comprehensive stock of books and periodicals relating to the humanities and social sciences for reference and research which cannot easily be done elsewhere. Leaflet *Applying for a Reader's Pass* available for guidance. Also exhibitions on literary and historical figures and a permanent exhibition on the history of printing and binding. Telephone enquiries welcome.

British Library Science Reference and Information Service
25 Southampton Buildings, London WC2A 1AW
☎0171 412 7494/7496 (General Enquiries)
Fax 0171 412 7495
Also at: 9 Kean Street, London WC2B 4AT (Life sciences enquiries)
☎0171 412 7288   Fax 0171 412 7217
And: Chancery House Reading Room, Chancery Lane, London WC2A 1AW
☎0171 412 7901   Fax 0171 412 7912

Open Southampton Buildings: 9.30 am to 9.00 pm Monday to Friday; 10.00 am to 1.00 pm Saturday. Kean Street and Chancery House Reading Room: 9.30 am to 5.30 pm Monday to Friday.
General enquiries tel as above; British and EPO Patent enquiries: 0171 412 7919; Foreign Patent enquiries: 0171 412 7902; Business enquiries: 0171 412 7454/7977.

Open Access
The national library for modern science, technology, medicine, business, patents, trade marks and designs, it is the most comprehensive reference collection in Western Europe of such literature from the whole world. The primary purpose is to make this information readily accessible, so no prior arrangement or reader's ticket is necessary. The library has enquiry and referral services and priced services (especially in business information, the environment, and industrial property); online database search; photocopying service; runs courses and seminars; and publishes a wide range of publications from newsletters to definitive bibliographies.

PRICED RESEARCH SERVICE CONTACT DETAILS:
Business Information Service:
☎0171 412 7457   Fax 0171 412 7453

Environmental Information Service:
☎0171 412 7955   Fax 0171 412 7954

STM search (science, technology and medicine):
☎0171 412 7477   Fax 0171 412 7954

British Library Social Policy Information Service

Great Russell Street, London WC1B 3DG
☎0171 412 7536   Fax 0171 412 7761

Open 9.30 am to 4.45 pm (last admissions 4.30pm) Monday to Friday

Access By British Library reader's pass

Provides an information service on social policy, public administration, and current and international affairs, and access to current and historical official publications from all countries, plus publications of intergovernmental bodies, including House of Commons sessional papers from 1715, UK legislation, current and back numbers of UK electoral registers, and up-to-date reference books on official publications and on the social sciences.

British Psychological Society Library

c/o Psychology Library, University of London, Senate House, Malet Street, London WC1E 7HU
☎0171 636 8000 ext. 5060
Fax 0171 436 1494

Open Term-time: 9.30 am to 9.00 pm Monday to Thursday; 9.30 am to 6.30 pm Friday; 9.30 am to 5.30 pm Saturday (holidays: 9.30 am to 5.30 pm Monday to Saturday)

Access Members only; Non-members £6 day ticket

Reference library, containing the British Psychological Society collection of periodicals - over 140 current titles housed alongside the University of London's collection of books and journals. Largely for academic research. General queries referred to **Swiss Cottage Library** which has a very good psychology collection.

Bromley Central Library

London Borough of Bromley - Leisure & Community Services, High Street, Bromley, Kent BR1 1EX
☎0181 460 9955   Fax 0181 313 9975

Open 9.30 am to 6.00 pm Monday, Wednesday, Friday; 9.30 am to 8.00 pm

Tuesday, Thursday; 9.30 am to 5.00 pm Saturday

Open Access

A large selection of fiction and non-fiction books for loan, both adult and children's. Also videos, CDs, cassettes, language courses, open learning packs for hire. Other facilities include a business information service, CD-ROM, Ramesis, local studies library, 'Upfront' teenage section, large reference library with photocopying, fax, microfiche and film facilities and specialist 'Healthpoint' and 'Careerpoint' sections. Specialist collections include: H. G. Wells, Walter de la Mare, Crystal Palace, The Harlow Bequest, and the history and geography of Asia, America, Australasia and the Polar regions.

CAA Library and Information Centre

Aviation House, Gatwick Airport, West Sussex RH6 0YR
☎01293 573725   Fax 01293 573999

Open 9.30 pm to 4.30 pm Monday to Friday

Open Access

Books, periodicals and reports on air transport, air traffic control, electronics, radar and computing.

Cambridge Central Library (Reference Library & Information Service)

7 Lion Yard, Cambridge CB2 3QD
☎01223 365252   Fax 01223 362786

Open 10.00 am to 7.00 pm Monday & Thursday; 10.00 am to 5.30 pm Tuesday & Friday; 1.00 pm to 7.00 pm Wednesday; 9.30 am to 5.30 pm Saturday

Access Open

Large stock of books, periodicals, newspapers, maps, plus comprehensive collection of directories and annuals covering UK, Europe and the world. Microfilm and fiche reading and printing services. On-line access to news and business databases. News databases on CD-ROM; Internet access. Monochrome and colour photocopiers.

Camomile Street Library

12-20 Camomile Street, London EC3A 7EX
☎0171 247 8895   Fax 0171 377 2972

Open 9.30 am to 5.30 pm Monday to Friday

Open Access

The new City of London lending library, replacing the Bishopsgate Library. Wide range of fiction and non-fiction books and language courses on cassette, foreign fiction, paperbacks, maps and guides for travel at home and abroad, children's books, a selection of large print, and collections of music CDs and of videos.

Cardiff Central Library

Frederick Street, St David's Link, Cardiff, Glamorgan CF1 4DT
☎01222 382116   Fax 01222 238642

Open 9.00 am to 6.00 pm Monday, Tuesday, Friday; 9.00 am to 8.00 pm Wednesday and Thursday; 9.00 am to 5.30 pm Saturday

General lending library with the following departments: leisure, music, children's, local studies, information, science and humanities.

Carmarthen Public Library

St Peter's Street, Carmarthen, Dyfed SA31 1LN
☎01267 233333 ext. 4833 Fax 01267 221839

Open 10.00 am to 7.00 pm Monday to Friday; 10.00 am to 1.00 pm Saturday.

Open Access
Comprehensive range of fiction, non-fiction, children's books and reference works in English and in Welsh. Large local history library - newspapers/census returns on microfilm. Large Print books, books on tape, CDs, cassettes, and videos available for loan.

Catholic Central Library

47 Francis Street, London SW1P 1QR
☎0171 834 6128

Open 10.00 am to 5.00 pm Monday to Friday; 10.00 am to 1.30 pm Saturday

Open Access For reference (non-members must sign in; loans restricted to members)
Contains books, many not readily available elsewhere, on theology, religions worldwide, scripture and the history of churches of all denominations.

Central Music Library (Westminster)

Victoria Library, 160 Buckingham Palace Road, London SW1W 9UD
☎0171 798 2192   Fax 0171 798 2181

Open 1.00 pm to 7.00 pm Monday to Friday; 10 am to 5.00 pm Saturday

Open Access
Located at Victoria Library, this is the largest public music library in the South of England, with extensive coverage of all aspects of music, including books, periodicals and printed scores. No recorded material, notated only. Lending library includes a small collection of CDs, cassettes and videos.

The Centre for the Study of Cartoons and Caricature

See under **Picture Libraries**

City Business Library

1 Brewers Hall Garden, London EC2V 5BX
☎0171 638 8215   Fax 0171 332 1847
☎0171 480 7638 (recorded information)

Open 9.30 am to 5.00 pm Monday to Friday

Open Access Local authority public reference library run by the Corporation of London.
Books, pamphlets, periodicals and newspapers of current business interest, mostly financial. Aims to satisfy the day-to-day information needs of the City's business community, and in so doing has become one of the leading public resource centres in Britain in its field. Strong collection of directories for both the UK and overseas, plus companies information, market research sources, management, law, banking, insurance, statistics and investment.

City of London Libraries

See **Barbican Library; Camomile Street Library; City Business Library; Guildhall**

Commonwealth Institute

Kensington High Street, London W8 6NQ
☎0171 603 4535   Fax 0171 602 7374

Open 11.00 am to 4.00 pm Tuesday to Friday; 1.00 pm to 4.45 pm Saturday

Access For reference
Special collection Books and periodicals on Commonwealth countries. Also a collection of directories and reference books on the Commonwealth and information on arts, geography, history and literature, cultural organisations and bibliography. The Commonwealth Literature Library includes fiction, poems, drama and critical writings.

Commonwealth Secretariat Library

10 Carlton House Terrace, London SW1Y 5AH
☎0171 747 6164   Fax 0171 747 6295

Open 9.15 am to 5.00 pm Monday to Friday

Access For reference only, by appointment
Extensive reference source concerned with economy, development, trade, production and industry of Commonwealth countries; also sub-library specialising in human resources

including women, youth, health, management and education.

Cornwall County Library
County Hall, Truro, Cornwall TR1 3AY
☎01872 322000   Fax 01872 70340
Open 9.30 am to 5.00 pm Monday to Friday
  Books, cassettes, CDs and videos for loan through branch or mobile networks. Reference, local studies, music and drama. *Special collections* on the visual arts and maritime studies. Opening hours vary at branch libraries throughout the county.

Coventry Central Library
Smithford Way, Coventry, Warwickshire CV1 1FY
☎01203 832314   Fax 01203 833163
Open 9.00 am to 8.00 pm Monday, Tuesday, Thursday, Friday; 9.30 am to 8.00 pm Wednesday; 9.00 am to 4.30 pm Saturday

Open Access
  Located in the middle of the city's main shopping centre. Approximately 120,000 items (books, records, cassettes and CDs) for loan; plus reference collection of business information and local history. *Special collections* Cycling and motor industries; George Eliot; Angela Brazil; Tom Mann Collection (trade union and labour studies); local newspapers on microfilm from 1740 onwards. Over 500 periodicals taken. Kurzweil reader and CCTV available for people with visual handicap. 'Peoplelink' community information database available.

Derby Central Library
Wardwick, Derby DE1 1HS
☎01332 255389   Fax 01332 369570
Open 9.30 am to 7.00 pm Monday, Tuesday, Thursday, Friday; 9.30 am to 1.00 pm Wednesday and Saturday

LOCAL STUDIES LIBRARY
25B Irongate, Derby DE1 3GL
Open 9.30 am to 7.00 pm Monday and Tuesday; 9.30 am to 5.00 pm Wednesday, Thursday, Friday; 9.30 am to 1.00 pm Saturday

Open Access
  General library for lending, information and Children's Services. The Central Library also houses specialist private libraries: Derbyshire Archaeological Society; Derby Philatelic Society. The Local Studies Library houses the largest multimedia collection of resources in existence relating to Derby and Derbyshire. The collection includes mss deeds, family papers, business records including the Derby Canal Company, Derby Board of Guardians and the Derby China Factory.

Devon & Exeter Institution Library
7 Cathedral Close, Exeter, Devon EX1 1EZ
☎01392 51017
Open 9.00 am to 5.00 pm Monday to Friday
Access Members only
  FOUNDED 1813. Contains over 36,000 volumes, including long runs of 19th-century journals, theology, history, topography, early science, biography and literature. A large and growing collection of books, journals, newspapers, prints and maps relating to the South-West.

Doncaster Libraries and Information Services
Central Library, Waterdale, Doncaster, South Yorkshire DN1 3JE
☎01302 734305   Fax 01302 369749
Open 9.30 am to 6.00 pm Monday to Friday; 9.30 am to 4.00 pm Saturday

Open Access
  Books, cassettes, CDs, videos, picture loans. Reading aids unit for people with visual handicap; activities for children during school holidays, including visits by authors, etc. Occasional funding available to support literature activities.

Dorchester Library
Colliton Park, Dorchester, Dorset DT1 1XJ
☎01305 224440/224448   Fax 01305 266120
Open 10.00 am to 7.00 pm Monday; 9.30 am to 7.00 pm Tuesday, Wednesday, Friday; 9.30 am to 5.00 pm Thursday; 9.00 am to 1.00 pm Saturday

Open Access
  General lending and reference library, including Local Studies Collection, special collections on Thomas Hardy, The Powys Family and T. E. Lawrence. Periodicals, children's library, playsets.

Dundee District Libraries
Central Library, The Wellgate, Dundee DD1 1DB
☎01382 434318   Fax 01382 434642
Open Lending Departments: 9.30 am to 7.00 pm Monday to Friday; 9.30 am to 5.00 pm Saturday. General Reference Department: 9.30 am to 9.00 pm Monday to Friday; 9.30 am to 5.00 pm Saturday. Local History

Department: 9.30 am to 5.00 pm Monday, Tuesday, Friday, Saturday; 9.30 am to 7.00 pm Wednesday and Thursday.

Access Reference services available to all; lending services to those who live, work or study within the City of Dundee District

Adult lending, reference and children's services. Art, music, audio and video lending services. Schools service (Agency). Housebound and mobile services. *Special collections*: The Ivory Collection; The Sturrock Collection; The Wighton Collection of National Music; The Wilson Photographic Collection; The Lamb Collection.

The Steps Film Theatre, a regional film theatre, is based in the Central Library under the licence of the Chief Librarian.

English Nature
Northminster House, Peterborough, Cambridgeshire PE1 1UA
☎01733 340345   Fax 01733 68834
Open 8.30 am to 5.00 pm Monday to Thursday; 8.30 pm to 4.30 pm Friday;
Access To *bona fide* students only. Telephone for appointment

Information on nature conservation, nature reserves, SSSIs, planning, legislation, etc.

Equal Opportunities Commission Library
Overseas House, Quay Street, Manchester M3 3HN
☎0161 833 9244   Fax 0161 835 1657
Open 9.00 am to 5.00 pm Monday to Friday
Access For reference (loans available)

Books and pamphlets on equal opportunities and gender issues. Non-sexist children's books and Equal Opportunities Commission publications. Also an information service with periodicals and press cuttings.

Essex County Council Libraries
County Library Headquarters, Goldlay Gardens, Chelmsford, Essex CM2 0EW
☎01245 284981   Fax 01245 492780
Essex County Council Libraries has 91 static libraries throughout Essex as well as 16 mobile libraries and three special-needs mobiles. Services to the public include books, newspapers, periodicals, CDs, cassettes, videos, pictures and CD-ROM as well as postal cassettes for the blind and subtitled videos. Specialist subjects and collections are listed below at the relevant library.

Chelmsford Library
PO Box 882, Market Road, Chelmsford, Essex CM1 1LH
☎01245 492758   Fax 01245 492536
Open: 9.00 am to 7.00 pm Monday to Friday; 9.00 am to 5.00 pm Saturday

Science and technology, business information, social studies, education and medical science.

Colchester Library
Trinity Square, Colchester, Essex CO1 1JB
☎01206 562243   Fax 01206 562413
Open: 9.00 am to 7.30 pm Monday, Tuesday, Wednesday, Friday; 9.00 am to 5.00 pm Thursday and Saturday

Local studies and music scores. Harsnett collection (early theological works 16th/17th-century); Castle collection (18th-century subscription library).

Grays Library
Orsett Road, Grays, Essex RM17 5DX
☎01375 383611   Fax 01375 370806
Open: 9.00 am to 7.30 pm Monday, Tuesday, Thursday, Friday; 9.00 am to 5.00 pm Wednesday and Saturday

Picture loans.

Harlow Library The High, Harlow, Essex CM20 1HA
☎01279 413772   Fax 01279 424612
Open: 9.00 am to 7.30 pm Monday, Tuesday, Thursday, Friday; 9.00 am to 5.00 pm Wednesday and Saturday

Language and literature.

Loughton Library
Traps Hill, Loughton, Essex IG10 1HD
☎0181 502 0181   Fax 0181 508 5041
Open: 9.00 am to 7.30 pm Monday, Tuesday, Wednesday, Friday; 9.00 am to 5.00 pm Saturday; closed Thursday

Jazz archive.

Saffron Walden Library
2 King Street, Saffron Walden, Essex CB10 1ES
☎01799 523178   Fax 01799 513642
Open: 9.00 am to 7.00 pm Monday, Tuesday, Thursday, Friday; 9.00 am to 5.00 pm Saturday; closed Wednesday

Victorian studies.

Southend Library
Victoria Avenue, Southend-on-Sea, Essex SS2 6EX
☎01702 612621   Fax 01702 469241

Open: 9.00 am to 7.00 pm Monday to Friday;
9.00 to 5.00 pm Saturday

Art, history and travel.

Witham Library
18 Newland Street, Witham, Essex CM8 2AQ
☎01376 519625   Fax 01376 501913
Open: 9.00 am to 7.00 pm Monday, Tuesday,
Thursday, Friday; 9.00 am to 5.00 pm
Saturday; closed Wednesday

Drama.

The Fawcett Library
London Guildhall University, Calcutta House,
Old Castle Street, London E1 7NT
☎0171 320 1189   Fax 0171 320 1188
Contact *Reference Librarian*
Open University term-time: 11.00 am to 8.30
pm Monday; 10.00 am to 8.30 pm
Wednesday to Friday (during vacation:
10.00 am to 5.00 pm Monday, Wednesday
to Friday)

Open Access members of staff and students at
London Guildhall University and to *bona fide*
researchers employed in higher education institutions funded by the (UK) Funding Councils
and DENI. Otherwise, full membership including borrowing rights £30 or £7 for full-time
students and the unwaged. Day fee (reference
only) £3 or £1.50 for students and the unwaged
    The Fawcett Library, national research
library for women's history, is the UK's oldest
and most comprehensive research library on all
aspects of women in society, with both historical and contemporary coverage. The Library
includes materials on feminism, work, education, health, the family, law, arts, sciences,
technology, language, sexuality, fashion and
the home. The main emphasis is on Britain but
many other countries are represented, especially the Commonwealth and the Third
World. Established in 1926 as the library of the
London Society of Women's Service (formerly
Suffrage), a non-militant organisation led by
Millicent Fawcett. In 1953 the Society was
renamed after and her and the library became
the Fawcett Library.
    Collections include: women's suffrage,
work, education; women and the church, the
law, sport, art, music; abortion, prostitution.
Mostly British materials but some American
and Commonwealth works. Books, journals,
pamphlets, archives, photographs, posters,
postcards, audiovisual materials, artefacts,
scrapbooks, albums and press cuttings dating
mainly from the 19th century although some
materials date from the 17th century.

Foreign and Commonwealth Office Library
King Charles Street, London SW1A 2AH
☎0171 270 3925   Fax 0171 270 3270

Access By appointment only
    An extensive stock of books, pamphlets and
other reference material on all aspects of historical, socio-economic and political subjects relating
to countries covered by the Foreign and
Commonwealth Office. Particularly strong on
colonial history, early works on travel, and photograph collections, mainly of Commonwealth
countries and former colonies, *c.* 1850s–1960s.

Forestry Commission Library
Forest Research Station, Alice Holt Lodge,
Wrecclesham, Farnham, Surrey GU10 4LH
☎01420 22255   Fax 01420 23653
Open 9.00 am to 5.00 pm Monday to
Thursday; 9.00 am to 4.30 pm Friday
Access By appointment for personal visits
    Approximately 10,000 books on forestry and
arboriculture, plus 500 current journals. CD-
ROMS include TREECD (1939 onwards).
Offers a Research Advisory Service for advice
and enquiries on forestry (tel: 01402 23000)
with a charge for consultations and diagnosis of
tree problems exceeding 10 minutes.

French Institute Library
17 Queensberry Place, London SW7 2DT
☎0171 589 6211   Fax 0171 581 5127
Head Librarian *Odile Grandet*
Deputy Head Librarian *Pascale Mukerjee*
Open 12.00 pm to 7.00 pm Tuesday to
Saturday

Open Access For reference and consultation
(loans restricted to members)
    A collection of over 40,000 volumes mainly
centred on French cultural interests with special emphasis on language, literature and history. Books in French and English. Collection
of 2000 videos; 250 periodicals; 1000 CDs
(French music); 50 CD-ROMs; Children's
library (8000 books); also a collection of rare
books and a special collection about 'France
Libre'. Inter-library loans; quick information
service; Internet access.

John Frost Newspapers
8 Monks Avenue, Barnet, Hertfordshire
EN5 1DB
☎0181 440 3159   Fax 0181 440 3159
Contact *John Frost, Andrew Frost*

A collection of 60,000 original newspapers

(1630 to the present day) and 100,000 press cuttings available, on loan, for research and rostrum work (TV and audiovisual documentaries/presentations). Historic events, politics, sports, royalty, crime, wars, personalities etc., plus many in-depth files.

Gloucestershire County Library Arts & Museums Service

Quayside House, Shire Hall, Gloucester GL1 2HY

☎01452 425020   Fax 01452 425042

Open Access
The service includes 39 local libraries - call the number above for opening hours; and seven mobile libraries telephone 01452 425039 for timetable/route enquiries

Goethe-Institut Library

50 Princes Gate, Exhibition Road, London SW7 2PH

☎0171 411 3452   Fax 0171 584 3180

Librarian *Regine Friederici*
Open 10.00 am to 8.00 pm Monday to Thursday; 10.00 am to 1.00 pm Saturday

Library specialising in German literature and books/audiovisual material on German culture and history: 27,000 books (4,800 of them in English), 144 periodicals, 14 newspapers, 2,750 audiovisual media (including 800 videos), selected press clippings on German affairs from the German and UK press, information service, photocopier, video facility for six viewers. Also German language teaching material for teachers and students of German.

Greater London Record Office Library

40 Northampton Road, London EC1R 0HB

☎0171 332 3822   Fax 0171 833 9136

Open 9.30 am to 4.45 pm Monday to Friday

Access For reference only
Covers all aspects of the life and development of London, specialising in the history and organisation of local government in general, and London in particular. Books on London history and topography, covering many subjects. Also London directories dating back to 1677, plus other source material including Acts of Parliament, Hansard reports, statistical returns, atlases, yearbooks and many complete sets of newspapers and magazines.

Guildford Institute of University of Surrey Library

Ward Street, Guildford, Surrey GU1 4LH

☎01483 62142

Librarian *Mrs Anne Milton-Worssell, BA, ALA*
Open 10.00 am to 3.00 pm Monday to Friday (under review and occasionally closed at lunchtime)

Open Access To members only
FOUNDED 1834. Some 10,000 volumes of which 7500 were printed before the First World War. The remaining stock consists of recently published works of fiction, biography and travel. Newspapers and periodicals also available. *Special collections* include an almost complete run of the *Illustrated London News* from 1843–1906, a collection of Victorian scrapbooks, and about 400 photos and other pictures relating to the Institute's history and the town of Guildford.

Guildhall Library

Aldermanbury, London EC2P 2EJ

☎0171 332 1839   Fax 0171 600 3384

Access For reference (but much of the material is kept in storage areas and is supplied to readers on request; proof of identity is required for consultation of certain categories of stock)
Part of the Corporation of London libraries. Seeks to provide a basic general reference service but its major strength, acknowledged worldwide, is in its historical collections. The library is divided into three sections, each with its own catalogues and enquiry desks. These are: Printed Books; Manuscripts; the Print Room.

PRINTED BOOKS
Open 9.30 am to 5 pm Monday to Saturday.
☎0171 332 1868/1870

Strong on all aspects of London history, with wide holdings of English history, topography and genealogy, including local directories, poll books and parish register transcripts. Also good collections of English statutes, law reports, parliamentary debates and journals, and House of Commons papers. Home of several important collections deposited by London institutions: the Marine collection of the Corporation of Lloyd's, the Stock Exchange's historical files of reports and prospectuses, the Clockmakers' Company library and museum, the Gardeners' Company, Fletchers' Company, the Institute of Masters of Wine, International Wine and Food Society and Gresham College.

MANUSCRIPTS
Open 9.30 am to 4.45 pm Monday to Saturday (no requests for records after 4.30 pm).
☎0171 332 1863

The official repository for historical records relating to the City of London (except those of the Corporation of London itself, which are housed at the Corporation Records Office). Records date from the 11th century to the present day. They include archives of most of the City's parishes, wards and livery companies, and of many individuals, families, estates, schools, societies and other institutions, notably the Diocese of London and St Paul's Cathedral, as well as the largest collection of business archives in any public repository in the UK. Although mainly of City interest, holdings include material for the London area as a whole and beyond.

PRINT ROOM
Open 9.30 am to 5.00 pm Monday to Friday.
☎0171 332 1839

An unrivalled collection of prints and drawings relating to London and the adjacent counties. The emphasis is on topography, but there are strong collections of portraits and satirical prints. The map collection includes maps from the capital from the mid-16th century to the present day and various classes of Ordnance Survey maps. Other material includes photographs, theatre bills and programmes, trade cards, book plates and playing cards as well as a sizeable collection of Old Master prints.

Guille-Alles Library

Market Street, St Peter Port, Guernsey, Channel Islands GY1 1HB
☎01481 720392   Fax 01481 712425

Open 9.00 am to 5.00 pm Monday, Tuesday, Thursday, Friday, Saturday; 9.00 am to 8.00 pm Wednesday

Open Access for residents; payment of returnable deposit by visitors
Lending, reference and information services.

Health Information Library (Westminster)

Marylebone Library, Marylebone Road, London NW1 5PS
☎0171 798 1039   Fax 0171 798 1044

Open 10.00 am to 8.00 pm Monday; 9.30 am to 8.00 pm Tuesday to Friday; 9.30 am to 5.00 pm Saturday; 1.30 pm to 5.00 pm Sunday

Open Access
Located in Westminster's Marylebone public library. Books, pamphlets and periodicals covering all aspects of medicine and the health services.

Hereford & Worcester County Libraries

Libraries Department, County Hall, Spetchley Road, Worcester WR5 2NP
☎01905 766240   Fax 01905 766244

Open Opening hours vary in branches across the county; all full-time libraries open at least one evening a week until 7.00 pm or 8.00 pm, and on Saturday until 1 pm

Access For reference to anyone; loans to members only (membership criteria: resident, educated, working, or an elector in the county or neighbouring authorities; temporary membership to other visitors. Proof of identity and address required)
Reference and lending libraries. Non-fiction and fiction for all age groups, including large print, sound recordings (CD, cassette, vinyl), videos, maps, local history, CD-ROMs at main libraries. *Special collections* Carpets and Textiles; Needles & Needlemaking; Stuart Period; Cidermaking; Beekeeping; Housman and John Masefield.

University of Hertfordshire Library

College Lane, Hatfield, Hertfordshire AL10 9AD
☎01707 284677   Fax 01707 284670

Open Term-time: 8.45 am to 9.30 pm Monday to Friday; 1.00 pm to 6.00 pm Saturday, Sunday; Holidays: 9.00 am to 5.00 pm Monday to Friday

Access For reference; loans available to members of HERTIS.
280,000 volumes and 2000 journals in science technology and social science, including law, across all three of the university's campuses. There are two other site libraries, one at Hertford (business), the other at Wall Hall, near Radlett (education and humanities). Desk research, postal interlibrary loans and consultancy undertaken by HERTIS Information and Research Unit which is based at Hatfield and has capacity for up to 300 subscribing companies and organisations.

HERTIS
See **University of Hertfordshire Library**

Highgate Literary and Scientific Institution Library

11 South Grove, London N6 6BS
☎0181 340 3343

Open 10.00 am to 5.00 pm Tuesday to Friday; 10.00 am to 4.00 pm Saturday (closed Monday)

Annual membership £33 single; £57 household

40,000 volumes of general fiction and non-fiction, with a children's section and extensive archives. *Special collections* on local history, London, and local poets Samuel Taylor Coleridge and John Betjeman.

Highland Libraries, The Highland Council, Cultural and Leisure Services Department

Central Services, 31A Harbour Road, Inverness IV1 1UA
☎01463 235713   Fax 01463 236986

Open Administration and support services: 8.00 am to 6.00 pm Monday to Friday; Libraries open to suit local needs

Open Access

Comprehensive range of lending and reference stock: books, pamphlets, periodicals, newspapers, compact discs, audio and video cassettes, maps, census records, genealogical records, photographs, educational materials, etc. Highland Libraries provides the public library service throughout the Highland Region with a network of 41 static and 12 mobile libraries.

Holborn Library

32-38 Theobalds Road, London WC1X 8PA
☎0171 413 6345/6

Open 10.00 am to 7.00 pm Monday and Thursday; 10.00 am to 6.00 pm Tuesday and Friday; 10.00 am to 5.00 pm Saturday (closed all day Wednesday)

Open Access

London Borough of Camden public library, specialising in law. Also includes the London Borough of Camden Local Studies and Archive Centre.

Sherlock Holmes Collection (Westminster)

Marylebone Library, Marylebone Road, London NW1 5PS
☎0171 798 1206   Fax 0171 798 1019

Open 10.00 am to 5.00 pm Monday; 9.30 am to 5.00 pm Tuesday to Friday; closed Saturday

Telephone for Access By appointment only

Located in Westminster's Marylebone Library. An extensive collection of material from all over the world, covering Sherlock Holmes and Sir Arthur Conan Doyle. Books, pamphlets, journals, newspaper cuttings and photos, much of which is otherwise unavailable in this country. Some background material.

Imperial College Library

See **Science Museum Library**

Imperial War Museum

Department of Printed Books, Lambeth Road, London SE1 6HZ
☎0171 416 5000   Fax 0171 416 5374

Open 10.00 am to 5.00 pm Monday to Saturday (restricted service Saturday; closed on Bank Holiday Saturdays and last two full weeks of November for annual stock check)

Access For reference (but at least 24 hours' notice must be given for intended visits)

A large collection of material on 20th-century life with detailed coverage of the two world wars and other conflicts. Books, pamphlets and periodicals, including many produced for short periods in unlikely wartime settings; also maps, biographies and privately printed memoirs, and foreign language material. Additional research material available in the following departments: Art, Documents, Exhibits and Firearms, Film, Sound Records, Photographs. Active publishing programme based on reprints of rare books held in library. Catalogue available.

Instituto Cervantes

22 Manchester Square, London W1M 5AP
☎0171 935 1518   Fax 0171 935 6167

Open 9.30 am to 1.00 pm and 2.00 pm to 5.00 pm Monday to Friday

Open Access For reference

Spanish literature, history, art, philosophy. Books, slides, tapes, records and films.

Italian Institute Library

39 Belgrave Square, London SW1X 8NX
☎0171 235 1461   Fax 0171 235 4618

Open 10.00 am to 1.00 pm and 2.00 pm to 5.00 pm Monday to Friday

Open Access For reference

A collection of over 26,000 volumes relating to all aspects of Italian culture. Texts are mostly in Italian, with some in English.

Jersey Library

Halkett Place, St Helier, Jersey JE2 4WH
☎01534 59991 (Lending)/59992 (Reference)
Fax 01534 69444

Open 9.30 am to 5.30 pm Monday,
Wednesday, Thursday, Friday; 9.30 am to
7.30 pm Tuesday; 9.30 am to 4.00 pm
Saturday

Access Open
  Books, periodicals, newspapers, CDs, cassettes, CD-ROMs, microfilm, specialised local
studies collection.

Kent Central Lending Library
Kent County Council Arts & Libraries,
Springfield, Maidstone, Kent ME14 2LH
☎01622 696511   Fax 01622 663573

Open 10.00 am to 6.00 pm Monday,
Tuesday, Wednesday, Friday; 10.00 am to
7.00 pm Thursday; 9.00 am to 4.00 pm
Saturday

Open Access
  300,000 volumes of non-fiction, mostly academic. English literature, poetry, classical literature, drama (including playsets), music
(including music sets). Strong, too, in sociology, art and history. Loans to all who live or
work in Kent; those who do not may consult
stock for reference or arrange loans via their
own local library service.

Lansdowne Library
Meyrick Road, Bournemouth, Dorset
BH1 3DJ
☎01202 556603   Fax 01202 291781

Open 10.00 am to 7.00 pm Monday; 9.30 am
to 7.00 pm Tuesday, Thursday, Friday; 9.30
am to 5.00 pm Wednesday; 9.00 am to 1.00
pm Saturday

Open Access
  General lending and reference library,
County Music Library, collection of Government publications. Children's section, periodicals.

The Law Society
50 Chancery Lane, London WC2A 1SX
☎0171 320 5810/11/12   Fax 0171 242 1309

Press Officer *Catherine Slaytor*
Head of Public Relations *Sue Stapely (LLB.
Hons/Solicitor)*

Open 8.30 am to 5.30 pm with out-of-house
answerphone and mobile phone back-up

Access Library restricted to solicitors/mem-
bers but press office available to all journalists
for advice, information and assistance.
  Provides all information about solicitors, the
legal profession in general, law reform issues
etc.

Leeds Central Library
Calverley Street, Leeds, West Yorkshire
LS1 3AB
☎0113 2478274   Fax 0113 2478268

Open 9.00 am to 8.00 pm Monday and
Wednesday; 9.00 am to 5.30 pm Tuesday,
Friday; 9.30 am to 5.30 pm Thursday;
10.00 am to 5.00 pm Saturday

Open Access to lending libraries; Reference
material on request

Lending Library covering all subjects.

Music Library contains scores, books and audio.

Information for Business Library holds
company information, market research, statistics, directories, journals and computer-based
information.

Art Library (in Art Gallery) has a major collection of material on fine and applied arts.

Local & Family History Library contains an
extensive collection on Leeds and Yorkshire,
including maps, books, pamphlets, local newspapers, illustrations and playbills. Census
returns for the whole of Yorkshire also available. International Genealogical Index and
parish registers.

Reference Library with over 270,000 volumes, including extensive files of newspapers
and periodicals plus all government publications since 1960. *Special collections* include
military history, Judaic, early gardening books,
and mountaineering.
  Leeds City Libraries has an extensive network of 65 branch and mobile libraries.

Leeds Library
18 Commercial Street, Leeds, West Yorkshire
LS1 6AL
☎0113 2453071

Open 9.00 am to 5.00 pm Monday to Friday

Access To members; research use upon application to the librarian
  FOUNDED 1768. Contains over 120,000
books and periodicals from the 15th century to
the present day. *Special collections* include
Reformation pamphlets, Civil War tracts,
Victorian and Edwardian children's books and
fiction, European language material, spiritualism and psychical research, plus local material.

Lincoln Central Library
Free School Lane, Lincoln LN2 1EZ
☎01522 549160 (Reference)/510800(Lending)
Fax 01522 535882

Open 9.00 am to 7.00 pm Monday, Tuesday,

Thursday, Friday; 9.00 am to 1.00 pm
Wednesday; 9.00 am to 12.30 pm Saturday

Linen Hall Library

17 Donegall Square North, Belfast BT1 5GD
☎01232 321707   Fax 01232 438586

Librarian *John Gray*

Open 9.30 am to 5.30 pm Monday, Tuesday,
Wednesday, Friday; 9.30 am to 8.30 pm
Thursday (5.30 pm in July and August);
9.30 am to 4.00 pm Saturday

Open Access For reference (loans restricted to
members)

FOUNDED 1788. Contains about 200,000
books. As well as general stock, there is a substantial Irish and local studies collection, with
over 80,000 items.

Literary & Philosophical Society of Newcastle upon Tyne

23 Westgate Road, Newcastle upon Tyne
NE1 1SE
☎0191 232 0192

Open 9.30 am to 7.00 pm Monday,
Wednesday, Thursday, Friday; 9.30 am to
8.00 pm Tuesday; 9.30 am to 1.00 pm
Saturday

Access Members; research facilities for *bona
fide* scholars on application to the Librarian

200–year-old library of 140,000 volumes,
periodicals (including 130 current titles), classical music on vinyl recordings and CD, plus a
collection of scores. A programme of lectures
and recitals provided. Recent publications
include: *History of the Literary and Philosophical
Society of Newcastle upon Tyne, Vol. 2 (1896-
1989)* Charles Parish; *Bicentenary Lectures 1993*
ed. John Philipson.

Liverpool City Libraries

William Brown Street, Liverpool LE3 8EW
☎0151 225 5429   Fax 0151 207 1342

Open 9.00 am to 7.30 pm Monday to
Thursday; 9.00 am to 5.00 pm Friday and
Saturday

Open Access

Arts and Recreations Library 50,000 volumes covering all subjects in arts and recreation.

Business & Information Library Business
and trade directories, plus all UK statutes and
law reports. Serves as a depository library for
UN and EC reports.

**General & Social Sciences/Hornby
Library** Contains stock of 68,000 volumes and
24,000 maps, plus book plates, prints and auto-
graphed letters. *Special collections* Walter Crane
and Edward Lear illustrations.

International Library Open-shelf and reserve
stocks on language, literature, geography and
history. *Special collection* British history, with
much on politicians and statesmen. 20,000
copies of British, American and European
plays, plus language tapes in twenty languages.

Music Library Extensive stock relating to all
aspects of music. Includes 128,000 volumes
and music scores, 18,500 records, and over
3000 cassettes and CDs. *Special collections* Carl
Rosa Opera Company Collection and Earl of
Sefton's early printed piano music.

**Record Office and Local History
Department** Printed and audiovisual material
relating to Liverpool, Merseyside, Lancashire
and Cheshire, together with archive material
mainly on Liverpool. Some restrictions on
access, with 30-year rule applying to archives.

Science and Technology Library Extensive
stock dealing with all aspects of science and
technology, including British and European
standards and patents.

London College of Printing & Distributive Trades: Department of Learning Resources

Elephant and Castle, London SE1 6SB
☎0171 514 6500   Fax 0171 514 6597

Access By arrangement

The Department of Learning Resources
operates from the three sites of the college at:
Elephant & Castle; Davies Street (W1); Back
Hill (Clerkenwell). Books, periodicals, slides,
CD-ROM, videos and computer software on
all aspects of the art of the book, printing, management, film/photography, graphic arts, plus
retailing. *Special collections* Private Press books
and the history and development of printing
and books.

The London Library

14 St James's Square, London SW1Y 4LG
☎0171 930 7705/6   Fax 0171 930 0436

Librarian *Mr A. S. Bell*

Open 9.30 am to 5.30 pm Monday to
Saturday (Thursday till 7.30 pm)

Access For members only (£100 p.a. 1995
price)

With over a million books and 8300 members, The London Library 'is the most distinguished private library in the world; probably
the largest, certainly the best loved'. Founded
in 1841, it is a registered charity and wholly

independent of public funding. Its permanent collection embraces most European languages as well as English. Its subject range is predominantly within the humanities, with emphasis on literature, history, fine and applied art, architecture, bibliography, philosophy, religion, and topography and travel. Some 6000-7000 titles are added yearly. Most of the stock is on open shelves to which members have free access. Members may take out up to 10 volumes; 15 if they live more than 20 miles from the Library. The comfortable Reading Room has an annexe for users of personal computers. There are photocopiers and CD-ROM workstations, and the Library also offers a postal loans service.

Prospective members are required to submit a refereed application form in advance of admission, but there is at present no waiting list for membership. The London Library Trust may make grants to those who are unable to afford the full annual fee; details on application.

Lord Louis Library
Orchard Street, Newport, Isle of Wight
PO30 1LL
☎01983 527655/823800 (Reference Library)
Fax 01983 825972

Open 9.30 am to 5.30 pm Monday to Friday (Saturday till 5.00 pm)

Open Access
General adult and junior fiction and non-fiction collections; local history collection and periodicals. Also the county's main reference library.

Manchester Central Library
St Peters Square, Manchester M2 5PD
☎0161 234 1900   Fax 0161 234 1963

Open 10.00 am to 8.00 pm Monday to Thursday; 10.00 am to 5.00 pm Friday and Saturday; Commercial and European Units: 10.00 am to 6.00 pm Monday to Thursday; 10.00 am to 5.00 pm Friday and Saturday

Open Access
One of the country's leading reference libraries with extensive collections covering all subjects. Subject departments include: Commercial, European, Technical, Social Sciences, Arts, Music, Local Studies, Chinese, General Readers, Language & Literature. Large lending stock and VIP (visually impaired) service available.

Marylebone Library (Westminster)
See **Health Information Library; Sherlock Holmes Collection**

Ministry of Agriculture, Fisheries and Food
Whitehall Place Library, 3 Whitehall Place, London SW1A 2HH
☎0171 270 8000/8421   Fax 0171 270 8419

MAFF Helpline 0645 335577 (local call rate) – general contact point which can provide information on the work of MAFF, either directly or by referring callers to appropriate contacts. Available 9.00 am to 5.00 pm Monday to Friday (excluding Bank Holidays)

Open 9.30 am to 5.00 pm Monday to Friday

Access For reference (but at least 24 hours notice must be given for intended visits)
Large stock of volumes on temperate agriculture.

The Mitchell Library
North Street, Glasgow G3 7DN
☎0141 287 2999   Fax 0141 287 2815

Contact *Mrs F. MacPherson*

Open 9.00 am to 9.00 pm Monday to Friday; 9.00 am to 5.00 pm Saturday

Open Access
Europe's largest public reference library with stock of over 1,200,000 volumes. It subscribes to 46 newspapers and more than 2,000 periodicals. There are collections in microform, records, tapes and videos, as well as CD-ROM, illustrations, photographs, postcards etc.

The library is divided into a number of subject departments including the language & literature department which contains a number of special collections, eg the Robert Burns Collection (5000 vols), the Scottish Poetry Collection (10,000 items) and the Scottish Drama Collection (1,650 items).

National Farmers' Union
164 Shaftesbury Avenue, London WC2H 8HL
☎0171 331 7200   Fax 0171 331 7382

Open 10.00 am to 4.30 pm Monday to Thursday

Access For reference only (by appointment)
NFU archive and current material.

National Library of Scotland
George IV Bridge, Edinburgh EH1 1EW
☎0131 226 4531/459 4531
Fax 0131 220 6662

Open Main Reading Room: 9.30 am to 8.30 pm Monday, Tuesday, Thursday, Friday; 10.00 am to 8.30 pm Wednesday;

9.30 am to 1.00 pm Saturday. Map Library: 9.30 am to 5.00 pm Monday, Tuesday, Thursday, Friday; 10.00 am to 5.00 pm Wednesday; 9.30 am to 1.00 pm Saturday. Scottish Science Library: 9.30 am to 5.00 pm Monday, Tuesday, Thursday, Friday; 10.00 am to 8.30 pm Wednesday.

Access To reading rooms and Map Library, for research not easily done elsewhere, by reader's ticket

Collection of over 6 million volumes. The library receives all British and Irish publications. Large stock of newspapers and periodicals. Many special collections, including early Scottish books, theology, polar studies, baking, phrenology and liturgies. Also large collections of maps, music and manuscripts including personal archives of notable Scottish persons.

National Library of Wales

Aberystwyth, Dyfed SY23 3BU
☎01970 623816   Fax 01970 615709
Open 9.30 am to 6.00 pm Monday to Friday; 9.30 am to 5.00 pm Saturday (closed Bank Holidays and first week of October)

Access To reading rooms and map room by reader's ticket, available on application

Collection of over 3.5 million books and including large collections of periodicals, maps, manuscripts and audiovisual material. Particular emphasis on humanities in printed foreign material, and on Wales and other Celtic areas in all collections.

The Natural History Museum Library

Cromwell Road, London SW7 5BD
☎0171 938 9191   Fax 0171 938 9290
Open 10.00 am to 4.30 pm Monday to Friday

Access To *bona fide* researchers, by reader's ticket on presentation of identification (telephone first to make an appointment)

The library is in five sections: general; botany; zoology; entomology; palaeontology and mineralogy. The sub-department of ornithology is housed at Zoological Museum, Akeman Street, Tring, Herts HP23 6AP (Tel 01442 834181). Resources available include books, journals, maps, manuscripts, drawings and photographs covering all aspects of natural history, including palaeontology and mineralogy, from the 14th century to the present day. Also archives and an historical collection on the museum itself.

Newcastle Literary and Philosophical Society Library

Westgate Road, Newcastle upon Tyne NE1 1SE
☎0191 232 0192
Librarian *Pat Southern*
Open 9.30 am to 7.00 pm (Tuesdays till 8.00 pm; Saturdays till 1.00 pm)

Access To members; scholars on application

Over 140,000 volumes, many of them old and rare. *Special collections* include 19th-century science and technology, history, exploration and travel, biography, literature, music, and local history.

Newcastle upon Tyne Central Library

Princess Square, Newcastle upon Tyne NE99 1DX
☎0191 261 0691   Fax 0191 261 1435
Open 9.30 am to 8.00 pm Monday and Thursday; 9.30 am to 5.00 pm Tuesday, Wednesday, Friday; 9.00 am to 5.00 pm Saturday

Open Access

Extensive local studies collection, including newspapers, illustrations and genealogy. Also business, science, humanities and arts, educational guidance unit, open learning resource centre, marketing advice centre. Patents advice centre.

Norfolk Library & Information Service

Norfolk and Norwich Central Library, Central Lending Service, 71 Ber Street, Norwich, Norfolk NR1 3AD
☎01603 215215
Central Reference & Information Service and Norfolk Studies
Gildengate House, Upper Green Lane, Norwich, Norfolk NR3 1AX
☎01603 215222   Fax 01603 215258
Open Leisure & Learning and Information & Research depts: 10.00 am to 8.00 pm Monday to Friday; 9.00 am to 5.00 pm Saturday. Local Studies: 10.00 am to 8.00 pm Monday to Friday; 9.00 am to 5.00 pm Saturday

Open Access

Reference and lending library with wide range of stock for loan, including books, recorded music, music scores, plays and videos. (The collections were severely damaged by fire in August 1994 and are in the process of being rebuilt.) Houses the 2nd Air Division Memorial Library and has a strong Local Studies Library. Extensive range of reference stock including business information. On-line database and CD-ROM services. Public fax and colour photocopying. Information brokerage provides in-depth research services.

Northamptonshire Libraries & Information Service

Library HQ, PO Box 259, 27 Guildhall Road, Northampton NN1 1BA
☎01604 20262   Fax 01604 26789

Since 1991 the Libraries and Information Service have run two to three programmes of literary events for adults each year. Programmes so far have included visiting authors, poetry readings, workshops and other events and activities. The programmes are supported by regular touring fiction displays, writers' advice sessions and dedicated notice boards in libraries across the country.

Northumberland Central Library

The Willows, Morpeth, Northumberland NE61 1TA
☎01670 512385   Fax 01670 519985

Open 10.00 am to 8.00 pm Monday, Tuesday, Wednesday, Friday; 9.30 am to 12.30 pm Saturday (closed Thursday)

Open Access
  Books, periodicals, newspapers, cassettes, CDs, video, microcomputers, CD-ROM, prints, microforms, vocal scores, playsets, community resource equipment. *Special collections* **Northern Poetry Library**: 12,000 volumes of modern poetry (see entry: **Organisations of Interest to Poets**); cinema: comprehensive collection of about 5000 volumes covering all aspects of the cinema; family history.

Nottingham Central Library

Angel Row, Nottingham NG1 6HP
☎0115 9412121   Fax 0115 9504207

Open 9.30 am to 7.00 pm Monday to Friday; 9.00 am to 1.00 pm Saturday

Open Access
  General public lending library: business information, the arts, local studies, religion, literature. Videos, periodicals, spoken word, recorded music. *Special collection* on D. H. Lawrence. Extensive back-up reserve stocks. Drama and music sets for loan to groups.

Nottingham Subscription Library Ltd

Bromley House, Angel Row, Nottingham NG1 6HL
☎0115 9473134

Librarian *Julia Nalepa*

Open 9.30 am to 5.00 pm Monday to Friday; also first Saturday of each month from 10.00 am to 12.30 pm for members only

FOUNDED 1816. Collection of 30,000 books including local history, topography, biography, travel and fiction.

Office of Population Censuses & Surveys Library

Library Services and Central Enquiry Unit, St Catherine's House, 10 Kingsway, London WC2B 6JP
☎0171 396 2236(Library)/2828(OPCS Data)
Fax 0171 396 2369

Open 9.30 am to 4.30 pm Monday to Friday

Access By appointment only
  All published Census data from 1801 onwards for the UK. Population and health statistics from 1837 onwards. Foreign censuses and statistics (incomplete; most are out-housed and require one week's notice for retrieval). International statistics (WHO, UN, etc). Government Social Survey reports, 1941 onwards. Small stock of books on demography, vital registration, epidemology, survey methodology, census taking.

Orkney Library

Laing Street, Kirkwall, Orkney KW15 1NW
☎01856 873166   Fax 01856 875260

Open 9.00 am to 8.00 pm Monday to Friday; 9.00 am to 5.00 pm Saturday. Archives: 9.00 am to 1.00 pm and 2.00 pm to 4.45 pm Monday to Friday

Open Access
  Local studies collection. Archive includes sound and photographic departments.

Oxford Central Library

Westgate, Oxford OX1 1DJ
☎01865 815549   Fax 01865 721694

Open 9.15 am to 7.00 pm Monday, Tuesday, Thursday, Friday (Wednesday and Saturday till 5.00 pm)

General lending and reference library including the Centre for Oxfordshire Studies. Also periodicals, music library, children's library and Business Information Point.

Penzance Library

Morrab House, Morrab Gardens, Penzance,
Cornwall TR18 4DQ
☎01736 64474

Librarian L. *Lowdon*

Open 10.00 am to 4.00 pm Tuesday to
Friday; 10.00 am to 1.00 pm Saturday

Access Non-members may use the library for
a small daily fee, but may not borrow books

A private subscription lending library of over
60,000 volumes covering virtually all subjects
except modern science and technology, with
large collections on history, literature and religion. There is a comprehensive Cornish collection of books, newspapers and manuscripts
including the Borlase letters; a West Cornwall
photographic archive; many runs of 18th- and
19th-century periodicals; a collection of over
2000 books published before 1800.

Plymouth Central Library

Drake Circus, Plymouth, Devon PL4 8AL
Fax 01752 385905

Open Access

LENDING DEPARTMENTS:

Lending ☎01752 385912; **Children's
Department** ☎01752 385916; **Music &
Drama Department** ☎01752 385914

Open 9.30 am to 7.00 pm Monday, Friday;
9.30 am to 5.30 pm Tuesday, Wednesday,
Thursday; 9.30 am to 4.00 pm Saturday

The Lending departments offer books on all
subjects; language courses on cassette and foreign language books; the Holcenberg Jewish
Collection; books on music and musicians,
drama and theatre; play sets; videos; song
index; cassettes and CDs.

REFERENCE DEPARTMENTS:

Reference ☎01752 385907/8; **Business
Information** ☎01752 385906; **Local
Studies & Natural History Department**
☎01752 985909

Open 9.00 am to 7.00 pm Monday to Friday;
9.00 am to 4.00 pm Saturday

The Reference departments include an extensive collection of Ordnance Survey maps and
town guides; community and census information; marketing and statistical information;
books on every aspect of Plymouth; naval history; Mormon Index on microfilm.

Plymouth Proprietary Library

Alton Terrace, 111 North Hill, Plymouth,
Devon PL4 8JY
☎01752 660515

Librarian *Camilla M. Blackman*

Open Monday to Saturday from 9.30 am
(closing time varies)

Access To members; visitors by appointment
only

FOUNDED 1810. The library contains
approximately 17,000 volumes of mainly 20th-
century work. Member of the Association of
Independent Libraries.

The Poetry Library

See under **Organisations of Interest to Poets**

Polish Library

238-246 King Street, London W6 0RF
☎0181 741 0474   Fax 0181 746 3798

Open 10.00 am to 8.00 pm Monday and
Wednesday; 10.00 am to 5.00 pm Friday;
10.00 am to 1.00 pm Saturday (library
closed Tuesday and Thursday)

Access For reference to all interested in Polish
affairs; limited loans to members and *bona fide*
scholars only through inter-library loans

Books, pamphlets, periodicals, maps, music,
photographs on all aspects of Polish history and
culture. *Special collections* Emigré publications;
Joseph Conrad and related works; Polish
underground publications; bookplates.

Poole Central Library

Dolphin Centre, Poole, Dorset BH15 1QE
☎01202 673910   Fax 01202 670253

Open 10.00 am to 7.00 pm Monday; 9.30 am
to 7.00 pm Tuesday to Friday; 9.00 am to
1.00 pm Saturday

Open Access

General lending and reference library,
including Healthpoint health information centre, HATRICS business information centre,
children's library, periodicals.

Press Association Library

292 Vauxhall Bridge Road, London
SW1V 1AE
☎0171 963 7000   Fax 0171 963
7065(News)/963 7066(Pics.)

Open News Library: 8.00 am to 8.00 pm
Monday to Friday; 8.00 am to 6.00 pm
Saturday; 9.00 am to 5.00 pm Sunday.
Picture Library: personal callers 9.00 am to
5.00 pm Monday to Friday

The national news agency offers public access
to over 14 million news cuttings on every subject from 1926 onwards, and over 5 million
colour and b&w photographs from 1902 to the

present day. Personal callers welcome or research undertaken by in-house staff.

Harry Price Library of Magical Literature

University of London Library, Senate House, Malet Street, London WC1E 7HU

☎0171 636 8000 ext 5031 Fax 0171 436 1494

Open 9.30 am to 5.15 pm Monday to Friday; 9.30 am to 1.00 pm, 2.00 pm to 5.15 pm Saturday (by prior appointment only); Monday evenings in term time (by prior appointment only)

Restricted access For reference only, restricted to members of the University and *bona fide* researchers (apply in writing)

Over 14,000 volumes and pamphlets on psychic phenomena and pseudo-phenomena; books relating to spiritualism and its history, to hypnotism, telepathy, astrology, conjuring and quackery.

Public Record Office

Ruskin Avenue, Kew, Richmond, Surrey TW9 4DU

☎0181 876 3444   Fax 0181 878 8905

Also at: Chancery Lane, London WC2A 1LR

Open 9.30 am to 5.00 pm Monday to Friday

Access For reference, by reader's ticket, available free of charge on production of proof of identity (UK citizens: banker's card or driving licence; non-UK: passport or national identity card. Telephone for further information)

Over 90 miles of shelving house the national repository of records of central Government in the UK and law courts of England and Wales, which extend in time from the 11th-20th century. Medieval records and the records of the State Paper Office from the early 16th-late 18th century, plus the records of the Privy Council Office and the Lord Chamberlain's and Lord Steward's departments, together with the records of the decennial censuses, 1841-1891, are held at Chancery Lane. Modern government department records, together with those of the Copyright Office, are held at Kew; these date mostly from the late 18th century. Under the Public Records Act, records are normally only open to inspection when they are 30 years old. Chancery Lane also houses a small permanent exhibition of records (open 10.00 am to 5.00 pm Monday to Friday; Census Rooms also open 9.30 am to 5.00 pm Saturday).

Reading Central Library

Abbey Square, Reading, Berkshire RG1 3BQ

☎0118 9509245   Fax 0118 9589039

Open 9.30 am to 5.00 pm Monday, Wednesday; 9.30 am to 7.00 pm Tuesday, Thursday, Friday; 9.30 am to 4.00 pm Saturday

Open Access

Lending library; county reference library; county local studies library, bringing together every aspect of the local environment and human activity in Berkshire; county business library; county music and drama library. Special collections: Mary Russell Mitford; local illustrations.

Public meeting room available.

Religious Society of Friends Library

Friends House, 173 Euston Road, London NW1 2BJ

☎0171 387 3601   Fax 0171 388 1977

Open 10.00 am to 5.00 pm Tuesday to Friday (closed last full week November and week preceding Spring Bank Holiday)

Access For reference, to members of the Society of Friends and to *bona fide* researchers on introduction or letter of recommendation

Quaker history, thought and activities from the 17th century onwards. Supporting collections on peace, anti-slavery and other subjects in which Quakers have maintained long-standing interest. Also archives and manuscripts relating to the Society of Friends.

Richmond Central Reference Library

Old Town Hall, Whittaker Avenue, Richmond, Surrey TW9 1TP

☎0181 940 5529   Fax 0181 940 6899

Open 10.00 am to 6.00 pm Monday, Thursday, Friday (Tuesday till 1.00 pm; Wednesday till 8.00 pm and Saturday till 5.00 pm)

Open Access

General reference library serving the needs of local residents and organisations.

Royal Geographical Society Library

1 Kensington Gore, London SW7 2AR

☎0171 589 5466   Fax 0171 584 4447

Open 10.00 am to 5.00 pm Monday to Friday

Access To the library and reading rooms restricted to use by Fellows and members

Books and periodicals on geography, topography, cartography, voyages and travels. The Map Room, open since 1854 to the general public for reference purposes only, houses map and chart sheets, atlases and RGS-sponsored expedition reports, for which an appointment is necessary. Photographs on travel and exploration are housed in the picture library.

Royal Society Library
6 Carlton House Terrace, London SW1Y 5AG
☎0171 839 5561   Fax 0171 930 2170
Open 10.00 am to 5.00 pm Monday to Friday
Access For research only, to *bona fide* researchers on application to the Head of Fellowship and Information Services.

History of science, scientists' biographies, science policy reports, and publications of international scientific unions and national academies from all over the world.

RSA (Royal Society for the Encouragement of Arts, Manufacturers & Commerce)
8 John Adam Street, London WC2N 6EZ
☎0171 930 5115   Fax 0171 839 5805
Archivist *Susan Bennett*
Open 10.00 am to 1.00 pm Monday,
Tuesday, Wednesday, Thursday and
2.00pm to 5.00 pm Wednesdays only
Access to fellows of RSA; by application and appointment to non-fellows (£6.00 for a yearly ticket)

Archives of the Society since 1754. A collection of approximately 5000 volumes; international exhibition material.

Royal Society of Medicine Library
1 Wimpole Street, London W1M 8AE
☎0171 290 2940   Fax 0171 290 2939
Open 9.00 am to 9.30 pm Monday to Friday;
10.00 am to 5.00 pm Saturday
Access For reference only, on introduction by Fellow of the Society (temporary membership may also be granted)

Books and periodicals on general medicine, biochemistry and biomedical science. Extensive historical material.

Royal Statistical Society Library
University College London, Gower Street,
London WC1E 6BT
☎0171 387 7050 ext. 2628
Fax 0171 380 7727/7373
Contact *D Chatarji*

Access RSS fellows registered with University College London Library

Statistics (theory and methodology), mathematical statistics, applied statistics, econometrics.

Science Fiction Foundation Research Library
Liverpool University Library, PO Box 123,
Liverpool L69 3DA
☎0151 794 2696/2733   Fax 0151 794 2681
Access For research, by appointment only (telephone first)

This is the largest collection outside the US of science fiction and related material – including autobiographies and critical works. *Special collection* Runs of 'pulp' magazines dating back to the 1920s. Foreign-language material (including a large Russian collection), and the papers of the Flat Earth Society. The collection also features a growing range of archive and manuscript material, including the Eric Frank Russell archive.

Science Museum Library
Imperial Institute Road, off Exhibition Road,
London SW7 5NH
☎0171 938 8234   Fax 0171 938 9714
Open 9.30 am to 9.00 pm Monday to Friday
(closes 5.30 pm outside academic terms);
9.30 am to 5.30 pm Saturday
Open Access Reference only; no loans

National reference library for the history and public understanding of science and technology, with a large collection of source material. Operates jointly with Imperial College Central Library.

Scottish Poetry Library
See under **Organisations of Interest to Poets**

Sheffield Libraries and Information Services
Central Library, Surrey Street, Sheffield
S1 1XZ
☎0114 2734711   Fax 0114 2735009
Sheffield Archives
52 Shoreham Street, Sheffield S1 4SP
☎0114 2734756   Fax 0114 2735066
Open 9.30 am to 5.30 pm Monday to
Thursday; 9.00 am to 1.00 pm & 2.00 pm
to 4.30 pm Saturday (documents should be
ordered by 5.00 pm Thursday for Saturday)
Access By reader's pass

Holds documents relating to Sheffield and

South Yorkshire, dating from the 12th century to the present day, including records of the City Council, churches, businesses, landed estates, families and individuals, institutions and societies.

Arts and Social Sciences Reference Service
☎0114 2734747/8

Open 10.00 am to 8.00 pm Monday; 10.00 am to 5.30 pm Tuesday, Thursday and Friday; 1.00 pm to 8.00 pm Wednesday; 9.30 am to 4.30 pm Saturday

Access For reference only
A comprehensive collection of books, periodicals and newspapers covering all aspects of arts (excluding music) and social sciences.

Music and Video Service
☎0114 2734733

Open as for Arts and Social Services above

Access For reference (loans to ticket holders only)
An extensive range of books, records, CDs, cassettes, scores, etc. related to music. Also a video cassette loan service.

Local Studies Service
☎0114 2734753

Open as for Arts & Social Sciences above (except Wednesday 1.00 pm to 5.30 pm)

Access For reference (but advance notice advisable)
Extensive material covering all aspects of Sheffield and its population, including maps, photos and taped oral histories.

Business, Science and Technology Reference Service
☎0114 2734736/7 (Business);
☎0114 2734742/3 (Science & Technology)

Open as for Arts & Social Sciences above

Access For reference only
Extensive coverage of science and technology as well as commerce and commercial law. British patents and British and European standards with emphasis on metals. Hosts the World Metal Index. The business section holds a large stock of business and trade directories, plus overseas telephone directories and reference works with business emphasis.

Sheffield Information Service
☎0114 2734760/1

Open 10.00 am to 5.30 pm Monday, Tuesday, Thursday and Friday; 1.00 pm to 5.30 pm Wednesday; 9.30 am to 4.30 pm Saturday

Full local information service covering all aspects of the Sheffield community and a generalist advice service on a sessional basis.

Shetland Library
Lower Hillhead, Lerwick, Shetland ZE1 0EL
☎01595 693868   Fax 01595 694430

Open 10.00 am to 7.00 pm Monday, Wednesday, Friday; 10.00 am to 5.00 pm Tuesday, Thursday, Saturday

General lending and reference library; extensive local interest collection including complete set of *The Shetland Times, The Shetland News* and other local newspapers on microfilm and many old and rare books; audio collection including *Linguaphone* courses and talking books/newspapers. Junior room for children and a weekly storytime for pre-school children. Disabled access and Housebound Readers Service (delivery to reader's home). Mobile library services to rural areas. Open Learning Service. Same day photocopying service. Publishing programme of books in dialect, history, literature.

Shoe Lane Library
Hill House, Little New Street, London
EC4A 3JR
☎0171 583 7178

Open 9.30 am to 5.30 pm Monday, Wednesday, Thursday, Friday; 9.30 am to 6.30 pm Tuesday

Open Access
Corporation of London general lending library, with a comprehensive stock of 48,000 volumes, most of which are on display. Some specialisation in graphics, advertising and illustrated works.

Shrewsbury Library
Castlegates, Shrewsbury, Shropshire
SY1 2AS
☎01743 255300   Fax 01743 255309

Open 9.30 am to 5.00 pm Monday and Wednesday; 9.30am to 1.00 pm Thursday; 9.30am to 7.30 pm Tuesday and Friday; 9.30 am to 4.00 pm Saturday

Open Access
The largest public lending library in Shropshire. Books, cassettes, CDs, talking books, videos, language courses. Strong music, literature and art book collection. Reference and local studies provision in adjacent buildings.

Spanish Institute Library
See **Instituto Cervantes**

St Bride Printing Library

Bride Lane, London EC4Y 8EE

☎0171 353 4660   Fax 0171 583 7073

Open 9.30 am to 5.30 pm Monday to Friday

Open Access

Corporation of London public reference library. Appointments advisable for consultation of special collections. Every aspect of printing and related matters: publishing and bookselling, newspapers and magazines, graphic design, calligraphy and type, papermaking and bookbinding. One of the world's largest specialist collections in its field, with over 40,000 volumes and 2000 periodicals (200 current titles), and extensive collections of drawings, manuscripts, patents, prospectuses, and printing and typefounding materials. Noted for comprehensive holdings of historical and early technical literature.

Suffolk County Council Libraries & Heritage

St Andrew House, County Hall, St Helens Street, Ipswich, Suffolk IP4 2JS

☎01473 230000   Fax 01473 225491

Open Details on application to St Andrew House above. Major libraries open six days a week

Access A single user registration card gives access to the lending service of 41 libraries across the county

Full range of lending and reference services. *Special collections* include Suffolk Archives and Local History Collection; Benjamin Britten Collection; Edward Fitzgerald Collection; Seckford Collection and Racing Collection (Newmarket). The Suffolk Infolink service gives details of local groups and societies and is available in libraries throughout the county.

Sunderland City Library and Arts Centre

28-30 Fawcett Street, Sunderland, Tyne & Wear SR1 1RE

☎0191 514 1235   Fax 0191 514 8444

Open 9.30 am to 7.30 pm Monday and Wednesday; 9.30 am to 5.00 pm Tuesday, Thursday, Friday; 9.30 am to 4.00 pm Saturday

The city's main lending and reference library. Local studies and children's sections, plus sound and vision department (CDs, cassettes, videos, talking books). The City of Sunderland maintains a further nineteen branch libraries. Special services available to housebound readers, hospitals and schools, plus two mobile libraries.

Swansea Central Reference Library

Alexandra Road, Swansea, West Glamorgan SA1 5DX

☎01792 655521   Fax 01792 645751

Open 9.00 am to 7.00 pm Monday, Tuesday, Wednesday, Friday; 9.00 am to 5.00 pm Thursday and Saturday. The library has a lending service but hours tend to be shorter - check in advance (Tel 01792 654065).

Access For reference only (Local Studies closed access: items must be requested on forms provided)

General reference material (approx. 50,000 volumes); also British standards, statutes, company information, maps, etc. Local studies: comprehensive collections on Wales; Swansea & Gower; Dylan Thomas. Local maps, periodicals, illustrations, local newspapers from 1804. B&w and colour photocopying facilities and microfilm/microfiche copying facility.

Swiss Cottage Library

88 Avenue Road, London NW3 3HA

☎0171 413 6533/4

Open 10.00 am to 7.00 pm Monday and Thursday; 10.00 am to 6.00 pm Tuesday and Friday; 10.00 am to 5.00 pm Saturday (closed all day Wednesday)

Open Access

Over 60,000 volumes and 400 periodical titles. Home of the London Borough of Camden's Information and Reference Services.

Theatre Museum Library & Archive

1e Tavistock Street, London WC2E 7PA

☎0171 836 7891   Fax 0171 836 5148

Open 10.30 am to 4.30 pm Tuesday to Friday

Access By appointment only

The Theatre Museum was founded as a separate department of the Victoria & Albert Museum in 1974 and moved to its own building in Covent Garden in 1987. The museum (open Tuesday to Sunday 11.00 am to 7.00 pm) houses permanent displays, temporary exhibitions, a studio theatre, and organises a programme of special events, performances, lectures and guided visits. The library houses the UK's largest performing arts research collections, including books, photographs, designs, engravings, programmes, press cuttings, etc. All the performing arts are covered but strengths are in the areas of theatre history, ballet, circus and stage design. The Theatre Museum has acquired much of the British Theatre Association's library and is providing reference access to its collections of play texts and critical works.

United Nations Office and Information Centre

18 Buckingham Gate, London SW1E 6LB
☎0171 630 1981   Fax 0171 976 6478

Open Information Centre: 9.30 am to 1.00 pm and 2.00 pm to 5.30 pm Monday to Friday. Reference Library: 10.00 am to 1.00 pm and 2.00 pm to 5.00 pm Monday, Tuesday, Wednesday, Thursday

Open Access To Information Centre only; Reference Library by appointment only

A full stock of official publications and documentation from the United Nations.

Victoria Library (Westminster)

See **Central Music Library**

Western Isles Libraries

Public Library, Keith Street, Stornoway, Isle of Lewis HS1 2QG
☎01851 703064   Fax 01851 705657

Open 10.00 am to 5.00 pm Monday to Thursday; 10.00 am to 7.00 pm Friday; 10.00 am to 1.00 pm Saturday

Open Access

General public library stock, plus local history and Gaelic collections including maps, printed music and cassettes; census records and Council minutes; music collection (cassettes). Branch libraries on the isles of Barra, Benbecula, Harris and Lewis.

City of Westminster Archives Centre

10 St Ann's Street, London SW1P 2XR
☎0171 798 2180   Fax 0171 798 2179

Open 9.30 am to 7.00 pm Monday to Friday; 9.30 am to 5.00 pm Saturday

Access For reference

Comprehensive coverage of the history of Westminster and selective coverage of general London history. 22,000 books, together with a large stock of maps, prints, photographs, and theatre programmes.

Westminster Reference Library

35 St Martin's Street, London WC2H 7HP
☎0171 798 2036 (General Media & Performing Arts)   Fax 0171 798 2040

Business and Official Publications:
☎0171 798 2034

Information for Business Service:
☎0171 976 1285 (fee-based service)

Open 10.00 am to 7.00 pm Monday to Friday; 10.00 am to 5.00 pm Saturday

Access For reference only

A general reference library with emphasis on the following: Art & Design (see separate entry); Performing Arts - theatre, cinema, radio, television and dance; Official Publications - major collection of HMSO publications from 1947, plus parliamentary papers dating back to 1906, and a ten-year file of key statistical publications from OECD, UN, Unesco, EU, etc.; Maps - an excellent map and town plan collection for Britain, plus international material; Business - UK directories, trade directories, company and market data; Periodicals - long files of many titles. One working day's notice is required for some monographs and most older periodicals. Official EU depository library - carries all official EU material.

The Wiener Library

4 Devonshire Street, London W1N 2BH
☎0171 636 7247   Fax 0171 436 6428

Open 10.00 am to 5.30 pm Monday to Friday

Access By letter of introduction (readers needing to use the Library for any length of time should become members)

Private library - one of the leading research centres on European history since the First World War, with special reference to the era of totalitarianism and to Jewish affairs. Founded by Dr Alfred Wiener in Amsterdam in 1933, it holds material that is not available elsewhere. Books, periodicals, press archives, documents, pamphlets, leaflets and brochures. Much of the material can be consulted on microfilm.

Vaughan Williams Memorial Library

English Folk Dance and Song Society, Cecil Sharp House, 2 Regent's Park, London NW1 7AY
☎0171 284 0523   Fax 0171 284 0523

Open 9.30 am to 5.30 pm Monday to Friday

Access For reference to the general public, on payment of a daily fee; members may borrow books and use the library free of charge

A multi-media collection: books, periodicals, manuscripts, tapes, records, CDs, films, videos. Mostly British folk culture and how this has developed around the world. Some foreign language material, and some books in English about foreign cultures. Also, the history of the English Folk Dance and Song Society.

Dr Williams's Library

14 Gordon Square, London WC1H 0AG
☎0171 387 3727   Fax 0171 388 1142

Open 10.00 am to 5.00 pm Monday,
Wednesday, Friday; 10.00 am to 6.30 pm
Tuesday and Thursday

Open Access To reading room (loans
restricted to subscribers)

Annual subscription £10; ministers of
religion and certain students £5

Primarily a library of theology, religion and
ecclesiastical history. Also philosophy, history
(English and Byzantine). Particularly important
for the study of English Nonconformity.

Wolverhampton Central Library

Snow Hill, Wolverhampton WV1 3AX
☎01902 312025   Fax 01902 714579

Open 10.00 am to 7.00 pm Monday to
Thursday; 10.00 am to 5.00 pm Friday and
Saturday

Archives & Local Studies Collection

42–50 Snow Hill, Wolverhampton WV2 4AB
☎01902 717703 10.00 am to 5.00 pm

Open Monday, Tuesday, Friday, Saturday
(Limited archive production between 12.00
pm and 2.00 pm; Archives must be booked
in advance on Saturdays); 10.00 am to 7.00
pm Wednesday; closed Thursday

General lending and reference libraries, plus
children's library. Also audiovisual library
holding cassettes, CDs, videos and music
scores.

York Central Library

Museum Street, York YO1 2DS
☎01904 655631/654144 (reference library)
Fax 01904 611025

Open 9.30 am to 8.00 pm Monday, Tuesday,
Friday; 9.30 am to 1.00 pm Wednesday;
9.30 am to 5.30 pm Thursday; 9.30 am to
4.00 pm Saturday

Reference Library 9.00 am to 8.00 pm
Monday, Tuesday, Wednesday, Friday; 9.00
am to 5.30 pm Thursday; 9.00 am to 1.00 pm
Saturday

General lending library plus reference library
incorporating local organisations database; local
studies library for York and surrounding area;
business information service; microfilm/fiche
readers for national and local newspapers; census returns and family history resource; general
reference collection. Maintains strong links
with other local history resource centres,
namely the Borthwick Institute, York City
Archive and York Minster Library. Audio
books service and music library.

Young Book Trust Children's Reference Library

Book House, 45 East Hill, London
SW18 2QZ
☎0181 870 9055   Fax 0181 874 4790

Open 9.00 am to 5.00 pm Monday to Friday

Access For reference only

A comprehensive collection of children's literature, related books and periodicals. Aims to
hold all children's titles published within the
last two years. An information service covers all
aspects of children's literature, including profiles of authors and illustrators. Reading room
facilities.

Zoological Society Library

Regent's Park, London NW1 4RY
☎0171 722 3333 ext. 6293 Fax 0171 586 5743

Open 9.30 am to 5.30 pm Monday to Friday

Access To members and staff; non-members
by application and on payment of fee

160,000 volumes on zoology including 5000
journals (1300 current) and a wide range of
books on animals and particular habitats. Slide
collection available and many historic zoological prints.

Picture Libraries

A-Z Botanical Collection Ltd
Bedwell Lodge, Cucumber Lane, Essendon,
Hatfield, Hertfordshire AL9 6JB
☎01707 649091   Fax 01707 649091
Contact *Jeremy Finlay*

150,000 transparencies, specialising in plants
and related subjects.

Action Plus
54-58 Tanner Street, London SE1 3LL
☎0171 403 1558   Fax 0171 403 1526

Specialist sports and action library with a vast
and comprehensive collection of small-format
colour and b&w images covering all aspects of
over 120 professional and amateur sports from
around the world. As well as personalities,
events, venues etc, also covers themes such as
success, celebration, dejection, teamwork,
effort and exhaustion. Offers same-day
despatch of pictures or alternatively, clients
with Macintosh and modem or ISDN links can
receive digital images direct.

Lesley & Roy Adkins Picture Library
Longstone Lodge, Aller, Langport, Somerset
TA10 0QT
☎01458 250075   Fax 01458 250858

Colour coverage of archaeology, heritage and
related subjects (UK and Europe), prehistoric,
Roman, medieval and recent sites and monuments, landscapes and countryside, housing, art
and architecture, towns, villages and religious
monuments. Prompt service. No service
charge if any pictures are used. Catalogue available.

The Advertising Archive Limited
45 Lyndale Avenue, London NW2 2QB
☎0171 435 6540   Fax 0171 794 6584
Contact *Suzanne or Larry Viner*

With half a million images, the largest collection of British and American press ads and
magazine cover illustrations in Europe. Visitors
by appointment. Research undertaken; rapid
service, competitive rates.

AFP (Agence France Presse)
See **Popperfoto**

AKG London Ltd, Arts and History Picture Library
10 Plato Place, 72-74 St Dionis Road,
London SW6 4TU
☎0171 610 6103   Fax 0171 610 6125
Contact *Julia Engelhardt*

Collection of 100,000 images with computerised
access to nine million more kept in the Berlin
AKG Library. *Specialises* in art, archaeology, history, topography, music, personalities and film.

Bryan & Cherry Alexander Photography
Higher Cottage, Manston, Sturminster
Newton, Dorset DT10 1EZ
☎01258 473006   Fax 01258 473333
Contact *Cherry Alexander*

70,000 colour transparencies, specialising in
polar regions, with emphasis on the wildlife
and native peoples of the Arctic.

Allsport (UK) Ltd
Allsport House, 3 Greenlea Park, Prince
George's Road, London SW19 2JD
☎0181 685 1010   Fax 0181 648 5240
Contact *Lee Martin*

A large specialist library with 6 million colour
transparencies, covering 130 different sports and
top sports personalities. Represented in 27
countries worldwide. Large studio and digital
wiring facilities through Macintosh picture desk.

Alvey & Towers
9 Rosebank Road, Countesthorpe,
Leicestershire LE8 5YA
☎0116 2779184   Fax 0116 2779184
Contact *Emma Alvey*

Collection of approximately 20,000 transparencies, mainly of the modern railway industry and all related supporting industries. In
addition, also covers architecture, gardens,
industry people, scenics, transport and travel.

Andes Press Agency
26 Padbury Court, London E2 7EH
☎0171 613 5417   Fax 0171 739 3159
Contact *Val Baker, Carlos Reyes*

80,000 colour transparencies and 300,000

b&w, specialising in social documentary, world religions, Latin America and Britain.

Heather Angel/Biofotos
Highways, 6 Vicarage Hill, Farnham, Surrey GU9 8HJ
☎01252 716700   Fax 01252 727464
Contacts *Rona Tiller, Val West*

Constantly expanding worldwide natural history, wildlife and landscapes: polar regions, tropical rainforest flora and fauna, all species of plants and animals in natural habitats from Africa, Asia (notably China and Malaysia), Australasia, South America and USA, urban wildlife, pollution, biodiversity, global warming. Catalogue available. Commissions undertaken. Complete picture/text packages a speciality.

Animal Photography
4 Marylebone Mews, New Cavendish Street, London W1M 7LF
☎0171 935 0503   Fax 0171 487 3038

Colour and b&w coverage of horses, dogs, cats, zoos, the Galapagos Islands, East Africa. Commissions undertaken.

Aquarius Picture Library
PO Box 5, Hastings, East Sussex TN34 1HR
☎01424 721196   Fax 01424 717704
Contact *David Corkill*

Over one million images specialising in cinema past and present, television, pop music, ballet, opera, theatre, etc. The library includes various American showbiz collections. Film stills date back to the beginning of the century. Interested in film stills, the older the better. Current material is supplied by own suppliers.

Aquila Photographics
PO Box 1, Studley, Warwickshire B80 7AN
☎0152785 2357   Fax 0152785 7507

Natural history library specialising in birds, British and European wildlife, North America, Africa and Australia, environmental subjects, farming, habitats and related subjects, domestic animals and pets.

Arcaid
The Factory, 2 Acre Road, Kingston upon Thames, Surrey KT2 6EF
☎0181 546 4352   Fax 0181 541 5230

The built environment, historic and contemporary architecture and interior design by leading architectural photographers. Covers international and British subjects, single images and series, with background information. Visitors welcome by appointment. Commissions undertaken.

Architectural Association Photo Library
34-36 Bedford Square, London WC1B 3ES
☎0171 636 0974   Fax 0171 414 0782
Contact *Valerie Bennett, Vanessa Norwood*

200,000 35 mm transparencies on architecture, historical and contemporary. Archive of large-format b&w negatives from the 1920s and 1930s.

Ardea London Ltd
35 Brodrick Road, London SW17 7DX
☎0181 672 2067   Fax 0181 672 8787

Wildlife, natural history, conservation and environmental topics in colour and b&w. Animals, birds, plants and fish in their natural habitat worldwide.

Art Directors Photo Library
Image House, 86 Haverstock Hill, London NW3 2BD
☎0171 485 9325/813 2128
Fax 0171 485 7776
Contact *Jack Stanley*

Work from 300 internationally recognised photographers is constantly updated. Of special interest are extensive files of backgrounds of all kinds, medical/hospital/pharmaceutical, business and industry, lifestyle, and wide-ranging travel/geographical, holiday sections. Catalogues free to professionals.

Artbank Illustration Library
8 Woodcroft Avenue, London NW7 2AG
☎0181 906 2288   Fax 0181 906 2289

Illustration and art library holding thousands of images by many renowned artists. Large-format transparencies. Catalogue available on faxed request. Represents a diverse group of UK and American illustrators for commissioned work. Portfolios available for viewing.

Aspect Picture Library Ltd
40 Rostrevor Road, London SW6 5AD
☎0171 736 1998/731 7362
Fax 0171 731 7362

Colour and b&w worldwide coverage of countries, events, industry and travel, with large files on art, namely paintings, space, China and the Middle East.

Audio Visual Services

Imperial College School of Medicine at St Mary's, London W2 1PG

☎0171 725 1739   Fax 0171 724 7349

Contact *B. Tallon*

Colour and b&w, mostly 35 mm colour. Clinical medicine, contemporary and historical, including HIV-AIDS material and history of penicillin. Commissions undertaken.

Autosport Photographic

38-42 Hampton Road, Teddington, Middlesex TW11 0JE

☎0181 943 5918   Fax 0181 943 5922

Contact *Tim Wright*

Collection of one million images of Formula 1, touring and club cars. Now incorporates Classic & Sportscar.

Aviation Images – Mark Wagner

42B Queens Road, London SW19 8LR

☎0181 944 5225   Fax 0181 944 5335

Contact *Mark Wagner*

150,000+ aviation images, civil and military, technical and generic. Mark Wagner is the photographer for *Flight International* magazine. Member of **BAPLA** and RAES.

Aviation Photographs International

15 Downs View Road, Swindon, Wiltshire SN3 1NS

☎01793 497179   Fax 01793 434030

The 250,000 colour photos comprise a comprehensive coverage of army, naval and airforce hardware ranging from early pistols to the latest ships. Extensive coverage of military and civil aviation includes modern together with many air-to-air views of vintage/warbird types. Commissions undertaken for additional photography and research.

Aviation Picture Library

35 Kingsley Avenue, London W13 0EQ

☎0181 566 7712   Fax 0181 566 7714

Contact *Austin John Brown, Chris Savill*

Specialists in the aviation field but also a general library which includes travel, architecture, transport, landscapes and skyscapes. *Special collections*: aircraft and all aspects of the aviation industry; aerial obliques of Europe, USA, Caribbean and West Africa; architectural and town planning. Commissions undertaken on the ground and in the air.

Axel Poignant Archive

115 Bedford Court Mansions, Bedford Avenue, London WC1B 3AG

☎0171 636 2555   Fax 0171 636 2555

Anthropological and ethnographic subjects, especially Australia and the South Pacific. Also Scandinavia (early history and mythology), Sicily and England.

Barnaby's Picture Library

Barnaby House, 19 Rathbone Street, London W1P 1AF

☎0171 636 6128   Fax 0171 637 4317

Contact *Mary Buckland*

Colour and b&w coverage of a wide range of subjects: nature, transport, industry and historical, including a collection on Hitler. Commissions undertaken.

Barnardos Photographic and Film Archive

Tanners Lane, Barkingside, Ilford, Essex IG6 1QG

☎0181 550 8822   Fax 0181 551 6870

Contact *John Kirkham*

Specialises in social history (1874 to present day), child care, education, war years, emigration/migration. Half a million prints, slides, negatives. Images are mainly b&w, colour since late 1940s/early 50s. Archive of 200 films dating back to 1905. Visitors by appointment Mon-Fri 9.30 am to 4.30 pm.

Colin Baxter Photography Limited

Woodlands Industrial Estate, Grantown-on-Spey PH26 3NA

☎01479 873999   Fax 01479 873888

Contact *Colin B. Kirkwood*

Over 50,000 images specialising in Scotland. Also the Lake District, Yorkshire, the Cotswolds, France, Iceland and a special collection on Charles Rennie Mackintosh's work. *Publishes* books, calendars, postcards and greetings cards on landscape, cityscape and natural history containing images which are primarily, but not exclusively, Colin Baxter's. Also publishers of the *Worldlife Library* of natural history books.

BBC Natural History Unit Picture Library

Broadcasting House, Whiteladies Road, Bristol, Avon BS8 2LR

☎0117 9746720   Fax 0117 9238166

Contacts *Helen Gilks, Colin Jackson*

This newly established picture library has 60,000 35mm stills of wildlife, landscape and filming, plus a unique collection of photographs relating to the early years of the Natural History Unit (founded in 1957). Represents the work of top wildlife photographers from around the world. Film footage and sound recordings also available.

The Photographic Library Beamish, The North of England Open Air Museum

Beamish, The North of England Open Air Museum, Beamish, County Durham DH9 0RG
☎01207 231811   Fax 01207 290933
Assistant Keeper, Resource Collections
Jim Lawson

Comprehensive collection; images relate to the North East of England and cover agricultural, industrial, topography, advertising and shop scenes, people at work and play. Also on laser disc for rapid searching. Visitors by appointment weekdays.

Earl Beesley Photography

10 The Green, West Drayton, Middlesex UB7 7PJ
☎01895 447473
Contact *Earl Beesley*

10,000 images of historic houses, stately homes, castles, landscapes, artifacts, ariel, ballet.

Ivan J. Belcher Colour Picture Library

57 Gibson Close, Abingdon, Oxfordshire OX14 1XS
☎01235 521524   Fax 01235 521524

Extensive colour picture library specialising in top-quality medium-format transparencies depicting the British scene. Particular emphasis on tourist, holiday and heritage locations, including famous cities, towns, picturesque harbours, rivers, canals, castles, cottages, rural scenes and traditions photographed throughout the seasons. Mainly of recent origin, and constantly updated.

The Berlitz Collection

33 Albury Avenue, Isleworth, Middlesex TW7 5HY
☎0181 847 3777   Fax 0181 568 2402
Contact *Brigitte Arora*

An extensive travel photography archive, commissioned specifically for the famous Berlitz travel list (*Berlitz Pocket Guides* and *Discovery* series). Covers destinations world-wide; comprehensive not only in its coverage of tourist attractions but also in its insight into local culture and lifestyle.

Andrew Besley PhotoLibrary

2 Reawla Lane, Reawla, Near Hayle, Cornwall TR27 5HQ
☎01736 850086   Fax 01736 850086
Contact *Andrew Besley*

Specialist library of 20,000 images of West Country faces, places and moods.

BFI Stills, Posters and Designs

British Film Institute, 21 Stephen Street, London W1P 2LN
☎0171 255 1444   Fax 0171 323 9260
Contact *Bridget Kinally*

Holds images from more than 60,000 films and TV programmes on 6 million b&w prints and over 500,000 colour transparencies. A further 20,000 files hold portraits of film and TV personalities and cover related general subjects such as studios, equipment, awards. Also holds original posters and set and costume designs. Visitors welcome by appointment only (from 10.00 am to 6.00 pm).

Birmingham Library Services Photographic Archives

See **Birmingham Library Services** under **Library Services**

Birmingham Repertory Theatre Archive and Sir Barry Jackson Library

See **Birmingham Library Services** under **Library Services**

Blackwoods Picture Library

See **Geoslides Photography**

Anthony Blake Photo Library

54 Hill Rise, Richmond, Surrey TW10 6UB
☎0181 940 7583   Fax 0181 948 1224

'Europe's premier source' of food and wine related images. From the farm and the vineyard to the plate and the bottle. Cooking and kitchens, top chefs and restaurants, country trades and markets, worldwide travel. Many recipes available to accompany transparencies. Commissions accepted. Free brochure available.

Boats & Boating Features (Keith Pritchard)

9 High Street, Southwell, Portland, Dorset
DT5 2EH
☎01305 861006   Fax 01305 861006
Contact *Keith Pritchard*

Around 20,000 colour transparencies of small
craft, historic and modern boats up to 100ft,
boating events, people and places in Britain and
overseas.

Chris Bonington Picture Library

Badger Hill, Nether Row, Hesket
Newmarket, Wigton, Cumbria CA7 8LA
☎016974 78286   Fax 016974 78238
Contact *Frances Daltrey*

Based on the personal collection of climber and
author Chris Bonington and his extensive travels
and mountaineering achievements; also work by
Doug Scott and other climbers, including the
Peter Boardman and Joe Tasker Collections.
Full coverage of the world's mountains, from
British hills to Everest, depicting expedition
planning and management stages, the approach
march showing inhabitants of the area, flora and
fauna, local architecture and climbing action
shots on some of the world's highest mountains.

Boulton and Watt Archive

See **Birmingham Library Services** under
Library Services

The Bridgeman Art Library

17-19 Garway Road, London W2 4PH
☎0171 727 4065   Fax 0171 792 8509
Marketing Manager *Sarah Pooley*

Fine art photo archive acting as an agent to
more than 600 museums, galleries and picture
owners around the world. Large-format colour
transparencies of paintings, sculptures, prints,
manuscripts, antiquities and the decorative arts.
The Library is currently expanding at the rate of
300 new images each week and recent additions
include the collections of the National Galleries
of Scotland, the Courtauld Institute Galleries
and San Diego Museum of Art. Catalogues of
stock are available in printed form and on CD-
ROM. Please call for a free brochure.

British Library Reproductions

British Library, Great Russell Street, London
WC1B 3DG
☎0171 412 7614   Fax 0171 412 7771
Twelve million books and approximately five
million other items available for photography.

Generally, photographs are made to order.
Material should be ordered as far in advance as
possible. All photography is done in-house by
staff only. Specialist subjects include illuminated
manuscripts, stamps, music, maps, botanical and
zoological illustration, portraits of historical figures, history of India and South-East Asia.

Brooklands Museum Picture Library

Brooklands Museum, The Clubhouse,
Brooklands Road, Weybridge, Surrey
KT13 0QN
☎01932 857381   Fax 01932 855465
Contact *John Pulford, Curator of Collections;*
Julian Temple, Curator of Aviation

About 40,000 b&w and colour prints and slides.
Subjects include: Brooklands Motor Racing
1907-1939; British aviation and aerospace 1908-
present day – particularly BAC, Hawker,
Sopwith and Vickers aircraft built at Brooklands.

Hamish Brown Scottish Photographic

26 Kirkcaldy Road, Burntisland, Fife KY3 9HQ
☎01592 873546
Contact *Hamish M. Brown*

Colour and b&w coverage of most topics and
areas of Scotland (sites, historic, buildings, landscape, mountains), also travel and mountains
abroad, Ireland and Morocco. Commissions
undertaken.

Bubbles Photolibrary

23A Benwell Road, London N7 7BL
☎0171 609 4547   Fax 0171 607 1410

Pregnancy, babies, children, teenagers, general
lifestyle, health, old age, medical, still lives of
food.

Caledonian Newspapers Picture Library

195 Albion Street, Glasgow G1 1QP
☎0141 552 6255   Fax 0141 553 2642

Over 6 million images: b&w and colour photographs from *c.*1900 from the *Herald* (Glasgow)
and *Evening Times*. Current affairs, Scotland,
Glasgow, Clydeside shipbuilding and engineering, personalities, World Wars I and II, sport.

Camera Press

21 Queen Elizabeth Street, London SE1 2PD
☎0171 378 1300   Fax 0171 278 5126
High-quality photofeatures and up-to-date

coverage of international events, celebrities, royals, fashion and beauty, and general stock.

Camera Ways Ltd
Picture Library
Court View, Stonebridge Green Road, Egerton, Ashford, Kent TN27 9AN
☎01233 756454   Fax 01233 756242
Contacts *Derek, Caryl, Jonathan, Steve*

Founded by award-winning film-maker and photographer, Derek Budd, the library specialises in rural activities and natural history. It contains 35mm and 6x4.5mm, colour and b&w images as well as 16mm film and video footage on Beta SP. Coverage includes: wildlife habitats, flora and fauna of Britain and Europe, traditional country crafts and people, village scenes, landscapes, gardens, coastal and aquatic life, dinosaurs, aerial surveys, storm damage and M.O.D. reserves. A creative service is available from their Technical Artist & Wildlife Illustrator; commissions undertaken in all aspects of commercial multi-media photography, 16mm film, broadcast and corporate video production. 35mm digital film scanning and transmission, image manipulation and page-making facilities also available with 'Adobe' software.

Capital Pictures
54a Clerkenwell Road, London EC1M 5PS
☎0171 253 1122   Fax 0171 253 1414
Contact *Phil Loftus*

300,000 images. *Specialises* in showbusiness, rock & pop, television, politics, royalty and film stills.

The Casement Collection
Erin Lodge, Jigs Lane South, Warfield, Berkshire RG12 6DP
☎01344 302067   Fax 01344 303158

Colour and b&w travel library, particularly strong on North America and the Gulf. Not just beaches and palm trees. Based on Jack Casement's collection, with additions by other photographers. Digitised images available.

J. Allan Cash Ltd
74 South Ealing Road, London W5 4QB
☎0181 840 4141   Fax 0181 566 2568

Colour and b&w coverage of travel, natural history, people, space, sport, industry, agriculture and many other subjects. New material regularly contributed by 300 plus photographers.

Central Press Collection
See **The Hulton Getty Collection**

The Centre for the Study of Cartoons and Caricature
The Templeman Library, University of Kent at Canterbury, Canterbury, Kent CT2 7NU
☎01227 823127   Fax 01227 823127
Contacts *Robert Edwards, Jane Newton*

Over 85,000 original cartoons, 1900–1996; 5000 books, papers, journals, catalogues, and assorted ephemera on cartoons, caricature, humour, satire and propaganda. *Specialises* in political and social cartoons – historical, British and international.

CEPHAS Picture Library
20 Bedster Gardens, West Molesey, Surrey KT8 1SZ
☎0181 979 8647   Fax 0181 224 8095

The wine industry and vineyards of the world is the subject on which Cephas has made its reputation. Around 50,000 images, mainly original 6x7 transparencies, make this the most comprehensive and up-to-date archive in Britain. Almost all the wine-producing countries of the world are covered in depth along with all aspects of the industry. CEPHAS also has a rapidly expanding food and drink department and a worldwide travel section which incorporates a major collection on France. Visitors welcome by appointment.

Christel Clear Marine Photography
Roselea, Church Lane, Awbridge, Near Romsey, Hampshire SO51 0HN
☎01794 341081   Fax 01794 340890
Contact *Nigel Dowden, Christel Dowden*

Over 50,000 images on 35mm and 645 transparency: yachting and boating from Grand Prix sailing to small dinghies, cruising locations and harbours. Recent additions include angling, fly fishing and travel. Visitors by appointment.

Christian Aid Photo Library
PO Box 100, London SE1 7RT
☎0171 620 4444   Fax 0171 620 0719

Pictures from Africa, Asia and Latin America, relating to small-scale, community-based programmes. Mostly development themes: agriculture, health, education, urban and rural life.

Christie's Images

1 Langley Lane, London SW8 1TH
☎0171 582 1282   Fax 0171 582 5632

Contact *Edward Schneider*

130,000 images of fine and decorative art; the largest collection of its kind in the UK.

The Cinema Museum

The Old Fire Station, 46 Renfrew Road, London SE11 4NA
☎0171 820 9991   Fax 0171 793 0849

Colour and b&w coverage (including stills) of the motion picture industry throughout its history, including the Ronald Grant Archive. Small collections on theatre, variety, television and popular music.

John Cleare/Mountain Camera

Hill Cottage, Fonthill Gifford, Salisbury, Wiltshire SP3 6QW
☎01747 820320   Fax 01747 820320

Colour and b&w coverage of mountains and wild places, climbing, trekking, expeditions, wilderness travel, landscapes and people from all continents. Geographical features, the Himalaya and the British countryside, both landscapes and country walking, are specialities. Commissions and consultancy work undertaken in all these fields. Researchers welcome by appointment.

Close-Up Picture Library

14 Burnham Wood, Fareham, Hampshire PO16 7UD
☎01329 239053

Director *David Stent*

Specialises in the close-up angle of all aspects of life: people, places, animal and bird-life and the environment in general. Also a wide range of pictures covering travel in Europe and the Orient, multicultural, ethnic and educational issues. Photographers with quality material always welcome: no minimum initial submission; 50% commission on 35mm.

Stephanie Colasanti

38 Hillside Court, 409 Finchley Road, London NW3 6HQ
☎0171 435 3695   Fax 0171 435 9995

Colour coverage of Europe, Africa, Asia, United Arab Emirates, the Caribbean, USA, Australia, New Zealand, the Pacific Islands and South America: people, animals, towns, agriculture, landscapes, carnivals, markets, archaeology, religion and ancient civilisations. Travel assignments undertaken. Medium-format transparencies (2″ square).

Michael Cole Camerawork

The Coach House, 27 The Avenue, Beckenham, Kent BR3 2DP
☎0181 658 6120   Fax 0181 658 6120

Contact *Michael Cole, Derrick Bentley*

Probably the largest and most comprehensive collection of tennis pictures in the world; incorporating the library of Le Roye Productions, a company which covered Wimbledon from 1945-70, and MCC coverage of all major tennis events, worldwide, since 1970. Also small travel picture library: English countryside, Venice, Moscow, US etc. 200,000 35mm colour slides, 3,600 2″ and 6x7cm colour transparencies, 270,000 b&w negatives and a vast quantity of b&w movie film.

Collections

13 Woodberry Crescent, London N10 1PJ
☎0181 883 0083   Fax 0181 883 9215

Contact *Laura Boswell, Brian Shuel*

250,000 colour and b&w images making a collection of collections about the British Isles. 'Our "area" collections aim to cover Great Britain, Ireland and the many smaller islands eventually – and we are doing well so far.' Subjects include two of Britain's major collections on pregnancy, birth, childhood and education by Anthea Sieveking and Sandra Lousada, the customs of Britain by Brian Shuel, landscapes by Fay Godwin, large collections of castles, waterways, railways, bridges and London, and a large variety of smaller specialities. Also building an unusual collection on the emergency services. Visitors welcome by appointment.

COMSTOCK Photolibrary

28 Chelsea Wharf, 15 Lots Road, London SW10 0QQ
☎0171 351 4448   Fax 0171 352 8414

Contact *Helena Kovac*

Extensive coverage of business, people, industry, science, futuristic, world travel, landscapes, medical and natural history. Also desktop photography and CD-ROM. Free catalogue on request. Provides access to over four million images.

Corbis UK Ltd

12 Regents Wharf, All Saints Street, London N1 7RLA
☎0171 843 4444   Fax 0171 278 1408

Contacts *Helen Menzies, Anna Calvert*

Access to a digital archive of over half a million

images, plus one of the world's largest picture sources, Bettmann. With over 17 million images, the archive is home to scores of individual collections including two of the most important news libraries: UPI (1907-90) and Reuters (1985 to the present day, from the original negatives). Specialist subjects include news events, sports, cinema, war, social history, entertainment, people, geography, and early coverage of the Wild West, native Americans and the American Civil War. Other major components provide comprehensive coverage of world history from woodcuts and engravings to early photographs. A 6000-image directory has been published and a free catalogue is available.

Sylvia Cordaiy Photo Library

72 East Ham Road, Littlehampton,
West Sussex BN17 7BQ
☎01903 715297   Fax 01903 715297
Contact *Sylvia Cordaiy*

Over 100,000 images on all formats, colour and b&w: architecture, world travel, wildlife, global environmental topics, landscapes, cities and rural scenes, veterinary work, the Antarctic, domestic and working animals, livestock. Huge files of card/calendar material and an archive of 17,000 b&w negatives. Visitors welcome.

Country Life Picture Library

King's Reach Tower, Stamford Street,
London SE1 9LS
☎0171 261 6337   Fax 0171 261 6216
Contact *Camilla Costello*

Over 150,000 b&w negatives and 15,000 colour transparencies dating back to 1897. Country houses, stately homes, churches and town houses in Britain and abroad, interiors of architectural interest (ceilings, fireplaces, furniture, paintings, sculpture), and exteriors showing many landscaped gardens. Visitors by appointment. Open Tuesday to Friday.

County Visuals

The Design Studio, Professional Services Dept, Kent County Council, Springfield, Maidstone, Kent ME14 2LT
☎01622 696209   Fax 01622 686170
Contact *Tony Hemsted*

A small but comprehensive library of colour transparencies specialising in the wide spectrum of attractions, activities, developments and general Kentish countryside scenes.

Philip Craven Worldwide Photo-Library

Surrey Studios, 21 Nork Way, Nork,
Banstead, Surrey SM7 1PB
☎01737 373737   Fax 01737 373737
Contact *Philip Craven*

Extensive coverage of British scenes, cities, villages, English countryside, gardens, historic buildings and wildlife. Worldwide travel and wildlife subjects on medium- and large-format transparencies.

CTC Picture Library

CTC Publicity, Longfield,
Midhurst Road, Fernhurst, Haslemere,
Surrey GU27 3HA
☎01428 655007   Fax 01428 641071
Contact *Neil Crighton*

One of the biggest specialist libraries in the UK with 250,000 slides covering world and UK agriculture, horticulture, and environmental subjects. Also a small section on travel.

Sue Cunningham Photographic

56 Chatham Road, Kingston upon Thames,
Surrey KT1 3AA
☎0181 541 3024   Fax 0181 541 5388

Extensive specialist collection on Brazil. Expanding coverage of other areas including Peru, Bolivia, Tanzania, Burundi, Zambia, Portugal, Spain, Hungary, Poland, Czech Republic and the UK. Colour and b&w. Member of **BAPLA**.

James Davis Travel Photography

65 Brighton Road, Shoreham, West Sussex BN43 6RE
☎01273 452252   Fax 01273 440116

Travel collection: people, places, emotive scenes and tourism. Constantly updated by James Davis and a team of photographers, both at home and abroad. Same-day service available.

Douglas Dickins Photo Library

2 Wessex Gardens, Golders Green, London NW11 9RT
☎0181 455 6221

Worldwide colour and b&w coverage, specialising in Asia, particularly India, Indonesia and Japan. Meeting educational requirements on landscape, archaeology, history, religions, customs, people and folklore.

C M Dixon

The Orchard, Marley Lane, Kingston, Canterbury, Kent CT4 6HJ
☎01227 830075   Fax 01227 831135

Colour coverage of ancient civilisations, archaeology and art, ethnology, mythology, world religion, museum objects, geography, geology, meteorology, landscapes, people and places from many countries including most of Europe, former USSR, Ethiopia, Iceland, Jordan, Morocco, Sri Lanka, Tunisia, Turkey, Egypt, Uzbekistan.

Dominic Photography

4B Moore Park Road, London SW6 2JT
☎0171 381 0007   Fax 0171 381 0008

Contact *Zoë Dominic, Catherine Ashmore*

Colour and b&w coverage of the entertainment world from 1957 onwards: dance, opera, theatre, ballet, musicals and personalities.

Philip Dunn Picture Library

Jasmine Cottage, Marston, Church Eaton, Staffordshire ST20 0AS
☎01785 840674/0860 523599
Fax 01785 840674

Contact *Philip Dunn*

Constantly expanding collection of some 50,000 b&w/colour images of travel, people, activities and places in Britain and overseas. Commissions undertaken.

Patrick Eagar Photography

5 Ennerdale Road, Kew Gardens, Surrey TW9 3PG
☎0181 940 9269   Fax 0181 332 1229

Colour and b&w coverage of cricket from 1965. Test matches, overseas tours and all aspects of the sport. Also a constantly expanding wine library (colour) of vineyards, grapes, cellars and winemakers of France, Italy, Germany, Lebanon, Australia, New Zealand, South Africa (and England). Digital photograph transmission by modem.

Ecoscene

The Oasts, Headley Lane, Passfield, Liphook, Hampshire GU30 7RX
☎01428 751056   Fax 01428 751057

Contact *Sally Morgan*

Expanding colour library of over 80,000 transparencies specialising in all aspects of the environment: pollution, conservation, recycling, restoration, natural history, habitats, education, landscapes, industry and agriculture. All parts of the globe are covered with specialist collections

covering Antarctica, Australia, North America. Sally Morgan, who runs the library, is a professional ecologist and expert source of information on all environmental topics. Photographic and writing commissions undertaken.

Edifice

14 Doughty Street, London WC1N 2PL
☎0171 405 9395   Fax 0171 267 3632

Contact *Philippa Lewis, Gillian Darley*

Colour coverage of architecture, buildings of all possible descriptions, gardens, urban and rural landscape. *Specialises* in details of ornament, period style and material. British Isles, USA, Africa, Europe and Japan all covered. Detailed list available, visits by appointment.

English Heritage Photographic Library

23 Savile Row, London W1X 1AB
☎0171 973 3338   Fax 0171 973 3330

Contact *Lucy Bunning, Celia Sterne*

Images of English castles, abbeys, houses, gardens, Roman remains, ancient monuments, battlefields, industrial and post-war buildings, interiors, paintings, artifacts, architectural details, conservation, archaeology.

The Environmental Picture Library Ltd

5 Baker's Row, London EC1R 3DB
☎0171 833 1355   Fax 0171 833 1383

Contacts *Daphne Christelis, Liz Somerville*

Rapidly growing stock of pictures on all environmental issues to illustrate the real problems as well as positive practices from local to global. Now supplying the Greenpeace collection. Colour transparencies and black & white prints.

EPA (European Pressphoto Agency)

See **Popperfoto**

European Passenger Service (Eurostar) and St Paul's Cathedral

426-432 Essex Road, London N1 3PJ
☎0171 704 0494   Fax 0171 226 0435

Contact *Philip Way*

1500 slides and photographs of Eurostar trains, facilities and stations; 1000 photographs of events in St Paul's Cathedral (1982-1985).

Mary Evans Picture Library

59 Tranquil Vale, Blackheath, London SE3 0BS
☎0181 318 0034   Fax 0181 852 7211

Collection of historical illustrations documenting

social, political, cultural, technical, geographical and biographical themes from ancient times to the recent past. Photographs, prints and ephemera backed by large book and magazine collection. Many special collections including Sigmund Freud, the **Fawcett Library** (women's rights), the Meledin Collection (20th-century Russian history) and individual photographers such as Roger Mayne. Brochure sent on request.

Express Newspapers Syndication
Ludgate House, 245 Blackfriars Road, London SE1 9UX
☎0171 922 7902/3/4/5/6 Fax 0171 922 7871
Syndication Manager *Jamie Maskey*

One and a half million images updated daily, with strong collections on personalities, royalty, showbiz, sport, fashion, nostalgia and events. Electronic transmission available.

Eye Ubiquitous
65 Brighton Road, Shoreham, East Sussex BN43 6RE
☎01273 440113   Fax 01273 440116
Contact *Paul Seheult*

General stock specialising in social documentary worldwide, including the work of Tim Page, and now incorporating the **James Davis Travel Library** (see entry).

Chris Fairclough Colour Library
Whinfields, Cranleigh Road, Ewhurst, Surrey GU6 7RN
☎01483 277992   Fax 01483 267984
Contact *Jane Eaton*

General colour library with special collections on religion, education, travel, children, people and places. Commissions undertaken and studio facility.

Falklands Pictorial
Vision House, 16 Broadfield Road, Heeley, Sheffield, South Yorkshire S8 0XJ
☎0114 2589299   Fax 0114 2550113

Colour and b&w photographs showing all aspects of Falklands life from 1880 to the present day.

Famous Pictures and Features
Studio 4, Limehouse Cut, 46 Morris Road, London E14 6NQ
☎0171 537 7055   Fax 0171 537 7056

Pictures and features agency with a growing library of colour transparencies dating back to 1985. Portrait, party and concert shots of rock and pop stars plus international entertainers, film and TV celebrities. The library is supplied by a team of photographers from the UK and around the world, keeping it up-to-date on a daily basis.

Farmers Weekly Picture Library
Quadrant House, The Quadrant, Sutton, Surrey SM2 5AS
☎0181 652 4914   Fax 0181 652 4005
Library Manager *Barry Dixon*

Britain's largest agricultural picture library holds more than 200,000 transparencies covering all aspects of farming and country life. The collection is updated daily.

Ffotograff
10 Kyveilog Street, Pontcanna, Cardiff CF1 9JA
☎01222 236879   Fax 01222 229326
Contact *Patricia Aithie*

Library and agency specialising in travel, exploration, the arts, architecture, traditional culture, archaeology and landscape. Based in Wales but specialising in the Middle and Far East; Yemen and Wales are unusually strong aspects of the library. Churches and cathedrals of Britain and Crusader castles. Abstract paintings and detailed photographic textures suitable for book covers.

Financial Times Pictures
1 Southwark Bridge, London SE1 9HL
☎0171 873 3671/3221   Fax 0171 873 4606
Contact *Suzie Kew*

One million colour and b&w portrait files of leading figures in commerce, industry and politics, plus city scenes and pictures of people at work in many trades and callings around the world. Visits by appointment.

Fine Art Photographic Library Ltd
2A Milner Street, London SW3 2PU
☎0171 589 3127   Fax 0171 584 1944
Contact *Linda Hammerbeck*

Over 15,000 large-format transparencies, with a specialist collection of 19th-century paintings.

Fogden Natural History Photos
Mid Cambushinnie Cottage, Kinbuck, Dunblane, Perthshire FK15 9JU
☎01786 822069   Fax 01786 822069
Contact *Susan Fogden*

Natural history collection, with special reference to rain forests and deserts. Emphasis on quality rather than quantity; growing collection of around 10,000 images.

Food Features

Hardwicke Court, Waverley Lane, Farnham, Surrey GU9 8ES
☎01252 784090   Fax 01252 784091
Contacts *Steve Moss, Alex Barker*

Specialised high-quality food and drink photography, features and tested recipes. Clients' specific requirements can be incorporated into regular shooting schedules.

Ron & Christine Foord Colour Picture Library

155B City Way, Rochester, Kent ME1 2BE
☎01634 847348   Fax 01634 847348
Specialist library with over 1000 species of British and European wild flowers, plus garden flowers, trees, indoor plants, pests and diseases, mosses, lichen, cacti and the majority of larger British insects.

The Football Archive

4th Floor, 2 Pear Tree Court, London EC1R 0DS
☎0171 336 6690   Fax 0171 490 1598
Contacts *Jamie Rainbow, Doug Cheeseman*

FOUNDED in 1995 as a specialist football library. Based on the work of FIFA's former director of photography, Peter Robinson, the library consists of over 100,000 colour and b&w images dating from the 1960s to the present day.

Forest Life Picture Library

231 Corstorphine Road, Edinburgh EH12 7AT
☎0131 334 0303   Fax 0131 334 4473
Contact *Douglas Green*

The official image bank of the Forestry Commission with 40,000 countryside images. Provides a comprehensive, single source for all aspects of forest and woodland management, employment, landscapes, tree species, wildlife, flora and fauna, conservation, sport and leisure.

Werner Forman Archive Ltd

36 Camden Square, London NW1 9XA
☎0171 267 1034   Fax 0171 267 6026
Colour and b&w coverage of ancient civilisations, the Near and Far East and primitive societies around the world. A number of rare collections. Subject lists available.

Formula One Pictures

Suite 8, King Harold Court, Sun Street, Waltham Abbey, Essex EN9 1ER
☎01992 787800   Fax 01992 714366
Contacts *John Townsend, Clive Rose*

500,000 35mm colour slides, b&w and colour negatives of all aspects of Formula One grand prix racing including driver profiles and portraits.

Robert Forsythe Picture Library

16 Lime Grove, Prudhoe, Northumberland NE42 6PR
☎01661 834511
Contact *Robert Forsythe, Fiona Forsythe*

25,000 transparencies of industrial and transport heritage; plus a unique collection of 50,000 items of related publicity ephemera from 1945. Image finding service available. Robert Forsythe is a transport/industrial heritage historian and consultant. Nationwide coverage, particularly strong on Northern Britain. A bibliography of published material is available.

Fortean Picture Library

Henblas, Mwrog Street, Ruthin, Clwyd LL15 1LG
☎01824 707278   Fax 01824 705324
Contact *Janet Bord*

30,000 colour and 45,000 b&w images: mysteries and strange phenomena worldwide, including ghosts, UFOs, witchcraft and monsters; also antiquities, folklore and mythology. Subject list available.

The Fotomas Index

12 Pickhurst Rise, West Wickham, Kent BR4 0AL
☎0181 776 2772   Fax 0181 776 2772
Contact *Arthur Allan*

General historical collection, mostly pre-1900. Subjects include London, topography, art, satirical, social and political history.

Fox Photos
See **The Hulton Getty Collection**

The Francis Frith Collection

The Old Rectory, Bimport, Shaftesbury, Dorset SP7 8AT
☎01747 855669   Fax 01747 855065
Contact *John Buck*

330,00 b&w photographs of British topography from 1860 to 1969 plus 6000 British towns and villages.

John Frost Newspapers
See under **Library Services**

Galaxy Picture Library
1 Milverton Drive, Ickenham, Uxbridge,
Middlesex UB10 8PP
☎01895 637463　　　　Fax 01895 623277
Contact *Robin Scagell*

Specialises in astronomy, space, telescopes, observatories, the sky, clouds and sunsets. Composites of foregrounds, stars, moon and planets prepared to commission. Editorial service available.

Garden and Wildlife Matters Photo Library
'Marlham', Henley's Down, Battle, East Sussex TN33 9BN
☎01424 830566　　　　Fax 01424 830224
Contact *Dr John Feltwell*

Collection of 80,000 6x4 and 35mm images. General gardening techniques and design; cottage gardens and USA designer gardens. 5000 species of garden plants. Flowers, wild and house plants, trees and crops. Environmental, ecological and conservation pictures, including sea, air, noise and freshwater pollution and Eastern Europe. Recycling in all its forms, agriculture, forestry, horticulture and oblique aerial habitat shots from Europe, USA and SE Asian rainforests.

The Garden Picture Library
Unit 12, Ransome's Dock, 35 Parkgate Road, London SW11 4NP
☎0171 228 4332　　　　Fax 0171 924 3267
Contact *Sally Wood*

Original colour transparencies featuring inspirational images of gardens, plants, outdoor living, people in the garden, swimming pools, conservatories, patios, indoor planting, water features, decorative details, landscapes and seasonal aspects on 35mm and medium formats. Special collections include al fresco food and the still life photography of Linda Burgess. In-house picture research can be undertaken on request and visitors are welcome by appointment. Promotional literature available on request.

Leslie Garland Picture Library
69 Fern Avenue, Jesmond, Newcastle upon Tyne, Tyne & Wear NE2 2QU
☎0191 281 3442　　　　Fax 0191 281 3442
Contact *Leslie Garland, ABIPP, ARPS*

The only general picture library between Leeds and Edinburgh, it contains images from North Yorkshire to the Scottish border, and from the North Sea to the Irish Sea. As well as covering the major cities, sights and scenes, the library also stocks images of an applied science, engineering and industrial nature. There is also a growing collection on Norway. Much of the work is on medium format. Brochure available on request. Qualified photographers available for commissioned work.

Ed Geldard Picture Collection
7 Ellergreen House, Nr Burnside, Kendal, Cumbria LA9 5SD
☎01539 728609
Contact *Ed Geldard*

Approximately 10,000 colour transparencies and b&w negs, all by Ed Geldard, specialising in mountain landscapes: particularly, the mountain regions of the Lake District; and the Yorkshire limestone areas, from valley to summit. Commissions undertaken. Books published: *Wainwright's Tour of the Lake District* and *Wainwright in the Limestone Dales.*

Genesis Space Photo Library
Greenbanks, Robins Hill, Raleigh, Bideford, Devon EX39 3PA
☎01237 471960　　　　Fax 01237 471960
Contact *Tim Furniss*

Contemporary and historical colour and b&w spaceflight collection including rockets, spacecraft, spacemen, Earth, moon and planets. Stock list available on request.

Geo Aerial Photography
4 Christian Fields, London SW16 3JZ
☎0181 764 6292/0115 9819418
Fax 0181 764 6292/0115 9815474/9819418
Contact *Kelly White*

Established 1990 and now a growing collection of aerial oblique photographs from the UK, Scandinavia, Asia and Africa - landscapes, buildings, industrial sites etc. Commissions undertaken.

GeoScience Features
6 Orchard Drive, Wye, Kent TN25 5AU
☎01233 812707　　　　Fax 01233 812707

Fully computerised and comprehensive library containing the world's principal source of volcanic phenomena. Extensive collections, providing scientific detail with technical quality, of rocks, minerals, fossils, microsections of botanical and animal tissues, animals, biology, birds, botany, chemistry, earth science, ecology, environment, geology, geography, habitats, landscapes, macro/microbiology, peoples, sky, weather, wildlife and zoology. Over 220,000 original colour transparencies in medium- and 35mm-format. Subject lists available on application. Incorporates the RIDA photolibrary.

Geoslides Photography
4 Christian Fields, London SW16 3JZ
☎0181 764 6292   Fax 0181 764 6292/0115 9819418
Contact *John Douglas*
Established in 1968. Landscape and human interest subjects from the Arctic, Antarctica, Scandinavia, UK, Africa (south of Sahara), Middle East, Asia (south and southeast); also Australia, via Blackwoods Picture Library. Also specialist collections of images from British India (the Raj) and Boer War.

Martin and Dorothy Grace
40 Clipstone Avenue, Mapperley, Nottingham NG3 5JZ
☎0115 9208248   Fax 0115 9626802
Colour coverage of Britain's natural history, specialising in trees, shrubs and wild flowers. Also ferns, birds and butterflies, habitats, landscapes, ecology. Subject lists available. Member of **BAPLA**.

Ronald Grant Archive
See **The Cinema Museum**

Greater London Photograph Library
Greater London Record Office & History Library, 40 Northampton Road, London EC1R 0HB
☎0171 332 3822   Fax 0171 833 9136
Contact *The Photograph Librarian*
A large collection on London, mostly topographical and architectural. Subjects include education, local authority housing, transport, the Thames, parks, churches, hospitals, war damage, pubs, theatres and cinemas. Also major redevelopments like the South Bank, The City, Covent Garden and Docklands.

Sally and Richard Greenhill
357A Liverpool Road, London N1 1NL
☎0171 607 8549   Fax 0171 607 7151
Colour and b&w photos of a social documentary nature: child development, pregnancy and birth, education and urban scenes in London and Northern England. Also Modern China

1971–89, Hong Kong, USA, longhouse life in Sarawak, and other material from around the world.

Greenpeace Communications
See **Environmental Picture Library**

V. K. Guy Ltd
Silver Birches, Troutbeck, Windermere, Cumbria LA23 1PN
☎015394 33519   Fax 015394 32971
Contact *Vic Guy, Pauline Guy, Mike Guy, Paul Guy, Nicola Guy*
British landscapes and architectural heritage. 20,000 5x4in transparencies, suitable for tourism brochures. Colour catalogue available.

Tom Hanley
61 Stephendale Road, London SW6 2LT
☎0171 731 3525   Fax 0171 731 3525
Colour and b&w coverage of London, England, Europe, Canada, India, the Philippines, Brazil, China, Japan, Korea, Taiwan, the Seychelles, Cayman Islands, USA. Also pop artists of the 60s, First World War trenches, removal of London Bridge to America, and much more. Current preoccupation with Greece, Turkey, Spain and Egypt, ancient and modern.

Robert Harding Picture Library
58–59 Great Marlborough Street, London W1V 1DD
☎0171 287 5414   Fax 0171 631 1070
Two million colour images covering wide range of subjects - people, beauty, art, architecture, cities, computer graphics, fashion, landscapes, lifestyle, space, sport, technology and travel. Many specialist collections, including: Tutankhamun, Chinese Exhibition, Beauty Bank, FPG B/W Historical Selects. Syndication of 25 titles from IPC Magazines, BBC Magazines and Burda Group.

Harpur Garden Library
44 Roxwell Road, Chelmsford, Essex CM1 2NB
☎01245 257527   Fax 01245 344101
Contact *Jerry and Marcus Harpur*
Jerry Harpur's personal collection of gardens in Britain, France, Australia, South Africa, the US, Morocco and Japan (35mm and 6x7, colour). Inspired partly by contemporary designers and horticulturalists but also includes historic gardens: formal gardens, front and back gardens, plant associations, gardens in all four seasons, garden containers, fences, hedges, herbs, hillsides, sea-

side, lawns, paths, paving, rock, arbours, scented, fruit and vegetables, ornaments, water and integrated gardens.

Jim Henderson AMPA Photographer

Crooktree, Kincardine O'Neil, Aboyne, Aberdeenshire AB34 4JD
☎01339 882149   Fax 01339 882149
Contact *Jim Henderson, AMPA*

Scenic and general activity coverage of the North-East Scotland–Grampian region and Highlands for tourist, holiday and activity illustration. Specialist collection of over 100 Aurora Borealis displays from 1989-1996 in Grampian. Large collection of recent images of Egypt: Cairo through to Abu-Simbel. Commissions undertaken.

Heritage and Natural History Photographic Library

37 Plainwood Close, Summersdale, Chichester, West Sussex PO19 4YB
☎01243 533822
Contact *Dr John B. Free*

Specialises in insects (particularly bees and bee-keeping), tropical and temperate agriculture and crops, archaeology and history worldwide.

John Heseltine Picture Library

2 Beaufort East, Lambridge, Bath, Avon BA1 6QD
☎01225 447080   Fax 01225 447028
Contact *John Heseltine*

Over 100,000 colour transparencies of landscapes, architecture, food and travel with particular emphasis on Italy and the UK.

Christopher Hill Photographic Library

17 Clarence Street, Belfast BT2 8DY
☎01232 245038   Fax 01232 231942
Contact *Janet Smyth*

A comprehensive collection of landscapes of Northern Ireland, from Belfast to the Giant's Causeway, updated daily. Images of farming, food and industry. 'We will endeavour to supply images overnight.'

Hobbs Golf Collection

5 Winston Way, New Ridley, Stocksfield, Northumberland NE43 7RF
☎01661 842933   Fax 01661 842933
Contact *Michael Hobbs*

Specialist golf collection: players, courses, art, memorabilia and historical topics (1300-present). 40,000+ images - mainly 35mm colour transparencies and b&w prints. Commissions undertaken.

David Hoffman Photo Library

21 Norman Grove, London E3 5EG
☎0181 981 5041   Fax 0181 980 2041
Contact *David Hoffman*

Social documentary library with an emphasis on drugs, policing, disorder, strikes, racism, homelessness, youth, protest, environmental, alternative energy, ecological and pollution issues. Colour and b&w images since the late 1970s, with recent pictures on a range of topical concerns. Mainly UK and Europe but good general files from USA, Venezuela and Thailand. Also a range of specialist files covering subjects from cycling to local authority services.

Holt Studios International Ltd

The Courtyard, 24 High Street, Hungerford, Berkshire RG17 0NF
☎01488 683523   Fax 01488 683511
Commercial Director *Andy Morant*

Specialist photo library covering world agriculture and horticulture both from a pictorial and a technical point of view. Commissions undertaken worldwide.

The Bill Hopkins Collection

See **The Special Photographers Library**

Kit Houghton Photography

Radlet Cottage, Spaxton, Bridgwater, Somerset TA5 1DE
☎01278 671362   Fax 01278 671739
Contact *Kit Houghton, Debbie Cook*

Specialist equestrian library of over 150,000 transparencies on all aspects of the horse world, with images ranging from the romantic to the practical, and many competition pictures including all Olympic Games from 1984. On-line facility available for transmission of pictures.

Chris Howes/Wild Places Photography

51 Timbers Square, Roath, Cardiff CF2 3SH
☎01222 486557   Fax 01222 486557
Contact *Chris Howes, Judith Calford*

Expanding collection of over 50,000 colour transparencies and b&w prints covering travel, topography and natural history worldwide, plus action sports such as climbing. *Specialist areas* include caves, caving and mines (with historical coverage using engravings and early photographs), wildlife, landscapes and the environment, including pollution and conservation. Europe (including Britain), USA, Africa and Australia are all well represented within the collection. Commissions undertaken.

The Hulton Getty Collection

Unique House, 21–31 Woodfield Road, London W9 2BA
☎0171 266 2662   Fax 0171 289 6392

The Hulton Getty Collection, the largest picture resource in Europe, holds over 15 million images from ancient history through the early years of photography up to present day. News events, sport, royalty, war, social history, people and places – photos, lithographs, etchings, engravings, woodcuts. A unique source of visual and reference material which includes the Keystone, Three Lions, Fox Photos and Central Press collections. Manages Mirror Syndication International. Also publishes material on CD-ROM (both Windows and Macintosh). Catalogue available.

Jacqui Hurst

66 Richford Street, Hammersmith, London W6 7HP
☎0181 743 2315/0860 563484
Fax 0181 743 2315

Contact *Jacqui Hurst*

A small library specialising in traditional and contemporary crafts, regional food producers and markets, British gardens, allotments, window boxes and plant portraits. The photos form illustrated essays of how something is made and finish with a still life of the completed object. Collection always being extended; available on request.

The Hutchison Library

118B Holland Park Avenue, London W11 4UA
☎0171 229 2743 (3 lines) Fax 0171 792 0259

Worldwide colour coverage of agriculture, architecture, industry, landscape, transport, ecology, energy, environment, families, festivals, human relationships, pregnancy, birth, leisure, modern life, peoples and religions, technology, lifestyles, travel, urban and country life, weather, wildlife. Collections include: Durrell-McKenna (birth, babies and human relationships); Disappearing World (ethnic minorities); Puttkamer (Amazon Indians); Long Search (world religions); Felix Greene (China, North

Vietnam, Tibet); Tribal Eye; Shogun Experience; Spirit of Asia; New Pacific.

Illustrated London News Picture Library

20 Upper Ground, London SE1 9PF
☎0171 805 5585   Fax 0171 805 5905

Engravings, photographs and illustrations from 1842 to the present day, taken from magazines published by Illustrated Newspapers: *Illustrated London News; Graphic; Sphere; Tatler; Sketch; Illustrated Sporting and Dramatic News; Illustrated War News 1914-18; Bystander; Britannia & Eve*. Social history, London, Industrial Revolution, wars, travel. Brochure available. Visitors by appointment.

The Image Bank

17 Conway Street, London W1P 6EE
☎0171 312 0300   Fax 0171 391 9111
4 Jordan Street, Manchester M15 4PY
☎0161 236 9226   Fax 0161 236 8723.
And: 14 Alva Street, Edinburgh EH2 4QG
☎0131 225 1770   Fax 0131 225 1660.
Contact, London *Paul Walker*
Contact, Manchester *Rowan Young*
Contact, Edinburgh *Roddy McRae*

Stock photography, illustration and film footage. Over 20 million constantly updated images from 450 photographers and 337 illustrators. Free catalogue available. Creative advertising, editorial and corporate commissions undertaken. For magazines, partworks and books, contact the publishing department. Visitors welcome.

Images Colour Library

15/17 High Court Lane, The Calls, Leeds, West Yorkshire LS2 7EU
☎0113 2433389   Fax 0113 2425605
12-14 Argyll Street, London W1V 1AB
☎0171 734 7344   Fax 0171 287 3933

A general contemporary library specialising in top-quality advertising, editorial and travel photography. Catalogues available. Visitors welcome. See also **Landscape Only**.

Images of Africa Photobank

11 The Windings, Lichfield, Staffordshire WS13 7EX
☎01543 262898   Fax 01543 417154
Contact *David Keith Jones, ABIPP, FRPS*

Over 120,000 images covering fourteen African countries: Botswana, Egypt, Ethiopia, Kenya, Malawi, Namibia, Rwanda, South Africa, Swaziland, Tanzania, Uganda, Zaire, Zambia and Zimbabwe. 'Probably the best collection of photographs of Kenya in Europe.' Wide range of topics covered. Very strong on African wildlife with over 80 species of mammals including many sequences showing action and behaviour. Popular animals like lions and elephants are covered in encyclopedic detail. Over 100 species of birds and many reptiles included. Other strengths are National Parks & Reserves, natural beauty, tourism facilities, tradition and modern people. Most work is by David Keith Jones, ABIPP, FRPS; several other photographers are represented. A colour brochure is available.

Imperial War Museum Photograph Archive

Lambeth Road, London SE1 6HZ
☎0171 416 5333   Fax 0171 416 5379

A national archive of photographs of war in this century. Mostly the two world wars but also other conflicts involving Britain and the Commonwealth. Mostly b&w. Visitors welcome. Appointments preferred.

The Interior Archive Ltd

7 Chelsea Studios, 410 Fulham Road, London SW6 1EB
☎0171 370 0595   Fax 0171 385 5403
Contact *Karen Howes*

Several thousand images of interiors, architecture, design and gardens.

International Photobank

Loscombe Barn Farmhouse, West Knighton, Dorchester, Dorset DT2 8LS
☎01305 854145   Fax 01305 853065

Over 275,000 transparencies, mostly medium-format. Colour coverage of travel subjects: places, people, folklore, events. Assignments undertaken for guide books and brochure photography.

The Isle of Wight Photo Library

The Old Rectory, Calbourne, Isle of Wight PO30 4JE
☎01983 531575   Fax 01983 531253
Contact *The Librarian*

Stock material represents all that is best on the Isle of Wight – landscapes, seascapes, architecture, gardens, boats.

Robbie Jack Photography

45 Church Road, Hanwell, London W7 3BD
☎0181 567 9616   Fax 0181 567 9616
Contact *Robbie Jack*

Built up over the last 13 years, the library contains over 250,000 colour transparencies of the performing arts – theatre, dance, opera and music. Includes West End shows, the RSC and Royal National Theatre productions, English National Opera and Royal Opera. The dance section contains images of the Royal Ballet, English National Ballet, the Rambert Dance Company, plus many foreign companies. Also holds the largest selection of colour material from the Edinburgh International Festival. Researchers are welcome to visit by appointment.

Jayawardene Travel Photo Library

7A Napier Road, Wembley, Middlesex HA0 4UA
☎0181 902 3588   Fax 0181 902 7114
Contacts *Marion Jayawardene, Rohith Jayawardene*

100,000 colour transparencies, specialising in worldwide travel and travel-related subjects. Most topics featured have been covered in depth, with more than 500 different images per destination. Regularly updated, all are originals and shot in 35mm- and medium-format. Commissions undertaken. New photographers welcome (please telephone first) – minimum initial submission: 300 transparencies.

Trevor Jones Thoroughbred Photography

The Hornbeams, 2 The Street, Worlington, Suffolk IP28 8RU
☎01638 713944   Fax 01638 713945
Contact *Trevor Jones, Gillian Jones*

Extensive library of high-quality colour transparencies depicting all aspects of thoroughbred horse racing dating from 1987. Major group races, English classics, studs, stallions, mares and foals, early morning scenes, personalities, jockeys, trainers and prominent owners. Also international work: USA Breeders Cup, Arc de Triomphe, French Classics, Irish Derby, Dubai racing scene, Japan Cup and Hokkaido stud farms; and more unusual scenes such as racing on the sands at low tide, Ireland, and on the frozen lake at St Moritz. Visitors by appointment.

Katz Pictures

13/15 Vine Hill, London EC1R 5DX
☎0171 814 9898   Fax 0171 814 9899
Contact *Alyson Whalley*

Contains an extensive collection of colour and b&w material covering a multitude of subjects from around the world – business, environment, industry, lifestyles, politics plus celebrity portraits from the entertainment world. Also Hollywood portraits and film stills dating back to the twenties. Represents *Life* and *Time* magazines for syndication in the UK and can offer a complete selection of material spanning over 50 years.

The Keystone Collection
See **The Hulton Getty Collection**

David King Collection
90 St Pauls Road, London N1 2QP
☎0171 226 0149   Fax 0171 354 8264
Contact *David King*

250,000 b&w original and copy photographs and colour transparencies of historical and present-day images. Russian history and the Soviet Union from 1900 to the fall of Khrushchev; the lives of Lenin, Trotsky and Stalin; the Tzars, Russo-Japanese War, 1917 Revolution, World War I, Red Army, Great Patriotic War etc. Special collections on China, Eastern Europe, the Weimar Republic, American labour struggles, Spanish Civil War. Open to qualified researchers by appointment, Monday to Friday, 10 – 6. Staff will undertake research; negotiable fee for long projects.

The Kobal Collection
4th Floor, 184 Drummond Street, London NW1 3HP
☎0171 383 0011   Fax 0171 383 0044

Colour and b&w coverage of Hollywood films: portraits, stills, publicity shots, posters, ephemera. Visitors by appointment.

Kodak Motoring Picture Library
National Motor Museum, Beaulieu, Hampshire SO42 7ZN
☎01590 612345   Fax 01590 612655
Contact *Simon Priestley, Jonathan Day*

A quarter of a million b&w images, plus 50,000 colour transparencies covering all forms of motoring history from the 1880s to the present day. Commissions undertaken. Own studio.

Kos Picture Source Ltd
The Glider Centre, Bishop's Waltham, Hampshire SO32 1BA
☎01489 896311   Fax 01489 892416
Managing Director *Lizzie Green*

Worldwide marine subjects from yachting to seascapes. Constantly updated, covering all aspects of water-based subjects.

Landscape Only
12-14 Argyll Street, London W1V 1AB
☎0171 734 7344   Fax 0171 287 3933

Premier landscape collection, featuring the work of top photographers Charlie Waite, Nick Meers, Joe Cornish and many others. Colour brochure available.

Frank Lane Picture Agency Ltd
Pages Green House, Wetheringsett, Stowmarket, Suffolk IP14 5QA
☎01728 860789   Fax 01728 860222

Colour and b&w coverage of natural history and weather. Represents Silvestris Fotoservice, Germany, and works closely with Eric and David Hosking, plus 200 freelance photographers.

André Laubier Picture Library
4 St James Park, Bath, Avon BA1 2SS
☎01225 420688

An extensive library of photographs from 1935 to the present day in 35mm- and medium-format. Main subjects are: archaeology and architecture; art and artists (wood carving, sculptures, contemporary glass); botany; historical buildings, sites and events; landscapes; nature; leisure sports; events; experimental artwork and photography; people; and travel. Substantial stock of many other subjects including: birds, buildings and cities, folklore, food and drink, gardens, transport. Special collection: *Images d'Europe* (Austria, Britain, France, Greece, Italy, Spain, Turkey and former Yugoslavia). Private collection: World War II to D-Day. List available on request. Photo assignments, artwork, design, and line drawings undertaken. Correspondence welcome in English, French or German.

The Erich Lessing Archive of Fine Art & Culture
c/o AKG London Ltd, Arts and History Picture Library, 10 Plato Place, 72-74 St Dionis Road, London SW6 4TU
☎0171 610 6103   Fax 0171 610 6125

Computerised archive of large-format transparencies depicting the contents of many of the world's finest art galleries as well as ancient archaeological and biblical sites. Over 70,000 pictures can be viewed on microfiche. Represented by AKG London Ltd.

Life File Ltd
76 Streathbourne Road, London SW17 8QY
☎0181 767 8832   Fax 0181 672 8879
Contact *Simon Taylor*

200,000 images of people and places, lifestyles, industry, environmental issues, natural history and customs, from Afghanistan to Zimbabwe. Stocks most of the major tourist destinations throughout the world, including the UK.

Lindley Library, Royal Horticultural Society

80 Vincent Square, London SW1P 2PE
☎0171 821 3050   Fax 0171 630 6060
Contact *Jennifer Vine*

18,0000 original drawings and approx. 8000 books with hand-coloured plates of botanical illustrations. Appointment is absolutely essential; all photography is done by own photographer.

Link Picture Library

33 Greyhound Road, London W6 8NH
☎0171 381 2261/2433   Fax 0171 385 6244
Contacts *Orde Eliason*

20,000 images of South Africa, India, Vietnam; also international musicians. Link Picture Library has an international network and can source material not in its file from Japan, USA, Holland, Scandinavia, Germany and South Africa. Original photographic commissions also undertaken.

London Aerial Photo Library

PO Box 25, Ashwellthorpe, Norwich, Norfolk NR16 1HL
☎01508 488320   Fax 01508 488282
Contact *Sandy Stockwell*

60,000 colour negatives of aerial photographs covering most of Britain, with particular emphasis on London and surrounding counties. No search fee. Photocopies of library prints are supplied free of charge to enquirers. Welcomes enquiries in respect of either general subjects or specific sites and buildings.

London Transport Museum Photographic Library

39 Wellington Street, London WC2E 7BB
☎0171 379 6344   Fax 0171 497 3527
Contacts *Hugh Robertson, Simon Murphy*

Around 100,000 b&w images from the 1860s and 10,000 colour images from c.1975. *Specialist collections* poster archive, underground construction, corporate design and architecture, street scenes, London Transport during the war. Collection available for viewing by appointment on Monday, Wednesday and Friday. No loans system but prints and transparences can be purchased.

The Ludvigsen Library Limited

73 Collier Street, London N1 9BE
☎0171 837 1700   Fax 0171 837 1776
Contact *Neil King, Brenda Stein*

Approximately 250,000 images (chiefly b&w with some colour transparencies) of automobiles and motorsport, mainly dating from the 1950s. Glass plate negatives from the early 1900s; Formula One, Le Mans, motor car shows, vintage, antique and classic cars from all countries. Includes the Dalton-Watson Collection and noted photographers such as Max le Grand and Rodolfo Mailander. Extensive research facilities.

Lupe Cunha Photos

19 Ashfields Parade, London N14 5EH
☎0181 882 6441   Fax 0181 882 6303
Children, health, pregnancy and general women's interest. Also special collection on Brazil. Commissions undertaken.

MacQuitty International Photographic Collection

7 Elm Lodge, River Gardens, Stevenage Road, London SW6 6NZ
☎0171 385 6031/384 1781
Fax 0171 384 1781
Contact *Dr Miranda MacQuitty*

Colour and b&w collection on aspects of life in over 70 countries: dancing, music, religion, death, archaeology, buildings, transport, food, drink, nature. Visitors by appointment.

Magnum Photos Ltd

Moreland Buildings, 2nd Floor, 5 Old Street, London EC1V 9HL
☎0171 490 1771   Fax 0171 608 0020
Head of Library *Heather Vickers*

FOUNDED 1947 by Cartier Bresson, George Rodger, Robert Capa and David 'Chim' Seymour. Represents over 50 of the world's leading photo-journalists. Coverage of all major world events from the Spanish Civil War to present day. Also a large collection of personalities.

The Raymond Mander & Joe Mitchenson Theatre Collection

The Mansion, Beckenham Place Park, Beckenham, Kent BR3 2BP
☎0181 658 7725   Fax 0181 663 0313
Contact *Richard Mangan*

Enormous collection covering all aspects of the theatre: plays, actors, dramatists, music hall, theatres, singers, composers, etc. Visitors welcome by appointment.

S & O Mathews Photography
The Old Rectory, Calbourne, Isle of Wight PO30 4JE
☎01983 531247   Fax 01983 531253

Landscapes, gardens and flowers.

MC Picture Library
119 Wardour Street, London W1V 3TD
☎0171 734 6710   Fax 0171 494 1839

Contact *Julia Cooper*

Leisure-related subjects – cookery, gardening, needlecraft, antiques, health and sex. Related text is often available.

Institution of Mechanical Engineers
1 Birdcage Walk, London SW1H 9JJ
☎0171 973 1289   Fax 0171 222 4557

Contact *Corporate Communications*

800 contemporary images on mechanical engineering can be borrowed free of charge.

Meledin Collection
See **Mary Evans Picture Library**

Lee Miller Archives
Burgh Hill House, Chiddingly, Near Lewes, East Sussex BN8 6JF
☎01825 872691   Fax 01825 872733

The work of Lee Miller (1907-77). As a photojournalist she covered the war in Europe from early in 1944 to VE Day with further reporting from the Balkans. Collection includes photographic portraits of prominent Surrealist artists: Ernst, Eluard, Miró, Picasso, Penrose, Carrington, Tanning, and others. Surrealist and contemporary art, poets and writers, fashion, the Middle East, Egypt, the Balkans in the 1930s, London during the Blitz, war in Europe and the liberation of Dachau and Buchenwald.

Mirror Syndication International
Unique House, 21-31 Woodfield Road, London W9 2BA
☎0171 266 1133   Fax 0171 266 2563

Head of Operations *Matthew Buttson*

Major photo library specialising in current affairs, personalities, royalty, sport, pop and glamour. Extensive British and world travel pictures, including the British Tourist Authority collection. Specialist film archive, the Picture Goer. Agents for Mirror Group Newspapers.

Syndicator of photos and text for news/features. Managed by the **Hulton Getty Collection Limited**.

Monitor Syndication
17 Old Street, London EC1V 9HL
☎0171 253 7071   Fax 0171 250 0966

Colour and b&w coverage of leading international personalities. Politics, entertainment, royals, judicial, commerce, religion, trade unions, well-known buildings. Syndication to international, national and local media.

Moroccan Scapes
Seend Park, Seend, Wiltshire SN12 6NZ
☎01380 828533   Fax 01380 828630

Contact *Chris Lawrence*

Specialist collection of Moroccan and Greek material: scenery, towns, people, markets and places, plus the Atlas Mountains. Over 16,000 images.

Motoring Picture Library
National Motor Museum, Trust Centre, Beaulieu, Hampshire SO42 7ZN
☎01590 612345   Fax 01590 612655

Contacts *Simon Priestley, Jonathan Day*

Over half a million b&w photographs and 60,000 transparencies on all aspects of motoring from the 1890s to the present day. The collection includes cars, commercials and motorcycles.

Mountain Camera
See **John Cleare**

Moving Image Communications Ltd
The Basement, 2-4 Dean Street, London W1V 5RN
☎0171 437 5688   Fax 0171 437 5649

Contact *Michael Maloney*

11,000 hours of quality archive and contemporary images; computer catalogued for immediate access. Collections include: Britain 1925-96, The Cuban Archive, Medical Technology, 1950's Classic Travelogues, Subaqua Films, Space Exploration, Vintage Slapstick, British Airways 1984-96, Seascapes and Landscapes, TVAM News/Interviews/Funnies 1983-92. In addition, Moving Image provides an external research and copyright clearance service. In-house researchers can locate images using long-established contacts with footage sources worldwide.

Museum of Antiquities Picture Library

University and Society of Antiquaries of Newcastle upon Tyne, Newcastle upon Tyne NE1 7RU

☎0191 222 7846   Fax 0191 222 8561

Contact *Lindsay Allason-Jones*

25,000 images, mostly b&w, of special collections including: Hadrian's Wall Archive (b&ws taken over the last 100 years); Gertrude Bell Archive (during her travels in the Near East, 1900–26); and aerial photographs of archaeological sites in the North of England. Visitors welcome by appointment.

Museum of London Picture Library

London Wall, London EC2Y 5HN

☎0171 600 3699 ext. 254 Fax 0171 600 1058

Contact *Gavin Morgan*

Comprehensive coverage of the history and archaeology of London represented in paintings, photographs and historic artefacts. Special files include Roman and medieval archaeology, costume, Suffragettes and Port of London.

National Galleries of Scotland Picture Library

National Galleries of Scotland, Belford Road, Edinburgh EH4 3DR

☎0131 556 8921, ext 319 Fax 0131 315 2963

Contacts *Deborah Hunter, Katharine May*

Over 30,000 b&w and several thousand images in colour of works of art from the Renaissance to present day. Specialist subjects cover fine art (painting, sculpture, drawing), portraits, Scottish, historical, still life, photography and landscape. Colour leaflet, scale of charges and application forms available on request.

National Maritime Museum Picture Library

Greenwich, London SE10 9NF

☎0181 312 6631   Fax 0181 312 6632

Manager *Chris Gray*

Over 3 million maritime-related images and artefacts, including oil paintings from the 16th century to present day, prints and drawings, historic photographs, plans of ships built in the UK since the beginning of the 18th century, models, rare maps and charts, instruments, etc. Over 50,000 items in the collection are now photographed and with the Historic Photographs Collection form the basis of the library's stock.

National Medical Slide Bank

Wellcome Centre Medical Photo Library, 210 Euston Road, London NW1 2BE

☎0171 611 8746   Fax 0171 611 8577

Contact *Julie Dorrington*

Specialist section of the **Wellcome Centre Medical Photographic Library**, it comprises 15,000 slides covering clinical and general medicine with associated pathology and medical imaging. 12,000 images on videodisc.

National Monuments Record

National Monuments Record Centre, Kemble Drive, Swindon, Wiltshire SN2 2GZ

☎01793 414600   Fax 01793 414606

The National Monuments Record is the first stop for photographs and information on England's heritage. Over 6.5 million photographs are held in three main collections, backed up by a detailed database. English architecture from the first days of photography to the present, air photographs covering every inch of England from the first days of flying to the present, and archaeological sites. The London office specialises in the architecture of the capital city – for more information phone 0171 208 8200.

National Portrait Gallery Picture Library

St Martin's Place, London WC2H 0HE

☎0171 306 0055 exts. 259/260/261

Fax 0171 306 0092/0056

Contact *Shruti Patel*

Over 700,000 images – portraits of famous British men and women dating from medieval times to the present day. Various formats/media.

National Railway Museum Picture Library

Leeman Road, York, North Yorkshire YO2 4XJ

☎01904 621261   Fax 01904 611112

1.5 million images, mainly b&w, covering every aspect of railways from 1866 to the present day. Visitors by appointment.

The National Trust Photographic Library

36 Queen Anne's Gate, London SW1H 9AS

☎0171 222 9251   Fax 0171 222 5097

Contact *Gayle Mault*

Collection of mixed-format transparencies covering landscape and coastline throughout

England, Wales and Northern Ireland; also architecture, interiors, gardens, painting and conservation. Brochure available on request. Profits from the picture library are reinvested in continuing the work of the Trust.

Natural History Museum Picture Library
Cromwell Road, London SW7 5BD
☎0171 938 9122/9035   Fax 0171 938 9169
Contact *Martin Pulsford, Lodvina Mascarenhas*

12,000 large-format transparencies on natural history and related subjects: extinct animals, dinosaurs, fossils, anthropology, minerals, gemstones, fauna and flora. No wildlife pictures but many images of historic natural history art. Commissions of museum specimens undertaken.

Natural History Photographic Agency
See **NHPA (Natural History Photographic Agency)**

Natural Science Photos
33 Woodland Drive, Watford, Hertfordshire WD1 3BY
☎01923 245265   Fax 01923 246067

Colour coverage of natural history subjects worldwide. The work of some 100 photographers, it includes animals, birds, reptiles, amphibia, fish, insects and other invertebrates, habitats, plants, fungi, geography, weather, scenics, horticulture, agriculture, farm animals and registered dog breeds. Researched by experienced scientists Peter and Sondra Ward. Visits by appointment. Commissions undertaken.

Nature Photographers Ltd
West Wit, New Road, Little London, Tadley, Hampshire RG26 5EU
☎01256 850661   Fax 01256 851157
Contact *Dr Paul Sterry*

Over 150,000 images on worldwide natural history and environmental subjects. The library is run by a trained biologist and experienced author on his subject.

Peter Newark's Pictures
3 Barton Buildings, Queen Square, Bath, Avon BA1 2JR
☎01225 334213   Fax 01225 334213
Over 1 million images covering world history from ancient times to the present day. Incorporates two special collections: American

history in general with strong Wild West collection; and the military collection: military/ naval personalities and events. Subject list available. Visitors welcome by appointment.

NHPA (Natural History Photographic Agency)
Little Tye, 57 High Street, Ardingly, West Sussex RH17 6TB
☎01444 892514   Fax 01444 892168
Library Manager *Tim Harris*

Extensive coverage on all aspects of natural history - animals, plants, landscapes, environmental issues. 120 photographers worldwide provide a steady input of high-quality transparencies. Specialist files include the unique high-speed photography of Stephen Dalton, extensive coverage of African and American wildlife, also rainforests, marine life and the polar regions. UK agents for the ANT collection of Australasian material. Loans are generally made direct to publishers; individual writers must request material via their publisher.

The Northern Picture Library
Greenheys Business Centre, 10 Pencroft Way, Manchester M15 6JJ
☎0161 226 2007   Fax 0161 226 2022
Wide selection of subjects from the UK and abroad. Mostly colour, some b&w. Industry, business, sport, farming, scenic, personalities, jazz musicians (and some classical), space, and many more. Special collection on the North West of England. Commissions undertaken.

NRSC - Air Photo Group
Arthur Street, Barwell, Leicestershire LE9 8GZ
☎01455 844513   Fax 01455 841785
Leading supplier of colour aerial photography in the UK. Commissions undertaken.

Observer Colour Library
PO Box 33, Edenbridge, Kent TN8 5PB
☎01342 850313   Fax 01342 850244
Half a million pictures from the *Observer* magazine, from 1962 to end 1992.

Only Horses Picture Agency
27 Greenway Gardens, Greenford, Middlesex UB6 9TU
☎0181 578 9047   Fax 0181 575 7244
Colour and b&w coverage of all aspects of the horse. Foaling, retirement, racing, show jumping, eventing, veterinary, polo, breeds, personalities.

George Outram Picture Library

See **Caledonian Newspapers Picture Library**

Oxford Picture Library

1 North Hinksey Village, Oxford OX2 0NA
☎01865 723404   Fax 01865 725294

Contact *Annabel Webb, Chris Andrews, Angus Palmer*

Specialist collection on Oxford: the city, university and colleges, events, people, spires and shires; also the Cotswolds, architecture and landscape from Stratford-upon-Avon down to Bath; the Chilterns and Henley on Thames, with aerial views of all of the above; plus Channel Islands, especially Guernsey and Sark. General collection includes wildlife, trees, plants, clouds, sun, sky and water. Commissions undertaken.

Oxford Scientific Films Photo Library

Long Hanborough, Witney, Oxfordshire OX8 8LL
☎01993 881881   Fax 01993 882808

Contact *Sandra Berry, Photo Library Manager*

Extensive collection of colour transparencies of wildlife and natural science images supplied by over 300 photographers worldwide, providing comprehensive coverage of behaviour, life histories, close-ups, high speed and some special effects, as well as environmental shots. Macro and micro photography. UK agents for Animals Animals and Photo Researchers, New York, Okapia, Frankfurt and Dinodia, India. Now also incorporating the Survival Anglia Photo Library. Research by experienced and specialist researchers. Visits by appointment.

Hugh Palmer

Knapp House, Shenington, Near Banbury, Oxfordshire OX15 6NE
☎01295 670433   Fax 01295 670709

Extensive coverage of gardens from Britain and Europe, stately homes, conservatories and garden buildings. Medium-format transparencies from numerous specialist commissions for books and magazines.

Panos Pictures

9 White Lion Street, London N1 9PD
☎0171 837 7505   Fax 0171 278 0345

Documentary colour and b&w library specialising in Third World and Eastern Europe, with emphasis on environment and development issues. Leaflet available. All profits from this library go to the Panos Institute to further its work in international sustainable development.

Papilio Natural History & Travel Library

44 Palestine Grove, Merton, London SW19 2QN
☎0181 687 2202   Fax 0181 687 2202

Contact *Robert Pickett, Justine Bowler*

40,000 colour transparencies of natural history, including birds, animals, insects, flowers, plants, fungi and landscapes; plus travel. Commissions undertaken. Full company information pack available. Visits by appointment only. Member of **BAPLA**.

Charles Parker Archive

See **Birmingham Library Services** under **Library Services**

David Paterson Photo-Library

88 Cavendish Road, London SW12 0DF
☎0181 673 2414   Fax 0181 675 9197

Travel, landscapes, nature from the UK, Europe, North Africa, the Himalayas, Japan, Scotland and the USA.

Ann & Bury Peerless Slide Resources & Picture Library

St David's, 22 King's Avenue, Minnis Bay, Birchington-on-Sea, Kent CT7 9QL
☎01843 841428   Fax 01843 848321

Contact *Ann or Bury Peerless*

Specialist collection on world religions: Hinduism, Buddhism, Jainism, Christianity, Sikhism. Geographical areas covered: India, Pakistan, Bangladesh, Sri Lanka, Thailand, Russia, Republic of China, Spain, Poland. 10,000 35mm colour transparencies.

Performing Arts Library

52 Agate Road, London W6 0AH
☎0181 748 2002   Fax 0181 563 0538

Colour and b&w pictures of all aspects of the performing arts, including classical music, opera, theatre, ballet and contemporary dance, musicals, concert halls, opera houses and festivals.

Photo Flora

46 Jacoby Place, Priory Road, Edgbaston, Birmingham B5 7UN
☎0121 471 3300

Specialist in British and European wild plants, with colour coverage of most British and many European species (rare and common) and habitats; also travel in India, Nepal, Egypt, China, Thailand and Tibet.

Photo Library International Ltd
PO Box 75, Leeds, West Yorkshire
LS7 3NZ
☎0113 2623005   Fax 0113 2625366

Contemporary colour coverage of most subjects, including industry.

Photo Press Defence Pictures
Glider House, 14 Addison Road, Plymouth, Devon PL4 8LL
☎01752 251271/491534   Fax 01752 222482
Contact *David Reynolds, Jessica Kelly*

Leading source of military photography covering all areas of the UK Armed Forces, supported by a research agency of facts and figures. More than 100,000 images. Campaigns in Aden, the Falklands, Ulster, the Gulf and Yugoslavia covered. Specialist collections include the Royal Marine Commandos and Parachute Regiment training. Visitors welcome by appointment.

Photo Resources
The Orchard, Marley Lane, Kingston, Canterbury, Kent CT4 6JH
☎01227 830075   Fax 01227 831135

Colour and b&w coverage of archaeology, art, ancient art, ethnology, mythology, world religion, museum objects.

Photofusion
17A Electric Lane, London SW9 8LA
☎0171 738 5774   Fax 0171 738 5509
Contact *Janis Austin*

Colour and b&w coverage of contemporary social issues including babies and children, disablement, education, the elderly, environment, family, health, housing, homelessness, people general and work. List available.

The Photographers' Library
81A Endell Street, London WC2H 9AJ
☎0171 836 5591   Fax 0171 379 4650

Covers people, lifestyles, commerce, holiday people, travel destinations, industry, landscapes, health. Brochure available.

Photomax
118-122 Magdalen Road, Oxford
OX4 1RQ
☎01865 241825   Fax 01865 794511
Contact *Max Gibbs, Barry Allday*

All aspects of the aquarium hobby are covered: aquarium fish, tropical freshwater, tropical marine, coldwater, marine invertebrates (tropical); aquarium plants; water lilies. Expanding. Commissions undertaken.

Photos Horticultural
169 Valley Road, Ipswich, Suffolk
IP1 4PJ
☎01473 257329   Fax 01473 233974

Colour coverage of all aspects of gardening in Britain and abroad, including extensive files on plants in cultivation and growing wild.

PictureBank Photo Library Ltd
Parman House, 30-36 Fife Road, Kingston upon Thames, Surrey KT1 1SY
☎0181 547 2344   Fax 0181 974 5652

250,000 colour transparencies covering people (girls, couples, families, children), travel and scenic (UK and world), moods (sunsets, seascapes, deserts, etc.), industry and technology, environments and general. Commissions undertaken. Visitors welcome. Member of **BAPLA**. New material on medium/large format welcome.

Pictures Colour Library
4th Floor, The Italian Building,
41 Dockhead, London SE1 2BS
☎0171 252 3300   Fax 0171 252 3345

Location, lifestyle, food, still life, sport, animals, industry and business. Visitors welcome.

Pitkin Pictorials Ltd
Healey House, Dene Road, Andover, Hampshire SP10 2AA
☎01264 334303   Fax 01264 334110
Contact *Sarah Pickering*

Colour transparencies of English cathedrals; plus a large collection of b&w prints. Also London and a few other cities. No visitors.

Popperfoto
The Old Mill, Overstone Farm, Overstone, Northampton NN6 0AB
☎01604 670670   Fax 01604 670635

Includes early colour from 1940s and b&w from 1870 to the present day. Subjects include Scott's 1910-12 Antarctic expedition, wars, royalty, sport, politics, transport, crime, topography, history and social conditions worldwide. Houses the EPA (European Pressphoto Agency), AFP (Agence France Presse), the Victory Archive (formerly the Conway Picture

Library), Reuters and UPI collections: worldwide news events, European politics and news in depth. The UPI collection commences 1932; Reuters from its start in 1985 to the present day. Also represents Bob Thomas Sports Photography.

PPL Photo Agency Ltd
68 East Ham Road, Littlehampton, West Sussex BN17 7BE
☎01903 730614   Fax 01903 730618
Contacts *Barry Pickthall, Jon Nash*

2 million pictures of sailing and boating, watersports, travel, water and coastal scenes.

Premaphotos Wildlife
Amberstone, 1 Kirland Road, Bodmin, Cornwall PL30 5JQ
☎01208 78258   Fax 01208 72302
Contact *Jean Preston-Mafham*, Library Manager

Natural history worldwide. Subjects include flowering and non-flowering plants, fungi, slime moulds, fruits and seeds, galls, leaf mines, seashore life, mammals, birds, reptiles, amphibians, insects, spiders, habitats, scenery and cultivated cacti. Commissions undertaken. Visitors welcome.

Press Association
See under **Library Services**

Professional Sport
8 Apollo Studios, Charlton Kings Mews, London NW5 2SA
☎0171 482 2311   Fax 0171 482 2441

Colour and b&w coverage of tennis, soccer, athletics, golf, cricket, boxing, winter sports and many minor sports. Major international events including the Olympic Games, World Cup soccer and all Grand Slam tennis events. Also news and feature material supplied worldwide. Computerised library with in-house processing and studio facilities; Macintosh photo transmission services available for editorial and advertising.

PWA International Ltd
City Gate House, 399-425 Eastern Avenue, Gants Hill, Ilford, Essex IG2 6LR
☎0181 518 2057   Fax 0181 518 2241
Contact *Terry Allen*

Over 250,000 images of beauty, cookery and craft plus a comprehensive library of story illustrations comprising work by some of the UK's best-known illustrators.

Railfotos
Millbrook House Ltd., Calthorpe House, 30 Hagley Road, Edgbaston, Birmingham B16 8QY
☎0121 454 1308
Fax 0121 454 4224 quote Millbrook House

One of the largest specialist libraries dealing comprehensively with railway subjects worldwide. Colour and b&w dating from the turn of the century to present day. Up-to-date material on UK, South America and Far East (except Japan), especially China. Visitors by appointment.

Redferns Music Picture Library
7 Bramley Road, London W10 6SZ
☎0171 792 9914   Fax 0171 792 0921

Music picture library covering every aspect of popular music from 1920s jazz to present day. Over 12,000 artists on file plus other subjects including musical instruments, recording studios, crowd scenes, festivals, etc. Brochure available.

Reed Consumer Books Picture Library
Michelin House, 81 Fulham Road, London SW3 6RB
☎0171 225 9212   Fax 0171 225 9053
Contact *Sally Claxton*

400,000 images of cookery and gardening.

Remote Source
See **Royal Geographical Society Picture Library**

Retna Pictures Ltd
1 Fitzroy Mews, Cleveland Street, London W1P 5DQ
☎0171 209 0200   Fax 0171 383 7151

Colour and b&w coverage of international rock and pop performers, actors, actresses, entertainers and celebrities. Also a general stock library covering a wide range of subjects, including travel, people, sport and leisure, flora and fauna, and the environment.

Retrograph Archive Ltd
164 Kensington Park Road, London W11 2ER
☎0171 727 9378/9426   Fax 0171 229 3395
Contact *Jilliana Ranicar-Breese*

'Number One for nostalgia!' A vast archive of commercial and decorative art (1860-1960). Worldwide labels and packaging for food, wine, chocolate, soap, perfume, cigars and cigarettes; fine art and commercial art journals, fashion magazines, posters, Victorian greeting cards, Christmas and Edwardian postcards, wallpaper and gift-wrap sample books, music sheets, folios of decorative design and ornament - Art Nouveau and Deco; hotel, airline and shipping labels; memorabilia, tourism, leisure, food and drink, transport and entertainment. Lasers for book dummies, packaging, mock-ups, film/TV action props. Colour brochure on request. Medium format. Colour, b&w and illustration. Picture research service. Design consultancy service. Victorian-style montages conceived, designed and styled (RetroMontages).

Reuters Television

40 Cumberland Avenue, London
NW10 7EH
☎0171 510 5647/5603   Fax 0171 510 8568
Colour coverage of international political leaders, personalities and locations on 35mm colour transparencies. Videoprints available from Reuters' international coverage.

Rex Features Ltd

18 Vine Hill, London EC1R 5DX
☎0171 278 7294/3362   Fax 0171 696 0974
Established in the 1950s. Colour and b&w coverage of news, politics, personalities, show business, glamour, humour, art, medicine, science, landscapes, royalty, etc.

Royal Air Force Museum

Grahame Park Way, Hendon, London
NW9 5LL
☎0181 205 2266   Fax 0181 200 1751
Contact *Christine Gregory*

About a quarter of a million images, mostly b&w, with around 1500 colour in all formats, on the history of aviation. Particularly strong on the activities of the Royal Air Force from the 1870s to 1970s. Researchers are requested to enquire in writing only.

The Royal Collection

Windsor Castle, Windsor, Berks
SL4 1NJ
☎01753 868286   Fax 01753 620046
Contact *Gwyneth Campling, Nicole Tetzner*

Photographic material of items in the Royal Collection, particularly oil paintings, drawings and watercolours, works of art, and interiors and exteriors of royal residences. 35,000 colour transparencies plus 25,000 b&w negatives.

Royal Geographical Society Picture Library

1 Kensington Gore, London SW7 2AR
☎0171 584 4381   Fax 0171 584 4381
Contact *Joanna Scadden, Daisy Jellicoe*

A strong source of geographical and historical images, both archival and modern, showing the world through the eyes of photographers and explorers dating from the 1830s to the present day. The 'Remote Source Collection' provides up-to-date transparencies from around the world, highlighting aspects of cultural activity, environmental phenomena, anthropology, architectural design, travel, mountaineering and exploration. Offers a professional and comprehensive service for both commercial and academic use.

Royal Opera House Archives

Royal Opera House, Covent Garden, London
WC2E 9DD
☎0171 240 1200   Fax 0171 212 9489
Contact *Francesca Franchi*

Information and illustrations covering the history of the three Covent Garden Theatres, 1732 to the present, including the three Royal Opera House Companies - Birmingham Royal Ballet, The Royal Ballet and The Royal Opera. Visitors welcome by appointment.

The Royal Photographic Society

The Octagon, Milsom Street, Bath, Avon
BA1 1DN
☎01225 462841   Fax 01225 448688
Contact *Debbie Ireland*

History of photography, with an emphasis on pictorial photography as an art rather than a documentary record. Photographic processes and cameras, landscape, portraiture, architecture, India, Victorian and Edwardian life.

RSPB Picture Library

The Lodge, Sandy, Bedfordshire SG19 2DL
☎01767 680551   Fax 01767 692365
Contact *Chris Sargeant*

Colour and b&w images of birds, butterflies, moths, mammals, reptiles and their habitats. Also colour images of all RSPB reserves. Growing selection of various habitats. Total number of slides now 65,000.

RSPCA Photolibrary

RSPCA Trading Limited, Causeway,
Horsham, West Sussex RH12 1HG
☎01403 223150   Fax 01403 241048

Photolibrary Manager *Tim Sambrook*

Over 25,000 colour transparencies and over 5000 b&w/colour prints. A comprehensive collection of natural history pictures representing the work of over 100 photographers. Has a unique photographic record of the work of the RSPCA including animal hospitals, veterinary treatment, wildlife rehabilitation work, cruelty to animals, animal welfare education, RSPCA inspectors at work, and other animal welfare issues such as environmental problems and cruel sports.

Russia and Republics Photolibrary

Conifers House, Cheapside Lane, Denham, Uxbridge, Middlesex UB9 5AE
☎01895 834814/0956 304384 (mobile)
Fax 01895 834028

Images of Russia and the Republics: cities, museums, cathedrals, markets, landmarks, landscapes, resorts, traditional costumes and dances, craftsmen at work.

S&G Press Agency

68 Exmouth Market, London
EC1R 4RA
☎0171 278 1223   Fax 0171 278 8480
Contact *Paul Kurton*

Over a million images covering every subject from A to Z. Dating back to the turn of the century, the collection is added to daily by a team of news and sports photographers employed by London News Service, Barratt's Photo Press and Sport & General Press Agency. *Specialises* in sport, celebrities, royalty, crime and general news.

Peter Sanders Photography

9 Meades Lane, Chesham, Buckinghamshire
HP5 1ND
☎01494 773674   Fax 01494 773674
Contact *Peter Sanders, Hafsa Garwatuk*

The world of Islam in all its aspects from religion and industry to culture and arts. Areas included are Saudi Arabia, Africa, Asia, Europe and USA. Now expanding to all religions.

Science & Society Picture Library

Science Museum, Exhibition Road, London
SW7 2DD
☎0171 938 9750   Fax 0171 938 9751
Contact *Angela Murphy, Venita Paul*

25,000 reference prints and 100,000 colour transparencies, incorporating many from collections at the Science Museum, the National Railway Museum and the National Museum of Film, Photography and Television. Collections illustrate the history of: science, industry, technology, medicine, transport and the media. Plus three archives documenting British society in the twentieth century.

Science and Technology Illustration Library

2 Pell Hill Cottages, Wadhurst, East Sussex
TN5 6DS
☎01892 783652   Fax 01892 784287
Contact *Peter Lafferty*

Expanding collection of original b&w/colour artwork on technology and all science subjects. Will commission new artwork if requested.

The Scottish Highland Photo Library

Unit 5, Castle Avenue Industrial Estate, Invergordon, Ross-shire IV18 0PQ
☎01349 852144   Fax 01349 852144
Contact *Hugh Webster*

100,000 colour transparencies of the Scottish Highlands and Islands. Not just a travel library; images cover industry, agriculture, fisheries and many other subjects of the Highlands and Islands. Submissions from photographers welcome. Commissions undertaken.

Seaco Picture Library

Sea Containers House, 20 Upper Ground, London SE1 9PF
☎0171 805 5831   Fax 0171 805 5926
Contact *Maureen Elliott*

Approx. 250,000 images of containerisation, shipping, fast ferries, manufacturing, fruit farming, ports, hotels and leisure.

Mick Sharp Photography

Eithinog, Waun, Penisarwaun, Caernarfon, Gwynedd LL55 3PW
☎01286 872425   Fax 01286 872425
Contacts *Mick Sharp, Jean Williamson*

Colour transparencies (6x4.5cm and 35mm) and black & white prints (5x4" and 6x4.5cm negatives) of subjects connected with archaeology, ancient monuments, buildings, churches, countryside, environment, history, landscape, past cultures and topography from Britain and abroad. Photographs by Mick Sharp and Jean Williamson, plus access to other specialist collections on related subjects. Commissions undertaken.

Phil Sheldon Golf Picture Library

40 Manor Road, Barnet, Hertfordshire
EN5 2JQ
☎0181 440 1986   Fax 0181 440 9348

An expanding collection of over 300,000 quality images of the 'world of golf'. In-depth worldwide tournament coverage including every Major championship & Ryder Cup since 1976. Instruction, portraits, trophies and over 300 golf courses from around the world. Also the Dale Concannon collection covering the period 1870 to 1940 and the classic 1960s collection by photographer Sidney Harris.

Skishoot Offshoot

28 Dalebury Road, London SW17 7HH
☎0181 767 0059   Fax 0181 767 6680
Contact *Caroline Ellerby*

Predominantly skiing and ski-related subjects, but also a travel library specialising in France. Commissions undertaken.

Skyscan Balloon Photography

Oak House, Toddington, Cheltenham,
Gloucestershire GL54 5BY
☎01242 621357   Fax 01242 621343

Unusual aerial views taken from a tethered balloon flown at heights of 80 to 800 feet all on medium-format transparency. This photo library of unique low-level pictures of British city and rural landscapes has a special collection of Heritage sites, the Cotswolds, London and the Thames Valley. Commissions undertaken.

SOA (Sabine Oppenländer Associates)

H Welbeck Mansions, Inglewood Road,
London NW6 1QX
☎0171 794 4567   Fax 0171 431 5385
Contact *Brigitte Boh, Jenny Williams*

75,000 colour slides, 10,000 b&w photos covering *Stern* productions, celebrities, sports, travel & geographic, advertising, social subjects. Representatives of Photonica, Voller Ernst, Interfoto and many freelance photographers. Catalogues available.

Solo Syndication Ltd

49-53 Kensington High Street, London
W8 5ED
☎0171 376 2166   Fax 0171 938 3165
Contact *Trevor York*

Access to three million images from *Daily Mail* and *Evening Standard* libraries. Leading collections of royalty and celebrity pictures, also crime portfolio. Available by bromide prints or by electronic transmission.

Sotheby's Picture Library

34-35 New Bond Street, London W1A 2AA
☎0171 408 5383   Fax 0171 408 5062
Contact *Joanna Ling*

A new source of images. Recently set up, the library mainly consists of several thousand selected transparencies of pictures sold at Sotheby's. Images from the 15th to the 20th century. Oils, drawings, watercolours and prints. 'Happy to do searches or, alternatively, visitors are welcome by appointment.'

South American Pictures

48 Station Road, Woodbridge, Suffolk
IP12 4AT
☎01394 383963/383279   Fax 01394 380176
Contact *Marion Morrison*

Colour and b&w images of South/Central America, Cuba, Mexico and New Mexico (USA), including archaeology and the Amazon. Frequently updated. There is an archival section, with pictures and documents from most countries.

The Special Photographic Library

21 Kensington Park Road, London
W11 2EU
☎0171 221 3489   Fax 0171 792 9112
Contacts *Chris Kewbank, Emma Griffiths*

Specialises in contemporary fine art photography, unusual in its style, technique or subject matter. Also has exclusive access to the Bill Hopkins Collection - an archive of thousands of vintage pictures dating back to the early 20th century.

Spectrum Colour Library

41-42 Berners Street, London W1P 3AA
☎0171 637 1587   Fax 0171 637 3681

A large collection including travel, sport, people, pets, scenery, industry, British and European cities, etc. All pictures are also available in digital format. Visitors welcome by appointment.

Frank Spooner Pictures Ltd

Unit B7, Hatton Square, 16-16A Baldwin's
Gardens, London EC1N 7US
☎0171 405 9943   Fax 0171 831 2483

Subjects include current affairs, show business, fashion, politics, travel, adventure, sport, personalities, films, animals and the Middle East. Represented in more than 30 countries and handles UK distribution of Harry Benson, and Gamma Presse Images of Paris. Commissions undertaken.

The Still Moving Picture Co.
67A Logie Green Road, Edinburgh EH7 4HF
☎0131 557 9697   Fax 0131 557 9699

Contact *John Hutchinson, Sue Hall*

250,000 colour, b&w and 16mm film coverage of Scotland and sport. The largest photo and film library in Scotland, holding the Scottish Tourist Board library among its files. Scottish agents for **Allsport (UK) Ltd**.

Still Pictures' Whole Earth Photolibrary
199 Shooters Hill Road, Blackheath, London SE3 8UL
☎0181 858 8307   Fax 0181 858 2049

Contacts *Theresa de Salis, Mark Edwards*

FOUNDED 1970, the library is a leading source of pictures illustrating the human impact on the environment, third world development issues, industrial ecology, wildlife, endangered species and habitats. 250,000 colour medium-format transparencies, 100,000 b&w prints. Over 100 leading photographers from around the world supply the library with stock pictures.

Stockfile
5 High Street, Sunningdale, Berkshire SL5 0LXS
☎01344 872249   Fax 01344 872263

Contact *Jill Behr, Steven Behr*

Specialist cycling- and skiing-based collection covering most aspects of these activities, with emphasis on mountain biking. Expanding adventure sports section.

Survival Anglia Photo Library
See **Oxford Scientific Films**

Telegraph Colour Library
The Innovation Centre, 225 Marsh Wall, London E14 9FX
☎0171 987 1212   Fax 0171 538 3309

Contact *Joanne Onion*

Leading stock photography agency covering a wide subject range: business, sport, people, industry, animals, medical, nature, space, travel and graphics. Free catalogue available. Same-day service to UK clients.

Three Lions Collection
See **The Hulton Getty Collection**

Patrick Thurston Photolibrary
10 Willis Road, Cambridge CB1 2AQ
☎01223 352547   Fax 01223 66274

Colour photography of Britain: scenery, people, museums, churches, coastline. Also various countries abroad. Commissions undertaken.

Rick Tomlinson Marine Photo Library
18 Hamble Yacht Services, Port Hamble, Hamble, Southampton, Hampshire SO31 4NN
☎01703 458450   Fax 01703 458350

Contacts *Rick Tomlinson, Sue Snow*

ESTABLISHED 1985. *Specialises* in marine subjects. 60,000 35mm transparencies of yachting, racing, cruising, Whitbread Round the World Race, tall ships, RNLI Lifeboats, Antarctica, wildlife and locations.

Topham Picturepoint
PO Box 33, Edenbridge, Kent TN8 5PB
☎01342 850313   Fax 01342 850244

Contact *Alan Smith*

Eight million contemporary and historical images, ideal for advertisers, publishers and the travel trade. Delivery on line.

B. M. Totterdell Photography
Constable Cottage, Burlings Lane, Knockholt, Kent TN14 7PE
☎01959 532001

Contact *Barbara Totterdell*

Specialist volleyball library covering all aspects of the sport.

Trades Union Congress Picture Library
See under **Library Services**

Tessa Traeger
7 Rossetti Studios, 72 Flood Street, London SW3 5TF
☎0171 352 3641   Fax 0171 352 4846

Food, gardens, travel and artists.

Travel Ink Photo & Feature Library
The Old Coach House, 14 High Street, Goring on Thames, Nr Reading, Berkshire RG8 9AR
☎01491 873011   Fax 01491 875558

Contact *Abbie Enock*

Around 60,000 colour images on-site covering

more than 100 countries (including the UK). With associate library in London, has access to nearly 200,000 transparencies. Topics range across travel, tourism, lifestyles, business, industry, transport, children, history activities. Specialist collections on Hong Kong, Greece, North Wales and the Cotswolds.

Peter Trenchard's Image Store Ltd
The Studio, West Hill, St Helier, Jersey, Channel Islands JE2 3HB
☎01534 869933   Fax 01534 889191
Contact *Peter Trenchard, FBIPP, AMPA*

Slide library of the Channel Islands - mainly tourist and financial-related. Commissions undertaken.

Tropix Photographic Library
156 Meols Parade, Meols, Wirral, Merseyside L47 6AN
☎0151 632 1698   Fax 0151 632 1698
Contact *Veronica Birley*

Leading specialists on the developing world in all its aspects. Environmental topics widely covered. Assignment photography undertaken at home and overseas. New collections welcome, especially parts of Africa and Latin America, and environmental; please write for details enclosing large s.a.e.. All submissions (35 mm+ colour transparencies only) must be accompanied by detailed accurate captions, prepared according to Tropix specifications.

Ulster Museum
Botanic Gardens, Belfast BT9 5AB
☎01232 381251   Fax 01232 681885
Contact *Mrs Pat McLean*

Affectionately known as the 'treasure house of Ulster', the Ulster Museum is a national museum for Northern Ireland. Specialist subjects: art - fine and decorative, late 17th-20th century, particularly Irish art, archaeology, ethnography, treasures from the Armada shipwrecks, geology, botany, zoology, local history and industrial archaeology. Commissions welcome for objects not already photographed.

Universal Pictorial Press & Agency Ltd
29-31 Saffron Hill, London EC1N 8FH
☎0171 421 6000   Fax 0171 421 6006
News Editor *Peter Dare*

Photo archive dates back to 1944 and contains approximately four million pictures. Colour and b&w coverage of news, royalty, politics,

sport, arts, and many other subjects. Commissions undertaken for press and public relations. Fully interactive digital photo archive accessible by Apple Mac via ISDN or modem. Full scanning and wire facilities for analogue and digital.

UPI
See **Popperfoto**

V & A Picture Library
Victoria and Albert Museum, South Kensington, London SW7 2RL
☎0171 938 8352/8354/8452
Fax 0171 938 8353

40,000 colour and half a million b&w photos of decorative and applied arts, including ceramics, ivories, furniture, costumes, textiles, stage, musical instruments, toys, Indian, Far Eastern, Islamic objects, sculpture, painting and prints, from medieval to present day.

The Victory Archive
See **Popperfoto**

Viewfinder Colour Photo Library
3 Northload Street, Glastonbury, Somerset BA6 9JJ
☎01458 832600   Fax 01458 832850

General colour library with an accent on travel. Over half the files are devoted to worldwide travel and detailed coverage of the British Isles. New specialist file on worldwide religions, including sacred sites, ceremonies and festivals. Transport, agriculture, occupations, leisure activities, landscapes, people and wildlife.

The Vintage Magazine Company Ltd
203-213 Mare Street, London E8 3QE
☎0181 533 7588   Fax 0181 533 7283

A large collection of movie stills and posters, photographs, illustrations and advertisements covering music, glamour, social history, theatre posters, ephemera, postcards.

Visions of Andalucia Slide Library
Apto 499, Estepona, Malaga 29 680, Spain
☎00 34 527 93647   Fax 00 34 527 93647
Contact *Chris Chaplow*

Specialist library covering all aspects of Spain and Spanish life and culture. Cities, white villages, landscapes, festivals, art, gastronomy, leisure, tourism. Commissions undertaken.

The Charles Walker Collection

12-14 Argyll Street, London W1V 1AB
☎0171 734 7344   Fax 0171 287 3933

One of the foremost collections in the world on subjects popularly listed as 'Mystery, myth and magic'. The collection includes astrology, occultism, witchcraft and many other related areas. Catalogue available.

John Walmsley Photo Library

April Cottage, Warners Lane, Albury Heath, Guildford, Surrey GU5 9DE
☎01483 203846   Fax 01483 203846

Specialist library of learning/training/working subjects. Comprehensive coverage of learning environments such as playgroups, schools, colleges and universities. Images reflect a multiracial Britain. Plus a section on complementary medicine with over 30 therapies from acupuncture and yoga to more unusual treatments like moxibustion and metamorphic technique. Commissions undertaken. Subject list available on request.

Warwickshire Photographic Survey

See **Birmingham Library Services** under **Library Services**

Waterways Photo Library

39 Manor Court Road, Hanwell, London W7 3EJ
☎0181 840 1659   Fax 0181 567 0605

A specialist photo library on all aspects of Britain's inland waterways. Top-quality 35mm- and medium-format colour transparencies, plus a large collection of b&w. Rivers and canals, bridges, locks, aqueducts, tunnels and waterside buildings. Town and countryside scenes, canal art, waterway holidays, boating, fishing, windmills, watermills, watersports and wildlife.

Wellcome Centre Medical Photographic Library

210 Euston Road, London NW1 2BE
☎0171 611 8348   Fax 0171 611 8577

Contact *Catherine Draycott, Heather Ercilla, Michele Minto, Julie Dorrington*

Approximately 160,000 images on the history of medicine and human culture worldwide, including modern clinical medicine. Incorporates the **National Medical Slide Bank**.

Eric Whitehead Photography

PO Box 33, Kendal, Cumbria LA9 4SU
☎015394 48894   Fax 015394 48294

Incorporates the Cumbria Picture Library. The agency covers local news events, PR and commercial material.

Elizabeth Whiting & Associates Ltd

21 Albert Street, London NW1 7LU
☎0171 388 0104   Fax 0171 387 1615

Contact *Elizabeth Whiting*

Approx. one million images of interiors, gardens and all home interest subjects.

Derek G. Widdicombe-Worldwide Photographic Library

Oldfield, High Street, Clayton West, Huddersfield, West Yorkshire HD8 9NS
☎01484 862638   Fax 01484 862638

Contact *Derek G. Widdicombe*

Around 150,000 images (mostly the work of Derek Widdicombe) in colour and b&w. Landscapes, seascapes, human interest, architecture, moods and seasons, buildings and natural features in Britain and abroad.

Wilderness Photographic Library

Mill Barn, Broad Raine, Sedbergh, Cumbria LA10 5ED
☎015396 20196   Fax 015396 21293

Contact *John Noble*

Striking colour images from around the world, from polar wastes to the Himalayas and Amazon jungle. Subjects: mountains, Arctic, deserts, icebergs, wildlife, rainforests, glaciers, geysers, exploration, caves, rivers, eco-tourism, people and cultures, canyons, seascapes, marine life, weather, volcanoes, mountaineering, skiing, geology, conservation, adventure sports, national parks.

David Williams Picture Library

50 Burlington Avenue, Glasgow G12 0LH
☎0141 339 7823   Fax 0141 337 3031

Colour coverage of Scotland and Iceland. Smaller collections of the Faroes, France and Western USA. Landscapes, historical sites, buildings, geology and physical geography. Medium format and 35 mm. Catalogue available. Commissions undertaken.

Vaughan Williams Memorial Library

English Folk Dance and Song Society, Cecil Sharp House, 2 Regent's Park Road, London NW1 7AY

☎0171 284 0523   Fax 0171 284 0523

Mainly b&w coverage of traditional/folk music, dance and customs worldwide, focusing on Britain and other English-speaking nations. Photographs date from the late 19th century to the 1970s.

Windrush Photos, Wildlife and Countryside Picture Agency

99 Noah's Ark, Kemsing, Sevenoaks, Kent TN15 6PD

☎01732 763486   Fax 01732 763285

Contact David Tipling

The whole environmental spectrum is covered. Specialist subjects include birds from around the world, and British wildlife. Worldwide wildlife and landscapes. Asian travel includes landscapes, people and tourist destinations from the region. A large collection of black and white images covering British wildlife and angling, and shooting scenes dating back to the 1930s. High quality photographic and features commissions are regularly undertaken for publications in the UK and overseas.

The Wingfield Sporting Art Library

The Old Nunnery, 191 Battersea Bridge Road, London SW11 3AS

☎0171 978 5990   Fax 0171 978 5990

Contact Mary Ann Wingfield

Sporting works of art, both historical and contemporary, covering 50 different sports. Commissions undertaken.

Woodfall Wild Images

14 Bull Lane, Debigh, Denbighshire LL16 3SN

☎01745 815903   Fax 01745 814581

Contacts David Woodfall, Martin Barlow

Environmental, conservation, landscape and wildlife photographic library. A constantly-expanding collection of images reflecting a wide range of subjects, 'from mammals to marine, insects to industry, rivers to rainforest, and pollution to people changing our world, for the better and for the worse'.

World Pictures

85a Great Portland Street, London W1N 5RA

☎0171 437 2121   Fax 0171 439 1307

Contacts David Brenes, Carlo Irek

600,000 colour transparencies of travel and emotive material.

WWF UK Photolibrary

Panda House, Weyside Park, Catteshall Lane, Godalming, Surrey GU7 1XR

☎01483 426444   Fax 01483 426409

Contact Heidi Cameron, Andrea Ballard

Specialist library covering natural history, endangered species, conservation, environment, forests, habitats, habitat destruction, and pollution in the UK and abroad. 9,000 colour slides (35mm), 550 medium format, 500 b&w prints, 100 b&w line drawings.

Yemen Pictures

28 Sheen Common Drive, Richmond TW10 5BN

☎0181 898 0150/876 3637
Fax 0181 898 0150

Large collection (4000 transparencies) covering all aspects of Yemen - culture, people, architecture, dance, qat, music. Also Africa, Australia, Middle East, and Asia.

York Archaeological Trust Picture Library

Piccadilly House, 55 Piccadilly, York YO1 1PL

☎01904 663000   Fax 01904 640029

Specialist library of rediscovered artifacts, historic buildings and excavations, presented by the creators of the highly acclaimed Jorvik Viking Centre. The main emphasis is on the Roman, Anglo-Saxon and Viking periods.

The John Robert Young Collection

61 De Montfort Road, Lewes, East Sussex BN7 1SS

☎01273 475216   Fax 01273 475216

Contact Jennifer Barrett

50,000 transparencies on travel, religion and military subjects.

Balancing the Books –
Tax and the Writer

'No man in this country is under the smallest obligation, moral or other, to arrange his affairs as to enable the Inland Revenue to put the largest possible shovel in his stores.

'The Inland Revenue is not slow, and quite rightly, to take every advantage which is open to it . . . for the purpose of depleting the taxpayer's pockets. And the taxpayer is, in like manner, entitled to be astute to prevent as far as he honestly can the depletion of his means by the Inland Revenue.'
    Lord Clyde, *Ayrshire Pullman v Inland Revenue Commissioners, 1929.*

Income Tax

What is a professional writer for tax purposes?
Writers are professionals while they are writing regularly with the intention of making a profit; or while they are gathering material, researching or otherwise preparing a publication.

A professional freelance writer is taxed under Case II of Schedule D of the *Income and Corporation Taxes Act 1988*. The taxable income is the amount received, either directly or by an agent, on his behalf, less expenses wholly and exclusively laid out for the purposes of the profession. If expenses exceed income, the loss can either be carried forward and set against future income from writing or set against other income which is subject to tax in the same year. If tax has been paid on that other income, a repayment can be obtained, or the sum can be offset against other tax liabilities. Special loss relief can apply in the opening year of the profession. Losses made in the first four years can be set against income of up to five earlier years.

Where a writer receives very occasional payments for isolated articles, it may not be possible to establish that these are profits arising from carrying on a continuing profession. In such circumstances these 'isolated transactions' may be assessed under Case VI of Schedule D of the *Income and Corporation Taxes Act 1988*. Again, expenses may be deducted in arriving at the taxable income, but, if expenses exceed income, the loss can only be set against the profits from future isolated transactions, or other income assessable under Case VI.

Expenses
A writer can normally claim the following expenses:
  (a) Secretarial, typing, proofreading, research. Where payment for these are

made to the author's wife or husband, they should be recorded and entered in the spouse's tax return as earned income which is subject to the usual personal allowances. If payments reach taxable levels, PAYE should be operated.

(b) Telephone, telegrams, postage, stationery, printing, maintenance, insurance, dictation tapes, batteries, any equipment or office requisites used for the profession.

(c) Periodicals, books (including presentation copies and reference books) and other publications necessary for the profession, but amounts received from the sale of books should be deducted. Some inspectors of tax allow only capital allowances on books (see (l) below).

(d) Hotels, fares, car running expenses (including repairs, petrol, oil, garaging, parking, cleaning, insurance, licence, road fund tax, depreciation), hire of cars or taxis in connection with:

    (i)   business discussions with agents, publishers, co-authors, collaborators, researchers, illustrators, etc.

    (ii) travel at home and abroad to collect background material.

(e) Publishing and advertising expenses, including costs of proof corrections, indexing, photographs, etc.

(f) Subscriptions to societies and associations, press cutting agencies, libraries, etc., incurred wholly for the purpose of the profession.

(g) Premiums to pension schemes such as the *Society of Authors Retirement Benefits Scheme*. Depending on age, up to 40% of net earned income can be paid into a personal pension plan.

(h) Rent, council tax and water rates, etc., the proportion being determined by the ratio which the number of rooms are used exclusively for the profession bears to the total number of rooms in the residence. But see note on *Capital Gains Tax* below.

(i) Lighting, heating and cleaning. A carefully estimated figure of the business use of these costs can be claimed as a proportion of the total.

(j) Accountancy charges and legal charges incurred wholly in the course of the profession including cost of defending libel actions, damages in so far as they are not covered by insurance and libel insurance premiums. However, where in a libel case, damages are awarded to punish the author for having acted maliciously the action becomes quasi-criminal and costs and damages may not be allowed.

(k) TV and video rental (which may be apportioned for private use), and cinema or theatre tickets, if wholly for the purpose of the profession, e.g. playwriting.

(l) Capital allowances for equipment, e.g. car, TV, radio, hi-fi sets, tape and video recorders, dictaphones, typewriters, desks, bookshelves, filing cabinets, photographic equipment. Allowances vary in the Finance Acts depending upon political and economic views prevailing. At present they are set at 25%. On motor cars the allowance is 25% in the first year and

25% of the reduced balance in each successive year limited to £2000 each year. In the case of motor cars bought after 11 March 1992 the limit is £3000 each year. The total allowances in the case of all assets must not exceed the difference between cost and eventual sale price. Allowances will be reduced to exclude personal (non-professional) use where necessary.

(m) Lease rent. The cost of lease rent of equipment is allowable; also on cars, subject to restrictions for private use and for expensive cars.

(n) Tax relief is available for three-year (minimum) covenants to charities. With effect from 1 October 1990 individuals can obtain tax relief on one-off charitable gifts subject to certain generous limits.

NB It is always advisable to keep detailed records. Diary entries of appointments, notes of fares and receipted bills are much more convincing to the Inland Revenue than round figure estimates.

It has recently been announced that there is a fundamental change in the method of assessment of income of the self-employed to the 'current year' basis. This will operate for most existing businesses with effect from 1996/7 but anyone who is just starting to write for profit should take professional advice as regards the date to choose for their accounting year end.

Capital Gains Tax

The exemption from Capital Gains Tax which applies to an individual's main residence does not apply to any part of that residence which is used exclusively for business purposes. The effect of this is that the appropriate proportion of any increase in value of the residence since 31 March 1982 can be taxed, when the residence is sold, at the maximum rate of 40% (at present).

Writers who own their houses should bear this in mind before claiming expenses for the use of a room for writing purposes. Arguments in favour of making such claims are that they afford some relief now, while Capital Gains Tax in its present form may not stay for ever. Also, where a new house is bought in place of an old one, the gain made on the sale of the first study may be set off against the cost of the study in the new house, thus postponing the tax payment until the final sale. For this relief to apply, each house must have a study, and the author must continue his profession throughout. On death there is an exemption of the total Capital Gains of the estate. Some relief from tax will be given on Council Tax.

NB Writers can claim that their use is non-exclusive and restrict their claim to the cost of extra lighting, heating and cleaning to avoid Capital Gains Tax liability.

Can a writer average out his income over a number of years for tax purposes?

Under Section 534 of the *Income and Corporation Taxes Act 1988,* a writer may in certain circumstances spread over two or three fiscal years lump sum payments, whenever received, and royalties received during two years from the date of first publication or performance of work. Points to note are:

(a) The relief can only be claimed if the writer has been engaged in preparing and collecting material and writing the book for more than twelve months.

(b) If the period of preparing and writing the work exceeds twelve months but does not exceed twenty-four months, one-half of the advances and/or royalties will be regarded as income from the year preceding that of receipt. If the period of preparing and writing exceeds twenty-four months, one-third of the amount received would be regarded as income from each of the two years preceding that of receipt.

(c) For a writer on a very large income, who otherwise fulfils the conditions required, a claim under these sections could result in a tax saving. If his income is not large he should consider the implication, in the various fiscal years concerned, of possible loss of benefit from personal and other allowances and changes in the standard rate of income tax.

It is also possible to average out income within the terms of publishers' contracts, but professional advice should be taken before signature. Where a husband and wife collaborate as writers, advice should be taken as to whether a formal partnership agreement should be made or whether the publishing agreement should be in joint names.

Is a lump sum paid for an outright sale of the copyright or part of the copyright exempt from tax?

No. All the money received from the marketing of literary work, by whatever means, is taxable. Some writers, in spite of clear judicial decisions to the contrary, still seem to think that an outright sale of, for instance, the film rights in a book is not subject to tax.

Is there any relief where old copyrights are sold?

Section 535 of the *Income and Corporation Taxes Act 1988* gives relief where not less than ten years after the first publication of the work the author of a literary, dramatic, musical or artistic work assigns the copyright therein wholly or partially, or grants any interest in the copyright by licence, and:

(a) the consideration for the assignment or grant consists wholly or partially of a lump sum payment, the whole amount of which would, but for this section, be included in computing the amount of his/her profits or gains for a single year of assessment, and

(b) the copyright or interest is not assigned or granted for a period of less than two years.

In such cases, the amount received may be spread forward in equal yearly instalments for a maximum of six years, or, where the copyright or interest is assigned or granted for a period of less than six years, for the number of whole years in that period. A 'lump sum payment' is defined to include a non-returnable advance on account of royalties.

It should be noted that a claim may not be made under this section in respect of a payment if a prior claim has been made under Section 534 of the *Income and*

Corporation Taxes Act 1988 (see section on spreading lump sum payments over two or three years) or vice versa.

Are royalties payable on publication of a book abroad subject to both foreign tax as well as UK tax?

Where there is a Double Taxation Agreement between the country concerned and the UK, then on the completion of certain formalities no tax is deductible at source by the foreign payer, but such income is taxable in the UK in the ordinary way. When there is no Double Taxation agreement, credit will be given against UK tax for overseas tax paid. A complete list of countries with which the UK has conventions for the avoidance of double taxation may be obtained from the Inspector of Foreign Dividends, Lynwood Road, Thames Ditton, Surrey KT7 0DP, or the local tax office.

Residence Abroad

Writers residing abroad will, of course, be subject to the tax laws ruling in their country of residence, and as a general rule royalty income paid from the United Kingdom can be exempted from deduction of UK tax at source, providing the author is carrying on his profession abroad. A writer who is intending to go and live abroad should make early application for future royalties to be paid without deduction of tax to HM Inspector of Taxes, Foreign Division, Prudential Building, 72 Maid Marian, Nottingham NG1 6AS. In certain circumstances writers resident in the Irish Republic are exempt from Irish Income Tax on their authorship earnings.

Are grants or prizes taxable?

The law is uncertain. Some Arts Council grants are now deemed to be taxable, whereas most prizes and awards are not, though it depends on the conditions in each case. When submitting a statement of income and expenses, such items should be excluded, but reference made to them in a covering letter to the Inspector of Taxes.

What if I disagree with a tax assessment?

Income Tax law requires the Inspector of Taxes to make an assessment each year calculating the amount of income tax payable on the 'profits' of the profession. Even though accounts may have already been submitted the assessment can quite possibly be estimated and overstated.

The taxpayer has the right of appeal within 30 days of receipt of the assessment and can request that the tax payable should be reduced to the correct liability which he must estimate as accurately as possible. However, if he underestimates the amount, interest can become payable on the amount by which he underpays when the correct liability is known.

What is the item 'Class 4 N.I.C.' which appears on my tax assessment?

All taxpayers who are self-employed pay an additional national insurance contribution if their earned income exceeds a figure which is varied each year. This contribution is described as Class 4 and is calculated in the tax assessment. It is additional to the self-employed Class 2 (stamp) contribution but confers no additional benefits and is a form of levy. It applies to men aged under 65 and women under 60. Tax relief is given on half the Class 4 contributions.

Value Added Tax

Value Added Tax (VAT) is a tax currently levied at 17.5% on:
- (a)   the total value of taxable goods and services supplied to consumers,
- (b)   the importation of goods into the UK,
- (c)   certain services from abroad if a taxable person receives them in the UK for the purpose of their business.

Who is Taxable?
A writer resident in the UK whose turnover from writing and any other business, craft or art on a self-employed basis is greater than £47,000 annually, before deducting agent's commission, must register with HM Customs & Excise as a taxable person. A business is required to register:

– at the end of any month if the value of taxable supplies in the past 12 months has exceeded the annual threshold; or

– if there are reasonable grounds for believing that the value of taxable supplies in the next 12 months will exceed the annual threshold.

Penalties will be claimed in the case of late registration. A writer whose turnover is below these limits is exempt from the requirements to register for VAT, but may apply for voluntary registration, and this will be allowed at the discretion of HM Customs & Excise.

A taxable person collects VAT on outputs (turnover) and deducts VAT paid on inputs (taxable expenses) and where VAT collected exceeds VAT paid, must remit the difference to HM Customs & Excise. In the event that input exceeds output, the difference will be repaid by HM Customs & Excise.

Outputs (Turnover)
A writer's outputs are taxable services supplied to publishers, broadcasting organisations, theatre managements, film companies, educational institutions, etc. A taxable writer must invoice, i.e. collect from, all the persons (either individuals or organisations) in the UK for whom supplies have been made, for fees, royalties or other considerations plus VAT. An unregistered writer cannot and must not invoice for VAT. A taxable writer is not obliged to collect VAT on royalties or other fees paid by publishers or others overseas. In practice, agents usually collect VAT for the registered author.

Remit to Customs
The taxable writer adds up the VAT which has been paid on taxable inputs, deducts it from the VAT received and remits the balance to Customs. Business

with HM Customs is conducted through the local VAT Offices of HM Customs which are listed in local telephone directories, except for tax returns which are sent direct to the Customs and Excise VAT Central Unit, Alexander House, 21 Victoria Avenue, Southend on Sea, Essex SS99 IAA.

Accounting

A taxable writer is obliged to account to HM Customs & Excise at quarterly intervals. Returns must be completed and sent to VAT Central Unit by the dates shown on the return. Penalties can be charged if the returns are late.

It is possible to account for the VAT liability under the Cash Accounting Scheme (Note 731), whereby the author accounts for the output tax when the

Taxable at the standard rate	Taxable at the zero or special rate	Exempt
Rent of certain commercial premises	Books (zero)	Rent of non-commercial premises
Advertisements in newspapers, magazines, journals and periodicals	Periodicals (zero)	Council Tax
	Coach, rail, and air travel (zero)	Postage
Agent's commission (unless it relates to monies from overseas, when it is zero-rated)	From 1.4.94 electricity (8%)	Services supplied by unregistered persons
Accountant's fees	Gas (8%)	Subscriptions to the Society of Authors, PEN, NUJ, etc.
Solicitor's fees *re* business matters	Other fuel (8%)	Wages and salaries
Agency services (typing, copying, etc.)		Insurance
Word processors, typewriters and stationery		Taxicab fares
Artists' materials		
Photographic equipment		
Tape recorders and tapes		
Hotel accommodation		*Outside the scope of VAT*
Motor-car expenses		PLR (Public Lending Right)
Telephone		Profit shares
Theatres and concerts		Investment income

NB This list is not exhaustive.

invoice is paid or royalties, etc., are received. The same applies to the input tax, but as most purchases are probably on a 'cash basis', this will not make a considerable difference to the author's input tax. This scheme is only applicable to those with a taxable turnover of less than £350,000 and, therefore, is available to the majority of authors. The advantage of this scheme is that the author does not have to account for VAT before receiving payment, thereby relieving the author of a cash flow problem.

It is also possible to pay VAT by nine estimated direct debits, with a final balance at the end of the year (see leaflet 732).

Registration

A writer will be given a VAT registration number which must be quoted on all VAT correspondence. It is the responsibility of those registered to inform those to whom they make supplies of their registration number. The taxable turnover limit which determines whether a person who is registered for VAT may apply for cancellation of registration is £44,000.

Voluntary Registration

A writer whose turnover is below the limits may apply to register. If the writer is paying a relatively large amount of VAT on taxable inputs – agent's commissions, accountant's fees, equipment, materials, or agency services, etc. – it may make a significant improvement in the net income to be able to offset the VAT on these inputs. An author who pays relatively little VAT may find it easier, and no more expensive, to remain unregistered.

Fees and Royalties

A taxable writer must notify those to whom he makes supplies of the Tax Registration Number at the first opportunity. One method of accounting for and paying VAT on fees and royalties is the use of multiple stationery for 'self-billing', one copy of the royalty statement being used by the author as the VAT invoice. A second method is for the recipient of taxable outputs to pay fees, including authors' royalties, without VAT. The taxable author then renders a tax invoice for the VAT element and a second payment, of the VAT element, will be made. This scheme is cumbersome but will involve only taxable authors. Fees and royalties from abroad will count as payments for exported services and will accordingly be zero-rated.

Agents and Accountants

A writer is responsible to HM Customs for making VAT returns and payments. Neither an agent nor an accountant nor a solicitor can remove the responsibility, although they can be helpful in preparing and keeping VAT returns and accounts. Their professional fees or commission will, except in rare cases where the adviser or agent is himself unregistered, be taxable at the standard rate and will represent some of a writer's taxable inputs.

Income Tax – Schedule D

An unregistered writer can claim some of the VAT paid on taxable inputs as a business expense allowable against income tax. However, certain taxable inputs fall into categories which cannot be claimed under the income tax regulations. A taxable writer, who has already offset VAT on inputs, cannot charge it as a business expense for the purposes of income tax.

Certain Services From Abroad

A taxable author who resides in the United Kingdom and who receives certain services from abroad must account for VAT on those services at the appropriate tax rate on the sum paid for them. Examples of the type of services concerned include: services of lawyers, accountants, consultants, provisions of information and copyright permissions.

Inheritance Tax

Inheritance Tax was introduced in 1984 to replace Capital Transfer Tax, which had in turn replaced Estate Duty, the first of the death taxes of recent times. Paradoxically, Inheritance Tax has reintroduced a number of principles present under the old Estate Duty.

The general principle now is that all legacies on death are chargeable to tax (currently 40%), except for legacies between spouses which are exempt, as are the first £200,000 of legacies to others. Gifts made more than seven years before death are exempt, but those made within this period are taxed on a sliding scale. No tax is payable at the time of making the gift.

In addition, each individual may currently make gifts of up to £3000 in any year and these will be considered to be exempt. A further exemption covers any number of annual gifts not exceeding £250 to any one person.

If the £3000 is not utilised in one year it, or the unused balance, can be given in the following year (but no later), plus that year's exemptions. Gifts out of income, which means those which do not reduce one's capital or one's living standards, are also exempt if they are part of one's normal expenditure.

At death all assets are valued: they will include any property, investments, life policies, furniture and personal possessions, bank balances and, in the case of authors, the value of their copyrights. All, with the sole exception of copyrights, are capable (as assets) of accurate valuation, and, if necessary, can be turned into cash. The valuation of copyright is, of course, complicated, and frequently gives rise to difficulty. Except where they are bequeathed to the owner's husband or wife, very real problems can be left behind by the author.

Experience has shown that a figure based on two to three years' past royalties may be proposed by the Inland Revenue in their valuation of copyright. However, it all depends. If a book is running out of print or if, as in the case of educational books, it may need revision at the next reprint, these factors must be taken into account. In many cases the fact that the author is no longer alive and able to make personal appearances, or provide publicity, or write further works, will result in lower or slower sales. Obviously this is an area in which help can be given by the publishers, and in particular one needs to know what their future intentions are, what stocks of the books remain, and what likelihood there will be of reprinting.

There is a further relief available to authors who have established that they have been carrying on a business, normally assessable under Case II of Schedule D, for at least two years prior to death. It has been possible to establish that copyrights are treated as business property and in these circumstances, 'business property relief' is available. This relief at present is at 100% on business assets including copyrights, so that the tax saving can be quite substantial. The Inland Revenue may wish to be assured that the business is continuing and consideration should therefore be given to the appointment, in the author's will, of a literary executor who should be a qualified business person or, in certain circumstances, the formation of a partnership between the author and his or her spouse, or other relative, to ensure that it is established that the business is continuing after the author's death.

If the author has sufficient income, consideration should be given to building up a fund to cover future liabilities. One of a number of ways would be to take out a whole life assurance policy which is assigned to the children, or other beneficiaries, the premiums on which are within the annual exemption of £3000. The capital sum payable on the death of the assured is exempt from inheritance tax.

Anyone wondering how best to order his affairs for tax purposes, should consult an accountant with specialised knowledge in this field. Experience shows that a good accountant is well worth his fee which, incidentally, so far as it relates to matters other than personal tax work, is an allowable expense.

The information contained in this section is adapted from **The Society of Authors** *Quick Guides to Taxation* (Nos 4 and 7), with the kind help of A. P. Kernon, FCA, who will be pleased to answer questions on tax problems. Please write to A. P. Kernon, c/o *The Writer's Handbook*. 45 Islington Park Street, London N1 1QB.

Company Index

The following codes have been used to classify the index entries:

A	UK Publishers	K	National and Regional Radio
A1	Irish Publishers	L	Film, TV and Video Producers
AB	Writer's Courses, Circles and Workshops	M	Theatre Producers
AA	European Publishers	N	US Publishers
AU	Audio Books	O	US Agents
B	Poetry Presses	P	US Press, Journals and Broadcasting
C	Poetry Magazines	Q	Professional Associations
D	Organisations of Interest to Poets	R	Arts Councils and Regional Arts Boards
E	UK Packagers	S	Bursaries, Fellowships and Grants
EE	Book Clubs	T	Prizes
F	UK Agents	U	Libraries
G	National Newspapers	V	Picture Libraries
H	Regional Newspapers	W	Small Presses
HH	News Agencies	X	Festivals
I	Magazines	Y	Editorial, Research and other Services
J	National and Regional Television	YY	Press Cuttings Agencies
J1	European Television Companies	Z	Literary Societies

Subject Index

Stop Press

Macmillan Publishers Ltd and Boxtree

See **UK Publishers** pages 16 and 65

Macmillan has bought Boxtree, the successful media tie-in publisher. Sarah Mahaffy, formerly Managing Director of Boxtree, joins Macmillan as Managing Director of Pan Macmillan, the trade publishing holding company.

Murray Pollinger

See **UK Agents** page 197

Murray Pollinger Literary Agency has been sold to David Higham Associates, which takes over from 19 July 1996.